The

Microtomist's
Formulary and Guide

The Microtomist's Formulary and Guide

by
Peter Gray, Ph.D., D.I.C., F.R.M.S.
Head, Department of Biological Sciences
University of Pittsburgh

THE BLAKISTON COMPANY, INC.
New York   Toronto

Library of Congress Catalog Card Number: 53-11567

PRINTED IN THE UNITED STATES OF AMERICA
BY THE MAPLE PRESS COMPANY, YORK, PA.

To
Freda

Preface

A few generations ago the English periodical *Punch* offered to its readers a "letter of advice to those about to be married": the applicants received the single word "Don't." The advice is pertinent for those about to write a source reference work.

You may well, in reading this book, become incensed at what you believe to be its inaccuracies, errors, and faulty arrangements. This is exactly how I felt, twenty years ago, when I struggled with the reference books on microtechnique which I was then using. You may decide, as I did, to try to write a better book.

You will find it a wearisome and disillusioning task. The research will, of course, be wholly delightful, but it will be followed by a period of brutal hard labor. Not only will you have to write, but then, if you are to produce a publishable book, it will have to be condensed and rewritten. Add to this the fact that the finished work has then to be reread four separate times as it goes through press, and you will join me in hoping that your activities do not too strongly resemble those of the dog mentioned in the Book of Proverbs.

This book would never have been completed without the help of the librarians of the University of Edinburgh, the Wood's Hole Marine Biological Laboratory, the University of Rochester, the Carnegie Library of Pittsburgh, and the University of Pittsburgh. I am especially indebted to Miss Lorena Garloch, and her assistants in the Reference Department of the University of Pittsburgh Library, for their extraordinary skill in tracking down obscure journals and securing them for me on inter-library loan.

The illustrations for this work, as for my *Handbook of Basic Microtechnique*, were prepared from my photographs and sketches by Mrs. Gloria Green Hirsch. I am glad that reviewers of the published book share my enthusiasm for her work.

The number of those, including the author and his wife, who have had a hand in typing this book is legion. It should be recorded, however, that Mrs. Mary Roman single-handed produced the first complete (1500 page) typescript and that Mrs. Dolores Johnson, and Miss Kristine Pallesen, have stood by the author during the distressing hurly-burly known as "getting the book into press."

Dr. James Lackey, then scientific editor of the Blakiston Company, encouraged me over long periods to persevere in producing a publishable book. His successor, Mr. William Keller, approved what had been done and, with Mr. Willard Shoener converted my efforts to their present form. My debt to these gentlemen, and to their editorial assistants, is immense.

Acknowledgement is made with thanks to the American Optical Company for figures 56, 57, and 84, to the Fisher Scientific Company for figures 34 and 38, and to the Carbide and Chemical Corporation for some of the data in Chapter 25. Permission to reproduce copyright material of the R. R. Bowker Company and the Oxford University Press is specifically acknowledged at the places where these reproductions occur.

PETER GRAY

EDINBURGH 1933
PITTSBURGH 1953

List of Contents

PART II—METHODS AND FORMULAS USED IN MAKING
MICROSCOPE SLIDES

Introduction

Scope of the Book

This work consists of two parts. Part I (Chapters 1–16) is a treatise on the art of making microscope slides from biological specimens. Part II (Chapters 17–28) is a classified list of the formulas and techniques used in this art.

Arrangement of Part I

Each chapter deals with a specific type of microscope slide and is divided into two parts. The first part discusses problems involved in the preparation of such a slide and the general methods by which these problems have been overcome. The second part is devoted to one or more specific examples which describe in detail the application of the general methods to the production of an actual slide. The few literature references in Part I are confined to places where the author is describing a method of which he lacks personal experience, or where he is giving opinions at variance with his own.

Arrangement of Part II

The chapters in Part II are devoted to specific types of formulas and give, where necessary, the techniques by which these formulas are used. Each chapter is subdivided decimally in accordance with a scheme given in full at the beginning of the chapter and explained in the first paragraph of the chapter. Every formula or technique is thus identified by a number which is used, together with two or three letters identifying the chapter, in all cross references. Thus:

DS 11.122 Mayer 1891

identifies a specific alum-hematoxylin of Mayer (he published five other alum-hematoxylin formulas) in any of the fifty places that reference is made to it. The formula is given only once and then in association with all the other alum-hematoxylin (DS 11.122) formulas in the book. These decimal reference numbers are added to the page numbers all through, thus making it easy to run down a given type of formula or technique.

Pet Names

Some biologists have a pernicious habit of omitting literature references and using what Conn 1938 (20540b, **13**:121) in a well-organized attack on them, calls "pet names." In cases where these pet names—such as *paracarmine* or *B 15*—have become embedded in the folklore of microtechnique, the present author puts them in italics, immediately after the decimal reference, thus:

DS 11.22 Mayer 1892 *paracarmine—compl. script.*

The appended *compl. script.* indicates that the word has occurred in a "great many writings." When only the originator of the technique appears to have used the pet name it is referred to with *auct.* Pet names should never be used in scientific writing but such sloppy scholarship as is inherent in a reference to "Bouin's Fluid" is almost worse. Bouin is the originator of many fixatives of which one happens to be popular at the moment; quite another was popular twenty years ago, when a casual reference to Bouin's Fluid meant a mercuric formaldehyde mixture.

Method of Giving Literature References

The author indicates, after every formula or technique, the source from which he is quoting. The form used varies according to the type of source and an example of each will be given.

1

DIRECT QUOTATIONS FROM BOOKS. The author's name, date, and page only are used, thus:

DS 11.120 Anderson Anderson 1929, 129

At the end of Part II there is a list of books cited where "Anderson 1929" is expanded to a full bibliographic reference.

INDIRECT QUOTATIONS FROM BOOKS. It too frequently happens that a book quotes a formula by name, either without giving a reference at all or with an incorrect reference. When the present author has been unable to find the original he uses the abbreviation *test*. Thus:

DS 11.123. Conklin *test*. 1930 Guyer Guyer 1930, 232.

This indicates that the volume in question contains, on page 232, a formula for Conklin's picro-hematoxylin but offers no information as to where the original can be checked.

Where the author of a book cited is quoting at second hand, the abbreviation *cit*. is used. Thus

DS 11.24 Vignal *test*. 1907 Böhm and Oppel *cit*. Henneguy Böhm and Oppel 1907, 118

indicates that, on page 118 of the volume in question, there is a statement to the effect that Henneguy proposed, following the method of Vignal, to prepare a picro-carmine by this particular method.

Where the author of a book cites himself, or the authors cite themselves, without reference, the abbreviation used is *test*. *ips*. (standing for *teste ipso* or *testibus ipsis*). Thus:

MS 31.22 Cajal 1925 *test*. 1933 *ips*. Cajal and de Castro 1933, 262

The present author would plead in self defense that he has tracked more than a thousand such references to the originals and that these *test*. and *cit*. references are used only where he has failed to find the original or where the original is incorrectly quoted.

DIRECT QUOTATIONS FROM JOURNALS. The author has used, in place of the name of the journal, the number assigned to that journal in the *World List of Scientific*

Periodicals (Oxford, The University Press, 1927). Thus:

DS 11.122 Carazzi 1911 23632, 28:273

indicates that Carazzi's formula is given on page 273 of volume 28 of the *Zeitschrift für wissenschäftliche Mikroskopie und für mikroskopische Technik*. The full titles of the two-hundred-odd journals cited will be found immediately preceding the index. The use of this number not only saves space, an important consideration in a volume of this magnitude, but also permits exact identification of the journal. The author decided to use these numbers quite shortly after he started checking references in the *J. Anat*. (either of two journals) and the *J. Bot*. (any one of three journals).

INDIRECT QUOTATIONS FROM JOURNALS. The abbreviations *test*., *test*. *cit*. and *test*. *ips*. are used with journal references exactly as described for book references.

UNPUBLISHED INFORMATION. The abbreviations *in verb*. and *in litt*. indicate that the author has received unpublished information either verbally or in a letter. Thus:

V 12.2 Fant 1932 *in verb*.

indicates that Mr. Fant told the author the unpublished composition of his sealing medium for glycerol mounts in 1932.

Slavonic Names

Where the author has cited Slavonic names from a Cyrillic alphabet original, he has transliterated according to the rules of the Library of Congress (Beetle, Clara, ed. *A. L. A. Cataloging Rules for Author and Title Entries*. Chicago, American Library Association, 1949, p. 246) without regard for the writer's preference as indicated in, say, a German summary of his paper. Thus *Yasvoyn*, not *Jasswoin*, is cited from the original. Slavonic names cited from a Latin alphabet original are transcribed directly even though this involves referring to the same individual by several names. Slavonic names cited at second hand are also transcribed directly, no matter how obviously they may have been mistransliterated.

Citing Latin alphabet names from Cyrillic alphabet originals has involved even more uncertainty. Russian writers not only omit references but also follow varying rules of transliteration, some taking a phonetic and others a literal approach. The name *Huygens*, for example, can be transliterated into a Cyrillic form which can then be phonetically transliterated in German as *Geugantz*. Thus Roskin 1946 attributes to an individual whose name may be transliterated *Shteve, Steeve, Stieve,* or *Stive* a fixative which resembles, but is not identical with, the formula attributed, also without reference, to Stieve by Romeis 1948. The author has given the one as Stieve *test.* 1946 Roskin—and the other as Stieve *test.* 1948 Romeis. Faulty scholarship can certainly increase the confusion originated by the architects of the Tower of Babel.

Names of Dyes

The author has, with one exception, changed the names of all dyes to accord with the synonym preferred by Conn 1946 (Conn, H. J. *Biological Stains* 5th ed. Geneva, N. Y., Biotech, 1946). The author prefers, however, to use the name *magenta*, rather than *basic fuchsin*, to describe the mixture of magenta O, magenta I, magenta II now sold as basic fuchsin. There is no discussion of the chemistry and synonymy of dyes in the present work; reference should be made to Conn (*op. cit.*). The author has not given certification numbers or dye content in formulas, since they are available for so few.

Names of Reagents Other than Dyes

The author has in almost all cases followed the usage preferred by *The Merck Index* 6th ed. Rahway, N. J., Merck, 1952. The terms *chromic acid, osmic acid,* and *picric acid,* though technically incorrect, are so universal in biological literature that they have been retained. Similarly the terms *alcohol* and *absolute alcohol* (abbreviated in the formulas to alc. and abs. alc.) have been used in place of *ethanol*.

Chemical names used are those customarily found on the label of the reagent bottle and are not accompanied by chemical formulas, or otherwise qualified, unless the reagent is found equally commonly in several forms. Thus *copper sulfate* indicates the usual reagent $CuSO_4.5H_2O$. On the rare occasions when reference is made to the anhydrous salt, it is referred to as *copper sulfate, anhydr.* In any case of doubt, reference should be made to the Merck Index.

Proprietary Compounds

Proprietary compounds of known composition, such as *amidol* and *salvarsan* have been referred to by the name preferred in the *Merck Index.* Proprietary compounds of secret composition have no place in contemporary science and have been ignored. It is fantastic that purveyors of reagents should be permitted to sell nostrums of secret composition, thus indicating a contempt for technicians equal to that shown by medicine men for the yokels they gypped with snake oil. The author would make it very plain that he does not extend this attitude to "brands" of mixtures or reagents selected for technicians' use. Every maker of microscope slides is indebted to those firms which select and blend materials specially for his use.

Quantities and Measures

The abbreviations ml. and Gm. have been omitted. It is to be presumed that all liquids will be measured in milliliters and all solids in grams. Formulas have been adjusted to give a rational total (usually 100) in terms of standard ingredients, no matter how the original was presented. This has been wearisome labor applied to thousands of formulas. It is doubtless convenient to make up a solution by adding fifteen drops of a 2.5% solution of this to 30 drops of a 1.25% solution of that and then to dilute to 15 milliliters with 30% alcohol. As a published instruction, however, it does not commend itself to writers of textbooks struggling to avoid duplication.

Index

The last section of the book is a single-alphabet, fully expanded, index, alphabetized according to the rules of the American Library Association (Beetle, 1949, *op. cit.*). These terms may require explanation.

A *single-alphabet index* is one in which all entries are placed in the same index. There are not separate indexes for authors, stains, etc. *Fully expanded* means that more than one entry leads to the information sought. For example, "Grenacher's alcoholic-borax-carmine" may be found whether the reader consults the word "Grenacher," "borax-carmine," alcoholic-borax-carmine," or "carmine." A condensed index, which saves the author work and the publisher money without regard to the reader's feelings, has "borax carmine *see* Grenacher," "carmine staining solutions, *see* author's name," etc. etc.

Those who do not think it necessary to have rules of alphabetization might try indexing *del Río-Hortega, 2BD fixative, CS-13 mountant*, and *van't Hooft*. The rules of the A.L.A. (*op. cit.*) may not be perfect but they are at least clearly expressed and easily available.

Part I

The Art of Making Microscope Slides

Foreword to Part I

The preparation of objects for microscopic examination—more colloquially known as "making microscope slides"—has a twofold purpose. On the one hand it may be desired to preserve in permanent form objects too small or too delicate to be handled by the ordinary methods of museum preparation. Second, and far more important, it may be necessary to make permanent preparations of objects and tissues in such a manner that their structure may be more clearly seen under the microscope. In both cases, the object is mounted on a slide, which is nowadays a standardized $3'' \times 1''$ strip of thin glass.

Originally microscope slides were very different and were usually made by taking a slip of ivory, about $2'' \times \frac{1}{2}''$, and drilling through it a hole of about $\frac{3}{8}''$ in diameter. This hole was then enlarged from each side, about a third of the way through, to a $\frac{1}{2}''$ diameter, thus leaving a ridge of ivory in the center. The depression on each side of the slide was fitted with a ring of spring steel and several disks of mica of a half-inch diameter were furnished with each slide. To make a mount, a piece of mica was inserted from one side and held in place by the slip ring, the object was placed on it and another disk of mica was then inserted from the other side and, in its turn, held in by a slip ring. This was the only type of slide available until about the middle of the 18th century when glass slides first made their appearance. These glass slides were, however, of very little use, with their talc covers which remained the greatest bar to the progress of microtomy.

Toward the close of the first half of the 19th century Messrs. Chance, Birmingham, England discovered how to make thin glass coverslips. They were for many years (Queckett 1855, 287) the only manufacturers, and until the discovery of oil immersion objectives microscopists were entirely dependent upon the increasing thinness with which these glasses could be supplied. Microscopists were still seeking for magnification rather than resolution, and by 1880 (Beale 1880, 351) a coverslip had been made sufficiently thin to permit the use of a $\frac{1}{50}$-inch "high dry" objective. Coverslips are now taken so much for granted that the contribution made to the development of biology through the introduction of thin glass is often overlooked. The earliest method of using these thin coverslips with glass slides was by holding the cover in place with the aid of a paper label which covered all the slide except the area immediately over the object. These labels were often fancifully engraved to the design of the individual technician and an excellent and well-illustrated description of their use is to be found in Martin 1872, pp. 46–52.

Microscope mounts, as made today, consist of three types. These are, first, *wholemounts*, in which organisms or pieces of organisms are mounted under a coverslip on a slide; second, *smear preparations*, in which either a cut surface or a viscous fluid is smeared on a slide to form a thin layer which is subsequently preserved under a cover glass; third, *sections*, in which thin slices of objects are mounted under a coverslip. Where objects are cut into a series of sections, each of which is mounted in consecutive order on a slide, the preparation is known as a *serial section*.

The simplest slide to prepare is that in which the object is mounted dry. An example of this is shown in Fig. 1 where a series of diatoms have been spread on a slide, and a coverslip placed over them. This coverslip is held in place by a ring of cement which is prevented from running under the edges of the coverslip by some

7

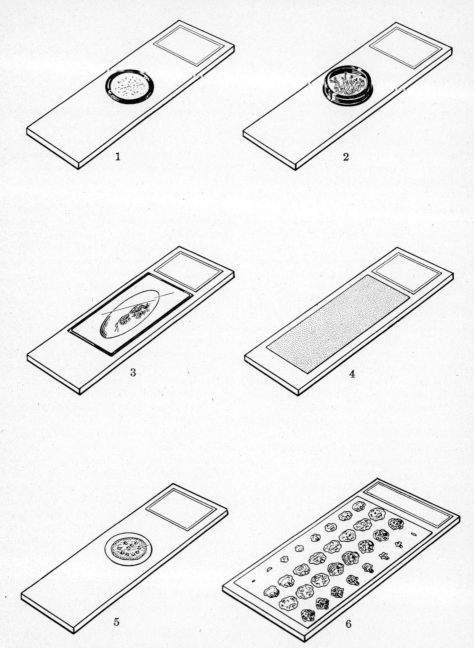

Figs. 1 to 6. Types of microscopical preparation. *1. Dry wholemount of diatoms. 2. Freshwater bryzoan in deep cell of formaldehyde. 3. Crustacean in oval cavity in glycerol jelly. 4. Smear preparation. 5. Single section of plant stem. 6. Serial section of embryo.*

form of thin cell, which may be either of cement or paper, and which serves the additional purpose of preventing the crushing of the object by the coverslip. Most wholemounts are, however, prepared in a preservative medium, which may be either aqueous, colloidal, or resinous. Many of these whole objects are relatively thick so that some method must be adopted of providing space for them under the coverslip. Fig. 2 shows an object mounted in a deep cell of glass, while Fig. 3 shows an alternative method in which a relatively thick slide has had an oval cavity ground into it. As will be seen from the figure these mounts are heavily varnished at the edges to prevent the evap-

oration of fluid or the withdrawal of water from the colloidal medium. Wholemounts prepared with resinous media, which harden and thus hold the coverslip in place, are frequently not varnished at the edges though some case can be made out (Gray 1936, *Microsc. Rec.*, 38) for the application of a ring of varnish around the edge of balsam mounts.

Smear preparations (Fig. 4) are almost invariably prepared in resinous media and equally invariably the edges of the coverslips are not varnished. Sections (Figs. 5 and 6), either single or serial, are universally mounted in resinous media and the edges of the coverslip are practically never varnished.

1

Dry Wholemounts

General Principles

A dry wholemount consists essentially of an object or objects enclosed within a small, usually cylindrical, box attached to the center of a microscope slide. The floor of this box is almost invariably the surface of the slide itself while the roof is formed by the coverslip. The sides of the box are produced by the attachment of a cell, which may be a thin ring of cement, a washerlike piece of paper or plastic, or a squat cylinder of the same materials. The object may be attached directly to the glass surface of the slide, if one desires to make a transparent mount, or the surface of the slide may be rendered opaque and the object then attached to whatever substance is used to blacken the surface. There are a number of decisions to be made before preparing a dry wholemount. The considerations governing these decisions will be discussed in the order in which they present themselves to the technician.

Selection of a Slide

If the object is to be prepared as a transparent wholemount one has no choice but glass. None of the transparent plastics at present available have a sufficiently hard surface to be worth using. They are unbreakable and easy to handle when first made, but will become so scratched after even a few months of use as to be worthless. The manufacturers of these slides point out that they may be repolished at intervals, but there seems little point in preferring them to glass which does not become scratched.

If the wholemount is to be prepared as an opaque object, which is the case in probably 90% of all dry wholemounts, there is little justification for using glass. It has two great disadvantages: first, it is very easily broken; second, it is one of the most difficult materials to which to cause adhesives to stick. In the early days of microscope mounting it was customary to employ slides of well-seasoned mahogany and, though this practice is today confined to the mounters of Foraminifera, a brief description of the preparation of these slides will be given. A piece of seasoned mahogany, 3″ by 1″ in section, is secured with the grain running parallel to the three-inch face. This block is set up on end in a vertical drill and a hole of the required diameter drilled as deeply into it as is possible with tools available. This hole should be about $\frac{1}{16}$ of an inch *smaller* than the size of the coverslip which will be used; that is, if $\frac{3}{4}$-inch coverslips are customary an $1\frac{1}{16}$-inch drill is used to make the hole. The actual size of the coverslips should be checked before drilling, since many coverslips which are sold as $\frac{3}{4}$-inch have a diameter of eighteen millimeters, or a trifle less than $\frac{45}{64}$. When the hole has been drilled, the block of wood is transferred to a circular saw and slices about $\frac{3}{16}$ of an inch in thickness cut from it. These slices are, in effect, $3″ \times 1″$ microscope slides with a hole of the required size in the center. A sheet of strong, thin card is then cut into $3″ \times 1″$ pieces, each of which is glued to the under side of one of the slides. The best way to do this without warping the wooden strip is to use shellac as an adhesive, either employing a very thick solution in alcohol and permitting it to dry under pressure, or coating the sheet before cutting with the thick solution which is allowed to dry and then pressed under heat onto the lower surface of the slide. Sheets of photographer's dry mounting tissue can be used for the same purpose, if a photographer's dry mounting press is available. This completes a wooden microscope slide with a built-in, white-bottomed, cell. If a black bottom is required a disk of black paper is punched, coated with ordinary starch

frame, the flanges of which are sufficiently deep to allow a thin slide to be slipped in as a cover.

Selection of a Coverslip

The chief difficulty in selecting a coverslip for a dry wholemount using a deep cell is to find one which is thick enough. The only value attaching to very thin coverslips is that they permit the use of high power objectives. Most dry whole-

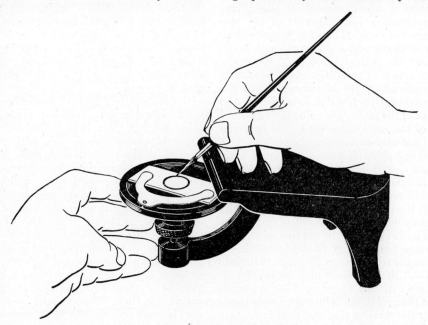

Fig. 7. Turning a ring on a slide.

paste on the underside, and pressed into position at the bottom of the hole.

Numerous variations on slides of this type are possible. To mount a number of small objects on the same slide it is only necessary to drill a number of small holes at the end of the wooden slab and thus secure a slide with as many built-in cells as is required. Special slides for Foraminifera are made where large collections are to be mounted. These consist of $3'' \times 1''$ slips of black card on the central two-thirds of which are printed 60 numbered divisions. At each end a section of thick card is glued on, so as to leave the black portion in the form of a shallow rectangular cell. The card so prepared slides into an aluminum

mounts are used with low power objectives. The thickness commercially sold as No. 3 is the thinnest which should be considered, unless high powers are certain to be used.

Selection of a Cell

A cell on a dry mount serves mainly to support the coverslip, and the thickness required is therefore the primary consideration governing selection. Where the object is only a few hundredths of an inch in thickness, as in the case of diatoms or the smaller Radiolaria, a cement cell is the simplest. For a dry mount it is difficult to find a better cement than "gold size" and the preparation of a cell with this medium will therefore be described. Cement cells are made with a turntable in the manner shown in Fig. 7. Turntables are of many patterns but consist essentially of a rest for the hand and of a rotating circular plate bearing clips to hold the slide. These plates have the center marked, usually with a series of concentric rings engraved round it. The center of the slide must first be marked, and this is readily done by placing the slide on a sheet of paper, running a pencil around its edges, and then drawing the diagonals of the rectangle so formed. The slide is replaced on the rectangle and a dot made with India ink at the point immediately above the intersection of the diagonals. The slide is transferred to the circular plate of the turntable with the dot over the central point of the plate. The cement ring should be of the same diameter as the coverslip and one of the circles on the plate may be used as a guide; if there are no guide lines, a ring should be marked on the underside of the slide of the same diameter as the coverslip to be used. The brush is charged with the cement and the table spun quite rapidly by means of the milled ring shown in Fig. 7. It is safer to use this milled ring than to use the edge of the turntable because the slide frequently projects slightly beyond the edge and may be tapped off center with the finger used for spinning. The charged brush is brought slowly down over the marked ring and held in contact with the spinning slide so that a circle of cement is drawn on the glass face. Remember that you are not painting a thin ring of varnish on the slide; you are endeavoring to build up a relatively thick layer of cement by allowing it to flow from the brush to the slide. The hairs of the brush should never touch the glass itself; only the cement should touch the glass and thus be drawn off. In making a dry wholemount it is not very important how wide the ring is, but a $\frac{3}{16}$-inch-wide ring for a $\frac{3}{4}$-inch coverslip will be about correct. As many slides as are likely to be required are prepared at one time and may be left to dry indefinitely. Cells prepared with an ordinary sample of good gold size are safe to use after about 24 hrs. Building up a thick ring of cement by the applica-

tion of successive coats is rarely satisfactory. A gold-size ring prepared in the manner described will have a thickness between one- and three-thousandths of an inch. If thicker rings are required, it is better to use cells made of paper, cardboard, tin, or plastic.

Paper rings are stamped from a sheet of the required thickness (a good quality bond paper runs from three- to five-thousandths of an inch) or from Bristol board (6- to 12-thousandths of an inch) or from cardboard (up to a thickness of about $\frac{3}{16}$ of an inch). The best board to use is the dense black bookbinder's board (once known as *millboard*) since cheap yellow strawboards have such a rough surface that they can be made to adhere only with difficulty to a glass slide. Shellac is a good adhesive for attaching paper, or thin card, to a glass slide. A sheet of bond paper is coated on one side with commercial shellac varnish and then dried. Rings of the appropriate size are stamped from this shellac-coated sheet, either by using two punches successively, or with a double punch. The outer diameter of the cell should be larger than that of the coverslip, while the inner diameter should be less, so that when the cover is laid in place there will be an appreciable overlap of paper both inside and outside. A large number of these stamped rings may be cut at one time. When required for use, one is centered on the slide and then pressed into place with a hot iron, raised to a temperature which will melt the shellac. When the slide has cooled, it is turned upside down and observed with light reflected from it at an angle. If the cell is perfectly attached no adjustment of the angle of observation will produce mirrorlike reflections from the underside of the cell; if any considerable area of the underside of the cell shows mirrorlike reflections, it is not properly attached and had better be rejected. Cardboard cells more than $\frac{1}{16}$ of an inch thick are not satisfactory, for they are so porous that they admit moisture in humid weather and allow fungus growth on the specimen. The outside of the cell may, of course, be covered with some waterproof cement, but this makes a clumsy looking mount and it is better to substitute either a plastic or a tin cell.

Most plastic cells seem to be stamped out of vulcanite, though there is no reason why the numerous other plastics available today should not be used. It is almost impossible to punch cells from sheets of plastic more than $\frac{1}{16}$ of an inch thick without special machinery, so that it is better to buy them than to prepare them one's self. Excellent cells may, however, be prepared by anybody in possession of a lathe by buying extruded tubing, readily available in many types of plastic, and cutting from it lengths of the appropriate thickness. Opaque plastic should never be used to prepare cells more than $\frac{1}{8}$ of an inch high, since the opaque wall interferes with the illumination of the contained object. Homemade cells are better prepared from tin than plastic, since an ordinary hammer and punch may be used to cut sheet tin, or sheet pewter, up to a thickness of nearly $\frac{1}{8}$ of an inch. When cells have been punched from sheet, rather than turned from a tube on a lathe, they will be found to have a turned-down edge where the punch came through. This edge must be removed before they are cemented by placing the cell on a sheet of fine sandpaper—sandpaper blocks sold for sharpening draftsmen's pencils are excellent—and rubbing it backward and forward until a visual inspection shows that all the undersurface has come in contact with the abrasive.

Cementing of cells to glass depends far more for its success on the cleanliness of the glass than on the cement selected. Gold size has the tremendous advantage that it will adhere firmly to slightly dirty glass, but it has the disadvantage that three or four days are required before it is sufficiently firm to continue mounting. If one is prepared to take the trouble to clean the glass thoroughly, almost any of the cements given in Chapter 28 under V 11.2 may be employed. To make a firm bond with liquid cements it is best to turn a ring of the cement in the appropriate place on the slide with a turntable, and to apply a thin coat of cement to the underside of the cell. When both these coats are dry another thin coat is applied either to the slide or the cell. The two are then pressed together and dried under pressure. An easy way to apply this pressure is to take a 500-gram brass weight, which is usually to be found somewhere about the laboratory, and lay it carefully on top of the cell; or one can place another slide on top of the cell and clip the two slides together with a strong spring paper clip. Whatever method, or cement, is employed, each slide must be inspected after it is dry to make sure that it is adhering perfectly over all, or almost all, of the base; minute air holes will admit moisture and lead to molding of the contained specimen. If the cell has been fixed with a cement under pressure, a small quantity of surplus cement will almost always have been extruded both outside and inside at the point of contact of the ring. That which has been extruded outside should be left in position, unless there is a great deal too much of it, but the material inside should be carefully scraped off with the edge of a scalpel. It is most unwise to endeavor to remove this cement with a solvent which is likely to loosen the cell.

Selection of a Background

No background other than the glass itself is necessary when the object is to be prepared as a transparent wholemount; but many objects prepared as a dry wholemount are better displayed against a black or colored background. This background may either be a varnish applied to the bottom surface of the cell, or a disk of the appropriately colored paper cemented in position. The best black paper is that used to wrap photographic plates, but colored papers of all types are available. The paper is punched into disks which are attached to the bottom of the cell with any adhesive. They will not be subjected to any strain, and office mucilage, or any of the formulas given in Chapter 28 under V 11.1 will be found satisfactory. If a black background is to be painted in place, the most satisfactory paint is the optical dead black, listed by some scientific suppliers or available occasionally from scientific instrument makers. The only one of these which may be prepared at home is the formula of Martin 1872 given in Chapter 28 under V 13.1. This is an excellent dead-black cement but, since it has a gold-size base, is very slow drying. The best colored backgrounds are the old wax and resin formulas, particularly those of Martin 1872, Oschatz 1842, and Mendeleef (1942); the formulas for these are in Chapter 28 under the heading V 12.2. These media have the advantage that they are thermoplastic so that they may be used both to provide a smooth background and to secure the adhesion of the object to the bottom of the cell. They must be applied molten, and this is readily done if the circular stage of the turntable is heated while a small quantity of the cement is melted in a capsule. The cement is then applied with a brush exactly as though it were a varnish and permitted to cool. These colored cement backgrounds were widely used in the old days and should receive more attention than is at present the case.

Selection of a Cement to Hold the Object in a Cell

This is the most difficult, as well as the most important, of the decisions which have to be made. A well-prepared dry wholemount should not have any visible cement obscuring the object, but the object must at the same time be so firmly held that it will stand the relatively rough handling to which most slides are subjected. If the slide is to be mounted as a transparent wholemount, there is nothing, in the author's opinion, which can compare with gum tragacanth; and a simple dispersion of this gum in water, with the addition of some preservative such as thymol, is better than any of the more complex formulas. Tragacanth has the useful property of being transparent in thin films, but these thin films are not strong enough to hold objects larger than diatoms or butterfly scales. To use this gum one takes the slide on which the selected cell has already been prepared and turns, with the aid of a turntable, a *very* thin uniform layer on the bottom of the cell. The preparation of this thin uniform layer requires experience and skill for which no description can substitute. The adhesive is then allowed to dry and

the objects are arranged on it in the required positions. As soon as all the objects have been laid on the dry film, it is placed in a moist, warm atmosphere which is usually secured by bending open-mouthed over the slide and breathing very slowly and carefully. This makes the layer of tragacanth sticky so that the objects adhere; it will dry again in a few moments. This was the method used to prepare those pictures, made with the scales of butterflies, or selected diatoms, which used to be a feature of the catalogs of old-time microscope preparers. There is, however, no reason why the method should not be employed for scientific purposes, for it is often desirable, particularly when dealing with diatoms, to arrange them in a selected pattern. Small objects of this type may readily be placed in position if they are picked up on the end of a hair attached to a needle-holder; if they do not stick to the hair at the first trial, it is only necessary to moisten it with the lips.

Gum tragacanth may also be used to attach larger objects (such as Foraminifera and Radiolaria) to a paper background but it will not stick satisfactorily to either a resinous or wax surface. For these larger objects it is necessary to take a very small sable brush and place a drop of tragacanth on the surface of the paper background which has previously been moistened. The individual object is then picked up and pressed into the surface of the drop, which is then allowed to dry. If the appearance of the preparation is not very important a fairly thick smear of the mucilage may be placed all over the paper and the objects sprinkled on; this gives, however, a clumsy and unfinished appearance.

The principal objection to the use of optical-dead-black varnish as a background is that aqueous adhesives will not adhere to it. Both gum arabic and gum tragacanth will stick for a certain length of time, but the author has never known a mount made with these adhesives in which the object did not loosen within a period of two or three months. Nothing is more annoying than to take the trouble to make a mount of selected foraminiferans and then, a few months later, to find one or two specimens rolling about inside the cell. If you are using an optical-dead-black based on gold size, clear gold size itself is the best cement. A series of fine drops of gold size are placed in the positions which the objects are subsequently to occupy, and the objects added one after another. This will result in perfect adhesion, but the slide will have to be left uncovered and flat for at least two or three days, to harden the gold size before the cover is attached. When using an optical-dead-

at a relatively high temperature and all too often this high temperature causes the dead-black cement to break away from the glass. When using these cements, a piece about one third of the size of the object which it is desired to attach is broken from the mass. These pieces of cement are placed on the bottom of the cell in the positions which the objects will occupy and the slide placed on a hot table to melt the cement. The author prefers

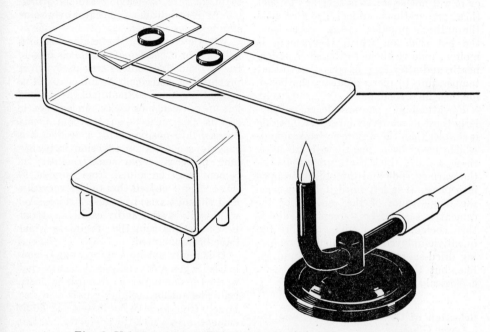

Fig. 8. Using a warm table to attach cells with marine glue.

black cement secured from a scientific supply house, it is necessary to secure some of the varnish medium in which the black has been suspended. The writer has seen hundreds of commercially prepared strewn slides of Radiolaria and Forami-nifera in which gum arabic had obviously been used on black varnish backgrounds and in which from a third to a half of all the specimens were loose. As a second choice to the varnishes, there may be employed one of the Canada-balsam-resin cements of the type of Fant 1932 (Chapter 28, V 12.2), or one of the Venice-turpen-tine cements of the type of Gage 1896. Unfortunately these cements have to be used

the type of table shown in Fig. 8 which consists of a strip of heavy metal, preferably copper, bent back twice on itself and mounted on four legs. The top of the upper strip projects beyond the bent portions. A burner is placed under this projection and adjusted to keep the end of the strip well above the boiling point of water. It will be seen that the temperature steadily diminishes from shelf to shelf, that of the upper shelf being highest, that of the second shelf being lower, while the bottom shelf is scarcely warm. To determine whereabouts on the shelf to place the slide it is only necessary to place a few chips of cement at about one-inch intervals along the first and second shelves. After a few moments it will be apparent which point is just at the melting point of the cement in question. The slide bearing the small pieces in the position where the objects are to be mounted is then placed at this point and each object is individually placed in its own little pool of molten cement. It must be left at this temperature long enough for the object to reach the temperature of the cement or it will not stick. It is best not to cool these preparations suddenly, so that it is the author's practice to take them from the hot shelf on which the cement is molten, remove them to the shelf underneath, and after they have cooled to that temperature to place them on the bench for their final cooling.

For attaching opaque objects, particularly those of relatively large size, nothing is simpler than the wax-resin backgrounds which have been mentioned. In using these, a fairly thick coating is applied to the warmed slide and the object dropped into place. It is left until it has reached the temperature of the cement, or the cement is seen to be "creeping," and is then cooled. These media are more frequently employed by botanists for mounting dried-spore cases of mosses, and the like, but they also work admirably for zoological specimens.

Selection of Cement for Attaching the Cover Glass

Before discussing the selection of a cement for the attachment of a cover glass, which is the last step in the preparation of a dry wholemount, it is necessary to insert a warning that the word dry as applied to dry wholemounts must be interpreted literally. If wholemounts are being made in an American laboratory in winter at an inside temperature of 70°F. and an outside temperature around 0°F., no difficulty will be encountered since the atmospheric humidity is practically nil. If, however, the humidity is relatively high some method of drying the specimen must be used. The writer has in his possession several imperfectly sealed dry whole-

mounts of ground sections of bone, made in Europe about forty years ago, which are entirely covered with fungus hyphae. The object may, it is true, be treated with some fungicide but this is rarely as effective as, and usually more trouble than, making sure that the mount is dry before sealing. If the object has been attached by one of the techniques which involves heating the slide and cement, it will probably have dried sufficiently, but it is desirable to make sure by leaving the uncovered mount overnight in a desiccator over some standard desiccant.

When a coverslip is to be attached to a gold-size or other cement cell, it is best to use the same cement as was used in the preparation of the cell. A thin coat of this cement is applied to the top of the cell and left until it becomes tacky. A clean coverslip is then placed on top and firmly pressed into position with a needle. It is easy to see whether adhesion is perfect and, if necessary, a small quantity of cement may be added from outside. It must be emphasized that only a very thin coat should be used because a thick layer will inevitably run in by capillary attraction and thus ruin the specimens which have been mounted.

It is really not important what cement is used when a coverslip is to be attached to the top of a paper, cardboard, or plastic cell. The author invariably uses gold size, largely from force of habit, but any liquid cement or varnish is adequate. A thin layer is painted on the upper surface of the cell and the coverslip pressed into place. The preparation should now be placed on one side until the adhesive is dry, and then finished with a coat of some black cement. Asphalt varnish [Benoit-Bazelle (1942) is an excellent formula] or Brunswick black (Beale 1880) both have the required characteristics of providing a waterproof seal while retaining a certain amount of flexibility. These formulas, and those of other suitable cements, are given under V 12.2 in Chapter 28. The old sealing-wax varnishes, and the modern cellulose-ester varnishes have the disadvantage that they tend to become brittle and break off after some years.

Specific Example

PREPARATION OF A STREWN SLIDE OF FORAMINIFERA OR RADIOLARIA

Wholemounts of the dried tests of Foraminifera, either fossil or recent, are customarily referred to as *strewn slides* even though the individual tests may be arranged in place. Tests of Foraminifera may be obtained either from sand, from marine sludge, or from fossil deposits, and the method by which the shells are separated is in each instance different. Radiolaria are almost invariably obtained from fossil deposits.

Forminiferal sands, which may be purchased or collected, are the best source of material. Large numbers of shells are thrown onto beaches in many parts of the world where they form whitish ridges. If such a ridge is observed it is only necessary to scoop off the surface with a spoon and to preserve it for further examination. Many scientific supply houses sell these sands. The separation of the dried shells from the sand is relatively simple. The whole may either be sprinkled onto the surface of a large vessel of cold water, in which case the majority of the shells will float, since they are filled with air; or carbon tetrachloride, the high specific gravity of which ensures that Foraminiferal shells with only a small quantity of air enclosed will rise to the surface, may be substituted for water. If only a few shells are required they may be picked from the surface of the flotation medium with a brush and laid to dry on a disk of fine filter paper. If all the shells are required, the surface layer containing the floating shells should be poured off through a fine sieve. Bolting silk is the best material from which to prepare this sieve, though fine brass screen wire may also be used.

The separation of tests from marine deposits dredged from the bottom is not so easy since they are, in this case, mixed not only with particles of sand but also with considerable quantities of fine sludge which may include some organic matter. If the sludge is free from organic matter, the mass may be passed through a series of sieves under a jet of running water; but even under these circumstances the tests will usually be discolored. Laporte 1946, p. 194 recommends that such tests be boiled in an alkaline solution of calcium hypochlorite (*eau de Javelle*) which serves the double purpose of bleaching the stains and removing any trace of organic matter which may remain. If the sludge is heavily contaminated with organic matter, the mass should be boiled for some time in a weak (2%) solution of sodium or potassium hydroxide before being sieved. Cushman 1940, p. 26 suggests also that tests may be separated as the old gold miners separated gold by rotating the mass in a flattened dish. The Foraminifera, being somewhat lighter than the rest of the material present, will collect round the edges of the dish, from which they may be jerked with a circular motion.

Tests of fossil Foraminifera may be obtained from sandy deposits. They are also found embedded in clay deposits, or chalk. Foraminifera concreted in limestone cannot, in most cases, be removed and made into wholemounts. Foraminiferal tests obtained from sandy deposits may be separated by flotation in the manner already described, but these shells are usually dirty either from chalk or clay, and must be thoroughly cleaned if a satisfactory mount is to be prepared. It is best to boil them after they have been separated in a 5% solution of sodium carbonate. After they have boiled for some time the beaker containing them is removed from the flame and the Foraminifera are allowed to settle to the bottom. The cloudy alkaline solution is then poured off and replaced with fresh solution and this is repeated until the tests are sufficiently clean. If the dirt is particularly tenacious, it may often be loosened by boiling the tests in a relatively small quantity of the alkaline solution which is then poured while boiling over a mass of cracked ice. This sudden temperature change will often loosen dirt which cannot be removed by any other method. When tests are cleaned in this manner it is essential that they should be thoroughly soaked, and preferably also boiled, in a large quantity of distilled water to remove the alkali.

Methods for the separation of foraminiferal tests from shale and clay deposits vary according to the degree of hardness of the deposit. The first exploratory step should always be to boil the mass in a 5% solution of sodium carbonate. If the solution speedily turns cloudy, it is evident that the material is being disintegrated satisfactorily and it is only necessary to continue boiling long enough for the tests to separate. The cloudy solution should be stirred up and poured off from time to time into a large cylinder of distilled water. This should be allowed to stand for about 10 minutes, to permit all the foraminiferal tests to fall to the bottom, and the cloudy supernatant liquid then poured off. This may be repeated as often as experience shows to be necessary to collect a mixture of foraminiferal tests and fragments of the shale mass at the bottom of the cylinder. Separation of the tests from the shale fragments may either be by hand under a binocular microscope, or the mass may be dried in an oven and sprinkled on cold water, or carbon tetrachloride, for the flotation method previously described. If the preliminary boiling in sodium carbonate does not result in a sufficiently rapid disintegration, two possible methods remain. The old method used to be to soak the mass thoroughly in water and then to freeze it; a household freezer giving temperatures of $-10°$ or $-20°$C. is excellent. The frozen piece is then removed and thrown into boiling water which almost invariably breaks the mass into smaller pieces. This process of alternately freezing and boiling is continued until the pieces have become sufficiently small to enable one to complete the separation of the tests with boiling alkali.

An interesting alternative method for shale has been suggested by Driver 1928 (*J. Pal.*, **1**:253) who subjects the pieces to the action of high pressure steam in a laboratory autoclave. The pressure is run up to about 20 lbs., maintained at this for a few minutes, and the autoclave then blown off to diminish the pressure as rapidly as possible. The repetition of this process results in the disintegration of materials which resist every other method.

The separation of foraminiferal tests from chalk is a relatively simple process. If one is only collecting the tests at random, so that it does not matter if many of the more fragile forms are broken, the old method of brushing under water has much to recommend it. A piece of chalk is held in one hand under the surface water and a brush (an old tooth brush is excellent) is scrubbed over the surface. Large numbers of tests, which fall to the bottom of the container, are removed by this method while the chalk remains in suspension and can be poured off. Tests prepared by this method are never clean and must subsequently be boiled in alkali to remove the adherent chalk. If it is desired to collect the greatest possible number of shells, chalk can often be disintegrated by boiling either in 5% potassium hydroxide or in 5% sodium carbonate; this is, however, a prolonged and messy business. Chalk may also be disintegrated by the freezing and thawing process, or by the autoclave process already mentioned.

The siliceous skeletons of radiolarians are cleaned altogether differently and it is difficult to improve on the method of Roudabush 1938 (*Ward's Bul.*, 9). No preliminary treatment is needed for the easily disintegrated Barbados earths though other material may have to be disintegrated by one of the methods already described. The disintegrated pieces are then boiled in 10% potassium hydroxide for about 20 minutes. Throw the whole mass into 10 times its own volume of water, stir vigorously, and allow to settle for 10 minutes. Pour off the milky solution; refill the beaker with water. Stir vigorously, allow to settle for 15 seconds and save the supernatant liquid. Repeat the process; the two batches of decanted water will be found to have most of the liberated radiolarians.

The pieces remaining at the bottom of the beaker can be again boiled with 10% potassium hydroxide and further batches of liberated radiolarians poured off and accumulated.

The cleaned radiolarians in the accumulated decantations are allowed to settle for about 20 minutes after the last batch has been added and the supernatant water poured off. Add carefully about twice as much nitric acid as there is sludge and boil for 20 minutes. Again wash with water, allow to settle and decant. Now carefully add twice as much 10% potassium hydroxide as there is sludge, boil for 20 minutes and again wash by decantation. The material is now nearly clean—if it is not, repeat the nitric acid-potassium hydroxide cycle.

Concentrate the nearly clean skeletons and then cover them with their own volume of ammonium hydroxide. Stir at intervals for about 10 minutes, then slowly add an equal volume of nitric acid. Wash thoroughly by decantation and examine the skeletons; if they are not now clean, repeat the ammonium hydroxide-nitric acid cycle. Concentrate the sludge as much as possible, wash it thoroughly with 95% alcohol, and then either allow to dry for strewn slides or store in alcohol and make balsam mounts in the manner described in Chapter 6.

After the foraminiferan tests or radiolarian skeletons are accumulated in a small watch glass, they should be dry and quite free from any of the reagents used to clean them. It is also necessary to have ready on the bench a binocular dissecting microscope, two fine sable brushes, slides on which cells have already been cemented, and a container of mucilage of gum tragacanth.

The author prefers to make all foraminiferal mounts in cells prepared from rings of vulcanite with bottoms of black paper. These should have been prepared the day before in the following manner. First take the required number of slides and clean them thoroughly. It is not necessary for the slides to be chemically clean —it is necessary only that the slide should be grease-free. A simple method of degreasing slides is to take a commercial scouring powder, of the type used for household purposes, and make it into a paste with water. This paste is smeared liberally on all surfaces of the required number of slides which are then dried. When the slide is dry, the scouring powder is removed by vigorous rubbing with a

soft cloth. While the slides are drying, the required number of vulcanite cells are laid out and a piece of fine sandpaper secured. Each cell is held on the sandpaper with the ball of the first finger and rubbed, with a circular motion, until all the lower surface has been abraded. The cell is then turned over and the process repeated. One side of the cell is then given a thin coat of gold size and placed with firm pressure on the center of a glass slide, which should then be left for three or four days. Any gold size which has been pressed out of the inner surface should be removed with the edge of a sharp pointed scalpel. A number of disks of black paper of the required size are then taken, coated on one side with any satisfactory adhesive, and pressed onto the bottom of the cell. It must be remembered that the cell should be of such a size that the coverslip, when laid on top, does not reach to the outer edge of the cell but only halfway across it. This may conveniently be done by using a ¾-inch cell with an 18-millimeter coverslip. The thickness of the cell selected is not of major importance but the writer usually prefers about $\frac{1}{32}$ of an inch when mounting Foraminifera.

Let us suppose first that it is desired to prepare, from the materials at hand, an ordinary strewn slide like those sold by biological supply houses. It is only necessary to moisten slightly the paper at the bottom of one of the prepared cells and to smear mucilage of tragacanth liberally over the surface. Plenty of tests are thrown onto the mucilage and the slide is placed on one side for about 10 minutes to dry. As soon as the mucilage is dry, the slide is inverted over the watch glass containing the tests and tapped sharply with the forefinger. This will cause all those tests which have not become attached to the mucilage to fall back into the stock, and will usually leave a continuous coat of foraminiferal tests over the black paper.

It is generally, however, more satisfactory to mount selected tests in the required position. In this case, the black paper on one of the prepared slides is thoroughly moistened and a fine sable brush is used to place small portions of mucilage of tragacanth in the positions which the selected tests are to occupy.

Each drop of tragacanth should be slightly smaller, both in breadth and in thickness, than the test which is going to be placed on it. These drops of mucilage are most conveniently placed in the correct position with the aid of a binocular dissecting microscope.

As soon as the drops have been placed the slide is pushed out of the field of the dissecting microscope and the watch glass, containing the specimens to be mounted, pushed into the field. A clean sable brush is then moistened with the lips. It should be sufficiently wet to cause the tip of the brush to come to a point but not sufficiently impregnated with saliva for any liquid to be showing. The tip of this brush is touched down onto the required specimen and held in the field of the dissecting microscope with the right hand, while the left hand pushes the watch glass of specimens out of place and replaces the glass slide. It cannot be emphasized too much that the paper must be liberally moistened or the drops of gum tragacanth will dry in the period of time that it takes to select tests. If, when the cell is replaced under the binocular microscope, it is observed that the mucilage is dry, do not attempt to remoisten it; place another drop of mucilage on top of the dry portion. The shell, on the tip of the fine brush, is now pressed down in the selected position. If it is not exactly as required, it may be adjusted with the tip of a needle. After all the tests required on any one slide have been placed in position, a fine sable brush is used to place a drop of water on top of each shell. This makes certain that there will be a perfect adhesion of the shell to the underlying mucilage.

On a very dry day (that is, one on which the relative humidity is below 20%) the preparations may be sealed immediately; on humid days it is best to place the slides in a desiccator overnight. In either case, the next step is simple. The top of each cell is spread with a *very* thin coat of gold size and a clean coverslip dropped into position. It is best to place one edge of the coverslip down first, supporting the other edge with a needle, and then to lower it by withdrawing the needle. As soon as it is in contact with the cell it is pressed down all round its circumference with a needle. It is not important that it should be in contact all over since further coats of cement will be placed on top. The initial coat of gold size is intended only to hold the coverslip in position through the next stages and it is better to have a very thin coat with an imperfect adhesion than to have a coat so thick that cement spreads onto the inner surface of the coverslip. The slides, with their attached covers, are then placed on one side, preferably in a desiccator, for a period of about 24 hours to set the gold size. The slide is finished on a turntable (Fig. 7) by turning onto the upper surface of the cell a coat of any selected cement. The author prefers either asphalt varnish, or Brunswick black, though any tough and flexible cement may be used. It is quite important that the cell should be accurately centered on the turntable, and though this may be roughly done with the aid of the concentric circles engraved on the table, it is usually necessary to spin it once or twice and to make necessary adjustments manually. If lack of experience renders this difficult, it is suggested that a needle should be held stationary above the edge of the cell and the turntable rotated slowly. The table should be stopped when the edge of the cell (presuming it to be eccentrically placed) is at the maximum possible distance from the needle. The cell is then pushed one half of this distance towards the needle, the needle replaced over the edge of the slide, turned as before, and readjusted. By this method even the most inexperienced can center a cell perfectly within a few moments. Only one coat of varnish is really necessary, though some people prefer to put on four or five, using the last coats to fill up the edge of the cell which is thus doubly protected. In the author's opinion this is not necessary and makes a clumsy mount.

If, through accident, a test becomes detached in one of these slides it may be repaired easily. The coverslip should be broken by a sharp blow with the handle of a scalpel and the pieces removed with a pair of forceps. The top of the cell is then scraped clean with a scalpel and the test recemented in place.

2

Fluid Wholemounts—Aqueous Type

General Principles

A fluid wholemount in an aqueous medium is essentially a miniature museum mount in which the glass jar has been replaced by a cell mounted on a microscope slide. With the exception of the selection of a slide—for none other than glass is suitable—the choices confronting the technician are very much those discussed in the preparation of dry wholemounts in the last chapter, though the selection is in each instance different. It is necessary to select successively a type of cell, a cement for attaching the cell to the slide, a cement for attaching the coverslip to the cell, and finally the mounting medium itself.

Selection of a Cell

The author prefers to use concave-ground glass slides instead of cells. At the present time these concave glass slides are both difficult to obtain, and unsatisfactory when obtained, from American sources. It is, however, possible to secure in Great Britain slides into which have been ground circular concavities from 9 to 20 millimeters in diameter, or oval concavities in many sizes. The use of cavity slides avoids the difficulties of attaching a cell, and the slides are more waterproof than any cell. It is to be hoped that American suppliers will make cavity slides available to technicians who wish to make wholemounts in fluid media.

If, however, cells must be used, the choice is very limited. It is a waste of time to take paper and cardboard cells and to endeavor, by soaking them in various resins, to make them take the place of a plastic or metal cell. Cells of vulcanite anb tin are obtainable or may be prepared with the aid of a punch. These should, before use, be flattened on both sides in the manner described in the last chapter. Where a very deep mount is required, it is better to use a glass cell which can be cut from thick-walled glass tube and ground flat on both faces. These cells are usually only obtainable in a ¾-inch size and care should be taken, as with other cells, to make sure that the edges of the coverslip selected will lie on the surface of the cell. It is difficult to seal a dry wholemount, and impossible to seal an aqueous wholemount, in which the edge of the coverslip and the edge of the cell coincide. An almost perfect relationship is that of an 18-millimeter coverslip to a ¾-inch cell, but unfortunately both 18 mm. and ¾-inch appear to be used interchangeably by scientific suppliers so that the measurements must be checked before mounting.

When very thin objects are to be mounted, a cell can be made from gold size in the manner described in the last chapter.

Selection of a Cell Cement

The selection of a cement to attach the cell to the slide is of far more importance in aqueous fluid mounts than in dry mounts. The cement must not only be capable of holding the cell firmly to the glass, but must also make a waterproof seal which must remain waterproof for many years. In the author's experience no varnish is satisfactory, and one is forced to turn to the thermoplastic cements. Among these marine glue (Chapter 28, V 12.2 Beale 1880) or, if this is not obtainable, the very similar cement of Harting 1880 are the best. The marine glue here specified bears no relation to the so-called marine glue commonly sold today. The old-style marine glue, which is essentially a mixture of rubber (or gutta-percha) with shellac is one of the most water-resistant cements ever invented. This style of marine glue can still be obtained from suppliers of microscope-mounting accessories in Europe but does not appear at present to be on the market in the United States. If it is unobtainable, and the technician is unwilling to make his own supply, gold size is the next best substitute. This gold size must, however, be of the old-fashioned kind specified for microscope mounting and not one of the new varnishes which are placed on the market for the benefit of gilders. It should perhaps be explained at this point that gold size was the material used by the early gilders to apply sheets of gold leaf on large areas. It was partially polymerized and partially oxidized linseed oil mixed with small quantities of resin and diluted with turpentine. To the old gilders it had the advantage that it took a long time to harden so that it retained a tacky surface, to which the gold leaf could be applied, over a long period. The advantage of this material to the maker of microscope slides is that both boiled linseed oil and turpentine will selectively "wet" glass—that is, they will displace a fine film of water from the surface of the glass. They can therefore be applied to damp glass to which they will remain adherent. Modern gilder's varnishes—sometimes called gold size—have the advantage to the modern gilder that they remain tacky for any specified period; to the microscope mounter they have the disadvantage that they are made in the interests of the gilder, not of the technician, and rarely contain ingredients which will adhere to moist glass surfaces.

The attachment of a cell with gold size was described in Chapter 1 and need only be briefly reiterated. The slide is placed on a turntable (Fig. 7) and a ring of gold size of about the width of the cell turned on the center of the slide. The undersurface of the cell is given a thin coat of gold size and both the slide and the cell are placed on one side until the varnished surfaces have become tacky. An additional thin coat of gold size is then applied either to the cell, or to the slide, and the two pressed together. Since, however, a waterproof seal is required, the cell must be pressed firmly against the slide until the cement has hardened, either by laying a heavy weight on top of the cell, or by placing another slide on top and clamping the two together.

The attachment of a cell with marine glue is an altogether different proposition. If a solution of marine glue is used, a thick ring is turned on the slide and a thick coat is applied to the underside of the cell. Both cell and slide are then warmed (the lowest step of the hot table shown in Fig. 8 may be employed) until all the solvent has been driven off. The slide is then laid on the upper shelf, which should be heated above the melting point of marine glue. The cell is placed on the now molten ring of cement and maintained in constant contact with it until its own coat of cement has melted and fused with the cement on the slide. The slide should next be transferred to the second or third shelf (which should be just below the melting point of the cement) and a heavy weight placed on top while the cement slowly solidifies. After a few minutes at this solidification temperature, the slide is removed, still with the weight or clips in position, and laid on one side to cool. It is then turned upside down and inspected to make sure that no air bubbles have been caught in the cement.

If solid marine glue is used, chips must be scraped from the block with a knife. A layer of these chips is then placed on one surface of the cell (which in this case must be of tin or some other metal) and the cell laid on the upper shelf of the hot table at a temperature which will melt the cement. A heated needle is used to remove as many air bubbles as possible from the molten cement and the glass slide is laid alongside it on the hot table. The hot slide is then pressed firmly to the molten cement on the upper surface of the ring. As soon as the ring is firmly pressed into place the slide is inverted, placed on the second shelf, and a heavy weight placed on top until the cement is cooled.

Whether gold size or marine glue be employed, care must be taken to remove those portions which have been extruded into the interior of the cell. These cements swell up and become white in the presence of water, and even a trace of remaining cement will give an unfinished appearance to the slide. The excess cement may be removed by scraping with a scalpel, and a final cleaning may be given with a 10% solution of potassium, or sodium, hydroxide, which is wiped over the inside of the cell with a piece of cotton held in a pair of forceps. The cell is then thoroughly washed and laid on one side to dry. It is best to cement cells onto slides in advance of requirements and thus secure an adequate reserve.

Selection of a Preservative Medium

The introduction of formaldehyde to microscopic technique was welcomed as the beginning of the millennium, and almost all of the older aqueous media were thrown overboard by mounters. This is to be regretted since formaldehyde is by no means a perfect medium, particularly for the preservation of small invertebrates and single-celled plants, so that attention should be given to the list of aqueous preservative media in Chapter 17 (P 11.1). These media are mostly variations on the fluid of Goadby which was a mixture of sodium chloride and ammonium alum—designed to approximate an isotonic solution—containing a very small quantity of mercuric chloride as a preservative. Some of these solutions (cf. Kronecker 1907) had an alkali added to preserve the green color of small algae. Another excellent preservative of green material is the solution of Ripart and Petit which is given in Chapter 18 (F 3000.0010 Ripart and Petit 1884) because it serves the dual purpose of fixation and preservation. A very similar formula was published by Woods in 1929 (Chapter 17, P 11.1) as a preservative for green algae.

Simple solutions of various reagents may also be employed. The best of these is formaldehyde, which for purposes of mounting should never be neutralized since, once subjected to this treatment, it is liable to develop precipitates. The ordinary 1 to 10 dilution of 40% formaldehyde, which is commonly employed for the preservation of gross biological specimens, is far too strong for microscope mounting of the type being discussed. It must be remembered that these strong solutions become greatly diluted from the water contained in the specimens placed in them, whereas in the case of a microscope mount the material will have already been impregnated with formaldehyde before being mounted. A dilution of 1 to 100 of the commercial 40% formaldehyde is adequate as a mounting fluid. Camphor water and chloroform water, which are merely saturated solutions of these reagents in distilled water, are also excellent preservatives for the more delicate Protozoa and Algae.

It must be emphasized that if glycerol is added to these media, the material will have to be handled by the special methods necessary for making glycerol mounts, which are described in the next chapter.

Selection of a Coverslip Cement

Though the cell is best attached to the slide with a thermoplastic cement, it must be obvious that a liquid cement must be used to attach the coverslip to a cell containing a fluid mounting medium. Numerous formulas have been developed for this purpose, and the author most warmly recommends either gold size, or the cements given under Behrens 1883 or Carany 1937 in Chapter 28 (V 12.1). These last two cements are quick drying, which is desirable, since at least three successive coats must be used properly to seal an aqueous wholemount. The first of these coats is designed to block off the water, and to provide a temporary support for a second layer of waterproof cement which would not adhere to the moist glass. This second coat of waterproof cement should always be an asphalt varnish (formulas are given in Chapter 28, V 11.2) and, if the black color is objected to, any colored varnish may be coated over the asphalt to provide a more finished appearance to the mount.

Sealing the Coverslip in Place

It was pointed out in the last chapter, and must be reiterated here, that before any sealing cement can be applied a protective barrier must be erected to prevent this cement from running in by capillary attraction and mixing with the contents of the cell. More wholemounts are spoiled by this running in of cement than by any other method. The procedure, when mounting on a flat slide, or one containing a concavity, is somewhat different from that which is used in sealing a cell. The former will be described first.

The process of attaching a coverslip and sealing it in place on an aqueous fluid mount in a concave slide is shown in section in Figs. 9–14. Fig. 9 shows a longitudinal section of the concave slide with the protective ring of cement in place. This ring should be the narrowest and the thickest which can be made with the aid of the finest sable-hair brush. It should certainly not be wider than $\frac{1}{64}$ of an inch, and if it can be built up to twice this depth, it will be all the better. This ring also assists in attaching the coverslip, so that the gold size should be given time to become tacky before the mount is made. It is a matter of convenience to run such rings on the turntable on the night before the mount is to be made. A ring made from a good specimen of gold size will remain tacky for at least 48 hours after it is turned. The diameter of this ring is quite critical. It should be at the outer edge about $\frac{1}{64}$ of an inch less than the diameter of the coverslip. If it is smaller than this, too big a space will be left between the edge of the cell and the coverslip; if it is larger than this, perfect sealing is impossible.

Fig. 10 shows the same slide after the object has been placed in the cavity and a sufficient quantity of the selected mounting medium placed on top of it. Notice that a great excess of the medium is provided and permitted to rise up in a convex meniscus. After this drop has been placed in position the mount should be inspected carefully to make quite certain that the fluid is in contact with the protective ring of varnish all the way around the edge. If the slide is perfectly clean it

may so happen that the meniscus does not extend to the varnish ring, leaving a small air gap which will result in a bubble—almost impossible to remove subsequently. The next step is that of placing the coverslip in position. The coverslip must *never* be let down from one side in the manner customarily taught in making balsam mounts. It must be held between the thumb and second finger and lowered horizontally until it is in the position shown in Fig. 11. It will be seen that the object remains in the central position in which it started whereas, if the cover were lowered from the side, the object would inevitably be pulled by capillary attraction to one corner whence it would be almost impossible to displace it.

Fig. 12 shows that the coverslip has been let down and pressed with a needle onto the surface of the tacky protective ring of gold size. The excess fluid has been pushed out and mopped up with a filter paper. Care should be taken to remove the whole of the fluid between the outer projecting edge of the coverslip and the ring to which it is attached. This is one of the most critical stages in the whole procedure. The needle used to press the coverslip in place should be run with a circular movement round the coverslip vertically above the protective ring, and pressure should be continued until the glass is clearly in contact with the gold size at all points. The slide is then placed on the turntable, centered, and a ring of the selected second cement applied round the edge.

The result of this is shown in Fig. 13, where it will be seen that the edge of the coverslip is firmly embedded in the cement which has run under as far as the protective barrier. The existence of the protective barrier and the overhang of the coverslip insure, therefore, that there shall be a good, thick layer of this cement in position. The slide is now laid on one side until this first protective layer is thoroughly dry and then (Fig. 14) as many rings of asphalt varnish turned over the top as are required. It is an excellent thing to apply two coats of asphalt varnish, naturally permitting the first to dry before applying the second, at the

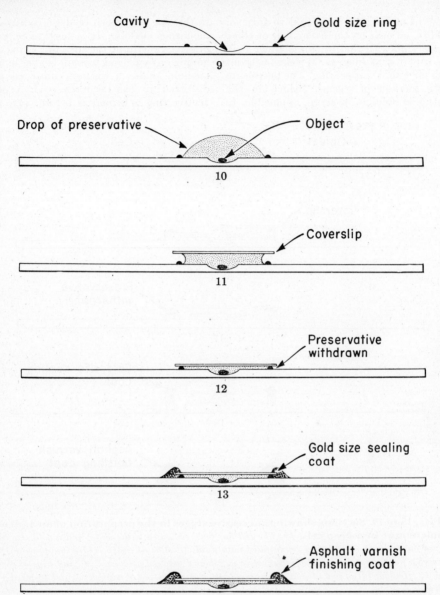

Figs. 9 to 14. Longitudinal section of a cavity slide showing successive stages in the preparation of an aqueous wholemount. *9. Protective ring of gold size turned. 10. Object placed in position in a large drop of preservative. 11. Coverslip held horizontally in contact with preservative. 12. Coverslip lowered and preservative withdrawn between protective ring and edge of coverslip. 13. Heavy sealing coat of gold size applied. 14. Finishing coat of asphalt varnish applied over gold size.*

time of making the slide and to turn an additional coat on top every two or three years. Slides treated in this manner may be kept for as long as 20 years without any air bubbles appearing. The petroleum jelly method of Spence, which in the author's opinion is more applicable to

to the side of the cell or dissolved in the mounting medium. It is best to remove dissolved air from the medium either by boiling or by placing a small beaker of the medium under a vacuum until all the dissolved air has been removed. A protective ring is turned as before (Fig. 15)

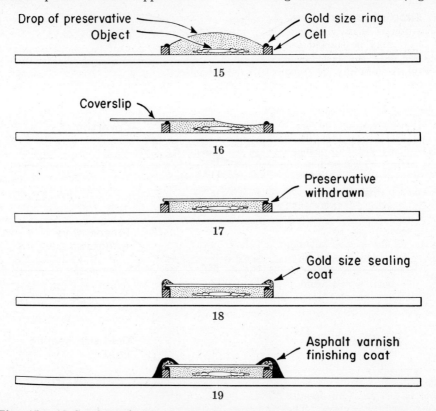

Figs. 15 to 19. Sections showing successive stages in the preparation of an aqueous wholemount in a deep cell. *15. The cell has been cemented to the slide, and a gold size ring turned on its inner edge, before being filled with fluid. 16. The coverslip is slid into position. 17. Coverslip pushed into place and preservative withdrawn between gold size ring and edge of coverslip. 18. Heavy sealing coat of gold size applied. 19. Finishing coat of asphalt varnish applied over gold size.*

glycerol than to aqueous mounts, is given in the next chapter. For a description of a modification of this method applied to aqueous mounts, refer to Spence 1940 (*Microscope*, **4**:121).

The method of mounting in a relatively deep cell is shown in Figs. 15–19. Particular care has to be taken in this case to prevent the appearance of air bubbles which may come from air either attached

but it will be seen, in this case, that this protective ring is on the inner edge of the upper surface of the cell. The cell is then filled with the preservative fluid, allowing an excess to rise in a concave meniscus. To make sure that no air is caught on the irregular surface of the inside of the cell one may now either place the whole under a vacuum or, more conveniently, take a clean brush and wipe the inside of the cell with it. Particular attention should be paid to the junction of the cell with the slide, where trapped air bubbles are often caught. The author finds it best not to lower the coverslip horizontally, as in the previous mount, but to slide the cover horizontally onto the cell. This is shown in Fig. 16 where the coverslip has reached halfway across. This illustration is slightly exaggerated since the cover may be started farther across and slid only the last few millimeters. Care must naturally be taken that the gold-size protective ring is sufficiently dry not to smear the coverslip as it is pushed. If, when the cover reaches nearly to the other side of the cell, a small air pocket is left, it may be filled with mountant and the coverslip pushed neatly into place. It is also possible to lower the coverslip from one side—that is, to place one edge in contact with one edge of the cell and to lower the other with a needle—provided that object is sufficiently large not to become displaced.

Fig. 17 shows the coverslip in place after it has been pressed in contact with the protective ring and after the mounting fluid has been wiped from the outside. This is more difficult, and must be done more carefully, than in the case of the flat mount previously discussed. A ring of the first sealing cement is then (Fig. 18) applied to fill the gap between the overlap of the coverslip and the protective ring on the inner edge of the cell. It is not necessary to do this on a turntable since this cement need not come onto the top of the coverslip at all but may be applied directly from the side. After this cement has had time to dry one should then build up (Fig. 19) several layers of asphalt varnish. So many layers are required to fill the angle between the cell and the coverslip that it is often desirable to use some cement containing a pigment. If a pigmented cement is used it should, however, be given a coat of waterproof asphalt varnish on the top before the slide can be considered finished. The purpose of a thick layer of cement, filling the angle between the cell and the slide, is to provide additional mechanical support to the cell. The most frequent cause of breakdown of thick aqueous mounts is either the complete detachment of the cell from the slide, or the cracking of the cement which holds the cell in place with the subsequent intrusion of small air bubbles.

Specific Examples

PREPARATION OF A WHOLEMOUNT OF MICROCYSTIS IN THE FLUID OF RIPART AND PETIT 1884

Wholemounts of unicellular algae prepared in any medium except balsam are rarely seen nowadays. These balsam mounts, though they display fairly clearly the internal structure of the alga, give the student not the faintest idea of what the material looks like in life. Nothing is more valuable for the laboratory instruction of classes, who will subsequently study in the field, than a series of wholemounts of phytoplankton preserved so as to resemble, as nearly as possible, the living material. It is the author's opinion that the solution of Ripart and Petit, used as described in this example, gives as close an approximation to the appearance of the living material as can be produced. Very weak solutions of formaldehyde are often used for the preservation of vials of phytoplankton concentrates for laboratory study, but it is not, in the writer's opinion, a satisfactory medium for the preparation of a wholemount.

The blue-green alga microcystis has been selected for the present example because it happens to be the most common alga found in large bodies of water in the district from which the author is writing. Other blue-green and green algae may just as well be prepared by the present method. It is a waste of time to endeavor to concentrate algal collections in the field. Several gallons of the greenish water containing these specimens should be collected and brought back to the laboratory for immediate processing.

There are two ways of concentrating the specimens. The first is to add to the fluid containing them considerable quantities of the required preservative, to permit the algae to settle to the bottom, and then to pour off the supernatant liquid. One of the modern *plankton* centrifuges will do the job twice as efficiently in half the time. These plankton centrifuges are built as miniature milk separators save for the fact that the vertical plates of the latter are missing. That is, the plankton centrifuge is merely a small cup which is rotated at high speeds while a continuous stream of the material to be concentrated is poured into the top. The plankton organisms, being the heavier, are collected round the edge while the cleared water passes out at the bottom. The material should be put through the separator twice and with its aid it is possible to concentrate five gallons of plankton into 100 milliliters in about five minutes. These concentrates must be processed immediately; within a space of ten minutes the available oxygen in the water will have been used up and the concentrate will die with a consequent degradation of its appearance.

The solution of Ripart and Petit, here recommended, may be used as a fixative for animal tissues as well as a preservative for plant tissues and is accordingly given in Chapter 18 under the heading F 4000.0010. It is a weak solution of copper acetate and copper chloride, acidified with acetic acid and with a small quantity of camphor added. More modern writers (Mayer 1920, p. 232) have suggested the substitution of thymol for camphor, and menthol may equally well be employed. It is unwise to use a saturated solution of any of these compounds, for crystals are likely to form through the slight evaporation which always takes place in a mount. One therefore takes equal quantities of a saturated solution of camphor or thymol, and distilled water, and then adds to each liter of this mixture two grams each of copper acetate and copper chloride together with seven milliliters of acetic acid. About ten times its own volume of preservative should be added to the concentrate, the bottle containing which is then carefully tilted backward and forward at intervals for the next twenty-four hours before the organisms are allowed finally to concentrate at the bottom of the jar and the supernatant reagent poured off. This preserved concentrate may be kept indefinitely in the dark and mounts made at any time.

Preparation of the actual mounts must be done on two successive days: on the first of these the cells are prepared and placed on one side to become hard; on the second the actual mount is made. Clean slides are absolutely necessary and may either be cleaned in the manner suggested in the last chapter, or may be chemically cleaned by one of the cleaning mixtures given in Chapter 28. The slides should be selected rather more carefully than usual for the most minute flaw in the surface of the slide will become apparent in an aqueous fluid mount, even though it would be invisible in a colloidal or resin medium of higher refractive index. Having selected and cleaned the slides, a ring of gold size is turned on each, care being taken that the ring is smaller in diameter than is the coverslip to be employed. An 18-millimeter ring and a ¾-inch coverslip form an excellent combination. It may be pointed out that this is the reverse of what is done when mounting in a tin, cardboard, or plastic cell where a ¾-inch cell is used with an 18-millimeter coverslip. In this case the purpose of the initial ring is not only to provide support to the coverslip but also to insure that the cement subsequently used for sealing shall not run in by capillary attraction and ruin the mount. The ring should be as narrow as can be drawn and should be about $\frac{1}{64}$ of an inch thick when in the fluid stain. With experience, and a fine sable brush, it is possible to draw these initial rings about $\frac{1}{64}$ of an inch in width, though $\frac{1}{16}$ is permissible and will be more likely in the hands of the inexperienced. As many rings are prepared as mounts are to be made and placed on one side until the next day. If, through some accident, mounting cannot be continued on the next day, or possibly the day after, it will be necessary to put a thin coat of fresh gold size over the dry coat and permit this to harden for 24 hours. The condition of the gold-size ring when mounting is critical; it must have dried to a rubbery, but not to a hard, consistency. For the final mounting one requires at hand the slides which have been prepared, the turntable which was used to draw the original ring, some clean coverslips, a pipet of the eye-dropper type, and the concentrate of algae.

A slide is centered on the turntable and a twist given to the turntable to make sure that the centering is accurate. A drop of the concentrated algae is placed in the center. If the slide is clean this drop will flow outwards until it reaches the cement ring where it will be held. Under no circumstances may the coverslip be placed on the preparation until the fluid touches the ring at all points. If it does not do so at once it may be brushed out with a small brush. It does not matter in the least if it flows over the ring but it will be impossible to avoid including air bubbles if it does not reach the ring. A coverslip, held between the thumb and the index finger of the right hand, is lowered horizontally until it touches the drop of algal suspension. It is then dropped in such a manner that it falls onto the ring which should be centered exactly under the coverslip. If it is not centered it is still possible to adjust it with a needle, provided it is not too far out, as long as it has been dropped and not pressed down. If it is initially pressed down, so as to make a contact with the gold size, nothing can be done and another slide must be taken in its place. As soon as the coverslip is centered a fine needle is taken and run round immediately over the ring to press the glass into contact with the slightly tacky gold size. Any of the algal suspension which has crept onto the top surface of the coverslip is removed with a soft cloth, remembering

to be very careful not to shift the coverslip; any fluid which has spread out over the slide may be wiped off as far as the edge of the coverslip itself. There will still remain a small quantity of the fluid between the ring, which is slightly smaller than the coverslip, and the edge of the coverslip itself. This must be removed, using the edge of a sheet of filter paper which is touched down to the fluid.

The withdrawal of this superfluous fluid from between the edge of the coverslip and the ring, is a critical part of the proceedings. The ring on which the coverslip rests is not sufficient to prevent evaporation but is sufficient to prevent the introduction of air mechanically while this superfluous fluid is being withdrawn. If, however, the coverslip is ever so slightly raised by the edge of the filter paper an air bubble will inevitably enter the mount which must then be thrown away. Assuming that all has gone well, and that the superfluous fluid has been withdrawn, a heavy ring of gold size is turned on and the mount placed on one side. The ring of gold size should be at least $\frac{1}{8}$ of an inch wide and as thick as the material can be persuaded to flow from the brush. The mount is then placed on one side and the next one taken.

A single ring of gold size will hold the mount in good condition for a few months but if permanence is desired it is better to add three other rings of gold size at daily intervals, then to wait a week and to turn on top of this a coat of asphalt varnish. The degree of permanence of these mounts is variable. The writer has one in his possession which is more than 20 years old and is as good as it was the day it was made.

PREPARATION OF A WHOLEMOUNT OF A ROTIFER BY THE METHOD OF HANLEY 1949

The method of Hanley is a modification of the well-known method published by Rousselet 1895 (11479, **5**:1) which has been quoted without alteration in the literature for more than 50 years. Hanley's method involves narcotization in his own narcotic (Chapter 19, AF 50 Hanley 1949) as a substitute for Rousselet's

narcotic (Chapter 19, AF 50 Rousselet 1895), and the substitution of formaldehyde for osmic acid in killing. These substitutions not only render the final preparation better and more permanent but also remove the difficulties both of working with osmic acid and of securing cocaine. This method is of great importance because satisfactory wholemounts of rotifers cannot be made in either resinous or gelatinous media, since no method of dehydration has yet been discovered which will not distort all save a very few of the toughest rotifers.

The collection of rotifers is relatively simple. Planktonic forms, either marine or fresh-water, may be taken in fine plankton nets and usually occur in considerable quantities where they occur at all. The tube or bottle at the end of the plankton net should be emptied into a considerable volume of water and kept well-oxygenated unless the specimens are to be prepared immediately. The usual methods of plankton concentration are very unsatisfactory for delicate rotifers, and it is better to rely on their attraction by light, and by high concentrations of oxygen. If, on the return to the laboratory, the quart or gallon of plankton suspension be placed on a bench and one side shaded while the other is brilliantly illuminated, all the planktonic rotifers will be found to concentrate at the surface on the illuminated side of the bottle. They may then be picked out without difficulty with a fine pipet and transferred to a watch glass for narcotization. If there are only a few rotifers present it may be necessary to take the jar into a darkened room and to illuminate one angle of it with a small spotlight (such as the Nicholas lamp used by embryologists) which will collect all the rotifers from half a gallon of water in a few minutes. If the jar is going to be left for some time under these conditions it is desirable to use some form of heat filter between the lamp and the jar.

The collection of sessile rotifers is more difficult. They will usually be found attached to the stems of water plants, and to the underside of water-lily leaves. It has been the author's experience that more rotifers will be found in relatively small ponds than in large lakes, and that if one could find a body of water several feet deep but of only a few hundred square feet of surface area, and if this water is relatively choked with large water weeds but contains only a small quantity of green algae, it is likely to contain many of the rarer forms of sessile rotifers. The

distribution of these forms is, however, very scattered and it is scarcely ever worth while to collect large quantities of water weeds with a drag and then to take them back to the laboratory and hunt through them. It is far more profitable to settle down and hunt the weeds as they are in the water, cutting from them short lengths of stem or small areas of leaf which bear the required forms. These are then placed in a large jar of water from the pond and brought back to the laboratory for further treatment.

The most difficult part of the preparation of a mount of the rotifer is to narcotize it correctly. Hanley (*Microscope*, **7**:155) has discovered that the use of alcohol in Rousselet's fixative is antagonistic to the cocaine in the same solution and that it is, therefore, by Rousselet's method necessary to use very large quantities of narcotic with a resultant very short interval between complete narcotization and death. With Hanley's narcotic the narcotization is relatively rapid but the interval between complete narcotization and death is relatively long. With Rousselet's fixative there is often only a period of from one to two seconds between the moment when the fixative can be applied and the moment when the rotifer dies and is then worthless. With Hanley's narcotic, this period is extended for as long as 10 to 15 seconds and only those who have mounted rotifers by Rousselet's method can appreciate how great is this advantage.

For the actual process of narcotization it is necessary to have two watch glasses, one containing the rotifers swimming in their normal environment, and the other a 10% solution of formaldehyde. These two watch glasses should be sufficiently far apart that fumes from the formaldehyde do not dissolve in the glass containing the rotifers. There is also required a supply of Hanley's narcotic, a fine pipet, and a dissecting microscope having a power sufficiently high to enable the rotifers to be seen clearly. For an average watch glass containing the rotifers two drops of Hanley's narcotic are added to the water and mixed by sucking the water in and out with a rather coarse pipet.

It does not matter that this treatment will cause the rotifers to contract for they will have ample opportunity, at this stage, to re-expand. The watch glass is then left alone for about 20 or 30 minutes, a further drop added and *very cautiously* mixed in; after a further five minutes another drop is mixed in with extreme caution and the rotifers watched under a microscope. The pH of the water, as Hanley points out, very greatly affects the rapidity of narcotization which may be complete in from 45 minutes to an hour and a half. No definite data are, however, available as to the adjustment of the pH in relation to the quantity of the narcotic so that one can only proceed by trial and error.

The author differs from Hanley as to the exact moment at which fixation or killing should take place. Hanley states that it is safe to pick out the rotifers and transfer them to the formaldehyde solution when they are moving sluggishly about but do not contract when they hit each other. He further says that it is too late to apply the killing agent when ciliary action has ceased. It has been the writer's experience that killing should always take place at the exact moment when the cilia cease to move. With Rousselet's narcotic this cessation of ciliary movement is followed within a second or two by death; it has been the writer's experience that with Hanley's narcotic one has at least ten seconds of leeway which permits one to flood the watch glass with a considerable quantity of 10% formaldehyde. Whichever method is adopted, as soon as the formaldehyde has been placed in the watch glass, it is rapidly withdrawn and replaced with fresh 10% formaldehyde in which the rotifers remain until they are ready for mounting. With Rousselet's method one used to add a drop or two of 2% osmic acid to kill the rotifers and then remove them very, very rapidly from the mixture through several changes of distilled water and then in to the formaldehyde for preservation. This method occasionally resulted in the destruction of the cilia, and it was also exceedingly difficult to avoid retaining sufficient osmic acid to cause subsequent darkening of the mount.

As Hanley's method of sealing a wet wholemount differs appreciably from the writer's, which was given in the description of the last example, Hanley's method will be given in some detail. The following description is taken almost verbatim from the paper of Hanley cited. If cement cells are used the cell is made beforehand and allowed to dry. When mounting, rotifers are picked out with a fine pipet and placed on the floor of the cell. The slide is then placed on the microscope stage and filled to excess with 2½% formaldehyde. The mount is examined under the microscope and any foreign bodies or air bubbles removed with a fine pipet—do not run a needle round inside the end of the cement ring to remove bubbles, "unless you are fond of cement scrapings in your mounts." Much of the excess fluid can be removed with the pipet, being careful not to remove the rotifers also, and a clean coverslip then placed on the mount with flat-ended forceps. The coverslip should float on the dome of fluid and then is tapped down smartly with the base of the forceps—if this is not done smartly enough the rotifers will be washed out. The surplus fluid is removed with filter paper, changing the point of application as the rotifers move, and when nearly all the surplus has been removed the cover can be pushed slowly into place with a bent wire.

It is important to notice that no wet cement is used on the cement cell. This is quite unnecessary with cement rings. (This is Hanley's opinion not the writer's.) If the cell is properly made, the cover glass when set down adheres so firmly to the cell that it can be broken before it will move, while, when wet cement is used, the cover cannot be centered once it has been applied.

The slide is then placed on a turntable and a thin ring of cement is run round and over the edge of the cover in the manner described in the last example.

In the matter of sealing the writer prefers the classical method of running several rings of gold size as a seal and finishing this with a flexible black varnish.

3

Fluid Wholemounts in Nonaqueous Media

General Principles

Nature of the Process

The mounting of whole objects in non-aqueous media is essentially the same process as mounting objects in aqueous media: that is, the objects are enclosed in the preservative medium in a very flat box, the floor of which is formed by the slide, the top of which is formed by the coverslip and the sides of which are formed either of cement, or by a cell. There are not, however, so many possible choices among cells and sealing media as is the case with aqueous mounts, for the choice of the medium itself dictates every subsequent step.

Choice of the Medium

Only three nonaqueous media are commonly used in mounting: these are glycerol, bromonaphthalene, and liquid petrolatum. These should never be used when any aqueous substitute is available, nor should a fluid medium be used if a mountant which will harden under the coverslip (see the next three chapters) can be employed in its place. Each of these three media will be discussed in their turn.

Glycerol is widely used as a mountant in those cases in which a water-miscible, high-refractive-index material is required and in which a medium of the type discussed in the next chapters cannot be employed. The principal reason that such media cannot be used is the difficulty of transferring delicate objects to, say, glycerol jelly without causing a collapse of their walls, while it is comparatively simple to get delicate objects into glycerol by evaporation. This technique is usually applied to nematode worms, and sometimes to small arthropods or very delicate coelenterates, which should be fixed in the ordinary manner and then transferred very gradually to alcohol and from alcohol to ½% glycerol in alcohol. The alcohol is then slowly evaporated, leaving the material in pure glycerol. It is almost impossible to seal a deep cell full of glycerol, and mounting in this material should be confined to cells built out of cement or to slides in which a concave hollow has been ground.

Sealing Glycerol Mounts with Dichromate Gelatin

There are three ways in which a glycerol-filled cell may satisfactorily be sealed. The first is with the aid of molten gelatin, applied from a turntable in the manner described in the last two chapters, and then varnished with any good cement; the second method involves the application of a molten resinous medium; the third method uses petrolatum. In the case of the first method it is better to use a solution of gelatin containing potassium dichromate, which becomes insoluble on exposure to light, than to use straight gelatin; and it is doubtful if the formula of Rüyter 1934 or 1935 (Chapter 28) can be improved.

A narrow ring of material is turned on the slide, in the manner previously described, the ring being made slightly smaller in diameter than the size of the coverslip to be used and just sufficiently thick to keep the coverslip from bearing on the object. This cement shrinks on drying so that a ring must be turned somewhat thicker than is customary with other cements. A number of slides may be prepared at the same time and left in a light place for an hour or two until the gelatin has become insolubilized. The object, together with a drop of glycerol, is placed in the middle of the cell and the coverslip lowered vertically as shown in Fig. 24 (Chapter 6). The coverslip is then held firmly in place, either with the finger or with one of the clips shown in Fig. 25, while all traces of exuded glycerol are removed with the aid of a rag moistened in alcohol. The slide is then placed on the turntable and a ring of molten dichromate gelatin turned over the edges of the coverslip. This ring of cement is cooled—it is not necessary to dry it— and the whole slide then thoroughly cleaned in 95% alcohol, either applied from a rag, or by waving the slide backward and forward in the fingerbowl of the reagent. Great care is necessary at this stage to avoid displacing the coverslip. The purpose of the ring of gelatin, in fact, is not so much to cement the coverslip in place as to provide a temporary seal which will hold the cover sufficiently long to permit the removal of exuded glycerol. As soon as the slide is dry, and glycerol-free, several coats of gold size are added, allowing ample time for each to dry, and then a final coat of asphalt varnish is turned on top. Slides prepared by this method have a very pleasing appearance but they require a great expenditure of time compared to the use of a thermoplastic resin cement.

Sealing Glycerol Mounts with Thermoplastic Resin Mixtures

The medium most usually recommended for heat-sealing glycerol mounts is Noyer (Chapter 28, V 12.2 Noyer 1918), a simple mixture of rosin and lanolin. The writer prefers the formula of Fant (V 12.2 Fant 1932), containing a quantity of dried Canada balsam, which appears to make it both easier to handle and more adhesive. Whichever medium is employed, the object in glycerol is placed under the coverslip and, after crudely wiping away the excess fluid, a layer of molten cement is applied to the

edge. For making large quantities of these preparations a most ingenious mechanism has been described by Banard (11360, **54**:29), but it is proposed here only to deal with the method of handling individual slides.

This method is shown in Fig. 20 where the objects are being mounted under a square coverslip. It is the author's opinion that no satisfactory seal can be made by this method on round coverslips. The dish in the left foreground contains the objects in pure glycerol and, immediately behind it in the center of the picture, there is a tin can containing the cement selected. The author always prepares the cement in such quantities as will just fill an empty boot-polish can, which is admirably adapted to the purpose. The tool being used is the same rather heavy brass tool which is shown being employed in the mounting of paraffin blocks in Fig. 65 (Chapter 12). An ordinary section lifter, sometimes recommended, is too thin and does not hold enough cement. In the illustration, it is presumed that the object has been placed under the coverslip, the coverslip lowered in place, the glycerol roughly wiped away, and the metal tool heated to about 150° to 200°C. This tool is now dipped into the can of cement, so that the edge accumulates molten cement along it, and then touched down on the edge of the coverslip. It will be noticed that the edge toward the front of the illustrations has already been finished and that the second edge is being applied. Before this was done, a minute drop of the cement was placed at one corner of the coverslip to hold it in position. Having finished two sides in this manner, it is easy to apply cement to the third side, but the whole trick of a successful mount lies in the method in which cement is applied to the fourth side. It will be obvious that this very hot cement, when it is applied to the coverslip, will cause an instantaneous expansion of the fluid. This does not matter as long as one side remains open. The last side, however, cannot be sealed in one piece, and it is necessary to apply the cement in such a manner that about a one-millimeter gap is left at a corner for the escape of the heated glycerol. The slide is then cooled, such glycerol as has been extruded from the corner is wiped away, and a small drop of very hot cement is applied at this place. Slides sealed in this manner will last almost indefinitely and require no further finishing beyond a brief wash in alcohol to

slip. The size of the drop is therefore critical but can only be learned by experience.

The slide is now placed on a warm table, kept a few degrees above melting point of the petrolatum employed, and molten petrolatum run under the cover from a pipet. Spence prefers to take a

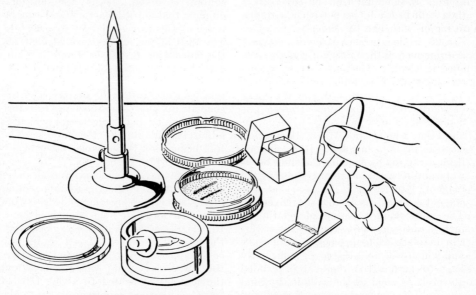

Fig. 20. Sealing a wholemount with Fant's cement.

remove excess glycerol. They are, however, clumsy in appearance compared to a ringed slide made with dichromate gelatin.

Sealing Glycerol Mounts with Petrolatum

This method, which was developed by Spence 1940 (*Microscope*, **4**:123) is the best yet developed, providing one is looking for chemical stability rather than mechanical strength. The object is lifted in a drop of glycerol and placed in the center of a clean slide. Three little squares of petrolatum-soaked paper or card, of a thickness sufficient to prevent coverslips crushing the object, are placed round, but not in contact with, the drop. The coverslip is now lowered vertically onto the drop which should spread out, when the coverslip is resting on the squares, until it occupies about half the area of the cover-

wisp of solid petrolatum on a toothpick and to let this melt and run under the coverslip. In either case, one is left with a bubble of glycerol surrounded by a thick layer of molten petrolatum. The slide is now chilled and any excess petrolatum scraped away. The mount is permanent in this form, but the petrolatum is so soft that the cover is liable to become detached when dust is wiped from it. A certain degree of mechanical strength can be given by turning on three or four rings of shellac, followed by three or four coats of asphalt varnish.

Sealing Other Non-aqueous Liquid Mounts

Mounting in liquid petrolatum is practically confined to blood films, on the assumption that this inert medium prevents the fading of methylene blue-eosin stains. These stains are, however, best kept dry, and many of the neutral mounting media described in Chapter 26, under the heading M 23.1, are less trouble to use, and probably just as good. Liquid petrolatum is difficult to seal, though the author has had most success with the hot-resin method described in the last paragraph. Even with this material, however, there is a slow diffusion of the brown resin through the liquid petrolatum which ultimately damages the slide. Since liquid petrolatum does not evaporate, it is sometimes preserved by holding a coverslip in place with a drop of cement at each corner. The quantity of cement used is thus so small that diffusion through the mounting medium is negligible, while the degree of adherence is sufficiently good for all normal handling. Bromonaphthalene is used only for mounting diatoms, when a medium of high refractive index is required. The only satisfactory cement for sealing is a de-waxed shellac prepared by the method of Hitchcock (Chapter 28, V 11.2). Both the preparation of the cell, and the process of mounting, are specialized procedures which are described in considerable detail in the second of the typical preparations which terminate this chapter.

Specific Examples

PREPARATION OF NEMATODES IN GLYCEROL

Nematodes are awkward objects from which to make wholemounts, for their thick cuticle permits only slow diffusion of reagents, and it is almost impossible to get them into either resinous or gelatinous media. The objection to shrinkage is not on aesthetic grounds, but on the basis that the folds and ridges of cuticle render it almost impossible to make out clearly those internal organs upon which classification depends. Nematodes are, therefore, almost invariably mounted in glycerol.

No difficulty will be experienced in collecting small nematodes from the blood, or when they are free-swimming (as Anguillula). The standard method of securing nematodes and their eggs from feces, however, is by flotation from a strong salt solution. Fresh specimens are collected and flooded with 10 or 15 times their volume of a 20% solution of sodium chloride. This may be added directly to the cardboard containers customarily used for such samples, and the unpleasant odor may be diminished by adding small quantities of nitrobenzene both to the salt solution and to the feces themselves. After the solids have settled, the top layer, on which the nematodes will be floating, is jerked into another dish with a quick movement of the wrist. It is almost impossible to pick the worms or eggs from the surface in a pipet so that, when a sample has been thus isolated, it should be diluted to a salt concentration of about 1% which allows the specimens to sink to the bottom. They may then be washed with weak saline until free of fecal matter. This method of collection cannot be used with fecal specimens which have been mixed with animal charcoal as a deodorant, because the charcoal also floats on the surface. Worms may, however, be collected from such samples by a modified Berlese funnel (see Chapter 4, Fig. 21). In this technique a plug of glass wool is placed at the bottom of an ordinary glass funnel and the fecal material poured in. The bottom of the funnel is then lowered into a tube of 1% salt solution until the liquid rises just to the lower edge of the fecal matter. A lamp, or some other heat source, is then placed above the feces. The worms endeavor to escape from the heat and, burrowing down through the feces, ultimately pass through the glass-wool plug and accumulate at the bottom of the tube of salt solution.

The collection of small nematodes from soil samples is much more difficult than from feces. The flotation method is practically impossible because in most soil samples there are large quantities of organic matter which will also float, while the modified Berlese funnel usually permits enough clay to sift down to make it difficult to separate the worms. Probably the best procedure is to dilute soil samples with a 1% salt solution and then survey small aliquots by strong transmitted light under a dissecting microscope. The nematodes may be recognized by their activity, picked out with a fine pipet, and transferred to fresh saline.

Whatever method has been employed, one is left with a collection of nematodes in salt solution. The solution should be changed frequently, until the worms are clean; for satisfactory wholemounts cannot be made if either dirt or mucus adheres to the outside. Heat is the only fixative which will penetrate a nematode rapidly. It is conventional, therefore, to fix worms in hot 70% alcohol, though hot water will, in point of fact, do equally well. The exact temperature is immaterial and usually 100 times as much 70% alcohol as there is saline around the worms is warmed until bubbles appear. This is usually at about 55° to 60°C. The hot alcohol is then rapidly flooded over the living worms, which are again collected by being allowed to settle to the bottom of the dish or tube. Most of the worms fixed by this method will be found to have straightened out, and the few which have not had better be thrown away.

The worms must next, very carefully and slowly, be transferred to absolute alcohol, in which they must remain until they are completely dehydrated. This transfer is best effected through 5% grades of alcohol; that is, from 70 to 75 to 80 to 85, etc. In the case of worms with very tough cuticles, a faster schedule may be employed. The reason the worms must be transferred to absolute alcohol before passing to glycerol is that it is almost impossible to get rid of water once it has got into the glycerol, and the high refractive index of the glycerol is lost if it is diluted. It is easy to find out how fast a schedule may be employed by taking one of the worms from 70% and throwing it directly into, say, 95% alcohol. If, after two or three hours in this, there is no sign of the collapse of the wall, the rest may follow it, but if the wall collapses one must experiment with 80% and so on until one has found the most rapid transfer which may be made. When the worms are all accumulated in absolute alcohol, a little glycerol is added. Assuming that the

worms are in 100 milliliters of absolute alcohol, it would be safe to add about 10 drops of glycerol, being very careful to shake rapidly and continuously so as to disperse the glycerol rapidly. The worms are left in this mixture for about 24 hours before a further 10 or 20 drops of glycerol are added and mixed. This schedule is continued until about 10 milliliters of glycerol have been added. The solution is then concentrated by evaporation, in a desiccator, at a rate which leaves the worms in concentrated glycerol at the end of about a week. It is easiest to suck air through with an aspirator, being careful that the air itself passes through a dehydration column before entering the desiccator. This method of preparation is laborious in the extreme, but it yields a product which looks exactly like a glass model. The author knows no other method which will produce clear nematodes without causing the collapse and wrinkling of the cuticle.

To make these cleared nematodes into permanent mounts, one now secures the necessary slides, coverslips, a metal tool of the type shown in Fig. 20, and a can either of Noyer's or Fant's cement. It is unnecessary to make a cell, or to use a concave slide, because the viscosity of the glycerol will hold the cover a reasonable distance away from the slide while the mount is being made, and the method of mounting embeds the coverslip so firmly that it does not subsequently shift. The slide is taken, cleaned by any preferred means, and the required specimen or specimens placed in the center in a drop of glycerol. Square coverslips should be employed and a little experience will soon show what amount will fill the coverslip to the edge. The coverslip should be lowered vertically to avoid displacing the worms, and, as soon as the glycerol has reached the edge, the heated metal tool is plunged into the cement and used to seal one edge. The success of the process depends on having the cement hot enough at the moment when it is applied. The opposite edge of the coverslip is then sealed, and these two seals connected by a third. The application of cement to the fourth side is, however, made in such a manner that a gap of about a millimeter will be left between the cement and one of the corners of the cover. This gap is necessary to permit the heat-expanded glycerol to escape. After the slide has thus been not quite sealed it is permitted to cool and a rag moistened with 95% alcohol is used to remove excess glycerol from the little vent which has been left. This vent is then itself sealed with a drop of very hot cement.

PREPARATION OF DIATOMS IN BROMONAPHTHALENE

Strewn slides of diatoms may be mounted dry in the manner described in Chapter 1. When it is necessary, however, to resolve fine structure, they should be prepared in a medium of high refractive index, and no resin has yet been found which is as satisfactory as bromonaphthalene. No one who has ever examined diatoms mounted in bromonaphthalene will ever wish to use any other medium and, though the process is tedious, the end result justifies the trouble taken.

Before mounting, diatoms must be collected and cleaned. The three great sources are fresh-water, sea-water, and fossil deposits. Diatoms occur in fresh water as part of the plankton, but are mostly found in the mud on the bottom of ponds or attached to weeds. No attempt should be made to separate diatoms from the weeds in the field; the collection should be taken back to the laboratory. The first rough separation is then carried out by cutting the plants into about ½-inch lengths and putting them into a flask with enough water to cover them, shaking vigorously, and then straining this water through coarse cloth into another container. More water is then added to the material, which is again shaken, and so on until after four or five washings, all the diatoms have been removed. These washings may be set on one side to settle for further treatment.

Diatoms may be separated from fresh mud by taking advantage of their phototropism. The mud, together with an adequate quantity of the water from which it was collected, is placed in a small saucer and a thin layer of cheesecloth is spread on the top. The mud should be sufficiently liquid to permit diatoms to pass through readily, but sufficiently solid to prevent the cheesecloth from sinking into it. If the dish be set in bright light for a day or two, the diatoms will migrate through the cheesecloth and form a dark greenish smear over its surface. The cloth is then removed, washed, and the diatoms accumulated in a small quantity of water.

The collection of diatoms from marine plants may follow the technique used for fresh-water plants, though the larger algae are better scraped with a blunt knife. These scrapings are then transferred to a jar of sea water where the diatoms and debris settle to the bottom. A rather large number of marine diatoms are, however, planktonic and can be collected from sea water with a centrifuge. A plankton-concentrating centrifuge is described in Chapter 2 and with its aid large volumes of water may be processed in a relatively short space of time. If such a planktonic centrifuge is not available, it will be necessary to collect the samples by towing behind the boat a long conical net of the finest obtainable bolting silk to the end of which is attached a small tube in which collect those specimens which have not passed through the net. Unfortunately the diatoms form a relatively small bulk, even though they may be numerous in quantity, of the total material collected, so that if there are many crustaceans among the plankton it is desirable to have a double net, the first layer of which will retain the crustaceans without permitting the diatoms to pass. Whatever method of concentration is adopted, however, one ends, as in the other processes described, by having a mixture of dirty diatoms and sludge accumulated in the bottom of the dish.

Diatoms also occur in guano, and in many fossil deposits, and must be roughly separated before cleaning. If the fossil deposit resembles guano, it is only necessary to shake it up in water and pass it through a coarse sieve to remove the sand and other extraneous material. Many of the more interesting diatoms, however, are found in hard aggregates which must be broken up before the frustules can be separated. Many methods of doing this have been described, but undoubtedly one of the most useful is the technique of Swatman (*Microscope*, **7**:132).

This technique utilizes the expansion and contraction which takes place on the sudden crystallization of a supersaturated solution of sodium acetate. The rock, or hard aggregate, containing the diatoms is roughly broken into ¼-inch pieces and placed at the bottom of an Erlenmeyer flask. Two or three times its own bulk of sodium acetate is then added, and thoroughly mixed in, before adding water to the extent of about 5% the total weight of the sodium acetate. The flask is then very carefully warmed, the flame being first applied to the sides and not to the bottom, until the sodium acetate is molten. Heating should then be continued until the material commences to boil and it should be maintained in a hot condition for as long as is required to cause the penetration of this supersaturated solution to every part of the aggregate. The flask is then cooled slowly, care being taken to avoid jarring, and when the solution is cold a single crystal of sodium acetate is dropped into it, which causes instant crystallization. As the flask will heat up greatly during crystallization, it is then recooled in water. The mass is remelted, recooled, recrystallized, and so on until a sufficient disintegration of the rock has taken place. Another method of arriving at the same result is to soak the pieces of material in water, to freeze them very rapidly (either in a freezer unit or in dry ice) then to drop them into warm water, refreeze them, and so on. This process is no more effective, however, and is usually much more trouble to carry out, than the sodium acetate procedure outlined. When the mass has sufficiently disintegrated, it is strained through a coarse sieve to get rid of the lumps and the diatomacious material allowed to form a sludge at the bottom.

Whatever method has been employed, one has now, from either fresh or fossil material, a sludge which should be transferred to a flask. This sludge contains diatoms together with various organic and inorganic impurities. The first thing is to get rid of any carbonates which may be present by adding hydrochloric acid cautiously (if there is a great deal of carbonate present effervescence may rise above the neck of the flask and cause a loss of material) until no further gas is evolved. The flask is then filled with water, the undissolved material allowed to settle, the water poured off, and the process repeated until all the soluble chloride has been removed. If there is any appreciable amount of clay present, it will also have been removed by this process, since even the smallest diatoms will settle relatively rapidly compared to the fine particles of clay. It is next necessary to remove any organic matter which may be present, and many methods have been proposed for this. The conventional method, also described by Swatman (*loc. cit.*), is to get the diatoms into concentrated sulfuric acid which is then heated to about 120°C. This chars the organic matter which is then oxidized by dropping *small* crystals of potassium chlorate into the hot acid. It should perhaps be emphasized that only exceedingly small crystals should be added, and that those who do not normally wear glasses should use some form of protection against the chance of spurting acid. If there is much organic matter present, the heated acid will be from black to dark brown in color, and chlorate is added until the color is reduced to yellow. The only safe method of removing the acid is to wait until it is entirely cold and then pour it in a slow and steady stream, while constantly stirring, into a relatively large volume of water. The diatoms settle out on the bottom. Some iron may still be present, either derived from a fossil deposit or from the chlorophyll of the plant debris. This is best removed by suspending the diatoms in 5% sodium hydroxide and bringing them to the boil. If there is any iron present it will appear as a brownish ferric hydroxide through which the diatoms will settle readily and which may then be poured off. After repeating this process several times, the diatoms are treated with hydrochloric acid to remove the last of the iron chloride and again washed by decantation.

It will probably happen, however, that many of the finest markings on the diatoms are still filled with finely divided clay which must be removed by treating the diatoms in the cold with a 10% dilution of ammonia. The frustules will be damaged if a hot or strong solution is used, and it is best to leave the diatoms in cold ammonia for two or three days, shaking at intervals, before washing them by decantation. The final stage in cleaning the diatoms is now to wash them with repeated changes of filtered distilled water until all traces of dissolved salts have been removed.

Some workers, after treating the diatoms with ammonia, repeat the sulfuric acid-potassium chlorate treatment as a final precaution. Another variant is to precede the original treatment with sulfuric acid and potassium chlorate by treatment with a hot mixture of two parts of sulfuric acid with one of nitric acid. This treatment is recommended when the original collection contains very large quantities of vegetable matter in addition to the diatoms. Swatman (*loc. cit.*) points out that if diatoms are collected from mud containing coal dust this will not be satisfactorily removed by any of the preceding processes and recommends that the diatoms be fused in a platinum crucible with pure potassium nitrate for removal of this contaminant.

It will have been observed, either in theory or practice, that many of the processes just described result in the production of noxious vapors, so that they cannot be properly carried out by anyone not having access to a chemical hood. To meet this objection Hendey 1938 (11360, **58**:49) has devised a most ingenious apparatus which will permit any of the processes described to be used in a living room.

All the methods so far described presume that the collector has been working close to his laboratory and has, therefore, not been faced with the problem of transporting large quantities of vegetable matter. A rough method of field cleaning (Swatman 1941: 11479, **1**:191) may be used to concentrate diatoms. As much

water as possible is drained from the rough sludge and replaced with 10% sulfuric acid. Potassium permanganate is then added, with constant stirring, until the solution remains pink after standing for a few minutes; then enough oxalic acid is added to dissolve the brown oxide sludge. The clear solution may be poured off and the diatoms roughly washed before being transferred to a tube.

By whatever method the diatoms have been cleaned, they are now presumed to be accumulated in clean distilled water. They should be roughly sorted into their kinds, since diatoms are much easier to handle under the surface of water with the aid of a fine pipet than they are when dry. The different kinds are then stored in small vials of distilled water to which a trace (about one-tenth of 1%) of formaldehyde is added with a view to discouraging organic growth. Larger quantities of formaldehyde should not be used, or a fine deposit will be found on the surface of the diatom when it is subsequently dried.

To mount a strewn slide of diatoms, it is only necessary to take a drop of the distilled water with the diatoms suspended in it, to let this evaporate on a coverslip, to dry the coverslip with heat, and then to mount it in the manner to be described subsequently. It may be presumed, however, that the worker wishes to prepare a slide in which the diatoms are arranged in some given order on the coverslip. It must not be thought for one moment that this method of arranging diatoms on the coverslip is of necessity confined to the production of artistic pictures. It is true that the method was developed by those who wished to build pictures, but it can also be used to line up in correct ranks all of the species found, for example, in one locality.

No method of arranging diatoms on, and attaching them to, a coverslip will compare with that of Bellido 1927 (11360, **47**:9). The description cited is one of very considerable complexity and goes into details not possible in the present place. It consists essentially, however, of coating a chemically clean coverslip with an exceedingly thin film of Bellido's cement (Chapter 28, V 11.1 Bellido 1897) which is then dried. Bellido recommends that the film be applied by dipping a needle into the cement and then drawing the flat of the needle sharply across the coverslip. This leaves an invisible film of dry gelatin on the cover, and individual diatoms may be placed on this film to which they will not adhere until the film is slightly moistened by breathing on it. The moment this has been done the diatoms are permanently attached.

Before individual diatoms may be selected for this technique, however, they must be dried. It is not safe to dry them on glass, to which they frequently adhere. It is better to attach a piece of mica to a slide with petrolatum and to evaporate the drop of water on this base. Individual diatoms may then be picked up on the end of a hair under the microscope. There is usually enough grease on a normal hair to permit the diatom to adhere. Bellido describes the ingenious idea of mounting a hair on the collar of a microscope objective in such a manner that the tip of the hair is in focus when the draw tube of the microscope is pulled halfway out. It follows that when the draw tube is pushed home the hair will be out of focus, and also well above the plane of the object which is in focus. It is possible, therefore, to press the draw tube fully home, search one of the squares of mica for the required specimen, pull out the draw tube until the hair is in focus, and then lower the microscope until the hair touches and picks up the object. Bellido recommends that the hair be moistened with a little bromonaphthalene and that the film of gelatin also be lubricated with the same reagent. He has also described, in the place quoted, a sealed chamber within which all these operations may be conducted without the risk of dust falling on the preparation. Another device for handling individual diatoms on a mechanically operated hair has been described by Meakin 1939 (*Microscope*, **4**:8). These mechanical devices are only necessary, however, for handling large quantities of rather small diatoms. A few months of practice with a hair mounted in any holder will enable the average worker to arrange diatoms directly. A mechanical device is, of course, almost necessary if one is endeavoring to arrange the diatoms according to any artistic pattern. In any event, as soon as the diatoms have been arranged one breathes very gently on the coated coverslip and pauses a moment or two. The coverslip is then examined under the microscope and a few of the larger and rougher diatoms very delicately probed with a hair. If they are found to be firmly attached, it may be assumed that the smaller diatoms are also attached. If, however, anything is found to be loose, one breathes again, and again probes until such a time as all the diatoms are fixed. These coverslips with the diatoms attached to them may now be laid on one side while the necessary cells for mounting are prepared.

There will be required a turntable, slides, a fine brush, a hot plate, and some de-waxed shellac (Chapter 28 V 11.2 Hitchcock 1884) which should be as thick as can conveniently be persuaded to flow from a brush of the size selected. A fine ring is then turned of a size slightly smaller than the coverslip. Save for the very largest diatoms a single ring of this cement will be sufficiently thick. It is absolutely necessary that these shellacked rings be baked if they are to become insoluble in the bromonaphthalene used for mounting. As soon, therefore, as the alcohol has evaporated from the shellac, the slides are placed on a hot plate, or for that matter, in an oven, and heated to just below the melting point of the shellac for at least 30 minutes. The cells, which would now be adequate for aqueous media, must be further processed for bromonaphthalene mounting by having the top ground flat. This is done by taking some of the finest available carborundum, making it into a slurry with water, and spreading this on a sheet of fine quality plate glass. The slide, with the cell down, is then laid on this glass and, with a *delicate* finger placed over the center of the cell, moved gently backward and forward for a few moments. It is then picked up, washed under the tap, and examined with a strong lens to make sure that there is a flat, smooth area over the whole of the top of the cell. The slide is then washed free of all traces of grit and dried in a dust-free place. As many prepared slides as are required now have a small drop of bromonaphthalene placed in each cell. If petrolatum was used to hold the coverslip in place while the diatoms were mounted on it, this should first be removed with ether to make quite certain that the diatom frustules are grease-free, dry, and clean. When one is satisfied as to this, the coverslip is lowered in place on top of the bromonaphthalene and then, with some blunt instrument (Bellido recommends a toothpick) pressed on the cell until it is firmly attached. If the coverslip is flat and if the cell has been properly ground, this seal is sufficiently good to permit one to remove any exuded bromonaphthalene with a cloth before turning on an additional layer of the shellac as a final seal. It is usually safer to follow this with another layer of some impermeable cement such as asphalt varnish.

Though this process may sound laborious, it actually takes less time by this means to mount one each of the 200–300 species that may be found in a fossil deposit on a single coverslip than it takes either to mount them individually on separate slides by any other means, or to endeavor to find them under a microscope if they are arranged at random.

4

Wholemounts in Gum Media

General Principles

Nature of the Process

. The preparations which have been described in the last two chapters are those in which the specimen is sealed in a preservative fluid. These mounts, as will be readily understood by anybody who has read the chapters, are difficult and laborious to prepare, so that most slides are made in a *mounting* as distinguished from a *preservative* medium. A *mounting medium*, used in this sense, is one which itself hardens and holds the coverslip in place while at the same time preserving the object contained in it. Mounting media may be divided into two large groups: first, those which are miscible with water; second, those which are not miscible with water, so that some initial treatment must be given to most objects before they are mounted. The media miscible with water are in themselves divisible into two types: first, those which are liquid at room temperature (dealt with in this chapter), second, those which are solid at room temperature and must be melted before they can be used. Water-soluble media are all colloidal dispersions of various materials, the colloids being in the sol phase for the media described in this chapter, and in the gel phase for the media described in the next.

Types of Gum Media Employed

Many formulas for mounting media of the sol-colloidal type are given in Chapter 27 under the heading M 11.1. They are dispersions of either natural or synthetic gums in water and must, therefore, depend for their hardening upon the evaporation of moisture from the edge of the coverslip. Were this to continue for an indefinite period, the media would naturally harden and crack; hence, most contain either glycerol or sorbitol to impart hygroscopic qualities. The prototype of all these media is Farrants', which is a simple dispersion of gum arabic in water to which has been added a small quantity of glycerol together with a preservative. All media derived from this follow the same pattern, differing mostly in the quantity of glycerol included and in the nature of the preservative selected. The fundamental objection to gum-arabic media is that it is difficult to obtain a pure sample of the gum, and one has to go through a wearisome process of filtration to avoid having the mount filled with sand grains and pieces of stick. Another objection to this type of medium is the low index of refraction, which leaves objects mounted in it relatively opaque when they are examined by transmitted light. This difficulty is overcome in Berlese's medium, to which chloral hydrate is added in considerable quantities with a view to increasing the index of refraction. The ordinary media of the Farrants' type have an index of refraction just over 1.3, while Berlese's medium and its modifications have indices of refraction as high as 1.47. Very few synthetic substitutes for water-soluble gums are available, the most promising at the present time being polyvinyl alcohol, which is used in the media of Downs, and of Gray and Wess. It is probable that the recent appearance on the market of water-soluble cellulose derivatives (for example, carboxymethyl cellulose) may lead to the ultimate suppression of gum arabic in mounting media.

Types of Objects Which May Be Mounted

Simple water-miscible liquid mountants are of far wider utility than is usually realized, for there has been a complete mental block on the part of most microscopists when faced with any mounting medium which is not a solution of a resin in a hydrocarbon. As a matter of fact, most simple objects such as the scales of fish, animal hairs, and the like, may be more readily mounted in aqueous media than in resinous ones. The actual process of mounting is so simple that it is regarded with distrust by those who have come to believe that only through complexity can good results be produced. With these media one merely takes the object which it is desired to mount, places it in the drop of mountant on the slide, and presses a coverslip onto the top. This process is not confined to relatively hard objects of the type described, but may also be applied to many protozoa and other small invertebrates. These do not make satisfactory permanent mounts by this method, for they ultimately reach a refractive index identical with that of the mountants and thus vanish; but a temporary mount of *Paramecium*, in one of these media, will show the internal structure to a class far

better than will the average stained mount, and will also give a far better realization of what the living object looks like. Objects most commonly mounted however, are small arthropods of the degree of transparency that does not require that the skeleton be cleared in the manner described in Chapter 6.

Gum mountants are not satisfactory in thick layers and the writer has never made a successful mount in a deep cell. There is no point in endeavoring to use shallow cells for these media, for the viscosity of the mountant is sufficiently high to prevent the coverslip from crushing small objects.

Finishing Slides in Gum Media

Exudate round the edges of the cover may be removed by washing with warm water, but it will be some time before the edges reharden. Moreover, no mounting medium containing glycerol or sorbitol can fail to absorb moisture from the air on humid days, and to lose it on dry days, so that it is usually better to finish the slide by applying a ring of varnish in the manner described in previous chapters. It does not matter what cement is employed, the writer's preference being for gold size, probably more from force of habit than from any other reason.

Specific Example

PREPARATION OF A WHOLEMOUNT OF A MITE BY THE METHOD OF BERLESE

The use of the name Berlese in the heading of this example is less an injunction to employ the mounting medium of that writer than a tribute to the method of collecting small arthropods which he introduced. This method is applied with the aid of the Berlese funnel which is seen in Fig. 21. This is a double-walled funnel, between the walls of which warm water may be placed and maintained at any desired temperature by applying a small flame to a projecting side arm. The temperature is not critical, so that no thermostatic mechanism is provided, but a thermometer may be inserted and used to read the temperature at intervals. A circle of wire

gauze with a mesh of about $\frac{1}{16}$ of an inch is placed at the bottom of the inner glass funnel, and whatever material to be searched for mites is placed loosely on this gauze. The lower end of the glass funnel is then attached with modeling clay to a tube containing whatever medium is being used for the collection of the specimens. If the specimens are merely to be stored, rather than mounted at once, 95% alcohol may be placed in the tube, and it is then unnecessary to seal it to the base of the funnel. If, however, the specimens are to be mounted directly in Berlese's medium, in which better mounts can be prepared from living than from preserved material,

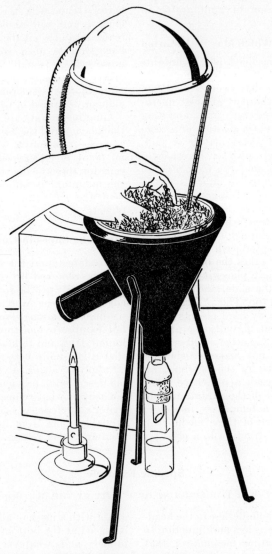

Fig. 21. Berlese funnel in use.

the funnel must be sealed to prevent the more active forms from working their way out of the tube.

After the mass has been placed in position a small lamp, certainly not of more than 15 watts, is mounted in any kind of a reflector some distance above the material. The animals in the material, therefore, find themselves surrounded by heat at the sides and plagued with light from above. As all of these animals are photophobic, they tend to move toward the lowest point of the mass from which they drop down the tube into the funnel. By this means it is possible in 10 or 15 minutes to collect the whole fauna from a large handful of any organic material which would, by any other means, take several hours to search. The use of the funnel is not, of course, confined to moss but may be used for hay, straw, shredded bark, or any other material from which small arthropods are customarily collected. The only difficulty in using this equipment is in preventing the heat from getting too great. Some people use so large a lamp above, and so high a temperature around the edges, that many small arthropods are killed before they have time to fall into the trap which has been laid for them. The outer water for most uses should be at a temperature of 30° to 40°C., while the lamp above should under no circumstances raise surface temperature of the material above 60°C. These temperatures are for a moderately dry moss sample, and may be considerably exceeded when one is dealing with a dry material such as straw. Wet moss of the sphagnum type, however, requires lower temperatures.

Assuming that permanent mounts are to be made, for record purposes, of all the small invertebrates which may be found in a moss sample, it is necessary to make adequate preparations to receive them while the moss is being treated. Two kinds of gum mountants are desirable: a high-refractive-index medium like Berlese, for the very heavy-walled forms such as the Oribatid mites and the Pseudoscorpionides; and a low-refractive-index mountant, like Gray and Wess, for the thinner-walled forms such as the Tyroglyphid and Gamassid mites. This last medium is also suitable for Thysanura and for Collembolla. Thick-walled beetles and fleas, if they are to be made into microscope slides, had better be treated as described in Chapter 6, and should be accumulated for this purpose in a tube of 95% alcohol. Sphagnum moss is also likely to yield a number of crustaceans, particularly Cladocera and Ostracoda. These are better mounted in glycerol jelly, in the manner described in the next chapter, and should be transferred as soon as they are found to 30% alcohol where they will die with their appendages extended. They should not, however, be permitted to remain in this weak alcohol for longer than is necessary to kill them, but should then be transferred to 95% alcohol. A considerable number of nematode worms are likely to turn up and should be treated as described in the last chapter, while a tube of some fixative should be provided to receive any small annelids which may be found in the gathering, and which must be fixed, stained, and mounted at once. A brush will also be required, a supply of clean 3″ × 1″ glass slides, and a number of coverslips.

All being ready, and observation showing that no further forms are falling through the Berlese funnel, the collecting tube beneath it is now inspected to see roughly what one has gathered. If there are a considerable number of Gamassid mites or active insects, it is necessary gently to open a portion of the tube by pushing away the modelling clay with the thumb and to let a minute drop of ether run down inside. When this has been done the tube is removed and the contents tipped out into a petri dish or similar container and the catch sorted.

A mite, or similar form, which is to be mounted, is then picked up on the tip of a brush and transferred to a drop of the mountant. As little water as possible should be transferred with it and the mite should be pushed under the surface of the gum with the point of a needle. The mount is then inspected under the low part of the microscope and, if any large quantity of air has been carried in with the mite, the bubbles are released with the aid of a fine needle and allowed to come to the surface before the coverslip is laid gently into place. The drop of gum should be of a considerable size and no endeavor should be made to press the coverslip down. If a reasonably thick layer of mountant is left almost any small arthropod will spread its legs like a textbook diagram before dying and will remain in this form indefinitely.

5

Wholemounts in Jelly Media

General Principles

Glycerol jelly is the only type of water-miscible medium known to most workers. Many objects, both plant and animal, which are usually prepared in glycerol jelly, are much better mounted by the method described in the last chapter, and the author would most warmly recommend to workers who have been using glycerol jelly that they try one of the methods there described.

Formulas for the jelly media, the use of which is described in the present chapter, are given in section M 12.1 of Chapter 26, and it will be seen that they are all essentially the same. That is, they consist of a dispersion of gelatin, which has been diluted with glycerol until the required index of refraction is obtained, and they have added to them some preservative. The older glycerol jellies, designed for use in European laboratories, do not in general contain sufficient glycerol to withstand the drying effects of an American laboratory. The author has in his possession many deep wholemounts of fairly large crustaceans which remained perfect for ten years in England but which dried and cracked after only two years in the United States. There is little to choose among any of the media, apart from the consideration just given, and practice will soon permit the mounter to select the one which works best in his hands.

Nature of the Process

Mounts prepared in glycerol jelly may be made either on flat slides or as deep wholemounts. Glycerol jelly can be used for larger objects than can the gum media of the last chapter and, except for botan-ical specimens, the use of glycerol jelly is largely confined to the preparation of permanent slides of unstained crustaceans. These media are solid at room temperature and must be melted before use. Material cannot be mounted directly from water unless the objects are soaked for a long time in molten jelly to allow some of the glycerol to penetrate. Mounts made from specimens taken directly from water are liable to have the jelly crack away from the object as it cools. Moreover, these media are not in their own right good preservatives so that material placed directly from water into them is liable partially to decompose before the mount stabilizes. It is conventional to transfer objects to these media from 50% alcohol, but it is better to harden the objects first in alcohol than to transfer them from alcohol to 50% glycerol and thence into the molten medium.

Process of Mounting

There are three separate stages in the preparation of glycerol-jelly mounts. The first is hardening the object; the second is getting the object from the hardening fluid into the 50% glycerol; and the third is the transfer from the 50% glycerol onto the slide.

As these mountants cannot be used for stained specimens, there is little object in using any fixative other than alcohol. The transfer from the hardening alcohol to the glycerol, however, must be by such stages as will insure that the object does not collapse through osmotic pressure. This makes it impossible satisfactorily to mount the majority of nematode worms in

46

jelly, and thus necessitates the glycerol technique described in Chapter 3. The author prefers to transfer objects from 95% alcohol to 70% alcohol and then to add, by such stages as are necessary, enough glycerol to this mixture to insure that, when the alcohol has been removed by evaporation, 50% glycerol will remain.

The two great difficulties in mounting material in these media are first to arrange the object on the slide before the jelly has time to solidify, and then to get the cover-

in which they are left until they are thoroughly permeated, and then placed in a stender dish on top of a water bath, seen in the left background of the picture. On this water bath, which is held about 10°C. above the melting point of the jelly, there is also placed the bottle containing the mounting medium and as many slides as will be required. A slide is taken, a molten drop of the medium placed on the warm slide, and the object to be mounted removed with a pipet and placed in this

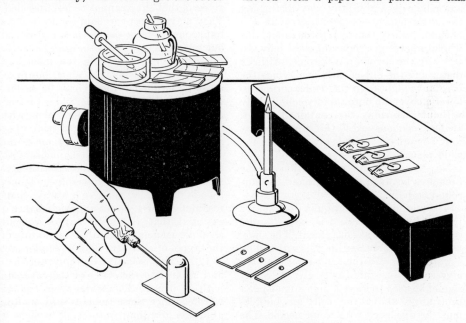

Fig. 22. Layout for jelly mounting.

slip into place without disarranging the object. The writer has invented a tool for overcoming these troubles, the use of which will be described in some detail. The layout, when one is mounting a number of objects, is shown in Fig. 22; the only object not commonly found in laboratories is the special tool shown in the left hand in the picture. This device is a short length of ¾-inch aluminum rod flattened at one end and rounded at the other. This aluminum rod is screwed to a short length of brass tube which terminates in a wooden handle. The procedure in mounting small objects is as follows. The objects themselves are accumulated in 50% glycerol,

drop. The slide is then removed from the water bath and examined under a microscope while a warmed needle is used to push the object into the required position. Make sure that it is in contact with the slide and that there is a considerable amount of jelly above it. In the center of the picture will be seen three slides which have so been treated and laid on one side until the medium has hardened. As many slides as are required may be treated in this manner so that one has a series of preparations, each of which contains a domed drop of solid jelly with the object lying in the required position at the bottom of it. Now take a cover glass of the required size, moisten the underside by breathing on it, or by smearing on it a little 50% glycerol, and then lay this slide on top of the domed drop of jelly. The cylinder of aluminum is then taken, warmed in the flame until it is somewhat above the melting point of the jelly, and pressed *gently* on top of the center of the slide until enough jelly has been melted to permit the cover to drop down to the required level. Very little practice is required before one can flatten down the coverslip without in any way disturbing the arrangement of the object at the bottom, which remains throughout this whole process in a layer of solid jelly. In this way the coverslip is flattened without disturbing the object, and one avoids the constant nightmare of endeavoring to lower a coverslip onto rapidly cooling jelly without disturbing the contained object. If the specimens are so thin that pressure may be applied, a clip is attached and the slide placed for a few minutes on a hot table, to permit an equalization of the pressures between the object and the surrounding jelly.

The method of mounting in deep cells is practically identical and is, with the described tool, just as convenient. The slide, with the cell cemented to it, is warmed on a water bath and then filled with molten glycerol jelly. Sufficient glycerol jelly should be used to leave a high domed layer protruding above the cell; air bubbles must be displaced with a hot needle. The object is then placed in the glycerol jelly, arranged in the required position within the cell, and then gently laid on one side to cool. A moistened coverslip is then placed in the center of the dome and pressed down with the warmed tool until it is flattened against the top of the cell. Large cells of this nature should always be placed on a hot plate for at least two or three hours before they are finally cooled, for the commonest cause of breakdown of deep jelly mounts is failure to permit the osmotic tension to equalize between the object and its surrounding medium before cooling.

Finishing Glycerol Jelly Mounts

Most glycerol jellies contain so much glycerol that they cannot be left unsealed. They may appear excellent for a few days but sooner or later the glycerol will spread out over the surface of the slide, even to the extent of moistening the label and causing it to fall off. The slide, however, must be cleaned before it can be sealed. Make sure that the slide is cold—a refrigerator is very convenient—and then with a sharp razor blade or scalpel trim away all the unwanted jelly. Then remove the smears that are left with a moist cloth and use another cloth moistened with 95% alcohol to remove any glycerol which may remain on the glass. There is always some residual glycerol, however, which makes it essential that the first coat of cement should be a gelatin-dichromate mixture of the type of Rüyter 1934 (Chapter 28, V 12.1). This is melted on the water bath and applied to the edges of the coverslip with a brush. The slide need not be warmed since these cements stay molten at quite low temperatures. The slide is placed on one side to dry and then given an additional coat of any waterproof cement. It is a worthwhile precaution, before applying the last coat of cement, to wipe off the slide with 95% alcohol to remove any trace of glycerol.

Specific Example

PREPARATION OF SMALL CRUSTACEANS IN GLYCEROL JELLY

The term small crustaceans, as here used, includes all specimens up to the size of a Gammarus, as well as the numerous larvae which are found both in fresh and salt waters. This group contains a large number of fascinating forms of universal distribution. A brief word must be said on methods of collection and preservation before passing to actual mounting.

Free-swimming crustaceans, whether marine or fresh-water, are collected by means of a plankton net. This is a long conical net, made by the professional from bolting silk, and by the amateur from the nearest woman's stocking. What distinguishes these nets from all others is that the lower end of the net, instead of being tied off, is blocked by a small glass tube tied firmly in place. These nets are towed slowly through the water, a process which results in the accumulation of large quantities of plankton within the net. The net itself is then very slowly and with constant shaking lifted from the water with the result that all those forms which have been accumulated in the net are washed down in the small glass tube, the contents of which may then be tipped out into another container. Unless one is on a very long collecting trip, it is better to bring home planktonic crustaceans alive, and for this purpose the contents of the tube should be tipped into at least a gallon of well-aerated water—fresh or salt as the case may be—for transference back to the laboratory. It is almost impossible to make a satisfactory preparation from the horrible messes which result from endeavoring to preserve directly the contents of an entire tube by throwing it into formaldehyde, a technique too often employed. When plankton samples are brought back to the laboratory they may again be concentrated with a plankton net or other device, and the still-living individuals are picked out with a pipet and transferred to a small bowl of clean, well-aerated water. Marine forms in particular should be washed in numerous changes of water to rid them of adherent phytoplankton which is almost impossible to remove from the fixed specimen. Though every mounter of microscope slides will go to endless lengths to narcotize many invertebrates, few ever appear to consider this necessary in the case of crustaceans. It is however much easier to identify specimens if their appendages are properly spread out, and the writer always kills crustaceans either with weak alcohol or with chloroform, a few drops of which are sprinkled on the surface of the water. As soon as they have dropped to the bottom they will be found to be flexible, and may then be picked out and placed on a slide, the appendages arranged more or less in the order required, and 95% alcohol cautiously dropped on them until they have stiffened in position.

Such specimens may then be transferred directly to a tube of 95% alcohol where they will retain the required shape until needed for mounting. Some small crustaceans are always found mixed up with weeds, both marine and fresh-water, from which they may be readily separated in the laboratory. Large masses of the weeds are brought back to the laboratory, and placed in shallow dishes with just sufficient water to cover them. The lack of oxygen in the water soon forces the crustaceans to detach themselves and gather round the edges of the bowl from which they may be removed with a pipet. There are a few marine copepods (*Dyspontius*, for example) which are considered exceedingly rare, for the reason that nobody ever collects them. These forms have sucking mouth-parts which they use to extract the juices of algae. They never become detached from these algae in the normal course of events. They may be readily collected by taking large masses of the specific alga, placing it in weak alcohol, shaking it vigorously, and then examining the sludge which is deposited at the bottom of the jar. Good hauls of these forms may also often be found at marine stations by going through the sludge which collects at the bottom of the jars in which both algae and ascidians have been stored.

There are also many small crustaceans which dwell in mosses, even in those which are apparently quite dry. These will not be secured if the moss is treated with a Berlese funnel in the way described in the last chapter. The only way to collect them is to soak the moss in some kind of narcotic until the crustaceans are stunned, then to rinse off the moss in a considerable volume of fluid which is allowed to settle, and to examine the sludge. The same process, applied to marine sands between tidemarks, often discloses small forms not found by any other means. Another fruitful way of collecting so-called rare forms is to go netting at night, since there are many marine crustaceans (Cumacea, for example) which become planktonic only at night. Parasitic forms, particularly copepods, are also often overlooked, particularly those which inhabit invertebrates.

No matter how these forms are collected, they should all be narcotized before killing, and should be killed in 95% alcohol and stored in this fluid, with a trace of glycerol, until required. When it is decided to mount them they are removed from 90% alcohol to 70% alcohol. After they have been permeated with this, glycerol is added little by little until the total concentration of glycerol is such that, if the alcohol be evaporated, a 50% glycerol-water mixture will be left. The final evaporation is best done at a temperature of 30° to 40°C. and is very conveniently conducted in a desiccator through which a current of air is drawn with any aspirator device. If the specimens are not very minute, it is desirable that the 50% glycerol should be poured off and replaced with the molten mounting medium in which the specimens should remain for an hour or two before mounting. Do not, however, transfer to the molten jelly more specimens than you are able to mount at one time, since prolonged soaking in the molten medium tends to soften them. The required number of slides are then warmed and a specimen, in a large drop of molten medium, placed on each. The specimen is then arranged with a needle and chilled rapidly. If there is not a large domed drop of medium over the top of the specimen, further medium is added from a pipet until there is a thick layer. When all the specimens have thus been mounted in the required position with a big dome of cooled jelly above them, a coverslip thinly smeared with 50% glycerol is laid on each. All of the slides may be provided with coverslips resting loosely on them before going further. The aluminum rod shown in Fig. 22 is now warmed and pressed down on the coverslip until the latter has come to rest on the specimen, or on the walls of the cell. A little practice is required to be able to do this without pressing down either so hard that one crushes the specimen or so long that one melts the jelly surrounding it.

If these specimens are mounted in a medium which does not contain sufficient glycerol, and which accordingly cracks and dries out when they are transferred to a drier environment, they may be remounted without very much difficulty by cracking the coverslip, soaking the specimen in 50% glycerol for a week or two, then removing the rest of the coverslip and remounting as though one had a fresh specimen.

6

Wholemounts in Resinous Media

General Principles

Mounting whole objects by the methods described in the last five chapters involves little preparation of the specimen but a great deal of preparation of the mount. In preparing wholemounts in resinous media a great deal of attention must be paid to the preparation of material, although the actual mounting is simple.

Resinous media are used for wholemounts not only because they permit mounting stained objects but more particularly because they impart to the specimen a great degree of transparency. This transparency comes from the increase in the index of refraction when the specimen is completely impregnated with the resin. These resins are not, however, miscible with water, hence the water must first be removed (*dehydration*) and then the dehydrant replaced with some material (*clearing agent*) with which the resin itself is miscible. Before these operations the specimen must be killed and hardened (*fixed*) and it is customary to stain the specimen in order to bring out those internal structures which would become invisible, were they not colored, through the increase in transparency. All of the following operations must, therefore, be conducted and will be discussed in turn:

1. narcotizing and fixing
2. staining
3. dehydrating
4. clearing
5. mounting

Narcotizing and Fixing Specimens

Hard objects such as small arthropods, hairs, and the like may be dehydrated and mounted directly into resinous media, but are far better prepared according to the manner described in Chapter 4. Most objects which are mounted in resinous media are, however, too soft to withstand the process of dehydration and clearing without special treatment. Though *hardening* and *fixing* agents were once considered as separate, they are now usually combined into a solution known as a *fixative*. Before dealing with fixatives, however, it is necessary to point out that few small animals, on being plunged into a fixative, will retain their shape, so that it is necessary first to narcotize them in some solution which will render them incapable of muscular contraction.

Narcotization may be caused either through the blocking of nerve impulses which cause contraction, or by some treatment which will inhibit the actual contraction of the muscle. For blocking nerve impulses there are a wide range of narcotics available (see Chapter 19, AF 50) and making a choice between them must be a matter of experience. It is to be recommended, in the absence of experience, that one of the solutions containing cocaine be first tried, since cocaine is the nearest approach to a universal narcotic known to the author. Should cocaine not be available, crystals of menthol may be sprinkled on the surface of the water containing the specimen. It is very important to distinguish between narcotization and killing, for a good wholemount cannot be made from a specimen which has been permitted to die in the narcotic.

Narcotization should always proceed slowly; that is, one should add a small quantity of narcotic at the beginning and increase the quantity later, adding the fixative only after the cessation of movement. This is easy to judge in the case of motile forms, which may be presumed to be narcotized shortly after they have fallen to the bottom, but in the case of sessile forms it is necessary to use a fine probe, preferably a hair, to determine the end point of narcotization.

Recommended Narcotics and Fixatives for Specific Objects

It must be pointed out that the primary purpose of fixing an object before making a wholemount is to retain as nearly as possible the natural shape. The fixative selected should, therefore, contain an *immobilizing agent* as well as a hardening agent. Gray 1933 (11360, **53**:14), in a discussion of the principles governing the selection of fixatives, came to the conclusion that there were only two good immobilizing agents. These were heat and osmic acid. It is therefore necessary, when dealing with highly contractile or imperfectly narcotized animals either to select a fixative containing osmic acid (Chapter 18, F 1000) or to heat the fixative. Neither osmic acid nor heat are good hardening agents and should not, therefore, be used alone. The best hardening agents for objects which are subsequently turned into resinous wholemounts appear to be chromic acid and formaldehyde, used either singly or in combination, and these solutions are usually acidified with acetic acid to assist in the preservation of internal structures, particularly nuclei. Reference to the classification of fixatives at the beginning of Chapter 18 will show a large number of solutions fulfilling these requirements and no specific recommendation need be made here. Mercuric chloride, particularly in the solution of Gilson 1898 (Chapter 18, F 3000.0014), is another good fixative to use before wholemounting. The following recommendations, drawn largely from Gray 1935 (*Microsc. Rec.*, **35**:4), and Gray 1936 (*Microsc. Rec.*, **37**:10), are to be taken only as suggestions representing the author's opinion and should be used as a basis for further experiment.

NONCONTRACTILE PROTOZOA. These do not require narcotization and may be fixed directly in a weak solution of osmic acid. The writer, however, much prefers his own technique (described at the end of this chapter) for the handling of these specimens.

INDIVIDUAL CONTRACTILE PROTOZOANS. These are very difficult to handle. Ten per cent methanol is quite a good narcotic for *Dileptus*, but 1% hydroxylamine seems better for *Spirostomum*. It is the writer's practice to try new forms with the following narcotics in the order given: 10% methanol, 1% hydroxylamine, 1% urethane, AF 51.1 Hanley 1949, AF 51.1 Rousselet 1895, and AF 51.1 Cori 1893 (Chapter 19). There are many forms, however, which do not respond to these narcotics and of which it appears almost impossible to make a good wholemount.

Individual rhizopods, as *Amoeba* and *Difflugia*, are best fixed to a coverslip in the following manner. Take a clean coverslip and smear on it a very slight quantity of fresh egg albumen. The solution of Mayer 1884 (Chapter 26, V 21.1), which is often recommended for the purpose, should be avoided, for the glycerol and preservative included in it inhibit the expansion of the animals. Each individual protozoan is placed in the center of a coverslip and left to expand. While this is going on a flask (or kettle) is fitted with a cork. Through this cork is inserted a glass tube the outer end of which has been drawn to a fairly fine point. The water in the flask is boiled to produce a jet of steam. As soon as the protozoan is satisfactorily expanded, the coverslip is picked up very gently and the underside passed momentarily through the jet of steam. This instantly hardens the protozoans in position and at the same time cements them to the coverslip through the coagulation of the egg white. The coverslip should then be transferred to any standard fixative solution for a few minutes before being washed and stored in alcohol.

Among the Suctoria, *Acineta* and *Dendrocometes* may be prepared by placing them in a good volume of water, sprinkling menthol crystals on the surface, leaving them overnight, and then adding sufficient 40% formaldehyde to bring the total strength to 4%. These forms may then be transferred to alcohol for staining and preparation as resinous wholemounts or may be mounted directly in formaldehyde as described in Chapter 2.

STALKED CILIATE PROTOZOANS. These forms are quite easy to fix provided one realizes that double narcotization is necessary: once for the stalk and once for the head. The author's technique is to narcotize with Rousselet's solution until the snapping movements have slowed up and then very gently to add weak hydrogen peroxide.

The specimens are then watched under a microscope and the selected fixative— which must contain osmic acid—is flooded onto them at the exact moment when the cilia straighten out and become stationary. This is satisfactory with *Carchesium*, *Zoothamnium* and *Vorticella*. *Opercularia* and *Epistylis* have noncontractile stalks and one need, therefore, only use hydrogen peroxide. The writer has never made a satisfactory mount of *Scathidium* or *Pyxicola*.

COELENTERATA. Hydroids are usually narcotized with menthol, though the writer prefers his own mixture (Chapter 19, AF 51.1 Gray) for the purpose, and fixed in a hot mercuric-acetic mixture. A description of the narcotization of *Hydra* is given in Chapter 9 and a detailed account of the preparation of Medusae in Chapter 20. Anthozoa, particularly the small ones likely to be prepared as wholemounts, can be narcotized with menthol, though magnesium sulfate is better.

PLATYHELMINTHES. Some of the smaller fresh water Turbellaria (e.g. *Vortex*, *Microstomum*) may be narcotized satisfactorily by adding small quantities of 2% chloral hydrate to the water in which they are swimming. Another good technique is to isolate the forms in a watch glass of water and place the watch glass under a bell jar together with a small beaker of ether. The ether vapor dissolves in the water and narcotizes these forms excellently. A detailed account of the method of handling the liver fluke is given in Chapter 20 and may be satisfactorily employed for other parasitic flatworms.

ANNELIDA. Small, marine, free-living Polychaetae make excellent wholemounts and do not usually need to be narcotized before killing. They should, however, be stranded on a slide and a very small quantity of the fixative dropped on them, so that they die in a flat condition which makes subsequent mounting possible. Much more realistic mounts are obtained by this means than if they are laboriously straightened before fixing, for they usually contract into the sinuous wave which they show when swimming. There seems to be no certain method of fixing the Nereids with their jaws protruding and one has to rely on chance to obtain one in this condition. The free-swimming larvae of marine polychaetes are very difficult to fix satisfactorily, because the large flotation chaetae usually fall out. The writer prefers for these, as for other marine invertebrate larvae, to concentrate a relatively large quantity of the plankton and then to flood over it three or four times its volume of Bouin's fixative (Chapter 18, F 5000.1010 Bouin 1897) at 70°C. The specimens are then allowed to settle, the fixative poured off, and replaced with 70% alcohol which is replaced daily until it ceases to extract yellow from the specimens. By hunting through a large mass of plankton so fixed, one can usually obtain a considerable number of specimens in a perfectly expanded condition.

Fresh water Oligochaetes are best narcotized with chloroform, either by adding small quantities of a saturated solution of chloroform in water, or by placing them in a small quantity of water under a bell jar in which an atmosphere of chloroform vapor is maintained. Leeches are difficult to handle and the author has had most success by placing them in a fairly large quantity of water to which is added, from time to time, small quantities of a saturated solution of magnesium sulfate. As soon as the leeches have fallen to the bottom considerably larger quantities of magnesium sulfate can be added, which will leave the leeches, in a short time, in a perfectly relaxed, but not expanded, condition. They should then be flattened between two slides and fixed in Zenker's fluid (Chapter 18, F 3700.0010 Zenker 1894). After the specimens have been fixed sufficiently long to hold their shape when the glass plates are removed, they are transferred for a couple of days to fresh fixative and then washed in running water overnight. If the crop contains any considerable quantity of blood, it will be necessary to bleach this before a satisfactory stained wholemount can be made; the specimens should, therefore, be transferred to the bleach of Murdoch 1945 (Chapter 19, AF 31.1) where they should remain for a few days.

BRYOZOA. Marine bryozoans may be narcotized without difficulty by sprinkling menthol on the surface of the water containing them. Subsequent fixation is best in some chromic-acetic mixture, for osmic acid tends to precipitate on the test and blacken the specimen. It may be pointed out that, for taxonomic purposes, dried wholemounts of the test prepared as described in Chapter 1 are of more value than are wholemounts with the expanded animal. It is usually recommended that fresh-water bryozoans be narcotized in some cocaine solution, but the writer has found menthol just as good and much easier to use. Fresh-water bryozoans should be fixed directly in 4% formaldehyde since they shrink badly in any other fixative.

GASTROTRICHA. These give excellent results by the special technique for minute fresh-water animals described at the end of this chapter.

SMALL CRUSTACEANS. These are sometimes prepared as resinous mounts, though the writer prefers to mount them in glycerol jelly in the manner described in Chapter 5. They may be narcotized in weak alcohol and fixed in almost any fixative.

OTHER ARTHROPODS. Wholemounts of most small arthropods are better made in gum media in the manner described in Chapter 4. A detailed description of the preparation of the skeleton of an insect for mounting in Canada balsam is among the typical preparations described at the end of this chapter.

Choice of a Stain

It is now to be presumed that, whatever method of narcotization and fixation has been employed, the specimens to be mounted have been washed free from fixative and accumulated either in water or 70% alcohol. The reason that so many formulas and methods for staining are given in Chapter 20, 21, and 23 is that no two people have ever agreed on the best method of staining anything. The suggestions which follow, therefore, are likely to be modified by every individual reading the book; but they are included for the sake of those inexperienced in making wholemounts.

SMALL INVERTEBRATES AND INVERTEBRATE LARVAE. These are best stained in carmine by the indirect process: that is, by overstaining and subsequent differentiation in acid alcohol. For most specimens the writer prefers Grenacher's alcoholic-borax-carmine (Chapter 20, DS 11.22 Grenacher 1879). As an alternative, particularly for marine invertebrates, he has frequently used the two formulas for Mayer's *paracarmine* (Chapter 20, DS 11.22 Mayer 1892a and 1892b). With these stains available there are very few small invertebrates or invertebrate larvae which cannot be prepared.

LARGER INVERTEBRATE SPECIMENS. Larger specimens are better stained by the direct process: that is, exposed for a considerable length of time to a very weak solution of stain and subsequently not differentiated. This process is described in considerable detail for the liver fluke in Chapter 20; the directions there given apply equally to earthworms, leeches, or medium-sized polychaetae.

VERTEBRATE EMBRYOS. These seem to stain more satisfactorily in hematoxylin than in carmine solutions, the author's preference being for the formula of Carazzi (Chapter 20, DS 11.122 Carazzi 1911). This formula is not very well known but may be used whenever the solution of Delafield is recommended. Detailed instructions for the use of this stain on a chicken embryo are given in Chapter 20. People who wish to produce a startling, rather than a useful, mount are recommended to try the technique of Lynch (Chapter 20, DS 13.7 Lynch 1930).

PLANT MATERIALS. Plant specimens for wholemounts often consist of only one, or at the most two, layers of cells and are easier to stain than zoological specimens. The nuclei may be stained either with safranin (Chapter 20, DS 11.42) or with any of the iron hematoxylin techniques (Chapter 20, DS 11.11) which in zoological procedures are rigorously confined to sec-

Dehydration is carried out by soaking the specimen in gradually increasing strengths of alcohol, it being conventional to employ 30%, 50%, 70%, 90%, 95%, and absolute alcohol. The writer prefers to omit from this series, unless the object is very delicate, both the 30% and the 50% steps in the process, thus starting with direct transfer from water to 70% alcohol. The only difficulty likely to be met in dehydration is in the handling of small specimens, for if they are in specimen tubes it

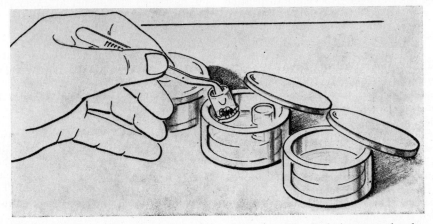

Fig. 23. Transferring objects between reagents with cloth-bottomed tubes.

tions. A contrasting plasma stain may be used after the nuclei have been well differentiated.

Dehydration

It is to be presumed that the specimens, plant or animal, stained or unstained, are now accumulated either in distilled water or in 70% alcohol according to the treatment which they have had. It is now necessary to remove the water from them before they can be transferred into a resinous mounting medium. Ethanol is widely used as a dehydrant and, at least in the preparation of wholemounts, only its nonavailability should make any substitute necessary. If substitution is necessary, acetone or methanol, in that order of preference, may be used, but they have the disadvantage of being more volatile than ethanol and, therefore, require more care in handling.

is almost impossible to transfer them from one to the other without carrying over too much weak alcohol. The writer has long since abandoned the use of tubes in favor of the device seen in Fig. 23. This is a short length of glass tube, open at both ends, with a small piece of bolting silk or other fine cloth tied across the lower end. The specimens are placed in these little tubes which (see illustration) are transferred from one stender dish to another with a minimum chance of contamination. These tubes are commercially available in England but in America must either be imported or homemade.

There is no means of judging when dehydration is complete save by attempting to clear the object. It is unwise to believe the label on an open bottle or jar if it says *absolute alcohol* because this reagent is hygroscopic and rapidly absorbs water from the air. One should, therefore, keep a quantity of anhydrous copper sulfate at the bottom of the absolute alcohol bottle and cease to regard the alcohol as absolute when the salt starts turning from white to blue. More wholemounts are ruined by being imperfectly dehydrated than by any other method, and even the smallest specimen should have at least 24 hours in absolute alcohol before being cleared.

If the specimen is to be mounted in Canada balsam, or one of the substitutes for it, it must next be cleared, but if it is to be passed directly to Venice turpentine the reader should turn to end of the chapter for a detailed description of this technique.

The Choice of a Clearing Agent

A clearing agent must be some substance which is miscible both with absolute alcohol and with the resinous medium which has been selected for mounting. The ideal substances for this purpose are *essential oils* for they impart just as much transparency to the specimen as does the resin used for mounting, so that one has, as it were, a preview of the finished specimen. The use of xylene or benzene, which is so widespread in the preparation of paraffin sections (see Chapter 12) has tended to spread into the preparation of wholemounts, for which purpose, in the author's opinion, they are worthless. They have a relatively low index of refraction; hence one cannot tell whether or not the slight cloudiness of the specimen is due to imperfect dehydration until after they have been mounted in balsam.

The writer's first choice is terpineol (synthetic oil of lilac) which has advantages possessed by no other oil. It is readily miscible with 90% alcohol, so that it will remove from the specimen any traces of water which may remain in it through faulty dehydration, and it has also the property of not making specimens brittle. The odor is very slight and rather pleasant. Oil of cloves is the most widely recommended essential oil for the preparation of wholemounts and it has only two disadvantages: its violent odor and the fact that objects placed in it are rendered brittle. If a small arthropod be cleared in oil of cloves, it is almost impossible to get

it into a wholemount without breaking off some appendages. Oil of cloves is, however, miscible with 90% alcohol. Oil of cedar (more correctly oil of cedarwood) has been recommended in the literature and has the advantage of having a pleasant odor and of not rendering objects brittle. Unfortunately it is very sensitive to water so that perfect dehydration in absolute alcohol is necessary before endeavoring to clear with it.

Two clearing agents, which are excellent for unstained specimens, are very little known. These are turpentine and acetic acid. The acid cannot be used with stains for obvious reasons, while the turpentine is a strong oxidizing agent and cannot, therefore, be used after hematoxylin, though it is perfectly safe with carmine. Absolute (glacial) acetic acid is miscible at all proportions both with water and with Canada balsam. If small arthropods are to be mounted in balsam, rather than in the manner described in Chapter 4, they may be dropped into acetic acid, left there until they are completely dehydrated, and then transferred directly to balsam. This little-known technique is strongly to be recommended.

Mounting Specimens in Balsam

Nothing is easier than to mount a specimen in a resinous medium, provided that it has been perfectly dehydrated and cleared. A properly made wholemount should be glass-clear, but it will not be clear in balsam unless it is clear in terpineol or clove oil. Not more than one in a thousand wholemounts has this vitreous appearance, and the worker who is accustomed to looking at rather cloudy wholemounts should take the trouble to dehydrate a specimen thoroughly, then to remove the whole of the dehydrating agent with a clearing agent, and then to mount properly in balsam.

The first step, therefore, in making a mount in, say, Canada balsam is to make quite certain that the specimen in its essential oil is glass-clear; the second step is to make certain that one has "natural" Canada balsam and not "dried" balsam which has been dissolved in xylene. Solutions of dried balsam in hydrocarbons are meant for mounting sections and are, for this purpose, superior to the natural balsam. Natural balsam is, however, just as preferable for wholemounts and is just as easy to obtain. If it is found to be too thick for ready use, it may be warmed gently until it reaches the desired consistency. A single small specimen is mounted by placing it in a drop of balsam on a slide and then lowering a coverslip horizontally (Fig. 24) until the central portion touches the drop. The coverslip is then released and pressed very gently until it just touches the top of the object. By this means it is possible to retain the object in the center of the coverslip and also, if one is using natural balsam which does not shrink much in drying, to avoid using cells for any but the largest object. Unfortunately most people are accustomed to mounting sections in thin balsam by the technique shown in Fig. 25: that is, by touching one edge of the coverslip to the drop and then lowering it from one side. The objection to this is that the balsam, as is seen in the figure, immediately runs into the angle of the coverslip, taking the object with it, and it is difficult to lower the coverslip in such a way that the object is left in the center. If one is mounting thin objects, or deep objects in a cell in which a cavity has been ground, it is desirable to hold the coverslip in place with a clip while the balsam is hardening. This process is seen in Fig. 25, the type of clip there shown being made of Phosphor bronze wire, and is far superior, in the writer's opinion, to any other type.

This description presumes that one is using natural Canada balsam, which is unquestionably the best resinous medium in which to prepare wholemounts. If one is using one of the thin resinous media, many formulas for which are given in Chapter 26 under the heading M 30, a very different technique will have to be adopted. In the first place these media are so thin that it is almost impossible to apply the coverslip as shown in Fig. 24, and one is forced to adopt the technique shown in Fig. 25. This difficulty may be avoided by placing the object on the slide, placing a drop of the medium over the object, and then placing the slide in a desiccator until most of the solvent has evaporated. A second layer is then placed on top, and a large drop, or rather a thick coat of varnish, is thus built up over the specimen. A coverslip is then applied and the slide warmed until the resin becomes fluid.

The best use for solutions of balsam in making wholemounts is in the preparation of delicate specimens or a large number of objects. The technique for the former is described in Chapter 20. In the latter case the objects are transferred from the clearing medium to a tube or dish of the solution of balsam in whatever hydrocarbon has been selected, and the solvent then evaporated. When the balsam which remains has reached a good consistency for mounting, each specimen is taken, together with a drop of balsam, and placed on a slide. A coverslip is then added. By this method large numbers of slides may be made in a short time. It is not necessary to use solutions of dried balsam, and the writer prefers, for this purpose, to dilute natural balsam with benzene.

Mounting large objects in a deep cell in Canada balsam is not to be recommended for the reason that the balsam becomes yellow with age and, in thick layers, tends to obscure the specimen. A wholemount of a 96-hour chicken embryo, for example, is of very doubtful value; but if it has to be made it is best first to impregnate it thoroughly with a fairly thin dilution of natural balsam. It is then placed in the cell, piling the solution up on top, and left in a desiccator. The cell is refilled as the evaporation of the solvent lowers the level. When the cell is finally completely filled with solvent-free balsam it is warmed on a hot table and the coverslip applied directly.

Finishing Balsam Mounts

If a mount has been properly made with natural balsam, and if the size of the drop has been estimated correctly, no finishing is required since no balsam will overflow the edges of the coverslip. Natural balsam takes a long time to harden and, if one has a fairly thick mount the coverslip of which is not supported, drying cannot be hastened by heating as this will liquify the balsam, causing the coverslip to tip

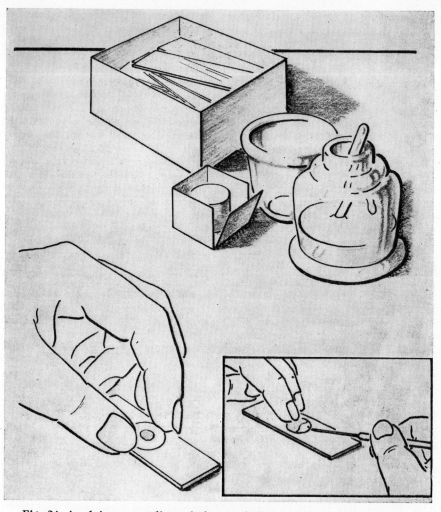

Fig. 24. Applying coverslip to balsam wholemount.
Fig. 25 (inset). Wrong way to apply coverslip to balsam wholemount.

to one side. Mounts in natural balsam are better put away for a month or two before any attempt is made to clean them. The slide should be cleaned, when it is sufficiently hard, first by chipping off any excess balsam with a knife and secondly by wiping away the chips with a rag moistened in 90% alcohol. This will leave over the surface of the slide a whitish film which may then be removed with a warm soap solution, and the slide may be polished before being labeled.

The writer prefers to apply a ring of some cement or varnish round the edge of his balsam mounts for two reasons. In the first place such a ring diminishes the rate of oxidation so that the mounts do not start going brown around the edges. In the second place, such slides are less likely to be damaged in students' hands because of the psychological effect produced by a well-finished slide. One must carefully avoid using any cement or varnish which is soluble in, or miscible with, balsam; the author prefers to use one of the numerous cellulose acetate lacquers which are available on the market. The method of applying such a ring has been described in

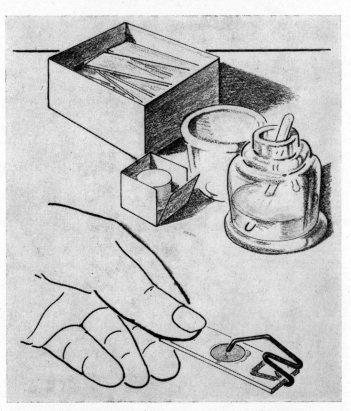

Fig. 26. Balsam wholemount ready for drying.

Chapter 1. With regard to labeling, it may be pointed out that no power on earth will persuade gum arabic, customarily used for attaching labels, to adhere to a greasy or oily slide: the portion of the slide to which the label is to be attached should, therefore, be cleaned more carefully than any other. The writer prefers to moisten both sides of the label, press it firmly to the glass, and to write on it only after it is dry.

Specific Examples

PREPARATION OF A WHOLEMOUNT OF PECTINATELLA

Though this exposition specifically applies to preparing wholemounts of the animal named, it applies equally well to the preparation of wholemounts of any other fresh-water bryozoan or, as a matter of fact, for any small invertebrate of about the same size and consistency. *Pectinatella* has been picked only for the reason that it has a habit of turning up on the walls of the aquaria in the writer's laboratory. If it does not turn up in aquaria in the reader's laboratory, it will be necessary for him to collect the specimen. Fresh-water bryozoans are rather like gold: that is, they oc-

cur where you find them. Profitable hunting grounds are the underside of the leaves of large water plants and the surface of branches of trees which have fallen into the water but have not yet had time to decay. An old trick of European collectors was to lower a length of rope into a pond in which bryozoans were known to occur, and to leave it there for the summer. It was astonishing how frequently, when these ropes were pulled up again in the fall, they were found to be covered with colonies of bryozoans.

However the bryozoans be obtained, it

is necessary next that they should be narcotized. The material on which they are living is cut up and the pieces placed in fingerbowl or aquarium of pond water. Distilled water and tap water are lethal to these forms. There should not be so many specimens that they touch each other on the bottom of the fingerbowl, and the fingerbowl itself should be completely filled with water. Fresh-water bryozoa are a little sensitive to heat and may not respond well to the high temperatures found in some laboratories. In this case it is as well to put the fingerbowl containing the specimens in a refrigerator, preferably one held at about 10°C, and to leave them there overnight. They may then be brought out and narcotized before they have time to suffer from the increasing temperature.

It is usually recommended that fresh-water bryozoans be narcotized with cocaine, either as a straight 2% solution, or in one of the mixtures the formulas for which are given in Chapter 19 under the heading AF 50. The writer prefers to use menthol which is both cheaper and easier to obtain. For an ordinary fingerbowl about a gram of menthol sprinkled on the surface will be sufficient. There is no means of foretelling how long it will take the specimens to become narcotized, therefore one must look at them at intervals until they are seen not to be contracting. This may not be due to narcotization, however, so one should take some very delicate instrument—a hair mounted on a wooden handle is excellent—and use this to push the individual polyps. If, on receiving a push, they contract sharply, it is evident that little narcotization has taken place and more menthol should be sprinkled on the surface. If, on being pushed with a hair, they contract slowly, it is evident that they are partly narcotized and one must be careful not to disturb them further for at least ten minutes, for if they contract in a narcotized condition they will not again expand. The right stage for killing has arrived when no amount of shoving with a hair will persuade the specimens to retract, and an examination under a binocular microscope shows the ciliary action on the lophophore not to have stopped. A tube is used to

siphon from the fingerbowl so much water that the remaining layer just covers the specimens. The fingerbowl is then filled with 4% formaldehyde, covered, and placed to one side.

One must be careful to distinguish at this point between a *killing* agent such as formaldehyde, and hardening and fixing agents. In the present instance it is unnecessary, since the stain to be used contains in itself an adequate mordant, to use a fixative which will combine with the proteins of the specimen, but it is necessary that they should be hardened in order that they may withstand the treatment to which they will be subjected in staining and dehydration. Four per cent formaldehyde hardens very slowly, and it is suggested that they should next be passed to alcohol for the hardening process.

It is desirable to flatten the specimens before hardening into the shape that they will be required to assume after mounting. It is to be presumed that the purpose of making a microscope slide is to study the object which has been mounted; and the depth of focus of microscope lenses is so slight that only relatively thin objects can be studied at one time. It is extraordinary how frequently this simple principle is overlooked, or how frequently people endeavor to flatten the object after it has been gotten into balsam when it is almost invariably so brittle that it will break up during the flattening process. Five minutes' work in arranging the parts before hardening makes all the difference between a first-class and a second-class mount. To arrange and flatten the objects for hardening, the 40% formaldehyde is replaced with water. The specimen is removed to a fingerbowl of clean distilled water where it is examined thoroughly to make sure it has no adherent dirt. The object is flattened by hardening it between two slides, but obviously, if it is just pressed between two slides it will be squashed rather than flattened. Anything may be used to hold the two slides apart, though in the present instance a very thick No. 3 or two No. 2 coverslips would give about the right separation. A glass slide is taken, and about an inch on each side of the center a thick No. 3 coverslip is placed and held in place by the capillary attraction of a drop of water. The specimen is taken from the water with a large eye-dropper type of pipet and placed in a considerable volume of water on the slide. It is then easy to arrange the parts with needles; but it is difficult to lower a second slide on top of the first without disarranging these parts. An alternative method is to place the slide with its coverslips in the fingerbowl with the specimen, to arrange its parts under water and to place the second slide on top. Whichever process is adopted, the slides are then tied or clipped, together and transferred to a jar of 95% alcohol, where they may remain for a week, or until next required. Each specimen is treated in this manner; and it is better not to try to flatten two or three specimens on one slide.

When it is desired to continue mounting the specimens, each slide is taken and placed in a fingerbowl of 95% alcohol before the cords which bind them together are cut, or the clips removed. Getting the two slides apart without damaging the specimen is not easy, particularly if the specimen tends to stick to one or the other of the slides. The simplest method is to insert the blade of a scalpel into the gap between the slides and, twisting it slightly sideways, see if the specimen is free. If the specimen shows signs of sticking to one slide, the other may be removed and the specimen washed from the slide to which it is stuck with a jet of 95% alcohol from a pipet. If it shows signs of sticking to both slides, it is still possible, by projecting a jet of 95% alcohol between them, to free it from both. Each slide is treated in due order until one has accumulated the whole of the flattened specimens in a dish of 95% alcohol. It must be understood that these specimens have been hardened flat so that no amount of subsequent treatment will ever swell them out again or prevent them from remaining in the required position.

It is recommended, if there are several specimens to handle, that a series of the little cloth-ended tubes shown in Fig. 23 be used. The only alternative is to handle each specimen with the aid of a section lifter with the consequent risk of damage. Though not nearly so satisfactory, it is also possible, at least for the process of staining and dehydration, to place the specimens all together in a small vial in which the different fluids used may be successively placed.

A wholemount of this type is best stained in carmine and the choice would lie between Mayer's carmalum (a detailed description of the use of which is given in Chapter 20), Grenacher's borax-carmine (also described in Chapter 20), and Mayer's paracarmine, which will accordingly be selected. Preparation of this stain (the formula for which is given in Chapter 20 under the heading DS 11.22 Mayer 1892) does not present any difficulty, but it should be noted that the differentiating solution is 0.2% solution of strontium chloride in 70% alcohol. Adequate supplies of this should be available before one starts staining.

The specimens are passed from 95% alcohol to 70% alcohol. They will naturally float, but as soon as they have sunk to the bottom it may be presumed that they are sufficiently rehydrated and either the cloth-ended tube containing them may be transferred to the dish of stain or the 70% alcohol may be poured out of the tube and stain substituted for it. One of the advantages of this stain is that it is relatively rapid in action—very few specimens will not be adequately stained in five to ten minutes—but it does not matter how long the materials remain in it. It is, therefore, often convenient to leave the specimens in overnight and to start differentiation the next morning. They are then either removed to the differentiating solution or, alternatively, the stain is poured off and the differentiating solution substituted for it. In the latter case three or four changes will be required, owing to the necessity of leaving some stain in the bottom of the tube to avoid pouring the specimens out with it. Unless the operator is quite experienced, it is safer to shake the tube so as to distribute the specimens thoroughly in the stain, and then to tip this into a large fingerbowl of differentiating solution from which the specimens may be subsequently picked out and transferred to a new tube of differentiator. It is tragically easy, in pouring off stain, to pour specimens with it down the sink. As soon as the stain has been washed off with the differentiating solution, a single specimen should be transferred to a watch glass and examined under a low power of the microscope. It is more than probable that little differentiation will be required, so that a simple rinse may be adequate. It is difficult to judge the exact degree of differentiation, but it must be remembered that the object will appear darker after clearing than it does in the differentiating solution. The internal organs should be sharply demarcated when the outer surface of the specimen is relatively free from stain. This may be judged in *Pectinatella* by placing a coverslip on the specimen and examining one of the branches of the lophophore under the high power of the microscope. Differentiation may be considered complete when only the nuclei in the cells of the lophophore are stained. The specimens are then washed in four or five changes of 70% alcohol, to remove the strontium chloride, before being placed for at least a day in 96% alcohol as the first stage of dehydration. They should then be transferred to two changes, with at least six hours in each, to a considerable volume of fresh 95% alcohol and may then be cleared. Absolute alcohol is not necessary if terpineol is the clearing agent.

There is some danger, if the specimens are transferred directly from 95% alcohol to a fluid as viscous as terpineol, that the specimens will become distorted through the very violent diffusion current. This may be avoided in the following manner: one takes a fairly wide (about an inch) glass vial and fills it about half full of terpineol. Ninety-five per cent alcohol is then carefully poured down the side of the vial (or on to a spoon held in the vial in the manner of a bartender making a *pousse-café*) so as to float a layer of alcohol on top of the terpineol. The specimens are now dropped into the alcohol and sink through it, coming to rest on the surface of the layer of terpineol into which they sink slowly without any strong diffusion currents. They will have sunk to the bottom after a little while, but there will still be alcohol diffusing upward from them. As soon as the diffusion currents have ceased, the alcohol should be drawn from the top of the tube with a pipet and the specimens transferred to clean terpineol. When they are in fresh terpineol, they should be examined carefully under a microscope to make sure that they are glass-clear without the least trace of milkiness. If they appear slightly milky they have either been insufficiently dehydrated, or the alcohol used for the dehydration has become contaminated with water. In either case they must be transferred to a tube of fresh alcohol for complete dehydration and then put back into terpineol. It is a waste of time to endeavor to prepare a balsam mount from a specimen which is not perfectly transparent in the clearing medium.

When all the specimens are in terpineol, take some clean slides, some clean ¾-inch circular coverslips, and a balsam bottle containing natural balsam. (The author's preference for the natural balsam rather than a solution of this material in some solvent has already been explained.) Place a drop of the natural balsam on each of, say, six slides, and then one at a time lift out six specimens from the terpineol and place them on top of the balsam. They will sink through the balsam slowly so that these six slides should be pushed on one side while a further six slides have drops of balsam put on them, and so on. As soon as the specimens have sunk to the bottom of the drop of balsam, a coverslip is held horizontally above, touched to the top of the drop, and then pushed down with a needle until the specimen is flattened firmly against the slide. As these specimens have been properly hardened and flattened there is no risk of their being damaged by drying the mount under pressure; therefore one can then apply a clip (see Fig. 26) and place the slides on a warm table to harden. Each slide is then cleaned, finished, and labeled as usual.

Preparation of a Skeleton of an Insect in Balsam

Two methods have already been described for preparing small insects as wholemounts. These are the use of the gum media given in Chapter 4, and the simple, though very little-known, method of dropping the insect directly into glacial acetic acid and then transferring it from this acid to balsam. Many small insects, or other arthropods, are too opaque for this method of preparation to render apparent any details of the endoskeleton, which is so frequently necessary for diagnostic purposes. These forms must, therefore, be skeletonized and rendered partially transparent before mounting.

Insects are skeletonized with 10% potassium hydroxide, which dissolves and removes the internal organs while at the same time softening the skeleton sufficiently for the specimen to be flattened and made into a wholemount. Some very skilled mounters of the past made a specialty of preparing whole insects without pressure, but these specimens are chiefly valuable as exhibits, and not as slides for study.

Let us suppose that we have an ant which is to be made into a transparent wholemount. It does not matter whether this specimen has been freshly collected or has been dried for some time; in either case it *must* be soaked for at least three or four days in 95% alcohol. Unless this precaution is taken, the strong alkali will dissolve the thin membrane which holds the joints together and the specimen will fall to pieces. Disregard of this simple precaution is responsible for more failures in this type of mount than anything else. After the specimen has been satisfactorily hardened in alcohol, it is transferred to water until it is rehydrated and then placed in the alkali. In the case of old and hardened specimens it is desirable first to drill a fine hole at the tip of the abdomen with a sharp needle. After 24 hours in the alkali, the specimen should be removed and stranded on a glass slide with the legs more or less in the position in which they will be mounted. The specimen is then gently stroked with a brush from the point of the head toward the tip of the abdomen, care being taken not to break off any of the appendages. The purpose of this stroking is to expel any of the viscera which may have been dissolved, either through the natural vent, or the small one which has been made with a needle. It has been stated that the specimen which we are examining, an ant, may be left for 24

hours before this is done, but in the case of thinner-walled and more delicate specimens, stroking must be done two or three times a day. The reason for this is that the hydrolysis of the internal organs causes great swelling and, unless some of this fluid is expelled at frequent intervals, the abdomen, thorax, and even the head will be swollen and stretched into an unnatural appearance. The process of gently stroking out the contained material either once or twice a day is continued until it is apparent that no further viscera remain in the animal. It must be emphasized again that it is quite impossible to make a good preparation if the specimen is just thrown into alkali and left there until it is sufficiently transparent. When all the viscera have been removed, the appendages are carefully arranged with needles as the specimen lies stranded on the slide, and a few drops of glacial acid dropped onto the specimen from a pipet. This instantly renders the specimen transparent and at the same time partially hardens the appendages in place. The specimen, however, has yet to be flattened and properly hardened before it can be mounted. A couple of thick coverslips, or a couple of pieces of cardboard of the same thickness as that desired in the final specimen, are laid one on each side of the specimen to support a second slide which is then placed on top. It is essential that the specimen should be flattened without producing any wrinkles in the softened chitinous exoskeleton and, unless the insect is naturally flat, this cannot be done merely by dropping a slide on top of it. Instead, the brush which was previously used for stroking is turned sideways, and rolled backward and forward along the insect, pressing out any wrinkles which may appear. A second slide is placed on top to hold the insect flat and, with the appendages in the position desired, two slides are tied or clipped together and placed in a jar of 95% alcohol until they are next required. They should not remain in alcohol for less than a week and may remain for an indefinite period without damage. After the specimen has been hardened and dehydrated in this manner, the two slides are very carefully separated, with the use of a fine pipet to

squirt in jets of alcohol to free the specimen. It does not matter if the specimen
should stick to one of the two slides for
it may then be mounted on this slide.
Whether, however, the specimen is free in
alcohol or adherent to one slide, it must
now be cleared, and the use of turpentine
for this purpose is strongly recommended.
As soon as the specimen has cleared, it is
placed in the center of the slide and a
considerable quantity of natural balsam
poured on top of it. Since this specimen
will not be danaged by heat, it should now
be warmed until the balsam is hot and as
liquid as water. This drives off the turpentine, as well as most of the natural solvent
of the balsam, so that when the coverslip
has been placed and the slide cooled it will
be finished. Excess balsam may then be
scraped and washed off in the usual manner and the specimen labeled.

The description just given is of the conventional method of preparing mounts of
this type and may be equally well applied
to parts as well as to entire insects. The
preparation of *demonstration mounts without pressure* is now a lost art, and there
appears to be no one alive to duplicate the
feats of the old mounters of the last century who were able to turn an entire
housefly into what appeared to be an amber glass model of itself. For the benefit,
however, of those who may wish to resur-
rect this art, the author would like to
offer a few suggestions as to a method by
which he has prepared passable, but not
good, slides of this type. The insect, relaxed exactly as if it were being prepared
for a museum specimen, is then "set" on a
glass slide, with the legs arranged in the
required position and held in place by
cementing the tip of each leg to the slide
with a small drop of molten gelatin.

A piece of wood is whittled down until
it can be slid between the insect and the
glass, thus stopping the legs from contracting and pulling the insect down in the
next stage of hardening. The glass with its
attached insect should then be placed in
95% alcohol and left for a week to harden.

If, at this stage, it is placed directly in
alkali, the ligaments of the legs will be
softened and the specimen will no longer
be set in a natural position. It is, however,
possible, after the specimen has been rehydrated, to drill a very small hole in the
back of the abdomen and to work a hypodermic needle forward until the tip of it
reaches to the head. A minute quantity of
10% potassium hydroxide is then injected
and the specimen left in a moist chamber
for two or three hours. The needle is then
reinserted and a further quantity of potassium hydroxide injected. By this time
some of the viscera will have been softened
sufficiently to come out of the hole on the
edge of the needle. Care must be taken
that none of the hydroxide gets onto the
legs, or onto any of the fine appendages,
and particularly that it does not run down
and dissolve the gelatin which is holding
the specimen in place. After three or four
days of making injections daily, the viscera of the insect will have been washed
out and the body itself commencing to
soften. The slide is then put into alkali,
where it remains until the legs of the
specimen start to soften and to be transparent. The specimen is then taken to
glacial acetic acid, and from glacial acetic
acid to xylene which is used to wash the
acetic acid from it. When all the acid has
been removed the specimen is transferred
to a weak solution of Canada balsam in
xylene, in which it remains until it is
thoroughly impregnated.

A deep cell (see Chapter 1) is next cemented to a glass slide, and the specimen
transferred to the cell which is filled to the
brim with a solution of balsam in xylene.
This is placed in the desiccator to evaporate, the cell being filled up as often as is
necessary. The cell, with its contained insect, is then slowly heated to drive off the
remainder of the solvent and finally closed
with a coverslip. The writer must again
confess, reluctantly, that such specimens
make magnificent show pieces that are
of very doubtful scientific value.

PREPARATION OF AN ALGA IN VENICE TURPENTINE

Venice turpentine is the natural balsam
which is exuded by the larch (*Larix de-*

cidua). It is a thick balsam, of about the
consistency of natural Canada balsam,

and takes its name, as do so many other resins, from the place from which it was first exported to England. The commonest commercial use of this material today is in the preparation of artist's pigments, so that it is usually better secured from an artists', than from a scientific, supply house. Many substitutes and impure specimens are on the market and, as the only value of Venice turpentine lies in its perfect miscibility with alcohol, any specimen should be tested by seeing whether an equal volume of the balsam and of 95% alcohol will make a perfectly clear mixture. If they do not, the specimen is not true Venice turpentine and is worthless for the technique which follows.

Zimmerman 1896, p. 18, recommends that, in any case, the raw resin should be diluted with twice its own volume of 95% alcohol, filtered, and then heated until the alcohol is evaporated from it. This method is, however, dangerous, unless the atmospheric humidity is practically nil. It is much simpler to get a first-class specimen of Venice turpentine in the first place.

This medium was first recommended for the preparation of botanical wholemounts by Pfeiffer and Wellheim 1892 (23632, **8**:29) but did not come into general use until it was reintroduced by Chamberlain 1915 (p. 97). This writer, however, complains that the original directions of Pfeiffer and Wellheim were diffuse; he cites, not their original paper on the mounting of objects in Venice turpentine, but another paper on the preparation of freshwater algae (Pfeiffer and Wellheim 1894; 10606, **26**:674). The present description is drawn from all the sources cited.

We will assume that we are dealing with *Spirogyra*, a form notoriously difficult to prepare as a satisfactory wholemount. It may be collected in quantity almost anywhere in the world, and should be transferred immediately after collection to a large volume of any chromic-acetic fixative; the formula of Lavdowsky 1894 (Chapter 18, F 6000.0010) is excellent for the purpose. After the masses of algae have been in the solution for a day or two, they should be washed in running water for 24 hours and then pieces should be selected for mounting. These pieces should

be relatively straight, and about ½ inch long, for it is a waste of time to take great masses of algae through the complicated processes which follow, and then to select finally only the few pieces which one desires to mount. The selected pieces should be carefully passed through 15%, 30%, 50% and 70% alcohol and finally into 90% alcohol in which they are to be stained.

Some specimens are so delicate that they will not stand transference from water to alcohol, no matter how gradual the transition phases may be, and for these the method of Chamberlain may be adopted. The algae are transferred from water to 10% glycerol and the water then evaporated until they are in pure glycerol. The glycerol is then washed out with 95% alcohol without risk of the specimen collapsing. This washing must, however, be thorough.

Assuming that we now have the specimens in 95% alcohol, it is recommended that they be stained by the technique of Chamberlain (Chapter 20, DS 13.5 Chamberlain 1915). For this there will be required a 1% solution of phloxine in 95% alcohol, a similar strength solution of anilin blue in the same solvent, and a 0.1% dilution of hydrochloric acid, also in 95% alcohol. The specimens are transferred from alcohol to the 1% phloxine solution, where they remain for about 24 hours. They are then rinsed in alcohol for a minute or two, or until most of the excess has been removed, and transferred to the anilin blue solution. They should remain in this until sufficient blue color is showing in the cytoplasm and until the cell walls themselves have just started to take this blue. They should not, however, remain in the blue for sufficiently long to obscure the bright red color of the nuclei. Chamberlain suggests that from three to thirty minutes may be necessary, but the writer has never had to use a longer period than five. It is obviously desirable to experiment with a few filaments until one has established the correct time and then stain all the rest of the filaments together. After the filaments have been stained in the blue, they should be transferred to the acid alcohol where they should remain until the excess blue has been removed from them. The object of this acid is not to remove blue from tissues which have already taken it, which it will not do, but to rinse off the outside and thus leave the red nuclei bright and clear. If, through any accident, the material has been left in the blue stain too long, it should be transferred to a large volume of 95% alcohol and left there until the whole of the blue color has been removed. This will also remove most of the red from the nuclei, and one must, therefore, start the whole process over again.

After the specimens have been stained they must be put into Venice turpentine. The reason for the selection of this material is that they may be passed directly to it from alcohol without the intervention of any clearing agent which would cause them to collapse. They cannot, of course, be passed directly from the alcohol to full-strength balsam but must be got into it by a process of evaporation. The exact strength to which one transfers them is immaterial, but the strongest which can be safely used is a mixture of ten parts of 95% alcohol to one part of the balsam. No difficulty at all will be occasioned in evaporating off the alcohol, provided it is done in an *absolutely* dry place. A large desiccator is, therefore, charged with silica gel. This material was not available at the time of the descriptions already cited but it provides what the earlier workers lacked —a material to be used in a desiccator which both provides an adequately dry atmosphere and absorbs a certain amount of alcohol vapor. The weak Venice turpentine containing the specimens is, therefore, placed in an evaporating basin, or crystallizing dish, and placed in a desiccator containing silica gel. As the alcohol is absorbed relatively slowly by the silica gel, it is preferable to have two desiccators and to transfer the dish from one to the other daily, thus avoiding saturating the atmosphere with alcohol. The evaporation of the alcohol should be continued until the Venice turpentine is as thick as the original specimen; and it may be necessary, after about two or three days have been spent in the evaporation, to transfer it to a desiccator containing a fresh batch

of silica gel in an oven at 30° to 40°C. This also renders the Venice turpentine more fluid and permits the mount to be more easily made.

When the Venice turpentine is sufficiently thick, a perfectly clean slide is taken and a small drop of Venice turpentine is placed on it. A needle is then dipped into the Venice turpentine and, with another needle, one of the short filaments of alga maneuvered alongside it; the first needle is then drawn slowly at an angle about 45 degrees from the Venice turpentine, so that the filament will remain lying along the side of it. The needle is then laid flat on the Venice turpentine on the slide and, by a rolling movement, the alga is transferred to the drop. As many filaments as are required should be transferred and the slide containing the specimens in Venice turpentine should then be placed in a desiccator.

One of the easiest errors to make in this technique is to leave a small quantity of alcohol in the Venice turpentine before starting to mount. If this is done, it is almost impossible to prevent the moisture in the breath from clouding the resin and ruining the whole long complex operation that has already been undertaken. When as many mounts have been prepared as are required, they are removed one at a time from the desiccator, a little fresh Venice turpentine placed on top of each and the coverslip applied. They may then be placed on a warm stage at a temperature of 30° to 40°C. and permitted to harden for a week or two.

It is difficult to clean a Venice turpentine mount for if one tries to dissolve off the excess Venice turpentine with alcohol, the coverslip may be dislodged. It is better to use only as much Venice turpentine as will exactly come to the edge of the coverslip to avoid having to clean at all. Vosseler 1889 (23632, **6**:292) recommends that the mount, as soon as it is made, should be *ringed* (as described in Chapter 2) with a solution of Canada balsam in xylene, and that the Canada balsam should then be hardened. This gives a very attractive and clean mount and is strongly to be recommended.

PREPARATION OF MINUTE FRESH-WATER ORGANISMS BY THE METHOD OF GRAY 1932

The technique here given, which is abridged from the original description of Gray 1932 (11360, **52**:370), permits one to prepare permanent mounts of individual microscopic organisms. It may be used equally well to mount an individual protozoan or an individual alga. It consists essentially of utilizing a special fixative which renders a layer of albumen on the slide intensely sticky so that the selected object, immediately after fixation, adheres to it.

The range of possible application of this method is very wide, the notable exceptions to its use being for rotifers, stalked ciliates (which cannot satisfactorily be narcotized), and nematode worms which cannot be mounted in balsam without great distortion. Almost anything else can be mounted, provided that its size lies between a total length of about three millimeters, and that of the smallest object which can be seen under a wide-field binocular microscope.

The reagents required, which can most conveniently be kept in drop bottles, are 70% alcohol, ether, 40% formaldehyde, glacial acetic acid, and the stock fixative solution (Chapter 18, F 3500.1010 Gray 1932) which consists of 1% each of picric acid and mercuric chloride in 90% alcohol. Before commencing to mount a series of specimens, it is also necessary to have some Mayer's albumen (Chapter 28, V 21.1 Mayer 1889), some clean slides, several small specimen tubes or vials for the preparation of the fixative, some strips of filter paper, a writing diamond, and, lastly, one or more coplin jars of 70% alcohol in which the mounts may be accumulated as they are made.

The required fixative is made up in small quantities according to the specimens which one desires to mount. When examining a sample of water without knowing what to expect, it is as well to accumulate three mixtures, each for specific organisms. These are:

A. *for protozoans*
stock fixative	10
ether	3
acetic acid	2
40% formaldehyde	5

B. *for heavily cuticularized forms (e.g. Gastrotricha)*
stock fixative	10
ether	1
acetic acid	4
40% formaldehyde	5

C. *for delicate larvae (e.g. Miracidia)*
stock fixative	10
ether	2
acetic acid	1
40% formaldehyde	5

The parts given are by volume and the author usually uses drops in making up these mixtures since only a very small quantity is required even in making many slides.

Half a dozen clean slides are now taken and smeared with a quantity of Mayer's albumen in the center of each. The layer should be considerably thicker than that which would be applied were one preparing to attach paraffin ribbons. The collection is now examined and any small object which it is desired to mount is taken up in a pipet with the least possible quantity of water and placed on the patch of albumen, beyond the limits of which the water should not run. The surplus fluid is then drawn off, sufficient, however, being left for the animal to swim naturally. The animal is watched until it is in a fairly normal position and a large drop of fixative then allowed to fall on it from above. Immediately the fixative has reached the water, diffusion currents of almost explosive intensity result, and considerable care must be taken to keep the rapidly moving object within the field of the dissecting microscope. If the object leaves the area of albumen, it must be guided back with a fine glass needle, the point of which will collect a capillary droplet of the fluid. When the animal is in the desired position over the albumen smear, all surplus fluid, which by now will have collected into drops moving slowly over the surface of the slide, is removed by the filter paper. The object is now closely watched under the dissecting microscope until the droplet of fluid, which will have collected round it, has so far evaporated as clearly to show the outlines of the object. When evaporation has proceeded this far, the slide is gently flooded with 70% alcohol. The correct point at which to do this is easily recognizable with practice but is difficult to describe in words other than the above. If evaporation be allowed to proceed too far, the animal, especially if it be spherical, is liable to become distorted; if it be arrested too soon, the animal is liable to become detached. A little practice will, however, readily allow one to determine the exact moment at which the alcohol must be added.

After the alcohol has been added to the slide and left for a few moments, a small circle is cut around the object with a writing diamond, as, once lost from the field of the dissecting microscope, such objects as small protozoans are almost impossible to distinguish from specks of dust acquired in the fixing process. The slide is then transferred to a coplin jar of 70% alcohol, for the specimen is firmly fixed in position and will not be detached through any subsequent process of staining and mounting.

Staining may be carried out by any method. It is customary to stain most small fresh-water animals in alum hematoxylin, most small fresh-water plants in some safranin solution, while the writer prefers, for gastrotrichans, one of the alum carmines which must be allowed to act over a long period.

It is possible with the aid of this method to mount 20 or 30 selected forms from a collection of fresh-water plankton in less than half an hour, and it will be found very useful to be able to examine a collection of fresh-water plankton with the assurance that any unknown form may be permanently attached to a slide for subsequent identification.

Smear Preparations from Fluid Material

General Principles

Every chapter up to the present has been concerned with the preparation of microscope slides from whole objects preserved in as nearly as possible their natural shape. Chapters 10 through 15 will be concerned with the preparation of thin slices or *sections* of objects. Between these extremes of a whole object and a thin slice there are two types of preparation, which are discussed in the next three chapters. *Smears*, discussed in this and the next chapter, are exactly what their name indicate: they are prepared by smearing some substance on a clean glass slide where it may be fixed, stained, and mounted. *Squashes*, the name of which is also self-explanatory, are prepared by squeezing either animal or plant materials in such a way that they disintegrate into their component cells, which may then be studied without reference to the relations which they previously had with each other.

Smears may either be prepared from fluids or from solid objects. A separate chapter is devoted to each. The present chapter deals with the preparation of thin layers of fluid so that the cells contained in them may be studied. Three operations are necessary in the preparation of smears of fluids: first, the smearing of the material itself into a layer of the required thickness; second, fixing this layer both to insure its adherence to the slide and to make sure that the contained cells remain in their normal shape; third, staining and mounting the fixed smear. Each of these operations will be discussed successively.

Preparation of the Smear

The first thing to do in the preparation of a smear is to make sure that chemically clean slides are available. The adherence of the smeared material to the slide will be excellent if it is a fluid containing considerable quantities of protein (as blood), even if the slide be not clean, but there are many fluids which are used in the production of smears which will not adhere at all save to an absolutely clean glass surface. Any method may be used for cleaning slides, but for this particular purpose the author prefers to use a household scouring powder, which consists of a soft abrasive together with some detergent agent. This powder is made into a thin cream with water and each slide is then dipped into this cream and stood in a rack to dry. As soon as it has dried the slides may be returned to a box, preferably each being separated from the other with a thin paper insert. As slides are commonly sold with these paper separators, it is only necessary to take a box and to save the separators when one dips the slide, returning them after they are dried to the same box with the same separators.

Two or three hundred slides may easily be prepared in this manner in a short time and stored against future use. For use the slide is polished with a clean linen or silk cloth. Smears often have to be made at unexpected moments, therefore it is a convenience to have slides at hand which may be rendered fit for use in a few moments.

The actual method of smearing the material varies greatly according to what is being used. Probably more smears are made of blood than of any other fluid, and the technique for the preparation of these is so well established that it will be described as a type. The material itself may either be taken from the puncture wound directly onto the slide, or (as in Fig. 27) removed from the puncture wound with a pipet and transferred to the slide. The drop is placed about ⅓ of an inch from one end of the slide, and a second slide (as

behind the first slide and distributed more or less uniformly on the under slide. A few people still try to conduct the operation in the reverse manner: by placing the second slide on top of the first, sloping it at a

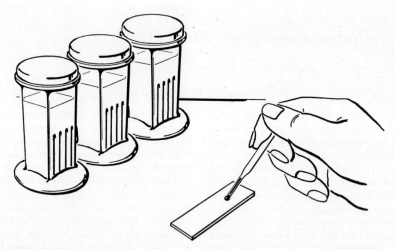

Fig. 27. Making a smear preparation. *a. Place the drop about an inch from the end of the slide.*

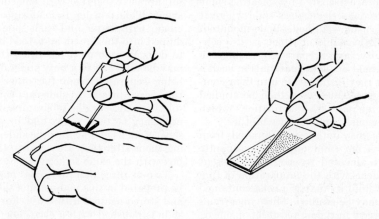

Fig. 28. Making a smear preparation—*(continued). b. Apply a second slide just in front of the drop.*
Fig. 29. Making a smear preparation—*(continued). c. Push the slide smoothly forward to spread the smear.*

shown in Fig. 28) placed on the drop. Capillary attraction will naturally distribute the fluid along the edge of the second slide which is then (Fig. 29) pushed sharply forward until it reaches the end of the bottom slide. The material of which the smear is being made is thus spread out

reverse angle to that shown, and then endeavoring to push rather than drag the material across the lower slide. The objection to this is that it results in crushing cells, though it must be admitted that it frequently gives a more uniform distribution of the material. The use of a glass slide for spreading has a great deal against it. There is a risk that the edge of the upper slide will scratch the lower, and though these scratches are not apparent in smears which are to be examined under an oil immersion objective, they are objectionable in a dry slide. It is also difficult to secure a slide which is entirely flat and which will thus make a layer of uniform thickness, for the thickness of the layer obviously depends on the degree of contact between the upper slide and the lower. The writer has recently been using a thin sheet of transparent plastic (methyl methacrylate) in place of glass and has obtained very much better results. To prepare such a sheet for use one cuts, or saws, a $3'' \times 1''$ rectangle from it and then polishes one of the edges by rubbing it briskly backward and forward on a sharpening stone or on a piece of fine sandpaper. This turns up a feather edge on both sides of the edge which has been flattened. This is removed by taking the slip and holding it at just about the same angle at which it will be used for preparing the smear and giving it one or two quick strokes on the finest sandpaper. The use of a soft material like this not only insures that there will be no scratches on the slide, but also guarantees that the edge used for smearing will always remain in contact with the slide. After two or three hundred smears have been made the piece of plastic may be thrown away and a new one taken.

The method described is the standard procedure for producing *thin smears*. These are necessary for those fluids, such as vertebrate blood or mammalian seminal fluid, which contain very large numbers of objects which must be separated as widely as possible if they are satisfactorily to be studied.

There are a number of fluids, however, from which thick smears must be made either because, as in the case of invertebrate blood, they contain relatively few cells or because, as in the case of malarial diagnostic smears, one is seeking for a parasite which is relatively sparsely distributed through the material. These thick smears are made with the aid of a loop of wire held in a needle-holder of the type found in bacteriological laboratories. This loop is dipped into the fluid to be examined, and used to spread it with a rotary motion in the center of the slide. This is very similar to the preparation of smears of bacterial material which is described in some detail in Chapter 21.

Fixing Smears

Smears may be fixed by drying, by alcohol, or in one of the conventional fixatives. When a smear is to be fixed by drying it is, as soon as it has been made, waved in the air and then set on one side for subsequent treatment. This procedure is excellent in the case of objects such as bacteria or erythrocytes, which do not change their shape after drying, or for materials such as white blood corpuscles, which it is not desired to preserve in their normal shape. No other object can, however, be considered satisfactory unless it has been fixed, and the simplest method of doing this is to pass the smear, just as it is drying, through a jet of steam. This technique has been described in Chapter 6 for mounting amebas and need not be repeated here.

All other smears should be fixed before they are dried and it is something of a problem to fix them without removing the material from the slide. It is obvious that if the material is freshly smeared onto a glass slide and then dropped into a fixative of some kind, it will be washed off. The logical solution to the problem is to use a fixative in a vapor phase, and nothing is better for this purpose than osmic acid. To use this material, a couple of glass rods are placed in a petri dish sufficiently far apart to permit the slide to rest on them without the smear touching them. A drop or two of a solution of osmic acid, usually of 2% strength is put on the bottom of the petri dish and the cover replaced. It must be emphasized that osmic acid fixes the mucous membrane of the nose and throat just as readily as it does a smear and every precaution must be taken to avoid inhaling the vapors. As soon as the smear is made, *and before it has time to dry*, it is placed face down across the two glass rods so that it is exposed to the vapor but not to the liquid. The cover is then replaced on the petri dish, and the slide left in place for about three or four minutes in the case of a thin smear, or for five to ten minutes in the case of a thick one. It is then transferred to distilled water to await staining.

It occasionally happens that a slide must be fixed in one of the conventional fluid fixatives. This is done with the same petri-dish and glass-rod setup as is used for vapor fixation, but in this instance the fixative is carefully poured into the petri dish, which must be level, until it has reached such a depth that, when the slide is laid across the glass rods, the under side of the slide with the smear on it is in contact with the fluid while the upper part is free from fluid. If the smear is reasonably thin and is laid carefully in place, it usually will not become detached. Thick smears, particularly those made with fluids containing very little protein, will not stand this treatment; they must either be fixed in the vapor phase, or else the fluid itself must be mixed with a small quantity of an adhesive, such as Mayer's albumen (Chapter 28, V 21.1 Mayer 1884).

Staining Smears

Blood smears are so universally stained with one or another of the methylene blue-eosinate mixtures (Chapter 20, DS 13.1 and 13.2) that it comes as something of a surprise to most people to learn that any stain which is suitable for sections may also be employed for smears. The advantage of methylene blue-eosinates for blood films is that the solvent methanol acts as a fixative so that they are stained and fixed in the same operation. When a blood smear is to be used for diagnostic purposes, these techniques are excellent, because the appearance of the various types of white corpuscle under this treatment is known to every technician. For research studies on the blood, however, it is strongly recommended that the worker experiment, first by fixing the blood film in osmic vapor in the manner described, and secondly by applying to it some other of the complex techniques described in Chapter 20. For materials other than blood there is no limit to the type of staining which may be employed, though it must be remembered that very thin films require a stain of considerable intensity if the finer structures are to be made out. Thus, for example, a thin smear of mammalian spermatozoa is best stained by one of the very dense iron hematoxylin techniques such as that of Bütschli (Chapter 20, DS 11.111 Bütschli 1892). The method for the application of these stains to smears differs very little, in most cases, from the method for the application of the same stains to slides, and no specific instruction need be given. Bacteriological staining methods, which differ from those used in botany and zoology, are given in Chapter 23 under the heading DS 23.2.

Typical Example

DEMONSTRATION OF MONOCYSTIS FROM THE SEMINAL VESICLE OF AN EARTHWORM

Few sporozoans are available for class demonstration purposes and the choice is practically limited to the inhabitants of the intestines of a cockroach or to the specimen at present under discussion, *Monocystis*.

The advantage of *Monocystis* is that all the forms from the sporozoite to the trophozoite occur in the seminal vesicle of the earthworm, and may therefore be made available on a single smear. The degree of infection among earthworms varies greatly, but it has been the author's experience that the larger the earthworm the more likely the chance of a heavy in-

festation. But it is no use making a whole lot of smears for class demonstration purposes until one has satisfied oneself by a preliminary survey of a single smear that the material will be satisfactory.

There is no need to kill or anesthetize the earthworm, which is simply pinned down in a dissecting tray and slit from the anterior end to about the 16th or 17th segment. The edges of this slit are pulled back and pinned into place disclosing the large white seminal vesicles.

There should be available, before making the smear, a petri dish in which are a couple of short lengths of glass rod, a supply of Schaudinn's fixative (Chapter 18, F 3000.0000 Schaudinn 1893), an adequate supply of clean glass slides, an eye-dropper-type pipet, some 0.8% sodium chloride, and some coplin jars of distilled water. Enough fixative is poured into the petri dish so that when a slide is laid on the pair of glass rods, its lower, but *not* its upper surface will be in contact with the fixative. This level is best established with a plain glass slide before the smears are started.

The seminal vesicle of the earthworm is slit and a drop of the contained fluid removed with the pipet. This pipet is then used to smear a relatively thick layer of the material on the center of one of the clean slides and, before it has time to dry, this slide is laid face down in the fixative for about two minutes. The slide is then removed, rinsed under the tap, and examined under a high power of the microscope after a coverslip has been placed over the smear. It is rather difficult to see the trophozoite stages in an unstained preparation, but no difficulty will be experienced in picking out the spore cases (*pseudo-navicellae*) owing to their relatively high index of refraction. It may be taken that adequate numbers of the parasites are present if not less than three or four of these spore cases occur within the field of a four-millimeter objective in a thick smear of this nature.

As soon as a satisfactorily infected worm has been found, the remainder of the material from the pipet is placed in a watch glass and diluted with 0.8% sodium chloride until it forms a dispersion about intermediate in thickness between cream and milk. As many smears as are required are made from this cream as rapidly as possible. The dilution in question will not retain the parasites in good condition for more than about five minutes, but if insufficient smears have been made in this time, it is easy to take a fresh supply of the seminal fluid from another vesicle and to dilute it in a fresh watch glass. The

cream should be spread with two slides in the manner described above, and each slide placed face downward in Schaudinn's fixative for three or four minutes before being removed to a coplin jar of distilled water.

After having been washed in water the smears should be transferred to 70% alcohol where they can remain until they are ready for staining. Any stain may be used but it is conventional to employ a hematoxylin mixture. The author prefers to use the old "triacid" stain of Biondi which is given in Chapter 20 under the heading DS 13.33 Biondi (1888). The advantage of this solution is that the orange G is picked up by the cases of the sporocysts, while the trophozoites are red with clear green nuclei. Nuclei of the spermatozoa and spermatids of the earthworm occupy so much of the cells in which they are found that they give the whole stain a greenish cast. This green background shows up the red trophozoites and the brilliant orange sporozoites.

The method of staining is easy. The solution, made in accordance with the directions given, is diluted to the extent of about 2% with distilled water. The slides are then placed in this diluted solution and left until examination under the low power of the microscope shows them to have been adequately stained and differentiated. They are then briefly rinsed in distilled water and dried. There is no necessity to use any dehydrating agent, such as alcohol, which will interfere with the staining, because the smears should be sufficiently thin and the objects in them sufficiently well fixed that drying will not distort them. To complete the mount, a drop of the mountant selected is added and a coverslip applied. Balsam may be used, but the writer considers it to have too high a refractive index, and for that reason prefers one of the "neutral" mountants, based on gum sandarac, the formulas for which are given in Chapter 26 under the heading M 23.1.

8

Smear Preparations from Cut Surfaces

General Principles

The last chapter described the preparation of smears from materials which were fluid; the present chapter deals with the method by which smears may be obtained from the surface of materials which have been cut into blocks.

Preparation of the Smears

There are only two methods of producing smears from the cut surface of solid bodies. Either the cut surface is rubbed on a clean slide, leaving behind a few cells which have been detached from it, or the cells are squeezed from a cut, and subsequently pressed out in the form of a smear. The former method is used for animal tissues and the latter for plant specimens.

The difficulty in preparing smears from the cut surface of animal tissue is not so much to secure material as to avoid securing unwanted cells. The blood content of the majority of organs is so high that, if a freshly cut surface be smeared on a piece of glass, the few cells which become detached will be obscured by the red blood corpuscles. The technique is, therefore, usually applied to the central nervous system, from the cut surfaces of which cells not only detach themselves very readily but which has also the advantage of being only slightly vascularized. The only difficulty in preparing a smear from a freshly cut surface of the central nervous system lies in finding a pair of forceps sufficiently wide and sufficiently blunt to hold the material without it disintegrating. Apart from this the technique is essentially that described in the last chapter. A perfectly clean slide is taken and rubbed with the cut surface of the material. These smears cannot be dried satisfactorily but must always be fixed, and it is necessary to use the technique, discussed in the last chapter, of placing the slide face down across a pair of glass rods lying in the bottom of the petri dish in such a manner that the lower surface, but not the upper surface, is in contact with the fixative. The fixative to be selected naturally varies according to the material to be studied, but fixatives containing mercuric chloride are usually to be preferred. Smears may also be fixed in osmic vapor, though they are not usually as satisfactory when prepared by this method as are smears prepared from fluid material.

The smear technique in plant microtechnique is largely confined to securing sporogenous tissue from anthers at various stages of their development. This technique, which was introduced by Taylor 1924 (3430, **78**:236), has the advantage that it permits the examination of chromosome material without the trouble of dehydrating, embedding, and sectioning. This smear technique must, however, be differentiated from the squash techniques, described in the next chapter, in which cells are dissociated. The smear technique can only be used for materials which can be squeezed out. There is some division of opinion as to whether a small quantity of adhesive (such as Mayer's albumen) should first be smeared on the slide, or whether the material extruded from the anther has enough protein to cause adhesion. In either case the anther is cut with a very sharp scalpel about one third of the distance from its base and placed on the slide with the cut end in the region where one wants the smear. The *back* of a scalpel is then rolled from a position about a millimeter from the cut edge, toward the cut edge. The material which is thus extruded is rapidly smeared with the back of the scalpel, the crushed anther removed, and the slide inverted on glass rods in a fixative. It has been found (Kauffman 1927, 20540b, **2**:88) that these smears are best stained with an iron hematoxylin technique (Chapter 20, DS 11.111).

In every other respect these smears are treated as though they had been prepared from a fluid material (see last chapter) but a single typical preparation applying one of these techniques will be given.

Typical Example

DEMONSTRATION OF NEGRI BODIES BY THE METHOD OF DAWSON 1934

The detection of Negri bodies is, of course, used in the diagnosis of rabies. A method for the demonstration of these bodies in sections is described in Chapter 21, and the method here described is intended less for permanent preparations than for a rapid diagnostic procedure. The description referred to contains detailed directions for the dissection of the horn of Ammon, which is the portion of the brain usually selected for these tests. We will assume, therefore, that the worker has dissected, following the necessary precautions as to his own safety, the brain of the diagnostic guinea pig in such a manner as to expose the horn of Ammon.

For the preparation of paraffin sections, the horn of Ammon is divided into small pieces, but for the preparation of smears it must be kept whole and a sharp razor used to trim away about the lower third leaving a freshly cut surface. If there is any quantity of extravasated blood present, it must be washed off with a gentle stream of normal saline or it will tend to obscure the picture.

To prepare the smear preparations there are required an adequate quantity of clean slides, a supply of methanol, a 2% solution of phloxine, and a quantity of Löffler's polychrome methylene blue. The preparation of the polychrome methylene blue solution is described in Chapter 20 (DS 11.44 Löffler 1890) and need not be repeated here. It is convenient to have the methanol and methylene blue solutions in drop bottles and to have the 2% phloxine and the 20% alcohol in coplin jars. If the slides are to be filed for reference, rather than used immediately for diagnosis, it is also desirable to have some neutral mountant (Chapter 26, M 23.1)

The entire horn of Ammon is then taken and dabbed once or twice in the center of one of the clean slides. If one endeavors to smear it, too much material usually comes off; but the vertical dabbing motion will provide a sufficiently thick film which, when moist, should appear as no more than a slight clouding of the surface of the slide. The slide is then waved gently backward and forward until it appears to be just about to dry. The material will be lost if methanol is added to it while it is completely wet, and the material will be distorted if it is permitted to become entirely dry; but only a little experience is necessary to enable one to adjudge the exact moment at which methanol should be dropped on the smear from the drop bottle. The slide may then be placed on one side to dry, if it is to be used immediately; it should be dropped into a coplin jar of methanol if it is not to be stained for, say, half an hour.

When the slides are to be stained they are waved in the air until the methanol has evaporated and then dropped into the 2% phloxine where they remain from two to five minutes. Upon being withdrawn from the phloxine, a stream of water from a wash bottle should be used very gently to remove the excess phloxine, the slide drained by its corner onto filter paper, and the polychrome methylene blue dropped onto the surface from a drop bottle. The methylene blue is left in place for 15 seconds, washed off with a stream of water from the wash bottle, and the slide then dropped into 20% alcohol where it may be left until no more color comes away. It may remain in the alcohol for 10 or 15 minutes without damage.

If the slide is required for immediate examination, nothing remains to be done save to remove it from the 20% alcohol, wave it about in the air until it is dry, and then examine it under the microscope with an oil immersion lens. If, however, the slide is to be filed for permanent reference, a drop of neutral mountant should be placed on the smear as soon as it has been dried and a coverslip added.

9

Squash Preparations from Solid Bodies

General Principles

Nature of the Process

Squash preparations are not, as their name might cause one to suppose, obtained merely by crushing an organ or animal in order that it may become thin enough to examine under the microscope. This would result in the hopeless distortion of the cells and their contents. A squash preparation, properly prepared, is obtained by causing the cells of animal or plant material to become separated one from the other without losing their individual shape in order that they may be spread out on a slide in a single layer for examination. This process is today much better known in botany than in zoology, though it was at one time the standard method of preparing histological specimens. Another fundamental difference between the smear and squash technique is that the former always employs fresh unfixed material while the latter should always employ a material which has been fixed previously.

Process of Maceration

The separation of cells of fixed plant or animal material through the hydrolysis of their interstitial tissue of cement is known as *maceration*. It does not matter what fixative has been used, though in the author's experience fixatives containing chromic or osmic acid, or mixtures of these, are best. Tissues are fixed in the ordinary way and the fixative thoroughly removed by washing before maceration commences. The two most common methods of maceration, either for animal or plant material, are acid hydrolysis and enzyme hydrolysis. Each will be described separately. Acid hydrolysis of plant tissues is almost always carried out in 10 % hydro-

chloric acid, in which the fixed tissue is soaked until a sample of it, placed under a coverslip, is found to disintegrate into its constituent cells when the coverslip is tapped lightly with a needle. Acid hydrolysis of animal tissues, however, has been carried out with almost any acid used for microscopy, and reference should be made to Chapter 19 (V 40) where many suggested mixtures are given. It may be pointed out that almost any acid fixative solution, if diluted with from 50 to 100 times its own volume of water, will act as a macerating agent.

Enzyme hydrolysis of animal tissues may be conducted either in an alkaline or an acid environment, and reference should be made to the methods of Jonsset 1903 and Langeron 1942 for examples of each of these. Abbreviated techniques for these methods are to be found in Chapter 19 under V 40 and need not be expanded here. Enzyme hydrolysis of plant tissues is of quite recent origin, and depends on the extraction of enzymes from sources which are customarily used in the digestion of plant material. Ensweller 1944 (20540b, 19, 109) suggests the extraction of various fungi but the method of Faberge 1945 (Chapter 19, V 41.1), of which a detailed description is given in one of the typical preparations following this chapter, is much to be preferred. The terminal point of enzyme maceration may be detected, exactly as is that of acid maceration, by whether or not the organism or tissue under examination disintegrates into its constituent cells.

Staining and Mounting Macerated Specimens

Though the process of maceration is itself quite easy, staining and mounting of the products of maceration present many difficulties. If the preparation is broken up under a coverslip, it is difficult to remove it without losing the cells, or to stain them with the coverslip in place; if the maceration is carried out in a small tube, it is difficult to concentrate the cells readily on the slide after they have been stained. Probably the simplest method in most cases is to treat the individual cells as though they were a culture of protozoans: that is, to stain them, dehydrate them, and get them into a small quantity of balsam, and then to place a drop of this balsam under the coverslip. As an alternative to this, the macerated material may

be smeared over the surface of a slide which has had an adhesive applied to it, or it may be diluted with an adhesive material such as Mayer's albumen and then treated as though it were a fluid smear. The objection to this treatment is that the majority of fixed cells are very brittle and will be damaged when the smear is made.

The selection of a stain is not difficult since each dissociated cell may be treated as a small wholemount. It is not worth while to double-stain macerated specimens, the true function of which is to present a clear picture of the shape, not the nature, of individual cells.

Typical Examples

PREPARATION OF MICROSPOROCYTES OF CROCUS FOR CHROMOSOME EXAMINATION

In the last chapter it was pointed out that material of this nature could be squeezed from the anther and spread over a slide with the back of a scalpel. This method inevitably leads to distortion both of the cells and of the chromosomes, and in the writer's opinion the method here described gives a better preparation. There is first the collection and fixation of the anthers, and second, the separation of the microsporocytes from the other cells of the anther by maceration.

The advantage of the crocus for this preparation is that it may be brought into flower in the laboratory at any season of the year. The anthers may be taken at any stage of their development, the most useful stage for demonstration preparations being that which is reached when the flower is just beginning to color. The flower is removed from the corm, the petals stripped away, and the anthers placed in fixative. Many fixatives may be used, though one of the best is Navashin (Chapter 18, F 6000.1010 Navashin 1912). The anthers are placed in several hundred times their own volume of this fluid which is, by convention, but probably unnecessarily, kept in the icebox. The anthers are removed after 24 hours and washed overnight in running water.

The method of maceration selected for this example is that of Faberge 1945; the abbreviated directions are in Chapter 19 under the heading V 41.1. This method

uses the stomach of the edible snail (*Helix pomatia*) which dissolves the interstitial tissue of plant cells. Edible snails are obtainable either by collection in the field or from restaurant supply houses. Snails obtained from the latter are usually in a state of hibernation from having been kept on ice and must be revived by being kept at room temperature for a day or two, after which they may be given a meal of lettuce and used on the day following. The snails are killed by drowning in warm water overnight, which leaves them fully expanded, and the stomach is then dissected out. The snail is removed from the shell and pinned down through the foot. The mantle cavity is then lifted in a pair of forceps and slit. As soon as the edges of this slit have been pulled back the crop (often miscalled the stomach) will be seen as a carrot-shaped body filled with brownish fluid. The fluid within the crop must now be withdrawn, either by the insertion of a hypodermic syringe, or by ligaturing the crop at each end, removing it, and then squeezing the contents into a tube. It is simplest to handle a good many snails at the same time, since the material removed may be preserved in an icebox with a drop of toluene on top.

The anthers, taken either from the water in which they have been washed or the alcohol in which they are stored, are placed in a drop or two of the enzyme solution. If the maximum number of slides are required, it is desirable to cut the anthers into pieces before placing them in the fluid. Maceration will usually be complete in about eight hours so that it is convenient to start the preparation in the evening and to examine individual pieces at intervals in the course of the next morning until one has determined that maceration is complete. The completion of maceration may be judged by the fact that the materials should be flabby, but not completely disintegrated.

At this stage the microsporocytes are extracted by gently squeezing either the anther, or each individual piece of anther, into a small drop of water. The microsporocytes themselves will not appear to be distinct but will appear as a gelatinous mass. This mass should be accumulated in a drop of water on a single slide and then small drops taken from it and made into smears on other clean slides. These smears need not be fixed, but may be permitted to dry on the slide to which they will adhere so well that they can be stained by any nuclear staining method. Aceto-carmine is in general use for temporary preparations, and a description of the use of this stain in plant material is given in Chapter 20.

PREPARATION OF A DISSOCIATED HYDRA

It is a little pathetic that the majority of elementary textbooks of biology should include an illustration showing the types of cell to be found in hydra and that instructors should then issue to the student a series of sections in which these cells are not visible. The illustrations have mostly been taken from older textbooks dating from the period when disassociation techniques for animal tissues were common. It would surely be more reasonable to show students slides which agree with the illustrations in the books they use.

Fixation is necessary before dissociation, and the only question to be settled is whether or not the finished slide should show muscle cells in an expanded condition, in which case the hydra will have to be narcotized before fixation, or whether it will be sufficient to kill the hydra without narcotization. It seems better, however, to show cells in the expanded condition and the hydra should therefore be collected from the tank or pond where they are growing, and accumulated in a watch glass of water which is kept in a cool place in subdued light so that the hydra may expand. A drop of 2% chloral hydrate is then added for each five milliliters of water in the watch glass. This should be mixed with the water by sucking in and out of a pipet. This is likely to cause partial retraction of the hydra but they will expand again. After about 10 minutes two or three more drops per five milliliters of water may be added and mixed in, as the hydra are usually by this time sufficiently narcotized not to con-

tract. The hydra should then be watched until touching with a hair causes no retraction. The watch glass is then very carefully picked up and placed in a fingerbowl. The reason for this is that hydra can most satisfactorily be fixed in large quantities of hot fixative. The solution of Perenyi (Chapter 18, F 6000.0040 Perenyi 1888) is excellent for this purpose. This fixative, which has few other uses, is made by dissolving ¾ of a gram of chromic acid in 135 milliliters of water and then adding to this 100 milliliters of ethanol. Seventeen and a half milliliters of strong nitric acid are then added and the solution placed on one side until it has turned violet. The fixative should be heated to 70°C. and then flooded suddenly over the narcotized hydra which should remain in the fixative for about two days before being removed for dissociation. An individual dissociated hydra may be prepared as a smear, but it is presumed in this case that a number of slides are being made for class issue, so that it is better to proceed by a different technique. The hydra are taken from the fixative (it is unnecessary to wash them) and placed in a few drops of the selected dissociating agent in the bottom of a small tube. The selection among the acid, dissociating media given in Chapter 19 under the heading AF 41.1 is not important, but the writer has been successful in the present preparation by the method of Hopkins as quoted by Roberts [Chapter 28, V 41.1 Hopkins (1895)]. This method requires first, 20% nitric acid, second, a saturated solution of potassium alum.

The tube containing the hydra is half filled with 20% nitric acid. The specimens may be left overnight for treatment the next morning or, if one is in a hurry, the tube may be very gently warmed (to a maximum of about 50°C.) for twenty minutes. In either case it will be found that the hydra, which had become hard in the fixative, are now flaccid and tender. The acid is removed, either by pouring or by withdrawing it with a pipet, and the tube filled with the saturated solution of potassium alum. The specimens will float for a brief time but, as soon as they have sunk to the bottom, the alum solution is poured off and replaced with fresh solution. The tube is now shaken gently until such time as each hydra has dissociated into its constituent cells. If this does not take place after shaking for a few minutes, it is necessary to withdraw the alum solution, replace it with nitric acid, and to continue macerating for a further period. It is not to be anticipated that all hydra out of a batch of 20 or 30 will disintegrate at the same time, but any large cell masses which remain may easily be picked out with the point of a needle after the tube containing the cells has been emptied into a watch glass.

Having thus secured a suspension of the cells in a solution of alum, it is necessary first to wash most of the alum from them, and then to get them into stain. For this purpose rinse the tube into a larger one which is filled with water, stir up, and allow the cells to settle. Any of the alum-carmine stains given in Chapter 20 (DS 11.21) may be used. Whichever one is chosen is poured over the cells after the supernatant water used in the last wash has been poured off. The time for staining is not important, three or four days being usually enough. Though the cells cannot be seen in the stain, it may be assumed that they have fallen to the bottom. The upper two-thirds of the stain is poured off before filling the tube with a weak (1%) solution of whatever alum was used in the preparation of the stain selected. The cells are again allowed to settle, the supernatant liquid poured off, the tube refilled with alum solution, and so on, until the wash solution is practically colorless.

The cells now have to be dehydrated; this is done by pouring off the alum solution, replacing it with, say, 30% alcohol, which is itself replaced with 70% alcohol, as soon as the cells have fallen to the bottom. At this stage a few cells should be withdrawn with a pipet, placed on a slide, covered, and examined under a high power of the microscope. Each cell should show the nucleus clearly stained dark red with a faint pink cytoplasm; if they appear too dark, a small drop of acetic acid should be added to the tube, mixed with the alcohol, and poured off after five minutes. The washing is continued until the alcohol no longer smells of acetic acid. It is easy to overdifferentiate at this point and unless the cells are grossly overstained, it is better to take them through without further differentiation occasioned by the wash in alum solution which they had immediately after staining. The 70% alcohol is now replaced with absolute alcohol in which the cells should be thoroughly stirred and then left overnight. A second change of absolute alcohol should be given; this should not be poured off but should be withdrawn with a pipet, so as to leave the cells accumulated in the least possible quantity of absolute alcohol at the bottom of the tube. The tube is then filled with benzene and left until the cells have again fallen to the bottom, when the benzene is withdrawn and replaced with fresh benzene, which is again replaced. The cells, which are now lying at the bottom of the tube in not more than a drop or two of benzene, should be covered with three or four drops of a strong solution of Canada balsam in benzene. The specimens should now be stirred up and left for an hour or two until they are thoroughly permeated with the balsam, a drop of which may then be removed, placed on a slide, and covered. By this method, as many slides may be made as there are drops of balsam; and, if the cell concentration has been kept reasonably heavy, it is usually better to use a very small (⅜ inch) coverslip in order to get as many slides as possible. A preparation of this size should contain two or three hundred cells and will give the student an excellent picture of all of the cell types found in hydra.

10

Ground Sections

Nature of the Process

Previous chapters have dealt with the preparation of whole specimens either mounted individually, smeared, or squashed on a slide. There are many specimens which, in order that their microscopic structure may be examined, have to be cut into thin structures. The more usual methods of cutting such materials are given in this and the next four chapters. The present chapter, which describes the preparation of sections of materials too hard to be cut by any conventional method, had better be ignored by anyone not specifically interested in this process. Sections of hard materials such as bone, the calcareous skeletons of coral, and even some of the hardest vegetable materials, must be prepared in two stages. The first of these stages is the preparation of a crude section from a half to one millimeter in thickness, while the second stage consists in grinding this down while leaving both sides polished.

Preparation of the Crude Section

It is presumed that we are dealing with material which cannot be cut with a knife and must, therefore, be cut with a saw. Most woodcutting saws are not hard enough for the purpose and the choice lies between the ordinary hacksaw, intended for cutting metal, and a jewelers' saw. The disadvantage of a hacksaw is that it is very coarse, so that only thick sections may be cut; the disadvantage of the jewelers' saw is that, unless it is guided by an expert hand, it will not cut a parallel-sided section. Whichever saw is selected, however, it should have relatively coarse

teeth, particularly if bone, or material containing very much animal matter, or material which has been embedded in resin, is to be cut. These materials choke the teeth of a fine saw; the tooth marks left by a coarse saw do not matter, for they will be ground and polished out. For very hard substances, such as teeth, it is often necessary to use a circular diamond saw, which is usually available in departments of geology where rock sections are cut. Even teeth, however, may be cut with a jewelers' saw provided that the blade be changed at intervals and that the entire operation be conducted under the surface of water.

Another type of preparation is that in which it is desired to preserve both the hard and the soft portions at the same time. A standard example of this is the preparation of a coral, of which it may be desired not only to section the calcareous skeleton but also to retain in position the soft parts of the animal within. This can only be done by embedding the material in some substance nearly as hard as the skeleton itself. A number of resins have been proposed for this purpose. The author always prefers, however, to use Canada balsam because, though it is gummy in the final grinding, it has the advantage that it need not be removed for mounting, and thus obviates one rather laborious stage of the process. As an alternative one may employ the process of Henrichi 1916 (4349, **6**:45) in which gum damar is substituted for balsam, though the method which is described involves the use of machinery not normally available in laboratories. The technique of embedding in balsam is described in some detail in the second example which follows the chapter and need not be repeated here.

Selection of Grinding and Polishing Agents

Once the initial sections have been prepared it is necessary that they should have one face polished, that this polished face should then be attached to some material, and that the other face be ground away and brought to a polish when the section is of the correct thickness. One technique for doing this is described in the first example at the end of this chapter, but some discussion must take place at this point as to the selection of grinding and polishing agents.

The initial flattening of one side of the section is best done with the aid of carborundum powder, using a grit of about 100-mesh. The 100-mesh carborundum itself is far too coarse to leave a surface which may be polished and an intermediate stage is required. In the writer's opinion, pumice is best used for this intermediate stage. We are now speaking of relatively soft material, such as bone or coral, and not of thin slices of rock which would require several stages of carborundum between 100-grit and pumice. One of the most difficult things to determine is when the scratches have finally been removed; this can never be seen when the sections are wet from grinding. It is, therefore, necessary at intervals to wash the surface of the section which is being ground, to dip it into alcohol, and then to warm it until dry. The surface of the section is then examined with a strong hand lens by reflected light, and grinding is ceased when it presents a uniform, dull surface unbroken by scratches.

The next stage is to bring this flattened surface to a high degree of polish. All the old directions recommend the use of rouge. The objection to rouge is its color, and the fact that it gets over everything on the bench and around the bench. The author most warmly recommends the substitution of *white rouge* (ceric oxide), which is rapidly replacing ordinary rouge in the polishing of glass, and is also excellent for microscopical specimens. It does not matter very much against what surface the abrasive has up to this time been rubbed, though glass is conventional. It is, however, impossible to get a fine surface with rouge on glass and one should, therefore, use a leather strop for the purpose. This does not mean a loose leather strop of the type used by barbers but rather a flat surface of horsehide which has been attached to a hardwood block. Rubbing the section up and down on this, while it is well lubricated with a slurry of white rouge, will soon bring it to a fine polish. There is no reason to get discouraged if, after polishing, the surface is found still to have a few fine scratches on it. The sections are going to be mounted in balsam which will hide most of the scratches.

The sections are then cemented, polished side down, to a slide and ground on some flat surface with coarse carborundum until they are of the required thickness. It is unfortunate that there is no adequate method of judging this thickness except by eye; experience is the only guide which may be reasonably followed. As soon as the section has been ground down to the required thickness it is then smoothed with pumice, polished with white rouge, and finally mounted. Practical application of the principles here discussed will now be given in the form of two typical preparations.

Typical Examples

PREPARATION OF A SECTION OF BONE

If the worker is interested only in the production of a section which will show the existence of Haversian canals, it is better to decalcify the bone (in one of the solutions given under AF 20 in Chapter 19) and to prepare sections by the paraffin technique described in Chapter 12. These sections, however, show neither the lamellae, lacunae, or canaliculi, which can only be demonstrated in a section prepared by grinding, in which all the calcareous parts remain intact.

The first thing is to secure a piece of dry bone. The majority of museums have old broken specimens from which they are only too glad to give away a bone or two. The example shown being sectioned in Fig. 30 is part of the femur of a horse which became accidentally broken. If no dried specimen of bone is available, and one is, therefore, forced to start with raw material, it is first necessary to boil the bone for four or five hours in water in order to remove as much of the protein material from it as possible. If, moreover,

handling bone because it combines the stiffness of a hacksaw with the thinness of a jewelers' saw. The first cut is made at right angles to the direction of the cut shown and a second cut (as seen in the illustration) is then made, parallel to the free surface that has been cut, and at right angles to the present position of the saw in the figure. Several slabs are cut, as uniformly as possible, but the saw kerf is stopped about a millimeter above the horizontal cut, and a second cut made, until (as is seen in the figure) as many

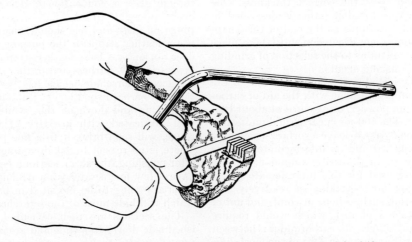

Fig. 30. Sawing slabs of bone for sectioning. *Note that the vertical kerfs have not been extended to meet the horizontal kerf.*

one is dealing with a long bone containing marrow, it is necessary that it should be cut with a hacksaw into short lengths in order that the marrow may be removed by boiling. The bone is then taken from the boiling water, dried for a day or two, and then defatted by being soaked in any fat solvent. About the cheapest and most convenient solvent available is naphtha, though if price is a secondary consideration one can, of course, use xylene. Three or four changes, each lasting a week, in a considerable volume of solvent must be made, and the bone should then be baked in a low-temperature oven until the solvent has been removed.

A series of thin slabs is then cut, as shown in Fig. 30. The saw there shown, which is a cheap imitation of a hacksaw, is the best that the author has found for

slabs as are required have been outlined. Each is then successively cut off. A convenient size slab for preparation of a microscope slide is approximately ¼ inch square, which is the size shown in the illustration.

Single sections may be handled without being attached to anything. Several blocks may, however, be ground down at the same time by cementing them to a slide as shown in Fig. 31. The hot table (shown in its entirety in Fig. 8) is heated to about 100°C. The slide is then liberally covered with natural balsam—not a solution in xylene—and the slabs laid in place. Each block of bone will have a jagged corner sticking from it, where it broke away just before the saw cut was complete, and these little jagged corners must be placed uppermost. One must also be careful that the thickest sections of bone are placed at the outside of the preparation, or it will be impossible to avoid the slide's wobbling while being ground. As soon as all the slabs of bone have been placed, the balsam is heated until it boils rapidly. The balsam usually catches fire during this process, but it may be extinguished by blowing on it. A pair of forceps is finally used to push each piece of bone into contact with the glass and the slide is cooled.

The scratches from the carborundum must now be polished out with pumice powder. One secures either another piece of glass or a flat hardwood board—they are equally good—and prepares on this a paste of pumice and water exactly as the carborundum paste was prepared. The slide is washed to remove the carborundum grains and then rubbed, with exactly the same motion, in a slurry of pumice until each section of bone is uniformly

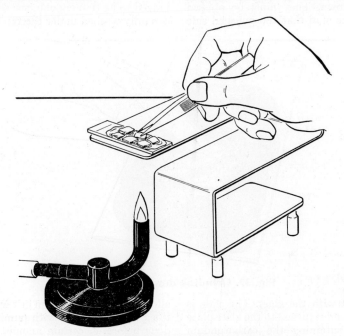

Fig. 31. Mounting bone slabs on glass slide.

While the section is cooling, a pool of water is poured on a slab of plate glass, and carborundum powder, of about 100 mesh, is sprinkled in until a thick cream is produced. The slide is then turned upside down in this cream, as shown in Fig. 32, and rubbed backward and forward with a circular movement, so as to grind down the bone. The grinding should be continued until the pieces of bone have been reduced to a uniform thickness. It may be necessary, from time to time, to add more water, and the specimen should be lifted at intervals to make sure that the abrasive fluid is underneath it, and not being pushed out by a wall of balsam.

smooth on the surface. Some people prefer to use a hardwood, rather than a glass, slab for the pumice. It is best to dry the surface of the bone and to examine it under a lens by strong reflected light to make sure that the scratches have been removed.

The sections are now polished on a horsehide strop cemented to a wood block. The strop is lubricated with a thick cream of either rouge or white rouge (ceric oxide). The slide should be rubbed rapidly with very little pressure; too much pressure is liable to dry the sections. If dried rouge is forced into the surface under pressure it is almost impossible to remove unless the specimens are reground with pumice. The final polish can be judged by eye and should be such as would be acceptable on, say, a polished ivory ornament.

The slide is then returned to the hot table seen in Fig. 31 and heated until the balsam is molten. Another slide is placed alongside the first, liberally smeared with balsam, and the sections transferred from the first slide to the second with the polished side down. They must be pressed hard to make sure that the polished side

necessary that the slide should not rock from side to side as it is pushed about, or the coverslips will become ground at the end before the sections of bone in the middle are thin enough. Experienced experts can often grind a section of bone until it is as thin as a number 1 coverslip, but this is not recommended to the beginner, for if the section is ground too thin it will suddenly disintegrate and all the work done so far will be lost. When the sections are judged to be thin enough, the slide is very carefully washed under the tap to remove

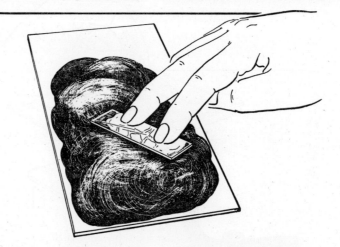

Fig. 32. Grinding down bone slabs.

is in contact with the glass. The slide is then cooled and returned to the glass plate (Fig. 32) containing the carborundum paste, on which it is now slowly and steadily ground until the sections are thin enough. The thickness may partly be estimated by holding the specimen up to a light and seeing how transparent it is becoming; the correct thickness has the transparency of a rather thin sheet of oiled paper. If the technician does not care to trust his judgment in the matter it is possible to take two number 3 coverslips and to cement one on each end of the slide. A thick number 3 coverslip is about the thickness of a good section of bone so that, if the bone is ground down until the coverslip just starts to be affected by the grinding compound, the sections may be presumed to be of the right thickness. To use this method satisfactorily, however, it is

all traces of carborundum grit and the sections then smoothed with pumice, as was done before. A certain amount of reduction in thickness may also be produced by the pumice though it is usually better to use carborundum. As soon as the scratch marks of the carborundum have been removed, the sections are again washed carefully under the tap and then polished. A coverslip is then placed on top of the preparation and the slide examined under various powers of the microscope, which will very soon disclose whether or not it is thin enough. If it is not thin enough to show the required structures it should be taken back to the carborundum, ground some more, then resmoothed and repolished in the manner described above. Several trials are often required before all the sections are found to be satisfactory.

There are two schools of thought as to

the mounting of these bone sections. Some people prefer to mount them dry, in which case the slide is placed in a jar of benzene and left until all the Canada balsam has been removed. Each individual section is then picked up on a section lifter, transferred to two or three fresh changes of benzene to remove the last of the balsam, and then dried under pressure between two glass slides; when it is dry it is then treated as any other dry wholemount (see Chapter 1). This method undoubtedly makes it easier to see the finer structure of the bone, but it is applicable only to very thin sections, for the additional transparency imparted by the balsam will be lost. It is usually more satisfactory to melt the balsam, to lift each section up, to place it in fresh balsam on its individual slide under a coverslip, and to heat it until all the air bubbles have been expelled. The coverslip is then held down with one of the clips shown in Fig. 25 and cooled.

All these operations can be conducted much more conveniently on the machinery made for grinding and polishing rock sections, but this description has been given for the benefit of those who lack such machinery. It has from time to time been recommended in the literature that one should grind sections of this kind down on microtome sharpening stones, using oil as a lubricant. The writer has had the most wretched results by this method; it is mentioned only in order that it may be avoided.

PREPARATION OF A TRANSVERSE SECTION OF A CORAL WITH POLYP IN PLACE

It must be understood, first of all, that the preparation here to be described will give a very much less satisfactory transverse section of a coral polyp than will the paraffin method described in Chapter 12. This method is intended only as a compromise between a paraffin section of a polyp and a ground section of a hard structure of the type described in the last example.

The living animal must first be narcotized, fixed, and hardened. It does not matter what coral be selected. The northern coral (*Astrangia danae*) is convenient both because of its wide distribution and because it may be obtained from biological supply houses. Supposing, however, it is to be collected fresh, a piece should be secured of about the size of an orange, or smaller, and brought back to the laboratory and left to expand in plenty of well-aerated sea water. It must, of course, be narcotized before fixation and a double process is best for this type of specimen. About 5% of its volume of a saturated solution of magnesium sulfate is therefore added to the water and the action of this narcotic is enhanced by sprinkling menthol on the surface. After about half an hour the polyps will be extruded from the coral in a partially narcotized condition and should be fixed. Perfect narcosis will result in such a small quantity of the polyp remaining in the coral that it is scarcely worth while sectioning it, whereas fixing an unnarcotized coral causes such a contraction of the polyp that the sections will be hard to interpret.

The fixative selected should be one which will harden the polyp as much as possible without having any effect on the calcareous structure surrounding it. The copper sulfate-mercuric chloride of Lo Bianco (Chapter 18, F 3400.0000 Lo Bianco 1890) is excellently suited for the purpose and about a gallon will be required for the fixation of a specimen of the size described. As much of the water as possible is now siphoned off from the vessel containing the coral specimen and the fixative added. The fixative should be stirred at intervals for the next two or three days and then the specimen should be transferred to fresh fixative for a period of about another week. The coral is then washed in running water overnight and placed in 4% formaldehyde, which should be changed daily until the whole of the fixative has been washed out of the specimen.

A coarse hacksaw is then used to cut the specimen into cubes of about an inch on a side, with due regard to the selection of pieces which will subsequently give good sections. These inch cubes are now washed in running water overnight, to get rid of the formaldehyde, and suspended in a considerable volume of 70% alcohol. It will be necessary to impregnate them with a resin;

they must, therefore, be completely dehydrated and cleared as though wholemounts were to be made of them (Chapter 6). This dehydration is very slow so that, after about two weeks in 70% alcohol, they should be placed for a further two weeks in 95% alcohol before being transferred for still another week into absolute alcohol. As considerable volumes are required it may be found more economical to substitute anhydrous acetone for the absolute alcohol.

The writer prefers to embed in Canada balsam but this must be freed of its contained essential oils if it is to become hard enough for grinding. It is very difficult to melt dry Canada balsam without obtaining a mass full of air bubbles and it is, therefore, better to take a pound or two of the natural balsam, place it in a wide evaporating dish and heat it to about 120°C., with due precautions against fire, until such time as a small drop placed on a cold plate hardens rapidly to a material which will crack and chip, rather than bend, when a knife is applied to it.

A solution of about 30% by weight of this essential-oil-free Canada resin in benzene is also required but may be made up from the commercial dried product.

After the specimen has been completely dehydrated it must, of course, be de-alcoholized in some material which is miscible with the resin and it is suggested that benzene be used. Three changes of benzene, with about a week in each, will be required; and it is desirable that some dehydrating agent, preferably silica gel or calcium sulfate should be kept in the vessel to remove the last traces of water. When the specimen is completely impregnated with benzene it is transferred to the solution of dry Canada balsam in benzene and left there for a week or two until it is impregnated. The solution is then transferred to an open vessel and warmed gently until as much as possible of the solvent has been removed. Care must be taken never to raise it to the boiling point of the solvent or bubbles may occur in the actual specimen which will wreck the subsequent preparation. The specimen is then immersed in molten balsam, which is maintained at about 100°C. until no further diffusion currents are seen. The beaker is then cooled until the balsam is completely hardened. The only practical method of removing this hardened block of clear balsam containing the specimen is to crack the beaker away from it with a hammer.

One is now left with a solid block of balsam containing the coral, and a saw is used to trim the specimen to shape. This trimming should result in a rectangular block, if we are dealing with *Astrangia danae*, of about a ½-inch side, by one inch long, with the polyp protruding from one end. Canada balsam is not easy to saw and it is recommended that the blade be kept lubricated at all times with a weak soap solution.

This rectangular block is now treated exactly as though it were a piece of bone and a series of slices of from ½ to one millimeter thick cut from it. These slices cannot, however, be handled all at one time in the manner described in the last example, but must be handled individually.

Each slice is therefore taken and ground flat with carborundum used in the manner described in the last example. Instead, however, of having the section cemented on a slide, it is held on the ball of the first finger and rubbed backward and forward until it is flattened. When it is flat, it will not be satisfactory to wash it under the tap, because many of the carborundum grains will be embedded in the balsam and one should, therefore, take a rag moistened with benzene and wipe the surface carefully until the carborundum grains are seen to be removed. Great care should be taken to do this in such a manner that the flatness of the center of the section, where there are only the soft parts embedded in balsam, is not disturbed. The section is then rubbed up and down with the finger using pumice on wood, and again washed and cleaned. These specimens do not polish well on leather and a sheet of velvet (which may be gummed to a wooden block) should be substituted. This velvet is liberally lubricated with white rouge in water and a polish put on the lower surface of the section. If the white rouge is sufficiently diluted with water, it is unlikely to become embedded in the balsam; therefore washing in water will remove it.

The section must now be mounted on the slide which it is finally to occupy, but this is done in exactly the opposite manner to that described in the last example, in which the slide was covered in balsam and the object pressed to it. In this case the section must be placed on a flat surface, a slide warmed rather above the melting point of the balsam and pressed down on to the specimen so as to melt the minimum possible quantity of balsam to permit perfect adherence. Only in this manner can one avoid disturbing the soft parts. The other side of the section is now ground down, smoothed, and polished exactly as described in the last example. It will, however, be much easier to estimate the thickness of a section of this type, for one can always observe the soft parts under the microscope. When the section has become sufficiently thin, it is only necessary to place a drop of natural balsam on top, apply a coverslip, and warm the whole while applying pressure.

Though this description has applied to the preparation of a coral, it may equally well be applied to the production of sections of bone with the bone marrow and blood cells retained in position. Those who prefer to grind their sections on oilstones with an oil lubricant should consult the description of Henrichi 1916 (4349, **6**:45).

11

Sections of Free Material

General Principles

Nature of the Process

A *section* is a thin slice cut from biological materials with a view to studying either the cells themselves, or their arrangement, neither of which can well be made out from a wholemount. If the

Though sections may be cut at any angle, they are usually taken through one of three planes (see Fig. 33), known as *transverse*, *sagittal*, and *frontal*. The purpose of this orientation of the material with relation to the plane of the section is to permit

Fig. 33. Standard section planes.

worker's only interest is, in the shape of the cells, as distinct from their structure, he should attempt some of the preparations described in Chapter 9, which will often be found better than sections for his purpose.

a better visualization of the structure of the whole, from an examination of sections. When the relation of organs is to be reproduced from sections, the process is known as *reconstruction* and is referred to briefly in Chapter 14. In theory a section can be made by cutting a thin slice from the object with a sharp knife. Few materials, however, are suitable for this, nor does this procedure yield sections of the same thickness. It is, therefore, customary to use an instrument known as a *microtome:* a device for advancing a block of tissue a given amount, cutting a slice from it, and then re-advancing it for the same amount, and so on. A full account of all the types of mechanism by which this result can be produced is to be found in Richards 1949 and need not be repeated here.

Another objection to the mere cutting of slices from an object is the nature of biological specimens themselves. Few of these are stiff enough to withstand the action of the knife without bending, and many contain cavities which would be crushed out of recognition as the section was taken. This makes it necessary, for most biological work, to surround and support the object to be cut with some material which will impregnate it. The medium most commonly used is wax. The technique for cutting wax sections is described fully in the next chapter. Nitrocellulose is also employed and is described in Chapter 13. Another method of stiffening the material, so that sections may be cut from it without crushing, is to freeze the specimen. This technique is described in Chapter 15. There are however, materials which may be cut without either the complicated microtomes described in these chapters or the support of impregnating substances. Sections which are so cut are known as *free* or *freehand sections*. These form the subject of the present chapter.

Microtomes for Free Sections

Even though the material itself is of the correct consistency to withstand the action of the knife, it is still necessary to have some mechanism which will produce sections of known thickness. The type of microtome usually employed in hard sectioning is shown in Fig. 34 and consists essentially of a disk, usually of polished plate glass, supported on a cylinder gripped in the hand. Within this cylinder there is some mechanism for holding specimens which terminates at its lower end on a

micrometer screw. When this screw is turned, the object in the holder is pushed above the surface of the glass plate. The collar of the micrometer screw is graduated, sometimes in thousandths of an inch, but more usually in hundredths of a millimeter. The unit commonly used to describe the thickness of a section is a

Fig. 34. Hand microtome.

micron which is one-thousandth of a millimeter; but hand sections are very rarely cut of less than 10-micron thickness and are usually better at two or three times this.

Methods of Holding the Material

Though the material itself may be suitable for cutting, it is rarely of a size and shape which may be gripped in the holder of the hand microtome without additional support. It must, therefore, be held in some substance which will itself cut readily and which may be easily shaped to support what is being cut. It is possible to embed the material either in wax or nitrocellulose before cutting a hand section, but if one is to go to this amount of trouble, it is usually better to use a complex microtome of the type described in Chapters 12 and 13. Vegetable tissues are usually employed to support objects for hand sectioning and the two best known are elder pith and carrots. Elder pith has the advantage that it may be stored indefinitely and cuts with a clean crisp action. Unfortunately the pith of the American elderberry (*Sambucus canadensis*) does not appear to be as suitable for the purpose as the pith of the

European elderberry (*S. nigra*). This difference between the two species may account for the disfavor in which elder pith is held in the United States, but in the writer's experience it is far more convenient than the carrot. The disadvantage of the carrot is that it must be absolutely fresh, and even if it is kept in water overnight it loses much of that crispness which is necessary for the production of a good section.

Almost all hand sections are cut from plant material, and most of them from leaves or stems. To support a leaf, a cylinder, of the right diameter to fit in the microtome is cut either from elder pith or carrot, split down the middle, and the leaf inserted. The holding screw is then tightened. Stems, however, cannot be held by this means and a hollow cylinder must be prepared with an outer diameter convenient to the microtome and an inner diameter which is slightly less than that of the stem to be gripped. This hollow cylinder is then split, the stem inserted, and the section cut. Of course, a few substances, such as cork or stiff plant stems, may be cut without any other support; these are, however, in the minority.

Hardening and Fixing Materials for Cutting

Many objects, which are in themselves unsuitable for sectioning by hand, may be made more suitable if they are fixed and hardened. A general discussion of the principles governing the selection of a fixative is given in Chapters 6 and 12; the formulas which have been suggested for the purpose are given in Chapter 18. If, however, one is to go to the trouble of hardening and fixing material in a formula designed to preserve the structure of the cells, it is usually worth while to go to the additional trouble of embedding the material and cutting sections as described in the next two chapters. For material to be hand sectioned it is sufficient that it be preserved in 90% alcohol. This process is equally applicable to the stems and leaves of the botanists, or to the very few animal materials, such as cartilage, which are suitable for the production of hand sections.

It must not be thought that objects embedded in nitrocellulose or wax should not, or cannot, be cut on a hand microtome. The study of the embryology of the frog is rendered much easier to elementary students if they are allowed to cut hand sections of blastulae, gastrulae and young larvae for themselves; and a word might be said at this point as to the method by which such blocks may be readily prepared in quantity. The larvae are fixed, dehydrated, cleared, and impregnated with wax in the manner described in Chapter 12. Instead of casting each into an individual block, however, a large slab of wax—the cheapest paraffin is suitable— is cast in a tray. A heated iron rod of about ½-inch diameter is then driven into the slab so as to make a little pool of molten wax. An impregnated larva, or egg, is then dropped into the hole and the process repeated. By this means a couple of hundred frog eggs may be embedded in ten minutes. The large block of wax, containing numerous eggs, is then cut with a saw into rectangles, the edges of which are trimmed with a knife until they will fit into a hand microtome. These blocks may even be cut without a hand microtome by placing the block on a bench and shaving off successive sections with a sharp scalpel.

Staining and Mounting Sections

Sections, which are taken individually from the knife and accumulated in a dish of 70% alcohol, should be treated as wholemounts rather than as sections. They may, that is, be directly mounted in either gum media (Chapter 4) or jelly media (Chapter 5) or they may be stained and mounted in resinous media in the manner described in Chapter 6.

It might be pointed out, however, that many sections may be double- or triple-stained (a process which is impossible with wholemounts) and that in theory any method of staining described in Chapters 20, 21, or 23 for wax or nitrocellulose sections may also be applied to a hand section. These are, however, much better applied to sections after they have been attached to a slide. If they are to be attempted, reference should be made to

Chapter 28 (V 21.3), where are given formulas and methods which may be used to attach individual sections. Sections which are not attached to slides must be transferred from one fluid to another with the device known as a *section lifter*, which is merely a small flattened sheet of metal held in a wooden handle.

Typical Examples

Preparation of a Transverse Section of the Leaf of Ligustrum

The leaf of the privet is, in the opinion of the writer, the easiest biological specimen from which a section may be pre-

It is necessary to have a hand microtome of the type already described, an old-fashioned hand razor, some freshly picked

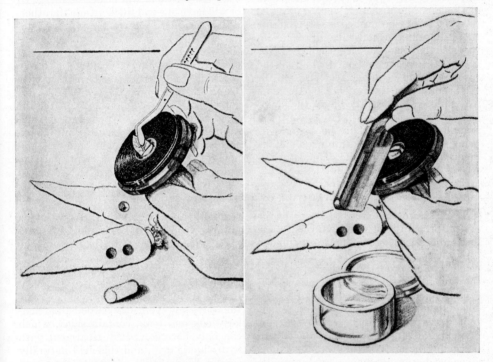

Fig. 35. Inserting a leaf into a split cylinder of carrot.

Fig. 36. Cutting a hand section. *The razor is drawn across the plate with gentle pressure and the section then washed into a stender dish.*

pared and is included in this place as an introduction to the art of cutting sections.

The leaves should be collected in summer and stored in a jar of 90% alcohol which must be changed as often as it becomes diluted from the extracted water or discolored by the extracted chlorophyll. If large quantities of alcohol are used in the first place it will be unnecessary to change it, but it must be agitated from time to time to avoid the accumulation of water at the bottom.

carrots, and a stender dish of 70% alcohol. The razor shown in the illustration (Fig. 35) is flat on one side and hollow-ground on the other. This is the best kind for hand sectioning, but if it is not obtainable a double hollow-ground razor may be used.

Next take a cork borer of such a size that it will bore out a cylinder which will fit reasonably well into the holder of the microtome. Then (Fig. 35) cut from a fresh carrot as many cylinders as are required. A leaf is then trimmed until it is the same width as the cylinder. The cylinder of carrot is split, inserted into the holder of the microtome, and the leaf pushed down into the center of the cylinder (Fig. 35).

The holder of the cylinder is now tightened and the razor used to slice off as much of the leaf and cork as projects above the level of the plate (Fig. 36). The micrometer screw at the bottom of the cylinder is then turned as far as is necessary to advance the carrot and leaf the thickness of the required section above the glass plate, and a section shaved off. The razor must not be pushed straight across the material, but must be drawn sideways, so that the whole length of the razor is used to cut the section. In Fig. 36 the razor is placed in the correct position for the beginning of the cut; but by the time it has passed through the block, the opposite end of the razor will be opposite the section. Notice also that the material is being sectioned with its thin edge, not its breadth, against the knife. This is neces-

sary whether one is cutting sections by hand or by any other means, because the less material cut at the same time, the less is the chance that it will be torn from its support.

The section on the knife is now brushed off into one of the stender dishes of alcohol, the micrometer screw advanced the same amount, another section cut, and so on. About twice as many sections should be cut as are ultimately required, for at least half of them will either be damaged or will have one end thicker than the other. The sections are therefore examined under the low power of a microscope and those which are not considered satisfactory are thrown away.

Stains used for materials of this type are given in Chapter 21 (DS 21.15), together with a specific example. After the sections have been stained as there described, they should be dehydrated exactly as if they were wholemounts and mounted in balsam in the manner described in Chapter 6.

PREPARATION OF A SECTION OF WOOD

The last process described is one of the easiest preparations which may be made in microtomy, whereas the present is one of the most difficult. The sectioning of wood belongs properly in this chapter on the preparation of freehand sections, because wood does not need to be embedded. The difficulty of cutting it lies in the fact that it is too hard to be cut by regular methods while being in general too soft to be cut by the method for ground sections given in Chapter 10. Some plant materials, such as the wood of the lignum vitae, or the ivory nut, may be cut by grinding techniques and make better sections by this method than by any other. A few woods, such as white pine cut parallel to the grain, are sufficiently soft to be cut in a hand microtome without any preparation. The present example deals with such woods as maple or oak, which fall between these two extremes.

The first thing to be done in the preparation of any section of wood is to cut a block, one end of which is of the size of the required section. A section size about ¼ inch square is usually adequate to demon-

strate the structure of the wood, and a number of blocks this size should be prepared with due regard to the plane of the section.

The wood must next be softened. This would be relatively simple if mechanical means alone could be employed. Unfortunately, however, many woods, particularly oak and teak, contain silica, which can only be removed by treatment with hydrofluoric acid, and this acid naturally cannot be made to penetrate the wood until all air has been removed. The blocks of wood are therefore boiled in distilled water for about ten minutes. A disk of glass—or of wire gauze—which will just fit inside the beaker, is placed on top of the pieces of wood, and a sufficient weight added on top to cause the blocks to sink to the bottom. The beaker is now transferred to some type of vacuum equipment and exhausted until bubbles are seen to cease leaving the wood. The vacuum is then released, the beaker returned to the flame, and again boiled for ten minutes. This process of alternate boiling and evacuation is continued until the wood no longer floats, a state showing that the greater part of air has been removed.

The blocks are now transferred to 50% commercial hydrofluoric acid, and a word of warning must be issued as to the danger of this material. Since it dissolves silica, it cannot be handled in glass vessels, and the choice lies between hard rubber and lead. Not only is the vapor extremely corrosive, but a burn from hydrofluoric acid on the skin is worse than that from any other chemical known to the writer. Extreme care should be taken, therefore, in transferring blocks to hydrofluoric acid, where they may remain until the silica has been dissolved from them. A block of ¼-inch oak will be satisfactorily desilicified in one day, but teak should remain for at least three or four. Observing the same precautions as before, the blocks of wood are removed from the hydrofluoric acid to running water and must be washed for at least three or four hours before they are safe to handle with the hand.

A block may now be removed from the water and mounted in any convenient microtome for cutting. The harder woods can never be satisfactorily cut on a hand microtome and the best mechanism is undoubtedly the sliding microtome described in Chapter 12. Exactly the same precautions in cutting a wood block on this microtome should be taken as in cutting a block of anything else. That is, the knife must be sloped at an angle towards the block so that the greatest possible length of knife is used to cut a single section, and the block must be so orientated that the knife enters at one corner rather than flat on the side. The sections as they are cut may be removed to water, and any tendency which they have to curl may be counteracted by warming the water.

An interesting variation of this standard technique was proposed at the same time by Crowell 1928 (20540b, **5**:149) and by Kisser (cited from Crowell). This method consists of mounting a dry block of wood in any type of microtome and directing onto its surface a jet of high-pressure steam. After the steam has acted for a moment or two, a single section is cut and the steam again applied for another few moments before cutting the next section, and so on. It is stated that by this means sections of the hardest material may be taken without the use of hydrofluoric acid.

Sections of wood are usually mounted in balsam, dehydrated, and cleared as described in Chapter 6. Sections which tend to curl may be tied between slides.

Sections of wood containing some natural color, as oak and mahogany, are best mounted unstained, but thin sections of colorless wood may become too transparent under this treatment. Almost any dye may be used, since the purpose is not to differentiate the parts but only to render them visible.

12

Paraffin Sections

General Principles

Nature of the Process

The last chapter discussed freehand sections, that is, sections of material which is in itself sufficiently strong and sufficiently coherent to hold together when cut in thin slices. The majority of objects to be sectioned, however, contain cavities which would collapse under the action of the knife, or are not of a shape or consistency which would enable one of them to be cut by hand. Objects of this nature must, therefore, be supported in a matrix which will itself section well, and those containing cavities must be impregnated throughout their whole substance with the embedding medium. Wax, nitrocellulose, and a variety of water-soluble materials have from time to time been suggested as impregnating and supporting agents, but the use of wax is so convenient and simple that only in special cases should any other material be employed.

The advantage of wax is not only that it readily passes from a solid to a molten state at temperatures which do not damage the material, but also that it is somewhat sticky, so that ribbons of sections may be prepared, each section being in the ribbon in the same order as it was cut from the object. Thus, if a rectangular block of wax is mounted in some kind of holder and then brought sharply down on a horizontal knife, the thin slice of wax which is cut off will adhere by its edge to the edge of the knife. If the block is then advanced by some mechanical device—such as a microtome—a small distance and again brought down on the knife, a second section will be cut off which will displace the first section, to which it will adhere on one edge, while the other edge remains attached to the knife. By the repetition of these movements a long ribbon may be produced. A ribbon of this type is seen in all the stages of its preparation in Figs. 65–70. Preparation of paraffin sections is quite a complex operation and involves the following stages:

1. Fixation of the material.
2. Dehydration, in order that the material may be impregnated with a fluid capable of dissolving wax.
3. The removal of the dehydrating agent with a material solvent of, or miscible with, molten wax.
4. The soaking of the cleared specimen in a molten wax for sufficiently long to insure that it shall become completely impregnated.
5. Casting the now impregnated specimen into a rectangular block of wax.
6. Attaching this block of wax to some holder which itself may be inserted into a suitable microtome.
7. The actual cutting of the sections of the block into ribbons.
8. The placing of these ribbons on a glass slide in such a manner that they will lie flat and that the contained section will be adherent after the wax has been dissolved away.
9. The removal of the wax solvent.
10. Staining and mounting.

Each of these operations will be dealt with in due order. This chapter terminates with a series of examples which describe in detail the application of the principles discussed to actual preparations.

Selection of a Fixative

Fixative formulas are given in Chapter 18; and the selection of the fixative for small invertebrates has already been discussed in Chapter 6. When one intends to section a small invertebrate, with the primary function of preserving its parts in as natural as possible a relation to each other, the same fixative should be employed as is recommended for those invertebrates intended to be made into wholemounts. The purpose in each case is to preserve the object in as natural a shape as possible without special regard to the preservation of the fine details of the cells themselves.

Something of the same consideration applies to blocks of tissue which are to be fixed in such a manner that their general structure, or histology will be displayed. In this case, however, there is no problem of contraction of parts, so that fixatives which would be quite useless for a whole animal may safely be applied to a block of tissue. Reference to Chapter 18 will show that there are between 600 and 800 solutions recommended for fixation, and there is no general agreement as to which is the best for any particular purpose. These notes are therefore written only for the benefit of the beginner who, presented with this bewildering display, lacks the experience on which to base his choice. The selections given below are modified from Gray 1933 (11360, **53**:15). The figures following the name and date refer to the decimal classification of Chapter 18 in which the formulas for these fixatives will be found. Specific suggestions for the employment of fixatives are to be found in many of the examples of the preparation of slides which occur in this book.

A. RECOMMENDED FIXATIVES FOR EM-BRYOS OR WHOLE ORGANS EXCEEDING 5 MM IN THICKNESS.

1. FOR USE WHEN THE PRESERVATION OF SHAPE IS OF PRIMARY IMPOR-TANCE.
Bensley 1915 F 1700.0010
Erlitzky 1877 F 4700.0000
Hoyer 1899 F 3700.0000
Lavdowski 1894 F 6000.0010
Maximov 1909 F 1700.1000

Müller 1859 F 7000.1000
Orth 1896 F 7000.1000
Régaud 1910 F 7000.1000

2. WHEN IT IS DESIRED, AS FAR AS POS-SIBLE, TO PRESERVE BOTH SHAPE AND PROTOPLASMIC DETAIL.
   a. *When shape is of greater importance*
   Helly 1903 F 3700.1000
   Petrunkewitsch 1933 F 4900.0040
   Rawitz 1895 F 5600.0040
   Smith 1902 F 7000.1010
   Zenker 1894 F 3700.0010
   b. *When protoplasmic detail is of greater importance*
   Fol 1896 F 1560.0000
   Gilson 1898 F 3000.0014
   Kohn 1907 F 3700.0010
   Mayer 1880 F 5000.0050
   Rabl 1894 F 2300.0000
   Tellysniczky 1898 F 3500.0010

B. RECOMMENDED FIXATIVES FOR SMALL PORTIONS OF ORGANS OR WHOLE OR-GANS OR EMBRYOS NOT EXCEEDING 5 MM. IN THICKNESS.

1. WHEN A GENERAL-PURPOSE FIXA-TIVE IS REQUIRED
Carleton and Leach 1938 F 3000.1000
Gatenby 1937 F 6700.0040
Gerhardt 1901 F 3600.1010
Schaudinn 1900 F 3000.0000

2. WHEN PROTOPLASMIC DETAIL IS OF GREATER IMPORTANCE
   a. *When nuclear fixation is especially required*
   Allen 1929 F 5600.1010
   van Beneden (1905) F 3000.0010
   Carnoy 1887 F 0000.0010
   Carnoy and Lebrun 1887 F 3000.0010
   Sanson (1928) F 0000.0010
   b. *When cytoplasmic detail is especially required*
   Champy 1911 F 1670.0000
   Flemming 1884 F 1600.0010
   Kultschitzky 1887 F 4700.0010
   Mann 1894 F 1300.0000
   Smith 1935 F 1670.0010

There are only two general precautions to be observed in the practical application of fixatives: first, that adequate volumes (at least 100 times the volume of the part to be fixed) be employed; second, that mixtures containing either chromic acid or potassium dichromate with formaldehyde be used in the dark. After fixation, tissues should be thoroughly washed in water if this is the solvent for the fixative, or in alcohol if the fixative is based on the latter. Objects are usually stored, after fixation and washing, in 70% alcohol; though if they are to be kept a long time before dehydration, it is recommended that 5% of glycerol be added to the alcohol. This glycerol must, however, be very thoroughly washed out before dehydration commences.

Choice of a Dehydrating Agent

Chapter 25 discusses the numerous organic solvents which from time to time have been proposed for the dehydration of biological specimens and the selection between them is not usually of great importance. The classic method of dehydration is to soak the object in a graded series of alcohols, usually 10 or 15% apart. Dehydration through gradually increasing strengths of alcohol may be vital when one is dealing with delicate objects containing easily collapsible cavities, such as chicken and pig embryos, but a block of tissue may be taken from water to 95% alcohol without any apparent damage. Even though one uses increasing strengths of alcohol, the series normally in employment at the present time is by no means satisfactory. It is customary, for example, to pass from water to 30% alcohol at one end of the series and to pass from 85% to 95% alcohol at the other. The diffusion currents between water and 30% alcohol are far greater and far more intense than those between 85 and 95%, and an intelligently graded series for delicate objects should run from water to 10% to 20% to 50% to 95% alcohol rather than through the conventionally spaced gradations. This is not at all in accordance with the recommendations in most textbooks but is based on the author's experience over a long time. In using this classic method of dehydration, it is not necessary to confine the technique to ethanol. Meth-

anol or acetone will dehydrate just as effectively, though they are rather more volatile.

There is a considerable vogue nowadays for the substitution for a straight dehydrating agent of some solvent which is both miscible with water and also with molten wax. The best known of these is dioxane, though n-butanol has also been recommended. The writer is not in love with these methods for, though the solvents involved are excellent dehydrating agents, they are relatively poor solvents of paraffin and frequently cause great shrinkage of delicate objects in the final transition between the solvent and the wax. For such purposes as the routine examination of the tissue blocks in a pathological laboratory, or for sectioning relatively sturdy plant materials, they may justifiably be employed. For sections intended, however, to retain intact structures on which research is subsequently to be conducted, it is most strongly recommended that the standard routine of passing from a dehydrating to a clearing reagent be retained.

Selection of a Clearing Agent

Reference should again be made to Chapter 25 for a list of the materials which have from time to time been recommended for de-alcoholizing, or clearing, biological specimens. The choice of a clearing agent in section cutting is of far more importance than the choice of a dehydrant, for there is not the slightest doubt that prolonged immersion in some of the volatile hydrocarbons, particularly xylene, leads to a hardening of the tissue with subsequent difficulty in sectioning. The classic method is to pass from alcohol to xylene, but the only apparent reason for the choice of xylene over toluene or benzene lies in the work of Squire (1892, page 80) who timed the evaporation rate of these three solvents from an open watch glass and found xylene to evaporate the most slowly. There is little choice in the solvent power of any of these three hydrocarbons on wax; the writer's preference is for benzene, though it seems impossible to shake the faith of the conventional that the more expensive xylene is a necessity both as a solvent for embedding media and as a clearing agent before them. These three hydrocarbons are so cheap, and are obtainable in such a pure form, that there seems no necessity to use any other clearing agent, unless one prefers the reagents which are supposed to combine the functions of both dehydration and clearing.

It is still occasionally recommended that essential oils, such as cedar oil, be used for clearing objects for embedding. There is no justification for this unless it is vital that the object be rendered transparent (rather than alcohol-free) in order that some feature of its internal anatomy may be oriented in relation to the knife. Essential oils are excellent for wholemounts, but they are not readily removed from the specimen by molten wax; therefore, if they must be used, they should always be washed out with a hydrocarbon before the wax bath. Relatively small traces of any essential oil will destroy the cutting properties of any wax mixture and, as they are nonvolatile, there is no chance of getting rid of them in the embedding oven.

Choice of an Embedding Medium

Formulas for the various wax mixtures used in the preparation of ribbons of sections will be found in Chapter 27 (E 21.1). It is to be presumed at the present time that no one will endeavor to use a plain paraffin but will use one of these mixtures. If, for some strange reason, a pure paraffin is preferred, then it is necessary to buy (in the United States by importation) a carefully fractionated and very expensive wax. Ordinary cheap paraffin is a mixture of a great variety of compounds of slightly different melting points, and it is essential in the use of pure wax that a wax of a very sharp melting point should be obtained.

The choice of an embedding medium should be dictated less by the nature of the specimen than by the conditions under which it should be cut. If pure paraffin is to be employed, it should be selected with such a melting point that the hardened wax will give a crisp section at the required room temperature. In the Europe of twenty years ago, when many writers were recommending a wax with a melting point of 52°C., the average laboratory

temperature in winter was between 50° and 60°F. A wax of 52°C. melting point, in an American laboratory kept between 70° and 80°F., is far too soft to cut any but the thickest sections. The use of waxes of 58°C., which are quite hard enough for cutting sections in an American laboratory, is unfortunate, since such use requires an oven temperature of at least 60°C. which results in many tissues becoming hard and brittle. As the introduction of any foreign substance automatically lowers the melting point of the wax, it is obviously desirable to use mixtures rather than the pure material. The writer's preference is naturally for his own composition (E 21.1 Gray 1944). The advantage of the mixtures there specified is that they have a relatively low melting point but soften very little before reaching the melting point. The degree of hardness (that is the thinness of the section which may be cut) may be controlled accurately by the proportion of resin added; and the writer has once secured, on a demonstration, a paraffin ribbon more than 20 feet long of 1-micron-thick sections. Media of this hardness, however, impregnate very slowly and should only be used for minute objects. For ordinary routine preparations the writer's preference is for any of the paraffin-rubber-bayberry-wax mixtures. The introduction of rubber undoubtedly increases the stickiness of the wax and makes it easier to secure continuous ribbons, while the bayberry wax not only prevents the crystallization of the paraffin but also lowers its melting point. The beginner is strongly recommended to experiment with several of the rubber-bayberry-wax compositions and to select after experiment that which gives him uniformly successful results in his own laboratory.

Technique of Dehydrating, Clearing, and Embedding

Before passing to the choice of a microtome and the method of using it, it is necessary to discuss briefly the actual operations which are involved in using the dehydrating, clearing, and embedding media selected. The techniques of dehydration and de-alcoholization do not differ materially from those used in the preparation of wholemounts which have been described in Chapter 6. The whole process could, however, be much simplified if people would only remember that water is heavier than the majority of dehydrating agents, and that the majority of dehydrating agents are lighter than most

The first prerequisite is some device which will maintain wax just at its melting point. Most people employ complex thermostatically controlled ovens for this purpose, but the exceedingly simple device shown in Fig. 37 has a great deal to recommend it. As will be seen, this consists essentially of a series of incandescent elec-

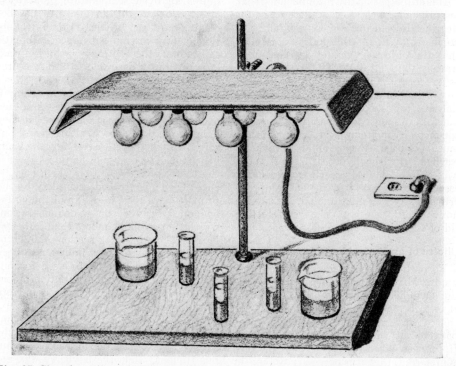

Fig. 37. Simple radiant heat embedding oven. *Height of the hood should be adjusted until the wax is melted for about one-half its depth.*

clearing agents. Translating this theory into practice it must be obvious that the object to be dehydrated should be suspended toward the top of a tall cylinder of dehydrant in order that the water extracted from it may fall toward the bottom of the vessel, and that an object for clearing should be held at the bottom of the vessel for the reverse reason. It is, indeed, practically impossible to dehydrate a large object unless it is so suspended. The process of impregnating the tissues with wax has not, however, previously been discussed and will be dealt with fully.

tric bulbs held, at a distance which may be varied, above a series of glass vials. Before commencing to embed one fills as many vials as one will require with wax, places them under the reflector, and turns on the current. After a little while it will be observed that the absorbed heat has melted the wax. The wax may be melted only at a small surface layer; it may be melted throughout the entire vial; or it may, as is required, be melted in the upper $2/3$ of the vial. If this last is not achieved the height of the lamp must be varied until, after an hour or two, each of the vials contains about $1/3$ of unmolten, opaque wax at the bottom and ⅔ of the clear molten material above. Thus, when the object is placed in one of these vials it will drop until it reaches the solidified layer, where it will remain in contact with molten wax at exactly the melting point of the wax. It is obvious that the room in which this operation is to be conducted must be at a fairly constant temperature and be free of drafts, but only a very large volume of embedding work justifies the purchase of an expensive thermostatically controlled oven. If such an oven is to be purchased it is highly desirable to avoid one in which the heat is distributed by convection. Such an old-

Vacuum ovens are occasionally required for the impregnation of the most difficult material but should be avoided whenever possible. If a vacuum oven is to be employed, moreover, it is necessary that all volatile solvents be removed from the material before it is placed in the vacuum so that it is always desirable to precede exposure in a vacuum oven by a considerable period of embedding in an ordinary oven.

Assuming that the material has been passed through dehydrating and clearing agents, and is now awaiting embedding, there are two main methods by which this

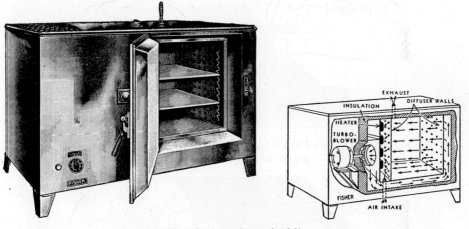

Fig. 38. Circulating air embedding oven.

fashioned convection oven is seen in Fig. 52 and is to be found all too frequently in laboratories. Unfortunately these ovens, as any cook could tell any microtomist, vary enormously in temperature from top to bottom. The thermostat is usually placed at the top and, in a fairly large oven, there may be as much as a ten-degree differential between the lowest shelf and the top one. The oven shown in Fig. 38 in which a circulating fan continuously moves the air and thus maintains a uniform temperature throughout the whole oven, is infinitely to be preferred. It is the high cost of such circulating-air ovens which leads the writer to believe that much more use should be made of the very simple radiant-heat embedding device discussed previously.

may be done. Either be the object may transferred directly to a bath of molten wax, or it may be passed through a graded series of wax-solvent mixtures. The writer is strongly in favor of the latter course. Let us suppose benzene has been selected as the clearing agent and that the object is in a vial containing a few milliliters of this solvent. Chips are then shaved from the block of embedding agent and added to the vial. These usually dissolve very slowly and form a thickened layer at the bottom of the tube through which the object to be embedded sinks. The average object will be satisfactory if left overnight. The tube is then placed in the embedding oven, maintained at a temperature slightly above the melting point of the wax, and as many further shavings as possible are

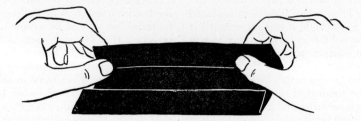

Fig. 39. Folding a cardboard box. *a. The two long edges of a rectangular card are folded to meet in the center.*

Fig. 40. Folding a cardboard box—*(continued). b. Folds are flattened out and the short edges are folded not quite to the center.*

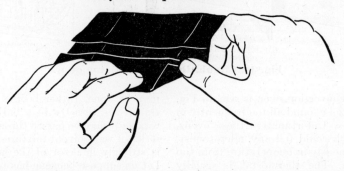

Fig. 41. Folding a cardboard box—*(continued). c. Corners are folded over.*

crammed into the tube. When these are completely molten, and most of the volatile solvent has evaporated, the object is removed with a pipet, or forceps, and placed in a dish of pure wax for an hour or two before being transferred to a second dish of pure wax for the time necessary to secure complete impregnation.

There is no method of forecasting how long an object will take to become completely impregnated with wax. It is very easy to find out, when one has started to cut sections, that the impregnation is not complete; but there is no basis save experience on which to base the timing in the different baths. If the object is to be transferred directly from solvent to wax, at least three baths should be employed, for nothing is more destructive to a good section than the presence of a small quantity of the clearing agent in the embedding medium. To an absolute beginner seeking

Fig. 42. Folding a cardboard box—*(continued). d. Edge of the fold is folded **back** over the creased corners.*

Fig. 43. Folding a cardboard box—*(continued). e. Box is opened and the corners pinched.*

Fig. 44. Folding a cardboard box—*(continued). f. Finished box.*

a rough guess, it may be said that a block of liver tissue of three-to-five-millimeter side will be satisfactorily impregnated with wax after 30 minutes in each of three baths, while a 96-hour chicken embryo will require at least two hours in each of three baths for its successful impregnation.

While the object is being impregnated with the wax it is necessary to decide what type of vessel will be used to cast the final block. This will depend more on the size of the object than on the preference of the worker. Very small objects may be most satisfactorily embedded in ordinary watch glasses (that is, ordinary thin-walled watch glasses not Syracuse watch glasses of the laboratory type) or in any other thin-walled glass vessel. Very large objects are often embedded with the aid of two thick L-shaped pieces of metal, which by being slid against each other may be caused to form a rectangular mold of varying dimensions. The writer himself regards these as very clumsy, and always prefers to prepare a cardboard or paper box than to endeavor to maneuver metal molds which are always getting jarred out of place at the wrong moment. The preparation of a paper or cardboard box is easy; the method preferred by the writer for large boxes is shown in Figs. 39–44.

Take a rectangular sheet of thin card or stout paper approximately twice as long as it is wide. The area of the floor of the box will be about ⅓ that of the sheet taken, but a little experience will soon show what size sheet to take for the box required. The sheet is laid on a flat surface and the long sides folded inwards (Fig. 39) until they very nearly meet in the middle. These folds are well creased with the thumbnail. The sheet of paper is then flattened again and the other two edges (Fig. 40) folded in the same manner. It is necessary, however, that this fold be much larger than the first fold made. These folds are also well creased with the thumbnail. The folded sheet is then laid out (Fig. 41)

Fig. 45 as there are boxes to be made. Center the sheet between the finger and the thumb (Fig. 46) and then fold up the sides (Fig. 47) creasing the paper where it is in contact with the edges of the block. Push up the end with the forefinger (Fig. 48) creasing both the paper in contact with the block and the flaps. Fold the flaps to the center (Fig. 49), being careful to get them straight and creasing them up the sides. Fold down the projecting flap (Fig. 50) and crease it firmly. Repeat these operations with the other side of the block and then slide the box off the end of the

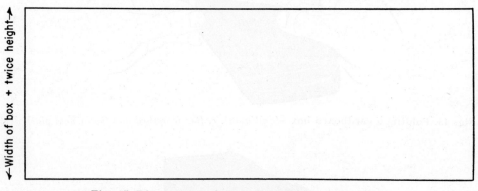

◄———— Length of box + twice height of box + twice length of flaps ————►

◄Width of box + twice height►

Fig. 45. Dimensions of sheet for folding a paper box.

and the corners folded in the manner shown. Since these end folds are larger than the side folds there will be an overhanging flap of paper at the top. After all four corners have been folded in, this overhanging flap (Fig. 42) is folded back over the triangular folded corner sections and this crease particularly firmly pressed with the thumbnail. When this has been done at each end, the box is finished and may be opened out as shown in Fig. 43. It will be found that the corners are not square but may be squared by pressing with the thumb and forefinger in the manner shown. The finished box is shown in Fig. 44.

There is a very convenient method of folding small boxes which requires a series of wooden blocks of cross-section equal to that of the boxes required. Take such a block (Figs. 46–51) and as many sheets of bond paper of the dimensions shown in

block (Fig. 51). It is well to have a series of these blocks made both in square and rectangular shapes. An additional advantage of this type of box is that one can put the data about the block on the flaps. Boxes cannot be made by this method much larger than $1'' \times \frac{1}{2}''$.

Some people prefer to cast a series of rectangular boxes from plaster of Paris. This can be done by any competent craftsman, but will not be described at this point.

After the box has been prepared we come to the actual process of embedding which is shown in detail in Figs. 52–55. Before starting it is necessary to make sure that the following items are available: (1) a dish of water of sufficient size that the finished block may be immersed in it (in the illustration an ordinary laboratory fingerbowl is in use); (2) some form of heat, an alcohol lamp being just as effective as a bunsen burner; (3) a slab of plate glass; (4) a wide-mouth, eye-dropper type pipet. It is presumed that the object itself is in the oven, which also contains a supply of molten medium. It must be emphasized that an object cannot successfully be impregnated with one kind of wax and embedded in another. Next wet the *underside* of the bottom of the paper box and press it into contact with the plate-glass slab. Then take from the oven (Fig. 52) a beaker of molten embedding material and fill the little paper box to the brim. The eye dropper is then heated in the flame to a temperature well above that at which the wax will melt, and is used to pick up the object from its own dish (Fig. 53) and to transfer it to the paper box. By the time this has been done, a layer of hardened wax will have been formed at the bottom of the paper box, so that the object will rest on the layer of solidified wax with a molten layer above. It will almost invariably happen that the surface has also cooled, so that a crust of cool wax will have been carried down with the object in the box. It is essential to get rid of this if the wax is to adhere through section cutting, and the pipet is again heated, used to melt the entire surface of the wax (Fig. 54), and to maneuver the object into the approximate position in which it is required to lie in the finished block. Then blow on the surface until the wax is sufficiently solidified to enable you to pick up the box carefully and (as shown in Fig. 55) to hold it on the surface of the water used for cooling. With most wax media it is desirable to cool the block as rapidly as possible; it should never be permitted to cool in air. It cannot, however, be pushed under the surface of the water, or the molten center is liable to break through the surface crust and thus destroy the block. After it has been held in the position indicated until it is fairly firm throughout, it may be pushed under the surface to complete the cooling.

The block may be left in water for any reasonable length of time; but if it is to be stored for days or weeks it is better kept in a 5% solution of glycerol in 70% alcohol. There seems to be a widespread delusion that because an object must be perfectly dehydrated before being impregnated with wax, it must subsequently be kept out of contact with fluids. Nothing could be further from the truth. As will be discussed later, when dealing with the actual technique of sectioning, it is often desirable to expose a portion of the object to be sectioned and leave it under the surface of water for some days, in order to get rid of the brittleness which has been imparted through the embedding process. Blocks which have been stored dry for a long period of time should always be soaked in a glycerol-alcohol mixture for at least a day before sectioning.

It is, in any case, undesirable to section a block as soon as it has been made, for it is necessary for successful sectioning that the block should be the same temperature throughout. If a block is made in the evening, it is better to take it out of the water and to leave it lying on the bench overnight in order that the temperature may be stabilized. Assuming, however, that we have such a block at hand, the next thing to do is to mount it in whatever holder is to be used.

Choice of a Microtome

Microtomes may be broadly divided into two classes. In the first of these the block remains stationary while the knife is moved past it; in the second group are those in which the block moves past a stationary knife. The first class (an example is shown in Fig. 56) is made by several manufacturers but is rarely used for the preparation of serial sections. They have the advantage that relatively large blocks may be cut, but they have the disadvantage that no ribbon can be obtained which is broader than the width of the knife. This microtome will not be discussed further in the present place, for a detailed description of its use is given in the next chapter on nitrocellulose sections, with which this type of microtome is often to be preferred.

A Minot, or rotary microtome, is shown in Fig. 57. In this type of microtome the rotation of the large wheel causes the block holder to move vertically up and down, in most instances through a distance of about three inches. The portion

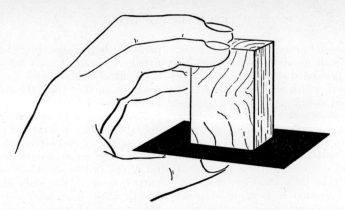

Fig. 46. Folding a paper box. *a. The block is centered on the sheet.*

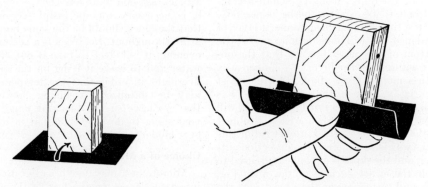

Fig. 47. Folding a paper box—(*continued*). *b. The sides are folded up.*

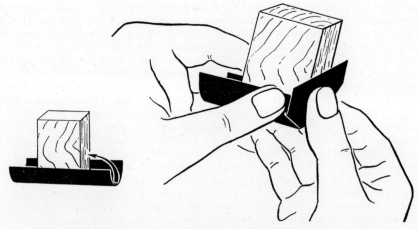

Fig. 48. Folding a paper box—(*continued*). *c. The end is folded up.*

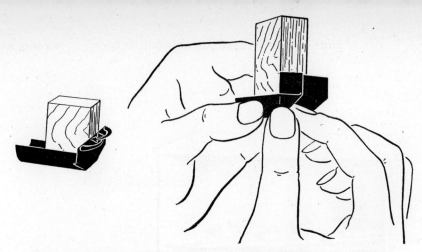

Fig. 49. Folding a paper box—(*continued*). *d. The flaps are folded in.*

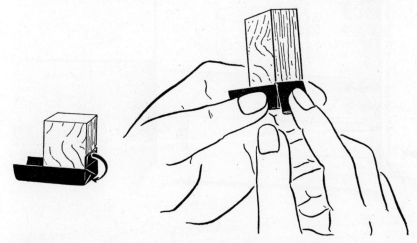

Fig. 50. Folding a paper box—(*continued*). *e. The end is folded down and creased.*

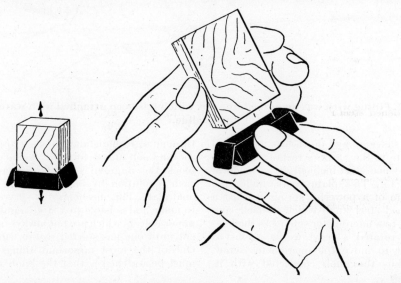

Fig. 51. Folding a paper box—(*continued*). *f. The cycle is repeated with the other end and the finished box removed.*

Fig. 52. Filling with wax an embedding box which has been attached with water to a glass slide.

which slides up and down has, at the end opposite to the block, a rectangular plate of hardened steel inclined at an angle of about 45°. This plate bears, under the pressure of a powerful spring, against a hardened steel knob which is itself connected to a micrometer screw. As the handle is rotated a pawl works against a ratchet to move the micrometer screw, and thus the knob connected with it, through a given distance for each rotation. As the knob moves forward, it moves the block the required distance forward at each revolution by bearing on the diagonal plate. This mechanism is very costly to make and is liable to a large number of minor defects which are not always apparent until one has started section cutting. One of the most important things that must be watched is that the knob which

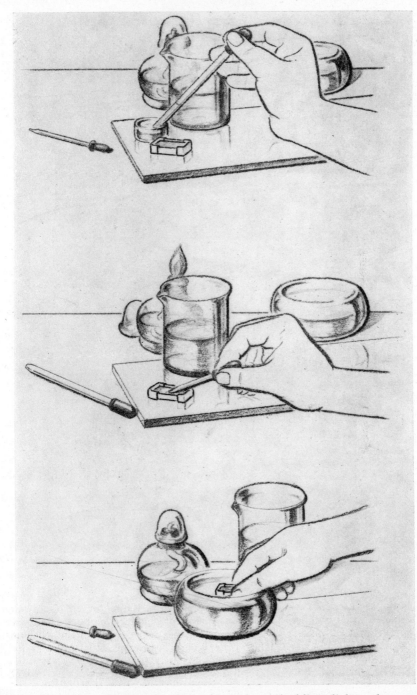

Fig. 53. (Top) Transferring the object from the embedding dish to the wax-filled paper box.

Fig. 54. (Middle) Remelting the wax around the object with a heated pipette.

Fig. 55. (Bottom) Cooling the wax block.

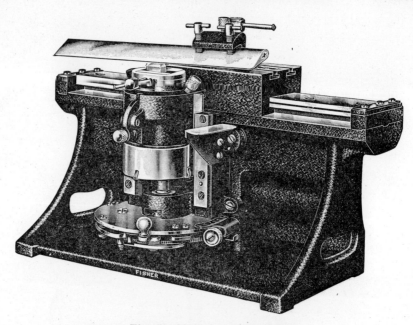

Fig. 56. Sliding microtome.

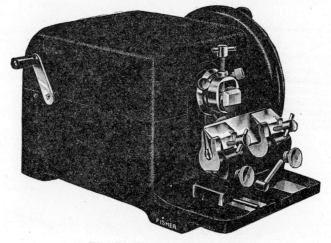

Fig. 57. Rotary microtome.

controls the section thickness must be so moved that an exact number of microns is indicated. If, for example, the knob is so moved that the indicator line lies between 9 and 10 microns, the pawl will not engage the ratchet perfectly but will chip off a small portion of brass at each revolution. It only requires a few weeks' operation under these careless conditions to destroy the ratchet wheel which will have to be replaced at the factory. No inexperienced student should ever be trusted with one of these machines until the mechanism of it has been explained to him and clearly demonstrated.

Knives and Knife Sharpening

The most important single factor in the production of good sections is the knife used in cutting. It does not matter how

much care has been taken in the preparation of the block or how complex a microtome is used, if the knife-edge is not perfect there is no chance of securing a perfect
section. Ordinary razors are not satisfactory for the production of fine sections,
and it is necessary to secure a microtome
knife, preferably from the manufacturer
of the microtome. Another type of microtome knife employs the edge of a safety-
razor blade in a special holder; these do
not, in the writer's hands, give such good
results as a solid blade.

Three types of solid blade are available:
first those which are *square-ground*, that
is, in which the main portion of the knife
is a straight wedge; second, those which
are hollow-ground, that is, in which both
sides of the knife have been ground away
to a concave surface, which results in a
relatively long region of thin metal towards the edge; third, knives which are
half-ground, that is, knives of which one
side is square- or flat-ground and the other
side hollow-ground. This last type of knife,
which the writer prefers, is a compromise.
There is no doubt that a square-ground
knife is sturdier than a hollow-ground
knife, a point of some importance when
cutting large areas of relatively hard tissues; but there is equally no doubt that a
hollow-ground knife can be brought more
readily to a fine edge. Microtome knives
must be sharpened frequently; but it is
necessary, before discussing how to do
this, to give a clear understanding of the
nature of the cutting edge itself.

If a wedge of hardened steel were to be
ground continuously to a fine edge, as in
Fig. 58, it would be utterly worthless for
cutting. After only a few strokes the fine
feather-edge, which would be produced by
this type of grinding, would break down
into a series of jagged saw teeth. A microtome knife, or for that matter any other
cutting tool, requires to have ground on
its cutting edge a facet of a relatively ob-
tuse angle, whether it be a square-ground
knife, as in Fig. 59, or a hollow-ground
knife as Fig. 60. The process of applying
this cutting facet to the tip is known as
setting; it is an exceedingly difficult operation to conduct, but one which must be
learned by every user of a microtome

knife. The actual grinding of the blade
itself to the correct angle, or to the correct
degree of hollowness, cannot be done in a
laboratory; the knife must be returned to
the manufacturer or to some scientific supply house adequately equipped with the
special machinery necessary. The cutting
facet, however, must be set at least once
a day if the blade is in continuous use.
The nature and purpose of this cutting
facet is best explained by reference to the
mechanism of cutting shown in Fig. 61.
Notice first that the knife blade itself
must be inclined at such an angle to the
block that the cutting facet is not quite
parallel to the face of the block. There
must be left a *clearance angle* to prevent
the knife from scraping the surface every
time that it removes a section. This clearance angle should, in cutting wax, be as
little as possible, and it is for this reason
that the blade holder of a microtome is
furnished with a device for setting the
knife angle. The knife angle should not be
set with reference to any theoretical consideration, but with regard only to securing this small clearance angle. The only
way to judge whether or not a satisfactory
clearance angle has been obtained is to
observe the sections as they come from
the knife. If the clearance angle is too
large, so that the section is not being cut
from the block but is being scraped from
it, the section will have a wrinkled appearance and will also usually roll up into a
small cylinder. If the clearance angle is too
small, so that the lower angle of the facet
is scraping the block after the tip has
passed, the whole ribbon of sections will
be picked up on the top of the block, which
will itself crack off when the knife point
reaches it. It is obvious that the knife
angle will be changed as the angle of
the cutting facet is changed, so that it
is desirable to maintain the cutting facet
of as uniform an angle as possible. This
angle is set onto the knife in the manner shown in Fig. 62. Notice that the knife
has been furnished with a handle and also
that a small split cylinder of steel has been
slipped over the back of the blade. This
split cylinder rests flat on the stone, as
does the edge of the blade, so that when
the knife is pushed forward (the figure

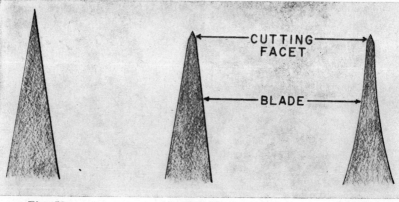

Fig. 58   Fig. 59   Fig. 60

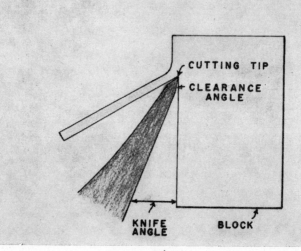

Fig. 61

Fig. 58. Knife ground as simple wedge without cutting facet.
Fig. 59. Flat ground knife showing cutting facet.
Fig. 60. Hollow ground knife showing cutting facet.
Fig. 61. Cutting action of knife on wax block.

shows it at the beginning of the stroke) the cutting facet is produced as the angle between the cutting edge lying on the stone and the enlarged temporary back which has been placed on the knife. Since a much blunter cutting facet is required for hard materials than for soft, it is strongly to be recommended that either two knives, or at least two sharpening backs, be secured. It does not matter what kind of stone is used for sharpening provided that it is of the finest obtainable grit, that it is dead flat, and that under no circumstancs whatever is it used for any purpose except the sharpening of microtome knives. It does not matter whether it be a *water stone*, to be lubricated with soap and water like the yellow Belgian stones commonly employed in Europe, or an *oilstone*, to be lubricated with mineral oil like the *pike* stones so commonly employed in the United States. It does matter, however, that it should be flooded with lubricant before starting, and that the knife should be drawn with a light pressure (notice that the finger is *behind* and *not* on top of the knife in the illustration) the entire length of the stone at each

itself. If the knife-edge is nicked to a deeper extent than about a quarter of a millimeter, the only thing to do is either to return the knife to the manufacturer to be reground, or try to avoid that portion of the blade containing the nick when cutting sections. It must be emphasized that the only purpose of setting is to produce a cutting facet, and that grinding, which cannot be done in the ordinary laboratory, is required for the removal of knife imperfections.

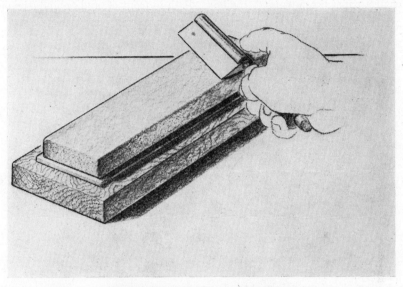

Fig. 62. Setting the cutting facet.

operation. If only the central portion of the stone is used, it soon becomes hollowed out and it thus becomes impossible to maintain a uniform angle. About three strokes on each side of the knife are quite enough to produce a perfectly sharp cutting facet; to continue beyond three strokes will have no effect other than to diminish the length of life of the knife.

This direction for the use of three strokes in setting applies, of course, only to knives which have been reasonably treated and not to those which through carelessness have acquired a nick in their edge. Where the nick is large it is almost impossible to remove it in setting, for the continual repetition of setting merely grinds away the edge of the knife and ultimately alters the thickness of the blade

The next question to arise is that of *stropping* the blade of the knife by pulling it backward across a leather surface in the manner shown in Fig. 63. If the knife has been set properly, stropping (the only purpose of which is to polish the facet) is quite unnecessary. The nature of the leather surface which is used for stropping makes it obviously impossible to pull the knife blade forward and there is a grave risk in pulling it backward, lest the facet, instead of becoming polished on its flat surfaces, will become rounded on its edges, and thus the work of setting be undone. Certainly no beginner should be permitted to use a strop until he has demonstrated his ability to set a knife-edge to the point where it will cut an excellent section without stropping. It is also strongly recommended to the beginner that he should examine the edge of a knife under the low power of a microscope before setting, after setting, and after stropping.

Mounting the Block

The knife being sharpened and the microtome selected, it now remains to trim the block to the correct shape and to attach it to the object holder of the microtome. The rough block of wax containing the object must be first removed from the mold or, if a paper box was used, the box

and it is essential that these should be exactly parallel to each other. A skilled microtomist can cut these edges parallel with a safety-razor blade without very much difficulty, but numerous devices have been described from time to time in the literature to enable one to do this mechanically. It does not matter if these two edges are exactly parallel with the plane of the object; it is only essential that they be parallel with each other. At this stage plenty of wax should be left both in front of, and behind, the object.

Fig. 63. Stropping a microtome knife.

cut away roughly with a knife. The block should now be held against a light so that the outlines of the contained object can be clearly seen. The block is then trimmed until the object lies in the center of a perfect rectangle, with the major axis of the object exactly parallel to the long sides. This is best achieved by finding first the major axis, at right angles to which the sections are to be cut, and trimming down one side of the block with a sharp safety-razor blade, taking off only a little wax at a time. If one tries to remove a large quantity of wax there is danger of cracking the block. When one side has been shaved to a flat surface, the other side is shaved parallel to it. The top and bottom surfaces of the block may now be shaved,

This trimmed block has now to be attached to some holder which can itself be inserted into the microtome. Since the majority of sections today are cut on a Spencer rotary microtome, we will describe the use of one of the holders supplied with this machine, though the ingenuity of man has not yet succeeded in devising a worse method of attaching a paraffin block to a microtome. The holder, which is seen in Fig. 64, consists of a disk of metal with a roughened surface attached to a cylindrical shank. This disk must first of all be covered with a layer of wax and it is extraordinarily difficult to get wax to adhere to these chromium-plated surfaces. If the worker is not entirely bound by convention, it would be much better for him to secure a series of small rectangular blocks of some hard wood like maple and to soak these for a day or two in molten wax. After they are removed, drained, and cooled it is the simplest thing in the world to attach a paraffin block to them and to hold them in the jaws of the microtome. Whether the metal holder or the wooden one are used, the technique is essentially the same. A layer bring these buttresses so far up the block that they reach the tip of the object to be cut. The metal should now be placed on one side and allowed to reach room temperature. Many people at this point throw the block and holder into a fingerbowl of water, which is all right provided the water is at room temperature. But there is no more fruitful source of trouble in cutting sections than to have the knife, the

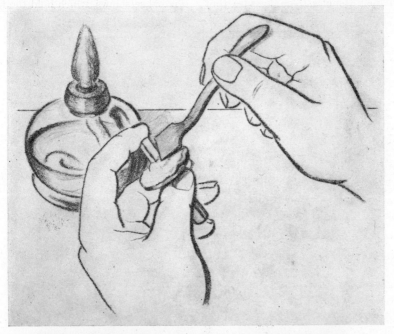

Fig. 64. Mounting the wax block on the block holder.

of molten wax is built up on the surface and allowed to cool. The block (see Fig. 64) is then pressed lightly onto this hardened wax and fused with it with the aid of a piece of heated metal. Some people use old scalpels but the writer prefers the homemade brass tool shown in the figure. Care must be taken to press only very lightly with the forefinger and to perform the whole operation as speedily as possible to avoid softening the wax in which the object is embedded. The metal tool should be heated to a relatively high temperature and touched lightly to the base of the block. If the block is very long, it is also desirable to build up small buttresses of wax against each side, being careful not to block, and the microtome at different temperatures. It is much better to mount the blocks the day before one intends to cut them and to leave them on the bench to await treatment. A final inspection is then made of the block to make certain that its upper and lower surfaces are flat, smooth, and parallel. Many people do not make the final cuts on these surfaces until after the block has been mounted in the block holder. The block and the block holder, after insertion in the jaws of the microtome, are seen in Fig. 65 and it will be noticed that setscrews on the apparatus permit universal motion to be imparted to the block so that it can be correctly orientated in relation to the knife. It is easy to discover whether or not the edges are parallel by lowering the block until it does not quite touch the edge of the knife, adjusting it until the lower edge is parallel, then lowering the block again and comparing the relation of the upper edge with the edge of the knife.

Cutting Paraffin Ribbons

The first step in cutting sections on this type of microtome is to make sure that

causes the two movable holding arms to hold the knife near its edge. The knife is now held in a pair of hemicylinders which may be moved so as to adjust the knife angle (see Fig. 61). The knife should be set at that angle which experience has shown to be desirable—no guide other than experience can be used—and the two setscrews which lock these inclinable hemicylinders in place then tightened. The two original setscrews, which hold the knife in

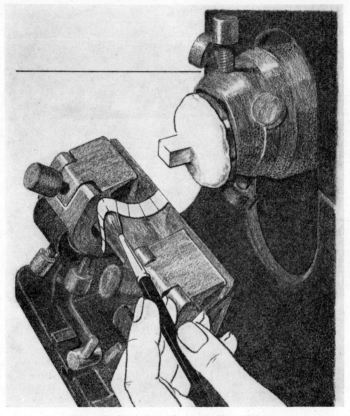

Fig. 65. Starting the paraffin ribbon.

every one of the setscrews seen in Fig. 65 is fully tight. The setscrews holding the block holder may be tightened in any order, provided that the result leaves the block correctly orientated, but those connected with the knife must be done in the correct order. First the knife is inserted into the holder and fixed firmly, but not tightly, in place by the two bearings at each end. The tightening of these screws

place, are now screwed up as tightly as the thumb can bear. This leaves two setscrews which come through the inclinable hemicylinders and bear on the bottom edge of the knife. These two setscrews should then be tightened simultaneously and uniformly. The effect of this is to force the knife upward and thus wedge it with extreme firmness in the knife holder.

Now that everything is tight the handle

on the back of the microtome is turned until the block is as far back as possible, and the entire knife is moved on its carriage until the edge of the blade is about ¼ inch in front of the block. A last-minute check is now made to make sure that the divisions of the setting device exactly coincide with the thickness desired; then the handle is rapidly rotated until the block

in the left hand, is slipped under the ribbon which is then raised in the manner shown in Fig. 65. Care should be taken that a few sections always remain in contact with the blade of the knife, for if the ribbon is lifted till only the edge of the section lies on the edge of the knife, the ribbon will usually break. As the handle is turned, the brush in the left

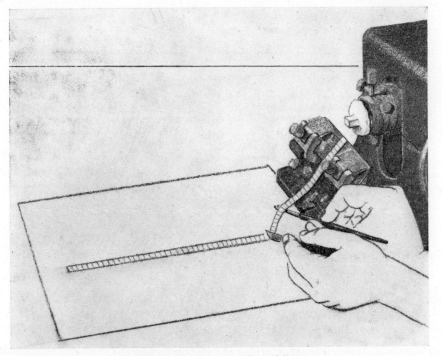

Fig. 66. Laying out the ribbon.

starts cutting. The front face will rarely be parallel to the blade of the knife, therefore a considerable number of sections will have to be cut until the entire width of the block is coming against the knife. No particular attention need be paid to the quality of this initial ribbon, which may be thrown away.

We will assume that all is going well and that the ribbon is coming off in a perfect condition; if it is not, refer to Table 1. The remaining operations of preparing and mounting the ribbon are far more clearly seen in illustration than by description. As soon as the ribbon is the width of the knife in length a dry soft brush, held

hand is moved away until the ribbon is the same length as the sheet of paper on which it is to be received. Legal size (foolscap) paper is quite commonly employed and is shown in Fig. 66. Notice that the left-hand edge of the ribbon has been laid flat some distance from the edge of the paper and that a loop, sufficiently large to avoid strain on the ribbon attached to the knife, is retained with the brush, while the ribbon is cut with a rocking motion with an ordinary scalpel or cartilage knife. The larger and colder this scalpel is, the less likelihood there will be of the section adhering to it. The purpose of leaving a good margin around the edge of the paper is that it may be desirable to interrupt ribbon cutting for some time and to continue later. In this case the worker should furnish himself with a little glass-topped frame which is laid over the paper to prevent the sections from being blown about. As the inexperienced worker will soon find out, the least draft of air, particularly the explosive draft occasioned by some

not be cut up until a sample has been flattened on a slide in order to determine the degree of expansion. Though the sections shown in the illustration are being mounted on an ordinary $3'' \times 1''$ slide, it would be more practical (for a ribbon as wide as this) to use a $3'' \times 1\frac{1}{2}''$ or even a $3'' \times 2''$ slide. The sections should never occupy the whole area of the slide,

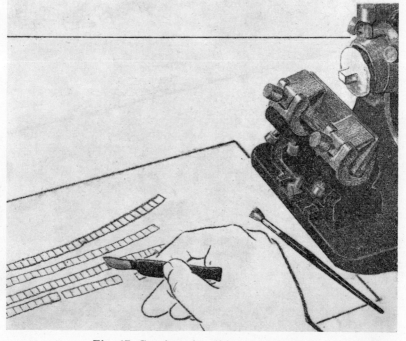

Fig. 67. Cutting the ribbon in lengths.

fool opening the door, is quite sufficient to scatter the ribbons all over the room. These operations of carrying the ribbon out with the left hand, transferring the brush to the right hand, and cutting the ribbon off, are continued until the whole of the required portion of the block has been cut and lies on the paper.

The ribbon must then be divided into suitable lengths for mounting on a slide (Fig. 67). Though in theory a section should be of the same size as the block from which it came, this practically never occurs in practice and it is usually safe to allow at least ten and sometimes twenty per cent for expansion when the sections are finally flattened. The ribbon should

but at least $\frac{1}{4}$ of an inch should be left at one end for subsequent labeling. When the decision has been made as to how many sections shall be left in each segment of ribbon, the first row of ribbons is then cut into the required lengths (Fig. 67). Then the worker must decide what shall be used to make them adhere to the slide. It is conventional to use the albumen adhesive of Mayer 1880 (Chapter 28, V 21.1), and to apply a thin smear of this on a clean slide with the tip of the little finger. The author prefers to dilute the selected adhesive two or three hundredfold with water, and to use this dilute adhesive in the next operation of flattening the sections.

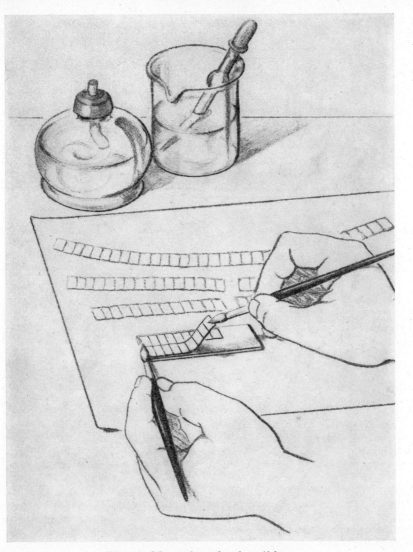

Fig. 68. Mounting the dry ribbon.

It will have been apparent to the worker from the moment that he started cutting the sections that they are not absolutely flat. They may be slightly crinkled, or slightly distorted, and must be flattened by being warmed on water heated just below the melting point of the wax. Some people place this water on the slide and then add the sections to it, but the writer prefers to lay the ribbons on the slide as shown in Fig. 68. This is not nearly so easy as it looks. Two brushes must be moistened with the tongue just enough to bring the hairs to a point. The two moist points are then delicately touched down (too much pressure will cause the ribbon to adhere to the paper) on each end of the selected piece of section. This piece is then lifted as shown in the illustration and placed on the slide. When a sufficient number have been accumulated the slide is then picked up carefully, reversed, and laid on top of the last three fingers of the left hand as shown in Fig. 69.

It is fatal to grasp the slide by the sides; if this is done, when the water is flooded on from the pipet, the meniscus coming to the edge of the slides will break against the fingers, to which the sections will permanently adhere. The technique shown is quite safe and the water containing the adhesive (if none has been applied to the slide) is then flooded on from a pipet in

tened, the slide is gently tilted backward towards the hand so as to run off the excess water against the thumb, leaving the sections stranded in place. The slide is now usually placed on a thermostatically controlled hot plate (seen at the back of Fig. 78) and dried. Most people leave their slides overnight but frequently an hour would be sufficient. Dryness can be

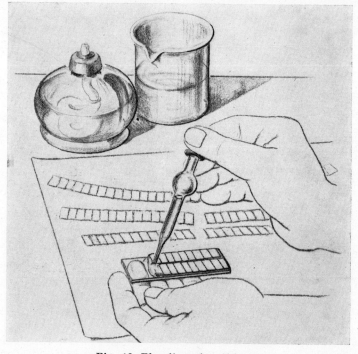

Fig. 69. Flooding the ribbons.

the manner shown. Enough fluid should be applied to raise a sharp meniscus at the edge of the slide.

The sections must now be flattened, and this is better done rapidly with a flame than slowly on a hot plate. Fig. 70 shows the slide being held over a small alcohol lamp, but a micro-bunsen can be employed equally well. The slide should be exposed to heat for a moment, withdrawn to give time for the heat to pass from the glass to the fluid, warmed again, and so on, until the sections are observed to be flat. The utmost care must be taken at this point for, if the paraffin is permitted to melt, the sections will not stick to the glass. As soon as the sections are flat-

gauged without the least trouble by the fact that a moist slide shows the wax to be more or less opalescent, while on a properly dried slide it is almost glass-clear.

The method just described is susceptible of several variations which may be briefly noticed. Some people do not drain the water from the slide, nor do they heat the slide over the lamp; they merely place the slide, as soon as the water has been added to it, on the thermostatically controlled hot plate so that the sections dry and flatten at the same time. The objection to this procedure is that dissolved air in the water used for flattening usually comes out in the form of bubbles which accumulate under the section, either causing it to fall off or at least making it very difficult to observe properly when mounted. There is also the risk in this procedure that the water will not stop at the edge of the slide, but will unexpectedly flood off, carrying the sections with it onto the surface of the hot plate.

Another procedure, frequently used by the author but not recommended for the inexperienced, is to blot the sections before putting them on the hot plate. A *water-saturated* piece of *coarse* filter paper

appearance, cause, and cure of the more common defects are shown in the pages which follow. These are by no means the only defects or the only cures which may be applied. Every user of the microtome should have in his hands a copy of Richards 1949, which lists many suggestions beyond those here given.

Staining and Mounting Sections

Assuming that all difficulties have been overcome, and that one now has a series of

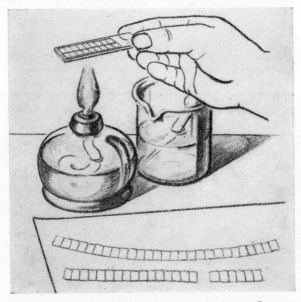

Fig. 70. Warming the flooded ribbons in order to flatten them.

is placed on the drained slide and pressed hard with a rubber roller, which squeezes much of the water out of both the paper and the sections. This makes sure that the sections are perfectly flattened in contact with the slide, but requires a strong nerve to try for the first time, because most people fear that the sections will stick to the paper. This has never happened in a good many thousands of slides which the author has made by this means. Slides so prepared are always free of air bubbles.

Before proceeding to a discussion of the next steps to be taken, it may be as well to revert to the moment when section cutting started, and to discuss the innumerable things that may happen, other than the production of a perfect ribbon. The

slides bearing consecutive ribbons, the paraffin must next be removed in order that the sections may be stained. It is conventional, though probably not necessary, to warm each slide over a flame (holding it as shown in Fig. 70) until the paraffin is molten. The slide is then dropped (as shown in Fig. 78) into a jar containing xylene, benzene, or some other suitable paraffin solvent. The jars shown in this figure are of the type known as *coplin jars*, which are usually employed when a relatively small number of $1'' \times 3''$ slides are to be handled. Larger numbers of small slides are more conveniently handled by being placed in racks, which may be moved from one rectangular jar to another. Individual slides may, of course, be handled in a coplin jar, but it is more convenient for these to have an ordinary round specimen tube, or vial, of just over 1-inch diameter, which maintains a single slide in an upright position without the necessity of using the relatively large quantities of fluid involved in a coplin-jar set. Coplin jars are not available for slides larger than 3″ by 1″; for these one is forced to use the rectangular jars.

It is necessary through the subsequent proceedings to be able to recognize instantly on which side of the slide the section lies. This is not nearly as easy as it

sounds; a lot of good slides have been lost by having the sections rubbed off. The simplest thing to do is to incline the slide at such an angle to the light that, if the section is on top, a reflection of the section is seen on the lower side of the slide. A diamond scratch placed in the corner is of little use because it becomes invisible when the slide is in xylene. The greatest care should be taken to remove the whole of the wax from the slide before proceeding further. It is usually a wise precaution to have two successive jars of xylene, passing the second jar to the position of the

Table 1

DEFECTS APPEARING IN RIBBONS WHILE BEING CUT

Fig. 71. Ribbon curved.

Possible Causes

1. Edges of block not parallel

2. Knife not uniformly sharp, causing more compression on one side of block than other

3. One side of block warmer than other

Remedies

1. Trim block

2. Try another portion of knife-edge or resharpen knife

3. Let block cool. Check possible causes of heating or cooling, such as lamps or drafts

Fig. 72. Sections compressed.

Possible Causes

1. Knife blunt

2. Wax too soft at room temperature for sections of thickness required

3. Wax warmer than room temperature

Remedies

1. Try another portion of knife-edge or resharpen knife. Compression often occurs through a rounded cutting facet (see Fig. 60) produced by overstropping

2. Re-embed in suitable wax or cut thicker sections. Cooling block is rarely successful

3. Cool block to room temperature

Table 1—(*Continued*)

Fig. 73. Sections alternately thick and thin, usually with compression of thin sections.

Fig. 74. Sections bulge in middle.

Possible Causes

1. Block, or wax holding block to holder, still warm from mounting
2. Block, or wax holding block to holder, cracked or loose
3. Knife loose
4. Knife cracked
5. Microtome faulty

Remedies

1. Cool block and holder to room temperature
2. Check all holding screws, Remove block from holder and holder from microtome. Melt wax off holder and make sure holder is dry. Re-coat holder and remount block. Cool to room temperature
3. Release all holding screws and check for dirt, grit, or soft wax. Check knife carriage for wax chips on bearing
4. Throw knife away
5. Return microtome to maker for overhaul

Possible Causes

1. Wax cool in center, warm on outside
2. Only sharp portion of knife is that which cuts center of block
3. Object impregnated with hard wax and embedded in soft, or some clearing agent remains in object

Remedies

1. Let block adjust to room temperature. This is the frequent result of cooling blocks in ice water
2. Try another portion of knife-edge or resharpen knife
3. Re-embed object

Table 1—(*Continued*)

Fig. 75. Object breaks away from wax or is shattered by knife.

Fig. 76. Ribbon splits.

Possible Causes

1. If object appears chalky and shatters under knife blade, it is not impregnated

2. If object shatters under knife but is not chalky, it is too hard for wax sectioning

3. If object pulls away from wax but does not shatter, the wrong dehydrant, clearing agent, or wax has been used

Possible Causes

1. Nick in blade of knife
2. Grit in object

Remedies

1. Throw block away and start again. If object irreplaceable, try dissolving off wax, redehydrating, reclearing and re-embedding

2. Soak block overnight in phenoglycerol mixture, rinse thoroughly, and dry, or spray section between each cut with celloidin, or dissolve wax and re-embed in nitrocellulose

3. Re-embed in suitable medium, preferably a wax-rubber-resin mixture. Avoid xylene in clearing muscular structures

Remedies

1. Try another portion of knife-edge

2. Examine cut edge of block. If face is grooved to top, grit has probably been pushed out. Try another portion of knife-edge. If grit still in place, dissect out with needles. If much grit, throw block away

Table 1—(*Continued*)

Fig. 77. Block lifts ribbon.

Possible Causes	Remedies
1. Ribbon electrified. (Check by testing whether or not ribbon sticks to everything else)	1. Increase room humidity. Ionize air, either with high frequency discharge or bunsen flame a short distance from knife
2. No clearance angle (see Fig. 60)	
3. Upper edge of block has fragments of wax on it (a common result of 2)	2. Alter knife angle to give clearance angle
4. Edge of knife (either front or back) has fragments of wax on it	3. Scrape upper surface of block with safety-razor blade
	4. Clean knife with xylene

No ribbon forms

Defect	Possible Causes
(1) Because wax crumbles	1. Wax contaminated with clearing agent
(2) Because sections, though individually perfect, do not adhere	2. Very hard, pure paraffin used for embedding
(3) Because sections roll into cylinders	3a. Wax too hard at room temperature for sections of thickness required
	3b. Knife angle wrong

Remedies

1. Re-embed. (*Note:* Wax very readily absorbs hydrocarbon vapors)
2. Dip block in soft wax or wax-rubber medium. Trim off sides before cutting
3a. Re-embed in suitable wax. If the section is cut very slowly, and the edge of the section held flat with a brush, ribbons may sometimes be formed
3b. Adjust knife angle

first, and replacing it with fresh xylene, after about ten or a dozen slides have passed through. It must be remembered that paraffin is insoluble in the alcohol which is used to remove the xylene, so that it is no use soaking a slide in a solution of xylene in wax and imagining that it will be sufficiently free from wax for subsequent staining. Some people go further than this and have the first two jars containing xylene, and then a third containing a mixture of equal parts of absolute alcohol and xylene, to make sure that the whole of the wax is removed. If even a small trace of wax remains, it will prevent the penetration of stains. Assuming that one is proceeding along the classic xylene-alcohol series, the slide is transferred from either the fresh xylene or the xylene-absolute-alcohol mixture, to a coplin jar of absolute alcohol. It is unfortunate that nobody seems yet to have placed on the market a coplin jar, or slide-staining dish, the lid of which is satisfactorily ground into position so that absolute alcohol,

soon, however, as the slide has been in water long enough to remove the alcohol, it should be withdrawn and examined carefully to make sure that it has been sufficiently dewaxed. If the water flows freely over the whole surface, including the sections, it is safe to proceed to staining by what ever manner is desired. If, however, the sections appear to repel the water, or if there is even a meniscus formed round the edge of the section, it is an indication that the wax has not been removed, and that the slide must again be

Fig. 78. Starting a slide through the reagent series.

which is very hygroscopic, remains uncontaminated. It does not matter if xylene is carried over into the absolute alcohol, but as soon as the first trace of a white flocculent precipitate appears in the alcohol—indicating that some wax is being carried over—the alcohol must be replaced.

The writer never bothers to use a series of graded alcohols between absolute alcohol and water. These graded series are necessary, of course, when one is dealing with the dehydration of whole objects which may be distorted, but the author has never been able to find the slightest difference between thin sections which have been passed from absolute alcohol to water, and those which have laboriously been downgraded through a series. As

dehydrated in absolute alcohol, passed back into a xylene-alcohol mixture, and thence again into pure xylene.

In the specific examples which conclude this chapter, and in numerous places throughout Chapters 20, 21, and 23, descriptions are given of individual staining methods. The purpose of this chapter is to discuss only the general principles involved in the preparation of paraffin sections, so that we may presume the section to have been already stained and returned (through such dehydrants as are specified in the method used) to xylene, and to be ready for mounting.

It is again assumed that the section will be mounted in one of the resinous media described in Chapter 26 (M 30), and

Canada balsam is so conventional that it may be taken as an example. The slide is removed from the xylene and drained (Fig. 78) and then placed on any convenient flat surface. A drop of the mountant is then placed on the surface of the sections. A coverslip of suitable size (Fig. 79) is then held at an inclined angle with a bent needle and slowly lowered so as to exclude all air bubbles. The edges of the slide are then roughly wiped and it is returned to the hot table shown in Fig. 78 to evaporate the solvent used for the resin. Though

This custom of evaporating the solvents from the surface of the slide rather than from the edge of the coverslip is nowadays considered old-fashioned; but there is no doubt that it produces a better and more durable slide than does the more usual procedure.

One very common accident, which may occur in the course of staining or dewaxing a slide, is that the individual sections show signs of becoming detached, either through not having been perfectly in contact with the slide when dried, or through having

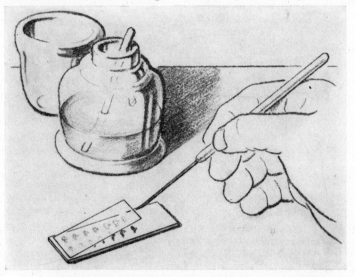

Fig. 79. Placing the coverslip on serial section slide.

this is the conventional method of operation it is by no means always the best. In particular there is a tendency to have a higher concentration of solvent along the edges of the coverslip than in the center, and it also takes a surprisingly long time for the whole of the solvent to be removed. It is much better, if one can spare the time, to place a relatively thin coat of mounting medium on top of the slide and then to leave the solvent to evaporate from this on the surface of a hot plate. There is no risk that the slide will dry out, for the mountant will act as a varnish. On the next day the slide is examined and, if it appears to be sufficiently varnished, the coverslip is placed on the surface and warmed while maintaining steady pressure. The slide will then be hardened as soon as it is cooled and may be cleaned and put away.

been exposed to some reagent which has a solvent action on the adhesive. The effects of this unfortunate accident may be minimized by having always on hand a coplin jar of the solution of Claoué 1920 (Chapter 28, V 21.1). This is a most admirable lacquer into which the slide may be dipped rapidly and withdrawn. This transparent lacquer hardens readily in place and holds the section attached without seriously interfering with subsequent observation.

Cleaning and Labeling Slides

No slide can be considered complete until it has been properly labeled, cleaned, and stored. Failure to clean a slide can cause rather serious damage for, if unwanted portions of Canada balsam are left lying about close to the edges or on the surface, and if the slide be then used

Table 2

DEFECTS APPEARING IN SECTIONS DURING COURSE OF MOUNTING

Defect	Cause	Remedy	Method of prevention
Sections appear wrinkled	1. Blunt knife used for cutting	1. None	1. Sharpen knife and cut new sections
	2. Water used for flattening too hot, so that folds in sections fused into position	2. None	2. Watch temperature of water used for flattening
	3. Sections unable to expand sufficiently: (a) because water used for flattening too cold (b) because area of water too small	3. None	3(a) Watch temperature of water used for flattening (b) Make sure that slide is clean, so that water flows uniformly over it
Sections have bubbles under them	1. Sections insufficiently flattened, so that air is trapped	1. If sections still wet, reflood slide with water and reheat to complete flattening	1. Check flatness of sections before draining slide
	2. Air dissolved in water used for flattening has come out and is trapped under sections in drying	2. If sections still wet, reflood slide with water, work out bubbles, and reheat to complete flattening	2. Use air-free (boiled) water for flattening. Drain slide thoroughly and blot off excess moisture. Squeeze sections to slide
Sections fall off slide	1. Wax melted in flattening	1. None	1. Watch temperature of water used for flattening
	2. Slide greasy	2. None	2. Use clean slides
	3. Alkaline reagents dissolve albumen adhesive. (Sections start to work loose in course of staining or dehydrating)	3. Treat slides with Claoué's solution (Chapter 28, V 21.)	3. See Chapter 28, V 21 for other section adhesives not alkali-sensitive
	4. Sections not flattened into perfect contact with slide	4. None	4. Sometimes caused by swelling of sections which causes center to lift. Squeeze sections to slide and dry as rapidly as possible

with an oil-immersion lens, the oil will dissolve a portion of the balsam which will be found very difficult to remove either from the surface of the coverslip or from the front lens of the immersion objective. The slide cannot be cleaned until it is thoroughly dried and if it has been mounted in a solution of resin, it will require several days on a hot plate or weeks at room temperature before the solvent has been removed. When, however, it is finally dried, which is when the resin on the edge can be cracked, the surface resin should be removed carefully with a blunt knife and the slide left overnight. If on examination the freshly cut edge is then found to be sticky, it is evident that more solvent has moved out and that the slide

Table 3

DEFECTS APPEARING IN SECTIONS AFTER STAINING AND MOUNTING

Defect	Cause	Remedy	Method of Prevention
Sections distorted	1. Blunt knife and soft wax	1. None, though prolonged flattening on warm water may help	1. Use suitable knife and embedding medium
	2. Ribbon stretched when picked up on hot day	2. As (1) above	2. Handle ribbons in short lengths or use harder wax
	3. Tissues not properly hardened before embedding	3. None	3. Use more suitable fixative or fix longer. Take extra care in dehydrating, clearing, and embedding
Sections appear opaque or have highly refractive lines outlining cells and tissues	1. Clearing agent evaporated before mountant added	1. None	1. Obvious
	2. Sections insufficiently cleared or cleared in agent not miscible with mountant	2. Soak off cover. Clear properly	2. Check quality and nature of clearing agents and mountants
Sections will not take stain, or stain irregularly	1. Wax not perfectly removed before staining	1. Return sections through proper sequence of reagents to xylene. Leave until wax removed. Restain	1. Change first jar of xylene frequently
	2. Section not uniform thickness	2. None	2. See table 1
	3. Tissue "old" (has been stored for a long time in alcohol or, worse still, fixative)	3. Return sections through proper sequence of reagents to water. Wash overnight. If not effective try a "tissue reviver" (Chapter 22, ADS 11)	3. Store all tissues embedded in paraffin blocks—never liquids
	4. Fixative not suitable before staining technique employed	4. Try mordanting sections in recommended fixative	4. Obvious
	5. Fixative not fully removed	5. Consult Chapter 10, ADS 11	5. Treat tissues as indicated
Sections contain fine opaque needles or granules	1. Imperfect removal of mercuric fixatives	1. Return sections through proper sequence of reagents to water. Treat 30 min. with Lugol's iodine, rinse, and bleach in 5% sodium thiosulfate. Restain	1. Treat tissues as indicated in Chapter 10, ADS 11

Table 3—*(Continued)*

Defect	Cause	Remedy	Method of Prevention
	2. Long storage in formaldehyde	2. None	2. Never store tissues in formaldehyde— always in paraffin blocks

is not yet ready. If, however, the removal of the dried balsam leaves no sticky residue, it is necessary to provide two finger bowls: one of 90% alcohol and the second of a moderately strong solution of soap and water. The whole slide is then dipped in the 90% alcohol and rubbed briskly until the excess balsam is removed. It is *immediately* (to avoid softening the balsam) rinsed in the soap solution, and then polished.

If the slides are unsatisfactory, tables 2 and 3 above may help to locate the trouble.

When dealing with valuable series of sections it is always as well to write the serial number of the slide, and some indication of its nature, on the glass in diamond before attaching the label. Labels are constantly becoming detached from slides and it is well to have a permanent record underneath them. It has already been pointed out that no two people agree as to what label adhesive to use. The author would only reiterate the counsel he has given in previous chapters: that both

sides of the label be licked thoroughly, that it then be pressed into position on the slide, allowed to dry slowly, and the requisite information written with waterproof India ink.

The violent objections which the author has expressed in previous chapters to storing wholemounts in vertical grooved filing cabinets, do not, of course, apply to sections, since the section is attached to the slide and cannot drift through the mountant. Storing in grooved trays, which hold the slide vertically, is undoubtedly the simplest method of storing such sections, but much space can be saved if they are placed in pouches of ordinary indexing cards. If two 5 by 3 index cards be taken, and one be cut down to 5 by 2, the smaller may then be stapled to the first card in such a manner as to leave a pocket into which a slide may be inserted. The full data may then be written on the index card, and these two-card pockets bearing the slides can be accumulated in ordinary card-file drawers.

Typical Examples

THE PREPARATION OF A TRANSVERSE SECTION OF THE SMALL INTESTINE OF THE FROG STAINED WITH HEMATOXYLIN-EOSIN

This is the simplest example of paraffin sectioning which can be imagined, and it may well serve as an introduction to this type of technique, either for a class or for an individual. The intestine of a frog has been selected, owing to the usual availability of this form in laboratories; but any small animal may be substituted in its place.

Before killing the frog it is necessary to have on hand a selected fixative and, since this is intended to be an example of the ut-

most simplicity, it is suggested that the cupric-nitric-paranitrophenol mixture of Petrunkewitsch (Chapter 18 F 4900.0040 Petrunkewitsch 1933) be employed. This fixative is entirely foolproof: objects may remain in it for weeks without damage, and it also permits excellent afterstaining by almost any known technique. If only a piece of intestine is to be fixed, 100 milliliters of fixative will be sufficient; but there is no reason why any other organ in the animal (with the exception of the central nervous system) should not be preserved in this fluid for subsequent investigation.

The frog is killed by any convenient method, but it is usually best for histological purposes to sever a large blood vessel and permit as much blood as possible to drain out from the heart before opening the abdominal cavity and removing the intestine. One or more lengths of about ⅓ of an inch should then be cut from the intestine and transferred directly to fixative where they may remain from a few hours to several weeks.

When they are next required the specimens should be removed from fixative, washed in running water for a few hours, and then transferred directly to 70% alcohol. The easiest method of washing objects of this size in running water is to take one of the coplin jars previously described, to fill it with water, insert the specimen, and then to attach a cover of coarse cheesecloth with a rubber band. This is then placed in the sink and a narrow stream of water permitted to fall on it from the tap. It will be found that the specimen will swirl round and round in the jar in a most satisfactory manner. This simple device saves all the trouble of rigging up glass tubes and boring corks to make the cumbersome apparatus sometimes recommended for the purpose.

The specimen is transferred, after twenty-four hours in 70% alcohol, to 95% alcohol. It is better to use a large volume of alcohol and to suspend the object in it than to use relatively small volumes which have to be frequently changed. It is recommended that a wide-mouthed stoppered jar of about 500 milliliters capacity be fitted with a hook in the center of its stopper, from which the object can then be suspended. The majority of stoppers for wide-mouthed glass jars have a hollowed undersurface which may be filled with plaster of Paris, and a glass hook (which is very easily bent from thin glass rod) may be inserted in the liquid plaster. This must naturally be done some days beforehand, and the plaster must finally thoroughly be dried out in an oven before the jar is used for dehydrating. If the worker does not wish to go to this much trouble, it is also easy to screw a small metal "pot hook" into the under surface of a plastic screw cover for a jar of the same size. Alcohol is, however, so hygroscopic that it is better to employ a glass-stoppered jar, the stopper being greased with stopcock grease, or petrolatum, for a permanent setup. An object as coarse as the one under discussion may be suspended in a loop of thread or cotton directly from the hook; or if this is not desirable, it may be enclosed in a small fold of cheese cloth for suspension. After twenty-four hours in this volume of alcohol, the object will be completely penetrated, and should then be transferred to absolute alcohol using the same volume in a jar of similar construction. It is useful to place about a quarter-inch layer of anhydrous copper sulfate at the bottom of the absolute alcohol jar, not only to make sure that the alcohol is absolute, but also to indicate, as it changes to blue, when this jar should be removed from service. Of the many de-alcoholizing (clearing) agents which may be used, the writer would in the present case select benzene because it is less liable to harden the circular muscles of the intestine than is xylene. As benzene is lighter than an absolute alcohol, it is not possible to employ the hanging technique for clearing, and the object should be placed in about 25 milliliters of benzene which should be changed when diffusion currents are seen to have ceased to rise from the object. This will take about six hours for an object of the size under discussion and a second bath of at least six hours should also be given.

It is now necessary to select the medium in which embedding is to be done and the writer would recommend the rubber paraffin of Hance (Chapter 17—E 21.1 Hance 1933) which must, of course, have been prepared some time before. The melting point of this medium is about 56°C. so that an oven should be available which is thermostatically controlled at about 58°C. This oven should contain three stender dishes as well as a 500 cc beaker containing about a pound of the embedding medium. The object is removed from benzene, drained briefly on a piece of filter paper, and placed in one of the stender dishes which has been filled to the brim with the molten embedding medium. Under no circumstances should a lid be placed on the stender dish since it is desirable that as much as possible of the benzol should evaporate while the process of embedding is going on. After about an hour the specimen should be removed to fresh wax in the second stender dish, where it may remain another hour, and then to the third stender dish where it should not remain for more than thirty minutes.

Shortly before the end of this last hour a decision should be made as to what type of vessel is to be used for casting the block, and it would be difficult to improve on a paper box (Fig. 50) for this object. The box having been made (it should be of ample size) it is moistened at the bottom and placed on a slab of glass in the manner described earlier in this chapter. The box should be about half filled with embedding material from the beaker and allowed to remain until the layer of wax has congealed on the bottom. An object like the one under discussion is best handled with an old pair of forceps rather than with a pipet. The forceps should be warmed in a flame to well above the melting point of the wax, and moved backward and forward across the surface so as to melt the surface film which has formed. The object is then rapidly picked up from its stender dish, placed in the wax, and enough fresh wax from the beaker added to make sure that there will be as much solid wax above as there is underneath the specimen. Blocks of this nature shrink greatly, and it will probably be best to fill the box entirely full. As soon as the box has been filled, the forceps should again be warmed and passed backward and forward around the object to make sure that no film of unmolten wax (which would cause it consequently to cut badly) remains. The wax in its box should now be blown on until it starts to congeal on the surface, then very carefully picked up with the fingers and lowered into a dish of water at room temperature until the water does not quite reach the top of the box. If it be thrust under the surface at this point, all of the molten wax will come out and the block

be rendered useless. As soon, however, as the block is seen to be congealed throughout, it is thrust under the surface of the water and something laid on it to keep it at the bottom. It should be left in the water for at least five or six hours and much better overnight.

One now sets up the microtome, and makes sure that the knife is sharpened in the manner previously described, and then mounts the block. The block having been trimmed to size and mounted as noted earlier, there remains only the actual cutting. The block should be trimmed so there is at least as much wax on each side of the object as there is in object itself. This amount of wax would be excessive were we preparing serial sections, but for the preparation of individual sections of this type, in an example given for the benefit of the beginner, this quantity is desirable. The handle of the microtome should now be rapidly rotated and the beginnings of the sections observed. There is no need to worry if the section curls to one side or the other during this preliminary period, since the entire area of the block will not be cut until twenty or thirty sections have been removed. As soon, however, as the knife is seen to be approaching the object, and the block in its entirety is being cut, the ribbon must be observed most carefully to see that it is suffering from none of those defects indicated in the table of defects. Should the ribbon not be coming perfectly, various suggestions given in the table may be tried until a perfect ribbon is secured. Since we are not, in this case, preparing a series of sections, it is unnecessary to cut a longer ribbon than will contain the actual number of sections required, with a few left over for emergencies. It is, however, a great mistake to throw partially cut blocks away, since they may be stored in a glycerol-alcohol mixture quite indefinitely, and one never knows when further sections may be required. The block, however, should be labeled before being placed in its solution by writing the appropriate information on a piece of paper and fusing this with a hot needle into an unwanted portion of the block.

Each section is now cut individually

from the ribbon and mounted on the slide in whatever manner has been selected. Since the use of the conventional Mayer's egg albumen (Chapter XXVIII V 21.1 Mayer 1880) has already been discussed, another medium will be used. The hydrolyzed starch of McDowell and Vassos (Chapter 8 V 21.1 McDowell and Vassos 1940) is very little known and well worth using. The directions given in the place just quoted should be used in the preparation of this thick, viscous liquid of which about four or five drops may then be added to about 50 cc of distilled water in an Erlenmeyer flask or beaker. The slides must be cleaned before the sections are mounted, and no two people have ever agreed as to what is the most desirable method of doing this. One way is first to rub the slide briskly with 1% acetic acid in 70% alcohol and dry it by waving in the air. Other methods of cleaning the slide, which yield equally good results can be found from the index. Several drops of the diluted adhesive are placed in the center of each slide and one of the individual sections then taken up with the tip of a moistened brush and placed on the adhesive. As soon as the section has been placed on the fluid, the slide is lifted up, warmed carefully over a spirit lamp until the section is flat but the paraffin not melted, and then the superfluous liquid removed carefully with the edge of a filter paper. The slide is then placed on a warm table to dry and, if the drying period is to be prolonged, it is as well to place a dust cover over it, since grains of dust falling upon the slide will adhere just as tenaciously to the adhesive used as will the specimen itself.

It is proposed in the present example to stain the slide in the simplest possible manner with coelestin blue B followed by phloxine. Various formulas for stains of the coelestin blue B type will be found in Chapter 20 under the heading DS 11.41; that preferred by the writer for its simplicity is recorded as "Anonymous 1936." There will also be required a solution of phloxine for counterstaining. Phloxine appears to work best from a weak alcohol solution. In Chapter 20 under the heading of DS 12.2 will be found the suggestion

that it be used in 0.2% solution in 10% alcohol. Any of the other dyes there recommended may, of course, be substituted.

Assuming the section now to be perfectly dry, it is turned upside down and the light is reflected from it to see whether or not the section is adherent to the glass. If there is any air gap between the section and the glass, a brilliant mirror will be formed and, in a preparation as simple as this, the slide had better be thrown away. Having selected those slides which are perfectly adherent, they are then warmed over a flame until the wax is melted and dropped into a jar of xylene, where they remain until the paraffin appears to have been removed. They are then passed to another jar of xylene where they remain for at least five minutes, and then to a jar of equal parts xylene and absolute alcohol where they remain for a further five minutes. This treatment is followed by five minutes in absolute alcohol and then by direct transference to distilled water. After they have been in distilled water for a few minutes, each slide should be lifted and inspected to make sure that the water is flowing uniformly over both the slide and section. If it tends to be repelled by the section, or a meniscus is formed around the section, this is evidence that the wax has not been completely removed, and the slide must be transferred first to 95% alcohol to remove the excess water, then to absolute alcohol until perfectly dehydrated, and then through absolute to xylene, where it remains until the wax has been completely removed before being brought down again as previously indicated. The slides may be taken down one at a time and accumulated in distilled water until they are required. When all the slides have been accumulated in distilled water, they are transferred to the coelestin B staining solution. The time in this varies, but ten to fifteen minutes will probably be sufficient to stain the nuclei. One of the most useful features of this stain is that it is almost impossible to overstain in it. Sections may be left overnight without staining the cytoplasm to a degree which requires differentiation. After the nuclei are blue-black, therefore, or after a time convenient to the operator has elapsed, the sections are transferred to fresh distilled water where they are thoroughly washed. Each slide is then taken individually and dipped up and down in the phloxine solution until a casual inspection shows the background to be yellow-pink. The intensity of stain for the background, in a case like this, is a matter of choice, some people preferring a faint stain and others a darker stain; it must be remembered, in judging the color, that the section will seem darker after it has been cleared than it does in water.

As soon as it has been found from a single slide what is the time required to produce the desired degree of staining, the remainder of the slides are placed in the phloxine solution together, left the appropriate time, and then transferred to distilled water until no more color comes away. The slides are then passed from distilled water to 95% alcohol where they are left for about five minutes, then to fresh 95% alcohol, where they are left for five or six minutes before being passed to absolute alcohol. The purpose of using the 95% alcohol is not to diminish diffusion currents but simply to save diluting the absolute alcohol by passing slides directly from water to it. After the slides have been for two or three minutes in absolute alcohol, a single slide is taken and passed into the absolute alcohol-xylene mixture for perhaps two minutes and then passed to xylene. This slide is then examined by reflected light against a black background and should be as nearly as possible transparent with only a faint opalescence. One of the commonest faults in mounting sections is dehydrating them imperfectly, for if there is any water which has been carried through the process into the xylene (in which water is soluble in the extent of about 1/3 of 1%) this water will be extracted by the section which is in itself an excellent dehydrating agent. There is a world of difference between a perfectly cleared (that is glass-clear) slide and one which is only more or less dehydrated so that it appears faintly cloudy. If the slide does not appear to be sufficiently dehydrated the whole of the remaining slides should be transferred to fresh absolute alcohol and another one tried. When it has become apparent from the examination of the test slide that dehydration is complete, the remaining slides may be run up through absolute alcohol and xylene and accumulated in the final jar of xylene.

As balsam was discussed in the body of this chapter, we suggest using at the present time the medium of Kirkpatrick and Lendrun (Chapter 26 M 34.1 Kirkpatrick and Lendrun 1939). Next clean the appropriate number of coverslips: in the present instance a 3/4-inch circle would be admirable. The author cleans his coverslips in the same manner as he cleans his slides: by wiping with a weakly acid, alcohol solution. Each slide is taken individually, drained by its corner, laid on flat surface, and a drop of mounting medium placed on top. The coverslip is then placed on the mounting medium and pressed down with a needle. It should not be pressed absolutely into contact with the slide or too thin a layer of mounting medium will be left; some experience is required to judge when the coverslip has been pushed down far enough. If this is done skillfully the surplus mounting medium will form a neat ring around the outer surface of the cover. If it does not do so, care should at least be taken that no portion of the cover is devoid of surplus mountant which will be sucked under the coverslip as the solvent evaporates. These slides should be left to dry at room temperature for about one day and then placed on a warm plate for about a week. After they are dried the surplus dry mounting medium should be scraped off with a knife and the excess remaining after scraping removed carefully with a rag moistened in 90% alcohol. The slides are again dried overnight and then should be ringed with some colored varnish using the technique described in Chapter 2. This ring does not assist the preservation of the mounting medium but it has always, in the writer's experience, assured that the slide when placed in the hands of students will be treated with more respect than a non-ringed slide. The slide, after labeling, is now complete.

PREPARATION OF SERIAL SECTIONS OF AN AMPHIBIAN EMBRYO

Heavily yolked embryos are among the most difficult objects from which to prepare satisfactory serial sections, as may be witnessed by the photographs which illustrate the work of many experimental embryologists. Though the example specifically taken is that of an amphibian embryo, the methods to be discussed may be used for any heavily yolked material such as fish, or even in the preparation of sections of the early stages (segmentation and the like) of bird embryos.

The crux of the entire matter lies in the selection of a fixative and it is doubtful whether a worse fixative for the purpose could be found than the picro-acetic-formaldehyde of Bouin, so generally employed. Two fixatives have been developed specifically for heavily yolked material: that of Gregg and Puckett (Chapter 18 F 3000.1010 Gregg and Puckett 1943) which is designed specifically for the eggs of frogs, and that of Smith (Chapter 18 F 7000.1010 Smith 1912) which was originally developed for the eggs of *Cryptobranchus*, but which the author has used successfully for a large variety of heavily yolked material. The author has used Smith for so many years that he is prejudiced in favor of this formula, and the fact that he has not been so successful with the formula of Gregg and Puckett may be due to the fact that he is less experienced with it and not that it is inherently incapable of giving equally good results. As the techniques of fixation involved are altogether different they will be discussed separately.

Let us assume first of all that we are using the fluid of Gregg and Puckett, which has been made up according to the formula given in Chapter 18. The mass of embryos and eggs, together with their gelatinous surrounding envelopes, are taken and placed in at least 50 times their own volume of the solution. The jar containing them should be turned upside down at intervals to insure that the fluid around them does not become diluted and they are then left for 24 hours. If the eggs are to be embedded and sectioned at once,

they may then be removed and washed in running water for 24 hours or, if they are to be stored for long periods, they may be moved to 2% formaldehyde directly from the fixative and may remain in this fluid, changed possibly after the first 48 hours, until they are required for use. The mass is then removed and broken into small clusters which are placed in a test tube or small flask about one-third filled with water. The flask is then shaken vigorously, which will remove a portion of the albuminous envelope, the dirty water poured off, fresh added, and the flask again shaken. After half a dozen treatments of this type the greater part of the albumen will have been removed. When as much of the jelly as possible has been removed by this mechanical treatment the eggs are transferred to a flask of 1% sodium hypochlorite and shaken gently and carefully. At intervals eggs will be found to detach themselves. These should be removed either with a section lifter or a small pipet to another flask containing water; by this means the whole of the remaining jelly will be removed. The eggs, which are now in water, should be carefully examined to see whether or not the vitelline membrane is still adherent. If it is still adherent, those which have it should be transferred back to fresh 1% sodium hypochlorite and stirred very gently, being examined at intervals under a binocular microscope, until the membrane has been removed. The eggs are then washed thoroughly to remove all traces of hypochlorite. It is better to do this with half a dozen changes of water rather than in running water, because the eggs at this stage are brittle and portions may be flaked off the outside if they are subjected to the bumping which seems to be an inevitable part of washing with running water.

Let us now examine Smith's method. The fixative must be made up immediately before use and large volumes are required in relation to the size of the objects. The author once fixed the entire yolk of a hen's egg, using two gallons of solution; and at least 500 milliliters should be employed for a cluster of a dozen or two amphibian eggs. The eggs are transferred to the solution which is immediately placed in a dark cupboard where it remains for about 48 hours. The original specifies that low temperature should be employed, but the writer has been unable to find the least difference in performance between heavily yolked eggs fixed at room temperature and those which have been fixed in a refrigerator. The solution should be changed once or twice during the forty-eight hours, or at least as often as it becomes dark green. It is inevitable that it should become greenish, but by changing solutions before a dark-green color appears, the deposition of chromium oxides on the surface of the egg and its membranes may be avoided. At the end of forty-eight hours the eggs are removed to large volumes of 2% formaldehyde *in the dark;* the solution must be changed as often as it becomes discolored and washing must continue until no further color comes away. After all possible color has been removed by the 2% formaldehyde, the jars may be taken from the cupboard and stored indefinitely at room temperature in the light. Most of the eggs or embryos will be found to have become detached from their gelatinous membranes in the course of this treatment, but the vitelline membrane is frequently left. It becomes brittle, however, and may be removed without difficulty with the aid of a couple of needles.

Whichever method of fixation has been employed, we are now left with the eggs or embryos in 2% formaldehyde. The process of embedding is different according to the technique to be used. By the technique of Gregg and Puckett the eggs are dehydrated through graded alcohols, allowing in the case of frog eggs two hours each at 35%, 50%, and 60%. It is also necessary to treat them with iodine to remove the mercuric chloride, and for this purpose they are placed in 70% alcohol, to which has been added about 5% of Lugol's iodine (Chap. 22 ADS 12.2 Lugol (1905)). The exact proportion of iodine is not important and technical directions usually read "add iodine until the fluid is the color of port"; but the author sees no reason why

this insult to a noble wine should be perpetuated. It requires a treatment of at least 48 hours to make sure that the mercuric residues are removed and the eggs are then transferred to 80% alcohol where they are washed until no further color comes away. They are then dehydrated for one or two hours each in 95% and absolute alcohol. Gregg and Puckett specify clearing in xylene for 30 minutes but the writer prefers cleaning in benzene, which does not seem to render the eggs so brittle. After complete clearing, they are then transferred to a mixture of one part of the hydrocarbon employed and two parts of soft (48°C.) paraffin at room temperature. They may remain in this mixture until next required. When embedding is finally to be completed this mixture is placed in an oven at 58°C. and allowed to remain until completely liquified. The eggs are then transferred to 52° paraffin for one hour and finally to whatever medium is chosen for embedding (Gregg and Puckett prefer 55° paraffin; the writer prefers rubber-paraffin) for another 3 or 4 hours.

In the alternative technique of Smith, the procedure is rather different. After the eggs are taken from formaldehyde they are passed through 35% and 50% alcohol for two or three hours each and then placed in Grenacher's alcoholic borax carmine for about two days. The formula for this fluid is given in Chapter 20 (DS 11.22 Grenacher 1879) and it must be most strongly recommended that one use the dry stock dissolved in 70% alcohol rather than the usual solution prepared direct. The eggs are removed from the stain to one-quarter of 1% hydrochloric acid in 70% alcohol and left there for about two hours or until the first rapid color clouds have died down. It is not intended to complete differentiation by this process, but only to remove the excess stain. They are then, exactly as in the previous technique, dehydrated through 95% and absolute alcohol before being cleared in whatever hydrocarbon is preferred. Smith prefers embedding in 52° paraffin but this, in the writer's experience, is too soft and will only permit the thickest sections. It is again recommended that one of the rubber paraffins with a melting point of from 50° to 55°C. be employed.

In any case we now have amphibian embryos and eggs accumulated in the embedding oven in whatever medium has been decided to use. It is usually necessary in cutting sections of this type that the orientation of the embryo in relation to the knife should be known; this is difficult to establish by ordinary means when one is dealing with a more or less spherical embryo. The method preferred by the writer for indicating one of the planes is to embed at the same time and alongside the spherical embryo a little rectangular block of liver or some other soft tissue. It is easy to dehydrate clear and impregnate with wax a piece of liver and keep this permanently in the embedding oven in paraffin. When one is ready to embed the eggs a small strip (in the case of the frog embryo about 3 mm. × 1 mm. × 1 mm.) is cut from this slab of liver, and is first of all laid in the paper box to which one has added the wax in the manner already described. The egg is then transferred to the same box and is most carefully orientated with regard to the strip of liver, so that if the liver be cut exactly at right angles, the egg will be cut in the desired plane. A strip of liver this size does not greatly increase the total area of this block, nor does it in any way interfere with whatever staining technique is employed for the sections. An identical procedure is followed, whether one is dealing with eggs fixed by the technique of Gregg and Puckett, or fixed and prestained by the technique of Smith.

After the block has been hardened under the surface of water (Smith specifies 70% alcohol for the purpose, but it does not appear to matter) it is removed, allowed to attain room temperature, and the sides trimmed away until the strip of liver is clearly seen. The block is then attached to the holder, mounted in the block holder of a microtome, and a ribbon is prepared in the usual manner. The only difficulty that is likely to arise is that, after the ribbons have been flattened and are drying, the entire yolky center of the embryo may rise in a dome. This event usually indicates that the vitelline membrane has

remained on the egg and there is nothing whatever that can be done about it. Such sections always become detached in the course of staining and are in any case worthless, for if they are varnished in place they will still be so domed as to render microscopic examination almost impossible. If, however, several successive batches of sections, in which one is quite certain that the vitelline membrane has been removed from the embryo, behave in this manner, it is sometimes possible to stop the trouble by drilling a little hole in the block until one just comes to the egg itself, and then soaking the block in glycerol-alcohol. Blocks so treated will, when cut, usually be found to lie flat on the slide. If this device fails it is strongly recommended that 70% alcohol be substituted for water used to flatten the sections (any of the customary adhesives may be mixed with alcohol of this strength just as readily as with water) and that the technique of using a wet blotter and a rubber roller be used, as described in the body of this chapter. It must be emphasized that these defects are uncommon in materials fixed in the manner described; they are mentioned only because they occur so frequently in the handling of amphibian embryos fixed and prepared by other methods.

After the ribbons have been flattened and dried, they are then put through the ordinary series of reagents until they are ready to be stained. The technique differs very greatly according to whether one is dealing with the technique of Gregg and Puckett or that of Smith. In the technique of the latter the slides are removed from absolute alcohol and flooded with the Lyons blue and picric acid mixture of Smith (Chapter 20 DS 12.221) for a period of about one minute. They are then returned to absolute alcohol until no color comes away, and cleared in xylene before being mounted in a resinous medium. The writer prefers this technique to any other because of the gross swelling which occurs in yolk when exposed to aqueous solutions of stains. The rising up of the center of the section, commented on in the last paragraph, is not confined to the time when the sections are flattening, but may also occur during staining; the center of many an excellent section has become detached from the slide simply for the reason that it has been handled in aqueous stains. The nuclei are not so clearly shown by carmine as by many other stains, but for valuable material the author has always used Smith as an insurance policy against losses. It is also easy with this stain to distinguish the various cells since the cell membranes themselves pick up the blue while the mass of the yolk retains the yellow of the picric acid.

Gregg and Puckett, on the contrary, take the sections down to water in the usual manner and then stain them in Delafield's hematoxylin [Chapter 20 DS 11.122 Delafield (1885)] differentiating in acid alcohol in the manner indicated until the nuclei alone remain clearly stained. They are then counterstained in eosin-orange (Chapter 20 DS 12.222 Gregg and Puckett 1943) before returning through the alcohols to xylene and then to the mountant. The author has never had the least success in staining amphibian embryos with hematoxylin because of the very strong affinity of this stain for the albumen granules in the yolk.

After staining the slides are cleaned and labeled in the usual manner and will show almost incredible improvement over the usual "Bouin's fixative-hematoxylin-eosin" technique which most modern embryologists appear to employ.

Preparation of a Sagittal Section of an Entire Mouse

This preparation is not recommended to the stern and dedicated research worker, whose only interest in the preparation of microscope slides is to demonstrate a thesis, but has been included for the benefit of those who, like the author, enjoy making a beautiful slide for its own sake. It may, of course, be argued by those who have to justify themselves that such sections form an admirable method of demonstrating the main relationships of mammalian anatomy to a large class. It is proposed, in fact, to prepare a sagittal (vertical-longitudinal) section of an entire mouse from the tip of its nose to the very last joint of its tail. This is a feat of great technical difficulty and requires attention, at odd moments, during several months. The author does not think that the end can justify the means: the beautiful preparation must be its own justification.

The mouse selected for the preparation should be of such a size that the section will fit onto a standard 3-inch by 1-inch slide, but sufficiently old to be covered in hair. A litter of freshly born white mice should, therefore, be watched until the young are completely clothed with hair; this will be between one and two weeks after birth. The next problem is to kill and fix the mouse in such a manner as to fulfill the conditions that the tail shall be straight, so that it can be included in a sagittal section, and that the fixative shall shall be able to penetrate to all parts. The tail must, of course, be curled under the body if the section is to be placed on a slide, and it must also be attached to some rigid structure so as to remain straight. It is desirable to kill the mouse in a relaxed condition: and injection of sodium amytal is probably the best. For those who do not have access to hyperdermic syringes and reagents of this type, however, it is quite satisfactory to kill with ether (not chloroform which stiffens the animal rapidly) though one has less time to work before rigor mortis sets in. Before killing the mouse one should have secured the finest possible needle obtainable and some very fine silk, not linen or cotton, thread. There is only one way of insuring that the tail shall coincide with the nose and that is to sew the two together. Therefore, as soon as the mouse is dead, open the jaws and insert a little wedge of wood so that they are partly opened (at the tip of the jaws the gap should be about 2 mm.) and then proceed to pull the tail around until the tip of it projects just beyond the nose. Using the fine needle and the fine silk sew the skin from *each side* of the tail to *each side* of the nose. It must be remembered that we are concerned only with getting half a dozen perfect sagittal sections and that anything outside the exact central plane will not show. Now take a glass rod, or a piece of plastic, and bind the tail to it with silk, being careful to bind only loosely lest the imprint of the silk show in the final section. Great care must be taken to keep the tail straight along the glass; it is then attached in front and in back to the body of the mouse exactly parallel to the spine. If this is done skilfully a median sagittal section will cut through the central portion of the central nervous system for its entire length and will show a central section of the tail to its very tip. It is just as well to kill the whole litter and to prepare them in this manner, since one or two specimens are bound to get out of alignment in the course of the subsequent operations. The writer thought at one time that the simplest method of maintaining the tail straight would be to hang the mouse from a loop of tape passed through its tail with a weight attached to the nose, but the objection to this is that though the tail remains dead straight, it does not remain exactly parallel to the spinal cord.

Before all this has been done, one should have decided on the fixative to be employed and have made up a sufficient quantity of it. Fixatives containing picric acid should be avoided at all costs, since the prolonged soaking in water which must inevitably accompany decalcification will cause the grossest swelling and vacuolation of picric-fixed materials. The writer's preference is for the dichromate-formaldehyde-acetic mixtures, preference being given to those which are based on the original solution of Müller and which thus contain sodium sulfate. Numerous formulas for these mixtures will be found in Chapter 18 under the general heading F 7000.1010, the writer has employed the mixture Böhm and Opel 1907 with success in a preparation of the present type. It must not be imagined that this, or any other fixative, will penetrate rapidly enough to fix an entire mouse before considerable autolysis has taken place in the internal organs; it will be necessary to make small openings in the sides if we are to have a successful preparation.

As soon, therefore, as the mouse has been firmly fixed in the manner described, a sharp scalpel should be taken and a series of slits made through the skin and peritoneum along each side of the abdomen. These slits should not be more than a millimeter or so in extent, or there may be a protrusion of the internal organs through them. Care must also be taken not to cut the liver, or any major blood vessel, or the entire abdominal cavity will fill up with blood, and the appearance of the finished preparation will be completely ruined. In addition to these slits down the side, about one third of each side of the head must be cut off with a fine saw so as to expose the outer surface of the brain. The use of bone forceps or wire cutters will cause distortion; a fine jewelers' saw is much better for the purpose. The cutting of blood vessels in this case does not make very much difference since there are few cavities into which the blood can flow.

The mouse, having thus been bound to its supports and a few small openings made, is wrapped in a fold of cheesecloth and suspended at about the center of at least one liter of the selected fixative. The jar containing the mouse and fixative should then be placed in a dark place for about two days. At the end of this time the mouse is removed and the fixative is replaced with new fixative. At this time also extend the size of the openings which have been made, since all of the blood will now be coagulated and the internal organs will be more or less firmly fixed in place. In extending these openings, remember actually that no more than the center half-millimeter of the mouse will ultimately be required, and certainly all of the limbs and considerable areas of both flanks may be removed. Some experience is necessary in deciding how much to remove. This is another reason why the entire litter of young mice should have been sacrificed at the same time rather than reliance placed on a single specimen. The mouse should now be placed in fresh fixative and left in the dark for a further period of about a week, the jar being examined at intervals to make sure that the fixative is not turning green. It will always turn green-brown, but should it become of a fairly dark-green color, it must immediately be replaced with new fixative. It is very difficult to overharden or overfix a specimen of this kind, and at least a month should be allowed to make sure that there is perfect fixation throughout while an exposure of six months will cause no damage.

After fixation is complete, the mouse (or mice) is removed from the fixative, and without removing from the cheese-cloth bags, hung in a jar through which running water flows from a tube reaching to the bottom. It (or they) should be washed for at least three days in running water before being removed and hung in a large jar of 20% alcohol or other de-hydrant. For those who find alcohol diffi-cult to obtain, either acetone, isopropanol, or methanol are equally good for dehydra-tion, but must in each instance be used in a fairly close series. Small objects may, as has been stated elsewhere, be passed with-out danger from water into absolute al-cohol, but as large an object as this mouse will have to be dehydrated very slowly. The mouse should be left in 20% alcohol for about five days and subsequently for about five days each in 50%, 70% and 90%. The experienced reader will have noticed that we have so far said nothing of decalcification which must obviously take place before the sections can be made. On the basis of the writer's experi-ence, born out by the earlier workers but apparently nowadays ignored, it would ap-pear that hardening in alcohol after fixa-tion yields a specimen which behaves very much better under the knife than does one which has been fixed only without the sub-sequent alcohol hardening. It is for this reason that he recommends that it be taken up in the manner described to 90% alcohol, left there for a week or two, and then brought down through the same series to water, where it is left until the whole of the alcohol has been re-moved. The specimen is now ready for decalcification.

For as large an object as this, particu-larly one which has been fixed in a di-chromate mixture, the method of von Ebner would be desirable. This solution, the formula for which is given in Chapter 19 under the heading AF 21.1 von Ebner (1891), employs a strong solution of sodium chloride to diminish the swelling of the tissues caused by the nitric acid used. It is also possible to use phloroglucin for the same purpose of diminishing the swelling; a typical formula is given in the same chapter as AF 21.1 Ferreri (1895). It has, however, been the writer's experi-ence that these phloroglucin formulas work better on smaller objects and he strongly recommends the formula of von Ebner in the present case.

Following this formula, the specimen is hung in a large volume of the solution and left for three or four days. At the end of this time a further 1% of nitric acid is added and the whole stirred up. This proc-ess of adding a milliliter of nitric acid per 100 milliliters is continued every third or fourth day until decalcification is com-plete. It is as undesirable to decalcify for too long a period as it is to leave patches of hard bone to wreck the knife, hence the worker will often find himself in a quan-dary as to how to determine when de-calcification is complete. The only way this can be done with complete success is by x-ray examination, for the least trace of undissolved calcium remaining will show clearly upon the x-ray plate or fluorescent screen. It is often possible to find some friendly dentist who will prepare an x-ray of the mouse at intervals, but if this is impossible one must judge on deli-cate probing with a needle. The two places which are usually, but by no means always, the last to decalicify are the inner ear and the molar teeth, and it is a reasonably safe assumption that if a fine needle can be passed through these with-out meeting more resistance than would be occasioned by tough leather, it is safe to continue. It is not safe to probe in the direction of the vertebrae, which are often slow in decalcification, because they are too close to the central area which will subsequently be sectioned. In the ab-sence of x-ray information it is much safer to decalcify too long than too short a time, and it will be suggested later that a solution be used to mordant the sections; this will undo, to a certain extent, any excessive hydrolysis which has taken place.

The decalcified mouse must now be thoroughly washed to remove all traces of acid, but water should not be used for this purpose since the removal of the salt is more rapid than the acid and bad hydrolysis may occur at this moment. The mouse should, therefore, be washed with weak (2%) formaldehyde, which should be changed at daily intervals for about a week. At the end of this time the mouse may be washed in running water overnight with safety, and may then be considered ready to be dehydrated and embedded. Before dehydration it is well to trim away as much of the material as can be removed without risk of displacing the remaining internal organs. The larger the piece to be dehydrated and embedded, the longer will the process take, and it is usually perfectly safe to reduce the preparation at this point to a slab of about ¼ of an inch thick. Do not hesitate to use fine ligatures of silk to hold in place any organ showing signs of diaplacement, for these ligatures will be missed by the knife as it takes the central section desired.

Dehydration and clearing can follow the ordinary procedure hanging the slab of tissue at the top of considerable volumes of 20%, 50%, 70%, 95%, and absolute alcohol before laying it at the bottom of a jar containing benzene, which may be changed once or twice. If the mouse has been reduced, as suggested, to a slab, possibly two or three days in each of these alcohols will be sufficient to provide perfect dehydration. As the block is going to be large, plain paraffin would be a most unsuitable embedding medium, the writer warmly recommends one of the rubber-paraffin media, the formula for which is given in Chapter 27 under the heading of E 21.1. In view of the large size of the specimen, the ordinary stender dishes used for embedding will have to be abandoned in favor either of beakers or crystallizing dishes. It is essential that the specimen should lie flat during the course of embedding, or it will inevitably become distorted, and the care thus far taken to maintain the tail in a straight line with the spine will be wasted.

The specimen should first be placed in a crystallizing dish filled with benzene, and about a half-inch layer of chips of the embedding medium should be placed on top of the specimen. The crystallizing dish should be left at room temperature for about a day—naturally covered with a plain sheet of glass—and should then be placed in a paraffin oven or warmed to about 50°C. It is necessary to use a special oven for this purpose, because the large quantity of benzol which evaporates from the preparation will be absorbed in any other wax in the oven and render it relatively useless for subsequent embedding. About three or four hours later, after the wax has become fluid, this mixture of benzene-paraffin may be enriched by pouring molten paraffin into it and carefully stirring it up. One should then at intervals of a few hours—it does not matter leaving it overnight—pour off about half of the fluid contained in the dish and replace it with fresh, molten paraffin. By this means, over a space of a day or two, the specimen may be passed by reasonable gradations from benzene to paraffin. This whole process should be watched and controlled with the utmost care, for it is easy for these slabs to twist out of shape in the course of impregnation. After the changes described the specimen should finally be removed very carefully to another crystallizing dish containing clean paraffin and left for at least a day to complete the impregnation with wax.

Casting of the block, which will be too large for a paper box, is one of the few cases in which L-shaped blocks of brass can profitably be employed. Alternatively, if L-shaped blocks are not available, take two 1-inch lengths of 1-inch-square brass to form the ends of the box which one is making and attach to them with sealing wax two thin sheets of brass along each side, thus making a metal box. This should be stood on a slab of plate glass. Now pour into this box, which should be at least three inches long by one inch wide and one-and-one-half inches deep, about a half an inch of wax and allow it to cool until it is solid. Then heat, in a small beaker, about a teaspoonful of wax to a temperature well above its melting point —it is probably safest to raise it to smoking heat—and then pour this suddenly onto the surface of the now hardened wax at the bottom of the box. By this means the surface is again molten and the box can be filled with wax which has been maintained in the oven at about its melting point. The object is then carefully placed in the box. At this point one may detach the tail from the rod of glass or plastic to which it has been attached. Then wait until the wax in which the specimen is lying commences to solidify and carefully fill the box to the very brim with molten wax. The whole must now be cooled as rapidly as possible. When the block has completely hardened it is slid out of its metal box and placed in a large jar of water at room temperature, where it may remain overnight or until one is prepared to deal with it.

In the examples previously given use has been made of the ordinary rotary microtome, but such an instrument is useless for the very large sections which we are about to cut. No microtome will serve save one of the slider type shown in Fig. 55. As these sliding microtomes have no possible justifiable use in the cutting of paraffin sections, save for very large objects, it is curious that so many of them (including the one shown in the illustration) have relatively small object holders provided. The jaws which are normally used to hold the metal object holder, however, can be adapted to hold a large piece of wood. The block under discussion had better be attached by melting the wax to a piece of hard wood, previously steeped in paraffin, of a size very little smaller than the block itself. After the block has been attached—it is very dangerous to try it before—it must be trimmed to the shape which will be used for actual cutting, which differs in every particular from the shape which must be used when cutting serial sections of small objects. For ribbon-cutting the block is always rectangular and the two sides must be exactly parallel. In the case of a very large block from which single sections are to be cut in one of these sliding microtomes, three sides of it may be left more or less rectangular, but the fourth side must come to an angle pointing to the blade of the knife. This angle is not important but should be between 40° and 60°. It does not matter whether the sloping side extends beyond the beginning of the object or not, and it is actually of no importance what shape the other sides are provided there is a 40° to 60° angle pointing towards the knife. This angle is for the purpose of presenting a small area of wax to the first cut. Large sections on a microtome of this type invariably roll themselves up into a cylinder which is very difficult subsequently to unroll. If, however, there is a sloping angle pointing towards the knife, the flat portion may be held with a brush against the knife and the whole section, therefore, retained more or less flat as it comes off.

Now take an old microtome knife and cut 25 or 30 micron sections from the top until one gets down to that part of the object which one wishes to cut. This preliminary flattening of the top surface of the block, and cutting away of the unwanted portions of the specimen, also shows how this particular block is behaving in relation to the microtome itself. If the sections curl hopelessly, in spite of the point of wax, it is evident that the knife is striking at the specimen too squarely and it should be adjusted to cut at an angle more like that of the knife shown in Fig. 83 which is, however, set for celloidin. A certain amount of maneuvering of the knife angle backward and forward will enable one to secure a cut in which at least half an inch of the pointed end of the wax remains straight, thus permitting a brush held in the left hand to be pressed down while the right hand completes the movement of the knife. Do not imagine that sections of this size will ever come off flat: it is enough if they are reasonably flat. Each section will have to be flattened independently in a bowl of water heated to from 5 to 10 degrees below the melting point of the embedding medium employed. The temperature is rather critical, but it may be established by experiments on unwanted sections, so that when the block has finally been trimmed down to the point where the 10 or 15 essential sections can be taken, all difficulties will have been ironed out. It is inevitable, as one cuts farther and farther into the object, that fine readjustments of the orientation will have to be made. These can only be made by trial and error, and one should never cut off too many sections until one has finally got the block lying in the exact plane required. It may be said that this plane may be determined reasonably when some portion of the vertebrae are being cut at the same time that the skin of the tail is being cut. Remember that after fine adjustment, the knife blade will have to be used as a plane to render flat the whole surface of the block before further complete sections can be taken. Finally, however, the moment comes which culminates all the months of work. The block is lying completely flat. One places a freshly sharpened knife in position and prepares to take the sections required.

Before this final operation it will be necessary to have cleaned, in any manner desirable, the required number of slides, and to have laid these at hand alongside the vessel of water which will be used for flattening. Now take the brush in the left hand, the knife in the right hand, slide the knife forward, grab the little curling tail of paraffin coming from the pointed end of the block, and with one smooth, continuous movement complete the section. This section, in a more or less wrinkled condition, will now be lying on the knife blade, from which it may be removed with the aid of two brushes. One brush held in the left hand is moistened with the lips and applied to the upper surface of the end of the section farthest from the edge of the blade, while the other is very gently slid under the section to loosen its attachment from the edge of the blade. Using one brush by adhesion from above and one brush to balance the other end of the section from below, now drop the section onto the warm water where it will completely expand. A slide is then taken in the right hand and a needle in the left, with a view to stranding the section in the right position on the slide.

The slide should be placed in the water and left for a moment or two until it reaches approximately the same temperature and then, while held pointing downwards at an angle of about 45°, approached to the section until that side of the section which is intended to be towards the upper end of the slide just touches the glass. The slide is then very slightly raised so as to strand the upper portion, which is then held in place with a needle while the whole slide is withdrawn at an angle of from 45 to 30° from the water. It is quite impossible to pass the slide horizontally under the section and then to raise it so that the section remains in place. It is only by withdrawing the slide at an angle, in the manner described, that one can hope to strand the section in the correct position. If the section is not in correct position on the slide, no attempt can be made to rearrange it. It is only possible to replace the slide in water with the hope that the section will float off so that a second attempt can be made. If the section is only slightly out of position on the slide it is much better to leave it alone, since the section usually breaks at the second attempt to strand it. As soon as the section has been stranded on the slide, the slide is removed from water, laid on a flat surface, a sheet of water-saturated coarse filter paper laid on top of it, and a rubber roller of the type used by photographers pressed down with considerable force so as to squeeze the water from the paper and the section at the same time. The section is then placed on a warm table to dry.

Nothing has been said about the use of an adhesive for attaching the section to the slide. Provided that the slide is perfectly clean and that the section is pressed firmly into contact with it, there should be no necessity for any adhesive at all. For those, however, who do not care to run this risk any adhesive mentioned in Chapter 28 under the heading of V 21.1 may be used either by smearing it on the slide, or mixed, to the extent of about 2%, in the water used for flattening.

As soon as the slides are dried they may be stained in any manner desired. For a specimen of this nature the writer's first preference is for the stain for Patay 1934 (abbreviated directions for which will be found in Chapter 20 under the heading DS 12.32 Patay 1934) or for the stain of Mallory (which will be found in the same chapter under the heading DS 13.41). Detailed descriptions of the use of both of these stains are given elsewhere.

If the slides have to be stored for any great length of time, or if the process of decalcification has been unduly prolonged, treat each slide before staining according to the method of Mullen and McCarter, which is given in Chapter 22 under the heading ADS 12.1 Mullen and McCarter 1941.

13

Nitrocellulose Sections

General Principles

Nature of the Process

As the name indicates, this chapter is concerned with the preparations of sections of material which has been impregnated with a solution of nitrocellulose. This process is not to be regarded as a substitute for the paraffin method described in the last chapter; it should be used only when paraffin will not give a satisfactory result. This is usually used either for exceedingly minute objects, the orientation of which in paraffin, or the retention of which in paraffin sections, is almost impossible, or for very large objects with numerous cavities which cannot well be supported with paraffin. Paraffin in large cavities tends to shrink away, while nitrocellulose solutions do not.

There are numerous disadvantages in the use of nitrocellulose. The worst for the research worker is the difficulty of preparing serial sections with the sections in their due order. This may be overcome to a certain extent by the process of double embedding (see the next chapter) but this itself is less satisfactory than straight embedding and should be used only for very small or very difficult objects.

One of the advantages of nitrocellulose embedding is that the process does not involve the use of heat; the materials are impregnated in solutions of increasing strength at room temperature, and these solutions are subsequently hardened either by evaporation or by chemical means. The size of the nitrocellulose molecules in the dispersions (usually called solutions) employed is so great that the material diffuses slowly and the the process is a long one. Various methods have been put forward for using nitrocellulose at high temperatures, but there appears to be little justification for them, because, if the material to be embedded will stand boiling, it will most certainly stand embedding in paraffin. These processes appear to have been introduced by those who are so accustomed to celloidin embedding that they do not wish to use anything else.

Materials Employed

Cellulose nitrate is not, as its name might indicate, a pure chemical, but is a mixture of a great number of different compounds, the relative proportions of which depend upon the method of manufacture. Few of these mixtures are suitable for cutting sections; and one should always be used which is specifically prepared for the purpose. The best known in the world, and for many years the only one known, was *celloidin*, supplied by Schering. Its place has been taken in the United States today by *Parlodion*, marketed by Mallinkrodt. It is unfortunate that the trade names of both of these should be so closely allied to *collodion*, which is a pharmaceutical solution of pyroxylin unsuitable for section cutting. Cellulose nitrates, other than those marketed under brand names, are broadly classified according to the viscosity of the standard solution. This viscosity is expressed in terms of the number of seconds taken by a steel ball of standard size to fall a standard distance through a standard column of the solution. The lowest viscosity normally marketed is that known as *5-second nitrocellulose* and is the only one which may be employed in microtechnique. Another point to be watched, in using other than a proprietary product, is the fact that some nitrocellulose mixtures are quite violently explosive when dry, whereas both celloidin and Parlodion, though they burn briskly if given the opportunity, do not ignite with explosive violence. Cellulose nitrates other than those indicated under brand names are always marketed in solution and should never be stored in the dry state. Many of the older books suggest that *chips* of nitrocellulose material, to be used for embedding, be stored under water. This advice is given not to lengthen the life of the chips, but only to avoid the risk of explosion.

Celloidin, which term will be used throughout the rest of this chapter whenever a nitrocellulose-embedding medium is meant, is soluble in a great variety of modern solvents, but most techniques are based on its use in a solution of a mixture of alcohol and ether.

Preparation of Solutions

Celloidin is not easily soluble in the alcohol-ether mixture usually employed, therefore a special method must be used to prepare the solutions. The chips of dried material are first removed from the bottle in which they have been kept and placed in a desiccator overnight. The only real enemy of the success of embedding in celloidin is water, and at no stage in the proceedings may one risk contamination. It is usual to carry in stock a 16% solution of celloidin, therefore, 16 grams of these dried chips should be weighed. These chips are placed in a *dry* bottle fitted with a glass stopper which has been tested for fit. Fifty parts of absolute alcohol are then poured over them. If this alcohol is not taken from an unopened new bottle, it is desirable that it be carefully dehydrated either with calcium sulfate or copper sulfate before being used for this purpose. The bottle is left at room temperature overnight, in order that the celloidin may swell, and when this swelling is complete 50 parts of *anhydrous* ether are added. The ordinary ether of commerce and the ether used for anesthetic purposes are worthless; one must employ the variety sold as *ether anhydrous by sodium*. Any

attempt on the part of the worker to remove water from commercial ether with sodium in his own laboratory will produce nothing but a serious explosion. The anhydrous ether should always be taken from a freshly opened can. The bottle is rotated slowly until the celloidin is completely dispersed through the mass. The selection of a solution of this strength is based on the fact that it is about the thickest solution which may reasonably be poured from a bottle. Not too much of the material should be prepared at one time, since ether always evaporates through even the best fitting stopper. The only method known to the writer of keeping the material satisfactorily is to secure one of the bottles, once common in pharmacies but now difficult to obtain, in which the ground glass stopper is itself covered with a domed cap—like that on a balsam bottle —ground to the neck. If such a bottle can be obtained, the outer cap, but *not* the inner, may be greased with glycerol and a relatively ether-tight seal thus secured. Under no circumstances should celloidin solutions be stored in an icebox in the hope of diminishing the rate of evaporation. If these cold solutions are then brought out into a warm room, moisture will condense all over the bottle and over the solution as it is being poured. In Chapter 27 under the heading E 22.1 will be found suggestions for various other solutions which have from time to time been made.

Infiltration of Objects with Nitrocellulose Solutions

In the course of embedding in paraffin, as described in the last chapter, it is just possible to get away with slightly imperfect dehydration. In impregnation with celloidin it is absolutely impossible. The prime prerequisite to the successful infiltration of a specimen is that it be perfectly dehydrated. For this purpose the specimen should be brought up in the conventional manner through such series of alcohols as may be necessary until absolute alcohol is reached. It should continue dehydration for some considerable time in at least two changes of absolute alcohol, the last of which has either been drawn from a sealed bottle, or from a bottle in

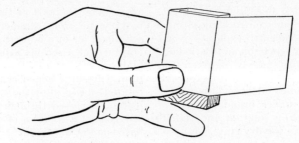

Fig. 80. Tying paper collar round wood block.

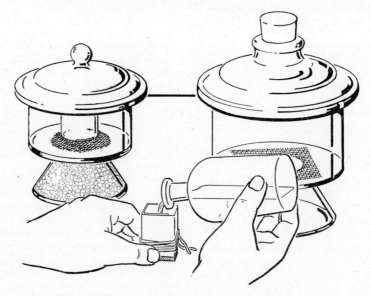

Fig. 81. Putting in first layer of celloidin.

which a considerable quantity of calcium sulfate or copper sulfate has been placed as a dehydrant. When the specimen is completely dehydrated, it is transferred to a mixture of equal parts of absolute alcohol and ether. The worker must remember always to use anhydrous ether and not the commercial variety. Specimens should remain in this mixture until they have been completely impregnated.

The actual process of getting the material impregnated with 16% celloidin may be done in two ways. Either the object may be placed in a considerable volume of a dilute solution, and evaporated, or it may be passed through solutions of increasing strength. The writer prefers the latter method since it is very difficult to

evaporate an alcohol-ether mixture slowly under dry conditions. Most people employ solutions of 2, 4, 8, and 16% celloidin prepared by dilution of the 16% stock. Every vessel used for dilution, as well as the diluent itself, must be absolutely dry. The object should be taken from the absolute alcohol-ether mixture, and placed in about 50 times its own volume of a 2% dilution in a glass-stoppered bottle, which should in turn be kept in a sealed desiccator while the impregnation is going on. The time of impregnation naturally varies according to both the size and the nature of the object, but it is a rough and ready rule for relative time that the material should spend proportionately as long in each solution as the concentration of the

Fig. 82. Transferring object in thick celloidin.

celloidin; that is, if the object were to take one hour in 2% it should have eight hours in 16%. As a measure of absolute time it may be said that an object the size of a frog's egg will require about one day in the 2% while a flower bud the size of a walnut should remain at least ten days. The writer prefers not to endeavor to transfer the object from one solution to another, but to pour off the weak solution and replace it with a stronger. There is no means of telling when impregnation is complete until one comes to cut the section; but two things must be remembered: one, that the specimen cannot be damaged no matter how long it be immersed in celloidin, two, that the most frequent cause of faulty sections is imperfect impregnation. When impregnation is complete it is necessary to prepare a block for cutting.

Casting Celloidin Blocks

Two methods may be employed to transform the celloidin from a liquid to a solid state. Either the alcohol-ether mixture may be permitted to evaporate, or it may be removed with another solvent, usually chloroform, in which celloidin is not itself soluble. The removal of the solvent with chloroform may also be done either in the liquid or in the vapor phase.

It is difficult to mount blocks of celloidin once they have been cast on an object holder, though the solution of Apáthy (Chapter 27, E 21.1 Apáthy (1942)) has been specifically developed for that purpose. It is, moreover, very nearly impossible to mount a celloidin block on any of the metal block holders supplied with standard microtomes. The worker is, therefore, advised to prepare for himself a series of small wooden blocks on which the object may be directly cast. These wooden blocks should be of hardwood and a whole series should be provided according to the size of the object which is to be cut. The smallest practical size is about $\frac{1}{2}'' \times \frac{1}{2}'' \times 1''$ and it should be understood that the block will be cast on the $\frac{1}{2}$-inch end. The largest practical size is dependent entirely upon the size of the object to be cut. These blocks should be cut, sanded as smooth as possible, baked in an oven at about 80°C. to remove as much water as possible, and then thrown directly into absolute alcohol. The absolute alcohol is replaced with absolute alcohol-ether and then with 2% celloidin. The blocks are transferred for several days to a solution of 4% celloidin and then withdrawn, stood on their ends in a desiccator, and dried. Once prepared, they may be used an indefinite number of times.

The process of casting the block is not difficult. First of all take a paper collar (ordinary bond paper is excellent) and tie it firmly round the edge of the block so that it projects upwards for a distance of about ½ inch (Fig. 80). This makes a box the floor of which is the end of the wooden block and the sides of which are of paper. Then pour into the bottom of this box about ¼ of an inch of 16% celloidin (Fig. 81) and place it in a desiccator (at the left in Fig. 81) where the alcohol and ether are allowed to evaporate until the surface of the block is firm when touched with a blunt needle. It is not required to be hard; it is only required to be sufficiently firm that an object placed on it will not sink. Remove the block from the desiccator and fill it to the brim with the 16% celloidin containing the object (Fig. 82). The object will sink through the liquid celloidin until it comes to the firm layer underneath. Needles are used to orientate it in the desired position, and it is then either placed in a desiccator to evaporate, or, better, placed in a desiccator in the base of which the desiccant has been replaced by a quantity of chloroform (at the right, Figs. 81 and 82). There is relatively rapid vapor exchange between the chloroform and the alcohol-ether, and the block by this means may be completely hardened overnight. If speed is vital, place the whole block in liquid chloroform as soon as the object has been oriented. By this means the block will be hardened in a few hours, but with some risk that the rapid diffusion currents set up may displace the object. The block should be stored in chloroform until required.

If the block is to be prepared by the method of evaporation, a box of paper is made and a layer of hardened celloidin set on the bottom. After the object has been oriented in the 16% celloidin, however, the block is placed in a desiccator to evaporate, and is filled up from time to time with 16% celloidin as it shrinks. Blocks hardened by evaporation are denser and tougher than those hardened with chloro-form. The chloroform technique is usually more satisfactory.

Cutting Sections in Celloidin

There are as many methods of cutting sections from celloidin blocks as there are workers who have done it, and space does not permit all the variations to be given here. Broadly speaking they fall into two classes: those in which the celloidin is cut dry, and those in which it is cut wet. Celloidin may be cut on any kind of microtome, but unless an attempt is to be made to serialize sections (which is far better done by the double embedding technique described in the next chapter) a sliding microtome should be used.

Celloidin cannot be cut by bringing a square edge of the block against the knife. Not only must the knife be set at an angle of about 30° to the direction of travel (Fig. 83) but the corner of the block must, as shown, be trimmed to an acute angle. The block, therefore, after being trimmed to the shape shown, is clamped by its wooden base in the holder and oriented in the desired position. If the block is being cut dry the knife is now slid forward and the sections removed to a watch glass. Do not worry if they are, as is more than probable, considerably curled. When enough sections have been accumulated they may be dealt with in the manner to be described later.

The author much prefers to cut his blocks after they have been moistened with oil of cedar. There is a double reason for this. Not only do the sections tend to stay flatter, but if the block is thoroughly impregnated with oil it will become glass-clear so that last-minute adjustments of orientation are easy. By this technique the block, which should have been chloro-form-hardened, is transferred directly to oil of cedarwood and left until it is glass-clear. When it is removed, as much as the cedar oil as possible should be wiped off with a cloth and the block mounted in the appropriate holder. Then take a finger-bowl, or beaker, of oil of cedarwood and, after having adjusted the knife to approximately the correct angle, moisten the blade of the knife with the oil. The knife is then slid forward to remove a section,

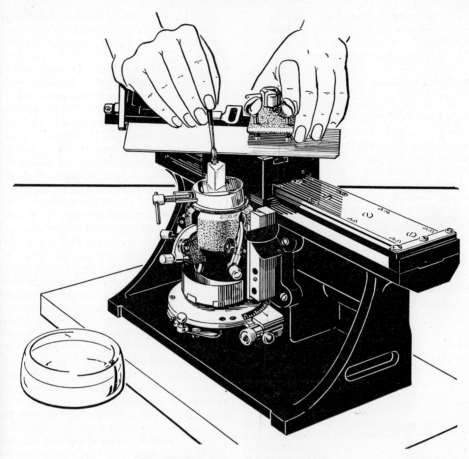

Fig. 83. Cutting celloidin sections.

and each section is received (Fig. 83) on a brush saturated with oil. From time to time the blade of the knife should be moistened with more cedar oil, and the sections as they come onto the knife may be left to accumulate—they will be held to the blade by the cedarwood—until a considerable area of the blade is covered. These sections may then be picked up with a brush moistened with oil of cedar and transferred to a container of the same fluid; or, if there are enough of them, they may merely be washed off the knife, which has been removed, and placed in the beaker or watch glass.

Both the methods just described presuppose that the object has been stained, as should usually be the case, before em-

bedding, and that the sections will require no further manipulation beyond flattening and mounting. When the sections are being cut with a view to staining them subsequently, the method of cutting a block moistened with 70% alcohol is to be preferred. By this method the block, which *must* have been hardened in chloroform, is placed directly in a considerable volume of 70% alcohol. Stronger alcohol should not be employed because it will tend to soften the block. After a day or two in 70% alcohol, most of the chloroform will have been removed, the block is then mounted in the usual manner, and sections are cut from it with a knife which is moistened with 70% alcohol. The blade must be moistened with a brush dipped in

70% alcohol each time a section is cut, and each section must be individually removed to a beaker of 70% alcohol in order to avoid evaporation and drying.

Staining Sections

It is usually desirable to stain objects before celloidin sections are cut, but when it is necessary to stain subsequently, and the sections have been prepared in 70% alcohol as described, they may be submitted to the action of any staining fluids exactly as though they were freehand sections. That is, they may be passed from one solution to another with the aid of a section lifter, washed in water, and in general handled with considerable roughness without any risk of damaging them. It must be remembered, of course, that alcohol solutions may not be employed or the celloidin will be hopelessly softened. The chief objection to this procedure is the tendency of some stains to be absorbed by the celloidin; it is difficult to find a plasma stain which will stain tissues without coloring celloidin. Nuclear staining is relatively easy, as is also metal staining, which is the process most usually applied to celloidin sections. No attempt should be made to flatten the section before it has been stained, but it should be passed through all the required techniques and then returned to 70% alcohol before mounting. A method of double staining a botanical specimen is given in the typical preparation which concludes this chapter.

Mounting Celloidin Sections on Slides

If the section has been cut in cedar oil from an object which has been prestained, nothing further is required than to remove the section from cedar oil, place it in the center of a clean slide, add a drop of the resinous mounting medium selected, and apply the coverslip. Any slight curl which tends to lift the coverslip may be easily pressed out, either by leaving a weight on the coverslip overnight or by using a small spring clip to hold the covership down.

If the section has been cut dry it will usually be found too curled to mount satisfactorily, and a different technique must be followed. In this case the section is placed in the approximate position on the slide, and the slide, with the section, placed in a small dish containing a little ether. Within a relatively short time the celloidin will have been softened sufficiently to be pressed flat on the slide and mounted in balsam under the coverslip.

If the section has been cut in 70% alcohol, and subsequently subjected to various staining procedures, it is necessary that it should be dehydrated before being mounted in balsam. It may be removed from 70% alcohol to a mixture of equal parts of absolute alcohol and chloroform, the former to dehydrate the specimen, the latter to prevent the dissolution of the celloidin. This mixture will often appear cloudy when the section is first put in, in which case it is only necessary to replace it with fresh solution and so on until both the section and the specimen remain unclouded. When an unclouded condition has been reached, the specimen may be dehydrated in oil of cedar, placed on the slide, and mounted as previously described.

It is occasionally necessary, though usually undesirable, to attach a number of celloidin sections to slides and then to stain them in position. The reason this is unsatisfactory is that it is hard enough to remove staining dyes from the celloidin matrix when both sides of the section are free in a watchglass, and nearly impossible when one side has been pressed against a glass surface. This method, however, must be employed if it is desired to serialize celloidin sections and some cogent reason prevents the use of the double technique described in the next chapter. Of the various methods given in Chapter 28 under the heading V 21.2, the writer prefers that of Heringa and ten Berge 1923 in which clean slides are coated with a 3% solution of gelatin and dried. When these slides are required they are soaked for a couple of hours in 5% sodium sulfate, rinsed, and again dried. The section is taken from 70% alcohol, pressed firmly to the slide— or the sections are lined up in their order and pressed firmly to the slide—and then dipped as soon as they are partially dry once or twice in absolute alcohol and chloroform. This gives a very reasonable adhesion. Another useful method of handling large numbers of celloidin slides is that of Linstaedt 1912, also described in Chapter 28, V 21.2. The method there given can be followed; it results, in effect, in the fusing of a large quantity of celloidin sections into a single sheet of celluloid, which may then be handled through stains, etc. as if it were a simple

section. It will be noticed that the sheet itself is made of celluloid—not celloidin—which is a material which does not readily pick up stains. The two methods of Longeron involve the removal of the celloidin after the sections have been mounted, and leaves one to wonder why celloidin should have been used, instead of paraffin, in the first place.

Typical Example

PREPARATION OF A TRANSVERSE SECTION OF A LILY BUD

It has already been pointed out that one of the best uses to which celloidin may be put is the preparation of sections of fine structures containing cavities which would not be held by paraffin. The example here selected is a case in point, for it would be almost impossible by the ordinary paraffin section technique to take a transverse section of a large flower and to maintain all the different parts in relation to each other. It would indeed be almost impossible to secure a section at all without gross collapse of the parts.

The bud of a lily has been selected because it is such admirable teaching material. Sections may be taken through a level which will show both the stamen and the pistil, and the material is sufficiently large to permit an elementary botany class to get a clear idea of the arrangement of the different parts with the use of magnifications no higher than those provided by a hand lens. The method of staining selected, however, is sufficiently good to permit the examination of the individual parts, by an advanced class, under the high power of the microscope.

The exact species of lily, provided it is one of the trumpet varieties known to florists, is quite immaterial, and the bud should be taken about a week before it is open. The best fixative to use for this kind of thing is one of the chromic-formaldehyde-acetic mixtures known to botanists under the general term of CRAF. Several formulas for these mixtures are given in Chapter 18 under the heading F 6000.1010; the fluids of Navashin 1912, Belling 1930, and Randolph 1935 are the ones widely used by botanists. It makes little difference which of these formulas

is employed, but they must be made up immediately before use to prevent the reduction of the chromic acid by the formaldehyde.

A lily bud 1½″ long × ½″ in diameter will need to be fixed for about four days in one of these fluids, which should be changed daily and kept in the dark. As soon as the bud is cut from the plant it should be immersed in the fixative and the extreme tip cut off to permit the contained air to leave. After fixation in these fluids, the bud should be washed for 24 hours in running water and then transferred through 20%, 50%, 70% and 90% alcohol (about a day or two in each) to 95% alcohol, which should be changed as often as it becomes discolored. It is necessary to remove the chlorophyll, or else this will subsequently diffuse into the celloidin, from which it is almost impossible to remove it. If the process of decolorization in 95% alcohol is too slow for the worker, he may transfer the bud to absolute alcohol until it is dehydrated, and then to chloroform where the remaining chlorophyll will be extracted very rapidly. The risk in this procedure, however, is that the chloroform will not subsequently be sufficiently removed, and will thus prevent proper infiltration by the celloidin. If chloroform is used, the bud must be removed as soon as bleached to absolute alcohol, which is changed as often as the least smell of chloroform remains. It is then put through at least 6 changes of 95% alcohol, with one day in each, before being transferred to fresh absolute alcohol to complete the dehydration.

The writer's preferred method of dehydration for large objects has already been described (Chapter 12) and should be employed in the case of the lily bud. Remember that almost nothing can prevent the production of a perfect celloidin section except imperfect dehydration of the specimen. One is only safe when the specimen has remained in a large vessel of absolute alcohol, containing copper sulfate at the bottom, for a period of 24 hours, at the end of which time not the slightest trace of color shall have been acquired by the copper sulfate.

A 16% solution of celloidin is then diluted to a strength of 2%. If the lily bud contains very large cavities—that is, if it was taken quite late in its development—it may be necessary, in order to avoid diffusion currents and some consequent bending of the internal structures, to start with a solution as weak as ½% celloidin rather than with the conventional 2%. It is best to fix and dehydrate several buds at one time and to take the first of these up through the conventional process. If this fails a slower method must be used. The bud is then passed to a mixture of equal parts of absolute alcohol and *anhydrous* ether until diffusion currents are no longer apparent. If only 20 or 30 milliliters of the fluid are used for a specimen of this size, it should be changed after about 3 hours and then left overnight in a fresh solution. There is a risk, if an object of this size is picked from alcohol-ether mixture and placed in another fluid, that the rapid evaporation will leave air bubbles; therefore, it is best to place it in a vessel with just enough alcohol-ether mixture to cover it and then to fill this vessel with 2% celloidin. The container is then rocked gently backward and forward to mix the celloidin, and the specimen is left for about 24 hours. This weak celloidin is now poured off, leaving enough of it to cover the object, and 4% celloidin is poured in. The 4% celloidin should be left for three or four days and then replaced in the same manner by 8% celloidin, in which the specimen should be left for at least a week. Eight per cent celloidin is sufficiently viscous to inhibit air bubbles when the specimen is transferred, and it should now be lifted from this thickish celloidin and put into the 16% solution. All these operations

should have been conducted in glass-stoppered bottles kept in a desiccator. The period of time in 16% celloidin is not critical but two or three weeks would be a safe period. The whole process is so long drawn out, that an extra week or two makes little difference; any endeavor to save even a few days in the final impregnation may undo all the previous work.

Now take a wooden block about 1″ × 1″ × 2″ and tie onto it a paper collar (Fig. 80) at least an inch taller than the bud. This is naturally a somewhat cumbersome arrangement; it will probably be best to use an ordinary 5″ × 3″ indexing card, rather than a piece of paper, in order to get the necessary stiffness. A large box of this kind will inevitably leak so that the overlapped edges should be held together with gum arabic, permitted to harden, and then dried in a desiccator. After this block, with its paper walls rising from it, has been thoroughly dried in a desiccator, the paper, and about half of the wooden block, is dipped in 8% celloidin and placed back in the desiccator. This procedure not only holds the paper more firmly in position but also provides an additional assurance against leakage. When this initial coat of celloidin has hardened, about ½ inch of 16% celloidin is poured into the bottom of the box, which is then returned to the desiccator and examined at intervals until the celloidin is found to have hardened sufficiently to bear the weight of the bud. The box is then filled with 16% celloidin and the bud is inserted. It does not matter in the least if the celloidin flows up over the side, but it will be very unfortunate if not enough of it is used. The writer finds that the best method of holding a large object like this in place in the box is to take a couple of entomological pins and drive them clear through the box and the specimen, in areas from which sections are not required. Using a long needle it is then possible to reach down and adjust both the bottom and the top of the long bud so that it lies essentially in the center of the box, held in place by the entomological pins driven through it. Fine pins of this nature do not make a sufficiently large hole to permit any leakage of celloidin. If the box is now not full of celloidin, it is topped off with the 16% solution and placed in a closed vessel (a desiccator is very convenient) in the bottom of which a small quantity of chloroform has been placed. After about a day it will be found that the block has set to a rather opaque jelly-like consistency and the whole thing —block, wood, pins, and paper—is then thrown into a large container of *anhydrous* chloroform. It should remain for a few days in the chloroform and then be transferred to a considerable volume of 70% alcohol, which is changed daily until no smell of chloroform is observed. The block —pins, paper, and all—may be kept in 70% alcohol until it is required.

When it is decided to start sectioning, the block is removed, the pins withdrawn (a pair of pliers will probably be necessary), and the paper shaved from the sides of the block with a sharp knife or razor. It has been presumed in the directions which have so far been given that the required sections will lie about one-third of the distance from the base of the block, since it is obvious that a block of this size will not have the stability to permit cutting at the top. Under these circumstances the upper two-thirds of the block should be removed, and it is safer to do this with a fine saw than with a knife. If it is decided that the portions of the upper block are also required, the block may be cut with a saw into as many pieces as are wanted, and each piece mounted on a celloidin-impregnated wooden block with the solution of Apáthy given in Chapter 27 under the heading E 22.1. Blocks mounted with Apáthy's cement are never as satisfactory, however, as those which have been cast directly onto a wooden block, as in the first case. The reason for the retention of the entire bud through embedding, is, of course, to avoid disturbing the exceedingly delicate relationships of the parts. This would certainly happen if one were to endeavor to embed one third of the bud without leaving the remainder of it attached for support. The lower third of the block on its wooden holder is now mounted in the object holder of a sliding microtome and oriented roughly in the position desired. The block will be found to be sufficiently clear, after one has planed off the

surface with a razor, to see down into it and select that point from which the desired sections will be cut. No difficulty will be experienced in cutting these sections provided the knife slopes back away from the block at an angle of about 30° and hits the corner rather than the edge of the block. Before cutting, provide a beaker containing 70% alcohol, in which the sections are to be accumulated, and another beaker and brush containing 70% alcohol, with which the knife blade and the surface of the block are to be liberally anointed while sectioning is in process. As each section comes off, it should be removed to the dish of 70% alcohol in which the sections may be stored until they are to be stained. It is excellent practice to accumulate a large number of these sections and then to issue them to a class for staining. Celloidin embedding is such a prolonged process that it is difficult to use in class periods, but there is nothing to prevent blocks or sections from being issued to classes to whom a detailed description of the manner in which they have been prepared is given.

A good combination for staining these sections is Delafield's hematoxylin and safranin. However, the ordinary Delafield's hematoxylin solution—the formula for which is given in Chapter 20 as DS 11.122 Delafield (1885)—cannot be used at full strength or it will be difficult to remove from the celloidin matrix. It is better to dilute the original solution with about 10 times its own volume of a 1% solution of ammonium alum. One-tenth of 1% hydrochloric acid in 70% alcohol and one of the solutions of safranin given in Chapter 20 under the heading DS 11.42, are also required. The safranin should be either in water or in an alcohol not stronger than 50%. The solution of Johansen 1940, for example, contains enough Cellosolve to soften a celloidin section undesirably. The formula of Chamberlain 1915 is that commonly employed.

Having accumulated these reagents in three dishes, and a spare dish of 70% alcohol, the sections are placed in safranin. It is difficult to overstain in this fluid and it is probably most convenient to leave it overnight. It should be left at least until it appears to be deeply stained. This will take not less than three or four hours. The next morning, if staining has taken place overnight, each section is transferred separately to acid alcohol and examined under a low power of the microscope until the safranin is observed to be almost removed from the cell walls. The sections are then transferred to distilled water, preferably through two changes, to remove the acid. As soon as the acid has been removed, they are placed in the diluted Delafield's hematoxylin and left there until the cell walls are deeply stained. This will take from five minutes to half an hour, depending on both the thickness of the section and on the nature of the specimen. The sections are then removed, one at a time, to acid alcohol, and left there until the stain has been removed from the celloidin matrix but not from the cell walls. As soon as this result has been achieved the sections are transferred to 70% alcohol, in which they are rinsed in several changes to remove the acid.

Now collect as many slides as are required, a mixture of equal parts absolute alcohol and anhydrous chloroform, and a bottle of whatever resinous medium has been selected as the mountant. The sections are transferred from 70% alcohol direct to absolute alcohol and chloroform, in which they are allowed to remain until dehydrated. Each section is then passed to cedar oil where it remains until it is clear. The sections are now taken one at a time and drained by the corner against a piece of filter paper. A drop of the resinous medium is placed on the slide, the section placed on this, another drop placed on top, and a coverslip applied. If the sections curl to a slight extent, this may be overcome, as has already been pointed out, by placing either a weight or a clip on the cover. If, however, the sections are badly curled, it is desirable to soften the celloidin somewhat. This may be done by using a mixture of cedar oil and clove oil (celloidin is readily soluble in the latter) in place of the pure cedar oil for the clearing. It is as well to try 10% clove oil in cedar oil at first and, if this does not render the sections flexible enough, to increase the quantity of clove oil until they can be flattened.

14

Sections from Double-embedded Material

General Principles

The only purpose of embedding objects first in celloidin and then in paraffin is to secure serial sections of material which cannot be handled by the paraffin method alone. This limits its utility to small objects which cannot with ease be oriented in paraffin, or alternatively, to small objects of which it is quite essential to obtain series, and which like many small arthropods, cannot be retained sufficiently firmly in a wax matrix to permit of sections being obtained.

It is possible to impregnate an object with celloidin (as described in the last chapter) and then to embed the impregnated object in paraffin. There are, however, much better ways available which shorten to a considerable extent this long process. These methods are based on the original suggestion of Peterfi 1921 (23632, **38**:342) that a solution of celloidin in methyl benzoate could profitably be substituted for the more conventional solutions.

By this method the small objects are dehydrated in the manner described in the last chapter, just as much care being necessary as though one were running a straight celloidin impregnation, but are then passed from the absolute alcohol-ether mixture to a celloidin solution containing methyl benzoate or methyl salicylate. These solutions mostly contain 1 % of celloidin. Formulas for some of them

will be found in Chapter 17 under the heading E 22.1. The advantage of methyl ester solutions is that the celloidin does not contract so much on hardening and the solutions may be dropped directly into a solution of chloroform to produce a solid block. Minute objects—usually small arthropods, invertebrate larvae, or protozoans—are first impregnated with the methyl ester solution, and then dropped into a beaker of anhydrous chloroform. Solidification is almost instantaneous and the little globule containing the object may be removed after five or ten minutes. As there is usually difficulty in orienting these minute objects, the author prefers to color the celloidin-embedding medium with the addition of 0.1 % of eosin. This enables the block to be trimmed to a rectangular shape which may itself be orientated without difficulty, for it is now clearly visible in paraffin.

Chips of the embedding medium are added to the chloroform, and this mixture is transferred to the oven until it is fluid. The small block is then removed, placed in pure embedding medium for as long as is necessary, and then made into a paraffin block as described in Chapter 12. These generalities are sufficient to introduce the process which is much better described in the form of the typical preparation which follows.

Typical Example

PREPARATION OF A SERIES OF SECTIONS, INTENDED FOR RECONSTRUCTION, OF A PLUTEUS LARVA OF ECHINUS

Echinoderm larvae are among the most difficult objects from which to cut perfect sections, and the only method by which their anatomy may reasonably be studied is in the form of reconstructions. The present example, since reconstruction has not been previously described, must be prefixed by a discussion of this process.

Reconstruction involves reproduction, either as a side view or as a solid model, of greatly enlarged areas of a section. This book is not the right place to discuss the process in detail, since it is no part of the making of microscope slides. A general understanding of the processes is, however, necessary in order to explain the steps which are taken in preparing the sections. To make a wax reconstruction, camera lucida drawings of the parts of the required sections are transferred to sheets of wax which have been cast of the same thickness as the section would be if it were magnified to the size of the drawings. The relevant portions of the wax are now cut out and piled on top of each other until a solid model, representing an enlargement of the section, has been built. Graphic reconstruction, on the contrary, is done on sheets of graph paper. Lines of the thickness which correspond to the magnification at which one is studying the section are drawn, these lines represent a side view of the section which is being reconstructed. It must be obvious that in both cases it is necessary to have one fixed, straight line running from front to back of the object in order to relate either the wax blocks or the lines drawn to some stable point. Were this not done, any curve, when reconstructed, would appear as a straight line. In reconstructing a vertebrate embryo the problem is simplified because either the center of the notochord, or the dorsal aorta, may be used as a point of reference. Invertebrate larvae, however, suffer from the disadvantage that they rarely have any structure which runs in a straight line through them and some straight lines must be synthesized. This is best done by embedding alongside the object a hair which has been thickly covered with lampblack. After the block has been cast the hair is withdrawn with a sharp jerk (it might really just as well be left in place) leaving a line of lamp black running from front to back. This line will appear as a dot in each successive section and each structure seen in the section may be orientated with regard to the lampblack line.

The first problem in dealing with echinoderm larvae is that of fixation. In the author's experience nothing is to be compared, for this purpose, with the "strong fluid" of Flemming (Chapter 18, F 1600.0010 Flemming 1884). Larvae from plankton samples or from breeding tanks, are accumulated in a small fingerbowl of clean sea water, each one then taken up in a pipet with the smallest possible quantity of sea water, and squirted rapidly into a large volume of fixative. They will be perfectly fixed in about 10 minutes and must immediately be removed to distilled water, in several changes of which they are washed. It is necessary to remove the fixative as rapidly as possible since the osmic acid is liable to deposit osmium hydroxides as a blackened layer over the tissue. Since these objects are to be embedded in celloidin and paraffin, it is necessary for them to be stained before embedding, or endless difficulties will result. The writer prefers, for echinoderm larvae, Mayer's "paracarmine," the formula for which will be found in Chapter 20 as DS 11.22 Mayer 1892a. Fixed specimens should be passed from 70% alcohol to 50% alcohol, which is then replaced with the stain in which the larvae are left from 24 to 48 hours.

It is easy to lose small larvae in changing the staining solutions. It is recommended, therefore, that the tube in which the staining is done be tipped out into a large fingerbowl of the differentiating solution, since the resultant dilution is light enough in color to enable one to see the small larvae floating about. These larvae are then picked out one at a time and placed in a clean tube of the differentiating solution for about half a day. They are then removed to distilled water for two changes of about one hour each, and from this passed through 30% alcohol, 50% alcohol, and back to 70% alcohol, in which they are well washed, and in which they may be preserved until required for sectioning. It may be added that the calcareous spines contained in later pluteus larvae are dissolved by the acetic acid in the fixative and no decalcification is necessary.

The specimens should now be looked over in order to select those in which the "arms" are relatively straight, and these should then be transferred to a tube of absolute alcohol and changed at intervals until they are completely dehydrated. The absolute alcohol is then replaced with a mixture of equal parts of absolute alcohol and anhydrous ether, which is changed once or twice. About three hours between changes will be enough to dehydrate objects of this size.

The embedding solution is prepared by taking 16% stock solution of celloidin in alcohol-ether and adjusting it with additions of alcohol-ether and methyl salicylate to the composition selected. The solution of Heinz 1923, for example (Chapter 17, 21.1 Heinz 1923), with which the writer has had excellent results, is obtained by diluting 12 milliliters of the 16% stock solution of celloidin to a total volume of 50 with a mixture of equal parts absolute alcohol and anhydrous ether, and then mixing with this 50 milliliters of methyl salicylate. The larvae are transferred directly from the alcohol-ether solution to this mixture and may remain for as long as required, but at least for 48 hours.

The author prefers, at this stage, to add a drop or two of a saturated solution of ethyl eosin in absolute alcohol to the medium, in order that the block cast from it may be sufficiently colored to be visible when embedded in wax. After the larvae have remained in this mixture long enough to become impregnated, the tube containing them is tipped into a watch glass. Each individual larva is then taken up in a pipet with a considerable amount of its embedding medium, and the pipet is held vertically until the larva has sunk to the bottom. The largest possible drop containing the larva is then extruded from the pipet into a beaker of anhydrous chloroform and finally shaken off the tip, so that a spherical globule of the embedding medium containing the larva falls into the chloroform, where it coagulates instantly. This is repeated with each of the successive larvae until the batch is finished. If orientation were not of importance, it would now be possible to proceed to paraffin embedding. In a case like this, however, orientation is of primary importance, and the author prefers to transfer, after about an hour in chloroform, each of the little globules to a tube of cedar oil where they remain until they are clear. Each globule is then trimmed, under cedar oil, until the larva lies in a rectangular block of celloidin with the long axis of the larva exactly parallel to the long sides of the rectangular block.

It is now necessary to prepare the hairs which will be used to provide the guide lines used in reconstruction. Take a number of human hairs and dip them into any sticky substance before rolling them backward and forward in a watch glass of lampblack. Remove each hair, shake off as much lampblack as possible, and lay the hair aside until required. When it is required for use, a bow of wood, or plastic, is strung with the hair, which therefore remains straight and under tension.

Now return the celloidin blocks to chloroform where they remain until most of the cedar oil has been removed. Then change to fresh chloroform and add enough chips of the embedding medium to cover the blocks. Now place the tube in the oven until the wax has dissolved in the chloroform. Pour off the chloroform-wax mixture and replace it with fresh wax, in which the objects may continue to impregnate for another hour before being cast into blocks.

Objects as small as this may be conveniently cast in a watch glass. Place a pipet full of wax in a watch glass, hold this touching the surface of a fingerbowl of water, and, as soon as the underside has hardened, transfer a celloidin block to it and orient the block roughly. Now lay one of the stretched hairs alongside the celloidin block, not quite touching, but absolutely parallel. Return the watch glass to the surface of the water so that the block will harden. Then detach the block from the watch glass and trim it, first cutting away the ends of the hair from the bow, and then jerking out the hair to leave a straight line of lampblack behind it. The block is then mounted and cut into serial sections as in Chapter 12.

The only difficulty which is likely to be

encountered is in making sure that the celloidin blocks and their contents adhere firmly to the glass slide. It will usually be found that when the ribbon is flattened on water there is a tendency for the celloidin block to bow up, and it will inevitably become detached in subsequent staining operations. The writer has found, however, that if a saturated solution of ether in water, instead of pure water, is used for flattening, and if each section is pressed firmly in place with wet filter paper and a rubber roller as described in Chapter 12, adhesion will be perfect. Any standard adhesive may be used. The writer's preference in this instance is for the egg albumen of Mayer (Chapter 28, V 21.1 Mayer 1884).

As the sections have already been stained, it is only necessary to remove the wax with xylene and to mount in whatever resinous medium is selected.

15

Frozen Sections

General Principles

Nature of the Process

The last three chapters have dealt with sectioning specimens which have been impregnated with some material to provide support, either through solidification (wax) or through the evaporation of the solvent (nitrocellulose). There are two circumstances under which neither of these processes may be used: first, when it is desired to preserve in the tissues some fatty material which would be dissolved by the reagents used prior to wax impregnation; second, when speed is of primary importance, as in the productions of quick sections from tumors for diagnostic purposes. In both cases recourse may be had to the method of frozen sections in which material is rapidly frozen until it is of a consistency which may be cut. Frozen sections should not, however, be employed on any occasion when the normal processes of embedding may be used.

Choice of a Microtome

Any of the microtomes previously discussed may be used for frozen sections with the aid of special attachments. The type of microtome shown in Fig. 84 is, however, specially made for the purpose and will be taken as the basis for the present discussion. It is essential in cutting frozen sections that the knife should slice rather than push, and this type of microtome produces this movement without the expensive sliding mechanism of the microtome shown in Fig. 56. The slicing effect is produced by mounting the knife to swing through the object when the handle on top is turned. This type of microtome is not as accurate, either as to the thickness of sec-

tion cut, or as to the repetition of this thickness, as is the big slider; but it is presumed that no one would cut frozen sections if thickness and reproducibility were primary objectives. The method of freezing the object will be discussed after we

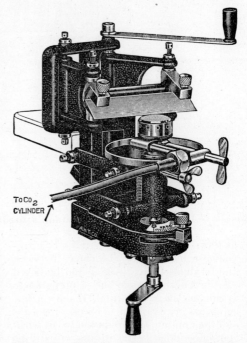

Fig. 84. Spencer clinical microtome fitted for freezing.

have dealt with the question of embedding the material in a supporting substance.

Choice of a Supporting Medium

Biopsy material delivered to a technician from the operating theater is usu-

157

ally cut without having been infiltrated with any material at all. The fact that this procedure gives sections which may be used for diagnostic purposes does not mean that it should be used for any other purpose. The sections so produced are of bad quality compared with sections cut in celloidin or paraffin; but if the material is first embedded in one of the media given in Chapter 27 under the heading E 10, it is possible to produce sections nearly as good

which it is desired to obtain the best possible section, and if time is of secondary importance, the method of Clark 1947 gives sections that are very nearly the equal of those which may be obtained by the paraffin method.

Choice of a Refrigerant

Blocks are nowadays usually frozen with carbon dioxide from cylinders. The cylinder is connected through a needle

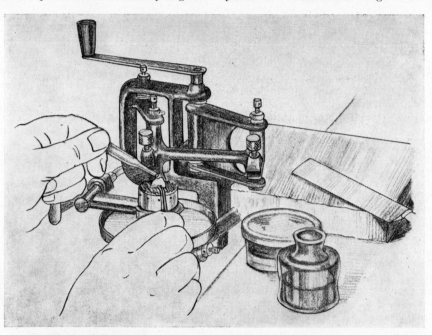

Fig. 85. Applying Anderson's medium to tissue about to be frozen.

as those obtained by the paraffin or nitro-cellulose techniques. The choice between the formulas there given should be based on the length of time one is prepared to spend on the preparation. If only a few moments are available in excess of the absolute minimum time required to cut without embedding, better results will still be obtained if the object is smothered in several layers of the solution of Anderson 1929. Much better results will be obtained, however, if the specimen, after it has been fixed in some material which will not alter its chemical nature, is soaked in this medium overnight in order to become impregnated. In dealing with materials of

valve to the object holder of the microtome, so that a jet of supercooled carbon dioxide may be projected against the underside of the object.

Other methods are available to those who lack carbon-dioxide cylinders. The standard method, prior to the introduction of carbon dioxide, was to replace the tube leading from the carbon-dioxide cylinder with a tube entering a bottle containing ether. Air was then blown through the bottle by a tube, which dipped under the surface of the ether, so that the vapor was projected onto the underside of the block. The head absorbed by the evaporation of the ether was very great and blocks could be frozen by this means almost as rapidly as with carbon dioxide. The stench and fire hazard which accompany this procedure, however, limit it to those who do not have access to carbon-dioxide cylinders.

Process of Cutting

The prime necessity for producing a good section is, of course, a sharp micro-

assumed that a carbon-dioxide cylinder has been attached to the tube leading to the microtome, and that a brief trial has shown the gas to be flowing satisfactorily.

Pick up with the pipet about half a cubic centimeter of the syrup, place this on the freezing table of the microtome, and turn on a small jet of carbon dioxide. Within a moment or two the gum will congeal and the carbon dioxide may be turned

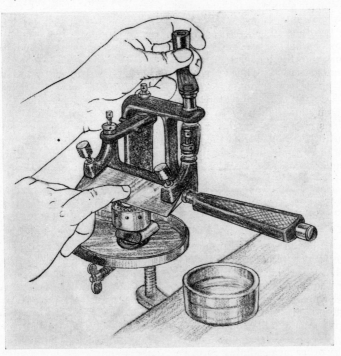

Fig. 86. Removing section from knife.

tome knife. The nature, care, and sharpening of microtome knives has already been discussed in Chapter 12. It may be pointed out here, however, that no provision is made for altering the cutting angle of the knife in most freezing microtomes, therefore, a knife, which is intended for use with a given microtome should be secured from the manufacturer.

Let us assume that we have slightly more than the minimum time, and that a section is to be made with the syrup of Anderson. Before cutting, set out a bottle of this syrup, a pipet of the eye-dropper type, and a jar of 70% alcohol in which to receive the sections as they are cut. It is

off. The object to be sectioned is then (Fig. 85) placed on top of this congealed layer of gum, and more gum is poured over the surface. Care must be taken that there is a layer of uncongealed gum beneath the object or it may loosen. Turn on the carbon dioxide and, as soon as the gum covering the object is congealing, pour on a little more gum so that the object becomes thoroughly covered. Next, turn off the carbon dioxide and insert the knife. Take an experimental cut across the top of the material and continue to shave it down with the thickness control set at 40 microns until the specimen is reached. Now reset the thickness control. No attempt should be made to cut sections thinner than 20 microns by this method; sections of 30 microns are usually good enough for diagnostic purposes.

The sections must be observed closely as they come from the block. If they crumble under the action of the knife, while the gum melts instantly on contact with it, it may be presumed that the block has not been frozen sufficiently hard, and the carbon dioxide should again be turned on for a few moments. It will only take a moment or two to establish the optimum condition under which only slightly curled sections appear on the blade of the knife. These preliminary cuts will, however, have soiled the blade which must now be washed with a drop of warm water to remove the gum and then used to cut as many sections as are required. As each section is cut it is removed from the blade of the knife to 70% alcohol. Most people working under pressure use the little finger (Fig. 86) for the removal of the section, though a number of very competent technicians prefer to use a brush. The gum quickly dissolves from the sections in 70% alcohol. The sections may then either be handled with a section lifter or attached to a slide with one of the adhesives given in Chapter 28 under the heading V 21.3.

Staining and Mounting Sections

Every pathological laboratory has its own well-established routine for staining frozen sections obtained from biopsy. Without wishing to suggest that this routine be altered, the writer would like to draw attention to the existence of the techniques of Kingsley (Chapter 20, DS 13.13 Kingsley 1935) which, standardized as a routine, permit the comparison of diagnostic frozen sections, if necessary, with permanent paraffin sections stained in an identical manner.

Typical Example

PREPARATION OF A SECTION OF FATTY MATERIAL EMBEDDED IN GELATIN BY THE METHOD OF CLARK 1947

The discussion of general principles given above was centered around the assumption that a freezing microtome is to be used for the production of diagnostic sections under pressure of time. The present description is of a method whereby a section of research quality may be obtained of material which cannot be sectioned by any other means. Let us suppose that it is necessary to section some fatty bodies, either from vertebrate or invertebrate material, with a view to making permanent slides in order to record such changes as may have taken place under varying conditions.

The fatty bodies are dissected out from wherever it is decided to secure them, and are placed in 4% formaldehyde until required. They may be left indefinitely but they should be hardened for at least a week.

Before embedding the pieces are washed in running water overnight. The technique of Clark 1947 (11431, **59**:337) requires a 25% dispersion of gelatin in water (made by soaking 25 grams of gelatin in water until it is thoroughly swollen, melted, and diluted to 100) and a 12.5% gelatin (which may either be prepared fresh or by the dilution of the 25% gelatin stock).

The tissue, after having been washed for at least 24 hours in running water, is placed in 12.5% gelatin in an oven at 37.5°C. A block of tissue of about ½-inch cube requires 24 hours in this solution before being transferred to 25% gelatin maintained at the same temperature. It should spend from 24 to 36 hours in this thick gelatin bath and should then be embedded in 25% gelatin exactly as though it were a paraffin block. That is, a paper box should be prepared in the manner described in Chapter 12. Molten gelatin is poured onto the bottom of the box and, as soon as it has solidified, the specimen is inserted and surrounded with further gelatin. The block is now placed in a refrigerator to harden and left there until required. When it is taken out for cutting, the paper is stripped from the outside, and the block trimmed until the object lies in the required orientation. This trimmed block is then left to harden in 2% formaldehyde for 24 hours.

The hardened block is now taken and placed on the freezing stage of a microtome, preferably a slider of the type shown in Fig. 55. The block is carefully oriented on the stage and chilled with the aid of a stream of carbon dioxide until sections may be taken from it. If the block has been properly made, and is cooled to the correct extent, it behaves almost exactly as though it were a nitrocellulose block.

Each section, as it is cut, is removed from the knife with a brush, and the sections are accumulated in 50% alcohol. Each section is then taken individually in a pair of forceps, dipped for a moment in 5% gelatin, and then placed in the center of a clean slide. These sections are flexible and may be flattened to the slide without difficulty. As soon as the surplus fluid has been drained off, the slide is placed in a coplin jar at the bottom of which are a few milliliters of 40% formaldehyde. Exposure to formaldehyde for about an hour will fix the section firmly; the process may be accelerated in an oven at a temperature of 37°C. The slides, after hardening in formaldehyde vapor, may be stored in 2% formaldehyde.

The next problem is that of staining and mounting. In the writer's opinion the best stain for the demonstration of fat in sections of this type is that of Lillie 1945 (Chapter 21 DS 22.4). This method requires a saturated solution of oil blue in 60% isopropanol, a 0.1% solution of Bismark brown R in water and some 5% acetic acid. The slides to be stained are removed from 2% formaldehyde, rinsed

briefly, and transferred to the blue solution where they should remain from five to ten minutes, or until examination under the low power of the microscope shows that the individual fat granules have absorbed the blue dye. They are then briefly rinsed in water and transferred to Bismark brown solution for one to two minutes. When they are removed from this solution they will appear to be a muddy brown, and should then be rinsed in 5% acetic acid until examination under the microscope shows the fat granules to be brilliant blue while the supporting connective tissues are stained brown. The slide should then be rinsed in water to remove the acetic acid and return to 2% formaldehyde to await mounting.

It is obvious that slides of this nature cannot be mounted in a resinous medium, for the necessary dehydrating and dealcoholizing agents would remove the fat from the sections. It is therefore necessary that they be either mounted in glycerol jelly in the manner described in Chapter 5, or (in the author's opinion this is better) in one of the gum media described in Chapter 4. The author has naturally a preference for his own formula (Chapter 26, M 13.1 Gray and Wess 1950). The sections can be mounted permanently in this media by removing them from 2% formaldehyde, rinsing them briefly in water, draining them, placing a drop of the mounting medium on top of each section, and applying a coverslip. The slides will be hard enough to handle in less than an hour, and will be as nearly permanent as any section of fatty material can be.

16

Injections

General Principles

Nature of the Process

Injection is the art of filling cavities in materials intended for microscopical examination, with some material which will render them more visible. In materials intended for gross dissection, the preparation of which is not described in this book, only the blood vessels are so treated and the idea has, therefore, developed that the process may only be applied to blood vessels. From the point of view of the microscopist any cavity may be filled whether it be blood, lymph, or bile vessels, or even the caniculi of bone (see Chapter 28, V 31.1 Altmann 1876). The material to be injected, if it is to be readily visible, must be either brightly colored or densely opaque. Though the term *injection* usually brings [to mind the insertion of materials under pressure, there are some cases, as in the example just mentioned, in which a vacuum may be used to displace a fluid or air and then replaced with the material being used. Injections may be prepared either as sections or as whole-mounts, but different methods and materials should be used for each. It will be necessary, therefore, to discuss first the selection of the injection medium, second the methods by which this medium may be inserted into the cavity which one desires to demonstrate, and lastly the method of preparing a permanent mount from the tissues so injected.

Before proceeding with this discussion, however, it is necessary to point out that injection is not the only, or even the best, means of showing fine vessels in a microscopic preparation. In Chapters 21 and 23 will be found methods of demonstrating both blood capillaries and bile capillaries by differential staining. These methods are usually less laborious than is the process of injection and should always be tried before an injection is undertaken.

Selection of an Injection Medium

The requirements of an injection mass are that it shall run readily into the vessels being injected, that it be readily visible when it is in the vessels, and that it remain in place through subsequent manipulations. The requirement that it should go into the vessels easily is met by providing a fluid medium of low surface tension which does not itself cause contraction of the muscular coats of the blood vessels. The condition of low surface tension is usually met by including in the medium a certain quantity of glycerol, though Hagmann 1940 (20540b, **15**:115) has recommended the inclusion of a wetting agent in a medium intended for injection of insect trachea. There is no reason why similar wetting agents should not be included in media intended for blood vessels.

The requirement that the injection should be visible when in position may be met in two ways. First one may incorporate with the injection mass a pigment finely enough divided to be apparently invisible but of a sufficiently large molecular size not to pass through the wall of the capillaries. The majority of injection masses are of this type and the detailed directions for preparation of them (Chapter 28, V 31.1) are largely devoted to the precipitation of a pigment of such fine grain size that it fulfills the required conditions. The second method of achieving the same result is to inject some material which can, with ease, be subsequently stained differentially. Thus Fischer 1902 (23681, **13**:277) recommended the injection of milk, the fat in which could subsequently be stained by any of the fat-staining methods (Chapter 21, DS 22.4). The objection to this type of mount, however, is that it cannot be dehydrated without the removal of fat, and must, therefore, be mounted in one of the aqueous mounting media discussed in Chapters 4 and 5, few of which have an index of refraction high enough to show the specimens properly. There is also the objection that, if the specimens are to be sectioned, a freezing technique must be used rather than the more conventional paraffin or nitrocellulose methods. A far better approach to this problem is that of Altmann 1878 (23632, **10**:191) who suggested the injection of dilute olive oil which could be stained, before embedding, with osmic acid. Various methods have from time to time been proposed for the injections of solutions of stains of such low penetrating power that they will not pass beyond the walls of the capillaries. Robin 1871, p. 40 and Hoyer 1882 (2981, **2**:19) suggested the injection of media containing silver nitrate which was subsequently "developed" with one of the solutions intended for the development of silver by metal-staining techniques (see Chapter 23, AMS 21.1).

The problem of ensuring that the blood vessels remain open while the injection medium is inserted into them is more difficult to solve. Glycerol in particular causes the blood vessels to contract, but this difficulty can be overcome in two ways. Either the animal may be killed with some substance which causes the greatest possible vasodilation, such as alcohol or amyl nitrite, or blood can be washed from the vessels with a normal citrate-saline, and then this fluid followed by some material, such as formaldehyde, which will fix and harden the blood vessels in an open condition. This was the universal practice of the older workers but is rarely done today.

The final difficulty is that of persuading materials to stay in place after they have been injected. This is not difficult in the preparation of wholemounts, in which cut surfaces of blood vessels are unlikely to be exposed. It is very difficult, however, in the case of materials which have to be sectioned and from the cut blood vessels of which material is likely to be washed, in the course of manipulation, if it is not specifically held in position. It is, therefore, desirable that the injection pigment should be incorporated in some mass which may be hardened in position. This again points up one of the advantages of using milk, which may be readily coagulated. Egg white, which may also be easily coagulated in position, is unsatisfactory for the reason that it is difficult to incorporate pigments with it. Gelatin, which may be set in position by cooling, and subsequently hardened by formaldehyde to a condition which cuts readily, is of almost universal employment.

An interesting method for obviating all of these difficulties is one of the oldest in microtomy. This consists of first injecting a solution of some material and, second, injecting after it a material which will cause a precipitation of a relatively gross pigment *in situ*. This method is of great antiquity and was apparently discovered by Doyère sometime before 1839 (see Cooper 1847, 156). Doyère himself recommended several solutions, but the author has only seen successful preparations prepared by the injection of 2% potassium dichromate followed by 2% lead acetate. This method, which is described in detail in one of the typical preparations following this chapter, has recently been rediscovered by various authors and yields finer injections of capillaries than are obtainable by any other method. It is not, of course, satisfactory for thin sections from which the material would be readily washed, but a thick section of a human kidney in the writer's collection, prepared by this method sometime before 1847, shows a better demonstration of the glomeruli than is obtainable by any other method.

Methods of Injection

There are two methods by which injection media may be inserted into fine blood vessels. In the first method an inert mate-

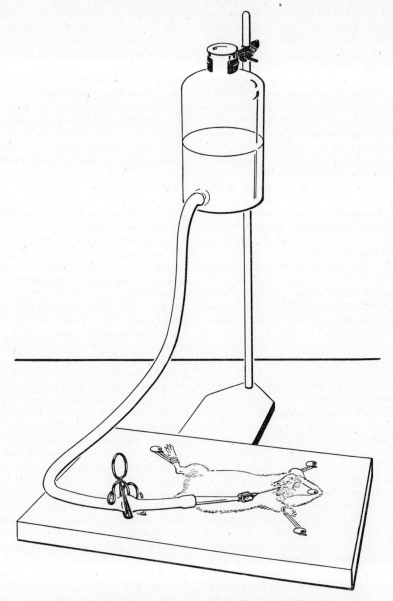

Fig. 87. Injecting a rat through the carotid artery.

rial, such as milk or a suspension of India ink, is injected into the blood stream, and the natural pumping action of the heart is utilized to carry it to the finest capillaries. The second method is to force the injection medium into the blood vessels of a dead animal in such a manner that it displaces the fluid already there. One method of *auto-injection* is described in considerable detail in one of the examples which terminate this chapter.

Forcing an injection material into the blood vessel of a dead animal is by no means as easy as it sounds. In the first place one has to secure some hollow tube which may be inserted into the blood vessel and held there firmly in spite of pressure being applied. An ordinary hypodermic needle cannot be used because it cannot be held firmly in the blood vessel; it is too smooth, even when tied in place, to withstand the pressure of the injection. The older books are filled with descriptions of injection "pipes" which had a little ridge of metal turned on their ends, around which a thread might be tied to hold them in position. These pipes were, however, mostly very large and could rarely be used with anything smaller than the dorsal aorta of a rabbit. It is very easy to turn a hypodermic needle into a good injection pipe by putting a little ridge of fine silk on it immediately behind the orifice. The only silk which is suitable is that used for tying trout flies, and is sold under the designation *six O*. The hypodermic should be held in a convenient holder, the end of the silk attached with a half-hitch just behind the orifice, wrapped around a half-dozen times, and then built up into a little ridge of four or five layers before being finished with a *whip finish*. A drop of any good lacquer or varnish is then used to impregnate the silk, and the minute injection pipe is ready. If the reader cannot understand this description it is recommended that he apply to the nearest tier of trout flies who will be able in ten minutes to prepare for him a dozen needles.

The next difficulty which must be faced is to attach to the other end of the needle some apparatus through which pressure may be maintained in order to drive in the injection medium. The ordinary hypodermic syringe, for which these needles are made, is singularly ill-adapted to the purpose. Pressure will have to be applied for a considerable time, and various devices have from time to time been proposed for leaning a weight of some kind upon the upper end of the plunger. The writer, however, has always had more success with the device shown in Fig. 87 in which a bottle containing the injection medium is suspended, at a height which may be varied, above the object being injected. The difficulty here is to secure a satisfactory attachment between the bottle and the hypodermic needle. In the

illustration, a piece of heavy-walled glass tube has been drawn out to approximately the right size and then ground at the tip, in the manner in which the tip of a hypodermic syringe is ground, to fit the needle. This can easily be done by any competent glass blower, but the process is beyond the facilities of most laboratories. It is, however, so necessary and so desirable, that the worker who intends to conduct a number of injections is well advised to have some of these glass tubes made. It must be emphasized that a method of detaching the needle from the supply must be available, since in almost all injection methods two or more fluids must be successively used. It is highly desirable to wash the excess blood from the animal by running a saline solution through the blood vessels before the insertion of the injection medium, and this obviously cannot be done unless the attachment to the needle may be readily changed. Equipment of the type shown is used, however, only when one desires to inject most of the capillaries of an entire animal and it cannot be used satisfactorily with a gelatin medium which has to be kept molten throughout the course of the injection. If such a warm injection is to be made, one must provide a heating jacket to surround the bottle containing the medium, and also immerse the entire animal in a tray of hot water until the injection is completed. Gelatin media, in fact, are far better adapted for the injection of small parts of animals (as described in one of the specific examples following this chapter) in which a hypodermic syringe may be used under the surface of warm water.

There are three very common causes of the failure which attends the first attempts of almost every individual to make an injection. The first of these is the failure to provide some means for the blood to get out when the injection medium is inserted. It is ridiculous to insert a needle into an artery and to expect an injection medium to be pushed through, unless some provision is made for the removal of the blood through the corresponding vein. One cannot, moreover, merely sever an artery and insert the needle into its end, or the bleeding from the other cut end will provide too ready a means of egress for the material inserted. One should, therefore, always slit the artery, slide the injection needle into the slit, and then ligate it in two places, the proximal ligature being for the purpose of holding the needle in place, and the distal ligature being for the purpose of sealing the other end of the slit.

The second great cause for failure lies in the stopping up of the blood vessels before an injection has reached them. This stoppage may be produced either by the natural contractions of the vessels themselves, or by the presence in the injection medium of some particle too coarse to pass through the finer capillaries. The contraction of the vessels themselves may be prevented by killing the animal with a vasodilating material, or by waiting before injection until rigor mortis has passed off. If the latter course is adopted one must, of course, wash the contained blood out of the blood vessels with a saline solution in order to prevent coagulation.

The last, and most frequent, cause of failure is that the blood vessels will burst before the medium has penetrated them. This is obviously due to the application of too great pressure, and is commonest among workers who use a hypodermic syringe and endeavor to push in the injection as if they were making a hypodermic injection of a drug. The rat shown in Fig. 87 was perfused, using the pressure shown, for a period of six hours with a glycerol-carmine mixture before the injection could be considered complete. It is occasionally possible, with very small organs, to complete an injection in a few moments, but it is usually far better to use a low pressure and take a long time, not only to avoid bursting of the vessels but also to prevent a gross swelling and distortion of them.

Mounting Injections

Injections may either be mounted as a wholemount in the manner described in Chapter 6, or prepared as sections by the methods described in Chapters 12, 13, and 14. In either case the material, after injection, should be fixed in a medium which will coagulate the injection material, if sections are to be cut, or which will remove the unwanted portions of the injection medium, such as glycerol, if wholemounts are to be made. The processes of dehydrating, clearing, and mounting, or embedding need not be described further since they have already been dealt with in the chapters indicated; but attention should be drawn to the fact that sections, if they are to be cut, should be relatively thick. The only purpose of an injection is to show the course of blood vessels and this cannot be done in an ordinary histological section of 10 or 12 microns in thickness. It is much better to cut a section of from $\frac{1}{10}$- to $\frac{1}{4}$-millimeter in thickness, and then to treat that as though it were a wholemount, being particularly careful that it is perfectly dehydrated and perfectly cleared so that the uninjected portions may be as transparent as glass. In sections of this type one may easily follow the course of even the finest blood vessels with the aid of a binocular dissecting microscope.

The general principles discussed in this chapter are illustrated by three quite different injections which will now be described.

Specific Examples

INJECTION OF THE BLOOD VASCULAR SYSTEM OF A 60-HOUR CHICK EMBRYO WITH INDIA INK

The trick of making these preparations, which are so widely used for teaching purposes, appears to be known to very few people and is, therefore, worthwhile describing here. The age of 60 hours for the chick has been specified in this example because this is the easiest size on which to learn the technique; but the method to be described can equally well, after some practice, be applied to any chicken embryo between the time when the heart is first formed and the end of the 96th hour, when the specimen becomes too big to inject conveniently. A description is given elsewhere (Chapter 20) of the removal of an embryo from the yolk and need not be repeated.

To prepare the medium, take any commercial India ink and dilute it with about ten times its volume of distilled water, to each 100 milliliters of which has been added one drop of ammonia. The use of tap water, particularly if slightly acid, tends to agglomerate the carbon particles and thus to make injection impossible. Next make a series of hollow glass needles of a size suitable for the injection. For these take short lengths of ordinary, soft-glass, 3-millimeter tubing, heat them in a flame until they are soft, remove them from the flame, and draw them out to about 1 millimeter in diameter; then return them to the flame, pulling sharply, when they are soft so as to secure a fine tip. This tip should be almost exactly the size of the Cuverian sinus of the embryo which is to be injected. It is simplest to prepare two or three dozens of these little injection needles, approximately the right size and then to select the best. One needle may be used for the entire batch but the exact size is vital to the success of the operation. In case the worker is unacquainted with the Cuverian sinus, he is recommended to look at the body of the embryo just along the side of the heart, where he will see that a large anterior and a large posterior vein come together to form the cross piece of a T, the stem of which passes downward towards the heart. This stem is the Cuverian sinus.

Now secure two stender dishes, one filled with the diluted India ink, and the other with physiological saline. Syracuse watch glasses, one for each embryo to be injected, should be placed in a dish of water at about 40°C., so that they may be warmed through, and a small beaker of any fixative, with an eye-dropper type pipet in it, should be at hand. Two pairs of fine forceps will be required, as well as the large scissors and blunt-nosed forceps used to remove the embryo. The injection is best made under a wide-angled dissecting binocular which is set up to transmit light through the embryo.

Now remove an embryo from the yolk and, after washing it in the manner described in Chapter 20, transfer it to one of the warmed watch glasses containing physiological saline. Drain out most of the saline so as to leave the embryo and

its surrounding extra-embryonic areas stranded on the bottom, and transfer the dish to the stage of the binocular microscope. A needle of the required size is now selected and attached to a short length of rubber tubing, terminating in a mouthpiece of the type sold for use with blood pipets. Dip this needle under the surface of the injection medium and suck until a considerable portion of the glass tube is filled. Remove the needle from the injection medium and transfer it to the dish of normal saline. Now give a very slight suck on the tube in such a manner as to fill the fine capillary portion of the tube with saline without drawing in enough to dilute the India ink in the body of the tube. This is the most vital stage in the proceedings, for if the fine capillary is left filled with India ink, this ink will flow out as soon as the needle touches the heart and the operator's view will be obscured.

After each injection is done, return the injection tube to the dish of normal saline and again refill the capillary tip with saline.

The only dissection of the embryo that is necessary is to split a hole through the pericardium. This may be readily done by tearing with two pairs of fine forceps, one held in each hand. Utmost care should be taken not to break any blood vessels in doing this, but a few minutes' practice on some embryos will be far more instructive than any amount of description. Now pick up the injection needle and take the mouthpiece at the end of the rubber tube between the teeth.

Provided the mouthpiece is kept in the teeth and the mouth kept open, no pressure can possibly be applied before it is required. Assuming the operator to be right-handed, so that the tube is in his right hand, the embryo is now turned so that its anterior-posterior axis is at about 45° to the operator with the head lying, as it were, to the northwest. The tip of the injection needle, which it is to be remembered is filled with saline and *not* with India ink, is now applied to the heart just at the bend. A sharp, short stab is used to drive the needle through until the end of the needle lies free in the cavity of the ventricle; a very slight and careful pressure is now applied with the mouth, while one watches the stream of saline coming out of the end to make sure that it is going into the ventricle. If the needle does not lie in the ventricle it may be withdrawn and a further stab made. A skilled operator can stab so as to bring the aperture of the needle into the ventricle nine out of ten times; this is the only skill which is required in the whole operation. As soon as the tip of the needle is seen to lie in the right place, blow *very gently* until a small quantity of India ink enters the heart. Even though the heart has stopped beating it will now usually start again under the action of the foreign substance inserted. Continue to blow gently so as to keep the ventricle at all times filled with India ink. It is practically impossible to inject into the blood vessels of the chick by pressure; one is forced to rely on the movements of the heart to drive the material round. If the ventricle is filled with India ink and emptied by contraction a

half-dozen times, the injection will be found to be perfectly satisfactory, even to the tip of the finest arteries.

The injection of the veins is slightly more difficult, since it must be undertaken by pressure and in this case the tip of the needle is inserted exactly into the junction of the anterior and posterior cardinal sinuses with the Cuverian sinus. In this case, as soon as the needle is in position, blow with a gentle continuous pressure, watching the other parts of the embryo, and cease instantly when the India ink has distributed itself to the ends of the veins. A really successful preparation will fill most of the veins as well as the arteries by injection through the ventricle.

Now remove the needle and drop a small quantity of the selected fixative onto the embryo. If this is done rapidly there will be no leakage of India ink from the tip of the ventricle, and the injection may then be turned into a wholemount by any of the methods described in Chapter 6.

Precipitation of Lead Chromate in the Glomeruli of a Rabbit Kidney

This is a preparation of great difficulty, not lightly to be undertaken by the inexperienced, but of which the beauty more than justifies the effort.

The method requires three solutions, each in the quantity of several hundred milliliters. The first solution is a physiological saline which has been saturated, by shaking, with amyl nitrite. Amyl nitrite is a vasodilator of great strength and should be handled carefully. The second solution is a 2% solution of potassium or sodium dichromate, and the third is a 2% solution of lead acetate. All three of these solutions should be passed through a filter immediately before use. There are also required three aspirator bottles, with tubes and glass tips set up in the manner shown in Fig. 87. Lastly a hypodermic needle will be required, with a silk ridge raised on it in the manner described above, and with a diameter approximately two-thirds that of the renal artery of a rabbit. It is also necessary to have a dish of such a depth that the kidney may be covered with physiological saline.

Now kill the rabbit, preferably with the aid of ether to which has been added a

considerable quantity of amyl nitrite. Ether produces unconsciousness quickly but death very slowly, and great care should be taken that the rabbit is completely dead before proceeding further.

Stretch the rabbit on a board, open the abdomen, push the intestines to one side to expose the kidney, and then carefully trace the course both of the renal artery and of the renal vein. These two are then ligated in two places with surgical silk and severed between the ligatures. Now dissect out the rest of the kidney until it is free from the body. It is far more important that the surface of the kidney should not be damaged than that it should be free of adherent tissues. Remove the kidney from the rabbit and transfer it to a dish of physiological saline, which is then placed under a binocular dissecting microscope. Insert the hypodermic needle into the renal artery and tie it firmly in place. Take care that the hypodermic needle is entirely filled with saline and that no air enters. This is why it is desirable to work under the surface of saline.

An aspirator bottle filled with amyl-nitrite-saturated saline is now arranged as shown in Fig. 87, and the ground end of the glass connection inserted into the hypodermic needle. This should be done under the surface of saline in order to avoid any possibility of air bubbles. Cut the renal vein above the first ligature and remove the clip from the rubber tube leading to the aspirator bottle. A stream of blood will immediately leave the renal vein as it is displaced by the saline being injected into the artery, and the perfusion should be continued until this stream of blood stops. Now replace the clip on the rubber tube and withdraw the glass connection from the hypodermic needle. Change the bloody saline in the dish for clean saline, being careful that at no time does the open end of the hypodermic needle have any opportunity to acquire an air bubble.

Now take the second aspirator bottle which contains the 2% potassium dichromate, remove the clip until a clear stream of chromate is flowing through the glass connection, and then attach the glass connection to the hypodermic needle. Open the clip again and allow the potassium dichromate to flow through until it is seen to have replaced the saline in its entirety. Replace the clip again, remove the dichromate-filled aspirator bottle, and replace the dichromate-contaminated saline in the dish with fresh saline. It is better to replace it two or three times to be quite certain that no dichromate remains in the dish. Before the last change of saline, briefly connect the aspirator bottle containing the saline and the hypodermic needle, and permit the saline to flow for about a couple of seconds to make sure that the hypodermic needle and its connections are again rendered free of dichromate. If this precaution is not taken, the needle is almost certain to become choked with lead chromate when the lead acetate is injected, and the solution in the dish will become so cloudy that one can no longer see what is going on.

As soon as there is no potassium dichromate anywhere except in the kidney, take the third bottle containing the 2% lead acetate and connect it to the hypodermic needle. Remove the clip and permit the lead acetate to flow until the entire kidney has assumed a dense, opaque yellow ap-

pearance. It is very improbable that any of the precipitated lead acetate will be forced through the fine capillaries of the glomeruli and out through the renal vein. The time necessary to precipitate the material within the glomeruli of the kidney may vary from five minutes to two or three hours but can readily be judged by eye. Even though only certain areas of the kidney go densely opaque yellow, the preparation should not be rejected since many sections may be obtained from even a small, properly injected, area. The kidney is now removed from the saline and thrown into 10% formaldehyde until it is next required.

The kidney will be sufficiently hardened to permit sectioning in about a week. At the end of this time, therefore, the kidney is transferred to a saline solution and cut into slices about two millimeters thick. Do not be alarmed that there will be liberated at this time considerable quantities of lead dichromate. The lead dichromate will not come out of the fine capillaries of the glomeruli, and each slice should be washed until it ceases to give rise to the clouds of yellow pigment which are, by this process, removed from almost all vessels except the finest ones. These two-millimeter slices should now be cut into sections about 100 microns thick ($\frac{1}{10}$ millimeter). This may be done either by embedding them in a very soft wax in the manner described in Chapter 12, or, far better, by embedding them in nitrocellulose in the manner described in Chapter 13. Whichever method is adopted, the sections should be mounted in balsam, and the utmost care should be taken to dehydrate and clear them thoroughly, so that the uninjected tissues appear glass-clear. After they are mounted these sections may be studied by transmitted light, in which case the glomeruli will be seen only as an opaque shadow; or they may be studied by reflected light, either after the slide has been placed on a black background, or after a piece of black paper has been attached to the undersurface. The examination of these specimens by reflected light will show the relationships of the glomeruli, and their attendant arterioles, better than any other method known to the author.

Injection of the Intestinal Capillaries of a Rabbit with Carmine-gelatin

The capillaries of the intestine may, of course, be injected with lead chromate in the manner described in the last example. This illustration is given, however, for the benefit of those who prefer the more conventional method of filling the fine capillaries with red gelatin for study.

The same rabbit may be used as was used in the last example provided that there are available two more aspirator bottles, one containing normal saline and the other 4% formaldehyde. While the kidney is being perfused with saline, in the manner described in the last example, remove a length of about two inches from the intestine, including a portion in which a branch of the mesenteric artery is seen to enter the intestine. Now place this in the dish with the kidney and attach it to its own aspirator system of normal saline, after having inserted a hypodermic needle into the artery exactly as described in the case of the kidney. Perfuse this specimen until all the blood has been removed. Now transfer it to another dish and perfuse, after the normal saline, 4% formaldehyde. It will be noticed that in this preparation, no precautions have been taken to open a relieving vein; the purpose of the perfusion with 4% formaldehyde is to expand the fine capillaries and permit them to set in this expanded condition. After the perfusion has gone on for about a couple of hours, remove the piece of intestine and transfer it to a jar of 4% formaldehyde, where it may remain until next required.

The writer has never found it practical to set up an elaborate arrangement of hot-water baths with a view to injecting fresh material with a gelatin mixture and, therefore, has always recommended that the material be fixed and hardened with the capillaries widely expanded. By this means it is possible to secure a specimen which may be injected relatively rapidly with a carmine-gelatin material held in a hypodermic syringe.

Of the many carmine-gelatin injection media, the formulas for which are given in Chapter 28 under the heading V 32.1, the writer prefers that of Moore 1929. About 100 milliliters of the selected mass will be required.

Before the injection can be made, the formaldehyde must be removed from the specimen. This may be done by washing the specimen for two or three days in running water, though it is usually safer in addition to perfuse it through the needle—which has, of course, remained attached to the artery throughout this period—using an aspirator system set on a shelf above the sink in which the specimen is being washed. When all of the formaldehyde has been removed, secure a vessel large enough to hold both hands, a one- or two-milliliter hypodermic syringe, and the specimen. Fill the dish with water heated to about 35°C. before placing in it the kidney and the hypodermic syringe. The temperature is not of importance, provided that it is above the melting point of the gelatin mixture. Melt the gelatin on a water bath and, when the kidney and needle have both been warmed through, remove the hypodermic syringe from the water bath, fill it in the ordinary manner with the injection mass, and then lower it into the water bath and attach it to the hypodermic needle. Now apply a slow and gentle pressure to the end of the plunger until a sufficient quantity of gelatin has been injected into the capillaries. The terminal point of the operation may be judged when reasonably large areas have become bright pink to red in color. Do not expect the injection to go into the whole length of the intestine; be satisfied if ¼ of an inch is well injected.

Now remove the hypodermic syringe and then drop the piece of intestine into ice water in order to chill and set the gelatin. As soon as the kidney is chilled it is transferred back to 10% formaldehyde, where it may remain until wanted for the production of sections of about 100 microns in thickness. In the present case excellent sections may be prepared by embedding in any low-melting-point wax, and cutting single sections on any kind of microtome. These sections are then attached to the slides by using very considerable quantities of adhesive, before being dewaxed and transferred to balsam in the manner described in Chapter 12.

Part II

Methods and Formulas Used in Making Microscope Slides

Foreword to Part II

Part I of this book described the methods of making microscope slides and contained specific information as to techniques and formulas only in the typical preparations which were appended to each chapter. This second part of the book contains specific information both as to techniques and formulas, but does not give general instructions as to the preparation of the slides except in a few typical preparations inserted into Chapters 20, 21, and 23, which deal with staining.

Classification

The 3500 specific formulas and methods which follow have been arranged according to a system of classification designed to bring similar methods and formulas together, and to make it easy for the worker to find that which he requires.

The primary division of this mass of material has been into chapters; within each chapter there is a decimal division of the contents. Each chapter is designated by one, two, or three letters which indicate the nature of the formulas and techniques contained in it. Thus, DS stands for dye stains, ADS for accessory dye stains, and so on. The complete decimal classification employed in each chapter is given at the beginning of each chapter, and, for purposes of cross reference, each formula or method is assigned the letter of its chapter and its own decimal designation. Thus a reference to DS 11.41 indicates division 11.41 of Chapter 20. The addition of the author's name and date to the decimal classification renders clear the identity of the method referred to, and permits it to be given in the least possible space. By this method it has been possible to ensure that no formula for a solution is given more than once, and that each solution is placed with other solutions of similar composition or properties. The method by which journal references have been added to these designations is explained in the Introduction.

Measurements and Units Employed

With the exception of the fixatives (Chapter 18) all formulas for solutions have been adjusted to give approximately 100 parts. The fixatives have been arranged to give either 250 parts when prepared from pure reagents, or 100 parts when prepared from the stock solutions described in the second part of Chapter 18. This exception, in the case of the fixatives, has been made since the writer has convinced himself, by inquiring among numerous workers, that 250 milliliters is the quantity of fixative most frequently prepared.

It is to be presumed, in the preparation of all the solutions, that fluids are measured by volume and solids by weight. The words *milliliter* and *gram* have, therefore, been omitted since their inclusion would have added 30 or 40 pages to the total length of the book. In a few cases where the context does not make it entirely clear that fluids are to be measured in volumes and solids by weight, the appropriate units have been given.

Saturated solutions are assumed to mean saturated solutions at room temperature, unless otherwise specified. It is also to be understood that the solvent of a saturated solution is water unless a specific statement to the contrary is made. In a few cases which might cause confusion, as in the case of dyes which are equally frequently dissolved in alcohol or water, the designation *sat. aq. sol.* has been used to indicate that water is the solvent.

The words "in water" have also been omitted following the words "wash," "rinse," etc. unless the context does not render the meaning of the instruction clear. It is also to be presumed, unless a specific designation to the contrary is made, that distilled water will be used in all operations.

Certain pharmaceutical abbreviations, used to shorten the technical directions for making up certain solutions, will be found expanded in the List of Abbreviations immediately preceding the "List of Books and Journals cited."

17

Preservatives

Decimal Divisions Used in Chapter

P 00 Generalities

P 01 GENERAL OBSERVATIONS

The distinction between *preservatives*, *fixatives*, and *mountants* is difficult to draw and has not always been observed in biological literature. As used in the present work, a *preservative* is distinguished from a *mountant* only in that the latter will hold the coverslip in place of its own accord, while the former requires that the coverslip be sealed in position by one of the methods described in Chapters 2 and 3. It does not, for example, appear justifiable to the writer to refer to the well-known lactophenol of Amman (P 12.2 Amman 1898) as a mountant, since it cannot be used for the preparation of permanent slides unless the edge of the coverslip is sealed. The distinction between *preservatives* and *fixatives* is more difficult to draw, but the author has endeavored to group in the present place all those fluids which are most usually employed for the actual preparation of a wholemount, or for the storage of material, as distinct from those fluids which are employed for the fixation of material before mounting or sectioning.

When the writer has been in doubt he has given a cross reference both in Chapter 18 and in the present chapter.

Probably the most widely used preservative today is a simple dilution of formaldehyde, opinion varying as to the exact concentration which may be employed. Certainly the 4% formaldehyde solutions (the so-called *10% formalin* so commonly referred to in the literature) is far too strong for the preparation of a microscope slide, and a dilution to at least $\frac{1}{10}$ of this concentration is perfectly adequate to prevent the growth of microorganisms in a sealed preparation. Alcohol by itself is practically worthless because of the difficulty of sealing it under a coverslip. Various mixtures of alcohol, glycerol, and formaldehyde have, from time to time, been employed, however, and are given below.

P 02 METHOD OF CLASSIFICATION OF FORMULAS

The formulas given below have been grouped according to their usage as much as their composition. In the first group (P 11.1) there are the few surviving simple solutions of inorganic reagents. These were once the most widely used class of preservatives, but they are now obsolete and scarcely ever employed, although they are the easiest of all fluids to seal. P 12.1 contains the organic reagents as distinct from the inorganic and is divided according to whether or not it contains phenol (P 12.1 are the alcohols, aldehydes, glycerine, etc., without phenol; 12.2 contains the phenol mixtures). A third group, P 12.3 below, contains miscellaneous organic reagents including complex mixtures of materials which, had they been used singly, would have been placed in groups P 12.1 or P 12.2. The classification P 13.1 contains all the other water-miscible preservatives which could not justifiably have been placed in either of the previous two classes.

P 10 Formulas

11 SOLUTIONS OF INORGANIC REAGENTS

11.1 Formulas

11.1 Assier *test.* **1882 Chevalier**   Chevalier 1882, 290
FORMULA: water 100, sodium chloride 10, acetic acid 1

11.1 Boitard 1921a   Boitard 1921, 49
FORMULA: water 100, ammonium alum 10, sodium chloride 11.5, mercuric chloride 1.2

11.1 Boitard 1921b   Boitard 1921, 379
FORMULA: water 86, sodium borate 8, boric acid 2, potassium nitrate 3, sodium chloride 1

11.1 Goadby *test.* **1855a Queckett**   Queckett 1855, 300
FORMULA: water 100, sodium chloride 6, potassium alum 3, mercuric chloride 0.15

11.1 Goadby *test.* **1855b Queckett**   Queckett 1855, 301
FORMULA: water 100, mercuric chloride 0.08, ammonium alum 2.4, sodium chloride 4.8
NOTE: Several other solutions were published by Goadby (Queckett, *loc. cit.*). These, however, appear to be the only ones widely used (cf. Robin 1871, 377 and Frey 1877, 136) for microscopial, as distinct from anatomical, preservation.

11.1 Kronecker *test.* **1907 Böhm and Oppel**   Böhm and Oppel 1907, 9
FORMULA: water 100, sodium chloride 0.6, sodium carbonate 0.006

11.1 Ralf *test.* **1872 Martin**   Martin 1872, 189
FORMULA: water 100, potassium alum 0.2, sodium chloride 0.2

11.1 Woods 1929   19938, **70**:637
FORMULA: water 100, copper acetate 0.5, acetic acid 4
METHOD: Fix 4 hrs. in above. Pour off solution and add ammonia till color changes to purple. Return objects and leave 1 hr. Transfer to 5% glycerol, concentrate by evaporation, and mount in M 12.1 Kaiser 1880
RECOMMENDED FOR: algae.

12 ORGANIC REAGENTS

12.1 Alcohols, Aldehydes, Ketones

12.1 Caberla 1878   23635, **30**:442
FORMULA: water 30, glycerol 10, 95% alc. 20

12.1 Francotte *test.* **1942 Langeron**   Langeron 1942, 1011
FORMULA: water 50, 95% alc. 20, glycerol 30

12.1 Gatenby and Painter 1937   Gatenby and Painter 1937, 222
FORMULA: water 50, glycerol 25, 95% alc. 25

12.1 Hantzch *test.* **1882 Chevalier** *cit.* **Rade**   Chevalier 1882, 325
FORMULA: water 60, 95% alc. 30, glycerol 10

12.1 Jäger *test.* **1937 Gatenby and Painter**   Gatenby and Painter 1937, 222
FORMULA: sea water 80, glycerol 8, 95% alc. 8

12.1 Moleschott *test.* **1871 Robin**   Robin 1871, 289
FORMULA: water 50, 95% alc. 25, acetic acid 25

12.1 Mönnig 1930   18640, **16**:199
FORMULA: water 90, 40% formaldehyde 10, chloroform *q.s.* to sat.
RECOMMENDED FOR: preservation of gorged ticks.

12.1 Newmarch 1938   *Microscope*, **2**:132
FORMULA: water 70, glycerol 25, 40% formaldehyde 5

12.1 Oudemann *test.* **1939 Scott** *cit.* **Morgenthaler**   *Microscope*, **3**:163
FORMULA: 95% alc. 60, water 27, glycerol 5, acetic acid 8

12.1 Pampel 1914   23635, **108**:290
FORMULA: water 60, 95% alc. 30, 40% formaldehyde 12, acetic acid 8
RECOMMENDED FOR: preservation of arthropoda for external studies.

12.1 Puppe 1899 *test.* **1922 Silvester**   4349, **8**:54
FORMULA: water 42, glycerol 42, alcohol 16

12.1 Railliet *test.* **1942 Langeron**   Langeron 1942, 871
FORMULA: water 93, 40% formaldehyde 5, acetic acid 2, sodium chloride 0.9

12.1 Robin 1871   Robin 1871, 289
FORMULA: water 20, 95% alc. 40, glycerol 40, acetic acid 4.5, nitric acid 2

12.1 Woods 1897   3430, **24**:206
REAGENTS REQUIRED: *A*. 95% alc.; *B*. water 95, glycerol 5, copper acetate 0.5, 40%
formaldehyde 1; *C*. water 95, glycerol 5, 40% formaldehyde 1
METHOD: [fresh plants] → *A*, few moments → water, few moments → [repeat cycle till
adherent air removed] → *B*, till blue-green → *C*, till no more color comes away → M
12.1 Wood 1897

12.2. PHENOLS AND MIXTURES CONTAINING PHENOL AND PHENOL DERIVATIVES

12.2 Alcorn and Yeager 1937   20540b, **12**:157
FORMULA: water 20, glycerol 40, lactic acid 20, phenol 10, acetic acid 0.3, orseillin BB
0.025
RECOMMENDED FOR: preserving and staining fungus-infected plant tissues.

12.2 Amann 1896   23632, **13**:18
FORMULA: lactic acid 20, phenol 20, glycerol 40, water 20
NOTE: This mixture is widely used in continental Europe but was ignored in England
and the United States until the formula was reprinted by **Linder 1929** (19938, **70**:430).
Although Linder correctly acknowledged the source of the formula, many subsequent
writers refer to "Linder's Medium" (cf. Carpenter and Nebel 1931; 19938, **70**:154).
In 1933 (19938, **77**:23) **Moore** suggested the addition of 0.5 phenosafranin to "Linder's Medium." This may account for the curious statement in Gatenby and Painter
1937, p. 692, that "Linder's Medium is [here is given Amman's mixture] . . . with a
small amount of carmine." Some additional confusion has been occasioned by the
fact that Linder (*loc. cit.*) cites an undated text by **Satory** as his source for Amman's
formula; Moore (*loc. cit.*) then cites the composition as "Satory's formula as given by
Linder." The stains of Maneval 1936 (DS 12.15) are designed for use before this
medium.

12.2 Amann 1899   23632, **16**:38
FORMULA: chloral hydrate 50, lactic acid 25, phenol 25

12.2 Amann 1899   *see also* S 41.1 Amann 1899a and b

12.2 Archibald and Marshall 1931   16035, **23**:272
     FORMULA: water 25, lactic acid 25, glycerol 25, phenol 25
     RECOMMENDED FOR: fixation and preservation of cercaria.

12.2 Bastian *test.* **1877 Frey**   Frey 1877, 135
     FORMULA: glycerol 90, phenol 6

12.2 Langeron 1942   Langeron 1942, 660
     FORMULA: chloral hydrate 40, phenol 40, lactic acid 20, sodium salicylate 10

12.2 Lepik 1928   16233, **18**:869
     FORMULA: 95% alc. 40, phenol 20, lactic acid 40, glycerol 20

12.2 Mukerji 1931   9940, **19**:281
     FORMULA: water 20, glycerol 20, lactic acid 40, chloral hydrate 10, 40% formaldehyde
     10, acetic acid 4

12.2 Linder 1929   *see* P 12.2 Amann 1896 (note)

12.2 Moore 1933   *see* P 12.2 Amann 1896 (note)

12.2 Priestly 1917a   13034, **2**:471
     FORMULA: phenol 20, glycerol 40, lactic acid, 20, water 20

12.2 Priestly 1917b   13034, **2**:471
     FORMULA: chloral hydrate 50, lactic acid, 25 phenol 25

12.2 Semmens 1937   *Microscope*, **1**:5
     FORMULA: water 50, lactic acid 40, glycerol 39, phenol 25

12.3 Other Organic Reagents, Including Mixtures of 12.1, and 12.2

12.3 Amann 1899   23632, **16**:38
     FORMULA: chloral hydrate 50, lactic acid 50

12.3 André   *see* V 51.1 André

12.3 Brazille 1908   5401, **33**:114
     FORMULA: water 50, 95% alc. 30, phenol 0.6, acetic acid 10

12.3 Bruin *test.* **1930 Guyer**   Guyer 1930, 71
     FORMULA: water 20, glucose 70, 95% alc. 5, camphor 0.5, glycerol 5
     NOTE: the camphor is dissolved in the alc. and the solution added to the other ingredients.

12.3 Brumpt *test.* **1942 Langeron**   Langeron 1942, 819
     FORMULA: water 97, 40% formaldehyde 7.5, picric acid 0.1, acetic acid 0.5
     RECOMMENDED FOR: mounting and preserving parasitic protozoans.

12.3 Brun 1889 *test.* **1937 Gatenby and Cowdry**   Gatenby and Cowdry 1937, 221
     FORMULA: water 70, glucose 20, glycerol 10, 95% alc. 5, camphor 0.5

12.3 Cole 1903   Cross and Cole 1903, 267
     FORMULA: water 30, glycerol 30, 95% alc. 30, acetic acid 0.3

12.3 Eckert 1931   20540b(abstr. 1932)**7**:68
     FORMULA: water 95, P 12.2 Amann 1896 5, copper chloride 0.2, copper acetate 0.2
     RECOMMENDED FOR: Either alone, or diluted 1:5 with P 12.3 Pfeiffer (1921) as a pre-
     servative for green algae.

12.3 Fabre-Domergue 1889   14901 (1889)
     FORMULA: water 60, glucose 40, methanol 20, glycerol 10, camphor *q.s.* to sat.

12.3 Gater 1928   4184, **19**:367
     FORMULA: water 40, acetic acid 6, chloral hydrate 60

12.3 Gerlach 1885   11360, **5**:541
FORMULA: sat. aq. sol. (*circ.* 1.5%) arsenic trioxide 100, gelatin 20, glycerol 60

12.3 Kaiserling 1897   22575, **147**:389
FORMULA I: water 100, 40% formaldehyde 20, potassium nitrate 1.5, potassium acetate 3
FORMULA II: water 100, potassium acetate 10, glycerol 20
NOTE: The first solution is intended for the fixation of slabs of pathological material, the color of which is redeveloped in 80% alc., before final preservation in the second solution. Both solutions are, however, excellent general-purpose preservatives.

12.3 Ordoñez 1865 *test.* **1882 Chevalier**   Chevalier 1882, 323
FORMULA: water 30, glycerol 75, tannin, 0.5

12.3 Pfeiffer *test.* **1931 Eckert**   20540b (abstr. 1932) **7**:68
FORMULA: acetic acid 30, methanol 30, 40% formaldehyde 30
RECOMMENDED FOR: preservation of green algae.

13 OTHER PRESERVATIVES INCLUDING MIXTURES OF 11 AND 12

13.1 Beale 1880   Beale 1880, 66
FORMULA: methanol 6, acetone 3, creosote 0.5, chalk *q.s.* to sat., water 95, camphor 1

13.1 Blaydes 1937   19938, **85**:126
FORMULA I: water 45, 95% alc. 45, 40% formaldehyde 5, acetic acid 5, copper sulfate 0.2
FORMULA II: water 25, 95% alc. 60, 40% formaldehyde 10, acetic acid 5, copper sulfate 0.2
RECOMMENDED FOR: preservation of color in green plants.

13.1 Chevalier 1882   Chevalier 1882, 319
FORMULA: water 60, glycerol 30, calcium chloride 6

13.1 Cole 1903   Cross and Cole 1903, 181
FORMULA: water 50, camphor to sat. glycerol 50, acetic acid 0.2, copper acetate 0.2, mercuric chloride 0.01

13.1 Frey 1877   Frey 1877, 136
FORMULA: water 90, glycerol 10, sodium chloride 2, mercuric chloride 1

13.1 Craig 1916   4349, **6**:56
FORMULA: water 80, glycerol 20, 40% formaldehyde 8, potassium acetate 8

13.1 Frost 1913   4349, **4**:41
FORMULA: sat. sol. thymol 100, cane sugar 44, potassium acetate 2, chloral hydrate 1, sodium fluoride 1

13.1 Gardiner 1898 *test.* **1931 Crafts**   20540b, **6**:127
FORMULA: water 60, glycerol 30, zinc chloride 2, iodine 0.2, potassium iodide "a trace"

13.1 Gibson *test.* **1905 Lee**   Lee 1905, 268
FORMULA: water 60, 95% alc. 30, glycerol 30, mercuric chloride 2, acetic acid 0.15

13.1 Grawitz 1887   7276, **27**:604
FORMULA: water 100, sodium chloride 15, sugar 4, boric acid 3, potassium nitrate 2

13.1 Haythorn 1915   4349, **5**:66
FORMULA: water 100, sugar 44, potassium acetate 4, arsenic trioxide 0.5

13.1 Jackson 1919 *test.* **1922** *ips.*   4349, **8**:75
FORMULA: water 100, 40% formaldehyde 2, cane sugar 10

13.1 Jores 1896   23681, **7**:134
FORMULA: water 100, 40% formaldehyde 10, sodium sulfate 2, magnesium sulfate 2, sodium chloride 1

13.1 Jores 1913   22264, **16**:357
FORMULA: P 13.1 Peck 1900 100, chloral hydrate 1

13.1 Kaiserling 1896   2813, **33**:775
FORMULA: water 57, 40% formaldehyde 43, potassium acetate 1.7, potassium nitrate 0.5

13.1 Kaiserling 1899   22264 (1899) 203
FORMULA: water 84, 40% formaldehyde 16, potassium nitrate 0.9 potassium acetate 1.8

13.1 Keefe 1926   19938, **64**:332
FORMULA: water 45, 95% alc. 45, 40% formaldehyde 5, glycerol 2.5 acetic acid 2.5, copper chloride 10, uranium nitrate 1.5
NOTE: **Jirouch 1929** (20540b, **4**:17) makes frozen sections of leaves preserved by this method and mounts in glycerol jelly.

13.1 Kirchner 1885 *test.* **1896 Zimmerman**   Zimmerman 1896, 41
FORMULA: water 90, glycerol 10, chrome alum 0.5
RECOMMENDED FOR: preservation of color in algae.

13.1 Klotz and Coburn 1916a   4349, **6**:51
FORMULA: water 100, 40% formaldehyde 0.5, chloral hydrate 1.0, sodium sulfate 0.55, sodium bicarbonate 0.5, sodium chloride 0.45, potassium nitrate 1.0, potassium sulfate 0.05

13.1 Klotz and Coburn 1916b   4349, **6**:53
FORMULA: water 100, 40% formaldehyde 0.5, chloral hydrate 1, sodium sulfate 1.6, potassium sulfate 0.025, sodium chloride 0.3, sodium bicarbonate 0.6

13.1 Klotz and MacLachan 1915   4349, **5**:59
FORMULA: water 100, 40% formaldehyde 3, chloral hydrate 3, sodium sulfate 0.7, sodium bicarbonate 0.6, sodium chloride 0.55, potassium sulfate 0.06, potassium nitrate 1.2

13.1 Mall 1902   590, **5**:433
FORMULA: water 80, glycerol 20, potassium hydroxide 1
RECOMMENDED FOR: preservation of mammalian embryos in which ossification studies are to be made in wholemounts.

13.1 Manesse *test.* **1921 Boitard**   Boitard 1921, 49
FORMULA: water 80, 95% alc. 20, potassium alum 10, potassium nitrate 10, sodium chloride 10

13.1 Melnikow-Raswedenkow 1896   23681, **7**:49
FORMULA: water 62.5, glycerol 37.5, potassium acetate 19

13.1 Melnikow-Raswedenkow 1895 *test.* **1922 Silvester**   4349, **8**:54
FORMULA: water 50, 40% formaldehyde 50, sodium acetate 3, potassium chlorate 0.5

13.1 Ordoñez 1865a   Chevalier 1882, 323
FORMULA: water 60, sat. aq. sol. camphor 20, glycerol 20, acetic acid 1

13.1 Ordoñez 1865b *test.* **1882 Chevalier**   Chevalier 1882, 323
FORMULA: water 100, glycerol 4, 95% alc. 4, mercuric chloride 0.03

13.1 Ordoñez 1865c *test.* **1882 Chevalier**   Chevalier 1882, 323
FORMULA: water 75, sat. aq. sol. camphor 15, glycerol 3, chromic acid 0.3

13.1 Pacini *test.* **1871 Robin**   Robin 1871, 376
STOCK SOLUTIONS: I. water 90, glycerol 10, mercuric chloride 0.9, sodium chloride 1.7; II. water 85, glycerol 15, mercuric chloride 0.4, acetic acid 0.75
WORKING SOLUTIONS: either of above diluted 1:3

13.1 Peck 1900   2813, 42
FORMULA: water 100, 40% formaldehyde 5, sodium sulfate 3.2, sodium bicarbonate 1.2, potassium chloride 0.6, potassium sulfate 0.05

13.1 Ripart and Petit 1884 *see* F 4000.0010 Ripart and Petit

13.1 Robin 1871   Robin 1871, 373
FORMULA: F 7000.0000 Müller 1859, 50, glycerol 50

13.1 Thwaite *test.* **1880 Beale**   Beale 1880, 65
FORMULA: 95% alc. 6, wood creosote 0.5, chalk in fine powder *q.s.* to sat., water 50, camphor water 50

13.1 Topping *test.* **1871 Robin**   Robin 1871, 375
FORMULA: water 50, glycerol 50, aluminum acetate 10

18

Fixatives

1370.0030   Osmic-mercuric-dichromate-formic
      .1000   Osmic-mercuric-dichromate-formaldehyde
1378.0000   Osmic-mercuric-dichromate-(other inorganic salts)
1380.0010   Osmic-mercuric-(other inorganic salts)-acetic
      .0030   Osmic-mercuric-(other inorganic salts)-formic
1400.0000   Osmic-cupric
      .0010   Osmic-cupric-acetic
1500.0010   Osmic-picric-acetic
      .0040   Osmic-picric-nitric
      .0050   Osmic-picric-sulfuric
1560.0000   Osmic-picric-chromic
      .1010   Osmic-picric-chromic-formaldehyde-acetic
1580.0000   Osmic-picric-(other inorganic salt)
1600.0000   Osmic-chromic
      .0010   Osmic-chromic-acetic
      .0020   Osmic-chromic-trichloracetic
      .0030   Osmic-chromic-formic
      .0060   Osmic-chromic-hydrochloric
      .1010   Osmic-chromic-acetic-formaldehyde
1670.0000   Osmic-chromic-dichromate
      .0010   Osmic-chromic-dichromate-acetic
      .0019   Osmic-chromic-dichromate-acetic-(other organic acids)
      .0090   Osmic-chromic-dichromate-(other organic acids)
1700.0000   Osmic-dichromate
      .0010   Osmic-dichromate-acetic
      .0030   Osmic-dichromate-formic
      .0040   Osmic-dichromate-nitric
      .1000   Osmic-dichromate-formaldehyde
      .1010   Osmic-dichromate-formaldehyde-acetic
1780.0000   Osmic-dichromate-(other inorganic salt)
1800.0000   Osmic-(other inorganic salt)
      .0010   Osmic-(other inorganic salt)-acetic
      .0030   Osmic-(other inorganic salt)-formic
F   2000   Platinic chloride in combination with fixative agents of higher numerical
           rank
2000.1000   Platinic-formaldehyde
      .1010   Platinic-formaldehyde-acetic
2300.0000   Platinic-mercuric
      .0010   Platinic-mercuric-acetic
      .1000   Platinic-mercuric-formaldehyde
      .1030   Platinic-mercuric-formaldehyde-formic
2356.0000   Platinic-mercuric-picric-chromic
2470.0000   Platinic-cupric-dichromate
2500.0010   Platinic-picric-acetic
      1030   Platinic-picric-formaldehyde-formic
2600.0000   Platinic-chromic
      .0010   Platinic-chromic-acetic
2700.0000   Platinic-dichromate
F   3000   Mercuric chloride in combination with fixative agents of higher numerical
           rank
3000.0000   Mercuric alone
      .0010   Mercuric-acetic
      .0012   Mercuric-acetic-trichloroacetic
      .0014   Mercuric-acetic-nitric
      .0020   Mercuric-trichloroacetic
      .0030   Mercuric-formic
      .0040   Mercuric-nitric
      .0060   Mercuric-hydrochloric
      .1000   Mercuric-formaldehyde
      .1010   Mercuric-formaldehyde-acetic

.1012   Mercuric-formaldehyde-acetic-trichloroacetic
.1020   Mercuric-formaldehyde-trichloracetic
.1310   Mercuric-formaldehyde-acetone-acetic
.3000   Mercuric-acetone
.3010   Mercuric-acetone-acetic
3400.0000   Mercuric-cupric
.1010   Mercuric-cupric-formaldehyde-acetic
.1014   Mercuric-cupric-formaldehyde-acetic-nitric
3470.1000   Mercuric-cupric-dichromate-formaldehyde
3500.0000   Mercuric-picric
.0010   Mercuric-picric-acetic
.0015   Mercuric-picric-acetic-sulfuric
.1000   Mercuric-picric-formaldehyde
.1010   Mercuric-picric-formaldehyde-acetic
3560.0040   Mercuric-picric-chromic-nitric
3600.0000   Mercuric-chromic
.0010   Mercuric-chromic-acetic
.0040   Mercuric-chromic-nitric
.1010   Mercuric-chromic-formaldehyde-acetic
3670.0000   Mercuric-chromic-dichromate
.0010   Mercuric-chromic-dichromate-acetic
3700.0000   Mercuric-dichromate
.0010   Mercuric-dichromate-acetic
.0030   Mercuric-dichromate-formic
.0040   Mercuric-dichromate-nitric
.1000   Mercuric-dichromate-formaldehyde
.1010   Mercuric-dichromate-formaldehyde-acetic
3780.0000   Mercuric-dichromate-(other inorganic salts)
.1000   Mercuric-dichromate-(other inorganic salts)-formalde-
hyde
3800.1000   Mercuric-(other inorganic salts)-formaldehyde
F   4000   Cupric salts in combination with fixative agents of higher numerical rank
4000.0010   Cupric-acetic
.0020   Cupric-trichloracetic
.0040   Cupric-nitric
.1000   Cupric-formaldehyde
.1010   Cupric formaldehyde acetic
.1090   Cupric-formaldehyde-(other organic acids)
4500.1010   Cupric-picric-formaldehyde-acetic
4600.1000   Cupric-chromic-formaldehyde
.1010   Cupric-chromic-formaldehyde-acetic
4700.0000   Cupric-dichromate
.0010   Cupric-dichromate-acetic
.1000   Cupric-dichromate-formaldehyde
4900.0040   Cupric-(other organic agent)-nitric
F   5000   Picric acid in combination with fixative agents of higher numerical rank
5000.0000   Picric alone
.0010   Picric-acetic
.0015   Picric-acetic-sulfuric
.0020   Picric-trichloroacetic
.0040   Picric-nitric
.0050   Picric-sulfuric
.0060   Picric-hydrochloric
.1000   Picric-formaldehyde
.1010   Picric-formaldehyde-acetic
.1020   Picric-formaldehyde-trichloroacetic
.1030   Picric-formaldehyde-formic
.1040   Picric-formaldehyde-nitric
.1090   Picric-formaldehyde-(other organic acid)
.1310   Picric-formaldehyde-acetone

5600.0000   Picric-chromic
.0010   Picric-chromic-acetic
.0040   Picric-chromic-nitric
.0050   Picric-chromic-sulfuric
.1000   Picric-chromic-formaldehyde
.1010   Picric-chromic-formaldehyde-acetic
5670.1000   Picric-chromic-dichromate-formaldehyde
5700.0000   Picric-dichromate
.0050   Picric-dichromate-sulfuric
.1010   Picric-dichromate-formaldehyde-acetic
5800.1010   Picric-(other inorganic salts)-formaldehyde
F   6000   Chromic acid in combination with fixative agents of higher numerical rank
6000.0000   Chromic alone
.0010   Chromic-acetic
.0030   Chromic-formic
.0040   Chromic-nitric
.0060   Chromic-hydrochloric
.0070   Chromic-oxalic
.1000   Chromic-formaldehyde
.1010   Chromic-formaldehyde-acetic
.1040   Chromic-formaldehyde-nitric
6700.0000   Chromic-dichromate
.0010   Chromic-dichromate-acetic
.0040   Chromic-dichromate-nitric
.1010   Chromic-dichromate-formaldehyde-acetic
6800.0000   Chromic-(other inorganic salts)
.0030   Chromic-(other inorganic salts)-nitric
F   7000   Dichromates without other primary fixative agents
7000.0000   Dichromate alone
.0010   Dichromate-acetic
.0040   Dichromate-nitric
.1000   Dichromate-formaldehyde
.1010   Dichromate-formaldehyde-acetic
.1030   Dichromate-formaldehyde-formic
.2000   Dichromate-acetaldehyde
7800.0010   Dichromate-(other inorganic salt)-acetic
.1000   Dichromate-(other inorganic salts)-formaldehyde
.1012   Dichromate-(other   inorganic   salts)-formaldehyde-tri-
chloroacetic
F   8000   Solutions with "other inorganic" primary fixative agents
8000.0010   (Other inorganic agent)-acetic
.0014   (Other inorganic agent)-acetic-nitric
.0030   (Other inorganic agent)-formic
.1000   (Other inorganic agent)-formaldehyde
.1010   (Other inorganic agent)-formaldehyde-acetic
F   9000   Solutions with "other organic" primary fixative agents.
9000.0010   (Other organic agent)-acetic
.4000   (Other organic agent)-(other modifier)

F 01 Method of Classification

No arrangement of formulas based on the intended application to tissues would appear to be in any way practical. The most diverse ingredients are used for the most diverse purposes, thus only a slight modification of a fixative intended by one writer for the preparation of brain tissue for subsequent gold staining (Smith 1930) is considered by another writer (Smith 1904) to be ideal for the preparation of large-yolked eggs. Under these circumstances one is forced to fall back on the ingredients themselves, which are surprisingly few in number and which may be conveniently classified into groups according to the presumptive role which they play in fixation. The first of these great groups contains mostly metallic salts, presumably intended to denature, or to form compounds with, the protoplasm. One or more of these ingredients is found in almost all fixative solutions, and they are, therefore, referred to in this classification as *primary fixative agents*.

PRIMARY FIXATIVE AGENTS

1. "Osmic acid" (osmium tetroxide)
2. Platinic chloride
3. Mercuric chloride
4. Cupric sulfate, nitrate, or chloride
5. "Picric acid" (2, 4, 6 trinitrophenol)
6. "Chromic acid" (chromium trioxide)
7. Potassium or sodium dichromate
8. Other inorganic salts
9. Other organic reagents

Since no one has yet proposed, nor is it to be hoped that anyone will propose, a mixture containing more than four of these agents, it is possible to indicate mixtures of them by using four numbers from the list above. Thus, 1000 represents a fixative containing only osmic acid, 1300, a fixative combining osmic with mercuric, 1360, an osmic-mercuric-chromic mixture, and so on.

These symbols are always written in their proper numerical order. Thus the combination 3600 would indicate a mercuric-chromic mixture without any other primary agent. The addition of osmic would produce the symbol 1360. The numerical rank assigned to these varying agents has been designed, as far as possible, to render this classification easy to handle.

The vast majority of fixatives are modified by the addition of one, but never more than two, *fixative modifiers*, which is the term here used to describe the commonly employed aldehydes and ketones. These are incorporated in the symbolic classification of a fixative by placing a decimal point after the symbol for the primary fixative agents and employing the first

two positions to the right of this decimal point for the fixative modifiers. The following list of fixative modifiers appear at present to be sufficient:

FIXATIVE MODIFIERS

(.) 1. formaldehyde
(.) 2. acetaldehyde
(.) 3. acetone
(.) 4. all other fixative modifiers

The only other common additions to fixative solutions are *acids*, of which never more than two appear to be employed in any one composition. It is, therefore, possible to indicate the acids as two further figures placed to the right of the modifier. For this purpose the fixative acids may be listed as:

FIXATIVE ACIDS

(.00) 1. acetic
(.00) 2. trichloroacetic
(.00) 3. formic
(.00) 4. nitric
(.00) 5. sulfuric
(.00) 6. hydrochloric
(.00) 7. oxalic
(.00) 8. all other inorganic acids
(.00) 9. all other organic acids

The combination of the agents with the modifiers and acids thus gives an eight-figure description which will indicate the composition of the fixative. This will be rendered clearer by a few further examples. Thus: 0000.1000, formaldehyde without other admixture; 0000.1010, formaldehyde-acetic; 0000.1012, formaldehyde-acetic-trichloroacetic; 1670.0010, osmic-chromic-dichromate-acetic.

The advantage of this method of classification is that it permits an indefinite expansion as new formulas appear in the literature. It also brings logically together formulas of similar composition, but of gradually increasing complexity. That some system of classification is necessary, is indicated by the fact that more than 300 classes of fixatives are at present in existence.

Additional difficulties are provided by two-solution formulas: that is, such a formula as those in which osmic acid and potassium dichromate, each in its own solution, are used successively in the course of fixation. These have been classified for the sake of simplicity as though both reagents were included in the same solution. The last case of ambiguity which occurs is that in which a complex salt, involving two primary fixative agents as one compound, is utilized. There are several formulas, for example, in which copper dichromate is specified as an ingredient. In these cases the formulas have been classified as though they were composed of a mixture of copper and dichromate rather than as prepared from the compound.

F 02 General Observations

The great confusion and diversity of opinion which occurs in the literature as to what constitutes a desirable quality for a fixative ingredient, is probably due to a similar disagreement as to what constitutes a desirable quality in a fixative mixture. In general, those who study the form of small invertebrates require first that a fixative should not interfere with the recognition of the object after fixation, that is, that its general shape shall not be distorted by the fluid applied to it. Cytologists, histologists, and pathologists, on the contrary, require as a first consideration that the inner structure of the cell constituent shall remain unaltered, or shall at least present on microscopic examination only those features which are thought to have been present in the original living cell. It is obvious that the first group of workers are dependent for their effect largely upon the osmotic pressure shown by the material or, alternatively, they require a solution that so rapidly and thoroughly hardens the outer coat that it will not become distorted by the passage of solutions through it. Thus Young (1935) gives directions for adjusting the osmotic pressure of solutions by the addition of sodium chloride, and Gray 1933 (11360, **53**:13) pointed out that the addition of sodium sulfate to potassium dichromate to give the solution of Müller improved the osmotic performance of the mixture. Heat is considered by many to be a desirable characteristic; Pantin (1946, 8) recommended heating fixatives for small marine invertebrate larvae. Heat should also possibly be applied to fixation of internal constituents of cells, since Thomas and Morris 1925 (10996, **48**:501) showed that the dichromates do not precipitate albumin unless they are heated either at the same time, or immediately after, the application of the reagent. The principal opponents of the view that the osmotic pressure of the solution is of primary importance are Baker and Crawford (*test*. Langeron 1942, 362) who showed that solutions with high osmotic pressure do not of necessity cause distortion; and Hirsch and Jacobs 1926 (1820, **18**:7) who denied emphatically that any improvement in fixing qualities could be found by the addition of sodium chloride to fixative solutions.

Those who desire to fix only the constituents of the living cell have been themselves sharply divided into two schools of thought. The first of these schools considered that the precipitating, or *coagulating* powers of the reagents employed were of primary importance. The second considered penetration and pH to be the most critical characteristic of a fixing fluid. The school which depended upon coagulation for fixation appears nowadays to be so thoroughly discredited that one can only refer to the summary of their work given in Böhm and Oppel (1907, 14). Here will be found a complex classification of fixatives based entirely upon the materials which were precipitated and rendered insoluble by the application of various reagents. There is, indeed, a fatal objection to this work which was pointed out by Bolles Lee (1905, p. 22). This is that the more organic dead materials are precipitated by the solution employed, the greater will be the artifacts produced. The case for cytologists and histologists is probably best given by Crétin (1925, LeMans) who considers that for neutral solutions, the total concentration of salts is important, but that for any solution containing acid, the pH must be carefully adjusted so that it is not below that of the isoelectric point of the proteins to be fixed. He considered a pH in the general vicinity of 4.2 to be the most desirable. His work was published at the same time as that of Gihei 1925 (3432, **39**:164), who gives a table showing the pH of a few fixatives, none of which, however, were as alkaline as the upper limit indicated by Crétin. This work was followed in 1928 by the detailed study of Zirkle 1928 (17191a, **4**:201) who came to the conclusion that there was a critical pH between 4.2 and 5.2. Fixative solutions more acid than this critical point were required for nuclear fixation, while those more alkaline gave better results in cytoplasmic studies. Jacquiert 1930 (6630, **104**:483) considered that a low pH with a suitable osmotic adjustment would give the more generally desirable fixative. This last study confirmed the work of Burchardt 1897 (6011, **12**:337) who recommended alkaline dichromate for cytoplasmic fixation and acid dichromate for nuclear fixation. This universal preference for acid fixatives must not cause one to lose sight of the work of Barnabo 1904 (3389, **13**:198) and 1905 (3389, **14**:139, 205) who stated that mercuric fixatives buffered with bicarbonate gave, in general, very much better pictures both of nuclear and cytoplasmic fixation than did the more usual acid mixtures. Another characteristic which may be mentioned is that the majority of materials used for fixation are either strongly reducing or strongly oxidizing materials. This was first brought forward as a basis for the construction of formulas by Unna and Golodetz 1912 (7175, **22**:10). They based their results on previous studies by Unna 1911 (1739, Fest. Waldeyer, 78) on the oxidizing and reducing properties of living tissues. This view, that oxidizing and reducing qualities should first be sought, is advocated very strongly by Langeron in the 1942 edition of his *Précis de Microscopie*.

The literature is so confused that no specific recommendations can be made for the theoretical production of a perfect fixative. The confusion which exists, however, with regard to the desirable qualities of a formula is very little compared to the confusion which has arisen in the practical preparation of these solutions. Authors have, in many instances, made no attempt to check the literature for the existence of a solution before they have invented one of their own. This duplication is all the more difficult to check for the reason that authors prepare their own solutions from any stock solution which happens to be on their shelves at the time. Thus various authors have recommended a few milliliters of a 2%, 3%, 4%, or 5% solution of potassium dichromate to be mixed with a few other milliliters of 0.25%, 0.5%, 1%, or 2% osmic acid. One of the most laborious features of the preparation of this work has been the reduction of all these formulas to a standard volume as though they had been prepared from dry salts. These standardized formulas are offered in two ways. First, together with the full citation to the original appearance, have been given the ingredients required to prepare 250 milliliters of solution from standard materials. This figure of 250 milliliters, rather than 100, has been taken as a matter of convenience since this is the quantity most usually made up. The names of chemicals have been given in full rather than in symbolic form for the reason that it is difficult to know where to draw the line. It is to be presumed that any biologist would not have the slightest difficulty in preparing the solution made up of $HgCl_2$ and HNO_3. It is felt, however, that the majority would be stopped cold by the directions to mix $(NO_2)_3$-C_6H_2OH, HCHO and CH_3COOH. To avoid the usual confusion between *formol*, *formaldehyde*, and *formalin*, the author has used the term 40% *formaldehyde* throughout, intending to indicate by this the fluid which comes in the bottle so labeled.

Formulas are also presented in an abbreviated, alphabetical list, permitting the preparation of the formulas referred to from standard solutions, which act, as it were, as the lowest common denominator of about 80% of fixatives employed. The explanation of this method, together with the list of fixatives, forms the second half of the present chapter.

F 03   Formulas Arranged by Classes

F 0000 SOLUTIONS WITHOUT PRIMARY OR SECONDARY FIXATIVE AGENTS

0000.0010 ACETIC ALONE

Acetic acid is never used nowadays in simple aqueous dilution because it causes rapid hydrolysis of the protoplasm. This hydrolysis is diminished by the presence of alcohol, therefore, the alcoholic dilutions given below can alone be recommended. These hydrolize cytoplasm rapidly, but do not greatly affect the nucleus. They are, therefore, mostly employed for the demonstration of nuclei or of materials containing considerable nucleic acid. Acetic acid is regarded by Gatenby and Cowdry (1928, 52) as "a substance most injurious to the finer elements of the cytoplasm, but in some cases it is indicated for a study of nuclear elements." Langeron (1942, 73), on the contrary, regards it as one of the most important fixative agents. Unless a rapid hydrolysis of the cytoplasm is required to bring nuclear elements into sharp contrast, it is strongly recommended that it be employed in mixture either with chromic acid or with mercuric chloride. Spiess 1953 (*in verb.*) states that the substitution of proprionic acid for acetic improves cytological fixation.

0000.0010 Bartelmez 1915a   1135, **25**:87
    FORMULA: abs. alc. 225, acetic acid 25

0000.0010 Bartelmez 1915b   1135, **25**:87
    FORMULA: abs. alc. 237.5, acetic acid 12.5

0000.0010 Bartelmez 1915c   1135, **25**:87
    FORMULA: alc. 152, chloroform 80, acetic acid 16

0000.0010 van Beneden and Heyt 1877   3678, **14**:218
    FORMULA: abs. alc. 125, acetic acid 125

0000.0010 Bradley 1948   20540b, **23**:29
    FORMULA: abs. alc. 95, acetic acid 31, chloroform 125

0000.0010 Carnoy 1887   6011, **3**:6
    FORMULA: abs. alc. 180, acetic acid 60

0000.0010 Carnoy 1887   6011, **3**:276
    FORMULA: abs. alc. 150, acetic acid 25, chloroform 75
    NOTE: Langeron 1934, p. 349 refers to this as "Carnoy or van Gehuchten."

0000.0010 Farmer and Shove 1905a   17510, **48**:559
    FORMULA: abs. alc. 214, acetic acid 36

0000.0010 Farmer and Shove 1905b   17510, **48**:559
    FORMULA: abs. alc. 167, acetic acid 73

0000.0010 Favorsky 1930   766, **70**: 376
    FORMULA: 50%–80% alc. 235 to 250, acetic acid 15 to 1
    NOTE: Use strong acid/weak alc. for tough tissues and vice versa.

0000.0010 Gilson 1897
    FORMULA: abs. alc. 80, acetic acid 80, chloroform 80

0000.0010 Hetherington 1922   11428, **9**:102
    FORMULA: abs. alc. 100, chloroform 75, acetic acid 25, phenol *q.s.* to make 250
    RECOMMENDED FOR: fixation and dehydration of nematodes.

0000.0010 Lendrum 1935   11431, **40**:416
    FORMULA: water 10, abs. alc. 75, chloroform 10, phenol 4, acetic acid 3

0000.0010 Moleschott 1871   *see* P 12.1 Moleschott 1871

0000.0010 Potenza 1939 *test.* **1942 Langeron**   Langeron 1942, 419
FORMULA: methanol 50, dioxane 200, paraldehyde 5, acetic acid 12.5

0000.0010 Sansom *test.* **1928 Gatenby and Cowdry**
FORMULA: abs. alc. 165, chloroform 75, acetic acid 7.5

0000.0010 Strauss 1909   23053a, **20**:3
FORMULA: 95% alc. 242.5, acetic acid 7.5

000.0012 Acetic-trichloroacetic

0000.0012 Davenport and Kline 1938   20540b, **13**:160
FORMULA: n-butyl alc. 150, n-propyl alc. 50, acetic acid 25, trichloroacetic acid 25

0000.0012 Hofker 1921   23632, **38**:130
FORMULA: abs. alc. 200, acetic acid 25, trichloroacetic acid 25

0000.0014 Acetic-nitric

0000.0014 Robin 1871   *see* P 12.2 Robin 1871

0000.0016 Acetic-hydrochloric

0000.0016 Jenkin 1920   *see* AF 21.1 Jenkin 1920

0000.0023 TRICHLOROACETIC-FORMIC

0000.0023 Davenport and Kline 1938   20540b, **13**:160
FORMULA: n-butanol 150, n-propyl alc. 50, trichloroacetic acid 25, formic acid 12.5

0000.0023 Davenport, McArthur and Bruesch 1939   20540b, **14**:22
FORMULA: n-butanol 160, n-propyl alc. 65, trichloroacetic acid 12.5, formic acid 12.5

0000.1000 FORMALDEHYDE ALONE

Formaldehyde in aqueous solution can scarcely be regarded as a fixative, though it is widely used as a preservative fluid. All figures given for the alcoholic dilutions which follow refer to cubic centimeters of the ordinary commercial so-called 40% formaldehyde. This solution becomes acid on standing, but may be buffered to a desirable pH, usually about 8.5, by the addition of borax. Another common procedure is to keep small chips of marble in the stock bottle; though this tends to cause a cloudy precipitate, if in no way interferes with its fixative value. Burke 1933 (608b, **9**:915) prefers pyridine (3 to 5%) as a neutralizing agent but this cannot (Warbritton 1937, 20540b, **12**:125) be used in mercuric mixtures. Koenig, Groat, and Windle 1945 (20540b, **20**:13) recommend the addition of from 2.5% to 5.5% of gum arabic to counteract the gross cell shrinkage produced by diluted formaldehyde.

0000.1000 Baker 1944   17510, **85**:1
FORMULA: water 225, 40% formaldehyde 25, calcium chloride 1

0000.1000 Benario 1894   7276, **20**:572
FORMULA: 90% alc. 250, 40% formaldehyde 2.5

0000.1000 Boeke 1910   766, **35**:193
FORMULA: water 100, 95% alc. 125, 40% formaldehyde 10

0000.1000 Bujor 1901   *see* AF 51.1 Bujor 1901

0000.1000 Burke 1933   608b, **9**:915
FORMULA: water 187.5, 40% formaldehyde 67.5, pyridine 12.5

0000.1000 de Castro 1916   21344, **14**:83
FORMULA: water 250, 40% formaldehyde 37.5, urea nitrate 3.75

0000.1000 Gulland 1900   23632, **17**:222
FORMULA: 95% alc. 225, 40% formaldehyde 25

0000.1000 Hampert 1926   22575, **259**:179
FORMULA: 95% alc. 130, water 35, 40% formaldehyde 85, potassium acetate 10

0000.1000 Hornell 1900   11976, **5**:86
FORMULA: 90% alc. 225, 40% formaldehyde 25

0000.1000 Jones *test.* **1915 Chamberlain**   Chamberlain 1915, 20
FORMULA: water 75, 95% alc. 170, 40% formaldehyde 5

0000.1000 Kaiserling   *see* P 12.3 Kaiserling 1928

0000.1000 Parker and Floyd 1895   766, **11**:156
FORMULA: 95% alc. 256, 40% formaldehyde 5

0000.1000 Schaffer 1908   23635, **89**:1
FORMULA: water 32, 95% alc. 128, 40% formaldehyde 80

0000.1000 Schaffer 1918   766, **51**:373
FORMULA: 80% alc. 160, 40% formaldehyde 80

0000.1010 Formaldehyde-acetic

These mixtures are valuable when it is necessary to avoid any metallic constituent, or to prevent the formation of the yellow color of picric mixtures. They are reasonably good general-purpose fixatives.

0000.1010 Armitage 1939   *Microscope,* **3**:213
FORMULA: water 125, dioxane 100, 40% formaldehyde 20, acetic acid 15

0000.1010 Becher and Demoll 1913   Becher and Demoll 1913, 43
FORMULA: water 150, 95% alc. 75, 40% formaldehyde 22, acetic acid 4

0000.1010 Bles 1905   21652, **41**:792
FORMULA: 70% alc. 225, 40% formaldehyde 17.5, acetic acid 7.5

0000.1010 Boule 1908a   15063, **10**:15
FORMULA: water 235, 40% formaldehyde 55, acetic acid 12.5

0000.1010 Boule 1908b   15063, **10**:15
FORMULA: 95% alc. 200, 40% formaldehyde 50, acetic acid 10, ammonia 1

0000.1010 Dietrich *test.* **1946 Roskin**   Roskin 1946, 91
FORMULA: water 150, 95% alc. 75, 40% formaldehyde 25, acetic acid 5

0000.1010 Dietrich   *see also* F 0000.1010 Kahle 1908 (note)

0000.1010 Fontana 1912   7176, **55**:1003
FORMULA: water 200, 40% formaldehyde 40, acetic acid 2
RECOMMENDED FOR: prior to MS 34.5 Fontana 1912 (*q.v.*).

0000.1010 Hosokawa 1934 *test.* **1942 Langeron**   Langeron 1942, 841
FORMULA: methanol 250, 40% formaldehyde 12.5, glacial acetic acid 2.5

0000.1010 Jackson 1922   4349, **8**:125
FORMULA: 90% alc. 200, 40% formaldehyde 25, acetic acid 25

0000.1010 Kahle 1908   23820, **21**:10
FORMULA: water 150, 95% alc. 65, 40% formaldehyde 30, acetic acid 5
NOTE: Kingsbury and Johannsen 1927, p. 8, refer this formula, without reference to "Dietrich or Kahle."

0000.1010 Lavdowsky 1894   7936a, **1**:361
FORMULA: 30% alc. 225, 40% formaldehyde 25, acetic acid 5
NOTE: Kupperman and Noback 1945 (1887a, **40**:78) recommend adding 1% ferric alum when tissues are to be hematoxylin stained.

0000.1010 Lüko 1910 *test.* **1910 Tellyesniczky**   Ehrlich, Krause, *et al.* 1910, **1**:472
FORMULA: 75% alc. 250, 40% formaldehyde 25, acetic acid 12.5
NOTE: Mayer 1920 (p. 30) refers to this formula as "Tellyesniczky." Tellyesniczky,
loc. cit. says clearly " . . . *eine Mischung, eingeführt vom Assistenten Bela V. Lüko.*"

0000.1010 Mahdissan 1935   1798, **85**:61
FORMULA: abs. alc. 150, chloroform 75, 40% formaldehyde 25, acetic acid 12.5

0000.1010 Murray and Fielding *test.* **1937 Findlay**   11360, **57**:138
FORMULA: water 115, abs. alc. 115, 40% formaldehyde 12.5, acetic acid 7.5

0000.1010 Podhradszky 1934   23632, **50**:285
FORMULA: water 225, 40% formaldehyde 25, acetic acid 12.5

0000.1010 Railliet   *see* P 12.1 Railliet (1942)

0000.1010 Roskin 1946   Roskin 1946, 292
FORMULA: water 200, 40% formaldehyde 50, acetic acid 7.5

0000.1010 Romeis 1948   Romeis 1948, 49
FORMULA: water 108, 95% alc. 112, 40% formaldehyde 25, acetic acid 5

0000.1010 Ruge 1942 *test.* **Langeron 1942**   Langeron 1942, 636
FORMULA: water 250, 40% formaldehyde 5, acetic acid 2.5

0000.1010 Scheuring 1913 *test.* **1948 Romeis**   Romeis 1948, 528
FORMULA: 95% alc. 120, 40% formaldehyde 120, acetic acid 10

0000.1010 Sikora 1917   23632, **34**:161
FORMULA: abs. alc. 175, acetic acid 30, 40% formaldehyde 30, chloroform 15
NOTE: With the addition of 1% of picric acid this becomes F 5000.1010 Leeuwen 1907
(*q.v.*).

0000.1010 Tellyesniczky   *see* F 0000.1010 Lüko 1910 (note)

0000.1020 Formaldehyde-trichloracetic

0000.1020 Champy 1913   1915, **52**:18
FORMULA: sat. aq. sol. phenol 200, 40% formaldehyde 48, trichloroacetic acid 3.6

0000.1020 Davenport, Windle, and Beach 1934   20540b, **9**:10
FORMULA: water 225, 40% formaldehyde 25, trichloroacetic acid 1.25

0000.1020 Heidenhain 1916   23632, **32**:365
FORMULA: water 200, 40% formaldehyde 37.5, trichloroacetic acid 12.5

0000.1030 Formaldehyde-formic

0000.1030 Szepsenwol 1935   6630, **120**:689
FORMULA: water 220, 40% formaldehyde 20, formic acid 10
RECOMMENDED FOR: prior to Szepsenwol 1935 MS 33.21 (*q.v.*) *via* 1% and 3% silver
nitrate.

0000.1040 Formaldehyde-nitric

0000.1040 Hoskins 1907   11689, **4**:176
FORMULA: water 225, 40% formaldehyde 20, nitric acid 6

0000.1040 McClung and Allen 1929   McClung 1929, 422
FORMULA: water 225, 40% formaldehyde 19, nitric acid 6.3

0000.1040 Wilhelmi 1909 *test.* **1920 Mayer**   Mayer 1920, 33
FORMULA: 90% alc. 195, 40% formaldehyde 18.75, nitric acid 7.5

0000.1080 Formaldehyde-(other inorganic acids)

0000.1080 Cohen 1934   20540b, **9**:104
FORMULA: water 225, metaphosphoric acid 9, 40% formaldehyde 25

0000.1200 Formaldehyde-acetaldehyde

0000.1200 Besta 1910   766, **36**:477
FORMULAS: A. water 200, 40% formaldehyde 50, acetaldehyde 5; B. water 250, ammonium molybdate 10
METHOD: [fix A, 2 days] → distilled water, 24 hrs. with frequent changes → B, 2 days

0000.1300 Formaldehyde-acetone

0000.1300 Bing and Ellermann 1901   1739, **3**:260
FORMULA: 40% formaldehyde 25, acetone 225

0000.4000 (OTHER MODIFIERS)

0000.4000 MacFarland and Davenport 1941   20540b, **16**:53
FORMULA: water 112, 95% alc. 112, chloral hydrate 12.5, formamide 25

0000.4010 (Other modifiers)-acetic

0000.4010 Grapnuer and Weissberger 1933   23833, **102**:39
FORMULA: methanol 50, dioxane 200, paraldehyde 5, acetic acid 12.5

F 1000 OSMIC ACID IN ALL COMBINATIONS

1000.0000 OSMIC ALONE

It cannot be too strongly emphasized that osmic acid is a dangerous material to handle. The vapor causes the death of tissues with which it comes in contact almost instantly and, indeed, it may be employed for fixation in the vapor phase. This vapor, applied to the cornea of the eye or to the membranes of the nose, can cause the most grave damage in a short space of time. Since osmic acid is very easily reduced in the presence of almost all organic material, solutions are difficult to keep. The writer prefers the addition of about .01% of potassium permanganate. This gives a pink color, which may easily be judged by the eye, so that the oxidation of the permanganate can be corrected by the addition of a few drops of a stronger solution. The product of the reduction, which is a dead black in color, appears to be some of the lower oxides. These lower oxides may again be easily oxidized (bleached) and it is customary to use various mixtures of hydrogen peroxide (see Chapter 19, AF 31.1 Overton 1890) for the purpose, but the specimen must be washed thoroughly or the oxides will be reprecipitated on the tissues. Osmic acid alone is rarely used save for very small objects. It has the great advantage that it gives a faithful picture of cytological detail. Olney 1953 (*Turtox News*, **31**:29) states that nitric acid may be substituted for osmic acid in fixative formulas.

1000.0000 Bizzozero 1885   1789a, 102
FORMULA: water 250, osmic acid 0.625, sodium chloride 0.19

1000.0000 Ewald 1897   23354, **34**:257
FORMULA: water 250, osmic acid 0.375, sodium chloride 1.25
NOTE: The above is recommended for amphibian and reptilian blood; for mammals the NaCl is increased to 0.65%.

1000.0000 Mann 1894   23632, **11**:479
FORMULA: water 250, osmic acid 2.5, sodium chloride 1.875

1000.0010 Osmic-acetic

These are excellent mixtures, and are probably as good as the osmic-chromic-acetic more usually recommended. The rapid fixing and hardening power of the osmic acid counteracts the swelling properties of the acetic. These fixatives can be recommended both for cytological and nuclear fixation.

1000.0010 Faber-Domergue 1889   *Ann. Micr.*, **1**:1, Paris
FORMULA: water 200, osmic acid 2.5, acetic acid 50

1000.0010 Fol 1896 *test*. **Poll 1910**   Ehrlich, Krause, *et al.* 1910, **2**, 345
FORMULA: water 250, osmic acid 0.25, acetic acid .25
NOTE: The fixative of **Schmidt 1896** (1780, **47**:47) is identical.

1000.0010 Hamann 1885 *test*. **1910 Poll**   Ehrlich, Krause, *et al.* 1910, **2**:345
FORMULA: water 250, osmic acid 1.25, acetic acid 1.25

1000.0010 Hertwig 1879   10899, **13**:457
FORMULA: water 250, osmic acid 0.06, acetic acid 0.25

1000.0010 Hertwig 1885   14555, **10**:337
FORMULA: water 250, osmic acid 1, acetic acid 2.5

1000.0010 Orr 1900   11431, **6**:387
FORMULA: water 250, osmic acid 4, acetic acid 0.5

1000.0010 Rawitz 1895   Rawitz 1895, 19
FORMULA: water or sea water 250, osmic acid 0.06, acetic acid 0.25

1000.0010 Schmidt 1896   *see* F 1000.0010 Fol 1896 (note)

1000.0010 Schwarz 1888   2701, **18**:3
FORMULA: water 250, osmic acid 0.5, acetic acid 2.5

1000.0010 Zacharias 1887   1780, **30**:111
FORMULA: abs. alc. 200, osmic acid 0.025, acetic acid 50, chloroform 0.25
NOTE: Mayer 1920, p. 37, refers this formula (without the chloroform) to 1888 (766, **3**:24), but see below.

1000.0010 Zacharias 1888   766, **3**:24
FORMULA: abs. alc. 200, osmic acid 0.04, acetic acid 50

1000.0019 Osmic-acetic-(other organic acid)

1000.0019 van Ermengen 1894   23684, **15**:969
FORMULA: water 250, osmic acid 1.5, acetic acid 2.5, tannic acid 12
RECOMMENDED FOR: fixation of bacterial smears before silver staining of flagella.

1000.0030 Osmic-formic

1000.0030 Henking 1891   23632, **8**:156
FORMULA: water 200, glycerol 40, osmic acid 0.025, formic acid 7.5, dahlia violet 0.1

1000.0030 Kerschner 1908   1780, **71**:522
FORMULA: water 225, osmic acid 0.5, formic acid 50

1000.0030 Viallane 1883 *test*. **1928 Gatenby and Cowdry**
                              Gatenby and Cowdry 1928, 210
FORMULA: *A*. water 250, osmic acid 2.5; *B*. water 160, formic acid 80
METHOD: [fresh tissues] → *A*, till lightly browned → *B*, 10 mins. → MS 23.21 Viallane 1883

1000.0040 Osmic-nitric

1000.0040 Kolossow 1892   *see* AMS 11.1 Kolossow 1892

1000.0040 Nicolas 1891   10157, **8**:3
FORMULA: water 250, osmic acid 1.25, nitric acid 7.5

1000.1010 Osmic-formaldehyde-acetic

1000.1010 Swank and Davenport 1934   20540b, **9**:11
FORMULA: *A*. water 225, 40% formaldehyde 25; *B*. water 250, osmic acid 0.82, acetic acid 2.5, potassium chlorate 0.625
METHOD: [fresh tissue] → *A*, 24 hrs. → *B*, directly without washing, 1 wk. → [sections.]

1000.1010 Swank and Davenport 1935   20540b, **10**:88
   FORMULA: water 200, osmic acid 0.025, 40% formaldehyde 30, acetic acid 2.5, potassium
   chlorate 1.5

1200.0000 OSMIC-PLATINIC

1200.0000 van der Stricht 1895   1825, **14**:469
   FORMULA: water 250, osmic acid 1, platinic chloride 2

1200.0010 Osmic-platinic-acetic

These once widely recommended cytological fixatives are doubtfully any better than plain
osmic-acetic mixtures.

1200.0010 Hermann 1889   1780, **34**:59
   FORMULA: water 250, osmic acid 1, platinic chloride 1.8, acetic acid 12.5

1200.0010 Meves 1908   1780, **72**:816
   FORMULA: water 250, osmic acid 0.15, platinic chloride 0.56, acetic acid 3.75

1200.0010 Niessing 1895   1780, **46**:147
   FORMULA: water 225, osmic acid 1, platinic chloride 13, acetic acid 25

1230.0010 OSMIC-PLATINIC-MERCURIC-ACETIC

1230.0010 Cox 1895   23632, **13**:498
   FORMULA: water 240, osmic acid 0.6, platinic chloride 4.5, mercuric chloride 6.5, acetic
   acid 36

1230.0010 Niessing 1895   1780, **46**:147
   FORMULA: water 235, osmic acid 0.5, platinic chloride 6.25, mercuric chloride 8.75,
   acetic acid 12.5

1236.0010 OSMIC-PLATINIC-MERCURIC-CHROMIC-ACETIC

1236.0010 Marchoux and Simond 1906   857, **20**:105
   FORMULA: water 250, osmic acid 0.75, platinic chloride 1.5, mercuric chloride 15, chromic
   acid 1, acetic acid 7

1250.0010 OSMIC-PLATINIC-PICRIC-ACETIC

1250.0010 vom Rath 1895   766, **11**:285
   FORMULA: water 250, osmic acid 0.5, platinic chloride 2.0, picric acid 3.0, acetic acid 4.0

1260.0000 OSMIC-PLATINIC-CHROMIC

1260.0000 Whitman 1883   651, **17**:1204
   FORMULA: *A.* 0.25% osmic in sea water; *B.* F 2600.0000 Eisig 1879
   METHOD: pelagic fish ova → *A*, 5–10 mins. → *B*, 2 days

1260.0010 Osmic-platinic-chromic-acetic

These mixtures are now rarely seen. The addition of the platinic acid is of very doubtful
value.

1260.0010 Besson 1904   Besson 1904, 750
   FORMULA: water 250, osmic acid 1.4, platinic chloride 1.4, chromic acid 2.1, acetic acid 14
   NOTE: Besson attributes this to "Borrel" but gives no reference.

1260.0010 "Borrel"   *see* F 1260.0010 Caullery and Mesnil 1905, *or* F 1260.0010 Marchoux
                         and Simond 1906, *or* F 1260.0010 Besson 1904

1260.0010 Brass 1884   23632, **1**:39
   FORMULA: water 250, osmic acid 0.2 to 0.3, platinic chloride 0.3 to 0.8, chromic acid 0.3
   to 0.8, acetic acid 0.3 to 0.8

1260.0010 Caullery and Mesnil 1905   1789, **6**:281
   FORMULA: water 240, osmic acid 1.3, platinic chloride 1.3, chromic acid 2.0, acetic acid 13
   NOTE: Langeron 1934, p. 339 refers to this mixture as "*Mélange de Borrel (1905)*" but
   offers no reference.

1260.0010 Marchoux and Simond 1906   857, 20:105
FORMULA: water 250, osmic acid 1.5, platinic chloride 1.5, chromic acid 2, acetic acid 14
NOTE: Poll 1910 (Ehrlich, Krause, *et al.* 1910, **2**, 348) refers to this formula (without reference) as "Borrel's mixture."

1260.0030 Osmic-platinic-chromic-formic

1260.0030 Pianese 1889   1886, 2:412
FORMULA: water 250, osmic acid 1, platinic chloride 1.5, chromic acid 0.13, formic acid 0.5

1268.0000 OSMIC-PLATINIC-CHROMIC-(OTHER INORGANIC SALTS)

1268.0000 Nebel 1934   7033a, 5:1
REAGENTS REQUIRED: *A*. 0.1% ammonium hydroxide; *B*. 0.5% thorium nitrate; *C*. water 230, osmic acid 5.75, platinic chloride 2.3, chromic acid 0.2
METHOD: [root tips] → *A*, 5 mins. → *B*, 3 hrs. → *C*, 24 hrs.

1268.0020 Osmic-platinic-chromic-(other inorganic salt)-trichloroacetic acid

1268.0020 Friedenthal 1908 *test. circ.* **1938 Wellings**   Wellings *circ.* 1938, 25
FORMULA: trichloroacetic acid 156, osmic acid 4, platinic chloride 4, chromic acid 8, uranium acetate 78

1270.0000 OSMIC-PLATINIC-DICHROMATE

1270.0000 Veratti *test.* **1900 Golgi**   Golgi 1900, 2:687
FORMULA: water 250, osmic acid 0.6, platinic chloride 0.08, potassium dichromate 4.0

1270.0010 Osmic-platinic-dichromate-acetic

1270.0010 Johnson 1895 *test.* **1905 Lee**   Lee, 1905, 43
FORMULA: water 250, osmic acid 0.5, platinic chloride 0.4, potassium dichromate 4.3, acetic acid 12.5

1300.0000 OSMIC-MERCURIC

These mixtures are cytological fixatives, and are worthless for nuclear preservation. They are best applied to small invertebrates in which the rapid killing action of the osmic is backed up by the hardening and mordanting action of the mercuric chloride.

1300.0000 Apáthy 1893   23632, 10:349
FORMULA: water 250, osmic acid 2.5, mercuric chloride 9

1300.0000 Apáthy 1897   14246, 12:495
FORMULA: water 250, osmic acid 1.25, mercuric chloride 8.75, sodium chloride 0.7

1300.0000 Braun 1895 *test.* **1910 Poll**   Ehrlich, Krause, *et al.* 1910, 2:351
FORMULA: water 250, osmic acid 0.013, mercuric chloride 17.5

1300.0000 Bühler 1898   22302, 31:316
FORMULA: water 250, mercuric chloride 17.5, osmic acid 0.125

1300.0000 Heidenhain 1896   23632, 13:186
FORMULA: water 250, osmic acid 1.25, mercuric chloride 8.75

1300.0000 Hirschler 1918   1780, 91:140
FORMULA: water 250, osmic acid 2.5, mercuric chloride 8.75

1300.0000 Kolster *test.* **1910 Poll**   Ehrlich, Krause, *et al.* 1910, 2:351
FORMULA: water 250, osmic acid 7.5, mercuric chloride 17.5, sodium chloride 1.25

1300.0000 Mann 1894   23632, 11:481
FORMULA: water 250, osmic acid 1.25, mercuric chloride 10, sodium chloride 2.25
NOTE: The original method calls for equal parts of 1% osmic and a sat. sol. mercuric chloride in 0.9% NaCl.

1300.0000 Pappenheim 1896   1789a, **145**:587
FORMULA: water 250, osmic acid 2.5, mercuric chloride 8.75

1300.0010 Osmic-mercuric-acetic

These are general-purpose fixatives, giving good preservation both of cytoplasmic and nuclear elements, as well as being much easier for after-staining than are osmic-acetic mixtures alone. The mercuric chloride may assist in preserving the osmic acid against reduction.

1300.0010 Colombo 1903   23632, **20**:282
FORMULA: water 250, osmic acid 1, mercuric chloride 7, acetic acid 0.5

1300.0010 Cox 1896   23632, **13**:498
FORMULA: water 200, osmic acid, 1.0, mercuric chloride 7.0, acetic acid 50.0

1300.0010 Drüner 1894   10899, **28**:296
FORMULA: water 240, osmic acid 0.125, mercuric chloride 12.5, acetic acid 12.5

1300.0010 Tschassownikow *test.* **1910 Spuler**   Ehrlich, Krause, *et al.* 1910, **2**:526
FORMULA: water 245, osmic acid 1.25, mercuric chloride 13, acetic acid 6.25

1300.0010 Zieglwallner 1911 *test.* **1928 Schmorl**   Schmorl 1928, 217
FORMULA: water 100, abs. alc. 125, osmic acid 1, mercuric chloride 3, acetic acid 25

1340.0000 OSMIC-CUPRIC-MERCURIC

1340.0000 Merton 1932   1798, **76**:171
STOCK SOLUTIONS: I. 2% copper sulfate; II. 2% osmic acid; III. sat. sol. mercuric chloride.
METHOD: [Paramecium on smear of V 21.1 Mayer 1884] → I, added to fluid on slide, 5 mins. → drain → vapor of II, 1 min. → III, on slide 10 mins. → 70% alc.

1350.0010 OSMIC-MERCURIC-PICRIC-ACETIC

1350.0010 Becher and Demoll 1913   Becher and Demoll 1913, 43
FORMULA: water 245, osmic acid 0.5, mercuric chloride 3.75, picric acid 0.75, acetic acid 5

1350.0010 vom Rath 1895   766, **11**:285
FORMULA: water 250, osmic acid 0.5, mercuric chloride 8, picric acid 1.4, acetic acid 2.2

1360.0010 OSMIC-MERCURIC-CHROMIC-ACETIC

1360.0010 Brouha *test.* **1930 Guyer**   Guyer 1930, 150
FORMULA: water 240, osmic acid 5, mercuric chloride 11.5, chromic acid 5, acetic acid 12.5

1360.0010 Cori *test.* **1910 Spuler**   Ehrlich, Krause, *et al.* 1910, **2**:526
FORMULA: water 250, osmic acid 0.003, mercuric chloride 15.3, chromic acid 0.08, acetic acid 0.03
NOTE: This may also be prepared by mixing 7 parts of 7% mercuric chloride with 1 part of F 1600.0010 Cori 1890.

1360.0010 Galescu 1908   6630, **65**:429
FORMULA: water 250, osmic acid 0.04, mercuric chloride 4.4, chromic acid 0.5, acetic acid 0.2

1360.0010 Podwyssozki 1886   2526, **1**:287
FORMULA: water 250, osmic acid 0.5, mercuric chloride 1, chromic acid 2, acetic acid 5

1370.0030 OSMIC-MERCURIC-DICHROMATE-FORMIC

1370.0030 Charipper 1928   763, **38**:401
FORMULA: water 240, osmic acid 1, mercuric chloride 10, potassium dichromate 5, sodium sulfate 2, formic acid 10

1370.1000 Osmic-mercuric-dichromate-formaldehyde

1370.1000 Levi 1918   1820, **11**:515
FORMULA: water 250, osmic acid 0.5, mercuric chloride 5.6, potassium dichromate 2.75, 40% formaldehyde 2.5

1378.0000 OSMIC-MERCURIC-DICHROMATE-(OTHER INORGANIC SALTS)

1378.0000 Benoit 1922   6630, **86**:1101
FORMULA: water 250, osmic acid 1.25, mercuric chloride 3.1, potassium dichromate 3.75, uranium nitrate 2.0, sodium chloride 0.5

1380.0010 OSMIC-MERCURIC-(OTHER INORGANIC SALTS)-ACETIC

1380.0010 Farkas 1914   23833, **45**:143
FORMULA: water 100, 95% alc. 125, osmic acid 1.25, mercuric chloride 4, acetic acid 25, sodium iodide 0.005

1380.0030 Osmic-mercuric-(other inorganic salts)-formic

1380.0030 Nebel 1932   23639b, **16**:251
FORMULA: water 225, osmic acid 2.5, mercuric chloride 3, uranium chloride 1, formic acid 25

1400.0000 OSMIC-CUPRIC

1400.0000 Gardner 1897   2981, **17**:398
FORMULA: water 250, osmic acid 0.2, copper acetate 14.0

1400.0000 de Waele 1899 *test.* **1920 Mayer**   Mayer 1920, 61
FORMULA: water 250, osmic acid 0.5, copper acetate 12.5

1400.0010 Osmic-cupric-acetic

1400.0010 Duboscq 1899   *see* DS 21.3 Duboscq 1899

1500.0010 OSMIC-PICRIC-ACETIC

No advantage can be secured by the addition of picric acid, which gives water-soluble precipitates, to such an excellent fixative as osmic-acetic alone. These formulas are, however, widely recommended in the literature.

1500.0010 Flemming 1882 *test.* **1920 Mayer**   Mayer 1920, 40
FORMULA: water 250, osmic acid 0.25, picric acid 0.6, acetic acid 0.25

1500.0010 Giesbrecht *test.* **1910 Poll** *cit.* **Lee and Mayer**
                                          Ehrlich, Krause, *et al.* 1910, **1**:345
FORMULA: sea water 250, osmic acid 0.1, picric acid 3, acetic acid 10

1500.0010 vom Rath 1895   766, **11**:289
FORMULA: water 250, osmic acid 0.3, picric acid 3, acetic acid 2.5

1500.0010 Schuberg *test.* **1920 Mayer**   Mayer 1920, 40
FORMULA: water 240, osmic acid 0.25, picric acid 2.7, acetic acid 7.5

1500.0010 Spüler 1892   1780, **40**:530
FORMULA: water 250, osmic acid 0.125, picric acid 3, acetic acid 1.5

1500.0040 Osmic-picric-nitric

1500.0040 Hill 1910   17510, **64**:1
FORMULA: water 250, osmic acid 0.05, picric acid 3, nitric acid 12.5

1500.0040 Rawitz 1895   Rawitz 1895, 24
FORMULA: water 250, osmic acid 0.7, picric acid 3, nitric acid 12.5

1500.0050 Osmic-picric-sulfuric

1500.0050 Erlanger 1895   14555, **22**:493
FORMULA: water 250, osmic acid 0.1, picric acid 3, sulfuric acid 5

1500.0050 Francotte *circa* **1890**   Francotte, 197
FORMULA: water 250, osmic acid 0.1, picric acid 0.5, sulfuric acid 5

1500.0050 Schuberg 1903   23635, **74** :155
FORMULA: water 250, osmic acid 0.4, picric acid 3, sulfuric acid 5

1560.0000 OSMIC-PICRIC-CHROMIC

Attention must again be drawn to the improbability that picric acid will impart additional qualities to an already good mixture, such as osmic-chromic alone.

1560.0000 Fol 1896 *test.* **1910 Poll**   Ehrlich, Krause, *et al.* 1910, **2** :348
FORMULA: water 250, osmic acid 0.01, picric acid 0.5, chromic acid 0.6

1560.1010 Osmic-picric-chromic-acetic-formaldehyde

1560.1010 Skovsted 1933   1032, **47** :227
FORMULA: water 190, osmic acid 1, picric acid 1.5, chromic acid 2.8, acetic acid 9, 40% formaldehyde 50, urea 3.8

1580.0000 OSMIC-PICRIC-(OTHER INORGANIC SALT)

1580.0000 Perriraz 1905   5392, **61** :213
FORMULA: water 175, 95% alc. 75, osmic acid 0.12, picric acid 0.75, silver nitrate 0.75
PREPARATION: Dissolve the osmic acid in the alc., and the salts separately in water. Add heated (50°C.) picric solution to silver nitrate, then osmic.

1600.0000 OSMIC-CHROMIC

The osmic-chromic mixtures share with the following class the distinction of being the best general-purpose fixatives. They give better cytological fixation than do the more strongly acid osmic-chromic-acetic, but the considerable number of formulas included under each class bear witness to their good qualities. When in doubt as to what fixative to choose for an object with which one has had no previous experience, it cannot be too strongly recommended that one from either this or the following class be employed.

1600.0000 Barret 1886a   17510, **26** :607
FORMULA: 50% alc. 250, osmic acid 0.5, chromic acid 0.5

1600.0000 Barret 1886b   17510, **26** :607
FORMULA: water 250, osmic acid 0.5, chromic acid 0.4

1600.0000 Barret 1886c   17510, **26** :607
FORMULA: water 250, osmic acid 0.25, chromic acid 0.65

1600.0000 Böhm and Oppel 1896   *see* F 1600.0000 Flesch 1879

1600.0000 Brock 1886   23635, **44** :333
FORMULA: water 250, osmic acid 0.04, chromic acid 0.25

1600.0000 Drew 1920   *see* ADS 12.1 Drew 1920

1600.0000 Flesch 1879   1780, **16** :300
FORMULA: water 250, osmic acid 0.25, chromic acid 0.6
NOTE: The formula given (without reference) by Böhm and Oppel in the 1896 edition of their *Taschenbuch* does not differ significantly from this.

1600.0000 Haug 1891   *see* AF 21.1 Haug 1891

1600.0000 Lo Bianco 1890   14246, **9** :443
FORMULA: water 250, osmic acid 0.05, chromic acid 2.5

1600.0010 Osmic-chromic-acetic

Flemming 1882 was the first of these excellent mixtures. The whole group is often referred to as "Flemming." "Flemming without acetic" (FWA) is just that, and belongs in the last class.

1600.0010 Baker 1945   Baker 1945, 97
FORMULA: water 237, osmic acid 1, chromic acid 2, acetic acid 13

1600.0010 Bělar 1929   *Meth. wiss. Biol.*, **1**:638
FORMULA: water 250, osmic acid 1, chromic acid 2, acetic acid 1.5

1600.0010 Bonn *test.* **1937 Gatenby and Painter**   Gatenby and Painter 1937, 675
FORMULA: water 240, osmic acid 0.3, chromic acid 1, acetic acid 7.5

1600.0010 Bonner *test.* **Meyer 1915**   Meyer 1915, 198
FORMULA: water 243, osmic acid 0.3, chromic acid 1.1, acetic acid 7

1600.0010 Burkhardt 1892 *test.* **1910 Poll**   Ehrlich, Krause, *et al.* 1910, **2**:248
FORMULA: water 250, osmic acid 1.7, chromic acid 2.5, acetic acid 20

1600.0010 Catcheside 1934   1032, **48**:601
FORMULA: water 250, osmic acid 0.4, chromic acid 4.5, acetic acid 3, maltose 3

1600.0010 Chamberlain 1906   3430, **42**:321
FORMULA: water 220, osmic acid 0.05, chromic acid 2.5, acetic acid 25

1600.0010 Cori 1890   23632, **6**:441
FORMULA: water 250, osmic acid 0.025, chromic acid 0.6, acetic acid 0.25

1600.0010 Duggar 1909 *test.* **1937 Gatenby and Painter**
                                        Gatenby and Painter 1937, 702
FORMULA: water 250, osmic acid 0.5, chromic acid 1.25, acetic acid 0.5

1600.0010 Ferguson 1904   *see* F 1600.0010 Mottier 1897 (note)

1600.0010 Fischler 1906   10606, **48**:42
FORMULA: water 250, osmic acid 0.27, chromic acid 1.0, acetic acid 6.5

1600.0010 Flemming 1882   Flemming 1882, 381
FORMULA: water 250, osmic acid 0.25, chromic acid 0.6, acetic acid 0.25
NOTE: This is "Flemming's first or weak mixture" (Gatenby and Cowdry 1928, 37).

1600.0010 Flemming 1884   23632, **1**:349
FORMULA: water 250, osmic acid 1, chromic acid 1.8, acetic acid 12.5
NOTE: This is "Flemming's second or strong formula" (Gatenby and Cowdry 1928, 37).

1600.0010 Flemming *test.* **1910 Meves**   Ehrlich, Krause, *et al.* 1910, **1**:476
FORMULA: water 250, osmic acid 0.5, chromic acid 1.8, acetic acid 12.5

1600.0010 Fol 1884 *test.* **1928 Gatenby and Cowdry**   Gatenby and Cowdry, 37
FORMULA: water 250, osmic acid 0.05, chromic acid 0.6, acetic acid 0.25

1600.0010 Friedmann *test.* **1900 Pollack**   Pollack 1900, 28
FORMULA: water 240, osmic acid 0.2, chromic acid 2.25, acetic 10

1600.0010 Gates 1907   3430, **43**:81
FORMULA: water 250, osmic acid 0.25, chromic acid 1.7, acetic acid 1.25

1600.0010 Jolly 1907   1823, **9**:142
FORMULA: water 250, osmic acid 0.75, chromic acid 1.5, acetic acid 2.5

1600.0010 Laguesse 1901 *test.* **1907 Böhm and Oppel**   Böhm and Oppel 1907, 358
FORMULA: water 250, osmic acid 3, chromic acid 0.8, acetic acid 0.6

1600.0010 Laguesse *test.* **1933 Cajal and de Castro**   Cajal and de Castro 1933, 28
FORMULA: water 240, osmic acid 1.6, chromic acid 1.6, acetic acid 1

1600.0010 Langendorf *test.* **1910 Poll**   Ehrlich, Krause, *et al.* 1910, **2**:347
FORMULA: water 250, osmic acid 0.5, chromic acid 1.25, acetic acid 75

1600.0010 Lehrmitte and Guccione 1909   20080, **19**:205
FORMULA: water 250, osmic acid 0.1, chromic acid 0.9, acetic acid 0.4

1600.0010 Lillie *test.* **1929 McClung and Allen**   McClung 1929, 423
   FORMULA: water 250, osmic acid 0.95, chromic acid 1, acetic acid 2

1600.0010 Meves 1910   Ehrlich, Krause, *et al.* 1910, **1**:476
   FORMULA: water 250, osmic acid 1, chromic acid 0.9, acetic acid 12.5

1600.0010 Meves and Duesberg 1908   1780, **71**:571
   FORMULA: water 250, osmic acid 0.25, chromic acid 1.0, acetic acid 6.25

1600.0010 Möbius 1887   14555, **12**:174
   FORMULA: sea water 250, osmic acid 0.25, chromic acid 0.7, acetic acid 0.25

1600.0010 Mottier 1897   10606, **30**:169
   FORMULA: water 250, osmic acid 0.75, chromic acid 2.0, acetic acid 12.5
   NOTE: **Ferguson 1904** (16953, 6) is identical.

1600.0010 Newton and Darlington 1919   11211, **21**:1
   FORMULA: water 250, osmic acid 1, chromic acid 1.5, acetic acid 7

1600.0010 Oguma and Kihara 1923   1825, **33**:493
   REAGENTS REQUIRED: *A.* F 0000.0010 Carnoy 1887; *B.* F 1600.0010 Flemming 1882
   METHOD: [small pieces] → *A*, 1 min. → *B*, 24 hrs.

1600.0010 Schmorl 1928   Schmorl 1928, 217
   FORMULA: water 120, 95% alc. 120, osmic acid 1, chromic acid 1.9, acetic acid 12.5

1600.0010 Showalter 1926   1032, **40**:713
   FORMULA: water 225, osmic acid 0.06 chromic acid 1, acetic acid 3

1600.0010 Sypkens 1904   17770a, .2.
   FORMULA: water 250, osmic acid 1, chromic acid 1.9, acetic acid 10

1600.0010 Taylor 1924   3430, **78**:236
   FORMULA: water 240, osmic acid 0.6, chromic acid 1, acetic acid 4, maltose 3

1600.0010 Yamanouchi 1908   3430, **45**:145
   FORMULA: water 250, osmic acid 0.2, chromic acid 1.0, acetic acid 27

1600.0020 Osmic-chromic-trichloroacetic

1600.0020 Winiwarter *test.* **1930 Guyer**   Guyer 1930, 217
   FORMULA: water 250, osmic acid 1, chromic acid 2, trichloracetic acid 4

1600.0030 Osmic-chromic-formic

1600.0030 Guthrie 1928 *test.* **1928 Gatenby and Cowdry**
        Gatenby and Cowdry, 1928, 66
   FORMULA: water 240, osmic acid 1.0, chromic acid 1.9, formic acid 12.5

1600.0060 Osmic-chromic-hydrochloric

1600.0060 Takahashi 1908   11135, **18**:167
   FORMULA: water 250, osmic acid 1.25, chromic acid 0.2, hydrochloric acid 0.05

1600.1000 Osmic-chromic-formaldehyde

1600.1000 Kaufman 1929   763, **42**:365
   FORMULA: water 237.50, osmic acid 1, chromic acid 1.9, 40% formaldehyde 12.5

1670.0000 OSMIC-CHROMIC-DICHROMATE

These are well-known cytological fixatives, particularly for protoplasmic inclusions. The next class (i.e., the present fixatives acidified) give reasonable nuclear fixation as well, but cannot compare with formulas specifically designed for that purpose.

1670.0000 Benda 1901 *test.* **1948 Romeis**   Romeis 1948, 231
   FORMULA: water 250, osmic acid 1, chromic acid 1.9, acetic acid 2.5

1670.0000 Champy 1911 *test.* **1942 Langeron**   Langeron 1942, 384
FORMULA: water 250, osmic acid 1.1, chromic acid 1.0, potassium dichromate 2.9

1670.0000 Nakamura 1928   13367, **55**:1
FORMULA: water 250, osmic acid 1, chromic acid 2, potassium dichromate 5

1670.0000 Nassanow 1923   1780, **97**:136
FORMULA: water 250, osmic acid 1.7, chromic acid 0.85, potassium dichromate 5

1670.0000 Severinghaus 1923   763, **53**:3
FORMULA: water 250, osmic acid 1.2, chromic acid 0.6, potassium dichromate 3.75

1670.0000 Zweibaum 1933   4285a, **10**:210
FORMULA: water 250, osmic acid 0.3, chromic acid 1, potassium dichromate 2.7

1670.0010 Osmic-chromic-dichromate-acetic

1670.0010 LaCour 1929   *LaCour's 2B—auct.*   14900, **124**:127
FORMULA: water 250, osmic acid 0.5, chromic acid 1.5, potassium dichromate 1.5, acetic acid 0.8, urea 1.5, sodium sulfate 0.8

1670.0010 LaCour 131   *LaCour's 2BD—auct.*   11360, **51**:119
FORMULA: water 250, osmic acid 0.6, chromic acid 1.0, potassium dichromate 1.0, acetic acid 1.5, saponin 0.1

1670.0010 LaCour 1931c   *LaCour's 2BE—auct.*   11360, **51**:124
FORMULA: water 240, osmic acid 0.5, chromic acid 1.4, potassium dichromate 1.5, acetic acid 0.75, saponin 0.05

1670.0010 Smith 1935a   *Smith's S1—auct.*   11211, **49**:119
FORMULA: water 250, osmic acid 0.8, chromic acid 1.25, potassium dichromate 0.6, acetic acid 1.5, saponin 0.06

1670.0010 Smith 1935b   *Smith's S2—auct.*   11211, **49**:119
FORMULA: water 250, osmic acid 0.8, chromic acid 1.2, potassium dichromate 1.6, acetic acid 1.0, saponin 0.1

1670.0019 Osmic-chromic-dichromate-acetic-(other organic acids)

1670.0019 Benda 1903   764, **12**:752
FORMULA: *A.* water 250, osmic acid 1, potassium dichromate 1.8, acetic acid 6.35; *B.* water 125, chromic acid 1.25, pyroligneous acid 1.25; *C.* water 250, potassium dichromate 5
METHOD: *A*, 8 days → water, 1 hr. → *B*, 24 hrs. → *C*, 24 hrs. → running water, 24 hrs.

1670.0090 Osmic-chromic-dichromate-(other organic acid)

1670.0090 Champy 1913   1915, **54**:307
FORMULA: *A.* water 250, osmic acid 1.25, chromic acid 1.15, potassium dichromate 3; *B.* water 175, chromic acid 2.5, pyroligneous acid 35; *C.* water 250, potassium dichromate 7.5
METHOD: *A*, 24 hrs. → distilled water , ½ hr. → *B*, 20 hrs. → distilled water, ½ hr. → *C*, 3 days → running water, 24 hrs.

1700.0000 OSMIC-DICHROMATE

These are the best known of all the cytoplasmic fixatives, particularly for the demonstration of mitochondria. They should not, however, be employed as general-purpose fixatives, for which use they were not intended.

1700.0000 Altmann 1890 *test.* **1928 Gatenby**   Gatenby and Cowdry
FORMULA: water 250, osmic acid 2.5, potassium dichromate 6.25
NOTE: Langeron 1942, 384 assigns an identical formula, without reference, to **Altmann 1894.**

1700.0000 Andriezen 1894   3579, **1** :909
  FORMULA: *A*. water 250, osmic acid 0.13, potassium dichromate 5; *B*. water 250, osmic
  acid 0.25, potassium dichromate 4.6
  METHOD: [thin slices, suspended by waxed threads] → *A*, 24 hrs. in dark → *B*, 48 hrs. →
  F 1700.0000 Golgi 1900 3½ to 6 days

1700.0000 Baker and Thomas 1933   Baker 1945, 97
  FORMULA: water 250, osmic acid 2.5, potassium dichromate 4.75

1700.0000 Berkely 1897   10920, **6** :1
  FORMULA: water 250, osmic acid 0.6, potassium dichromate 6

1700.0000 Cajal 1890   23632, **7** :332
  FORMULA: water 250, osmic acid 0.4, potassium dichromate 6

1700.0000 Cajal 1891   6011, **8** :130
  FORMULA: water 250, osmic 0.25, potassium dichromate 6.5

1700.0000 Dekhuyzen 1903   6628, **137** :415
  FORMULA: sea water 250, osmic acid 0.68, potassium dichromate 5.4

1700.0000 Gedoelst 1889   *see* F 1700.0000 Golgi 1880 (note)

1700.0000 van Gehuchten *test.* **1927 Kingsbury and Johannsen**
                                       Kingsbury and Johannsen 1927, 89
  FORMULA: water 250, osmic acid 0.5, potassium dichromate 6

1700.0000 Golgi 1880 *test.* **1903** *ips.*   Golgi 1903, **1** :162
  FORMULA: water 250, osmic acid 0.4, potassium dichromate 4
  NOTE: This method was republished by Golgi in 1883 (*test. ipsi, loc. cit.* **2** :504). An
  identical formula is given by **Gedoelst 1889** (6011, **5** :131).

1700.0000 Golgi 1900 *test.* **1903** *ips.*   Golgi 1903, **2** :685
  FORMULA: water 250, osmic acid 0.7, potassium dichromate 5
  NOTE: This formula is identical with the third solution of Andriezen 1894 (see above)
  but is listed as Golgi 1900 for convenience.

1700.0000 Kolossow 1897 *test.* **1928 da Fano**   Gatenby and Cowdry 1928, 608
  FORMULA: water 250, osmic acid 0.63, potassium dichromate 10

1700.0000 Lo Bianco 1890   14246, **9** :435
  FORMULA: water 250, osmic acid 0.05, potassium dichromate 12.5

1700.0000 Löwenthal 1893   23632, **10** :309
  FORMULA: water 250, osmic acid 0.5, potassium dichromate 5

1700.0000 Marchi 1886   19460, **12** :50
  FORMULA: water 250, osmic acid 0.88, potassium dichromate 1.7, potassium sulfate 0.8

1700.0000 Mettler 1932   20540b, **7** :102
  FORMULA: water 250, osmic acid 0.5, potassium dichromate 6

1700.0000 Metzner 1907 *test.* **1920 Mayer**   Mayer 1920, 53
  FORMULA: water 250, osmic acid 9.4, potassium dichromate 4.5
  NOTE: The formula is originally given in terms of a "sat. sol. dichromate." This is here
  taken to represent a 7.5% sol.; the original may have used anything between 7% and
  12%.

1700.0000 Roskin 1946   Roskin 1946, 97
  FORMULA: water 165, osmic acid 3.3, potassium dichromate 2.1

1700.0000 Schultze 1904   23632, **21** :7
  FORMULA: water 250, osmic acid 1.25, potassium dichromate 5.6

1700.0000 Timofecheff *test.* **1933 Cajal and de Castro**   Cajal and de Castro 1933, 125
  FORMULA: water 240, osmic acid 0.8, potassium dichromate 8

1700.0000 Windle 1926   11135, **40**:229
    FORMULA: water 250, osmic acid 0.4, potassium dichromate 7.5

1700.0000 Wlassow 1894   2526, **15**:543
    FORMULA: water 250, osmic acid 0.1, potassium dichromate 0.6, sod. chloride 2.0

1700.0000 Zietschmann 1903   23635, **74**:1
    FORMULA: water 250, osmic acid 0.75, potassium dichromate 3.2, potassium sulfate 1.6

1700.0010 Osmic-dichromate-acetic

This is a much neglected group of general-purpose fixatives, indicated for histological study in which it is desired to preserve the lipoid constituents of the cell.

1700.0010 Bensley 1911   590, **12**:297
    FORMULA: water 250, osmic acid 1, potassium dichromate 4, acetic acid 0.75

1700.0010 Bensley and Bensley 1938   Bensley and Bensley 1938, 45
    FORMULA: water 250, osmic acid 1, potassium dichromate 5, acetic acid 1.25

1700.0010 Hoehl 1896   1739, (1896):32
    FORMULA: water 250, osmic acid 0.5, potassium dichromate 6, acetic acid 5

1700.0010 Oxner 1905   10899, **40**:589
    FORMULA: water 255, osmic acid 0.6, potassium dichromate 5.25, acetic acid 12.5

1700.0030 Osmic-dichromate-formic

1700.0030 Oxner 1905   10899, **40**:589
    FORMULA: water 255, osmic acid 0.6, potassium dichromate 5.25, formic acid 15

1700.0040 Osmic-dichromate-nitric

1700.0040 Dekhuyzen 1903   6628, **137**:415
    FORMULA: sea water 250, osmic acid 0.9, potassium dichromate 6.25, nitric acid 1.2
    NOTE: The original formula, which is said to be isotonic with sea water, requires 250 ml. of a 2.5% solution of potassium dichromate in sea water, to be mixed with 25 ml. of N nitric acid and 54 ml. of 2% osmic acid.

1700.1000 Osmic-dichromate-formaldehyde

The apparently irrational mixtures that comprise this and the next few classes are in reality of the utmost value, not only for the cytological and neurological studies for which they were originally intended, but also for the fixation of embryos and of small invertebrates. Where nuclear fixation is as important as cytoplasmic fixation, the acidified mixtures should be used.

1700.1000 Fish 1895   21400a, **17**:319
    FORMULA: water 250, osmic acid 0.025, potassium dichromate 2.5, 40% formaldehyde 0.5, potassium sulfate 2.5

1700.1000 dell'Isola 1895 *test.* **1928 da Fano**   Gatenby and Cowdry 1928, 609
    FORMULA: water 235, osmic acid 0.25, potassium dichromate 12.5, 40% formaldehyde 37.5

1700.1000 Maximow 1909   23623, **26**:179
    FORMULA: water 225, osmic acid 0.5, potassium dichromate 5, potassium sulfate 2.5, 40% formaldehyde 25

1700.1000 Mislawsky 1913   23632, **81**:394
    FORMULA: water 200, osmic acid 0.125, potassium dichromate 6, 40% formaldehyde 50

1700.1000 Murray 1919   1200, **6**:77
    FORMULA: *A.* water 225, potassium dichromate 5.6, potassium sulfate 2.25, 40% formaldehyde 25; *B.* water 250, potassium dichromate 6.5, potassium sulfate 2.5; *C.* water 250, osmic acid 5
    METHOD: [whole organ or large piece] → *A*, overnight → *B*, thin slices, 2–7 days → *C*, 2 days → running water, 12 hrs.

1700.1000 Schridder *test.* **1928 Gatenby and Cowdry**   Gatenby and Cowdry 1928, 330
FORMULA: *A.* water 225, potassium dichromate 5.5, potassium sulfate 2.25, 40% formaldehyde 25; *B.* water 250, potassium dichromate 6, potassium sulfate 2.5; *C.* water 250, osmic acid 5
METHOD FOR MITOCHONDRIA AND FATS IN BIRDS AND MAMMALS: *A,* 2 days → *B,* 2–4 days → *C,* 2 days → running water, 24 hrs.

1700.1000 Smirnow 1895   1780, **52**:202
FORMULA: water 250, osmic acid 0.375, potassium dichromate 9.5

1700.1010 Osmic-dichromate-formaldehyde-acetic

1700.1010 Swank and Davenport 1934   20540b, **9**:11
FORMULA: *A.* distilled water 225, 40% formaldehyde 25; *B.* water 250, osmic acid 0.85, potassium dichromate 0.34, potassium sulfate 0.8, acetic acid 5

1780.0000 OSMIC-DICHROMATE-(OTHER INORGANIC SALTS)

1780.0000 Cajal 1933a   Cajal and de Castro 1933, 29
FORMULA: water 250, osmic acid 0.5, potassium dichromate 6, ferric chloride 12

1780.0000 Cajal 1933b   Cajal and de Castro 1933, 29
FORMULA: water 240, osmic acid 0.4, potassium dichromate 4.8, potassium ferricyanide 1.2

1800.0000 OSMIC-(OTHER INORGANIC SALTS)

1800.0000 Bensley and Bensley 1929   590, **44**:79
FORMULA: water 250, osmic acid 5, ferric chloride 1.25

1800.0000 Busch 1898   15058, **17**:476
FORMULA: water 250, osmic acid 0.75, sodium iodate 2.5

1800.0000 Kolossow 1898   1780, **52**:1
FORMULA: water 250, osmic acid 1.25, uranium nitrate 6.25

1800.0010 and .0030 Osmic acid-(other inorganic salts)-(acids)

1800.0010 Frenkel 1893   766, **8**:539
FORMULA: water 250, osmic acid 1.25, acetic acid 1.25, palladium chloride 1.9

1800.0030 Pianese 1899   1886, **2**:412
FORMULA: water 250, osmic acid 1, cobalt chloride 2, formic acid 0.5

F 2000 PLATINIC CHLORIDE IN COMBINATION WITH FIXATIVE AGENTS OF HIGHER NUMERICAL RANK

Platinic chloride is a valuable and neglected fixative agent. Its main value lies in its mordanting power for after-staining, for it appears to interfere less with the staining properties of the tissues than any other reagent. It is stated by Langeron (1942, 372) to have all the advantages of chromic acid with none of the disadvantages resulting from the discoloration of the tissue. It is particularly valuable in mixtures with chromic acid where it inhibits the production of chromic oxide, which causes such gross discoloration and prevents good after-staining.

2000.1000 PLATINIC-FORMALDEHYDE

2000.1000 Cajal 1893 *test.* **Pollack 1900**   Pollack 1900, 133
FORMULA: water 150, platinic chloride 0.08, 40% formaldehyde 100

2000.1010 Platinic-formaldehyde-acetic

2000.1010 Bouin 1900   1825, **17**:211
FORMULA: water 200, platinic chloride 1.8, 40% formaldehyde 50, acetic 12.5

2000.1010 Retterer 1900   11024, **36**:508
FORMULA: water 125, platinic chloride 6.25, 40% formaldehyde 125, acetic 7.5

2300.0000 PLATINIC-MERCURIC

This is an admirable fixative, particularly before complex staining techniques. Where nuclear fixation is of importance the acidified mixtures of the next class should be used.

2300.0000 Becher and Demoll 1913   Becher and Demoll 1913, 43
FORMULA: water 250, platinic chloride 0.7, mercuric chloride 3.75

2300.0000 Rabl 1894   23632, **11**:165
FORMULA: water 250, platinic chloride 0.625, mercuric chloride 4

2300.0010 Platinic-mercuric-acetic

2300.0010 Bouin *test*. **1910 Spuler**   Ehrlich, Krause, *et al*. 1910, **2**:523
FORMULA: water 240, platinic chloride 1.6, mercuric chloride 5.6, acetic acid 24

2300.0010 Hoffmann 1908   23635, **89**:598
FORMULA: 25% alc. 250, platinic chloride 1.25, mercuric chloride 4.5, acetic acid 12.5

2300.0010 Lenhossék 1898   1780, **51**:220
FORMULA: water 250, platinic chloride 1.25, mercuric chloride 6.4, acetic acid 12.5

2300.1000 Platinic-mercuric-formaldehyde

2300.1000 Szüts 1913   23632, **29**:290
FORMULA: water 190, platinic chloride .625, mercuric chloride 7.6, 40% formaldehyde 62.5

2300.1030 Platinic-mercuric-formaldehyde-formic

It is unfortunate that the name of Bouin should be so widely associated with picric-formaldehyde-acetic mixtures. Undoubtedly the best general-purpose fixative which he contributed is the only present occupant of this class. It gives a better general-purpose fixation than does the more generally employed "Bouin's fluid," and permits better and more billiant after-staining.

2300.1030 Bouin 1898   2844, **6**:54
FORMULA: water 180, platinic chloride 1, mercuric chloride 4.2, 40% formaldehyde 60, formic acid 30

2356.0000 PLATINIC-MERCURIC-PICRIC-CHROMIC

2356.0000 von Pacaut 1906   1823, **8**:438
FORMULA: water 250, platinic chloride 0.1, mercuric chloride 17.5, picric acid 3.5, chromic acid 5
NOTE: This formula is referred by Mayer 1920 to Pacaut 1905 see 6593 (1905):407. Spuler 1910 (Ehrlich, Krause, *et al*. 1910, **2**:522) refers to Pacaut 1905 but gives the 1906 journal reference.

2470.0000 PLATINIC-CUPRIC-DICHROMATE

2470.0000 Burkhardt 1897   6011, **12**:335
FORMULA: water 240, platinic chloride, copper dichromate 9

2500.0010 PLATINIC-PICRIC-ACETIC

2500.0010 vom Rath 1895   766, **11**:282
FORMULA: water 250, platinic chloride 1.25, picric acid 3, acetic acid 2.5

2500.1030 Platinic-picric-formaldehyde-formic

2500.1030 Bouin and Bouin 1898 *test circ*. **1938 Wellings**
                    Wellings *circ*. 1938, 31
FORMULA: water 180, platinic chloride 0.9, picric acid 1, 40% formaldehyde 45, formic acid 23

2600.0000 PLATINIC-CHROMIC

The purpose of the platinic constituent of these mixtures is to prevent the discoloration of tissues by the chromic acid. The fixative picture obtained does not differ from chromic alone, or chromic-acetic, in the two classes here given.

2600.0000 Eisig 1878   14246, 1 :341
    FORMULA: water 250, platinic chloride 0.32, chromic acid 1.25
    NOTE: This solution is frequently referred to **Whitman** who republished it (Whitman 1885, 153, 238) without reference.

2600.0000 Merkel 1870 *test.* **1910 Poll**   Ehrlich, Krause, *et al.* 1910, 1 :224
    FORMULA: water 250, chromic acid 0.5, platinic chloride 0.5

2600.0000 Whitman 1885   *see* F 2600.0000 Eisig 1878 (note)

2600.0010 Platinic-chromic-acetic

2600.0010 Brass 1884   23632, 1 :39
    FORMULA: water 250, platinic chloride 0.35 to 0.85, chromic acid 0.35 to 0.85, acetic acid 0.35 to 0.85

2600.0010 Lavdowsky 1894   764, 4 :355
    FORMULA: water 250, platinic chloride 0.12, chromic acid 2.4, acetic acid 12.5

2700.0000 PLATINIC-DICHROMATE

2700.0000 Roncoroni *test.* **1900 Pollack**   Pollack 1900, 106
    REAGENTS REQUIRED: *A.* F 7000.0000 Müller 1859; *B.* 0.8% platinic chloride

F 3000 MERCURIC CHLORIDE IN COMBINATION WITH FIXATIVE AGENTS OF HIGHER NUMERICAL RANK

Mercuric chloride is probably the best known and most widely used fixative agent. It has many disadvantages. In the first place, it is a dangerous poison, which can be absorbed through the skin (of those sensitive to it) and produce chronic, cumulative mercury poisoning. Unless the individual desiring to use these solutions is satisfied that he is not sensitive to mercury, he should wear rubber gloves when handling the solution. Even those not sensitive should take the utmost precautions to prevent contact of this dangerous material with the bare skin. The second disadvantage is that once a material has been placed in mercuric solution, it cannot be handled with any metal instrument, but must be manipulated entirely with instruments of glass, wood, or plastic. Mercuric chloride has also a tendency to render materials brittle. The last disadvantage is that this reagent tends to cause a precipitate of small crystals in the tissues unless it is washed out either by very prolonged washing in water, or by relatively prolonged washing in solutions of iodine, which must then themselves be removed by subsequent washing in alcohol. Against these disadvantages is the fact that mercuric fixatives permit the most brilliant after-staining of almost any class. Mercuric chloride is not usefully employed in simple aqueous solution, but is occasionally useful, in the formulas which follow, in alcohol solution.

3000.0000 MERCURIC ALONE

3000.0000 Apáthy *test.* **1920 Mayer**   Mayer 1920, 56
    FORMULA: 50% alc. 250, mercuric chloride 9, sodium chloride 1.25

3000.0000 Giemsa 1909 *test.* **1938 Mallory**   Mallory 1938, 41
    FORMULA: water 165, 95% alc. 85, mercuric chloride 11.5

3000.0000 Heidenhain 1888   16155, **43** (Suppl.): 40
    FORMULA: water 250, mercuric chloride 22, sodium chloride 1.25

3000.0000 Lenhossék 1899 *test. circ.* **1938 Welling**   Welling 1938, 29
    FORMULA: water 115, 95% alc. 135, mercuric chloride 9, sodium chloride 11

3000.0000 Löwit 1887   20170, **95** :144
    FORMULA: water 250, mercuric chloride 0.2, sodium sulfate 6, sodium chloride 2.5

3000.0000 Neukirch 1909   *see* DS 22.6 Neukirch 1909

3000.0000 Pietschmann 1905   1683, **16**:63
FORMULA: 90% alc. 250, mercuric chloride 0.9

3000.0000 Prowazeko 1906 *see* F 3000.0000 Schaudinn 1893 (note)

3000.0000 Rothig 1900   1780, **36**:354
FORMULA: water 225, 95% alc. 25, mercuric chloride 15.7

3000.0000 Schaudinn 1893   13635, **57**:19
FORMULA: 60% alc. 250, mercuric chloride 5.5
NOTE: Prowazeko 1906 (23632, **23**:1) specifies 90% alc. for the above solutions.

3000.0000 Schaudinn 1900   23831, **13**:197
FORMULA: 30% alc. 250, mercuric chloride 10

3000.0000 Schmorl 1928   Schmorl 1928, 29
FORMULA: water 235, mercuric chloride 11, sodium chloride 1.25

3000.0010 Mercuric-acetic

The mercuric-acetic mixtures share with the chromic-acetic mixtures the honor of being the most popular fixatives. It is probable that they deserve this. They are simple to make up, stable in solution, easy to handle, and do not harden as badly as does mercuric chloride alone. They permit the most brilliant after-staining, and are widely used for the fixation of marine forms. They can be confidently recommended to the inexperienced worker, provided that he remembers to wash out the mercury thoroughly and not to handle the fixed object with any metal instrument until washing is complete.

3000.0010 Altman 1890 *test.* **1920 Mayer**   Mayer 1920, 59
FORMULA: water 200, mercuric chloride 3.5, acetic acid 50

3000.0010 Apáthy 1896   14246, **12**:495
FORMULA: water 150, alc. 100, mercuric chloride 5, acetic acid 1.25

3000.0010 Béguin *test.* **1910 Spuler**   Ehrlich, Krause, *et al.* 1910, 521
FORMULA: water 225, mercuric chloride 16, acetic acid 25

3000.0010 van Beneden *test.* **1905 Lee**   Lee 1905, 54
FORMULA: water 190, mercuric chloride to sat. (*circ.* 20), acetic acid 60
NOTE: Both Lee 1905, 54 and Mayer 1920, 53 attribute this solution to van Beneden, but neither quotes a reference.

3000.0010 Bignami *test.* **1896 Kahlden and Laurent**   Kahlden and Laurent 1896, 127
FORMULA: water 250, mercuric chloride 2.5, acetic acid 2.5, sodium chloride 2

3000.0010 Borgert 1900   23831, **14**:207
FORMULA: water 190, mercuric chloride 13.5, acetic acid 60

3000.0010 Carazzi *test.* **1920 Mayer**   Mayer 1920, 56
FORMULA: 30% alc. 240, mercuric chloride 5.2, acetic acid 8.3

3000.0010 Carnoy and Lebrun 1887   6011, **13**:68
FORMULA: abs. alc. 80, acetic acid 80, chloroform 80, mercuric chloride to sat. (*circ.* 60
NOTE: The original authors attribute this mixture to Gilson, by whom it was never published. It is, however, frequently referred to as "Gilson's Mixture." Langeron 1934, 344 calls it "Gilson (1897)" but gives no reference.

3000.0010 Carter 1919   1032, **13**:213
FORMULA: water 125, 95% alc. 125, mercuric chloride 7.5, acetic acid 7.5

3000.0010 Cholodkowsky *test.* **1910 Spuler**   Ehrlich, Krause, *et al.* 1910, **2**:521
FORMULA: water 250, mercuric chloride 17.5, acetic acid 1.25

3000.0010 Coker 1902   3430, **33**:90
FORMULA: water 250, mercuric chloride 0.9, acetic acid 2.5

3000.0010 Cornwall 1937   *Microscope*, **1**:137
FORMULA: water 250, chromic acid 1.25, acetic acid 2.5

3000.0010 Davidoff 1889   14246, **9**:118
FORMULA: water 190, mercuric chloride 13.2, acetic acid 60

3000.0010 Eisig 1898   14246, **13**:89
FORMULA: sea water 190, mercuric chloride 9.5, acetic acid 60

3000.0010 Eltringham 1930 *fixative B—auct.*   Eltringham 1930, 44
FORMULA: water 145, 95% alc. 100, mercuric chloride 10, acetic acid 9
RECOMMENDED FOR: whole insects not larger than a housefly.

3000.0010 Gilson 1897 *see* F 3000.0010 Carnoy and Lebrun 1887 (note)

3000.0010 Goto 1898   11130, **10**:239
FORMULA: water 250, mercuric chloride 4.2, acetic acid 3.75, glycerol 11.25

3000.0010 Hein *test*. **1910 Spuler**   Ehrlich, Krause, *et al*. 1910, **2**:521
FORMULA: sea water 245, mercuric chloride 20, (or to sat.), acetic acid 5

3000.0010 Jäger *test*. **1928 Schmorl**   Schmorl 1928, 432
FORMULA: water 165, 95% alc. 85, mercuric chloride 1.7, acetic acid 0.3

3000.0010 Kaiser 1891   2842, **7**:4
FORMULA: water 250, mercuric chloride 8.3, acetic acid 7.5

3000.0010 Kolster *test*. **1910 Spuler**   Ehrlich, Krause, *et al*. 1910, **2**:521
FORMULA: water 250, mercuric chloride 20, acetic acid 2.5, sodium chloride 1.25

3000.0010 Laidlaw *test*. **1936 Pappenheimer and Hawthorne**
                                                          608b, **12**:627
FORMULA: water 250, mercuric chloride 10, acetic acid 12.5

3000.0010 Lang 1878   766, **1**:14
FORMULA: water 250, mercuric chloride 15, acetic acid 17.5, sodium chloride 20

3000.0010 Langeron 1942   Langeron 1942, 387
FORMULA: water 22.5, mercuric chloride 13.5, acetic acid 7.5

3000.0010 Lapp *test*. **1910 Spuler**   Ehrlich, Krause, *et al*. 1910, **2**:251
FORMULA: 50% alc 250, mercuric chloride 9, acetic acid 5

3000.0010 Lenhossék 1897   1780, **51**:215
FORMULA: 25% alc. 250, mercuric chloride 12.5, acetic acid 12.5

3000.0010 Lo Bianco 1890   14246, **9**:443
FORMULA: water 210, mercuric chloride 11.5, acetic acid 42.5

3000.0010 Mingazzini 1893   19353, **3**:47
FORMULA: 30% alc. 190, mercuric chloride 9, acetic acid 62.5

3000.0010 Ohlmacher 1897   11189, **3**:671
FORMULA: abs. alc. 200, chloroform 37.5, mercuric chloride 50, acetic acid 12.5
NOTE: This formula is referred by Spuler 1910 (Ehrlich, Krause, *et al*. 1910, **2**:521) to
1899.

3000.0010 Oxner *test*. **1910 Spuler**   Ehrlich, Krause, *et al*. 1910, **2**:521
FORMULA: water 240, mercuric chloride 17.5, acetic acid 7.5

3000.0010 vom Rath 1895   766, **11**:286
FORMULA: abs. alc. 250, mercuric chloride 1.25, acetic acid 5

3000.0010 Pearl 1903 *test. circ.* **1938 Wellings** Wellings *circ*. 1938, 29
FORMULA: water 225, mercuric chloride 16, acetic acid 25

3000.0010 Roskin 1946   Roskin 1946, 94
FORMULA: water 235, mercuric chloride 14, acetic acid 15

3000.0010 Schmorl 1928   Schmorl 1928, 29
FORMULA: water 250, mercuric chloride 7.5, acetic acid 1.5

3000.0010 Sherlock *test.* **1930 Eltringham**   Eltringham 1930, 46
FORMULA: water 238, mercuric chloride 17, acetic acid 12

3000.0010 Spuler 1910   Ehrlich, Krause, *et al.* 1910, **2**:521
FORMULA: abs. alc. 250, mercuric chloride 10, acetic acid 7.5

3000.0010 Wenrich and Geiman 1933   20540b, **8**:158
FORMULA: water 200, abs. alc. 50, mercuric chloride 8, acetic acid 5

3000.0010 Woltereck *test.* **1910 Spuler**   Ehrlich, Krause, *et al.* 1910, **2**:251
FORMULA: water 100, 90% alc. 150, mercuric chloride 9, acetic acid 25

3000.0012 Mercuric-acetic-trichloroacetic

This mixture is thought by many to be superior to mercuric-acetic, but the author has never seen any evidence, as apart from opinion, that this is true.

3000.0012 Heidenhain 1909   23632, **25**:405
FORMULA: water 250, mercuric chloride 17.5, acetic acid 2.5, trichloroacetic acid 5
NOTE: This is *Heidenhain's Subtriessig* or *Heidenhain's sub-tri-acetic* of some authors. It is given by Cajal and de Castro 1933 as a decalcifying solution, for which purpose it is probably excellent.

3000.0014 Mercuric-acetic-nitric

The formula of Gilson 1898 below is, in the author's opinion, one of the finest general-purpose fixatives which can be employed by those without previous experience of fixation. Objects may be left in it for weeks at a time without becoming unduly hardened. It holds a very reasonable balance between cytoplasmic and nuclear fixation, and it is particularly good before any of the more complex triple and quadruple stains. It was once more widely employed than it is at present, but it seems to have been removed from popular esteem through the present passion for Bouin's picro-formol-acetic.

3000.0014 Carazzi *test.* **1910 Spuler**   Ehrlich, Krause, *et al.* 1910, **2**:522
FORMULA: water 250, 70% alc. 25, mercuric chloride 5, acetic acid 1.25, nitric acid 3.75, sodium chloride 2.5

3000.0014 Duggar 1909 *test.* **1937 Gatenby and Painter**
Gatenby and Painter 1937, 701
FORMULA: water 225, 96% alc. 25, mercuric chloride 8.5, acetic acid 1.7 nitric acid 4

3000.0014 Gilson 1898   6011, **14**:374
FORMULA: water 220, 60% alc. 25, mercuric chloride 5, acetic acid 1, nitric acid 4.5

3000.0014 Petrunkewitsch 1901   23831, **14**:576
FORMULA: water 150, 95% alc. 100, mercuric chloride to sat., acetic acid 45, nitric acid 5

3000.0020 Mercuric-trichloroacetic

3000.0020 Huber *test.* **1943 Cowdry** *cit.* **Addison**   Cowdry 1943, 95
FORMULA: 95% alc. 250, mercuric chloride 7.5, trichloroacetic acid 3.75

3000.0030 Mercuric-formic

3000.0030 Altmann 1890 *test.* **1920 Mayer**   Mayer 1920, 09
FORMULA: water 200, mercuric chloride 3.5, formic acid 50

3000.0030 Ruffini 1905   23635, **79**:150
FORMULA: water 235, mercuric chloride 6.25, formic acid 16

3000.0040 Mercuric-nitric

3000.0040 Apáthy and Boeke *test.* **1910a Spuler**   Ehrlich, Krause, *et al.* 1910, **2**:524
FORMULA: water 240, mercuric chloride 15, nitric acid 10

3000.0040 Apáthy and Boeke *test.* **1910b Spuler**   Ehrlich, Krause, *et al.* 1910, **2**:524
FORMULA: water 240, mercuric chloride 25, nitric acid 10

3000.0040 Frenzel 1886   1780, **26**:232
FORMULA: 80% alc. 125, sat. sol. mercuric chloride in 80% alc. 125, nitric acid 10
NOTE: Mercuric chloride is about 20% soluble in 80% alc.; the 125 parts quoted above
therefore contain about 25 of the dry salt.

3000.0040 Kostanecki and Siedlecki 1896   1780, **48**:184
FORMULA: water 250, mercuric chloride 9, nitric acid 7.5

3000.0040 Saling 1906 *test.* **1937 Gatenby and Painter**   Gatenby and Painter 1937, 389
FORMULA: water 125, 95% alc. 100, mercuric chloride 5, nitric acid 10

3000.0060 Mercuric-hydrochloric

3000.0060 Meyer 1912 *test.* **1915** *ips.*   Meyer 1915, 198
FORMULA: 95% alc. 250, mercuric chloride 12.5, hydrochloric acid 1

3000.1000 Mercuric-formaldehyde

These are very bad fixatives, save for a few specialized purposes for which some have been
recommended by their inventors.

3000.1000 Bouin 1900   1825, **17**:211
FORMULA: water 190, mercuric chloride 11.25, 40% formaldehyde 62.5

3000.1000 Brinkmann 1903   14246, **16**:367
FORMULA: water 220, mercuric chloride 8.8, 40% formaldehyde 30, sodium chloride 2.2

3000.1000 Carleton and Leach 1938   Carleton and Leach 1938, 33
FORMULA: water 225, mercuric chloride 16, 40% formaldehyde 25

3000.1000 Dawson and Friedgood 1938   20540b, **13**:17
FORMULA: water 225, mercuric chloride 9, 40% formaldehyde 25, sodium chloride 1.8

3000.1000 Downey 1913   8545, **15**:25
FORMULA: water 225, mercuric chloride 20, 40% formaldehyde 25, sodium chloride 2.2

3000.1000 Eltringham 1930 *fixative A—auct.*   Eltringham 1930, 44
FORMULA: water 225, mercuric chloride 15, 40% formaldehyde 25
RECOMMENDED FOR: soft parts of insects free of chitin.

3000.1000 Gilson (1905)   *see* P 13.1 Gilson (1905)

3000.1000 Heidenhain 1916a   *Heidenhain's weak mixture—compl. script.*
23632, **32**:365
ᴋᴏʀᴍᴜʟᴀ: water 200, mercuric chloride 10, 40% formaldehyde 50, sodium chloride 1.25

3000.1000 Heidenhain 1916b   *Heidenhain's strong mixture—compl. script.*
23632, **32**:365
FORMULA: water 125, mercuric chloride 10, 40% formaldehyde 125, sodium chloride 1.25

3000.1000 "J.A." *test.* **1937 Findlay**   11360, **57**:294
FORMULA: water 225, mercuric chloride 6.25, 40% formaldehyde 25

3000.1000 Rosenthal 1900 *test.* **1907 Böhm and Oppel**   Böhm and Oppel 1907, 202
FORMULA: sat. sol. picric acid 250, 40% formaldehyde 12.5
USE: fixation of adipose tissues before DS 22.4 techniques.

3000.1000 Schmorl 1928   Schmorl 1928, 29
FORMULA: water 200, mercuric chloride 11.25, sodium chloride 1.25, 40% formaldehyde
50

3000.1010 Mercuric-formaldehyde-acetic

These are slightly better than the preceding class, but they are not nearly as good as
straight mercuric-acetic mixtures. There seems to be no reason for the inclusion of the
formaldehyde in a general formula of this nature.

3000.1010 Böhm and Oppel 1907   Böhm and Oppel 1907, 114
FORMULA: water 200, mercuric chloride 12.5, 40% formaldehyde 25, acetic acid 12.5

3000.1010 Bouin 1900   1825, **17**:211
FORMULA: water 190, mercuric chloride 1.8, 40% formaldehyde 50, acetic acid 12.5

3000.1010 Cox 1891   1780, **37**:16
FORMULA: water 150, mercuric chloride 10.5, 40% formaldehyde 50, acetic acid 25

3000.1010 Destin *test.* **1943 Cowdry**   Cowdry 1943, 61
FORMULA: water 230, chromic acid 2.3, 40% formaldehyde 15, acetic acid 5

3000.1010 Gregg and Puckett 1943   20540b, **18**:179
FORMULA: water 225, 40% formaldehyde 20, acetic acid 5, mercuric chloride 12.5

3000.1010 Gough and Fulton 1929   *see* ADS 12.2 Gough and Fulton 1929

3000.1010 Heinz 1910   2526, **29**:369
FORMULA: water 200, mercuric chloride 8.8, 40% formaldehyde 50, acetic acid 1.25

3000.1010 Spuler 1910   Ehrlich, Krause, *et al.* 1910, **2**:521
FORMULA: water 225, mercuric chloride 6.75, 40% formaldehyde 25, acetic acid 0.25

3000.1010 Stieve *test.* **1948 Romeis**   Romeis 1948, 74
FORMULA: water 190, mercuric chloride 11.5, 40% formaldehyde 50, acetic acid 10

3000.1010 Stieve *test.* **1946 Roskin**   Roskin 1946, 94
FORMULA: water 190, mercuric chloride 2, 40% formaldehyde 50, acetic acid 10

3000.1010 Worcester *test.* **1929 McClung and Allen**   McClung 1929, 420
FORMULA: water 200, mercuric chloride 14, 40% formaldehyde 22.5, acetic acid 25

3000.1012 Mercuric-formaldehyde-acetic-trichloroacetic

3000.1012 Heidenhain 1916 *Susa—compl. script.*   23632, **32**:365
FORMULA: water 200, mercuric chloride 11.25, 40% formaldehyde 50, acetic acid 10,
trichloroacetic acid 5, sodium chloride 1.25
NOTE: This mixture, named by its inventor, Susa, was first published in 1916 (*loc. cit.*)
but the formula involved using Heidenhain 1916 F 3000.1000; the rationalized
formula from dry salts did not appear till 1917 (23632, **33**:233). This formula is still
beloved of some pathologists.

3000.1012 McNamara, Murphy, and Gore 1940   *see* AF 21.1 McNamara, *et al.* 1941.

3000.1012 Romeis 1918   23422, **6**:101
FORMULA: water 176, mercuric chloride 6, 40% formaldehyde 60, trichloroacetic acid 4

3000.1020 Mercuric-formaldehyde-trichloroacetic

3000.1020 Hartz 1950   *Tech. Bull.*, **20**:77
FORMULA: water 200, mercuric chloride 12, 40% formaldehyde 50, trichloroacetic acid
0.2

3000.1020 Romeis 1918 *test.* **1920 Mayer**   Mayer 1920, 56
FORMULA: water 220, mercuric chloride 12.5, 40% formaldehyde 12, trichloroacetic
acid 5

3000.1310 Mercuric-formaldehyde-acetone-acetic

3000.1310 Sz.-Györgyi 1914   23632, **31**:23
FORMULA: acetone 185, mercuric chloride 6, 40% formaldehyde 60, acetic acid 7.5

3000.3000 Mercuric-acetone

3000.3000 Held 1897   1739, (1897):227
FORMULA: water 150, acetone 100, mercuric chloride 2.5

3000.3010 Mercuric-acetone-acetic

3000.3010 Lepine and Santter 1936   42852, **13**:287
FORMULA: abs. alc. 80, mercuric chloride 20, acetone 80, acetic acid 80

3400.0000 MERCURIC-CUPRIC

Mercuric-cupric mixtures are excellent fixatives for small invertebrates, and have been widely used for the fixation of marine forms. As histological fixatives they are inferior.

3400.0000 Lo Bianco 1890   14246, **9**:443
FORMULA: water 250, mercuric chloride 1.75, copper sulfate 25

3400.1010 Mercuric-cupric-formaldehyde-acetic

3400.1010 Becher and Demoll 1913   Becher and Demoll 1913, 48
FORMULA: water 230, copper sulfate 5, mercuric chloride to sat. 40% formaldehyde 20, acetic acid 1.25

3400.1010 Nelis 1900   3678, **72**:6
FORMULA: water 210, mercuric chloride 17.5, 40% formaldehyde 35, acetic acid 1.25, copper sulfate 5

3400.1014 Mercuric-cupric-formaldehyde-acetic-nitric

3400.1014 Stappers 1909   6011, **25**:356
FORMULA: water 220, 60% alc. 25, mercuric chloride 5, copper nitrate 5, 40% formaldehyde 12.5, acetic acid 1, nitric acid 4.5

3470.1000 MERCURIC-CUPRIC-DICHROMATE-FORMALDEHYDE

3470.1000 Kingsbury 1912   763, **6**:48
FORMULA: water 225, mercuric chloride 7.5, copper sulfate 2.5, copper dichromate 6.25, 40% formaldehyde 25

3500.0000 MERCURIC-PICRIC

Mercuric-picric mixtures, whether acidified or modified with formaldehyde, are doubtfully an improvement over mercuric alone. There seems to be no reason for incorporating picric acid with its attendant disadvantages of color. These mixtures have, however, been widely used in the past and are still sometimes recommended for embryological purposes.

3500.0000 Baumgärtel 1918   *see* DS 23.5 Baumgärtel 1918

3500.0000 Imhof *test.* **1910 Spuler**   Ehrlich, Krause, *et al.* 1910, **1**:251
FORMULA: water 250, mercuric chloride 6.3, picric acid 1.0

3500.0000 Jeffry *test.* **1915 Chamberlain**   Chamberlain 1915, 29
FORMULA: sat. sol. mercuric chloride in 30% alc. 187, sat. sol. picric acid in 30% alc. 63

3500.0000 Lenhossék 1897   1780, **51**:215
FORMULA: water 250, mercuric chloride 8.75, picric acid 1.6

3500.0000 Mann 1894   23632, **11**:479
FORMULA: water 250, mercuric chloride 20, picric acid 2.5, sodium chloride 2.0

3500.0000 Rabl 1894   23632, **11**:165
FORMULA: water 250, mercuric chloride 4.5, picric acid 0.75
NOTE: Ehrlich, Krause, *et al.* 1910, **1**:478, attribute an identical formula to **Zilliacus 1905**

3500.0000 Zilliacus 1905   *see* F 3500.0000 Rabl 1894 (note)

3500.0010 Mercuric-picric-acetic

3500.0010 Becher and Demoll 1913   Becher and Demoll 1913, 43
FORMULA: water 245, mercuric chloride 3.75, picric acid 0.75, acetic acid 5

3500.0010 Böhm and Oppel *test.* **1910 Spuler**   Ehrlich, Krause, *et al.* 1910, **2**:523
FORMULA: *A*. water 237.5, mercuric chloride 6.5, acetic acid 12.5; *B*. water 250, picric acid 3
METHOD: [reptile eggs] → *A*, 2–3 hrs. → *B*, 12–24 hrs. → 70% alc.

3500.0010 Fish 1896 *test.* **1920 Mayer**   Mayer 1920, 57
FORMULA: water 250, mercuric chloride 1.25, picric acid 0.25, acetic acid 2.5

3500.0010 Lenhossék 1907   10157, **24**:293
FORMULA: water 210, 95% alc. 30, mercuric chloride 12.5, picric acid 3 (to sat.), acetic acid 12.5

3500.0010 Michaelis *test.* **1948 Romeis**   Romeis 1948, 71
FORMULA: water 250, mercuric chloride 3.6, picric acid 0.6, acetic acid 3

3500.0010 Tellyesniczky 1898   1780, **52**:242
FORMULA: water 250, mercuric chloride 8.75, picric acid 1.6, acetic acid 2.5

3500.0010 Völker *test.* **1910 Spuler**   Ehrlich, Krause, *et al.* 1910, **2**:251
FORMULA: water 240, mercuric chloride 8, picric acid 1.25, acetic acid 12.5

3500.0010 Winge 1930   23639b, **10**:699
FORMULA: abs. alc. 150, mercuric chloride 2, picric acid 2.5, acetic acid 25, urea 7.5, chloroform 75

3500.0015 Mercuric-picric-acetic-sulfuric

3500.0015 Lang *test.* **1910 Spuler**   Ehrlich, Krause, *et al.* 1910, **2**:523
FORMULA: water 250, mercuric chloride 15, picric acid 3, acetic acid 12.5, sulfuric acid 5

3500.1000 Mercuric-picric-formaldehyde

3500.1000 Crétin 1938   Le Mans, 48
FORMULA: water 225, mercuric chloride 6.5, picric acid 1.5, 40% formaldehyde 25

3500.1000 Kingsley 1937   8545, **57**:87
FORMULA: water 230, mercuric chloride 15, picric acid 0.5, 40% formaldehyde 20, sodium chloride 1.75

3500.1000 Mann 1894   23632, **11**:479
FORMULA: water 250, mercuric chloride 6.25, picric acid 2.5, 40% formaldehyde 25

3500.1000 Mann 1898   22246, **12**:39
FORMULA: water 250, mercuric chloride 6.25, picric acid 2.5, 40% formaldehyde 12.5

3500.1000 "Mann"   *see* F 3500.1000 Spuler 1910 (note)

3500.1000 Spuler 1910   Ehrlich, Krause, *et al.* 1910, **2**:522
FORMULA: water 180, mercuric chloride 6.3, picric acid 1.0, 40% formaldehyde 60
NOTE: Spuler (*loc. cit.*) attributes this, without citing his source, to Mann.

3500.1010 Mercuric-picric-formaldehyde-acetic

These are, to all intents and purposes, a picro-formaldehyde-acetic improved by the addition of mercury. This improvement doubtfully justifies the use of the mixture for general purposes.

3500.1010 Branca 1899   11024, **35**:767
FORMULA: water 210, mercuric chloride 15, picric acid 2.5, 40% formaldehyde 40, acetic acid 3.75

3500.1010 Gray 1932   11360, **52**:370
STOCK SOLUTION: 95% alc. 250, mercuric chloride 2.5, picric acid 2.5
WORKING SOLUTIONS: A. stock 125, 40% formaldehyde 62.5, acetic acid 25, ether 37.5
                   B. stock 125, 40% formaldehyde 62.5, acetic acid 50, ether 12.5
                   C. stock 140, 40% formaldehyde 70, acetic acid 14, ether 28
NOTE: A detailed description of the uses of these fluids is given in Chapter 16.

3500.1010 Pfuhl 1932 *Supiformeis—auct.*   23507a, **31**:18
    FORMULA: water 200, mercuric chloride 6, picric acid 1, 40% formaldehyde 50, acetic
    acid 12.5

3500.1010 Yokum 1918   22084, **18**:337
    FORMULA: 95% alc. 140, ether 25, picric acid 1.25, mercuric chloride 2.5, 40% formalde-
    hyde 62, acetic acid 25

3560.0040 MERCURIC-PICRIC-CHROMIC-NITRIC

3560.0040 Hennings 1900   23632, **17**:311
    FORMULA: water 86, abs. alc. 128, mercuric chloride 8, picric acid 0.3, chromic acid 0.2,
    nitric acid 36
    NOTE: This is stated by the author to soften chitin.

3600.0000 MERCURIC-CHROMIC

Mercuric-chromic mixtures are good fixatives, though the mercuric constituent tends to
make small forms more brittle than do the simple chromic fixatives. They are in general to be
recommended for cytoplasmic rather than nuclear fixation.

3600.0000 Lo Bianco 1890   14246, **9**:443
    FORMULA: water 250, mercuric chloride 1.2, chromic acid 0.7

3600.0000 Mann 1898   22246, **12**:39
    FORMULA: water 250, mercuric chloride 6.25, chromic acid 6.25

3600.0010 Mercuric-chromic-acetic

3600.0010 Novak 1902 *test.* **1910 Poll**   Ehrlich, Krause, *et al.* 1910, **1**:225
    FORMULA: water 200, mercuric chloride 2, chromic acid 0.25, acetic acid 50

3600.0040 Mercuric-chromic-nitric

3600.0040 Kingsbury and Johannsen 1927   Kingsbury and Johannsen 1927, 75
    FORMULA: water 185, mercuric chloride 7.5, F 6000.0040 Perenyi 1882 65
    RECOMMENDED FOR: stated to prevent hardening of chitinized structure.

3600.1010 Mercuric-chromic-formaldehyde-acetic

3600.1010 Gerhardt 1901   766, **20**:244
    FORMULA: water 225, mercuric chloride 4.25, chromic acid 0.7, acetic acid 6.25, 40%
    formaldehyde 62.5

3600.1010 Hertwig 1905 *test. circ.* **1938 Wellings**   Wellings *circ.* 1938, 29
    FORMULA: water 220, mercuric chloride 5.25, chromic acid 0.75, 40% formaldehyde 25,
    acetic acid 7.5

3600.1010 Novak 1901   766, **20**:244
    FORMULA: water 225, mercuric chloride 5.3, chromic acid 0.75, 40% formaldehyde 25,
    acetic acid 7.5

3600.1010 Röthig 1904 *test.* **1948 Romeis**   Romeis 1948, 552
    FORMULA: water 217, mercuric chloride 5.4, chromic acid 0.75, acetic acid 7.5, 40%
    formaldehyde 25

3670.0000 MERCURIC-CHROMIC-DICHROMATE

3670.0000 Williamson and Pearse 1923   11025, **57**:193
    FORMULA: water 250, mercuric chloride 12.5, potassium dichromate 5, chromium fluoride
    5
    PREPARATION: Boil the dichromate and fluoride 30 minutes. Cool, filter, and add mercuric
    chloride to filtrate. Boil till solution is complete.

3670.0010 *Mercuric-chromic-dichromate-acetic*

3670.0010 Ruffini 1927   Ruffini 1927, 7
FORMULA: water 250, mercuric chloride 3, chromic acid 1.8, potassium dichromate 1.2, sodium sulfate 0.6, acetic acid 12
NOTE: A second formula (*loc. cit.* p. 63) reduces the acetic acid to 3.

3700.0000 MERCURIC-DICHROMATE

Mercuric-dichromate fixatives are among the better known cytoplasmic reagents. They are probably better for this purpose than the mercuric-chromics of the previous classes.

3700.0000 Bensley 1910   763, **4**:379
FORMULA: water 125, 95% alc. 125, mercuric chloride 32, potassium dichromate 2.5
NOTE: The original formula calls for a mixture of equal parts 2% dichromate and a sat. sol. $HgCl_2$ in abs. alc. Spuler 1910 (Ehrlich, Krause, *et al.* 1910, **2**:254), quotes this formula as "Bensley 1896" but gives no further reference.

3700.0000 Bensley and Bensley 1938   Bensley and Bensley 1938, 37
FORMULA: water 250, mercuric chloride 12.5, potassium dichromate 6.25

3700.0000 Cox *test*. 1895 Rawitz   Rawitz 1895, 17
FORMULA: water 250, mercuric chloride 2.5, potassium dichromate 2.5, potassium chromate 2

3700.0000 Duthie 1937   *see* F 3700.0000 Lane (1910) (note)

3700.0000 Foa 1891 *test*. 1920 Mayer   Mayer 1920, 52
FORMULA: water 250, mercuric chloride 5, potassium dichromate 5, potassium sulfate 2.5

3700.0000 Foa 1895   11360, **37**:287
FORMULA: water 250, mercuric chloride 10, potassium dichromate 6.25, sodium chloride 1.25
NOTE: Spuler 1910 (Ehrlich, Krause, *et al.* 1910, **2**:254) refers to this formula as "**Nickiforow-Foa**" but gives no reference.

3700.0000 Hoyer 1899   1780, **54**:97
FORMULA: water 240, mercuric chloride 4, potassium dichromate 3.2

3700.0000 Lane *test*. 1910 Spuler   Ehrlich, Krause, *et al.* 1910, **2**:254
FORMULA: water 125, 96% alc. 125, mercuric chloride 32, potassium dichromate 4.4
NOTE: The original calls for a mixture of equal parts 3½% dichromate and a sat. sol. $HgCl_2$ in 96%. **Duthie 1937** (Gatenby and Cowdry 1937, 420) calls for 2½% dichromate.

3700.0000 Marrassini *test*. 1910 Spuler   Ehrlich, Krause, *et al.* 1910, **2**:254
FORMULA: water 250, mercuric chloride 2.5, potassium dichromate 5.0

3700.0000 Nickiforow   *see* F 3700.0000 Foa 1895 (note)

3700.0000 Salkind 1917   23632, **29**:540
FORMULA: water 250, mercuric chloride 10, potassium dichromate 6.25, chloral hydrate 10

3700.0000 Wlassow *test*. 1910 Spuler   Ehrlich, Krause, *et al.* 1910, **2**:254
FORMULA: water 200, mercuric chloride 0.3, potassium dichromate 0.12, sodium chloride 6.0

3700.0000 Wolbach 1919   11343, **41**:75
FORMULA: water 250, mercuric chloride 15, potassium dichromate 6.7

3700.0010 *Mercuric-dichromate-acetic*

These are some of the better general-purpose fixatives. The addition of acetic acid adds a reasonable nuclear fixation to the excellent cytoplasmic fixation afforded by the principal constituent.

3700.0010 Bensley and Bensley 1938   Bensley and Bensley 1938, 44
FORMULA: water 237.5, mercuric chloride 12, potassium dichromate 6, acetic acid 12.5

3700.0010 Bowie 1925   763, **29**:57
FORMULA: water 250, mercuric chloride 12.5, potassium dichromate 6.25, acetic acid 5

3700.0010 Dahlgrens 1897   766, **13**:149
FORMULA: water 240, mercuric chloride 8, potassium dichromate 2.5, acetic acid 12.5, potassium sulfate 1.25

3700.0010 Kohn 1907   1780, **70**:273
FORMULA: water 250, mercuric chloride 3.2, potassium dichromate 5.8, acetic acid 12.5

3700.0010 Kultschitzky 1897   1780, **49**:8
FORMULA: 50% alc. 245, mercuric chloride 0.625, potassium dichromate 5, acetic acid 2.5

3700.0010 Lavdowsky 1893   23632, **10**:4
FORMULA: water 250, mercuric chloride 0.35, potassium dichromate 12.5, acetic acid 5

3700.0010 Leigh-Sharpe 1921   *in verb* 1921
FORMULA: water 250, mercuric chloride 12.5, potassium dichromate 7.5, acetic acid 12.5

3700.0010 Long and Mark 1912 *test.* **1937 Gatenby and Painter**
                                         Gatenby and Painter 1937, 366
FORMULA: water 225, mercuric chloride 5, potassium dichromate 5, acetic acid 25

3700.0010 Sonnenbrodt 1908   1780, **72**:416
FORMULA: water 240, mercuric chloride 1.6, calcium dichromate 1.4, acetic acid 8

3700.0010 Spuler 1910   Ehrlich, Krause, *et al.* 1910, **2**:527
FORMULA: water 250, mercuric chloride 6.5, potassium dichromate 4.25, acetic acid 3.75, potassium sulfate 2.125

3700.0010 Zenker 1894   14674, **41**:533
FORMULA: water 240, mercuric chloride 12.3, potassium dichromate 5, acetic acid 12.5, potassium sulfate 2.5
NOTE: The "Zenker-formol" of most authors is F 3700.1010 Heidenhain 1916. **Ralston and Wells 1939** (591b, **3**:72) double the quantity of acid and use the resultant fluid for decalcification.

3700.0030 Mercuric-dichromate-formic

3700.0030 Guthrie 1928 *test.* **Gatenby and Cowdry**   Gatenby and Cowdry 1928, 65
FORMULA: water 240, mercuric chloride 12.5, potassium dichromate 5, formic acid 12.5, potassium sulfate 2.5

3700.0040 Mercuric-dichromate-nitric

3700.0040 Angelucci *test.* **1895 Rawitz**   Rawitz 1895, 17
FORMULAS: *A.* 3% nitric acid; *B.* F 7000.0000 Müller 1850
METHOD: [vertebrate retina] → *A*, ½ to 2 hrs. → *B*, 10 days

3700.0040 Whitney *test. circ.* **1938 Wellings**   Wellings 1938, 35
FORMULA: water 238, mercuric chloride 12.5, potassium dichromate 6.25, sodium sulfate 2.5, nitric acid 12.5

3700.1000 Mercuric-dichromate-formaldehyde

3700.1000 Baley 1937   11431, **44**:272
FORMULA: water 225, mercuric chloride 3.4, potassium dichromate 3.4, 40% formaldehyde 25

3700.1000 Bensley 1910   2975, **29**:3
FORMULA: water 225, mercuric chloride 12.5, potassium dichromate 6.25, 40% formaldehyde 25

3700.1000 Bensley and Bensley 1938   Bensley and Bensley 1938
FORMULA: water 225, mercuric chloride 11, potassium dichromate 5.5, 40% formaldehyde 25

3700.1000 Danchakoff *test.* **1930 Guyer**   Guyer 1930, 215
    FORMULA: *A.* water 250, mercuric chloride 12.5, potassium dichromate 6.25, sodium
    sulfate 3; *B.* 40% formaldehyde
    NOTE: Add 5 to 10% *B* to *A* immediately before use.

3700.1000 Ellermann 1919   23632, **36**:56
    FORMULA: water 230, mercuric chloride 12.5, potassium dichromate 12.5, 40% formalde-
    hyde 25, potassium sulfate 2.5

3700.1000 Harvey 1907a   590, **6**:207
    FORMULA: water 165, mercuric chloride 3, potassium dichromate 4, 40% formaldehyde
    85

3700.1000 Harvey 1907b   590, **6**:208
    FORMULA: water 190, mercuric chloride 4.5, potassium dichromate 1.9, 40% formalde-
    hyde 60

3700.1000 Helly 1903   23632, **20**:414
    FORMULA: water 240, mercuric chloride 12.5, potassium dichromate 5, 40% formalde-
    hyde 12.5, potassium sulfate 2.5

3700.1000 Klein 1906   590, **5**:323
    FORMULA: water 100, 96% alc. 125, mercuric chloride 30, potassium dichromate 4, 40%
    formaldehyde 25

3700.1000 Maximov 1909   23632, **26**:177
    FORMULA: water 250, mercuric chloride 12.5, potassium dichromate 6.25, 40% formalde-
    hyde 25, sodium sulfate 2.5

3700.1010 Mercuric-dichromate-formaldehyde-acetic

3700.1010 Hamazaki 1935   22575, **295**:703
    REAGENTS REQUIRED: *A.* water 250, mercuric chloride 7.5, potassium dichromate 5,
    acetic acid 12.5; *B.* 4% formaldehyde
    METHOD: [small pieces of muscle] → *A*, 3 days → *B*, 1 day

3700.1010 Heidenhain 1916   23635, **32**:365
    FORMULA: water 225, mercuric chloride 11.25, potassium dichromate 4.5, 40% formal-
    dehyde 25, acetic acid 11.5, potassium sulfate 2.15
    NOTE: This is the **Zenker-formol** of most authors.

3700.1010 Held 1909 *test.* **1933 Cajal and de Castro**   Cajal and de Castro 1933, 245
    FORMULA: water 250, mercuric chloride 7.5, potassium dichromate 6.25, sodium sulfate
    2.5, 40% formaldehyde 1.25, acetic acid 7.5

3700.1010 Kolmer 1912   766, **42**:47
    FORMULA: water 215, mercuric chloride 3, potassium dichromate 9.75, 40% formalde-
    hyde 10, acetic acid 25

3700.1010 Krueger 1911   1820, **6**:173
    FORMULA: water 215, mercuric chloride 11, potassium dichromate 4.5, acetic acid 11,
    40% formaldehyde 25, potassium sulfate 2.2

3700.1010 Meeker and Cook 1928   1883, **57**:185
    FORMULA: water 200, mercuric chloride 10, potassium dichromate 5, sodium sulfate 5,
    acetic acid 25, 40% formaldehyde 25

3780.0000 MERCURIC-DICHROMATE-(OTHER INORGANIC SALTS)

3780.0000 Schiller 1930 *solution 131—auct.*   23639b, **11**:63
    FORMULA: water 250, mercuric chloride 0.15, potassium dichromate 5, uranium acetate
    0.2, magnesium acetate 2.5

3780.1000 Mercuric-dichromate-(other inorganic salts)-formaldehyde

3780.1000 Benoit 1922   6630, **86**:1101
FORMULA: *A.* water 250, mercuric chloride 3.1, potassium dichromate 3.75, uranium nitrate 2.0, sodium chloride 0.5; *B.* 2% formaldehyde
METHOD: [fix *A*, 4 hrs.] → *B*, 12 hrs. → wash

3800.1000 MERCURIC-(OTHER INORGANIC SALTS)

3800.1000 Dominici 1905   8545, **2**:219
FORMULA: water 220, mercuric chloride 15, 40% formaldehyde 30. Add sufficient tincture of iodine to produce a deep wine color

F 4000 CUPRIC SALTS IN COMBINATION WITH FIXATIVE SALTS OF HIGHER NUMERICAL RANK

Cupric salts are never used alone for fixation. They are good fixatives in general, owing to their power of mordanting tissues, particularly those which it is desired subsequently to stain in hematoxylin.

4000.0010 CUPRIC-ACETIC

4000.0010 Behrens 1898 *test.* **1920 Mayer**   Mayer 1920, 232
FORMULA: water 250, acetic acid 2.5, copper chloride 0.5, copper nitrate 0.5, phenol 2.5

4000.0010 Ripart and Petit 1884 *test.* **1884 Carnoy**   Carnoy 1884, 94
FORMULA: water 125, camphor water 125, acetic acid 1.8, copper acetate 0.5, copper chloride 0.5
NOTE: The camphor water employed is the pharmaceutical saturated solution of camphor in water; Mayer (Mayer, 1920, 232) suggests the substitution of thymol.

4000.0020 Cupric-trichloroacetic

4000.0020 Friedenthal 1907   20189, 209
FORMULA: water 190, copper acetate 8.75, trichloroacetic acid 60

4000.0040 Cupric-nitric

4000.0040 Petrunkewitsch 1933   19938, **77**:117
STOCK SOLUTIONS: I. water 250, copper nitrate 30, nitric acid 20; II. water 250, phenol 10, ether 15
WORKING SOLUTION: stock I 60, stock II 180

4000.1000 Cupric-formaldehyde

4000.1000 Gelderd 1909   6011, **25**:12
FORMULA: sea water 250, copper nitrate 5, 40% formaldehyde 12.5

4000.1000 Stappers 1909   6011, **25**:356
FORMULA: water 220, copper nitrate 5, 40% formaldehyde 30

4000.1010 Cupric-formaldehyde-acetic

4000.1010 Emig 1941   Emig 1941, 71
FORMULA: methanol 75, water 67, copper acetate 0.75, 40% formaldehyde 75, acetic acid 7.5
RECOMMENDED FOR: algae.

4000.1090 Cupric-formaldehyde-(other organic acids)

4000.1090 Zirkle 1931   7033a, **2**:85
FORMULA: water 217.5, 40% formaldehyde 25, proprionic acid 7.5, copper hydroxide to excess

4500.1010 CUPRIC-PICRIC-FORMALDEHYDE-ACETIC

The original purpose of Hollande in the mixture given below was to increase the picric acid content of the well-known picric-formaldehyde-acetic of Bouin. The characteristics of the fixative are, however, changed by the addition of copper, and it cannot be regarded as a modified Bouin though it is found in some textbooks under this name.

4500.1010 Hollande 1918 6630, **81**:17
FORMULA: water 250, copper acetate 6.25, picric acid 10, 40% formaldehyde 25, acetic acid 2.5
PREPARATION: Add picric acid to the copper solution. Filter and add other ingredients.

4500.1010 Kostoff and Kendall 1929 11211, **21**:113
FORMULA: water 187, copper oxide 7.5, picric acid 2, 40% formaldehyde 37.5, acetic acid 25, urea 2.5

4600.1000 CUPRIC-CHROMIC-FORMALDEHYDE

4600.1000 Zirkle 1928 17191a, **4**:201
FORMULA: water 225, chromium sulfate 12.5, 40% formaldehyde 25, copper hydroxide to excess

4600.1010 Cupric-chromic-formaldehyde-acetic

4600.1010 Benda *test.* **1911 Mallory and Wright** Mallory and Wright 1911, 386
FORMULA: water 225, copper acetate 12.5, chrome alum 6.25, acetic acid 12.5, 40% formaldehyde 25
NOTE: This is an adaptation of ADS 12.1 Weigert 1891 to fixative purposes. *See also* DS 21.22 Jakob 1913.

4600.1010 Jakob 1913 *see* DS 21.22 Jakob 1913

4700.0000 CUPRIC-DICHROMATE

The formula of Erlitzky here given was one of the first fixatives to be widely employed. These mixtures are primarily cytoplasmic fixatives and are not very useful, even after the addition of acid, for the preservation of nuclei.

4700.0000 Erlicki *see* F 4700 Erlitzky 1877

4700.0000 Erlitzky 1877 17035, **5**:739
FORMULA: water 250, potassium dichromate 6.25, copper sulfate 1.25
NOTE: This solution is to be found in almost every text as "Erlicki," presumably copying the statement in Lee 1885, 403 that "This modification of Müller is known in Germany as Erlicki's solution." The second edition of Lee (1890) gives a reference to a Polish journal. The fifth edition (1900) adds a reference to 1897 (*Progrès Médicale*, No. 39). This incorrect "1897" was continued to the 7th edition where a printer's error changed 39 to 31. This double error has continued to the 11th edition (Gatenby and Beams 1950, 35). These compound errors have been copied by many other texts in which 39 and 31 have been treated both as volume and page numbers. Moreover, the French paper gives the name as Erlitzky.

4700.0000 de la Iglesia 1904 *test.* **1910 Poll.** Ehrlich, Krause, *et al.* 1910, **1**:234
FORMULA: 50% alc. 250, potassium dichromate to sat., copper acetate to sat.

4700.0000 Zirkle 1934 17191a, **20**:169
FORMULA: water 250, copper sulfate 2.5, potassium dichromate 3.1, ammonium dichromate 3.1

4700.0010 Cupric-dichromate-acetic

4700.0010 Aigner 1900 20170, **38**:109.
FORMULA: water 250, copper sulfate 2.9, potassium dichromate 6.25, acetic acid 2.5

4700.0010 Kultschitzky 1887 23632, **4**:348
FORMULA: 50% alc. 250, copper sulfate to sat., potassium dichromate to sat., acetic acid 0.5 cc.

4700.0010 Rubaschkin 1904 1780, **63**:577
FORMULA: water 250, copper acetate 2, potassium dichromate 7, acetic acid 12, 40% formaldehyde 25

4700.0010 Wolters *test*. **1896 Kahlden and Laurent**   Kahlden and Laurent 1896, 73
FORMULA: water 125, 95% alc. 125, cupric sulfate, potassium dichromate, *a.a.* to sat., acetic acid 0.75

4700.1000 Cupric-dichromate-formaldehyde

4700.1000 Kenyon 1896   11135, **6**:133
FORMULA: water 200, copper sulfate 5, potassium dichromate 9.5, 40% formaldehyde 50

4700.1000 Strong 1903   11135, **13**:296
FORMULA: water 125, 40% formaldehyde 125, copper dichromate 6.25

4900.0040 CUPRIC-(OTHER ORGANIC AGENT)-NITRIC

4900.0040 Petrunkewitsch 1933   19938, **77**:117
FORMULA: water 100, 96% alc. 150, ether 12.5, copper nitrate 5, nitric acid 7.5, paranitrophenol 12.5
NOTE: *See also* Roskin 1946.

4900.0040 Roskin 1946   Roskin 1946, 97
FORMULA: water 100, dioxane 150, copper nitrate 5, nitric acid 7.5, paranitrophenol 12.5
NOTE: This is stated by Roskin (*loc. cit.*) to be a modification of Petrunkewitsch 1933.

4900.0040 Waterman 1937   20540b, **12**:21
FORMULA: water 100, dioxane 150, copper nitrate 5, nitric acid 7.5, paranitrophenol 12.5, ether 12.5 (added after other ingredients have stood 2–3 days and been filtered)

F 5000 PICRIC ACID IN COMBINATION WITH FIXATIVE AGENTS OF HIGHER NUMERICAL RANK

5000.0000 PICRIC ALONE

Picric acid is not a good fixative. It forms, with the cytoplasmic constituents of the cell, compounds which are easily water-soluble, so that fixation in any of the mixtures containing no other primary fixative constituent than picric acid always shows huge vacuoles. Special after-treatment is also required for the removal of picric acid, and it is notoriously almost impossible to secure differentiation of histological structures after fixation in picric mixtures. These considerations do not, however, prevent their being the most popular class of fixatives in use at the present time.

5000.0000 Gage *test*. **1920 Mayer**   Mayer 1920, 39
FORMULA: water 125, 95% alc. 125, picric acid 0.5

5000.0010 Picric-acetic

The acidified picric mixtures given in this class and the next three classes have nothing to recommend them for any purpose save an occasional special technique. They give wretched preservation of cytoplasmic constituents, and there are many better fixatives for nuclei.

5000.0010 Armitage 1939   *Microscope*, **3**:213
FORMULA: water 100, picric acid 1.1, acetic acid 25, dioxane 125

50000.0010 Allen and McClung 1950   Jones 1950, 60
FORMULA: water 125, dioxane 100, picric acid 1.2, acetic acid 25

5000.0010 Bigelow 1902   4604, **40**:66
FORMULA: water 240, picric acid 3, acetic 12.5
NOTE: The original formula calls for a saturated solution of picric acid in 5% acetic.

5000.0010 Boveri 1887   10899, **21**:433
FORMULA: water 250, picric acid 3, acetic acid 2.5

5000.0010 Davidoff 1899   14246, **9**:118
FORMULA: water 190, picric acid 2.4, acetic acid 60

5000.0010 Deegener 1909   23831, **27**:634
FORMULA: 45% alc. 240, picric acid 1.6, acetic acid 12.5
NOTE: Deegener (*loc. cit.*) refers to this as **"Zimmer's mixture,"** but quotes no reference. Mayer 1920 indexes it as *"Zimmer's Gemisch"* but quotes the journal reference of Deegener's paper.

5000.0010 Dobell 1914   1798, **34**:133
FORMULA: 90% alc. 180, picric acid 40, acetic acid 67.5

5000.0010 Eltringham *fixative D—auct.*   Eltringham 1930, 46
FORMULA: 95% alc. 200, chloroform 37.5, picric acid 2, acetic acid 12.5
RECOMMENDED FOR: general insect histology.

5000.0010 Gulick 1911   1820, **6**:339
FORMULA: water 250, picric acid 1, acetic acid 7.5

5000.0010 Hertwig *test.* **1895 Rawitz**   Rawitz 1895, 22
FORMULA: water 100, picric acid 1.1 (to sat.), acetic acid 3–5

5000.0010 Kingsbury and Johannsen 1927   Kingsbury and Johannsen 1927, 9
FORMULA: abs. alc. 200, chloroform 35, picric acid 2, acetic acid 15

5000.0010 Potenza 1939 *test.* **1942 Langeron**   Langeron 1942, 419
FORMULA: water 125, picric acid 1.5, acetic acid 25, dioxane 100

5000.0010 Zimmer 1909 *see* F 5000.0010 Deegener 1909

5000.0015 Picric-acetic-sulfuric

5000.0015 Blanc *test.* **1895 Maggi**   Maggi 1895, 112
FORMULA: water 100, picric acid 0.1, acetic acid 0.6, sulfuric acid 0.3

5000.0015 Nemeč 1899   10606, **33**:314
FORMULA: sat. sol. picric acid 250, acetic acid 1.25, sulfuric acid 1.25

5000.0015 Patterson 1907   2975, **13**:252
FORMULA: F 5000.0050 Kleinenberg 1879 230, acetic acid 20

5000.0020 Picric-trichloroacetic

5000.0020 Crétin 1941   6630, **135**:355
STOCK: I. dioxane 100, picric acid 25; II. water 35, trichloroacetic acid 5, methanol to make 100
WORKING SOLUTION: stock I 50, stock II 60
RECOMMENDED FOR: fixation of starch and glycogen in tissues held at 1–3°C.

5000.0040 Picric-nitric

5000.0040 Eltringham 1930   Eltringham 1930, 94
FORMULA: water 250, picric acid 2.6, nitric acid 10

5000.0040 Kingsbury and Johannsen 1927   Kingsbury and Johannsen 1927, 9
FORMULA: water 237, nitric acid 13, picric acid *q.s.* to sat.

5000.0040 Mayer 1880   14246, **2**:5
FORMULA: water 250, picric acid 4, nitric acid 6.25

5000.0040 Zimmermann 1896 *test.* **1922 Schneider**   Schneider 1922, 323
FORMULA: *A.* 3% nitric acid; *B.* 1% picric acid in 95% alc.
METHOD: [plant material] → *A*, 24 hrs. → water, 24 hrs. → *B*, 12 hrs. → 96% alc., thorough wash

5000.0050 Picric-sulfuric

5000.0050 Kleinenberg 1879   17510, **19**:208
FORMULA: water 250, picric acid 0.75, sulfuric acid 5
NOTE: **Langenbeck 1898** (11373, **14**:303) is this solution made with sea water. **Mayer 1880** (14246, **2**:2) is the same solution as Kleinenberg, made another way; Mayer 1920 (p. 40) is incorrect in supposing it to be "stronger."

5000.0050 Langenbeck 1898   *see* F 5000.0050 Kleinenberg 1879 (note)

5000.0050 Mayer 1880   *see* F 5000.0050 Kleinenberg 1879 (note)

5000.0050 Wistinghausen 1891   14246, **10**:47
   FORMULA: water 250, picric acid 0.75, sulfuric acid 1.25

5000.0060 Picric-hydrochloric

5000.0060 Becher and Demoll 1913   Becher and Demoll 1913, 43
   FORMULA: water 250, hydrochloric acid 20, picric acid *q.s.* to sat.

5000.0060 Mayer 1880   14246, **2**:5
   FORMULA: water 250, picric acid 5, hydrochloric acid 5

5000.1000 Picric-formaldehyde

These mixtures appear to have nothing whatever to recommend them but are still quoted in the literature.

5000.1000 Aniline 1903 *test.* **1920 Mayer**   Mayer 1920, 39
   FORMULA: 70% alc. 225, picric acid to sat. (*circ.* 15), 40% formaldehyde 25

5000.1000 Graf 1897 *test.* **1910 Blum**   Ehrlich, Krause, *et al.* 1910, **1**:489
   FORMULA: water 225, picric acid 2.8, 40% formaldehyde 25
   NOTE: Blum 1910 (Ehrlich, Krause, *et al.* 1910, **1**:488) quotes four other "picric-formal-
   dehydes of Graf"; this is the most usual.

5000.1000 Mayer 1920   Mayer 1920, 31
   FORMULA: sea water 200, picric acid 0.25, 40% formaldehyde 25

5000.1000 Rossman *test.* **1947 Davenport** *cit.* **Deane,** *et al.*
                                           20540b, 63, 401
   FORMULA: abs. alc. 225, picric acid 22.5, 40% formaldehyde 25

5000.1000 Verhoeff 1926 *test.* **1938 Mallory**   Mallory 1938, 258
   FORMULA: water 95, 95% alc. 130, picric acid 2.7, 40% formaldehyde 25

5000.1010 Picric-formaldehyde-acetic

These are today the most widely used general-purpose fixatives. They have nothing what-ever to recommend them for any purpose save the demonstration of nuclei in meiosis, for which the original Bouin 1897, undoubtedly the best-known fixative at present employed, was developed. Bouin himself recommended his fluid for no other purpose than the demon-stration of nuclear figures in the testis of the rat, and it is difficult to understand how its use has become so widespread. It is almost impossible to secure sharp cytoplasmic staining after any of these mixtures. Their use should be confined entirely to that for which they were orig-inally proposed, that is, the demonstration of nuclear figures.

5000.1010 Allen 1929a   *Allen's PFA₂—auct.*   McClung 1929, 425
   FORMULA: water 190, picric acid 2.4, 40% formaldehyde 25, acetic acid 25

5000.1010 Allen 1929b   *Allen's PFA₈—auct.*   McClung 1929, 425
   FORMULA: water 225, picric acid 2.8, 40% formaldehyde 12.5, acetic acid 12.5

5000.1010 Allen 1929c   *Allen's PFA₃—auct.*   McClung 1929, 425
   FORMULA: water 190, picric acid 2.4, 40% formaldehyde 35, acetic acid 25, urea 2.5

5000.1010 Bauer 1933   23639b, **33**:143
   FORMULA: dioxane 212.5, picric acid 75, 40% formaldehyde 25, acetic acid 12.5
   RECOMMENDED FOR: preservation of glycogen in tissues.

5000.1010 Becher and Demoll 1913   Becher and Demoll 1913, 48
   FORMULA: water 25, 95% alc. 140, picric acid 2.6, 40% formaldehyde 67.5, acetic
   acid 17.5

5000.1010 Belar 1929   23639b, **10**:76
FORMULA: water 30, 95% alc. 120, picric acid 1, 40% formaldehyde 60, acetic acid 15
NOTE: Belar refers this solution, without reference, to "Bouin-Duboscq."

5000.1010 Bouin 1897   *Bouin's Fluid—compl. script.*   1823, **1**:229
FORMULA: water 190, picric acid 2.4, 40% formaldehyde 60, acetic acid 12.5
NOTE: This is the "Bouin's Fluid" of most authors, but see also Bouin F 2000.1010,
F 2300.0010, F 2300.1030, F 3000.1000 and F 3000.1010. For "alcoholic Bouin"
(see F 5000.1010 Brasil 1905. See also note under Roskin 1946 who also recommends
(Roskin 1946, 97), following the suggestion of **Waterman 1937** (20540b, **2**:23) that
dioxane be substituted for water in the above; for partial dioxane substitution see
Puckett 1937. **Kupperman and Noback 1945** (1887a, **40**:75) recommend adding 1%
ferric alum when tissues are subsequently to be stained in hematoxylin.

5000.1010 Brasil 1904   *alcoholic Bouin—compl. script.*   1915, **4**:74
FORMULA: 80% alc. 150, picric acid 1, 40% formaldehyde 60, acetic acid 15
NOTE: Many authors refer this, without reference, to "Duboscq-Brasil."

5000.1010 Brumpt *test.* **1942 Langeron**   *see* P 12.3 Brumpt

5000.1010 Carothers 1916   11373, **2**:445
FORMULA: water 225, picric acid 2.5, acetic acid 25, 40% formaldehyde 62, urea 2.5

5000.1010 Claverdon 1943   19938, **97**:168
FORMULA: isopropyl alc. 137.5, acetone 75, picric acid 12.5, 40% formaldehyde 12.5,
acetic acid 12.5

5000.1010 Dammin 1937   *see* DS 23.32 Dammin 1937

5000.1010 Debaisieux 1935   6011, **44**:273
FORMULA: 80% alc. 167, picric acid 3.3, 40% formaldehyde 67, acetic acid 16

5000.1010 Dobell 1923   16035, **15**:365
FORMULA: 95% alc. 225, picric acid 18, 40% formaldehyde 62.5, acetic acid 12.5,
chloroform 0.1

5000.1010 Duboscq-Brasil 1905   *see* F 5000.1010 Brasil 1904

5000.1010 Gendre 1937   4285a, **14**:262
FORMULA: sat. sol. picric acid in 95% alc. 200, 40% formaldehyde 37.5, acetic acid 12.5

5000.1010 Gilbert 1935   591, **22**:52
FORMULA: sat. sol. (*circ.* 6%) picric acid in 70% alc. 190, acetic acid 7.5, 40% formaldehyde 38

5000.1010 Ingelby 1925   11360, **1925**:423
FORMULA: water 180, picric acid 3, 40% formaldehyde 63, acetic acid 5, potassium
bromide 2

5000.1010 Langeron 1934   Langeron 1934 p. 344
STOCK FORMULA: water 180, 40% formaldehyde 60, picric acid to sat.
WORKING FORMULA: stock 95, acetic acid 5

5000.1010 van Leeuwen 1907   23833, **32**:316
FORMULA: abs. alc. 175, picric acid 2.5, acetic acid 30, 40% formaldehyde 30, chloro-
form 15
NOTE: For "Leeuwen without picric"   *see* F 0000.1010 Sikora 1917.

5000.1010 Lenoir 1929   6630, **101**:1203
FORMULA: stock formula I. water 180, 40% formaldehyde 60, picric acid to sat. at
50°C.; stock formula II. water 180, acetic acid 60, picric acid to sat. at 50°C.
WORKING FORMULA: stock I 75, stock II 25
NOTE: The original specifies "neutral formol" but this appears to be quite unnecessary.

5000.1010 Lillie 1944   4349, **24**:35
FORMULA: water 212.5, picric acid 2.2, 40% formaldehyde 25, acetic acid 12.5

5000.1010 Puckett 1937   20540b, **12**:97
FORMULA: water 125, dioxane 85, picric acid 1.6, 40% formaldehyde 40, acetic acid 10.6

5000.1010 Roskin 1946   Roskin 1946, 92
FORMULA: water 250, picric acid 1.9, 40% formaldehyde 60, acetic acid 12
NOTE: Roskin (*loc. cit.*) refers to this as "Bouin's mixture" without reference. It is
certainly not the mixture of Bouin 1897 (*q.v.*), which is given by Roskin as "a good
modification of Bouin's mixture."

5000.1010 Schweitzer 1942 *test.* **1946 Roskin**   Roskin 1946, 200
FORMULA: methanol 175, picric acid 0.8, 40% formaldehyde 37, acetic acid 15, chloroform 37

5000.1010 Smith *test.* **1930 Guyer**   Guyer 1930, 223
FORMULA: water 110, 95% alc. 110, picric acid 1.5, 40% formaldehyde 12.5, acetic
acid 12.5

5000.1010 Waterman 1937   *see* F 5000.1010 Bouin 1897 (note)

5000.1010 Wetzel 1925   1798, **51**:209
FORMULA: water 145, 95% alc. 35, picric acid 1.2, 40% formaldehyde 72, acetic acid 18

5000.1020 Picric-formaldehyde-trichloroacetic

5000.1020 Bouin *test.* **1934 Langeron**   Langeron 1934, 345
FORMULA: water 190, picric acid 2.4, 40% formaldehyde 60, trichloroacetic acid 0.25

5000.1020 Crétin 1937   4285a, **14**:163
FORMULA: 95% alc. 45, water 10, picric acid 4, 40% formaldehyde 45, trichloroacetic
acid 2

5000.1020 Moreaux 1910   2844, **19**:265
FORMULA: water 210, picric acid 3 (to sat.), 40% formaldehyde 37, trichloroacetic acid 6

5000.1020 Roskin 1946   Roskin 1946, 93
FORMULA: water 240, picric acid 1.9, 40% formaldehyde 60, trichloroacetic acid 0.1

5000.1020 Stieve *test.* **1948 Romeis**   *Tripiform—auct.*   Romeis 1948, 76
FORMULA: water 210, picric acid 2.2, 40% formaldehyde 15, trichloroacetic acid 0.75

5000.1030 Picric-formaldehyde-formic

5000.1030 Lillie 1944   4349, **24**:35
FORMULA: water 85, picric acid 0.9, 40% formaldehyde 10, formic acid 5

5000.1040 Picric-formaldehyde-nitric

5000.1040 Hollande 1911   1833, **13**:133
FORMULA: abs. alc. 81, 40% formaldehyde, sat. with picric acid 18, nitric acid 1.5,
benzene 4.5

5000.1090 Picric-formaldehyde-(other organic acids)

5000.1090 Foley 1938   20540b, **13**:5
FORMULA: abs. alc. 245, picric acid 0.5, 40% formaldehyde 2.5, monochloroacetic
acid 2.5

5000.1090 Schabadasch 1939 *test.* **1948 Romeis**   Romeis 1948, 256
FORMULA: 95% alc. 137.50, calcium picrate 87.50, 40% formaldehyde 12.5, mono-
chloroacetic acid 12.5
RECOMMENDED FOR: fixation of glycogen in tissues.

5000.1310 Picric-formaldehyde-acetone-acetic

5000.1310 Claverdon 1943   19938, **97**:168
FORMULA: isopropyl alc. 137, picric acid 12.5, 40% formaldehyde 12.5, acetone 75,
acetic acid 12.5

5000.1310 van Walsen 1925   23632, **42**:439
FORMULA: water 130, picric acid 1.5, 40% formaldehyde 35, acetic acid 2.5, acetone 85

5600.0000 PICRIC-CHROMIC

The addition of chromic acid to picric-acid mixtures probably undoes some of the damage occasioned by the picric, in that the tissues after sectioning appear less vacuolated. The presence of the picric acid, however, continues to cause diffused staining.

5600.0000 Fol *test.* **1885 Whitman**   Whitman 1885, 237
FORMULA: water 250, picric acid 0.3, chromic acid 0.63
NOTE: Gatenby and Cowdry 1928, 57 state that they have seen this formula "with the addition of a trace of acetic acid, quoted as 'liquid of Haensel'"; they do not say where or when.

5600.0000 Haensel   *see* F 5600.0000 Fol (1885) (note)

5600.0000 Kahlden and Laurent 1896   Kahlden and Laurent 1896, 70
FORMULA: water 250, picric acid 0.25, chromic acid 0.375

5600.0010 Picric-chromic-acetic

5600.0010 Haensel   *see* F 5600.0000 Fol (1885) (note)

5600.0040 Picric-chromic-nitric

5600.0040 Rawitz 1895   Rawitz 1895, 24
FORMULA: water 250, picric acid 1, chromic acid 1.25, nitric acid 2

5600.0050 Picric-chromic-sulfuric

5600.0050 Fol *test.* **1910 Mayer**   Ehrlich, Krause, *et al.* 1910, **2**:401
FORMULA: water 250, picric acid 0.5, chromic acid 0.88, sulfuric acid 3.3

5600.0050 Lo Bianco 1890   14246, **9**:443
FORMULA: water 250, picric acid 1.5, chromic acid 1.25, sulfuric acid 5

5600.10000 Picric-chromic-formaldehyde

5600.1000 Cohen 1935   20540b, **10**:25
FORMULA: water 225, chromium sulfate 11.25, 40% formaldehyde 25, picric acid to sat.
NOTE: Salicylic acid may be substituted for picric acid.

5600.1000 Masson *test.* **1947 Paquin and Goddard** *cit.* **Warren**
         4349, **27**:195
FORMULA: water 187.5, picric acid 2.2, chrome alum 7.5, 40% formaldehyde 67.5
PREPARATION: Soak the alum in the formaldehyde for 1 hour before adding the picric acid dissolved in the water. Leave for 24 hours and filter.

5600.1010 Picric-chromic-formaldehyde-acetic

These are some of the best nuclear fixatives that have ever been developed, but they should be confined exclusively to the fixation of tissues for the demonstration of nuclear figures. They give very poor cytoplasmic fixation.

5600.1010 Allen 1918   *Allen's PFA₁₅—auct.*   11373, 31, 135
FORMULA: water 190, picric acid 2.4, chromic acid 3.8, 40% formaldehyde 60, acetic acid 7.5, urea 5

5600.1010 Allen 1929a *test.* **1929 McClung**   *Allen's B₃—auct.*
         McClung 1929, 425
FORMULA: water 190, picric acid 2.4, chromic acid 2.5, 40% formaldehyde 35, acetic acid 25, urea 2.5

5600.1010 Allen 1929b *test.* **1929 McClung**   *Allen's PFA₁₆ or B₁₆—auct.*
         McClung 1929, 425
FORMULA: water 190, picric acid 1.6, chromic acid 2.5, 40% formaldehyde 50, acetic acid 12.5, urea 2.5

5600.1010 Bachuber 1916   2975, **30**:294
     FORMULA: water 190, chromic acid 3.75, picric acid 2.4, 40% formaldehyde 37, acetic
     acid 25

5600.1010 Painter 1924   763, **27**:77
     FORMULA: water 225, picric acid 2.5, chromic acid 3.75, acetic acid 25, 40% formaldehyde
     62, urea 5

5670.1000 PICRIC-CHROMIC-DICHROMATE-FORMALDEHYDE

5670.1000 Chura 1925   23632, **42**:55
     FORMULA: water 200, picric acid 0.16, chromium fluoride 1, chrome alum 1, potassium
     dichromate 4.75, formaldehyde 50
     RECOMMENDED FOR: fix 24 hours. Then transfer to ADS 12.1 Chura 1925a, if chromosomes
     are to be stained, or to ADS 12.1 Chura 1925b for mitochondria.

5700.0000 PICRIC-DICHROMATE

5700.0000 Schultze 1904   23632, **21**:7
     FORMULA: water 250, picric acid 0.125, potassium dichromate 7.5

5700.0050 Picric-dichromate-sulfuric

5700.0050 Vialleton 1887   915, **6**:168
     FORMULA: water 250, picric acid 0.4, potassium dichromate 1.25, sulfuric acid 2.5

5700.1010 Picric-dichromate-formaldehyde-acetic

5700.1010 Lenoir 1930   6630, **103**:1253
     FORMULA: water 50, 95% alc. 100, ammonium dichromate 6, 40% formaldehyde 50,
     water 38, acetic acid 12, picric acid to sat.

5800.1010 PICRIC-(OTHER INORGANIC SALTS)-FORMALDEHYDE

5800.1010 Goodrich 1919   17510, **64**:38
     FORMULA: water 190, picric acid 2, water 1, potassium iodide 0.25, iodine 0.125, 40%
     formaldehyde 56, acetic acid 11

5800.1010 Turchini 1919   6630, **82**:1131
     FORMULA: water 250, picric acid 2, ammonium molybdate 17, 40% formaldehyde 50
     RECOMMENDED FOR: fixation of thiazin dyes in tissues.

F 6000 CHROMIC ACID IN COMBINATION WITH
FIXATIVE AGENTS OF HIGHER NUMERICAL RANK

6000.0000 CHROMIC ALONE

     Chromic acid used alone can scarcely be considered a fixative; it is rather a hardening
agent. It has a very low penetration and is used as a fixative only for marine forms containing
large quantities of water.

6000.000 Lo Bianco 1890   14246, **9**:443
     FORMULA: 35% alc. 250, chromic acid 1.25

6000.0000 Howell 1884 *test*. 1910 Poll   Ehrlich, Krause, *et al*. 1910, **1**:222
     FORMULA: 30% alc. 250, chromic acid 0.125

6000.0000 Klein 1878   17510, **18**:315
     FORMULA: 30% alc. 250, chromic acid 0.275

6000.0000 Pritchard 1873   17510, **13**:427
     FORMULA: 75% alc. 250, chromic acid 2.5

6000.0000 Vlakovic *test*. 1926 E. W. B. *cit*. Wilkie   11360, **46**:287
     FORMULA: water 30, 95% alc. 220, chromic acid 0.7

6000.0010 Chromic-acetic

These are magnificent fixatives. The cytoplasmic fixation afforded by the chromic acid is coupled with nuclear fixation by the acetic. The only disadvantage is that they tend to discolor the tissues, which sometimes renders after-staining difficult. They are as standard in botanical practice as are the osmic-chromic-acetic mixtures for zoological purposes.

6000.0010 Ammerman 1950　　　　　　　　　20540b, **25**:197
FORMULA: water 238, chrome alum 3, 40% formaldehyde 30, acetic acid 2
RECOMMENDED FOR: heavily yolked embryos and insect larvae.

6000.0010 Arnold 1888　　　　　　　　　　1780, **31**:541
FORMULA: water 250, chromic acid 0.75, acetic acid 1.25

6000.0010 Bataillon 1904　　　　　　　　　1756, **18**:1
FORMULA: water 225, chromic acid 2.25, acetic acid 25

6000.0010 Becher and Demoll 1913　　　　Becher and Demoll 1913, 24
FORMULA: water 100, chromic acid 0.25, acetic acid 0.1

6000.0010 Claussen 1908　　　　　　　　　2626, **26**:144
FORMULA: water 250, chromic acid 1.25, acetic acid 2.5

6000.0010 Czermak 1893　　　　　　　　　1823, **42**:581
FORMULA: water 250, chromic acid 0.625, acetic acid 2.5
NOTE: M'Ilroy and Hamilton 1901 (11024, **40**) is identical. Yamanouchi 1906 (3430, **41**:425) requires the same ingredients dissolved in sea water.

6000.0010 Demarbaix 1889　　　　　　　　6011, **5**:25
FORMULA: water 250, chromic acid 1.3, acetic acid 7.5

6000.0010 Ehler *test*. **1910 Poll** *cit*. **Lee und Mayer**　　Ehrlich, Krause, *et al*. 1910, **1**:223
FORMULA: water 250, chromic acid 2, acetic acid 0.5
NOTE: Gatenby and Cowdry (1928, 36) quote, without reference, an "Ehler's Chromacetic" which is identical with F 6000.0010 Lo Bianco 1890.

6000.0010 Ehler　　*see* F 6000.0010 Lo Bianco 1890a (note)

6000.0010 Faussek 1900　　　　　　　　　14246, **14**:88
FORMULA: water 250, chromic acid 2.5, acetic acid 0.6

6000.0010 Felix 1891 *test*. **Poll 1910**　　　Ehrlich, Krause, *et al*. 1910, **1**:223
FORMULA: water 250, chromic acid 6.25, acetic acid 2.5

6000.0010 Fick 1893　　　　　　　　　　　23635, **56**:529
FORMULA: water 250, chromic acid 1.25, acetic acid 0.25

6000.0010 Flemming 1882 *test*. **1928 Gatenby and Cowdry**
　　　　　　　　　　　　　　　　　　　Gatenby and Cowdry 1928, 35
FORMULA: water 250, chromic acid 0.50, acetic acid 0.25

6000.0010 Fol *test*. **1910 Poll**　　　　　Ehrlich, Krause, *et al*. 1910, **1**:224
FORMULA: water 270, chromic acid 0.45, acetic acid 2.5

6000.0010 Friedländer 1889　　　　　　　Friedländer 1889, 33
FORMULA: water 250, chromic acid 0.4, acetic acid 2.5

6000.0010 Gates 1908　　　　　　　　　　3430, **43**:81
FORMULA: water 250, chromic acid 1.75, acetic acid 1.25

6000.0010 Gates and Latter 1927　　　　11360, **47**:280
FORMULA: water 250, chromic acid 2.5, acetic acid 2.5
NOTE: Another formula in the same paper reduces the chromic acid to 1.5.

6000.0010 Hertwig 1892　　　　　　　　　1780, **39**:353
FORMULA: water 250, chromic acid 2.5, acetic acid 0.5

6000.0010 King *test*. **1910 Poll**　　　　Ehrlich, Krause, *et al*. 1910, **1**:223
FORMULA: water 225, chromic acid 0.625, acetic acid 25

6000.0010 Kopsch 1897   *see* F 6000.0010 Virchow (1897) (note)

6000.0010 Lavdowsky 1894   764, **4**:355
FORMULA: 10% alc. 250, chromic acid 0.5, acetic acid 1.25

6000.0010 Lo Bianco 1890a   *Bianco's Chromacetic 1—auct.*
                                              14246, **9**:443
FORMULA: water 250, chromic acid 2.5, acetic acid 12.5
NOTE: Ehler *test.* **1928 Gatenby and Cowdry** (Gatenby and Cowdry 1928, 36) is identical
with this, but see also Ehler (1910).

6000.0010 Lo Bianco 1890b   *Bianco's Chromacetic 2—auct.*
                                              14246, **9**:443
FORMULA: water 25, chromic acid 0.25, acetic acid 250

6000.0010 M'Ilroy and Hamilton 1901   *see* F 6000.0010 Czermak 1893 (note)

6000.0010 Müche 1908   2626, **26**:8
FORMULA: water 250, chromic acid 2.5, acetic acid 2.5

6000.0010 Schaffner 1906   3430, **41**:183
FORMULA: water 250, chromic acid 0.75, acetic acid 1.75

6000.0010 Simons 1906   3430, **41**:183
FORMULA: water 250, chromic acid 0.625, acetic acid 0.25

6000.0010 Virchow *test.* **1897 Kopsch**   1780, **51**:184
FORMULA: water 225, chromic acid 0.5, acetic acid 25
NOTE: This formula is often attributed to Kopsch (*loc. cit.*) but must not be confused
with F 7000.1000 Kopsch 1896.

6000.0010 Yamanouchi 1906   *see* F 6000.0010 Czermak 1893 (note)

6000.0010 Zimmermann 1893   1780, **41**:367
FORMULA: sea water 240, chromic acid 0.62, acetic acid 12.5

6000.0030 Chromic-formic

6000.0030 Rabl 1884   1455, **10**:215
FORMULA: water 250, chromic acid 0.8, formic acid 0.25

6000.0030 Rohl *test.* **1910 Poll**   Ehrlich, Krause, *et al.* 1910, **1**:223.
FORMULA: water 250, chromic acid 0.75, formic acid 0.25

6000.0040 Chromic-nitric

6000.0040 Haug 1891   *see* AF 21.1 Haug 1891

6000.0040 Perényi 1882   23833, **5**:459
FORMULA: water 165, 90% alc. 75, chromic acid 0.5, nitric acid 10

6000.0040 Perényi 1888   23833, **11**:139
FORMULA: water 135, abs. alc. 100, chromic acid 0.75, nitric acid 17.5

6000.0040 Robin 1871   Robin 1871, 305
FORMULA: water 250, potassium chromate 5, nitric acid, 1.25

6000.0060 Chromic-hydrochloric

6000.0060 Busch 1877   *see* AF 21.1 Busch 1877

6000.0060 Calvet 1900 *test.* **1910 Poll**   Ehrlich, Krause, *et al.* 1910, **1**:224
FORMULA: water 250, chromic acid 0.425, hydrochloric acid 0.31

6000.0070 Chromic-oxalic

6000.0070 Graf 1898 *test.* **1910 Poll**   Ehrlich, Krause, *et al.* 1910, **1**:224
    FORMULA: 30% alc. 250, chromic acid 0.75, oxalic acid 8

6000.1000 Chromic-formaldehyde

Chromic-formaldehyde mixtures must be prepared immediately before use, and it is desirable to use them in the dark. Chromic-formaldehyde alone, without acidification, is of no value save for cytoplasmic fixation.

6000.1000 Braus 1896   7137, **5**:307
    FORMULA: water 180, chromic acid 0.625, 40% formaldehyde 60

6000.1000 Levitsky 1910   2626 **28**:540
    FORMULA: water 225, chromic acid 0.4, 40% formaldehyde 25

6000.1000 Lo Bianco 1890   14246, **9**:443
    FORMULA: water 125, sea water 110, chromic acid 1.25, 40% formaldehyde 12.5

6000.1000 Marina 1897   19443, **2**:20
    FORMULA: 90% alc. 250, chromic acid 0.25, 40% formaldehyde 12.5

6000.1000 Nemeč *test.* **1937 Gatenby and Painter**   Gatenby and Painter 1937, 678
    FORMULA: water 232, chromic acid 2.3, 40% formaldehyde 18

6000.1000 Prokofieva 1934   7033a, **5**:498
    FORMULA: water 190, chromic acid 6.25, 40% formaldehyde 60

6000.1010 Chromic-formaldehyde-acetic

This class of fixative is widely shown to botanists under the generic name *CRAF*.

6000.1010 Belling 1928   20540b (abstr.) **4**:94
    FORMULA: water 185, chromic acid 2.5, acetic acid 25, 40% formaldehyde 40

6000.1010 Belling 1930   Belling 1930, 244
    FORMULA: stock I. water 212, chromic acid 3.5, acetic acid 38; stock II. water 117,
      40% formaldehyde 133; stock III. water 185, 40% formaldehyde 65
    WORKING SOLUTIONS: *A.* stock I 125, stock II 125; *B.* stock I 125, stock III 125
    RECOMMENDED FOR: Use solution *A* for general nuclear fixation; solution *B* for metaphase
      preparations only.

6000.1010 Destin *test.* **1929 McClung and Allen**   McClung 1929, 422
    FORMULA: water 250, chromic acid 2.5, 40% formaldehyde 15, acetic acid 5

6000.1010 Gatenby and Painter 1937   *see* F 6000.1010 Navashin 1912 (note)

6000.1010 Guyer 1930   Guyer 1930, 218
    FORMULA: water 160, chromic acid 1.6, acetic acid 10, 40% formaldehyde 85

6000.1010 Karpenchenko 1924   14, **387**:11211
    FORMULA: water 235, chromic acid 1, acetic acid 7.5, 40% formaldehyde 7.5
    NOTE: This formula is attributed to "Navashin 1924" by Semmens 1939 (*Microscope*,
    3:4).

6000.1010 Marchoux 1910 *test.* **1928 Gatenby and Cowdry**
                                       Gatenby and Cowdry 1928, 65
    FORMULA: water 120, chromic acid 0.8, 40% formaldehyde 120, acetic acid 75.
    NOTE: Gatenby and Cowdry (*loc. cit.*) cite this formula as "from **Perez 1910** (1915,
    5:11)." The journal reference is incorrect and the writer has never found any other
    source for the formula.

6000.1010 Navashin 1912   23253, 42, 28
    FORMULA: water 188, chromic acid 2, 40% formaldehyde 50, acetic acid 12
    NOTE: Gatenby and Painter 1937, 677 recommend the reduction of the chromic acid
    to 1.6.

6000.1010 Perez 1910 *see* F 6000.1010 Marchoux 1910 (note)

6000.1010 Randolf 1935   20540b, **10**:95
 FORMULA: stock I. water 230, chromic acid 2.5, acetic acid 20; stock II. water 175,
  40% formaldehyde 75
 WORKING SOLUTION: stock I 125, stock II 125

6000.1010 Retterer 1900   11024, **36**:508
 FORMULA: water 160, chromic acid 4.8, acetic acid 20, 40% formaldehyde 80

6000.1010 Weber 1930   22073, **9**:319
 FORMULA: stock I. water 220, chromic acid 3.3, acetic acid 30; stock II. water 120,
  40% formaldehyde 130
 WORKING SOLUTION: stock I 125, stock II 125

6000.1010 Winge 1930   23639b, **10**:699
 FORMULA: water 205, chromic acid 1.9, 40% formaldehyde 26, acetic acid 18.5

6000.1040 Chromic-formaldehyde-nitric

6000.1040 Yao-Nan 1927   4285a, **4**:71
 FORMULA: water 88, chromic acid 0.15 40% formaldehyde 12, nitric acid 0.2, sodium
  chloride 0.75

6700.0000 CHROMIC-DICHROMATE

6700.0000 Rutherford *test.* **1878 Marsh**   Marsh 1878, 68
 FORMULA: water 250, chromic acid 0.5, potassium dichromate 1

6700.0000 Weigert 1896   7936a, **6**:10
 FORMULA: water 250, potassium dichromate 12.5, chromium fluoride 5

6700.0010 Chromic-dichromate-acetic

 Chromic-dichromate mixtures are intended for cytoplasmic fixation; both the chromic
and the dichromate fix specific elements of cytoplasm.

6700.0010 Burckhardt 1897   6011, **12**:335
 FORMULA: water 230, chromic acid 1.5, potassium dichromate 3.8, acetic acid 12.5

6700.0010 Goldsmith *test.* **1930 Guyer**   Guyer 1930, 218
 FORMULA: water 237.5, chromic acid 1.9, potassium dichromate 2, acetic acid 12.5

6700.0010 Maximow 1916   6630, **79**:462
 FORMULA: *A.* Champy 1913 F 16700.0090; *B.* water 60, chromic acid 30, acetic acid 0.6;
  C. 3% potassium dichromate
 METHOD: fix *A*, 3–4 days → wash → *B*, 24 hrs. → wash → *C*, 3 days → wash → [sections
  stained by DS 13.22 Kull 1913 or DS 22.21 Baker and Thomas 1933]

6700.0010 Stockwell 1934 *see* ADS 12.2 Stockwell 1934

6700.0040 Chromic-dichromate-nitric

6700.0040 Gatenby 1937   Gatenby and Painter 1937, 380
 FORMULA: water 235, chromic acid 2.25, potassium dichromate 4.5, nitric acid 15

6700.0040 Kollmann 1885   1739, **51**:296
 FORMULA: water 250, chromic acid 5, potassium dichromate 12.5, nitric acid 5

6700.1010 Chromic-dichromate-formaldehyde-acetic

6700.1010 Semmens 1939 *CS33—auct.*   *Microscope,* **3**:5
 FORMULA: water 238, chromic acid 3.75, ammonium dichromate 2.5, 40% formaldehyde
  12.5, acetic acid 0.6

6800.0000 CHROMIC-(OTHER INORGANIC SALTS)

6800.0000 Bhaduri and Semmens 1942   11360, **62**:21
 FORMULA: water 250, chromic acid 2.5, sodium uranate 2.5

6800.0000 Lenoir 1926   19076, **38**:720
  FORMULA: water 250, chromic acid 2.5, potassium iodide 2.5

6800.0010 Chromic-(other inorganic salts)-acetic

6800.0010 Semmens 1939a *CS19—auct.*   *Microscope,* **3**:4
  FORMULA: water 249, chromic acid 2, ammonium uranate 0.65, acetic acid 1
  NOTE: The ammonium uranate is prepared as follows. Wash 10 uranium trioxide by
    stirring and decantation with 20 5% hydrochloric acid. Dissolve residue in 20 conc.
    hydrochloric acid, filter and add ammonia to filtrate until precipitation complete.
    Wash and dry ppt.

6800.0010 Semmens 1939b *Flemming-uranic—auct.*   *Microscope,* **3**:5
  FORMULA: water 238, chromic acid 1.9, sodium uranate 2.5, acetic acid 12.5
  NOTE: The sodium uranate is prepared as the ammonium uranate of "a," with the
    substitution of *N* sodium hydroxide for ammonia.

6800.0010 Semmens 1939c *Benda-uranic—auct.*   *Microscope,* **3**:5
  FORMULA: water 250, chromic acid 1.5, sodium uranate 2, acetic acid 2.5

6800-0030 Chromic-(other inorganic salts)-formic

6800.0030 Pianese *test.* **1904 Besson**   Besson 1904, 750
  FORMULA: water 250, chromic acid 1, cobalt chloride 20, formic acid 0.3

F 7000 DICHROMATE WITHOUT OTHER PRIMARY FIXATIVE AGENTS
7000.0000 DICHROMATE ALONE

Dichromate alone is an adequate general-purpose bulk fixative when it is desired to
preserve large masses of material. The cytological and histological pictures obtained from
this fixative, however, are not so good as those obtained with other classes.

7000.0000 Cajal 1890   23632, **7**:332
  FORMULA: water 250, potassium dichromate 9

7000.0000 Cole 1884   Cole 1884b, 21
  FORMULA: water 185, 95% alc. 65, potassium dichromate 3.6, sodium sulfate 2

7000.0000 Gerlach 1872 *test.* **1928 Gatenby and Cowdry**
                                                    Gatenby and Cowdry 212
  FORMULA: water 250, ammonium bichromate 5

7000.0000 Golgi 1903   Golgi 1903, **1**:163
  FORMULA: water 250, potassium dichromate 5

7000.0000 Hamilton 1878   11025, **12**:254
  FORMULA: 25% alc. 250, potassium dichromate 4.8, potassium sulfate 2.4

7000.0000 Müller 1859 *Müller's Fluid—compl. script.* 22302, **10**:80
  FORMULA: water 250, potassium bichromate 6.25, potassium sulfate 2.5

7000.0010 Dichromate-acetic

7000.0010 Tellyesniczky 1898   1780, **52**:242
  FORMULA: water 250, potassium dichromate 7.5, acetic acid 12.5
  NOTE: This is the "Tellyesniczky's Fluid" of most authors, but *see also* F 0000.1010 and
    F 3500.0010.

7000.0040 Dichromate-nitric

7000.0040 Benda *test.* **1900 Pollack**   Pollack 1900, 30
  REAGENTS REQUIRED: *A.* 10% nitric acid; *B.* 1% potassium dichromate
  METHOD: [fresh tissue] → *A* 24 hrs. → *B* 14 days

7000.1000 Dichromate-formaldehyde

The apparently irrational dichromate-formaldehyde mixtures, including the next class
with the addition of acetic acid, are excellent fixatives for heavily yolked material. They
exercise less hardening effect, and render this material less brittle, than any other group.
Though the majority have been proposed for the purpose of cytoplasmic fixation only, they
are to be widely recommended in embryological practice. These mixtures must be prepared

immediately before use and fixation should always take place in the dark. It is desirable to wash them out with a weak solution of formaldehyde, also in the dark, until such time as no further color comes away.

7000.1000 Bock 1924 23632, **40**:318
FORMULA: water 240, potassium dichromate 5, sodium sulfate 2, 40% formaldehyde 10

7000.1000 Braus 1896 7137, **5**:307
FORMULA: water 190, potassium dichromate 4.8, 40% formaldehyde 60, potassium sulfate 2.4

7000.1000 Bubenaite 1929 23632, **46**:359
FORMULA: A. water 225, 40% formaldehyde 25, B. water 250, potassium dichromate 6

7000.1000 Cajal *test.* **1933** *ips.* Cajal and de Castro 1933, 282
FORMULA: water 250, potassium dichromate 10, 40% formaldehyde 37.5

7000.1000 Durig 1895 766, **10**:659
FORMULA: water 225, potassium dichromate 7.5, 40% formaldehyde 25

7000.1000 Eisath 1911 14370, **20**:3
FORMULA: water 250, potassium dichromate 7, sodium sulfate 4, 40% formaldehyde 37

7000.1000 Fish 1895 21400a, **17**:319
FORMULA: water 250, potassium dichromate 7.5, 40% formaldehyde 2.51

7000.1000 Hultgren and Andersson *test.* **1910 Poll** Ehrlich, Krause, *et al.* 1910, **1**:232
FORMULA: water 250, potassium dichromate 5, potassium sulfate 2.5, 40% formaldehyde 10

7000.1000 Kopsch 1896 766, **11**:727
FORMULA: *A.* water 200, potassium dichromate 7.5, 40% formaldehyde 50; *B.* water 250, potassium dichromate 8.75
NOTE: *See* MS 34.1 Kopsch 1896.

7000.1000 Kose 1898 *see* F 7000.1000 Stilling 1898 (note)

7000.1000 Lachi 1895 14425, **5**:15
FORMULA: water 187, potassium dichromate 7.5, 40% formaldehyde 63

7000.1000 Landsteiner 1903 2526, **33**:237
FORMULA: water 240, potassium dichromate 3, potassium sulfate 1.5, 40% formaldehyde 12.5

7000.1000 Mettler 1932 20540b, **7**:102
FORMULA: *A.* water 125, 40% formaldehyde 125; *B.* water 250, potassium dichromate 7.5
METHOD: [brain exposed but not removed from body] → *A*, 3–5 days → [brain removed to *B* 1 wk. in dark] → thin slices to fresh *B*, changed when discolored, 2 wks. in dark → F 1700.0000 Mettler 1932
NOTE: Before metal staining, neutral formaldehyde must be employed.

7000.1000 Möller 1899 23635, **66**:85
FORMULA: water 200, potassium dichromate 6, 40% formaldehyde 50

7000.1000 Müller 1899 *Müller-formol—compl. script.* 1780, **55**:11
FORMULA: water 225, potassium dichromate 1.5, 40% formaldehyde 25

7000.1000 von Orth 1896 23632, **13**:316
FORMULA: water 225, potassium dichromate 5.6, 40% formaldehyde 25, potassium sulfate 2.25
NOTE: The liquid of **Schridde 1910** (*test.* 1937 Gatenby and Painter, 396) is identical.

7000.1000 Pfeiffer and Jarisch 1919 23422, **10**:1
FORMULA: water 225, potassium dichromate 8, 40% formaldehyde 25

7000.1000 Régaud 1910 1823, **11**:291
FORMULA: *A.* water 200, potassium dichromate 5, 40% formaldehyde 50; *B.* water 250, potassium dichromate 7.5
METHOD: *A.* 5 days in dark, changing every 24 hrs. → *B*, 8 days, changing every 24 hrs.

7000.1000 del Río-Hortega 1928 *test.* **1933 Cajal and de Castro**

Cajal and de Castro 1933, 281

FORMULA: water 225, potassium dichromate 15, chloral hydrate 15, 40% formaldehyde 25

7000.1000 del Río-Hortega 1929   3231, **9**:21

FORMULA: water 225, potassium dichromate 4.5, 40% formaldehyde 25
NOTE: This solution must be made with pure distilled water and borax-neutralized formaldehyde if used before metal staining.

7000.1000 Sánchez *test.* **1933 Cajal and de Castro**   Cajal and de Castro 1933, 128

FORMULA: water 225, potassium dichromate 5, 40% formaldehyde 25

7000.1000 Schreiber 1898   766, **14**:275

FORMULA: *A.* water 237, potassium dichromate 0.9, 40% formaldehyde 16; *B.* water 225, potassium dichromate 4.4, 40% formaldehyde 3.8

7000.1000 Schridde 1910   *see* F 7000.1000 von Orth 1896 (note)

7000.1000 Smirnow 1898   1780, **52**:202

FORMULA: water 200, potassium dichromate 10, 40% formaldehyde 50

7000.1000 Smith 1930   *Turtox News*, **8**:91

FORMULA: *A.* water 225, 40% formaldehyde 25; *B.* water 250, potassium dichromate 10
METHOD: [fresh tissues] → *A*, till required → thin slices, *B* 3–5 days → distilled water, thorough wash → blot → MS 34.1. Andriezen 1884

7000.1000 Stilling 1898   1780, **52**:176

FORMULA: water 225, potassium dichromate 6.25, 40% formaldehyde 25
NOTE: The formula of **Kose 1898** (20181, **6**:224) is identical.

7000.1000 Strong 1895   766, **10**:494

FORMULA: *A.* water 250, potassium dichromate 8.75, 40% formaldehyde 8.75; *B.* water 163, potassium dichromate 7.5, 40% formaldehyde 87
NOTE: *See* MS 34.1 Strong 1895.

7000.1000 Whitehead 1932   11431, **35**:415

FORMULA: water 220, potassium dichromate 6, 40% formaldehyde 30

7000.1000 Wiesel 1902   764, **19**:481

FORMULA: *A.* water 225, potassium dichromate 2.5, 40% formaldehyde 25; *B.* 2% potassium dichromate
METHOD: [fresh tissue] → *A*, 4 days → *B*, 2 days

7000.1010 Dichromate-formaldehyde-acetic

This class of fixatives is warmly recommended by Romeis 1948, p. 58, under the generic name of *Kaformacet.*

7000.1010 Böhm and Davidoff 1905   Böhm and Davidoff 1905, 27

FORMULA: water 225, potassium dichromate 5, 40% formaldehyde 25
PREPARATION: Add the formaldehyde after complete solution of dichromate.

7000.1010 Böhm and Oppel 1907   Böhm and Oppel 1907, 114

FORMULA: water 225, potassium dichromate 2.25, sodium sulfate 1.25, 40% formaldehyde 12.5, acetic acid 12.5

7000.1010 Cummings 1925   11135, **38**:401

FORMULA: water 250 potassium dichromate 8.5, 40% formaldehyde 10, acetic acid 12.5

7000.1010 Haver 1927   11431, **30**:621

FORMULA: water 225, potassium dichromate 5.6, sodium sulfate 2.25, 40% formaldehyde 12.5, acetic acid 12.5

7000.1010 Held 1909   65, **31**:196

FORMULA: water 240, potassium dichromate 2.5, 40% formaldehyde 8.8, acetic acid 4.0

7000.1010 Joseph 1918   1798, **38**:164

FORMULA: water 175, potassium dichromate 5.4, 40% formaldehyde 50, acetic acid 25

7000.1010 Lillie 1948   Lillie 1948, 35
FORMULA: water 220, potassium dichromate 3.3, 40% formaldehyde 22, acetic acid 11

7000.1010 Romeis 1948   Romeis 1948, 58
FORMULA: water 212.5, potassium dichromate 6.5, 40% formaldehyde 25, acetic acid 12.5

7000.1010 Semmens 1939 *CS32—auct.*   *Microscope*, **3**:5
FORMULA: water 238, ammonium chromate 10, methenamine 10, acetic acid 2.5
NOTE: The methenamine is decomposed to formaldehyde by the acid.

7000.1010 Smith 1912   11373, **23**:91
    FORMULA: water 230, potassium dichromate 2.5, acetic acid 6.25, 40% formaldehyde
    12.5
    RECOMMENDED FOR: heavily yolked embryos.

7000.1010 Wittmaack *test.* **1910 Poll**   Ehrlich, Krause, *et al.* 1910, **1**:233
FORMULA: water 210, potassium dichromate 12.5, 40% formaldehyde 25, acetic acid 7.5

7000.1030 Dichromate-formaldehyde-formic

7000.1030 Ciaccio 1910   22575, **199**:381
FORMULA: water 210, potassium dichromate 9.8, 40% formaldehyde 40, formic acid 1

7000.2000 Dichromate-acetaldehyde

7000.2000 Vassale and Donaggi 1895   14425, **6**:82
FORMULA: water 250, potassium dichromate 8.75, acetaldehyde 12.5

7800.0010 DICHROMATE-(OTHER INORGANIC SALT)-ACETIC

7800.0010 Russell 1941   4349, **21**:47
FORMULA: water 250, potassium dichromate 6.25, zinc chloride 15, acetic acid 12.5

7800.1000 Dichromate-(other inorganic salts)-formaldehyde

7800.1000 Gross and Lohaus 1932   23632, **49**:168
    FORMULA: sodium borate-HCl buffer, pH 7.6 250, potassium dichromate 2.5, calcium
    chloride 2.5, 40% formaldehyde 10

7800.1000 La Manna 1937   23632, **54**:257
    FORMULA: *A.* 4% formaldehyde; *B.* water 250, potassium dichromate 15, zinc chloride
    12.5
    METHOD: *A*, 3 days → *B*, 1 day, 56°C.

7800.1012 Dichromate-(other inorganic salts)-formaldehyde-acetic-trichloroacetic

7800.1012 Kolmer *test.* **1938 Walls**   20540b, **13**:69
    FORMULA: water 217, potassium dichromate 4.5, uranium acetate 1.9, 40% formaldehyde
    9, acetic acid 23, trichloroacetic acid 12
    RECOMMENDED FOR: whole eyes.
    NOTE: Walls (*loc. cit.*) refers to this formula, without reference, as "Kolmer's Fluid."
    This term is more usually applied to F 3700.1010 Kolmer 1912.

F 8000 SOLUTIONS WITH
"OTHER INORGANIC" PRIMARY FIXATIVE AGENTS
8000.0010 (OTHER INORGANIC AGENT)-ACETIC

8000.0010 Belar 1929   23639b, **10**:76
    FORMULA: water 125, 95% alc. 125, zinc chloride 13, acetic acid 13

8000.0010 Juel *test.* **1915 Meyer**   Meyer 1915, 198
    FORMULA: water 125, 95% alc. 125, zinc chloride 5, acetic acid 5

8000.0010 Rawitz 1909   23632, **25**:385
    FORMULA: water 100, 95% alc. 125, phosphotungstic acid 10, acetic acid 25

8000.0014 (Other inorganic agent)-acetic-nitric

8000.0014 Gilson 1890   6011, **6**:122
FORMULA: water 80, 95% alc. 20, zinc chloride 5, acetic acid 1.25, nitric acid 1

8000.0030 (Other inorganic agent)-formic

8000.0030 Carpenter and Nebel 1931   19938, **74**:154
FORMULA: water 250, ruthenium tetroxide 0.1, formic acid 1

8000.1000 (Other inorganic agent)-formaldehyde

8000.1000 Aoyama 1930   23632, **46**:490
FORMULA: water 210, 40% formaldehyde 40, cadmium chloride 2.5

8000.1000 Baker 1944   17510, **85**:1
FORMULA: water 225, calcium chloride 1, 40% formaldehyde 25

8000.1000 Besta 1905   19460, **39**:1
FORMULA: water 190, 40% formaldehyde 60, tin ammonium chloride 10

8000.1000 Cajal 1914   21344, **12**:127
FORMULA: water 187, abs. alc. 63, 40% formaldehyde 37, uranium nitrate 2.5

8000.1000 Drew 1920   11360, **40**:295
FORMULA: water 200, cobalt nitrate 5, sodium chloride 2, 40% formaldehyde 50

8000.1000 da Fano 1920   11360, **40**:157
FORMULA: water 250, 40% formaldehyde 37.5, cobalt nitrate 2.5

8000.1000 Fish 1896   21400a, **17**:319
FORMULA: water 200, 40% formaldehyde 50, zinc chloride 15, sodium chloride 88

8000.1000 Krohntal 1899   23632, **16**:235
FORMULA: water 235, lead formate 2, 40% formaldehyde 15

8000.1000 Lawrentjew *test*. **1933 Cajal and de Castro**   Cajal and de Castro 1933, 360
FORMULA: water 80, 95% alc. 80, 40% formaldehyde 80, arsenic trioxide 1

8000.1000 Lison 1931   1825, **41**:343
FORMULA: water 250, lead acetate 10, 40% formaldehyde 25

8000.1000 Merland 1935   4285a, **12**:290
FORMULA: water 250, neutralized 40% formaldehyde 37.5, sodium bromide 25, cobalt nitrate 5

8000.1000 Michmanns 1946   11431, **58**:93
FORMULA: water 225, cobalt nitrate 2.5, calcium chloride 1, 40%, formaldehyde 25

8000.1000 Penfield 1930   608b, **5**:445
FORMULA: water 200, 40% formaldehyde 50, potassium iodide 15, urea 10

8000.1000 del Río-Hortega 1925 *test*. **1928 da Fano**   Gatenby and Cowdry 1928, 644
FORMULA: water 225, 40% formaldehyde 25, uranium nitrate 3.75

8000.1000 Slonimski and Cunge *test*. **1948 Romeis**   Romeis 1948, 470
FORMULA: water 250, potassium ferricyanide 4, 40% formaldehyde 25, sodium chloride 10

8000.1000 Warthin 1916   4349, **6**:71
FORMULA: water 250, 40% formaldehyde 25, calcium chloride 0.05, potassium chloride 0.05, sodium bicarbonate 0.025, sodium chloride 2.25

8000.1010 (Other inorganic agent)-formaldehyde-acetic

8000.1010 Salkind 1916   6630, **79**:16
FORMULA: acetic acid 30, lead subacetate 30, water 150, 40% formaldehyde 30

F 9000 SOLUTIONS WITH
"OTHER ORGANIC" PRIMARY FIXATIVE AGENTS

9000.0010 Sannomiya 1926   8542a, **4**:363
FORMULA: abs. alc. 250, acetic acid 12.5, sulfosalicylic acid 7.5

9000.0000 Bank and Davenport 1940   20540b, **15**:9
  FORMULA: water 125, 95% alc. 125, formamide 10, chloral hydrate 6

9000.1000 Huseby 1946   16913, **61**:122
  FORMULA: water 225, resorcinol 12 to 20, 40% formaldehyde 25

9000.4000 Davenport, Windle, and Rhines 1947   Conn and Darrow 1947, 1C$_2$, 24
  FORMULA: paranitrophenol 12.5, water 112, 95% alc. 112, formamide 25

F 04 Basal Fixative Solutions

04.0 EXPLANATION

These basal fixative solutions were originally suggested by Gray 1933 (11360, **53**:13) where he published a brief list of the more common fixatives which could be prepared by their aid. This list was slightly amplified, and formed an appendix to the tenth and eleventh editions of Lee's *Microtomist's Vade Mecum*.

Briefly, the method involves having available standardized solutions, through the mixture and dilution of which it is possible to prepare about 80% of commonly employed fixatives. The original method of Gray involved the preparation of two series of such solutions, known as the *aqueous* and *alcoholic* series, but the latter has now been suppressed, since experience has shown it to be impractical. The system of numbering the solutions used in this volume differs from that originally proposed and is based on the numerical classification used in the first part of this chapter. That is, the number designating the stock solution corresponds to the number used to designate this ingredient in the list of formulas which have already been given. All the solutions employed are stable except the osmic acid, the preparation of which is described in the next paragraph.

References to the original citations of the fixatives, indicated in the following list by the author's name and date only, will be found in the preceding section of this chapter. They may be traced either from the alphabetical index or by taking the first four numbers at the head of the column. This will give, in that order, the numerical designation of the class in which the fixative belongs. The addition of the symbols for modifier and acid is readily made by simple inspection.

04.1 LIST OF SOLUTIONS

The following solutions are of sufficient strength to require dilution for the preparation of any of the fixatives shown. The first two columns in this tabular material show the two most commonly employed diluents. The last column shows such other ingredients as must be added to secure the required fixative. It is understood that when the ingredient is liquid, a volume is indicated and when the ingredient is solid, a weight is indicated.

Solution 1—2% osmic acid
  NOTE: This should be prepared in chemically clean glassware in filtered, triple-distilled water, to which has been added enough potassium permanganate (approximately 0.01%) to give a faint pink color. This pink color should be maintained by the addition of a few drops of potassium permanganate solution whenever necessary.
Solution 2—1% platinic chloride
Solution 3—7% mercuric chloride
Solution 4—5% copper sulfate
Solution 5—a saturated aqueous solution of picric acid.
Solution 6—2% chromic acid
Solution 7—7.5% potassium dichromate
Solution 8—7.5% potassium dichromate and 3% sodium sulfate
  NOTE: This is a triple-strength Müller's 1859 fixative. The previous solution (7) may be substituted for it by those who do not believe in the efficacy of the sulfate content of Müller.
Solution 9—40% formaldehyde
Solution 10—glacial acetic acid

04.2 FORMULAS ARRANGED ALPHABETICALLY

BASAL SOLUTIONS

REFERENCE	H_2O	95% alc.	1 · 2% OsO_4	2 · 1% H_2PtCl_6	3 · 7% $HgCl_2$	4 · 1% $CuSO_4$	5 · Sat. sol. picric acid	6 · 2% CrO_3	7 · 7.5% $K_2Cr_2O_7$	8 · sol. 7 +3% Na_2SO_4	9 · 40% formaldehyde	10 · acetic acid	Other additions
Aigner 1900	43					23			33			1	
Allen 1918							75	1.5			25	5	2 urea
Allen 1929							75	1			15	10	1 urea
Allen 1929	25						50	1			20	5	1 urea
Allen 1929							75				15	10	1 urea
Allen 1929a							75				10	10	
Allen 1929b							90				5	5	
Allen and McClung 1950	60						50					10	40 dioxane
Altmann 1890	60		50		20							20	
Altmann 1890	15		50		20								20 formic acid
Altmann 1890	16.5		50						35				
Altmann 1894									33.5				
Ammerman 1950	87		2.5								12	0.8	1.2 chrome alum
Andriezen 1894	80								17		15		
Aoyama 1930	85		50								15		1 $CdCl_2$
Apáthy 1893	31	40			50								
Apáthy 1896	25				29							5	
Apáthy 1897		50	25		50								0.25 NaCl
Apáthy (1920)	10				85								0.5 NaCl
Apáthy and Boeke (1910)	80				14								4 HNO_3
Apáthy and Boeke (1910)	85												5 HNO_3
Armitage 1939							40	15			10	10	50 dioxane
Arnold 1888	85							1.5				0.5	
Bachuber 1916	90						75				15	10	
Baker 1944	90										10		0.4 $CaCl_2$
Baker 1945	35	20						40				5.2	
Baker and Thomas 1933	25	50							25				
Baley 1937	52	10			20				18		10		
Barret 1886a	30	50	10					10					
Barret 1886b	92	10	10					8					
Barret 1886c	92	5	5					13					
Bartelmez 1915a		90										10	

BASAL SOLUTIONS

REFERENCE	H_2O	**95%** alc.	1 2% OsO_4	2 1% H_2PtCl_6	3 7% $HgCl_2$	4 1% $CuSO_4$	5 Sat. sol. picric acid	6 2% CrO_3	7 7.5% $K_2Cr_2O_7$	8 sol. 7 +3% Na_2SO_4	9 40% formaldehyde	10 acetic acid	Other additions
Bartelmez 1915b		95										5	
Bartelmez 1915c		60										10	chloroform 30
Bataillon 1904	45											10	
Becher and Demoll 1913a	87.5							45				0.1	
Becher and Demoll 1913b	35	30						12.5				1.6	
Becher and Demoll 1913c	50		10		18		26				85	2	
Becher and Demoll 1913d	50.5			28	21.5								
Becher and Demoll 1913e	52				21.5		24.5					2	
Béguin (1910)	40				90							10	
Belar 1929a	40		20					40				0.6	
Belar 1929b	30	120	5								60	15	
Belar 1992c	50	50						50				5	5 $ZnCl_2$
Belling 1928	24										10	16	
Benario 1894	9	90									1	1	
Benda 1901	41		20					38					
Benda 1903a	65		20									2.5	
Benda 1903b	25							25	10				50 pyrolignious acid
van Beneden and Heyt 1887		50										50	
Benoit 1922a	37		25		18				20				0.8 $UO(NO_3)_2$ 6 H_2O 0.2 NaCl
Benoit 1922b	72				18				20				0.8 $UO(NO_3)_2$ 6 H_2O 0.2 NaCl
Bensley 1911	52		20						22			0.3	
Bensley and Bensley 1929			100										0.5 $FeCl_3$
Bensley and Bensley 1938					70				30				
Bensley and Bensley 1938	7				63				30		10		
Bensley and Bensley 1938	53		20		68				32			5	
Bensley and Bensley 1938	50		12.5						27			0.5	
Berkely 1897	50								35		25		4 $SnCl(NH_4)Cl_2$
Besta 1905	75										20		2 acetaldehyde
Besta 1910a	80												

REFERENCE	H_2O	95% alc.	1 — 2% OsO_4	2 — 1% H_2PtCl_6	3 — 7% $HgCl_2$	4 — 1% $CuSO_4$	5 — Sat. sol. picric acid	6 — 2% CrO_3	7 — 7.5% $K_2Cr_2O_7$	8 — sol. 7 +3% Na_2SO_4	9 — 40% formaldehyde	10 — acetic acid	Other additions
Besta 1910b	100												4 $(NH_4)Mo_7O_{27}$, 4 H_2O
Bigelow 1902							95					5	
Bignami 1896	87				14							1	0.8 NaCl
Bing and Ellerman 1901											10		90 acetone
Bizzozero 1885	87.5		12.5										0.75 NaCl
Blanc 1895	96						4					0.25	0.12 H_2SO_4
Bles 1905	20	70									7	3	
Bock 1924	69										4		
Boeke 1910	35	55								27	10		
Böhm and Davidoff 1905	63								27		10	5	
Böhm and Oppel 1907	15				70						10	5	
Böhm and Oppel 1907	78									12	5	5	
Böhm and Oppel (1910)a					95								
Böhm and Oppel (1910)b							100						
Bonn (1937)	71		6					20				3	
Bonner (1915)	69		6					22				3	
Borgert 1900					75							25	
Bouin 1897							75				25	5	
Boule 1908a	63				70						22	5	
Bowie 1925									30			2	
Bradley 1948		38	2.5		100							12	50 chloroform
Bühler 1898	50		3.5										
Burckhardt 1892	40							2.5				8.2	
Burckhardt 1897								30	20			5	
Burke 1933	68		15								27		5 pyridine
Busch 1898	85												1 $NaIO_3$
Cajal 1890a	53								47				
Cajal 1890b	60		8						32				
Cajal 1891	60		5						35				
Cajal 1893	56.8			3.2							40		

BASAL SOLUTIONS

REFERENCE	H_2O	95% alc.	1 — 2% OsO_4	2 — 1% H_2PtCl_6	3 — 7% $HgCl_2$	4 — 1% $CuSO_4$	5 — Sat. sol. picric acid	6 — 2% CrO_3	7 — 7.5% $K_2Cr_2O_7$	8 — sol. 7 +3% Na_2SO_4	9 — 40% formaldehyde	10 — acetic acid	Other additions
Cajal 1914	75	25											
Cajal (1933)	33										15		
Cajal 1933a	58		10								15		5 $FeCl_3$
Cajal 1933b	66		8										0.5 $K_3Fe(CN)_6$; .125 HCl
Calvet 1900	90							8.5	52				1 NaCl
Carazzi (1910)	75	7			29				32			0.5	
Carazzi (1920)	40	30			30				26			3.3	
Carleton and Leach 1938					90						10		
Carnoy 1887a		75										25	
Carnoy 1887b		60										10	30 chloroform
Carnoy and Lebrum 1887		30										30	30 chloroform
Carter 1919	7	50							40			3	1.5 urea nitrate
de Castro 1916	100										15		1.2 maltose
Catcheside 1934			8					90			1		
Caullery and Mesnil 1905			26	26				40	15			5.5	
Chamberlain 1906	40		2.5					50	16			10	
Champy 1911	43		22					20					
Champy 1913a	33		22					20					
Champy 1913b	20							50					
Champy 1913c	60								40				35 pyrolignious acid
Champy 1913d	50		50									0.5	1.5 NaI
Cholodkowsky (1910)	50				100								
Chura 1925	54						5.5		25		20		0.4 each $CrF_3.4H_2O$ and $NH_4Cr(SO_4)_2.12H_2O$
Ciaccio 1910	30								53		16	1	0.4 formic acid
Claüssen 1908	75							25					
Cohen 1934	90										10	1	3.6 $2H_3PO_4.H_2O$
Coker 1902	94	25			5.2							1	
Cole 1884	55	25			40					20			
Colombo 1904	40		20					12.5			20	0.2	
Cori 1890	85		0.5					1.6				0.1	
Cori (1910)	10		0.06		87.5							0.0125	

REFERENCE	H_2O	95% alc.	BASAL SOLUTIONS										Other additions
			1 2% OsO_4	2 1% H_2PtCl_6	3 7% $HgCl_2$	4 1% $CuSO_4$	5 Sat. sol. picric acid	6 2% CrO_3	7 7.5% $K_2Cr_2O_7$	8 sol. 7 +3% Na_2SO_4	9 40% formaldehyde	10 acetic acid	
Cox 1891					60						20	10	0.8 K_2CrO_4
Cox (1895)	72				14				14				
Cox 1896	20		20		40							20	
Crétin 1938					40						10		
Cummings 1925	45						50				4	5	
Czermak 1893	87.5							12.5	45			1	
Dahlgrens 1897	35				45					15		5	
Davenport, Windle, and Beach 1934	90										10		0.5 trichloroacetic acid
Davidoff 1889a					75							25	
Davidoff 1889b							75					25	
Dawson and Friedgood 1938	38				52		50				10		0.7 NaCl
Deegener 1909		45					50					5	
Demarbaix 1889	71							26			6	3	
Destin (1929)	50							50			6	2	
Destin (1943)	46							46			10	2	
Dietrich (1946)	60	30									10	2	
Dobell 1919	8	32					68				12	10	
Dominici 1905	20		2.5		80							5	iodine to wine color
Drüner 1894	41	10			72							0.7	
Duggar 1909a	65				49			25				0.2	1.6 HNO_3
Duggar 1909b	50		10						40		10		
Durig 1895	65							40				0.2	
Ehlers (1910)	48							40		37	15		
Eisath 1911	70			6.25									
Eisig 1878	5				85			25					
Eltringham 1930a							100				10		10 HNO_3
Eltringham 1930b							100					1	2 H_2SO_4
Erlanger 1892			5										5 tannic acid
van Ermengen 1894	70		30										0.5 NaCl
Ewald 1897	100		2.5										

BASAL SOLUTIONS

REFERENCE	H_2O	95% alc.	1 — 2% OsO_4	2 — 1% H_2PtCl_6	3 — 7% $HgCl_2$	4 — 1% $CuSO_4$	5 — Sat. sol. picric acid	6 — 2% CrO_3	7 — 7.5% $K_2Cr_2O_7$	8 — sol. 7 +3% Na_2SO_4	9 — 40% formaldehyde	10 — acetic acid	Other additions
Faber-Domergue 1889	30		50								15	20	$Co(NO_3)_2$ 6 H_2O
da Fano 1920	100											10	0.002 NaI
Farkas 1914		50	25		25							15	
Farmer and Shove 1905a		85										29	
Farmer and Shove 1905b		71										0.25	
Faussek 1900	50							50				5	
Favorsky 1930		95											
Fick 1893	75		5.5					25				0.1	
Fischler 1906	72		0.5					20				2.5	
Fish 1895a	65										0.2		
Fish 1895b	55									35			
Fish 1896a	80						8		40		5		6 $ZnCl_2$, 35 NaCl
Fish 1896b	85				7						20		
Flemming 1882a	82.5		5		7			12.5				0.1	
Flemming 1882b	75		5				20					0.1	
Flemming 1882c	95							5				0.1	
Flemming 1884	45		20					37.5				5	
Flemming (1910)	55		10					37.5				5	
Flesch 1879	85		5					12.5		35			
Foa 1891	35			30									
Foa 1895	27			50					33	35	0.1		0.6 NaCl
Fol 1884	85		1				10	12.5				1	
Fol (1885)	73							12.5					
Fol 1896a	95		5										
Fol 1896b	73		0.25				10	12.5				1	
Fol (1910)a	17						65	17				1	1.3 H_2SO_4
Fol (1910)b	72.5							7.5					
Fontana 1912	84						17						
Francotte 1890	63		20								16	0.8	2 H_2SO_4
Frenkel 1893	75		25									0.5	0.75 $PdCl_2.2 H_2O$
Friedländer 1889	91							8				1	
Friedmann (1900)	62		4					50				4	

REFERENCE	H_2O	95% alc.	1 — 2% OsO_4	2 — 1% H_2PtCl_6	3 — 7% $HgCl_2$	4 — 1% $CuSO_4$	5 — Sat. sol. picric acid	6 — 2% CrO_3	7 — 7.5% $K_2Cr_2O_7$	8 — sol. 7 +3% Na_2SO_4	9 — 40% formaldehyde	10 — acetic acid	Other additions
Gage 1890	33	50											
Galesescu 1908	65		0.8									0.08	
Gatenby 1937	20				25		17	10	24				6 HNO_3
Gates 1907	65		5					50				0.5	
Gates 1908	65							35				0.5	
Gates and Latter 1927	50							35				1	
van Gehuchten (1927)	58		10					50	32				
von Gelei and Horvath 1931					95						5	2.5	
Gerhardt 1901	35				24			14			25		
Gerlach 1872	100												2 $(NH_4)_2Cr_2O_7$
Giemsa 1909		34			66							4	
Giesbrecht (1910)			2				95						
Gilson 1898	65	6	2		30							0.4	1.2 HNO_3
Goldsmith	46							38	11			5	
Golgi 1880	70		8						22				
Golgi 1900	58		16.5						26				
Golgi 1903	73								27				
Goto 1898	75				24								
Graf 1897	55						90				10	1.5	4.5 glycerol
Graf 1898	20	30			70			15				2	
Gregg and Puckett 1943											8	3	3.2 oxalic acid
Gulick 1911	63	90					34				3	10	
Gulland 1900	37.5		20					37.5		30			5 formic acid
Guthrie 1928a					70					30			5 formic acid
Guthrie 1928b	34							28			34	4	
Guyer 1930	75		20								34	0.5	
Hamann 1885	50				70						20		
Hamilton 1878	10	25			25						25		
Hartz 1950	40				17					25		5	0.2 trichloroacetic
Harvey 1907a	27								10			5	
Harvey 1907b	60								22	30	34	5	
Haver 1927										30	5	5	

BASAL SOLUTIONS

REFERENCE	H_2O	95% alc.	1 2% OsO_4	2 1% H_2PtCl_6	3 7% $HgCl_2$	4 1% $CuSO_4$	5 Sat. sol. picric acid	6 2% CrO_3	7 7.5% $K_2Cr_2O_7$	8 sol. 7 +3% Na_2SO_4	9 40% formaldehyde	10 acetic acid	Other additions
Heidenhain 1888					100								0.5 NaCl
Heidenhain 1896	25		25		50							1	2 trichloroacetic acid
Heidenhain 1909					100						20		1.25 NaCl
Heidenhain 1916a	23				57						50		0.5 NaCl
Heidenhain 1916b	80				50						15	5	5 trichloroacetic acid
Heidenhain 1916c					63					27	10	5	
Heidenhain 1916d	15				65						20	4	2 trichloroacetic acid
Heidenhain 1916e													2 trichloroacetic acid, 0.5 NaCl
Heinz 1901	30				50						20	0.5	
Held 1897	45				15								40 acetone
Held 1909a	60								13		3.5	1.6	
Held 1909b	19				43					35	0.5	3	
Held (1933)					97							3	
Helly 1903	37				70					30	5	5	
Hermann 1889	99		20	37.5								0.1	
Hertwig 1879	85		1.2									1	
Hertwig 1885	50		15					50					
Hertwig 1892	42				30			15				0.2	
Hertwig 1905	77		1		17						10	3	5 HNO_3
Hill 1910			50		50								
Hirschler 1918			10						30				
Hoehl 1896	60				25							2	
Hoffmann 1908	25			25								15	10 trichloroacetic acid
Hofker 1921		80										10	
Hornell 1900	10	100							20		10		
Hoyer 1899	50				21								
Huber (1943)		57			43								1.5 trichloroacetic acid
Hultgren and Anderson (1910)	65									35	4		
Ingelby 1925			5								25	5	
dell'Isola 1895	25						75		67		15		2 KBr

BASAL SOLUTIONS

REFERENCE	H_2O	95% alc.	1. 2% OsO_4	2. 1% H_2PtCl_6	3. 7% $HgCl_2$	4. 1% $CuSO_4$	5. Sat. sol. picric acid	6. 2% CrO_3	7. 7.5% $K_2Cr_2O_7$	8. sol. 7 +3% Na_2SO_4	9. 40% formaldehyde	10. acetic acid	Other additions
"J.A." 1937	35				35						10	0.1	
Jäger (1928)	56	34			10							5	
Johnson 1895	55		10	7.5				30	23			1	
Jolly 1907	45		15										
Jones (1915)	30	68											
Joseph 1918	72								28		2	10	
Kahlden and Laurent 1896	84						8.5				20		
Kahle 1908	60	26									12		
Kaiser 1891	50				47							2	
Karpenchenko 1924	74		40					20				3	
Kaufman 1929	17		10					38			3	3	
Kerschner 1908	80										5		20 formic acid
King (1910)	77.5							12.5					
Klein 1878	60	35					100	5.5				10	
Kleinenberg 1879													2 H_2SO_4
Kohn 1907	51				18				31			5	
Kolmer 1912	17				17				52		4	10	
Kolmer (1938)	59								24		3.6	9.2	0.75 $UO(NO_3)_2$,6 H_2O, 5 trichloro-acetic acid
Kolossow 1897	35		12.5						53				
Kolossow 1898	75		25										2.5 $UO_2(NO_3)_2$,6 H_2O
Kolster (1910)	40				99							1	0.5 $NaCl$
Kopsch 1896a	53								40		20		
Kopsch 1896b	50				50				47				
Kostanecki and Siedlecki 1896													2.8 HNO_3
Krueger 1911										25	10	4.4	
Kultschitzky 1897	18	50			63				27				
Lachi 1895	35				5				40		25	1	

BASAL SOLUTIONS

REFERENCE	H_2O	95% alc.	1 — 2% OsO_4	2 — 1% H_2PtCl_6	3 — 7% $HgCl_2$	4 — 1% $CuSO_4$	5 — Sat. sol. picric acid	6 — 2% CrO_3	7 — 7.5% $K_2Cr_2O_7$	8 — sol. 7 +3% Na_2SO_4	9 — 40% formaldehyde	10 — acetic acid	Other additions
LaCour 1929	52		10					30	8			0.3	0.6 urea
LaCour 1931	63		12					20	5			0.6	0.04 saponin
Laguesse 1901	34		60					16				0.25	
Laguesse (1933)	36		32					32				0.4	
Laidlaw (1936)	38				57						5	5	
Landsteiner 1903	78									17			
Lane (1937)					70				30			7	
Lang 1878					100								8 NaCl
Langendorf (1910)	35		10					25				30	
Langeron 1942	20				77							3	
Lapp (1910)	30	50			50				67			2	
Lavdowsky 1893	60				2							1	
Lavdowsky 1894a		27		2.5								2	
Lavdowsky 1894b	100							5			10	5	
Ladvowsky 1894c	80	10						10				0.5	
Lehrmitte and Guccione 1909	80		2	18								0.2	
Lenhossék 1897a		25			75							5	
Lenhossék 1897b	40			25	50		50						
Lenhossék 1898	50				36							5	
Lenhossék 1899	50				50								4.5 NaCl / 1 KI
Lenoir 1926	50							50					
Levi 1918	82		10		35			8	15		1		
Levitsky 1910	61		19					20			10	0.83	
Lillie (1929)							85				10		
Lillie 1944a	69										10	4.5	5 formic acid
Lillie 1948	17							17	18		9	17	
Lo Bianco 1890a	17				65								
Lo Bianco 1890b	25				66								
Lo Bianco 1890c	40										5		
Lo Bianco 1890d	25	35					50	25					
Lo Bianco 1890e	25							25					45 sea water
Lo Bianco 1890f	25		2				50	25	75				2 H_2SO_4

BASAL SOLUTIONS

REFERENCE	H₂O	95% alc.	1 2% OsO₄	2 1% H₂PtCl₆	3 7% HgCl₂	4 1% CuSO₄	5 Sat. sol. picric acid	6 2% CrO₃	7 7.5% K₂Cr₂O₇	8 sol. 7 +3% Na₂SO₄	9 40% formaldehyde	10 acetic acid	Other additions
Lo Bianco 1890g	50		1					50					
Lo Bianco 1890h	50							50					
Lo Bianco 1890i	5							5				5	
Long and Mark 1912	35				28							100	
Löwenthal 1893	63		10						27			10	
Löwit 1887	99				1.2				27				2.4 Na₂SO₄, 10 H₂O, 1 NaCl
Lukö 1910	20	80									10	5	
Mann 1894a	50		50										0.75 NaCl
Mann 1894b	25		25		50								0.9 NaCl
Marchi 1886	63		17.5							22			
Marchoux and Simond 1906a			28	28				43				6	
Marchoux and Simond 1906b			14	14	50			22				3	
Marchoux 1910	29							16.5			48	3	
Marina 1897		95						5			5		
Marrassini (1910)	50				14				37				
Masson (1947)	45		10				75			35	25		3 chrome alum
Maximow 1909	90										10		2 HNO₃
McClung and Allen 1929	6										7.5		2 Na₂SO₄.10 H₂O
Meeker and Cook 1928	80				57				27		10	10	
Merkel 1870	50		10	10				10					
Mettler 1932a	60												
Mettler 1932b	58								40		50		
Mettler 1932c			5						32				
Meves and Duesberg 1908a	70		3					20				2.5	
Meves and Duesberg 1908b	90			11								1.5	
Meves 1910	65		20				20	18				5	
Michaelis (1948)	59				21				6.5		8	1.2	
Milovidov 1928	61							25				25	
Mingazzini 1893		25			50								

BASAL SOLUTIONS

REFERENCE	H_2O	95% alc.	1 2% OsO_4	2 1% H_2PtCl_6	3 7% $HgCl_2$	4 1% $CuSO_4$	5 Sat. sol. picric acid	6 2% CrO_3	7 7.5% $K_2Cr_2O_7$	8 sol. 7 +3% Na_2SO_4	9 40% formaldehyde	10 acetic acid	Other additions
Mislawsky 1913	46		2.5						32		20	3	
Müller 1899	48								32		20		
Mottier 1897	40		15									5	
Müche 1908	50							40				2.5	
Müller 1859	65							50	8	35	80		
Müller 1899.	12	80									10		
Murray 1919a	60									30			
Murray 1919b	65									35			
Murray 1919c		100											
Nakamura 1928	13	20						15	27				
Nassanow 1923	20	30						40	25		20		
Navashin 1912	35							46			7	5	
Neméc (1937)	47		20					30					6.4 HNO_3
Newton and Darlington 1919	47		25									5	
Nicholas 1891	70		20		50							5	
Niessing 1895	25			2.5	30							3	
Novak 1901	42							15				3	
Nowack 1902	45				23			5				23	
Orr 1900	20	80									10	0.2	
von Orth 1896	60									30	10		
Oxner 1905a	47	10							23			5	
Oxner 1905b	47	10							23				5 formic acid
Oxner (1910)					97								
von Pacaut 1906		50		4.5	50		50	0.15				3	
Pappenheim 1896		98			50								
Parker and Floyd 1895	80										2		6 KI, 4 urea; 4 HNO_3
Penfield 1930	55	30						10			20		6.4 HNO_3
Perényi 1882	37	40						15					
Perényi 1888	45	30					20						0.05 $AgNO_3$
Perriraz 1905	45		4.8						42				
Pfeiffer and Jarisch 1919	48										10		
Pfuhl							34				20	5	
Pianese 1899a	45	20		30	34			4					0.2 formic acid; 0.8 $CoCl_2.6\,H_2O$
Pianese 1899b	80	20		30									0.2 formic acid

BASAL SOLUTIONS

REFERENCE	H_2O	95% alc.	1 — 2% OsO_4	2 — 1% H_2PtCl_6	3 — 7% $HgCl_2$	4 — 1% $CuSO_4$	5 — Sat. sol. picric acid	6 — 2% CrO_3	7 — 7.5% $K_2Cr_2O_7$	8 — sol. 7 $+3\%$ Na_2SO_4	9 — 40% formaldehyde	10 — acetic acid	Other additions
Pietschmann 1905		95			5								
Podhradszky 1934	85		20								10		
Podwyssozki 1886	30	25						40				5	5 $HgCl_2$
Pritchard 1873	25	25						50				2	
Rabl 1884	85							15					0.1 formic acid
Rabl 1894a	50				25		25						
Rabl 1894b	62.5			12.5	25								
vom Rath 1895a			10	40			50					1.6	
vom Rath 1895b			10		45		45					1	
vom Rath 1895c			6				100					1	
Rawitz 1896a	20						20	40					0.8 HNO_3
Rawitz 1896b	95		0.5									0.04	(sea water may be used)
Rawitz (1905)			5				90						5.6 HNO_3
Régaud 1910a	50								30		20		
Régaud 1910b	60								40				
del Río-Hortega 1925	90										10		1.5 $UO_2(NO_3)_2.$ 6 H_2O
del Río-Hortega 1928	10								80		10		6 chloral hydrate
del Río-Hortega 1929	66								24		10		0.1 formic acid
Rohl (1910)	85							15					2 trichloroacetic acid; 0.6 NaCl
Romeis 1918a	20				70						10		
Romeis 1918b	61				34						24		1.6 trichloroacetic acid
Romeis 1948a	43	45									10	2	
Romeis 1948b	45								40		10	5	
Roskin 1946a	6						65				24	5	
Roskin 1946b	11						65				24		0.24 trichloroacetic acid
Roskin 1946c	14	66										6	
Roskin 1946d	22								12				
Röthig 1900		10			90								

BASAL SOLUTIONS

REFERENCE	H_2O	95% alc.	1 2% OsO_4	2 1% H_2PtCl_6	3 7% $HgCl_2$	4 1% $CuSO_4$	5 Sat. sol. picric acid	6 2% CrO_3	7 7.5% $K_2Cr_2O_7$	8 sol. 7 +3% Na_2SO_4	9 40% formaldehyde	10 acetic acid	Other additions
Röthig 1904	41				31			15			3	10	
Ruffini 1905	60				35								6.5 formic acid
Ruffini 1927	36				17			36	6.5			5	
Ruge (1942)	97										2	1	
Russel 1931	63								33		4		
Rutherford (1878)	45							50	5				
Saling 1906	28	40			28								4 HNO_3
Salkind 1917	15				57						10		14 chloral hydrate
Sánchez (1933)	63								27				
Sansom (1928)	17								27			5	30 chloroform
Schaffer 1908	15	65						15			32	0.7	
Schaffer 1918	85	51									35		
Schaffner 1906		50			35								
Schaudinn 1893		65			65								
Schaudinn 1900		35											
Scheuring 1913	37	48									48	4	
Schmorl 1928a	57				63								0.5 $NaCl$
Schmorl 1928b	16				43							0.6	
Schmorl 1928c	90				64				4.5		20		0.5 $NaCl$
Schreiber 1898a	75								24		6.5		
Schreiber 1898b	60										1.5		
Schridder (1928a)	65									30	10		
Schridder (1928)b							85			35			
Schridder (1928)c	10						87						
Schuberg 1903	5		100									3	2 H_2SO_4
Schuberg (1920)	60		7.5				4						
Schultze 1904a	45		5						40				
Schultze 1904b	90		25						30				
Schwarz 1888	44		10									1	
Severinghaus 1932	88		24					12	20			1.2	
Showalter 1926	87.5		1.2					20					
Simons 1906								12.5				0.1	
Smirnow 1895	53		7.5						50				

BASAL SOLUTIONS

REFERENCE	H_2O	95% alc.	(1) 2% OsO_4	(2) 1% H_2PtCl_6	(3) 7% $HgCl_2$	(4) 1% $CuSO_4$	(5) Sat. sol. picric acid	(6) 2% CrO_3	(7) 7.5% $K_2Cr_2O_7$	(8) sol. 7 +3% Na_2SO_4	(9) 40% formaldehyde	(10) acetic acid	Other additions
Smith 1912	88								14		5	2.5	
Smith 1930a	90										10		
Smith 1930b	47		16						53			0.6	
Smith 1935a			16					25	3.2			0.4	0.6 saponin
Smith 1935b			16					22	8.5			0.6	0.04 saponin
Spuler 1892			2.5				100						
Spuler 1910a	45				45						10	1	
Spuler 1910b					35		35				35		
Spuler 1910c	47			17	30							1.5	
Stieve (1946)	59				17						20	4	
Stieve (1948)a	10									23	20	4	
Stieve (1948)b	9				66		85				6		0.3 trichloroacetic acid
Stilling 1895	58								32		10		
Stowell 1884	28	60						2.5				3	
Strauss 1909		97											
van der Stricht 1895	40		20	40									
Strong 1895a	50								47		3.5		
Strong 1895b	25								40		35		
Swank and Davenport 1934a	90										10		
Swank and Davenport 1934b	73		16.5									1	0.25 $KClO_3$
Swank and Davenport 1934c	90												
Swank and Davenport 1934d	67		17							14		2	
Swank and Davenport 1935	93		6.25								12	1	0.6 $KClO_3$
Sypkens 1904	40		20					36				4	
Szepsenwol 1935	88										8		
Szmonowicz 1896			14		84								4 formic acid
Szüts 1913	20			12.5	43						25		

BASAL SOLUTIONS

REFERENCE	H_2O	95% alc.	1 — 2% OsO_4	2 — 1% H_2PtCl_6	3 — 7% $HgCl_2$	4 — 1% $CuSO_4$	5 — Sat. sol. picric acid	6 — 2% CrO_3	7 — 7.5% $K_2Cr_2O_7$	8 — sol. 7 +3% Na_2SO_4	9 — 40% formaldehyde	10 — acetic acid	Other additions
Takahashi 1908	72		25					3.75					0.02 HCl
Taylor 1924	66		12	20								1.6	1.2 maltose
Tellyesniczky 1898a					50							1	
Tellyesnickzy 1898b	60		16				50					5	
Timofecheff (1933)	42		25						40	42			
Tschassownikow (1910)					75							2.5	
Vassale and Donaggi 1895	53		12.5	2.5									5 acetaldehyde
Veratti (1900)	60		50										
Viallane 1883a	50												
Viallane 1883b	65						14						35 formic acid
Vialleton 1887	80							10	6.5			10	1 H_2SO_4
Virchow (1897)	80				45			15					
Vlakovic (1926)		85			46								
Völker (1910)							45					5	
Wenrich and Geiman 1933	32	20							32			2	
Whitehead 1932	56	77.5									12		
Wilhelmi 1909	52		8						40		7.5		2.4 HNO_3
Windle 1926	45							38					
Winge 1930	36		20	40							10	7.5	4 trichloroacetic acid
Winiwarter (1930)	75						25						0.5 H_2SO_4
Wistinghausen 1891	20								67				
Wittmaack (1910)	65								33		10	3	
Wlassow 1894	100		2		2.5				1				0.8 NaCl
Wlassow (1910)	10				50								3 NaCl
Woltereck (1910)		40										10	
Worcester (1929)	78							19			9	10	81 $HgCl_2$
Yamanouchi 1908			3.8									0.1	0.1 chloroform
Zacharias 1887		80	0.5		70					30		20	
Zacharias 1888		80	0.75		17							20	
Zenker 1894	3											5	
Zieglwallner 1911		50	20									10	
Zietschmann 1903	62		16							22			
Zweibaum 1933	60		6					20	14				

19

Accessory Fixative Formulas

Decimal Divisions Used in Chapter

AF 00 General Observations and Classification of Formulas

The formulas included in this chapter are those which are used either immediately before, or immediately after, fixation, and which would therefore seem to warrant the title *Accessory fixative solutions*. The formulas are arranged according to the use for which they are intended, and therefore fall logically into the classification indicated above.

AF 10 Fixative Removers

Most fixatives may be removed from tissues by the simple process of washing either in alcohol or in water. The principal exceptions to this statement are fixatives containing picric acid or mercuric chloride. Much of the yellow picric stain cannot be removed, since it results from the combination of picric acid with various of the proteins present. Some of these picric compounds are soluble in water, and if picric material be washed for a long period, many of the cells will be found to be heavily vacuolated. This may be required if studies of the nucleus only are being

254

made and, in this case, even more of the cytoplasm can be dissolved by washing in weakly alkaline solutions. Lithium carbonate solutions are often suggested, though they are no more effective than sodium carbonate solutions of the same molar concentration. The three special formulas given below (AF 11.1) for the removal of picric from material have specific functions indicated under each.

The removal of fixatives which contain mercuric chloride is a far more difficult and vital matter. It has long been known that sections or wholemounts prepared from mercuric-fixed materials tend to develop needlelike crystals, or black granules, presumably of mercuric chloride. The formation of these crystals cannot always be prevented, even by prolonged washing in water or alcohol, and it has become customary to treat sections with a solution of iodine in potassium iodide, on the ground that the mercuric iodide so formed will itself form a complex with the excess potassium iodide and thus be removed. The exact composition of the solution employed is not a matter of any great importance, and the several formulas given below (AF 12.1) may be diluted or increased in strength at the option of the worker. The last division of fixative removers (AF 13) gives two formulas for the prevention of precipitates, which occasionally occur in materials which have been fixed and stored in formaldehyde for a long period. One formula, which might more properly belong in the divisions on bleaches (AF 30), is used to remove the black material deposited by osmic acid on the outside of small specimens.

AF 11 FOR USE AFTER PICRIC MIXTURES
AF 11.1 FORMULAS

11.1 Bolcek 1930   23632, **47**:334
   FORMULA: abs. alc. 80, nitric acid 10, origanum oil 20, cedarwood oil 10
   RECOMMENDED FOR: treatment of picric-fixed materials before celloidin embedding.

11.1 Cappell *test.* **Carleton and Leach 1938**   Carleton and Leach 1938, 31
   REAGENTS REQUIRED: A. 70% alc.; B. 5% sodium thiosulfate
   METHOD: alternate sections between A and B
   RECOMMENDED FOR: removal of yellow color from mounted sections before staining.

11.1 Lenoir 1930   6630, **103**:1253
   FORMULA: water 70, 95% alc. 30, ammonium acetate 10
   RECOMMENDED FOR: removal of yellow color from picric-fixed specimens before embedding or making wholemounts.

AF 12 FOR USE AFTER MERCURIC MIXTURES
AF 12.1 FORMULAS

12.1 Gram 1884   *Gram's iodine—compl. script.*   8645, **2**:6
   FORMULA: water 5, iodine 1, potassium iodide 2, water to 300

12.1 Haug 1889   23632, **8**:11
   FORMULA: water 50, glycerol 50, ADS 12.2 Lugol (1905) 2, potassium iodide 1
   RECOMMENDED FOR: removal of mercury fixatives.

12.1 La Cour 1931   11360, **51**:123
   FORMULA: 80% alc. 100, potassium iodide 1, iodine 1
   RECOMMENDED FOR: removal of mercuric chloride fixatives.

12.1 Lugol (1905) *test.* **1905 Lee**   *Lugol's iodine—compl. script.*
                                                        Lee 1905, 62
   FORMULA: water 110, iodine 6, potassium iodide 4
   PREPARATION: Dissolve iodine and potassium iodide in 10 water. Dilute to 100.

AF 13 FOR OTHER USES

AF 13.1 Formulas

13.1 Lhotka and Ferreira 1950   20540b, **25**:27
FORMULA: water 100, chloral hydrate 20
RECOMMENDED FOR: removal of "bound" formaldehyde from tissues.

13.1 Overton 1890   23632, **7**:10
FORMULA: alc. 70% 100–250, hydrogen peroxide 10
RECOMMENDED FOR: bleaching overfixed or blackened osmic acid preparations.

13.1 Schridde 1906 *test.* **1938 Mallory**   Mallory 1938, 40
FORMULA: water 70, 95% alc. 30, ammonium hydroxide 0.5
RECOMMENDED FOR: removal of precipitates from formaldehyde-fixed tissues before
embedding.

13.1 Verocay 1908   23681, **19**:769
FORMULA: water 80, 96% alc. 20, potassium hydroxide 0.01
RECOMMENDED FOR: prevention of precipitate in formaldehyde-fixed tissues before
embedding.

AF 20 Decalcifying Fluids and Methods for Softening Chitin

These two groups of methods have been thrown together for the reason that they solve
essentially the same problem, that is, to soften material normally so hard that it cannot be
sectioned. The removal of calcium has for many years been achieved principally with acids
in which the calcium carbonate and phosphate are soluble. These acids naturally lead to a
gross hydrolysis of the tissues, unless this hydrolysis is restrained by the addition of some
other agent. The agents used to restrain swelling are very varied and will be noticed as a
part of all the formulas given under the heading AF 21.1. Fairly recently attempts have been
made to remove the calcium in solutions that are either neutral or very slightly alkaline.
In 1938 Wilkes (14900, **142**:958) proposed the removal of the calcium through a base
exchange similar to that used in the softening of water, and employed for this purpose a
30% solution of sodium hexametaphosphate. Dotti, Paparo, and Clarke 1951 (*Tech. Bull.*,
21:475) used a base exchange resin (Win—3000) in combination with 10 to 20% formic acid;
Birge and Imhoff 1952 (*Tech. Bull.*, **22**:16) use a slightly alkaline chelating agent.

The softening of chitin (AF 23.1 below) is a problem which has not yet satisfactorily been
solved. *Diaphanol* was once recommended for the purpose, but is no longer on the market,
and the preparation of its principal constituent (chlorodioxyacetic acid) is so dangerous
that it cannot be recommended in the ordinary laboratory. The technique of Jurray 1937
has given better results in the author's hands than any other, but it will only work on
certain insects, and then its reaction cannot always be forecast accurately.

21 EMPLOYING ACID MEDIA FOR DECALCIFICATION

21.1 Formulas

21.1 Andeer 1884   23730, **33**:193
FORMULA: water 100, phloroglucinol 0.01, hydrochloric acid 3

21.1 Anonymous 1946   4349, **26**:13
FORMULA: water 85, 40% formaldehyde 10, nitric acid 5

21.1 Bayerl 1885   1780, **23**:35
FORMULA: water 100, chromic acid 1.5, hydrochloric acid 0.5

21.1 Belloni 1939 *test.* **1943 Cowdry**   Cowdry 1943, 35
FORMULA: water 100, formaldehyde 6, formic acid 50

21.1 von Beust *test. circ.* **1938 Wellings**   Wellings *circ.* 1938, 230
FORMULA: water 100, 40% formaldehyde 10, formic acid 10
RECOMMENDED FOR: embryonic teeth.

21.1 "Bielschowsky-Agduhr"   *see* ADS 21.1 Cajal 1933a (note)

21.1 Bodecker 1937   11147, **16**:143
FORMULA: methanol 100, celloidin 6, nitric acid 4.5
RECOMMENDED FOR: enamel of teeth.

21.1 Brain 1950   11360, **70**:313
FORMULA: water 100, formic acid 5, calcium phosphate 2
RECOMMENDED FOR: teeth (*see* E 24.1 Brain 1950, Chapter 27).

21.1 Busch 1877a   1780, **14**:481
FORMULA: water 100, chromic acid 2, hydrochloric acid 3

21.1 Busch 1877b   1780, **14**:481
REAGENTS REQUIRED: *A.* water 100, chromic acid 0.1, potassium dichromate 1; *B.* water
100, potassium dichromate 1, nitric acid 2
METHOD: [fixed tissues] → *A*, several days → *B*, till decalcified → rinse → 95% alc.

21.1 Cajal 1933a   Cajal and de Castro 1933, 39
REAGENTS REQUIRED: *A.* 20% formaldehyde; *B.* 4% nitric acid; *C.* 80% pyridine
METHOD: [fresh tissue] → *A*, 1–3 days → *B*, till decalcified → wash, 24 hrs. running
water → *C*, 24 hrs. → 95% alc., till pyridine removed.
NOTE: The method attributed, without reference, to "**Bielschowsky-Agduhr**" by Cajal
1933, 40 differs from the above only in the omission of *C*.

21.1 Cajal 1933b   Cajal and de Castro 1933, 40
FORMULA: water 86, 40% formaldehyde 11, nitric acid 3

21.1 Carleton and Leach 1938   Carleton and Leach 1938, 211
REAGENTS REQUIRED: *A.* water 80, nitric acid 10, 40% formaldehyde 10; *B.* 5% sodium
sulfate
METHOD: [fresh or fixed bones] → *A*, till decalcified → *B*, till free from acid → [sections]

21.1 de Castro 1925a   21344, **23**:427
FORMULA: water 65, alc. 35, chloral hydrate 5, nitric acid 3

21.1 de Castro 1925b   21344, **23**:427
FORMULA: water 40, 95% alc. 60, urethan 2, nitric acid 3

21.1 de Castro 1925c   21344, **23**:427
FORMULA: water 40, 95% alc. 60, aprobarbital 2, phenobarbital 2, nitric acid 4
NOTE: These solutions are primarily intended for materials subsequently to be metal
stained. The author has translated the hypnotics and sedatives from European
proprietary trade names to the terms preferred in contemporary American usage.

21.1 de Castro 1926   21344, **23**:427
FORMULA: water 50, 95% alc. 50, chloral hydrate 2.5, nitric acid 3.4
RECOMMENDED FOR: use before silver staining of nerves in bone or teeth.
NOTE: 1 urethan or 0.6 diethylamine barbiturate may be substituted for chloral hydrate,
in which case the alcohol should be increased to 60%.

21.1 Crétin 1925   Le Mans, 48
FORMULA: water 90, potassium iodide 22.5, iodine 25, trichloroacetic acid 10
RECOMMENDED FOR: decalcification after F 3500.1000 Crétin 1925 fixation.

21.1 David 1935   19938, **82**:179
REAGENTS REQUIRED: *A.* 10% nitric acid; *B.* 5% sodium sulfate
METHOD: [fresh bone] → *A*, till decalcified → *B*, 24 hrs. → running water, 24 hrs.

21.1 von Ebner *test.* **1891a Haug**   23632, **8**:3
FORMULA: water 100, nitric acid 2, sodium chloride 18
NOTE: Add 1 nitric acid daily until decalcification complete.

21.1 von Ebner *test.* **1891b Haug**   23632, **8**:7
FORMULA: water 15, 95% alc. 85, hydrochloric acid 0.4, sodium chloride 0.4

21.1 Evans and Krajian 1930　　　　　　　　　1789a, **10**:477
FORMULA: water 75, sodium citrate 10, formic acid 25

21.1 Ferreri *test.* **1895 Rawitz**　　　　　　　　Rawitz 1895, 28
FORMULA: water 100, nitric acid 10, phloroglucinol 1

21.1 Fieandt and Sazen 1936　　　　　　　23632, **53**:125
REAGENTS REQUIRED: *A.* water 90, 40% formaldehyde 10, sulfuric acid 5,; *B.* 4% formal-
dehyde; *C.* water 90, 40% formaldehyde 10, lithium sulfate 5; *D.* 5% lithium sulfate
METHOD [chrome-fixed material] → *A*, 4–6 wks. → *B*, 1 wk. → *C*, 1 wk. → *D*, 1 wk. →
wash
RECOMMENDED FOR: inner ear.

21.1 Fischer *test. circ.* **1938a Wellings**　　　　Wellings *circ.* 1938, 42
FORMULA: water 225, 40% formaldehyde 12.5, trichloroacetic acid 2.5, sodium chloride
25
RECOMMENDED FOR: teeth.

21.1 Fischer *test. circ.* **1938b Wellings**　　　　Wellings *circ.* 1938, 43
FORMULA: water 67, formic acid 33, 40% formaldehyde 5
RECOMMENDED FOR: teeth.

21.1 Gairns 1944　　　　　　　　　20540b, **19**:127
REAGENTS REQUIRED: *A.* 10% nitric acid; *B.* 2% potassium alum; *C.* 5% sodium
bicarbonate
METHOD: [formol-fixed teeth and bones] → 70% alc. 1 day → *A*, changed alternate days,
till decalcified → rinse → *B*, 12 hrs. → rinse → *C*, 24 hrs. → [paraffin sections]

21.1 Gage *test.* **1937 Gatenby and Painter** *cit.* **Fish**　　　Gatenby and Painter 1937, 252
FORMULA: water 100, ammonium alum 2.5, nitric acid 5

21.1 de Galantha 1937　　　　　　　　4349, **17**:72
FORMULA: water 25, nitric acid 10, 95% alc. 100, sat. sol. picric acid 5, olive oil 10

21.1 Gomori 1933　　*see* MS 33.1 Gomori 1933, sol. D.

21.1 Gooding and Stewart *test.* **1938 Carleton and Leach**
　　　　　　　　　　　　　　　Carleton and Leach 1938, 211
FORMULA: water 75, formic acid 25, 40% formaldehyde 5

21.1 Haug 1891a　　　　　　　　　23632, **8**:3
FORMULA: water 100, chromic acid 1, hydrochloric acid 1

21.1 Haug 1891b　　　　　　　　　23632, **8**:3
FORMULA: water 100, osmic acid 0.1, chromic acid 0.25

21.1 Haug 1891c　　　　　　　　　23632, **8**:7
FORMULA: water 30, 96% alc. 70, hydrochloric acid 3, sodium chloride 0.5

21.1 Haug 1891d　　　　　　　　　23632, **8**:7
FORMULA: water 30, 96% alc. 70, nitric acid 3, sodium nitrate 0.25

21.1 Haug 1891e　　(*Haug's slow decalcifier—compl. script.*)
　　　　　　　　　　　　　　　23681, **2**:193
STOCK SOLUTION: nitric acid 20, phlorogucinol 2, water 80
PREPARATION OF STOCK: Dissolve phloroglucinol in warm (*not* hot) acid and dilute to 100.
WORKING SOLUTION: water 100, stock solution 20

21.1 Haug 1891f　　(*Haug's rapid decalcifier—compl. script.*)
　　　　　　　　　　　　　　　23632, **8**:11
FORMULA: water 30, 95% alc. 70, phlorogulcinol 1, nitric acid 5
PREPARATION: Dissolve phloroglucinol in warm (*not hot*) acid. Cool, add water and
alcohol.

21.1 Heidenhain *test.* **1933 Cajal and de Castro**　*see* F 3000.0012 Heidenhain 1909

21.1 Hennings 1900   *see* F 3560.0040 Hennings 1900

21.1 Hopewell-Smith *test. circ.* **1938 Wellings**   Wellings *circ.* 1938, 42
REAGENTS REQUIRED: *A.* 10% hydrochloric acid; *B.* nitric acid; *C.* sat. sol. lithium
carbonate
METHOD: [fixed teeth varnished with celloidon] → 100 *A*, 2 days → add 1.5 *B*, leave
2 days → add further 1.5 *B*, leave 2 days → wash → *C*, 20 mins.
NOTE: Wellings (*loc. cit.*) states that **Choquet** recommends adding 1% palladium chloride to *A*.

21.1 Jenkin 1926   11431, **24**:166
FORMULA: water 10, 95% alc. 73, acetic acid 3, hydrochloric acid, 4, chloroform 10
NOTE: This is also a fixing and dehydrating agent.

21.1 Katz *test.* **1895a Rawitz**   Rawitz 1895, 28
FORMULA: water 100, chromic acid 0.4, nitric acid 5

21.1 Katz *test.* **1895b Rawitz**   Rawitz 1895, 28
FORMULA: water 100, chromic acid 0.4, nitric acid 10, palladium chloride 0.01

21.1 Kingsbury and Johannsen 1927   ·   Kingsbury and Johannsen 1927, 78
FORMULA: water 100, potassium alum 3.5, nitric acid 5

21.1 Kristensen 1948   20540b, **23**:151
FORMULA: water 82, formic acid 18, sodium formate 3.5

21.1 Langeron 1942   Langeron 1942, 357
REAGENTS REQUIRED: *A.* water 45, 40% formaldehyde 5, formic acid 50; *B.* 4% formaldehyde
METHOD: [formaldehyde-fixed objects] → *A*, till decalcified → *B*, thorough wash

21.1 Marsh 1878   Marsh 1878, 67
FORMULA: water 100, chromic acid 1, nitric acid 0.75

21.1 McNamara, Murphy, and Gore 1940   11284, **25**:874
FORMULA: water 80, 95% alc. 10, trichloroacetic acid 6, nitric acid 1, 40% formaldehyde
8, mercuric chloride 2

21.1 Ralston and Wells 1939   591b, **3**:72
FORMULA: water 100, potassium dichromate 2, mercuric chloride 5, sodium sulfate 1,
acetic acid 10
NOTE: This is F 3700.0010 Zenker 1894 with the acetic acid content doubled.

21.1 Richman, Gelfand, and Hill 1947   1887a, **44**:92
FORMULA: water 100, nitric acid 8, formic acid 10
METHOD: The object is placed in a perforated porcelain capsule suspended in the liquid.
One platinum electrode is inserted in the object, the other in the free liquid. An EMF
of +6 volts is applied to the object. At 30°C. large objects are completely decalcified
in 2–4 hrs.

21.1 Rosbach and Leavitt 1952   *Tech. Bull.*, **22**:198
FORMULA: water 95, trifluoroacetic acid 5
NOTE: This is said to give complete decalcification of teeth in 5 or 6 days without loss of
cytological detail.

21.1 Rousseau 1897   23632, **14**:207
FORMULA: water 20, 96% alc. 80, nitric acid 20
NOTE: It is recommended that the object be embedded in celloidin before decalcification.

21.1 Schaffer 1903   23632, **19**:460
REAGENTS REQUIRED: *A.* 3% nitric acid; *B.* 5% sodium sulfate
METHOD: [fixed material, embedded in celloidin] → water → *A*, till decalcified → wash
→ *B*, 24 hrs. → *B*, fresh solution, 24 hrs. → wash

21.1 Schmorl 1928a   Schmorl 1928, 44
FORMULA: water 90, 40% formaldehyde 10, nitric acid 10

21.1 Schmorl 1928b   Schmorl 1928, 48
FORMULA: water 100, potassium dichromate 2, sodium sulfate 1, nitric acid 0.3

21.1 Schridde 1910 *test.* **1937 Gatenby and Painter**   Gatenby and Painter 1937, 252
FORMULA: water 90, 40% formaldehyde 10, nitric acid 10

21.1 Seiler 1881   Seiler 1881, 43
FORMULA: water 100, chromic acid 0.5, nitric acid 1
NOTE: **Gatenby and Cowdry 1937,** 253, attribute to "Seiler" (without reference) a fluid
containing half the quantity of chromic and three times the quantity of nitric.

21.1 Tello 1932 *test.* **1933 Cajal and de Castro**   Cajal and de Castro 1933, 369
FORMULA: water 95, nitric acid 5, chloral hydrate 15

21.1 Thoma 1891   23632, **8**:191
REAGENTS REQUIRED: *A.* 1% nitric acid in 95% alc. *B.* 95% alc. rendered milky with
chalk
METHOD: [fixed tissues] → *A*, changed daily till decalcified → *B*, changed daily, till
acid-free

21.1 Waldeyer *test.* **1891 Haug**   23632, **8**:4
REAGENTS REQUIRED: *A.* 0.17% chromic acid; *B.* 0.25% chromic acid; *C.* 0.5% chromic
acid; *D.* water 100, chromic acid 0.5, nitric acid 2
METHOD: [fresh tissue] → *A*, 2 days → *B*, 2 days → *C*, 4 days → *C*, till decalcified

21.1 Welling *circ.* **1938**   Welling *circ.* 1938, 37
REAGENTS REQUIRED: *A.* water 100, potassium dichromate 1, chromic acid 0.1; *B.* water
100, chromic acid 0.1, nitric acid 2
METHOD: [embryos] → *A*, frequently charged, several wks. → *B*, frequently changed,
till decalcified

21.1 Wilson 1934   11431, **39**:531
REAGENTS REQUIRED: *A.* 4% formaldehyde in 0.9% sodium chloride; *B.* ether 50, abs.
alc. 50; *C.* ether; *D.* 20% nitric acid; *E.* sat. aq. sol. lithium carbonate
METHOD: [tissue blocks] → *A*, 2–3 days → thorough wash abs. alc. via graded alc. series
→ *B*, 1 hr. → *C*, 2 changes, 1 hr. each → *B*, 1 hr. → water, via graded alc. series → *D*,
in vacuo, till effervescence ceases (20 mins.–3 hrs.) → *E*, large volume, *in vacuo*, till
effervescence ceases (few mins.) → wash → [paraffin sections]

AF 22 EMPLOYING ALKALINE OR NEUTRAL MEDIA
FOR DECALCIFICATION

22.1 Birge and Imhoff 1952   *Tech. Bull.*, **22**:16
FORMULA: ethylene diamine tetraacetic acid, tetrasodium 10, water 100
NOTE: This salt which is *Versene*, and its close relatives *Calsol*, *Versenate*, and *Sequestrene*,
chelate with metal ions to form nonionized compounds. The decalcifying action is
slow, but is stated by the authors to have no action on the staining quality of the
tissues.

22.1 Kramer and Shipley *test.* **1929 Shipley**   McClung 1929, 260
FORMULA: water 70, citric acid 25, magnesium oxide 1.3, ammonia 30, hydrochloric acid
q.s. for pH 7.5
PREPARATION: Dissolve the citric acid with heat in 30 hot water, add the magnesium
oxide and stir to solution. Cool, add ammonia, dilute to 100, leave 24 hours and filter.
Adjust to pH 7.5 with hydrochloric acid.

22.1 White 1923   11431, **26**:425
FORMULA: adjust a 6% solution of acetic acid to pH 7.5–8 with ammonia

AF 23 METHODS FOR SOFTENING CHITIN

23.1 FORMULAS

23.1 Cox *test.* **1930 Eltringham**   Eltringham 1930, 93
REAGENTS REQUIRED: *A.* 10% potassium hydroxide; *B.* 33% acetic acid
METHOD: [fixed insects] → *A*, 24 hrs. → wash, 6 hrs. → *B*, 1 day → wash, 6 hrs. → paraffin, via usual reagents
NOTE: **Eltringham** (*loc. cit.*) finds "even the elytra of small beetles . . . sufficiently softened for sectioning in 58° paraffin."

23.1 Eltringham 1930a   Eltringham 1930, 94
REAGENTS REQUIRED: A 6% sodium hypochlorite; *B.* F 5000.0040 Eltringham 1930
METHOD: [fixed insects] → water → *A*, 36 hrs., 60°C. → wash, 4 hrs. → *B*, 6 days, 60°C. → 70% alc., boil 1 min. → 70% alc., 24 hrs. → paraffin, via cedar oil

23.1 Eltringham 1930b   Eltringham 1930, 95
REAGENTS REQUIRED: *A.* 6% sodium hypochlorite; *B.* F 5000.0050 Kleinenberg 1879
METHOD: [alc. fixed insects] → *A*, 24 hrs., 60°C. → wash → *B*, boil, 1 min. → *B*, 60°C., 4 days → 70% alc. boil → paraffin, via cedar oil

23.1 Eltringham 1930c   Eltringham 1930, 95
REAGENTS REQUIRED: *A.* F5000.0050 Kleinenberg 1879
METHOD: [living insects] → *A*, boil 10 mins. → *A*, 6 days, 60°C. → 70% alc., boil → paraffin, via cedar oil

23.1 Henking 1891   23632, **8**:156
FORMULA: water 30, 95% alc. 70, hydrochloric acid 0.2, pepsin 0.1
NOTE: This is intended to soften fixed and stained insect eggs before sectioning.

23.1 Hennings 1900   *see* F 3560.0040 Hennings 1900

23.1 Kingsbury and Johannsen 1927   *see* F 3600.0040 Kingsbury and Johannsen 1927

23.1 Jurray 1937   11360, **57**:15
FORMULA: chloral hydrate 50, phenol 50
METHOD: [insects fixed in F 3000.0010 Carnoy and Lebrun 1887] → mixture, 12–24 hrs. → paraffin, via chloroform

23.1 Roonwall 1935   *see* AF 23.1 Slifer and King 1933 (note)

23.1 Slifer and King 1933   19938, **78**:366
FORMULA: water 20, 95% alc. 80, phenol 4
RECOMMENDED FOR: insect eggs which are treated 24 hours between fixation and sectioning.
NOTE: **Roonwall 1935** (23833, **110**:17) prefers 1–2% phenol.

AF 30 Bleaching Agents

The formulas here given are designed to remove natural pigments, and particularly melanin, from specimens of which it is desired to make wholemounts. The classic method is that of Mayer 1880, which may be safely employed on almost any material. These methods mostly depend on the use of nascent chlorine, nascent hydrogen, or sulfur dioxide, which are liberated under conditions designed to prevent, as far as possible, damage to the specimens.

AF 31.1 FORMULAS

31.1 Alfieri *test.* **1910 Mosse** *cit.* **Mayer**   Ehrlich, Krause, *et al.* 1910, **1**:715
REAGENTS REQUIRED: *A.* 0.1% potassium permanganate; *B.* 0.3% oxalic acid
METHOD: [whole objects or sections] → *A*, till bronze → water, thorough wash → *B*, till bleached → wash

31.1 Grenacher 1885   23632, **2**:244
FORMULA: water 15, 95% alc. 45, glycerol 30, hydrochloric acid 3
NOTE: Though not technically a bleaching mixture, this was recommended by Grenacher for the removal of pigment from the eyes of arthropods.

31.1 Grynfelt and Mestrezat 1906   6630, **61**:87

FORMULA: water 55, barium chlorate 25, sulfuric acid 4.25

PREPARATION OF STOCK: Dissolve barium chlorate in 35 warm water. Cool below 30°C. Mix sulfuric acid in 20 water. Add to chlorate solution in small portions with constant agitation. Filter.

WORKING SOLUTION: 90% alc. 100, stock solution 15

31.1 Langeron 1942   Langeron 1942, 670

FORMULA: water 100, sodium perborate 17, oxalic acid 6

PREPARATION: Dissolve sodium perborate in water. Add oxalic acid to solution.

NOTE: This is equivalent to "12-vol." hydrogen peroxide.

31.1 Mayer 1880   14246, **2**:8

FORMULA: potassium chlorate 0.1, hydrochloric acid 0.1, 70% alc. 100

PREPARATION: Mix potassium chlorate and hydrochloric acid in flask. Leave till chlorine freely produced. Add alc.

31.1 Mayer 1881   14246, **2**:8

FORMULA: potassium chlorate 0.1, hydrochloric acid 0.3, 70% alc. 100

PREPARATION: Mix potassium chlorate and hydrochloric acid. Wait few moments. Add 70% alc.

31.1 Monckeberg and Bethe 1899   1780, **54**:135

FORMULA: water 100, sodium bisulfite 2, hydrochloric acid 1

31.1 Murdock 1945   4349, **25**:71

FORMULA: acetone 50, hydrogen peroxide (3%) 50, ammonia 0.06

RECOMMENDED FOR: removal of laked blood pigments in formaldehyde-fixed tissue.

31.1 Lundvall 1927   766, **62**:353

FORMULA: 95% alc. 90, 40% formaldehyde 10, oxalic acid 6

RECOMMENDED FOR: synchronous preservation and bleaching of small vertebrates in which it is intended to stain bone or cartilage. See particularly DS 21.11 Lundvall 1927.

31.1 Tomlinson and Grocott 1944   *see* DS 23.33 Tomlinson and Grocott 1944 (note)

AF 40 Macerating and Digesting Agents

These were at one time very much more widely used than they are now, for it appears to be the present custom to endeavor either to see everything in sections, or to reconstruct from sections what the structure would have looked like had it not been cut to pieces. It is a great deal simpler, in many cases, to macerate the tissues in order that individual cells may be separated. The process of maceration involves the solution, either by acid hydrolysis or enzyme hydrolysis, of the materials which attach the cells one to another. At the same time that this solution is going on, it is necessary to provide a fixative which will prevent swelling or dissociation of the cells themselves. There is naturally a rather critical time factor, and the process can only be handled properly by trial and error. It may be added that almost any fixative, if diluted with 20 or 30 times its volume of water, will in fact become a macerating agent. Even 30% alcohol, the use of which is usually attributed to Ranvier (Lee 1890, 241) will produce disassociation of many tissues.

AF 41 METHODS USING HYDROLYSIS

AF 41.1 FORMULAS FOR ACID HYDROLYZING SOLUTIONS

41.1 Apáthy 1898   23632, **10**:49

FORMULA: water 30, glycerol 30, 95% alc. 30, acetic acid 5, nitric acid 5

41.1 Becher and Demoll 1913a   Becher and Demoll 1913, 24

FORMULA: water 100, osmic acid 0.25, chloral hydrate 3

41.1 Becher and Demoll 1913b   Becher and Demoll 1913, 23

FORMULA: water 30, 95% alc. 30, glycerol 30, nitric acid 5, acetic acid 5

41.1 Drost *test.* **1895 Rawitz**   Rawitz 1895, 7
FORMULA: sea water 100, osmic acid 0.05, chromic acid 0.125, acetic acid 0.05

41.1 Felix *test.* **1942 Langeron** *cit.* **Mann**   Langeron 1942, 351
FORMULA: 30% alc. 100, salicylic acid to sat.

41.1 Freude 1879   20170, **78**:102
FORMULA: water 50, glycerol 35, hydrochloric acid 15

41.1 Gage 1892   21400a, **14**:120
FORMULA: water 75, 95% alc. 25, picric acid 1

41.1 Goodrich 1942   17510, **83**:245
FORMULA: water 100, ADS 12.2 Lugol 0.25, sodium chloride 0.9, boric acid to sat.

41.1 Haller 1887   14555, **11**:321
FORMULA: water 50, glycerol 25, acetic acid 25

41.1 Harlow 1928   3420, **85**:226
REAGENTS REQUIRED: *A.* sat. aq. sol. chlorine; *B.* 3% sodium sulfite
METHOD: [match-size pieces of wood] → boil → *A*, 2 hrs. → *B*, 80°–90°C., 15 mins. →
[repeat *A* → *B* cycle till wood fails to turn red in *B*] → wash → section or tease
RECOMMENDED FOR: separation of wood fibers.

41.1 Hertwig 1879   *see* F 1000.0010 Hertwig 1879 (note)
This is given as a macerating agent by Gatenby and Painter 1937, 246. It was intended
in the original as a fixative.

41.1 Hertwig *test.* **1895 Rawitz**   Rawitz 1895, 7
FORMULA: water 100, osmic acid 0.025, acetic acid 1

41.1 Hopkins *test.* **1895 Rawitz**   Rawitz 1895, 7
REAGENTS REQUIRED: *A.* 20% nitric acid; *B.* sat. aq. sol. potassium alum
METHOD: [fresh tissues] → *A*, till soft, → wash → *B*, till sufficiently disintegrated

41.1 Klebs *test.* **1895 Rawitz**   Rawitz 1895, 9
FORMULA: water 100, sucrose 5, sulfuric acid 5

41.1 Konigstein 1895   20170 (1895) 71
FORMULA: water 30, glycerol 30, hydrochloric acid 30

41.1 Kuhne 1862 *test.* **1895 Ranvier**   Ranvier 1895, 79
NOTE: Under this reference, also cited by Gatenby and Painter 1937, 246, a method of producing a serious explosion is described. The original, which must surely be misquoted,
is not available to the author.

41.1 Ludwig 1872 *test.* **1883 Cole**   Cole 1883, 135
FORMULA: 90% alc. 80, hydrochloric acid 20
METHOD: [vertical slices of fresh kidney] → macerant, boil with reflux, 1–3 hrs. → leave
to settle → decant → add water, leave 24 hrs. → shake → mount selected tubules.
RECOMMENDED FOR: isolation of renal tubules.

41.1 MacCallum 1900 *test.* **1905 Böhm and Davidoff**   Böhm and Davidoff 1905, 23
FORMULA: water 40, glycerol 40, nitric acid 20

41.1 Masson 1929   4349, **12**:81
FORMULA: 95% alc. 90, nitric acid 10

41.1 Mobius 1887   *see* F 1600.0010 Mobius 1887 (note)

41.1 Rogers *test.* **1927 Kingsbury and Johannsen**   Kingsbury and Johannsen 1927, 82
FORMULA: water 80, picric acid 1, acetic acid 20
RECOMMENDED FOR: disassociation of striped muscle.

AF 41.2 Formulas for Alkaline Hydrolyzing Solutions

41.2 Behrens, Kossel and Schiefferdecker 1889   Behrens, Kossel and Schieffer-
decker 1889, 156
REAGENTS REQUIRED: *A*. water 67.5, potassium hydroxide 32.5; *B*. water 50, acetic acid
50
METHOD: [fresh tissue] → *A*, on slide, till macerated → drain → *B*, dropped on slide →
DS 11.2 stain if required → M 11 or M 12 mountant.

41.2 Reinke 1892   766, **8**:582
FORMULA: water 50, glycerol 20, 95% alc. 20, lysol 10

AF 41.3 Formulas as for Neutral Hydrolyzing Solutions

41.3 Arnold 1898   1780, **52**:135
FORMULA: water 100, potassium iodide 10, iodine 0.15

41.3 Gage 1895 *test.* **1896** *ips.*   Gage 1896, 177
FORMULA: water 99.5, 40% formaldehyde 0.5, sodium chloride 0.6

41.3 Gage 1897   21400a, **19**:179
FORMULA: water 100, potassium dichromate 0.25, sodium sulfate 0.1, sodium chloride 0.9

41.3 Landois 1885 *test.* **1937 Gatenby and Painter**   Gatenby and Painter 1937, 245
REAGENTS REQUIRED: *A*. water 100, ammonium chromate 1.25, potassium phosphate
tribasic 0.5, sodium sulfate 0.6; *B*. solution *A*. 50, DS 11.26 Beale 1857 50
NOTE: Gatenby and Painter give a reference to "1780, n.v., 445" which is incorrect.

41.3 Moleshott and Borine 1872 *test.* **1875 Ranvier**   Ranvier 1875, 242
FORMULA: water 100, 95% alc. 20, sodium chloride 1

41.3 Schiefferdecker 1886   1780, **28**:305
FORMULA: water 60, glycerol 30, methanol 3
NOTE: This formula was republished by the same author in 1911 (23632, **28**:318).

41.3 Soulier 1891 *test.* **1905 Lee**   Lee 1905, 302
FORMULA: F 4000.0010 Ripart and Petit 50, 2% sodium thiocyanate 50
NOTE: Soulier is reported (*loc. cit.*) to have added thiocyanates to a large number of
fixatives.   The mixture here given is thought by Lee to be the best.

AF 42 METHODS USING ENZYME DIGESTION
AF 42.1 Formulas

42.1 Faberge 1945   20540b, **20**:1
PREPARATION: Extract stomach contents of *Helix pomatia*. Preserve with 1 drop toluene
RECOMMENDED FOR: removal of cell wall from plant tissues for smear preparation of
chromosomes. This technique is described in detail in Chapter 9.

42.1 Hoehl 1897   1739, n.v., 136
FORMULA: water 100, sodium carbonate 0.3, pancreatin 0.25

42.1 Jousset 1903   1863, **15**:289
FORMULA: water 100, glycerol 1, hydrochloric acid 1, sodium fluoride 0.3, pepsin 0.1

42.1 Kuskow 1895   1780, **30**:32
FORMULA: water 100, pepsin 0.5, oxalic acid 3

42.1 Langeron 1942   Langeron 1942, 353
FORMULA: water 100, sodium hydroxide 0.2, pancreatin 0.3, thymol to sat.
NOTE: Use at 37°C.

AF 50 Narcotizing Agents

Narcotizing agents as here given are not intended for use on animals which will subsequently recover, but are intended to leave in a relaxed condition small invertebrates and larvas which are subsequently to be fixed. It is hoped by the worker that these relaxed specimens will not contract out of their normal shape on the application of fixative. One of the best methods of narcotizing small marine invertebrates is with the aid of carbon dioxide, for many of these forms have a natural response of endeavoring to increase their surface area when they find their oxygen supply being diminished or the concentration of carbon dioxide in their environment rising. Carbon dioxide is best used for this purpose by taking one of the devices commercially sold for aerating drinks, filling it with sea water, and saturating this with carbon dioxide. In some fresh-water invertebrates heat will produce the same effect.

Many poisons have from time to time been regarded as narcotics and thus **Zebrowski 1926** (21400a, **45**:258) has recommended a 2% solution of strychnine sulfate for planaria; this same reagent was recommended for rotifers by **Pritchard 1851**, 39. Magnesium sulfate is widely used for marine coelenterates, since an excess of magnesium ions in the water apparently has the effect of inhibiting muscular contraction in these forms.

Either ether or chloroform may be used in the vapor phase by the process of exposing small invertebrates swimming under a coverslip to an atmosphere of a volatile anesthetic. This process was first recommended by **Beauchamp 1904** (5401, **29**:26) who used it for Vorticella and other stalked ciliates. In the experience of the writer cocaine, or cocaine hydrochloride, is still, in spite of the flood of synthetic substitutes, the best narcotic for general use.

AF 51.1 Formulas

51.1 Baker *test.* **1937 Gatenby and Painter**   Gatenby and Painter 1937, 10
FORMULA: water 90, 90% alc. 10, cocaine hydrochloride 0.6

51.1 Bujor 1901   1915, **10**:49
FORMULA: water 100, sodium chloride 0.9, ether 10, 40% formaldehyde 10
RECOMMENDED FOR: anesthetizing and killing cestodes before regular fixation.

51.1 Cori 1893   23632, **55**:626
FORMULA: water 90, methanol 10, chloroform 0.3, sodium chloride 0.6

51.1 Gray 1935   *Micr. Rec.* (1935) 35
REAGENTS REQUIRED: *A.* Rousselet 1895 AF 51.1; *B.* 3% hydrogen peroxide 10, water 90
METHOD: [stalked ciliate protozoa] → *A*, added drop by drop, till cilia start slowing → *B*, added drop by drop till cilia stop → fixative, instantly

51.1 Gray 1952   Gray 1952, 14
FORMULA: menthol 48, chloral hydrate 52
PREPARATION: Grind in a mortar until an oily fluid results.
METHOD: Place a few drops on the surface of water containing animals to be narcotized.

51.1 Hanley 1949   *Microscope,* **7**:156
FORMULA: water 90, ethylene glycol monoethyl ether 10, eucaine hydrochloride 0.3

51.1 Langeron 1942   Langeron 1942, 1013
FORMULA: water 50, methanol 50, cocaine hydrochloride 5
NOTE: This is called "concentrated liquid of Rousselet" by Langeron. See, however, AF 51.1 Rousselet 1895.

51.1 Lo Bianco *test.* **1937 Gatenby and Cowdry**   Gatenby and Cowdry, 1937, 11
FORMULA: sea water 40, water 10, 95% alc. 30, glycerol 20

51.1 Morrison 1948a   *Turtox News,* **26**:54
FORMULA: water 93, methanol 7, cocaine hydrochloride 0.03

51.1 Morrison 1948b   *Turtox News,* **26**:54
FORMULA: water 70, 95% alc. 7, methanol 5, hydroxylamine hydrochloride 0.1

51.1 Rousselet 1895 11479, **5**:1
FORMULA: water 90, methanol 10, cocaine hydrochloride 0.6
NOTE: *See also* AF 51.1 Langeron 1942.

51.1 Volkonsky 1933 3919, **67**:135
FORMULA: isotonic saline 100, aprobarbital 0.3, phenobarbital 0.3, chlorobutanol 0.06

51.1 Waddington *test.* **1937 Gatenby and Painter** Gatenby and Painter 1937, 11
FORMULA: water 50, sat. sol. chloroform 50, cocaine 0.5

51.1 de Waele 1934 899a, **12**:492
FORMULA: buffer pH 6 100, sodium taurocholate 1
RECOMMENDED FOR: evagination of scolices of cysticerci.

20

Formulas and Techniques for Dye Stains of General Application

DS 00 Generalities

DS 00 GENERAL OBSERVATIONS

The term *dye staining* as used in the present work applies to those methods by which objects or parts of objects are colored. It is distinguished from metal staining (Chapter 23) more by convention than by any scientific actuality, for some of the methods employed involve the application of salts of metals for the production of color, while some of the metal-staining techniques involve the deposition of colored compounds in the same manner.

The terms *dye, pigment, stain,* and *lake* have become so hopelessly confused in biological literature as almost to have lost their original meaning. Technically a stain (and the process of staining) involves only the addition of color to an otherwise colorless material. The term *dye* should be applied to those stains which remain on the material on which they are deposited and cannot subsequently be removed by normal techniques. A *pigment*, as the term is customarily used in other than biological literature, refers to a solid color matter not in a state of solution. But the use of the term *dye* for ruthenium red is widely current in biological literature even though the material itself is a finely divided suspension of an insoluble material. A *lake*, in nonbiological literature, is an insoluble compound of a dye and some other material, usually a metal, which is used to hold it in place upon the dyed material. Though still technically correctly employed with regard to the mordant staining with hematoxylin, carmine, and the like, the term should also be applied to many other methods of staining, such as the eosin-azur stains.

The necessity for staining specimens intended for microscopical examination is not nearly as great as the widespread use of the process would lead one to suppose. Many writers have stressed the undesirability of the current habit of staining every object which is to be examined under the microscope, and one cannot do better in this respect than quote the words (in the writer's translation) of Langeron 1942, 485: "Histological science has certainly not progressed in proportion to the enormous number of staining reagents which have been placed at its disposal. One cannot too often repeat that staining is not the whole of histology and that the first duty of the microtomist is not to be a dyer but to know how to study through a microscope. That is the art which the former masters possessed fundamentally and which it would be desirable to see a little better cultivated today." It would be to the great advantage of students preparing microscope slides if they were deprived of access to coloring reagents until they had made at least a hundred slides without the aid of the reagents. This is particularly true in the preparation of wholemounts, in many of which more details of structure are brought out by the varying refractive index of the organs, than they do by soaking them in red and blue solutions which tend in many instances only to obscure the finer structures. These remarks do not apply with nearly so much force to the staining of sections, though it is probable that such structures as ciliated epithelium can be better distinguished in an unstained than in a stained preparation. The true value of staining is realized when it provides either a specific coloration of an organ or cellular structure which is to be studied, or alternatively when it provides a contrast between two such structures. A lesser, and a less necessary, purpose is to render apparent through the introduction of color those very few structures, the refractive index of which so closely approximates either that of the mounting medium or of their neighboring structures as to render them indistinguishable as uncolored objects.

Contemporary opinion on the theoretical composition of materials used for staining has altered very little since the original account of Witt 1876 (2627, 9:522) who first advanced the now widely held theory that the presence of color in a chemical is conditioned by the presence of certain groups or radicals known as *chromophores*, and that materials known to contain these groups should be called *chromogene*. The power of imparting this color to other substances is given to a chromogen by the presence of an *auxochrome*. The majority of auxochromes are either alkali or acid radicals which impart the property of solubility to the materials under discussion. It is unfortunate that the partial absorption of these theories by biologists should have left them with the almost universal habit of classifying dyes either as *basic* or *acidic*, according to the nature. of the auxochrome, and left them also endeavoring theoretically to forecast the performance of such a dye on the basis of its alleged physical reaction.

There are in point of fact four main ways in which a color may be caused to remain diffused throughout or adherent to, a particular structure. The first of these, *surface adsorption*, is a physical reaction and is dependent both on the charge upon the ionized dye and upon the materials on which this dye is precipitated. It might be imagined, and has indeed been widely stated, that it is thus only necessary to know the isoelectric point of the protein involved and the pH of the dye solution to be able to secure a perfect differential absorption at all times. This is to a considerable extent true in the case of vital staining or of proteins whose nature has not been altered. In the latter instance, for example, the dried smears, used either in the staining of blood or the staining of bacteria, fulfill the requirements. In these circumstances the control of the pH of the staining solution is all that is required to secure reproducible and perfect results. As soon, however, as a fixative is employed which denatures the proteins, the problem becomes more complex; and there is no method save that of trial and error by which the desirable pH of a dye solution may be determined. This does not mean that pH should not be more widely controlled, for there is little doubt that many of the troubles of the early microtomists, who were forced to specify a particular source for a particular dye, were due to the influence on the pH of the final solution of various impurities left in the commercial product by different manufacturers.

Another physical reaction involved in the staining of tissues is the saturation of a material with a dye and the subsequent precipitation of the dye in place by the use of solvents for dehydrating in which the dye is not soluble. These methods are little used and difficult to control. Lastly, in a few cases, a definite chemical combination is entered into between the dyestuff and the tissue which is being differentially stained. A common and obvious case of this is the use of alizarin red S to stain boney structures or the calcareous plates of invertebrates. In this case colored lake ("calcium alizarinate") is formed between the bone and dye, resulting in a quite sharp differential staining after the extraction of the excess dye with alkalis in which the lake is insoluble.

It is difficult to maintain today the old distinction between *direct* and *indirect* staining. In the former instance the stain was applied from a very weak solution on the assumption that it would be differentially absorbed by varying structures and tissues. Actually, however, in the majority of these methods, the density of the tissue controls the degree of absorption. Indirect methods are those in which the dye is applied from a relatively strong solution and is subsequently dissolved away, or extracted, from the unwanted structures either by a solvent or by some additional chemical reagent.

The last method of staining which is commonly employed is that of *mordant* staining, in which the tissue is first caused differentially to absorb a substance with which the dye subsequently makes an insoluble compound. Nuclear stains are the most widely used by this method, although it is probable that in many instances the metals employed in fixative solutions do themselves act as mordants. In the majority of cases tissues fixed by methods other than those specified for a particular staining technique may be rendered available for this technique if the sections attached to the slide are mordanted in the required fixative before staining.

DS 02 METHOD OF ARRANGE-MENT OF FORMULAS

The original method of classification for stains was to divide them into *basic* (*i.e.*, nuclear staining), *acid* (*i.e.*, plasma stain-

ing), and *neutral* groups. This method has been rendered obsolete by the employment of dyes in formulas which alter their basic staining reactions. The method of classification adopted by Langeron in the numerous editions of his *Précis de Microscopie* is based upon the chemical nature of the dyes themselves, and would appear at first sight to be the most logical. This is not, however, as good in practice as in theory, for it results in the widespread separation of formulas which, in laboratory practice, are, or should be, interchangeable.

The classification given at the beginning of this chapter has been erected on the principal that those solutions which may be profitably interchanged for each other upon the laboratory bench should have their formulas published under the same heading. The first step has, therefore, been the removal of "Techniques of Special Application" to Chapter 21. This chapter does not contain all those stains which have been proposed for special purposes, but only those which experience has shown to be otherwise valueless. The triple stain of Kull 1913, for example, which is widely employed for the demonstration of mitrochondria, has many other uses, and is accordingly placed with Rhamy 1930, which it resembles. Both are, however, mentioned as cross references in the division of the special section for which they were proposed.

Each of these two chapters has been further divided into convenient subdivisions, which in some cases are founded upon the components of the solutions, in other cases upon their practical use. The result is that every formula is accompanied either by those formulas or by references to those formulas, which may be employed as a substitute.

DS 10 Dye Staining Techniques of General Application

It cannot be too strongly emphasized that the selection of a dye staining technique for the general purposes of histology, embryology, and cytology is a matter in which the investigator should use his own initiative rather than rely on his knowledge of what has been done before. In too many cases a relatively worthless tech-

nique has been applied year after year for no other reason than that it has become conventional to do so. Were this reasoning to be taken to its logical conclusion and techniques utilized only for the original purpose for which they had been invented, we should find that the use of Bouin's picro-formaldehyde-acetic fixative would be entirely confined to the study of the spermatogenesis of rats, and that the majority of the carmine stains, now widely employed for staining whole-mounts, would be confined to the pre-staining of tissues prior to embedding, so that the nuclei might be stained in sections subsequently to be cut from them.

The dye staining techniques of general application are here divided into the three broad headings of those primarily intended for nuclear staining (DS 11), those primarily intended for providing a contrast to a previously applied nuclear staining (DS 12), and those intended for application to sections in which both the nuclei and background are to be stained in the same operation (DS 13).

DS 11 NUCLEAR STAINING TECHNIQUES

This section includes those techniques customarily employed for staining nuclei in general, and they are to be kept distinct from those special techniques intended for the study of the nucleus as such, which are to be found in Chapter 21 (DS 22.1).

Nuclear staining techniques are here classified solely on the basis of the reagents employed and of the manner of their employment. Prior to the use of stains in microtomy, hematoxylin was widely employed in the dye industry for obtaining purples and blacks, the former with the aid of alum mordants, and the latter with the aid of iron mordants. This division has been fairly closely followed in microtomy and is used as the basis for the division into mordant staining and direct staining which follows. The selection between these two methods must be made entirely on the purpose for which the method is intended.

The use of carmine is of greater antiquity than is the use of hematoxylin. The original use of carmine in textile dyeing was with the aid of a whole range of mordants, which enabled the dyer to select colors ranging from a brilliant scarlet to a dead black. In general the methods of microtomy utilize only the red aluminum mordants and to a lesser extent, the black iron mordants. The main use of carmine in microtomy, however, is in direct staining with the aid of solutions containing aluminum mordants. There is considerable misapprehension about the degree of alkalinity of the various formulas. Early workers tended to say that a solution was too alkaline on the sole basis of the fact that it was prepared with a sodium salt rather than with the more expensive lithium compounds or with borax. The rediscovery in Germany in the 1930's of some of the older sodium-carmines has led to their inclusion in the present work.

Brazilin and saffron are also to a minor extent employed in the staining of nuclei; and they terminate the list of the so-called natural dyes.

The synthetic dyes form a large group which are here subdivided according to which dye is used. Too much attention cannot be drawn to the oxazine dyes described by Becher 1921, which have been rediscovered at intervals. They have never replaced hematoxylin, but it must appear to most microtomists they are ultimately destined to do so. They have the advantage over hematoxylin stains in that they are relatively acid-fast once they have adhered to the nucleus, and therefore give a whole range of dark blue and black nuclear stains which can be employed before counterstaining methods involving acid materials. There is some confusion between the use of nuclear stains in zoology and botany and the use of the same stains for the preparation of bacteria. Nuclei and bacteria have essentially the same staining reactions, and a method which may be utilized for one can without difficulty be adapted to the other.

DS 11.1 HEMATOXYLIN STAINS

DS 11.10 TYPICAL EXAMPLES

Demonstration of spermatogenesis in the rat testis using the iron hematoxylin stain of Heidenhain 1892

The laboratory white rat is one of the best forms in which to show spermatogenesis, for the reason that it has a continuous breeding period and all stages are therefore available in almost every section examined. Baker 1945, 180 recommend the salamander *Triturus* for this purpose because of the very large chromosomes which it possesses. It is a disadvantage, however, that spermatogenesis in Triturus occurs only in the summer months immediately following the breeding cycle.

The rats selected should be young males, and are most conveniently killed with chloroform. The scrotal sac is then opened by a median incision, the testes are removed, and the epididymis trimmed away. The testes should be placed on a clean glass plate and slashed with a sharp scalpel or razor about two-thirds of the way through. The slashes should be spaced a few millimeters apart and should be made before the testes are thrown into the selected fixative solution. Few fixatives for this purpose can improve on the fluid originally suggested by Bouin 1897 (Chapter 18, F 5000.1010). This fixative today has many uses of doubtful validity; but for this, the material which it was originally designed to preserve, it has rarely been surpassed. At least 100 milliliters of fixative should be employed for a normal size testis, and the bottle containing it should be reversed once or twice during the first few hours to avoid the accumulation of diluted fluid at the bottom. The length of time allowed for fixation is not of any great importance, but it should, in any case be overnight, and should not in general exceed several weeks. After the object is removed from the fixative, it may be washed for about an hour in running water before being transferred to 70% alcohol to complete the removal of the picric acid. It must be emphasized that washing it in water after putting it in picric-acid fixatives results in considerable vacuolation of the cytoplasm. This does not in the present instance interfere with the study of the nucleus. After three or four changes of 70% alcohol, leaving the testes in a considerable volume of solution for at least two or three days between changes, the final removal of the picric acid may be completed by adding a small quantity of dry lithium carbonate to the alcohol used for washing. It will be impossible to remove the whole of the yellow color, some of which is caused by combination of the picric acid with the albuminoids present, but the last alcohol used for washing

should be only very faintly tinted with yellow. It is not the color of the fixed material to which objection is raised during the passage of the material through paraffin; it is the fact that unless most of the picric acid be removed, there will be a crystallization which will damage the tissues.

Small pieces may now be removed from the testis itself for embedding. It is best to select a piece about one millimeter in from the surface and of about a two-millimeter side. These should be embedded in paraffin and cut about five microns thick in the usual manner. These sections should then be attached to a slide. Particular attention must be paid to the fact that the slides are clean and that not too much of whatever adhesive is employed be allowed to remain.

The dry sections attached to the slide should now be warmed on the underside until the paraffin melts, placed in xylene until the paraffin is completely removed, and then run down in the ordinary way through absolute alcohol and lower-percentage alcohols to distilled water. They should then be lifted from the distilled water and examined carefully. If there is a tendency for the water to gather in droplets on the slide, or if upon shaking the water from the slide each section appears to retain around itself an adherent coat of water, it is an indication that the wax was not properly removed in the xylene or that the xylene itself is so old as to have a wax content too high to be useful. Such slides must be returned through the alcohols to absolute alcohol and thence to clean xylene, in which they should be left for a few minutes before again being brought down to water and reexamined. There is no more common cause of the failure of the stains to take than the imperfect removal of the wax.

Only two solutions are required for staining. These are a $2\frac{1}{2}\%$ solution of ferric alum and a $1\frac{1}{2}\%$ solution of hematoxylin. The only difficulty in making the ferric alum solution is to secure a pure and unoxidized sample of the reagent. Most of the crystals in a new bottle are of a clear violet color, but after it has been opened for some time, particularly if the stopper be loose, most of the crystals become covered with a brownish deposit which must be scraped off with a knife before the solution is prepared for staining. If the brown powder on the outside of the crystal forms a layer of any thickness, it is better to reject the whole and secure a fresh supply of the reagent. Hematoxylin itself has little staining effect, the color being produced by the formation of lakes with hematin, an oxidation product of hematoxylin. It was customary in former times to prepare considerable quantities of solution, which was kept with the stopper loose in the bottle for a period of at least one month before use. For the purpose of Heidenhain's technique, however, it is far more important that a small quantity of the ferric alum be carried over into the hematoxylin solution than that the latter should be aged. The staining will be both simpler and more effective if a few drops of hematoxylin be placed in the iron alum solution and a few drops of the iron alum solution be placed in the hematoxylin. Both solutions should, of course, be filtered immediately before use if the finest slides are required for the reason that chromosome figures in a rat can be obscured by even a very small particle of dust.

The slides are now taken from distilled water and placed in the mordant solution. It matters very little how long they remain in this solution, although the usual directions call for overnight. The ideal time varies with every type of tissue studied and is greatly dependent on temperature. If the solutions be heated to 50°C., with the understanding that this will cause a swelling of the section and a general obscuring of the finer details, the period may be shortened to as little as 10 minutes. But the finest stains are those secured by leaving the sections in the mordant solutions at room temperatures. On removal from the mordant solution the sections should be rinsed *very* briefly in distilled water. The purpose of the rinse is to remove the surplus mordant from the surface of the slide without extracting it from the tissues. The slides are then placed in the hematoxylin solution, in which they should remain for approximately the same length of time as they have been in the

mordant. It is not of importance how long this be though from three to 24 hours is customary period. Sections may be removed from time to time from the staining solution and examined with the naked eye. A successful preparation shows the whole section to have become completely blackened, although a slight bluish tinge in the black is permissible. If the sections have not become completely blackened in 24 hours, it is only necessary to replace them, after a brief rinse, in the mordant solution and leave them there, say a further period of 24 hours, before returning them to the stain.

If, however, the sections are sufficiently blackened on removal from the staining solution, it remains only to differentiate them, that is, to extract the color from all portions of the sections except the chromosomes. This is customarily done with the same solution in which they were mordanted, though, of course, a fresh solution or a stronger solution may be employed if desired. Differentiation at the commencement of the process goes relatively slowly so that all of the slides, which are presumable being carried in a glass rack, may be removed and placed in the ferric alum solution. The actual time in which differentiation takes place cannot be forecast because it depends on a large number of uncontrollable factors. But it is never less than five minutes nor very often more than a few hours. Sections should therefore be withdrawn from the ferric alum every four or five minutes and examined briefly under the low-power of a microscope. It is a matter of great convenience in controlling differentiation of chromosomes in this type of preparation if an ordinary student microscope can be fitted with a glass plate over the stage so that a slide wet with ferric alum can be placed, without fear of damage to the instrument, on the surface of the stage for examination. It is not uncommon for a beginner to place the slide upside down on the surface of the stage with the subsequent loss of all the sections. This can readily be avoided if the worker will make it a matter of routine, as he lifts the slide from the mordant, to hold it at an angle between himself and a light source so that the light is reflected from the surface. If the sections are, as they should be, on the upper surface of the slide when it is placed on the stage, they will appear to be double through the reflection from the under surface as well as the upper surface of the glass. A good rule is never to place an unmounted slide on the stage of the microscope until the double reflection has been seen.

If a low-power examination of the section shows the nuclei to be standing out clearly, the entire tray should be removed to distilled water, because from this time on differentiation is very rapid and each slide must be controlled separately. If, however, the nuclei are not sharply defined and a considerable degree of black or bluish color remains in the background, then the entire tray may be left in the iron alum for as long as is necessary. When this preliminary differentiation, down to the distinction of the nuclei under low power, has been completed, it is necessary to continue differentiation while examining the slides at frequent intervals under a very high power of the microscope. It is a matter of convenience if a water immersion objective is available. It is obviously impossible to place immersion oil on a wet slide, while the short working distance of a high-dry objective renders it particularly liable to cloud from the evaporation and recondensation of the water. Water immersion objectives are usually of three millimeter equivalent focus. This provides a sufficiently wide field to permit differentiation to be observed, while at the same time it has a magnification sufficiently high for satisfactory control. Each slide should now be taken separately and returned to the ferric alum for a few minutes and then reexamined. The various phases of mitosis and meiosis do not retain the stain to the same degree and care must be taken that the color is not washed completely out of the other chromosomes by examining only metaphase figures in which the color is retained longer than in any other. Considerable practice is required to gauge accurately the exact moment at which to cease the differentiation, which may be stopped almost instantly by placing the slides in a slightly

alkaline solution. In Europe most tap waters are sufficiently alkaline for this purpose and are generally specified; but in the cities of the United States it is often best to add a very small quantity of lithium carbonate or sodium bicarbonate to the water which is used to stop differentiation. Slides may be left in water for any reasonable period of time; the process is complete when the slide turns from a brown to a blue color.

The slides are then rinsed in distilled water, upgraded through the various percentages of alcohols, dehydrated, cleared, and mounted in balsam in the usual manner. Slides which have on them sections required for examination over a long period of time should have the sections some distance from the edge of the coverslip because, as the balsam oxidizes inward from the edge, it tends to remove the color of the stain from the chromosomes, leaving them a rather unpleasant shade of brown. If this happens to a valuable slide, however, the matter can be remedied by the utilization of a green light which will make the chromosomes again appear black.

Preparation of a wholemount
of a 48-hour chicken embryo,
using the alum hematoxylin
stain of Carazzi 1911

Fertile eggs are relatively easy to secure and should be incubated at a temperature of 103°F. for the required period of time. The term *48-hour chick* is relatively meaningless, because the exact stage of development which will have been reached after two days in the incubator depends not only on the temperature of the latter, but also on the temperature at which the egg was stored prior to its incubation, and even on the age of the hen. It is therefore desirable, if any very specific age of development be required, to start a series of eggs in the incubator at three- or four-hour intervals and then to fix and mount them at the same time.

For the removal of the embryos from the egg there are required first a number of fingerbowls, or any kind of circular glass dishes of five to six inches diameter and two to three inches depth, a number of Syracuse watch glasses, a large quantity of a 0.9% solution of sodium chloride, a pair of large dissecting scissors, a pair of fairly fine forceps, a pipet of the eye-dropper type, some coarse filter paper, and a pencil. No very great accuracy is required in making up the normal salt solution, although it is customarily specified that the temperature of the solution should be 102 to 103°F. Anywhere within 10 degrees on either side of these figures, however, is relatively safe.

The egg is removed from the incubator and placed in one of the fingerbowls which is then filled with enough warm normal saline to immerse the egg completely. If the operator is rather skilled, it is, of course, possible to break the egg into the warm saline as though one were breaking it into a frying pan. But it is recommended that the inexperienced worker prepare several hundred embryos before attempting to do this. The method by which he can be assured of securing a perfect embryo on every occasion is first to crack open the air space which lies at the large end of the egg and then to let the air which lies within it bubble out through the warm saline. This permits the yolk to fall down out of contact with the upper surface of the shell, which may now be removed, as he works from the air space toward the center with a pair of blunt-nose forceps. Again a matter of practice is involved, for a skilled operator can remove this shell in large portions, while the inexperienced one should work very carefully to avoid puncturing the yolk. If the yolk is punctured it is simpler to throw the egg away and start with another one. After about half of the shell has been removed, it will be quite easy to tip the yolk with the embryo lying on top of it out into the saline.

The next operation is to cut the embryo from the yolk by a series of cuts made well outside the blood vessel *sinus terminale* which marks the limits of the developing embryonic structures. To do this with success requires more courage than experience. Just as soon as the vitelline membrane is punctured, the yolk starts squirting out through the hole and render-

ing the fluid milky so that the embryo is obscured. The smaller the hole which is cut, the more violently does the yolk squirt out. Thus, the larger the scissors which are employed, the more easily will the embryo be removed. The easiest method is to take a pair of blunt forceps in the left hand and grip the extra-embryonic areas of the chick well outside the *sinus terminale*. Use a certain amount of drag, so that the vitelline membrane is wrinkled, and then make a transverse cut with a large pair of scissors directly away from you, about a third of an inch outside the *sinus terminale* on the side of the embryo opposite to that which is held by the forceps. This initial cut should be at least an inch long and should be made firmly. Two cuts at right angles to the first, each an inch in length, should then be run on each side of the embryo. The part gripped with the forceps should then be released, and the free edge where the first cut was made should be gripped so that the embryo can be folded back away from the yolk. It is now relatively easy by a fourth cut to sever all connections between the embryo and the underlying materials. The embryo, held by the forceps in the left hand, will now be free in the saline solution. The embryo is much stronger than it looks and will not be damaged provided the tip of the forceps is kept under the surface of the solution.

The embryo must now be transferred to clean saline, preferably in another finger-bowl. This transfer may be made either with a very wide-mouthed pipet of the eye-dropper type or by scooping it up in a smaller watch glass with plenty of saline and transferring it to the fresh solution. Here it should be picked up again by one corner with the forceps and waved gently backward and forward. This is to remove from it the adherent vitelline membrane (which may, however, already have fallen off) as well as to wash from it such yolk as may remain. At this stage the embryo should be examined to make sure that the heart is beating and that it is in a fit condition for fixation.

The embryo is now scooped out on one of the Syracuse watch glasses with as little water as possible. Next it is necessary to persuade it to flatten out on the bottom in an upside down position, that is, so that that portion of the embryo which was previously in contact with the yolk is now directed toward the operator. To determine which side of the embryo is uppermost requires considerable practice, unless the primary curvature of the head toward the right has already started. The best point of examination is the heart, which lies, of course, on the lower surface of the embryo. Having maneuvered the embryo in the saline in the watch glass until it is upside down, the water should now be drained off with the aid of a pipet which is run rapidly with a circular motion round and round the outside of the blastoderm while the water is being drawn up. As experience will soon show, any attempt to drain the water up a stationery pipet will result in the embryo being drawn out in the direction in which the water is being sucked. A little practice with the pipet being run round and round the outside the blastoderm and about a millimeter away from it will enable the operator to strand the embryo so that it is perfectly stretched in all directions. Under no circumstances should a needle be used to arrange the embryo, or the point will adhere to the blastoderm from which it cannot be detached without damage. If the embryo is not flattened and spread out satisfactorily, it is only necessary to add a little clean saline with a pipet and repeat the operation.

A piece of coarse filter paper or paper towel is now taken and cut into a rectangle of such size that it will fit easily into a syracuse watch glass. An oval or circular hole is then cut in the middle of this (most easily done by bending it in two and cutting from it a semicircle) of such a size as will exactly cover those areas of the embryo which it is desired to retain. That is, if only the embryo is required, the hole may be relatively small; if it is necessary to retain the whole of the area vasculosa with its *sinus terminale*, the hole must be correspondingly enlarged. The hole must not, however, be larger than the blastoderm removed from the egg, because the next step causes the unwanted extraembryonic regions to adhere to the paper, leaving the embryo clear in the center. By this means alone will the embryo be prevented from contracting and distorting when fixative is applied to it. Having prepared a rectangle of a suitable size with a suitable hole in the center, such data as are pertinent may be written on the edge in pencil. The paper is then dipped in clean saline. If the saline used has already become contaminated with egg white, a sharp puff should be directed at the whole to make quite certain that a film of moisture does not extend across it because the bubbles so produced always disrupt the embryo if this film is left. The rectangle of filter paper is now dropped on top of the stretched embryo in such a manner that the embryo does not become distorted. That is a great deal easier than it sounds, though a few false trials may be made by the beginner. The writer's procedure is to place one end of the rectangle on the edge of the watch glass nearest to him, taking care that it does not touch the blastoderm, and then to let it down sharply. The edges of the blastoderm must be in contact with at least two-thirds of the periphery of the hole if it is to remain stretched. As soon as the paper has been let down, the end of a pipet or a needle should be used to press lightly on the edges of the paper where it is in contact with the blastoderm, to make sure that it will adhere.

The embryo is now ready to be fixed, and the choice of a fixative must naturally be left to the discretion of the operator. The author's preference, when hematoxylin is subsequently to be employed for staining, is for the mercuric-chromic-formaldehyde mixture of Gerhardt (Chapter 18, F 3600.1010 Gerhardt 1901). The disadvantage of the customarily used picric formulas is that they interfere seriously with subsequent staining by hematoxylin. The fixative should be applied from an eye-dropper type pipet in the following manner. First a few drops are placed on the center of the embryo so that a thin film of fixative is spread over it. After a moment or two a little more may be added with a circular motion on the paper which surrounds the embryo. The paper should again, at this point, be pressed onto the periphery of the blastoderm with a needle, or the end of the pipet, to make sure that adherence is perfect. The whole should be left for a moment or two before being very gently shaken from side to side to make quite certain that the embryo is not sticking to the watch glass. If it is sticking, the end of the pipet containing the fixative should be slid under the edge of the paper and a very gentle jet of fixative used to free the embryo. As soon as the embryo is floating freely in fixative the Syracuse watch glass may be filled with fixative and placed on one side while the same cycle of events is repeated with the next embryo. After about 10 minutes in the fixative, the paper may be picked up by one corner and moved from reagent to reagent without the slightest risk of the embryo becoming either detached or damaged. The paper must not be picked up with a pair of metal forceps unless these have been waxed, or the mercuric chloride in the fixative will damage the metal. It is the writer's custom to leave the embryos in the watch glass for about 30 minutes before picking them out and transferring them to a large jar of the fixative which is preferably kept in a dark cupboard. The total time of fixation is not important, but it should be not less than one day nor more than one week. When the embryos are removed from the fixative they should be washed in running water overnight and then be stored in 70% alcohol.

When one is ready to stain a batch of embryos it is only necessary to transfer them from alcohol back to distilled water, leaving them there until they are thoroughly rehydrated, and then to transfer them to a reasonably large volume of Carazzi's hematoxylin (DS 11.122 Carazzi 1911) in which they may remain overnight. It is a mistake to stain them initially for too short a period, for the result will be that the outer surface of the embryo becomes adequately stained while the inner structures do not. This defect, however, is very difficult to detect until the embryo is finally cleared for mounting. When the embryos are removed from the stain, at which time they should appear a deep purple, they should be transferred to a large fingerbowl of distilled water and rocked gently backward and forward

until most of the stain has been removed from the papers to which they are attached. Each embryo should now be taken separately and placed in 0.1% hydrochloric acid in 70% alcohol. The color will immediately start to change from a deep purple to a pale bluish-pink. They should remain in this solution until, on examination under a low power of the microscope, all the required internal structures appear clearly differentiated. Most people differentiate too little, forgetting that the pale pink of the embryo will be changed back to a deep blue by subsequent treatment and that the apparent color will also increase in density when the embryo is cleared. No specific directions for the extent of the differentiation can be given beyond the general advice to differentiate far more than you anticipate to be necessary. After the embryos have been sufficiently differentiated each one should be placed in alkaline tap water, either as it occurs in nature or as it is rendered alkaline with the addition of sodium bicarbonate. Here it should remain until all the acid has been neutralized and the embryo itself has changed from a pink back to a blue coloration. It may then be dehydrated in the ordinary manner through successive alcohols, and it is the author's custom to remove it from its paper only when it is in the last alcohol and before it is placed in the clearing reagent. Some persons place it in the clearing reagent attached to its paper and remove it only before mounting. Any clearing reagent may be tried at the choice of the operator. The author's preference for chicken embryos is terpineol which has the advantage of not rendering these delicate structures as brittle as do many other reagents. The mountant may be Canada balsam or any of its synthetic substitutes.

Preparation of a series of demonstration slides, each having six typical transverse sections of a 72-hour chicken embryo, using the acid alum hematoxylin stain of Ehrlich 1896

The last example described in some detail the manner in which a chicken embryo may be removed from the yolk and fixed in a Syracuse watch glass where it is stretched by a collar of filter paper. Exactly the same procedure should be followed in the present instance, save that it is not necessary to make the hole in the paper a size larger than will accommodate the embryo itself. The same fixative recommended there should be employed, but after the removal of the fixative, the embryo should be embedded in paraffin and cut by the methods described in Chapter 12. A complete ribbon of serial sections should be taken from the whole embryo.

It is presumed for the purpose of this example that the reader wishes to have a series of slides for class use, on each of which will be arranged, in order, transverse sections through the region of the eye, the ear, the heart, and the anterior, middle and posterior abdominal regions. These regions will be found all that is required for teaching an elementary class the development of the eye, ear, and heart, and the closure of the amnion and neural folds. It is first necessary to identify those sections which will show the required structure and to isolate the portions of ribbon containing them. Provided the sections are placed against a background of black paper, this is relatively simple with the aid of a long-arm binocular dissecting microscope. This microscope may be swung over the ribbons and will supply sufficient magnification to enable the regions of the ribbon to be identified by a competent microtomist. If the operator has had little practice at this, it might be desirable to stain the embryo in carmine before embedding, preferably with one of the alum-carmines given in section DS 11.21 below. Each portion which contains the selected sections is then cut from the ribbon with a sharp scalpel moved with a rocking motion, picked up on a camel's-hair brush, and transferred to another sheet of black paper. The rest of the ribbon may now be thrown away.

The sections in each of the selected strips of ribbon are then counted to determine the maximum number of slides which may be made—the ear sections are usually the limiting factor—and the pieces of ribbon are trimmed so that each contains approximately the same number of sections. The required number of slides are then cleaned and a few drops of the usual adhesive added to an ounce or so of filtered distilled water in a small flask.

The only difficulty of this procedure is in fixing each section in its correct place on the slide. A single slide is taken, placed in front of the operator, and covered lightly with the dilute adhesive. The fluid should extend to the edge of the slide, but should not be raised in a meniscus sufficiently high to cause any appreciable slope of the fluid from the center of the slide toward the edges. The end section is then cut from each of the ribbons with a sharp scalpel with a rocking motion. These sections are then placed in the correct order (but without any regard to symmetry) on the surface of the fluid on the slide. To secure these sections in the required position it is now necessary to have two fine brushes, a mounted needle, and a bunsen or spirit lamp.

The last section, that is, that section which is required to lie farthest from the label on the slide, is now secured in position with a brush held in the left hand, while the second section is maneuvered with a brush held in the right hand until its edges touch those of the first section. Both sections will be held together by capillary attraction when the brush is removed. The needle is then warmed in the flame and used to fuse the edges of the sections together in two spots. If the entire edge is melted it will create a ridge which will prevent the compound ribbon from lying flat against the slide. Two minute spots fused together with the point of the needle are quite sufficient to hold the section in place. The brush is again picked up with the right hand and used to guide the next section into its appropriate place. This section is then spotted into position with the tip of the warm needle, and so on, until all the sections have been fused into a continuous ribbon. The ribbons are then flattened with heat and drained as described in Chapter 12. The sections are now, in the ordinary course of events, left on the warm table until they are entirely dry before they are dewaxed in xylene and brought down to 90% alcohol through absolute alcohol in the usual manner.

Ehrlich's acid alum hematoxylin (DS 11.123 Ehrlich 1896) has been selected for this typical example because it is one of the best, though at the same time one of the most frequently misused, of the hematoxylin stains. The method given for its preparation should be rigorously followed, that is, the hematoxylin should be dissolved in a mixture of acetic acid and absolute alcohol, and the glycerine, water, and ammonium alum should be added to the bottle. The bottle should then be shaken vigorously and the mixture allowed to ripen with the bottle stopper loose for some months. "Artificially" ripened hematoxylin does not give as good a preparation, but there is no reason why this stain should not be prepared in half-gallon lots at routine intervals so that a sufficiently ripened solution is always available. When it has once been ripened, which can be told both by the "fruity" smell and by its dark color, it remains in a fit condition to use for many years. One of the most frequently omitted precautions is that of maintaining the concentration of the ammonium alum by adding about 100 grams per liter to the bottle in which the hematoxylin is kept after it has been sufficiently ripened. This stain should never be diluted but should always be used full strength by the method now to be described.

Each slide, or all the slides together in a glass tray, are taken from the 95% alcohol and placed in full-strength Ehrlich's hematoxylin solution for a few minutes. The exact time is not important, but they should be examined at intervals to make sure that they are not becoming overstained. If the technician is inexperienced, it is recommended that a period of one minute be used, and that they should then be examined under a low power of the microscope. The nuclei should appear quite densely stained, the background being only lightly stained. Each slide is then removed individually from the tray, wiped on the underside with a clean cloth, and then differentiated with 95% alcohol (*never* with acid alcohol) dropped onto it from a drop bottle or from a pipet. It will be observed at once that the drops of the viscous hematoxylin solution are rolled back from the section by the 95% alcohol, and that after this has continued for a short time the nuclei become more distinct and the background less distinct. The exact point at which differentiation should cease is determined by the operator, but it is better, in general, since the sections are not to be counterstained, to discontinue differentiation when the nuclei are clearly defined against the background. Each section is then transferred directly to a saturated solution of lithium chloride in 70% alcohol, in which it turns from pink to blue. If the conventional method of differentiating these stains with acid alcohol is followed, it results in a hopelessly diffuse stain. The purpose of the 95% alcohol is to utilize the surface tension of the stain to hold it in the nuclei. If the slide is placed in acid 70% alcohol, it will be found that the stain diffuses out from the nuclei which, instead of appearing clear and sharp, appear blurred around the edges as does an out-of-focus photograph. Differentiation by rolling back the stain with 95% alcohol gives a clear, sharp stain which is as well differentiated as any of the ferric alum mordant stains, but which has the advantage of giving a greater transparency and also of staining the background sufficiently to render it apparent for class demonstration purposes.

The slides may remain in the saturated solution of lithium chloride in 70% alcohol for as long as is required. They are subsequently passed directly through the higher alcohols to xylene and mounted in balsam or some synthetic substitute.

11.11. MORDANT HEMATOXYLIN STAINING

Mordant staining with hematoxylin results, in general, in black nuclei, heavily and densely stained, from which the stain is with difficulty removed by subsequent treatment. It is therefore to be recommended in those cases in which it is desired to follow with a complex counterstaining, particularly those which involve the use of an acid rinse. The method most commonly employed is still that of Heidenhain 1892, from which the majority of the other formulas have been derived. These variations are for the most part in the concentration of the solutions employed or in the temperature at which they are used. The technique of Régaud 1910 is very frequently specified in Europe as a prior staining for complex after-staining methods. During the early part of the present century, the substitution of ferric chloride for ferric alum as a mordant was followed in many circles. Mordants other than iron are rarely employed, although the introduction of copper by Faure 1924 has provided histologists with a staining method considered by many people to be a definite improvement. **Diamond 1945** (*Tech. Bull.*, **6** :68) finds that the addition of .1% of a wetting agent (Tergitol 7) improves the stain.

11.111 After Ferric Alum Mordants

11.111 Benda 1893   2246, **7** :161
REAGENTS REQUIRED: *A.* ADS 12.1 Benda 1893 35, water 65; *B.* 1% hematoxylin; *C.* ADS 12.1 Benda 1893 5, water 95
METHOD: [sections] → water → *A*, 24 hrs. → rinse → *B*, till black → *C*, till differentiated → balsam, via usual reagents

11.111 Bütschli 1892   Bütschli 1892, 80
REAGENTS REQUIRED: *A.* 2% ferric acetate; *B.* 0.5% hematoxylin
METHOD: [sections of protozoans] → *A*, 24 hrs. → rinse → *B*, 3 hrs. → distilled water → balsam, via usual reagents

11.111 Diamond 1945   519b, **15** :68
REAGENTS REQUIRED: *A.* 4% ferric alum; *B.* water 100, hematoxylin 0.5, Tergitol 7 0.1; *C.* sat. aq. sol. picric acid
METHOD: [sections or smears] → water → *A*, 5 mins. → rinse → *B*, 5 mins. → rinse → *C*, till differentiated, 3–5 mins. → tap water, till blue → balsam, via carbol-xylene

11.111 Dobell 1914   1798, **34** :139
REAGENTS REQUIRED: *A.* 1% ferric alum in 70% alcohol; *B.* 1% hematin in 70% alcohol; *C.* 0.1% HCl in 70% alcohol
METHOD: [thin sections or protozoan smears] → 70% alcohol → *A*, 10 mins. → *B*, 10 mins. → 70% alcohol, quick rinse → *C*, till differentiated → 70% alcohol, wash → counterstain → balsam, via usual reagents

11.111 Freitas 1936   1345, **31** :707
REAGENTS REQUIRED: *A.* 0.5% ferric alum in 70% alc.; *B.* 1% hematin in 70% alc. 60 phosphate buffer pH 7.6 30; *C.* 0.3% picric acid
METHOD: [sections] → *A*, 1 hr. → *B*, 1 hr. → wash → *C*, till differentiated → wash → balsam, via usual reagents

11.111 French 1923   626, **3** :213
REAGENTS REQUIRED: *A.* 3.5% ferric alum; *B.* 95% alc. 98, hematoxylin 1, sat. aq. sol. lithium carbonate 2; *C.* 1% ferric alum
METHOD: [sections or smears] → *A*, overnight → rinse → *B*, overnight → wash → *C*, till differentiated → wash
NOTE: Solution *B* is attributed, without reference, to **Rosenbush.**

11.111 Galiano 1928   *see* DS 13.6 Galiano 1928

11.111 Haggquist 1933   23632, **50** :77
REAGENTS REQUIRED: *A.* 5% ferric chloride; *B.* 1% hematoxylin; *C.* 1% ferric chloride.
METHOD: [sections] → water → *A*, 1 hr. → quick rinse → *B*, 1 hr. → wash → *C*, till differentiated → wash → balsam, via usual reagents

11.111 Hance 1933   19938, **77** :287
STOCK FORMULA I: 10% hematoxylin in 95% alcohol
REAGENTS REQUIRED: *A.* 2.5% ferric alum; *B.* water 100 ml., stock I 10 ml., 2.5% sodium bicarbonate 0.1
METHOD: [sections] → *A*, ½ to 2 hrs. → distilled water, rinse → *B*, ½ hr. → tap water, rinse → *A*, till differentiated → tap water, till blue → balsam, via usual reagents

NOTE: In preparing *B* solution, the bicarbonate should be added until the color changes from yellow to plum. This color change is of more importance than the quantity of alkali required to produce it.

11.111 Heidenhain 1892   *Festchr. Kölliker*, 118

REAGENTS REQUIRED: *A*. 2.5% ferric alum; *B*. 0.5% hematoxylin, "ripened" at least on month

METHOD: distilled water → *A*, 30 mins. to 24 hrs. → distilled water, rinse → *B*, 30 mins. to 24 hrs. → tap water, rinse, → *A*, till differentiated→ tap water, till blue → balsam, via usual reagents

NOTE: **Murray 1919** (1200, **16**:77) substitutes 3.5% ferric alum for *A*, above. **Masson 1912** (4956, **87**:291) substitutes 4% ferric alum for *A* and 1% hematoxylin for *B*, mordanting and staining 5–10 minutes at 50°C. See also DS 12.31 Masson 1912. A detailed description of the use of this stain in the demonstration of chromosomes is given under DS 11.10.

11.111 Hirsch and Bretschneider   *see* DS 21.21 Hirsch and Bretschneider 1938

11.111 Kofoid and Swegy 1915   16599, **51**:289

REAGENTS REQUIRED: *A*. 0.4% ferric alum in 50% alc.; *B*. 0.50% hematoxylin in 70% alc.

METHOD: [smears] → 50% alc. → *A*, 10 mins. → rinse, 50% alc. → *B*, 30 mins. → *A*, till differentiated → wash thoroughly

RECOMMENDED FOR: protozoan smears.

11.111 Laudau   *see* DS 21.212 Laudau 1924

11.111 Loyez   *see* DS 21.212 Loyez

11.111 Markey, Culbertson, and Giordano 1943   *see* DS 23.33 Markey, *et al.* 1943

11.111 Masson 1912   *see* DS 11.111 Heidenhain 1892 (note)

11.111 Murray 1919   *see* DS 11.111 Heidenhain 1892 (note)

11.111 Régaud 1910   1823, **11**:291

REAGENTS REQUIRED: *A*. 5% ferric alum; *B*. water 80, hematoxylin 1, glycerol 10, 90% alcohol 10; *C*. ADS 21.1 Masson 1942

METHOD: distilled water → *A*, 30 mins., 50°C → distilled water, rinse → *B*, 30 mins., 50°C. → distilled water, wash → *C*, till differentiated → tap water, till blue → balsam, via usual reagents

NOTE: A detailed description of the use of this stain before a complex contrast is given under DS 12.30 below.

11.111 Rosenbush   *see* DS 11.111 French 1923 (note)

11.111 Shortt 1923   9940, **10**:836

REAGENTS REQUIRED: *A*. 2.5% ferric alum; *B*. water 95, hematoxylin 1, phenol 5

METHOD: identical with 11.111 Heidenhain

11.112 After Ferric Chloride Mordants

11.112 Cole 1926   19938, **64**:452

STOCK SOLUTIONS: abs. alc. 100, sodium hydrosulfite 1, hematoxylin 5

REAGENTS REQUIRED: *A*. ADS 12.1 Cole 1926; *B*. Stock 3, ammonia 0.5, water 100; *C*. 0.1% hydrochloric acid; *D*. 0.01% ammonia

METHOD: water → *A*, on slide, 5 mins. → rinse → *B*, on slide, 10 mins. → *C*, till differentiated → *D*, till blue → balsam, via usual reagents

11.112 Mallory 1900   11189, **5**:18

REAGENTS REQUIRED: *A*. 10% ferric chloride; *B*, 1% hematoxylin; *C*. 0.25% ferric chloride

METHOD: [sections] → distilled water → *A*, 3–5 mins. → *B*, on slide, draining and renewing till precipitate ceases to form, till blue-black, 3–5 mins. → tap water, wash → *C*, till differentiated → tap water, wash → balsam, via oil of cretan origanum

11.113 After Other Mordants

11.113 Apáthy 1888   23632, **5**:47
REAGENTS REQUIRED: *A*. 1% hematoxylin; *B*. 1% potassium dichromate
METHOD: [sections] → water → *A*, overnight → *B*, till stain first produced sufficiently differentiated → water, till yellow color removed → balsam, via usual reagents

11.113 Bensley and Bensley 1938   Bensley and Bensley 1938, 79
REAGENTS REQUIRED: *A*. sat. sol. copper acetate; *B*. 5% potassium chromate; *C*. 1% hematoxylin; *D*. water 80, ADS 21.1 Weigert 1885, 20
METHOD: [sections] → water → *A*, 5 mins. → rinse → *B*, dip → rinse → *C*, 2 mins. → *A*, 1 min. → *D*, till differentiated → balsam, via usual reagents

11.113 Drew 1920   *see* DS 22.0 Drew 1920

11.113 Fajerstajn 1901   *see* DS 21.212 Fajerstajn 1901

11.113 Heidenhain 1884   1780, **24**:468
REAGENTS REQUIRED: *A*. 0.3% hematoxylin; *B*. 0.5% potassium chromate
METHOD: [whole objects or sections] → water → *A*, overnight → rinse → *B*, till dark stain first produced sufficiently differentiated → water, till yellow color removed → balsam, via usual reagents

11.113 Knower 1930   19938, **72**:172
PREPARATION OF STOCK SOLUTION: Dissolve 5 hematoxylin in 100 abs. alc. Add 1 sat. sol. sodium metabisulfite.
REAGENTS REQUIRED: *A*. ADS 12.1 Cole 1916; *B*. stock 4, water 8, ammonia 1, 95% alcohol 100; (Mix in order given; leave first three ingredients 30 seconds before diluting); *C*. 0.1% hydrochloric acid; *D*. sat. sol. lithium carbonate in 70% alcohol
METHOD: [sections from material fixed in any copper-containing fixative (see Chapter 18, F 1400, F 2400, F 3400, F 4000)] → 95% alcohol → *A*, 5 mins. → 95% alcohol, quick rinse → *B*, 5 mins. → *C*, till differentiated → *D*, 2 mins. → balsam, via usual reagents
NOTE: Though this was originally intended as a nerve stain, it is far too good a general-purpose stain to be omitted from this section. The original calls for "sodium bisulphite," which is not soluble to the extent indicated; however "the bisulphite of commerce usually consists chiefly, or almost entirely, of sodium pyrosulphite" (Merck Index, 5th ed., 1940, 506). Sodium pyrosulfite, which is commonly sold as "metabisulfite," is soluble to the required extent and is accordingly specified in the formula given above.

11.113 Kulschitzky 1889   766, **4**:223
FORMULA: water 98, acetic acid 2, hematoxylin 1
USE: For general purposes as DS 11.113 Knower 1930. For nervous elements see Chapter 21 DS 21.212. The formula of **Wolters 1890** (23632, **7**:466) differs only in containing 2 parts hematoxylin.

11.113 Mallory 1936   *Lead hematoxylin*   *see* DS 21.212 Mallory 1936

11.113 Nissl 1894   466, **51**:245
REAGENTS REQUIRED: *A*. 2% ferric acetate in 90% alc.; *B*. 1% hematoxylin in 70% alc.; *C*. 1% hydrochloric acid in 70% alc.
METHOD: [sections of brain] → *A*, 30 mins. → rinse → *B*, 30 mins. → rinse → *C*, till differentiated → balsam, via usual reagents

11.113 Schultze 1904 23632, 21:5
REAGENTS REQUIRED: *A*. F 1600.0010 Flemming 1882; *B*. sat. sol. hematoxylin in 70%
alc.; *C*. 1% potassium dichromate in 50% alc.; *D*. bergamot oil
METHOD: [sections of material fixed, or mordanted, in *A*] → 50% alc. → *B*, 24 hrs. →
wash → *C*, 1 hr. → 95% alc. → *D*, till differentiated → balsam

11.113 Wolters 1890 *see* DS 11.113 Kulschitsky 1889 (note)
23632, 7:466

11.12 DIRECT HEMATOXYLIN STAINING

Hematoxylin cannot be used in direct staining unless some mordant is incorporated with
the solution for the purpose of fixing the stain on the material to be colored. The term *direct
staining* is used in this case in contrast to *mordant staining* and must not be confused with
the term *direct staining* as opposed to *indirect staining*. The former indicates merely that the
object is stained in a relatively strong solution for a length of time sufficient to impregnate
the whole and that it is subsequently exposed either to an acid solution or to a solution of the
mordant with a view to extracting it from those objects which it is desired to bring into contrast. The term *indirect staining*, as used in this same sense, indicates the employment of a
very weak solution in order to permit a differential absorption of the stain by those parts
of the object to be stained (usually the more dense) which it is intended to bring out. As a
generality it may be said that direct staining, in this sense, is usually applied to sections
while indirect staining is better for the preparation of wholemounts, provided that one has
the leisure to wait for the somewhat lengthy process to finish.

The direct-staining formulas are divided into four classes according to the mordant which
is incorporated. The first group, incorporating iron mordants, is used almost exclusively for
staining the central nervous system in sections; their use and variations are more fully
described in Chapter 21. It is doubtful that these stains could ever be employed for indirect
staining of wholemounts, but for staining nuclei they are far better than the other three
classes, though less widely employed.

The next two divisions include these formulas containing alum mordants and acid-alum
mordants, the separation of these two being necessitated by the large number of formulas
to be found in each. Both are employed for sections and for wholemounts, the best known
being unquestionably the formula of Delafield (1885). This reagent has the advantage of
being almost foolproof, but it has to be ripened for a considerable period before it can be
employed: **Watson 1945** (11360, **63**:21) recommends barium peroxide for ripening these
solutions. The formula of Carazzi 1911 is almost identical but may be used as soon as it is
prepared. It is strongly recommended to the attention of those whose staining has previously
been confined to Delafield. The formula of Mayer 1896 was once very widely employed for
staining wholemounts, but it has nowadays fallen somewhat into disuse. It also required
ripening for a considerable period before employment.

The formulas incorporating an acid, usually acetic, in addition to the alum mordant are
among the best of the general-purpose stains. The formula of Ehrlich 1886 is the most widely
known, though any of the others can be recommended.

The alum-mordant formulas are the only ones which can be employed in great dilution for
indirect staining. It is usually a waste of time to employ acid-alum formulas for this purpose.
The diluent to be employed should have the same composition as the formula itself, without
the inclusion of hematoxylin. It is a mistake to follow the very wide recommendation that
0.1% hydrochloric acid be employed. This reagent is difficult to remove from the object
before its final mounting and leads ultimately to the breakdown of the color.

In all cases hematoxylin stains should be "blued" after they have been differentiated, in
some alkaline solution, preferably containing free ions of an alkali metal. Lithium carbonate
is widely used, though a weak solution of calcium chloride, adjusted with ammonium hydroxide to a pH of about 8, is more satisfactory. The old exhortation to use tap water originated
in Europe where most of the tap waters are alkaline. The majority of city tap waters in the
United States are worthless for this purpose.

The chrome-hematoxylins and copper-hematoxylins, which form the fourth class, are of
comparatively recent introduction or, at least, of comparatively recent acceptance. The
formulas of Hanson 1905 and of Liengme 1930 are, however, excellent reagents and should
be tried for sections in those instances in which the more customary formulas do not yield

satisfactory results. The phosphomolybdic and phosphotungstic hematoxylins of Mallory, though originally intended for staining nervous structures, are useful for a more general purpose. Mayer's 1891 "haemacalcium" was originally intended for staining wholemounts of small marine invertebrates and is admirable for the purpose.

11.121 Formulas Incorporating Iron Mordants

11.121 Anderson 1929   Anderson 1929, 129
STOCK SOLUTIONS: I. 0.5% hematoxylin in 50% alc. 100, 2% calcium hypochlorite 5; II. water 100, ferric alum 3, sulfuric acid 2.5
WORKING SOLUTION: stock solution I 60, stock solution II 30
NOTE: Overstaining of sections rarely occurs but may be corrected with 0.1% hydrochloric acid in 70% alcohol.

11.121 Barrett 1932   *see* DS 22.11 Barrett 1932

11.121 Faure 1924   6639, **90**:87
REAGENTS REQUIRED: *A*. 90% alcohol 100, hematoxylin 3.2; *B*. ADS 12.1 Faure 1924; *C*. 1% hydrochloric acid; *D*, sat. aq. sol. lithium carbonate
METHOD: [distilled water] → *A* + *B*, (equal parts), 5 secs. → wash, tap water → *C*, quick rinse → wash, tap water → *D*, till blue → wash → [counterstain, if desired] → balsam, via usual reagents

11.121 Hansen 1905   23632, **22**:55
FORMULA: water 100, ferric alum 4.5, hematoxylin 0.75
PREPARATION: Dissolve the alum in 65 water. Dissolve the dye in 35 water. Mix. Boil. Cool. Filter.

11.121 Held *test.* **1937 Gatenby and Painter**   Gatenby and Painter 1937, 374
REAGENTS REQUIRED: *A*. 5% ferric alum; *B*. water 95, DS 11.124 Held 1937 5
METHOD: [water] → *A*, 24 hrs. → *B*, 12–24 hrs. → *A*, till differentiated → balsam, via usual reagents

11.121 Janssen 1897   6011, **14**:207
FORMULA: water 70, ferric alum 5, hematoxylin 1, abs. alc. 5, glycerol 15, methanol 15
PREPARATION: Dissolve the alum in the water and the hematoxylin in the alc. Mix. Leave 1 week. Filter and add remaining ingredients.
NOTE: This formula is recommended by **Lillie and Earle 1939** (20540b, **14**:53) as a substitute for Weigert 1904.

11.121 Kefalas 1926   11360, **46**:277
FORMULA: acetone 100, ferric chloride 1, hydrochloric acid 0.05, hematoxylin 1

11.121 Krajian 1950   Krajian 1950, 196
FORMULA: water 50, 95% alc. 50, hematoxylin, ferric alum, ferric chloride, potassium iodide *a.a.* 6
PREPARATION: Dissolve salts in water and dye in alc. Mix.
NOTE: This formula, designed for bacteriology (see DS 23.222 Krajian 1950), is an excellent general-purpose hematoxylin.

11.121 La Manna 1937   23632, **54**:257
FORMULA: water 100, hematoxylin 1, ferric chloride 3

11.121 Lillie and Earle 1939   608b, **15**:765
STOCK SOLUTIONS: I. 95% alc. 50, glycerol 50, hematoxylin 1; II. water 100, ferric alum 15, ferrous sulfate 15
WORKING STAIN: stock I, 50, stock II 50

11.121 Lillie 1940   1789a, **29**:705
FORMULA: water 100, ferric chloride 1.2, hematoxylin 1, hydrochloric acid 1

11.121 Morel and Bassal 1909 11024, **45**:632
STOCK SOLUTIONS: I. 95% alc. 100, hematoxylin 1; II. water 100, ferric chloride 2, copper acetate 0.04, hydrochloric acid, 1
WORKING SOLUTION: stock I 50, stock II 50

11.121 Olivecrona 1917 *see* DS 21.21 Olivecrona 1917

11.121 Paquin and Goddard 1947 4349, **27**:198
FORMULA: water 75, 95% alc. 25, glycerol 13, ferric alum 5, ammonium sulfate 0.7, hematoxylin 0.8
PREPARATION: Dissolve the dye in the glycerol and alc. with gentle heat. Cool and add, with constant agitation, the other ingredients dissolved in the water. Leave 24 hours.

11.121 Rozas 1935 23632, **52**:1
REAGENTS REQUIRED: *A.* water 74, 95% alc. 6, glycerol 20, ferric alum 1, aluminum chloride 1.2, hematoxylin 0.6; *B.* 20% ferric alum
METHOD: [sections] → water → *A*, 12–24 hrs. → *B*, till differentiated → balsam, via usual reagents

11.121 Seidelin 1911 *see* DS 11.121 Weigert 1904 (note)

11.121 Thomas 1943 4285a, **20**:212
FORMULA: water 60, dioxane 40, acetic acid 6, hematoxylin 2.5, ferrous chloride 6, ferric chloride 1.5, ferric alum 3, hydrogen peroxide 1
PREPARATION: Dissolve the hematoxylin in the dioxane and add the hydrogen peroxide. Dissolve the salts in the water and acid. Filter into the hematoxylin solution.

11.121 Verhoeff 1908 *see* DS 21.13 Verhoeff 1908

11.121 Weigert 1903 *test.* **1910** *ips.* Ehrlich, Krause, *et al.* 1910, **1**:231
STOCK SOLUTIONS: I. 0.4% ferric chloride; II. 1% hematoxylin in 95% alcohol
REAGENTS REQUIRED: *A.* stock I 50, stock II 50; *B.* ADS 21.1 Masson 1942
METHOD: [distilled water] → *A*, 1–2 hrs. → distilled water, rinse → *B*, till differentiated → tap water, till blue → balsam, via usual reagents

11.121 Weigert 1904 23632, **21**:1
STOCK SOLUTIONS: I. water 95, ferric chloride 0.6, hydrochloric acid 0.75; II. 1% hematoxylin in 95% alc.
REAGENTS REQUIRED: *A.* stock I 50, stock II 50
METHOD: [distilled water] → stain, till sufficiently colored → distilled water, wash → tap water, till blue → balsam, via usual reagents
NOTE: See Chapter 21, DS 21.212 for use of these reagents in nerve staining. Weigert diluted his B stock from a 10% stock just before use and specified a German pharmaceutical preparation, here reduced to terms of laboratory reagents, for his solution *A*.
Seidelin 1911 (16035, **4**:94) used 3 stock *A* to 2 stock *B* in preparing solution *A*.

11.121 Yasvoyn *test.* **1946 Roskin** Roskin 1946, 150
STOCK SOLUTIONS: I. 0.1% hematoxylin; II. 2.5% ferric alum
WORKING SOLUTIONS: add II with constant stirring to 20 drops I until solution just remains blue
METHOD: [sections] → stain, 2–5 mins. → 70% alc. if differentiation required → balsam, via usual reagents

11.122 Formulas Incorporating Alum Mordants

11.122 Belloni 1939 *test.* **1943 Cowdry** Cowdry 1943, 35
FORMULA: water 100, potassium alum 3, hematoxylin 0.15, chloral hydrate 0.1, potassium hydroxide 0.01

11.122 Böhmer 1868 1780, **4**:345
STOCK SOLUTIONS: I. 3.5% hematoxylin in abs. alc.; II. 0.3% potassium alum
WORKING FORMULA: stock I 10, stock II 90

11.122 Bullard, *in verb.* **Harpst 1951**

FORMULA: water 225, 95% alc. 35, glycerol 33, acetic acid 3.5, ammonium alum 6, mercuric oxide 0.8, hematoxylin 0.8

PREPARATION: Dissolve the dye in 15 of 50% alc. with 2 acetic acid. Heat and add 2 ammonium alum in 25 water. Boil, add mercuric oxide, and filter. Add remaining ingredients to cold filtrate.

NOTE: The author has not been able to discover any literature reference for this solution which is widely used in pathological laboratories.

11.122 Cajal and de Castro 1933   Cajal and de Castro 1933, 77

PREPARATION OF STOCK: To 100 of a 5% solution of hematoxylin add 5 ammonia. Evaporate to dryness.

STAINING SOLUTION: 2% solution of above powder in 50% alc. 50; 5% ammonium alum 50

11.122 Carazzi 1911   23632, **28**:273

REAGENTS REQUIRED: *A*. water 80, potassium alum 5, hematoxylin 0.1, potassium iodate 0.02, glycerol 20; *B*. 0.1% hydrochloric acid in 70%

METHOD FOR WHOLE OBJECTS: water → 1*A* + 10 water, 3 to 10 mins. → distilled water → *B*, if differentiation necessary → tap water till blue → balsam, via usual reagents

METHOD FOR SECTIONS: water → *A*, till sufficiently stained, 5 mins. to 12 hrs. → distilled water, wash → tap water, till blue → balsam, via usual reagents

NOTE: A detailed description of the use of this stain in the preparation of a wholemount is given under DS 11.10 above.

11.122 Delafield *test.* **1885 Prudden**   23632, **2**:288

REAGENTS REQUIRED: *A*. water 70, ammonium alum 3, hematoxylin 0.6, abs. alc. 4, glycerol 15, methanol 15 .

METHOD: as Carazzi 1911

NOTE: The original calls for preparation from sat. aq. sol. ammonia alum and 16% hematoxylin solution.

11.122 Friedländer 1882   Friedländer 1882, 92

FORMULA: water 30, glycerol 30, 95% alc. 30, hematoxylin 0.6, potassium alum 0.6

11.122 Gage 1892 *test.* **1896** *ips.*   Gage 1896, 178

FORMULA: water 100, potassium alum 4, chloral hydrate 2, 95% alc. 2, hematoxylin 0.1

11.122 de Groot 1912   23632, **29**:182

FORMULA OF SOLVENT: 95% alc. 65, water 27, glycerol 8

FORMULA OF STAIN: 95% alc. 65, water 27, glycerol 8, hydrogen peroxide 0.75, hematoxylin 0.2, calcium chloride 1.5, sodium bromide 0.75, ammonium alum 2.2, potassium ferricyanide 0.08

PREPARATION OF STAIN: Take 100 solvent. Mix 1.5 solvent with 0.75 hydrogen peroxide and dissolve 0.2 hematoxylin in this. In 25 solvent dissolve 15 calcium chloride and 0.75 sodium bromide. Add this to the hematoxylin solution and dissolve 1.1 ammonium alum in the mixture. In 40 solvent dissolve 0.08 potassium ferricyanide and add this to mixture. In the remaining solvent dissolve 1.1 ammonium alum and add to the mixture.

11.122 Harris 1900   11032, **3**:777

FORMULA: 95% alc. 5, hematoxylin 0.5, potassium alum 10, water 100, mercuric oxide 0.25

PREPARATION: Dissolve the hematoxylin in alc. Dissolve alum in water and raise to boiling. Pour hot solution on hematoxylin. Boil and throw mercuric oxide into boiling solution. Cool rapidly. Filter.

NOTE: **Mallory 1938,** 72 suggests the addition of 5% acetic acid.

11.122 Harris and Power *test.* **1884 Cole**   Cole 1884b, 42

FORMULA: hematoxylin 20, alum 60, water 100, abs. alc. 6

PREPARATION: Grind the hematoxylin in a mortar with the alum, adding water in small portions while grinding. Filter and add alcohol.

11.122 Haug *test.* **1900 Pollock**   Pollock 1900, 84
FORMULA: water 100, aluminum acetate 5, abs. alc. 5, hematoxylin 5.5
PREPARATION: Add the hematoxylin dissolved in the alc. to the acetate dissolved in the water.

11.122 Kleinenberg 1876 *test.* **1907 Böhm and Oppel**   {Böhm and Oppel 1907, 103
STOCK SOLUTIONS: I. water 30, 95% alc. 70, calcium chloride to sat., ammonium alum to sat.; II. Stock I 12, sat. sol. pot. alum in 70% alc. 88; III. sat. alc. sol. hematoxylin
WORKING SOLUTION: stock II 100, stock III 3

11.122 Kleinenberg *test.* **1884 Cole**   Cole 1884b, 42
FORMULA: sat. sol. calcium chloride in 70% alc. 15, sat. sol. potassium alum in 70% alc. 85, sat. sol. hematoxylin in abs. alc. 1

11.122 Launoy 1904 *test.* **1907 Böhm and Oppel**   Böhm and Oppel 1907, 356
FORMULA: water 100, potassium alum 0.5, hematin 1

11.122 Lee 1905   Lee 1905, 188
FORMULA: water 100, hematoxylin 0.1, ammonium alum 5, sodium iodate 0.02, chloral hydrate 5

11.122 Lillie 1948   *see* DS 11.123 Lillie 1941 (note)

11.122 Löwenthal 1892   *see* DS 13.6 Löwenthal 1892

11.122 Mallory 1938   Mallory 1938, 70
FORMULA: water 100, potassium alum 5, hematoxylin 0.25, thymol 0.25

11.122 Martinotti 1910   23632, **27**:31
FORMULA: water 70, glycerol 15, methanol 15, hematin 0.2, ammonium alum 1.5
PREPARATION: Dissolve alum in 60 water. Add hematin dissolved in 10 water. Add other ingredients to mixture.

11.122 Mayer 1891   14246, **10**:172
FORMULA: water 100, 95% alc. 5, ammonium alum 5, hematoxylin 0.1
PREPARATION: Add the hematoxylin dissolved in the alc. to the alum dissolved in the water. Ripen some months.
NOTE: Mayer (*loc. cit.*) also recommended the addition of 2% acetic acid to the above, when used for sections.

11.122 Mayer 1896 *Mayer's Glycheaemalum—auct.*   14246, **12**:310
FORMULA: water 70, glycerol 30, ammonium alum 5, hematoxylin 0.4
PREPARATION: Grind the hematoxylin to a stiff paste with a little of the glycerol. Mix the other ingredients and use the solution to wash out the mortar with successive small doses.

11.122 Mayer 1901   23632, **28**:273
FORMULA: water 100, potassium alum 5, hematoxylin 0.1, sodium iodate 0.02
NOTE: **Mayer 1903** (23632, **20**:409) substitutes ammonium alum for potassium alum.

11.122 Prudden 1885   *see* DS 11.122 Delafield (1885)

11.122 Rawitz 1895a   Rawitz 1895, 62
FORMULA: water 65, glycerol 35, potassium alum 1, hematoxylin 1

11.122 Rawitz 1895b   Rawitz 1895, 63
FORMULA: water 50, hematin 0.25, ammonium alum 1.5, glycerol 50

11.122 Rindfleisch *test.* **1877 Frey**   Frey 1877, 100
STOCK SOLUTIONS: I. sat. aq. sol hematoxylin; II. sat. aq. sol. (*circ.* 14%) ammonium alum
WORKING SOLUTION: water 85, stock I 10, stock II 5

11.122 Sass 1929   20540b, **4**:127

FORMULA: water 100, ammonium alum 5, hematoxylin 0.1, sodium iodate 0.1

NOTE: *See also* DS 11.123 Sass 1929.

11.122 Tribondeau, Fichet, and Dubreuil 1916   6630, **79**:288

FORMULA FOR STOCK SOLUTION: 95 alc. 100, water 22, silver nitrate 2, sodium hydroxide 1, hematoxylin 5

PREPARATION OF STOCK SOLUTION: Add the hydroxide dissolved in 20 water to the silver nitrate dissolved in 2 water. Wash ppt. by decantation and transfer to flash with reflux condenser. Dissolve the hematoxylin in alc. and add to silver suspension. Raise to boiling, cool, filter.

WORKING SOLUTION: 5% potassium alum 100, stock 5

11.123 Formulas Incorporating Acid Alum Mordants

11.123 Anderson 1923 *test.* **1929** *ips.*   Anderson 1929, 192

REAGENTS REQUIRED: *A*. water 90, abs. alc. 5, hematoxylin 0.25, calcium hypochlorite 0.4, ammonium alum 2, acetic acid 5; *B*. 0.1% hydrochloric acid

PREPARATION OF *A*: Add the hypochlorite to 20 water. Leave 4 hours. Filter. Add filtrate to hematoxylin dissolved in water. Dissolve other ingredients in rest of water. Add this to dye solution.

METHOD: water → *A*, 2–3 mins. → *B*, till differentiated → tap water, till blue

11.123 Anderson 1929   Anderson 1929, 129

FORMULA: water 70, 95% alc. 5, acetic acid 5, calcium hypochlorite 4, ammonium alum 3, hematoxylin 0.5

PREPARATION: as Anderson 1923.

11.123 Apáthy 1897   14246, **12**:712

FORMULA: water 45, 95% alc. 25, glycerol 35, hematoxylin 0.3, acetic acid 1, salicylic acid 0.03, ammonium alum 3

PREPARATION: Dissolve the hematoxylin in 10 water, 25 alc. Allow to ripen for some months. Dissolve the alum and acids in 35 water. Add to dye solution; then add glycerol.

11.123 Cole 1903   Cross and Cole 1903, 170

FORMULA: water 32, 95% alc. 32, glycerol 29, acetic acid 7.5, hematoxylin 0.6, ammonium alum 0.6

PREPARATION: Add alum dissolved in water to hematoxylin dissolved in alc. Add other ingredients to mixture.

11.123 Conklin *test.* **1930 Guyer**   Guyer 1930, 232

FORMULA: water 80, DS 11.122 Delafield 1885 20, F 5000.0050 Kleinenberg 1879 4

11.123 Ehrlich 1886   23632, **3**:150

REAGENTS REQUIRED: *A*. water 30, 95% alc. 30, glycerol 30, acetic acid 3, hematoxylin 0.7, ammonium alum to excess; *B*. sat. 70% alc. sol. lithium carbonate.

PREPARATION OF *A*: Dissolve hematoxylin in the alc. and acid. Dissolve 1 ammonium alum in water and glycerol. Mix with dye solution. Allow to ripen for some months. Add excess (*circ.* 10) ammonium alum to ripened solution.

METHOD FOR SECTIONS: 90% alc. → *A*, ½ to 2 mins. → 90% alc. applied from drop bottle, till differentiated → *B*, till blue → balsam, via usual reagents

NOTE: The passage of sections to water before staining, or the use of water to differentiate, results in a diffuse stain. A detailed description of the use of this stain for sections is given under DS 11.10 above.

11.123 Harris 1900   *see* DS 11.122 Harris 1900 (note)

11.123 Langeron 1942   Langeron 1942, 523

REAGENTS REQUIRED: *A*. DS 11.122 Mayer 1901 100, chloral hydrate 5, citric acid 0.1; *B*. 0.1% HCl in 70% alc.

METHOD: [sections or whole objects] → distilled water → *A*, (sections) 10 mins. *or A*, (whole objects) 24 to 48 hrs. → *B*, till differentiated → tap water till blue → balsam, via usual reagents

11.123 Lillie 1941   20540b, **16**:5

FORMULA: water 70, glycerol 30, acetic acid 20, hematoxylin 0.5, sodium iodate 0.1

PREPARATION: Add the iodate to the dye dissolved in the water. Leave overnight. Add other ingredients.

NOTE: This formula was republished, without any reference to its previous publication, by Lillie 1942 (20540b, **17**:90).

11.123 Mallory 1938 *see* DS 11.122 Harris 1900 (note)

11.123 Mann 1892 *test.* **1934 Langeron**   Langeron 1934, 475

FORMULA: water 35, 95% alc. 32, glycerol 25, acetic acid 3, hematin 0.6, potassium alum 3.5

PREPARATION: Dissolve the dye in the acid. Add mixed alc. and glycerol. Then add alum dissolved in water.

11.123 Masson *test.* **1934 Langeron**   Langeron 1934, 475

FORMULA: water 100, acetic acid 2, hematin 2, potassium alum 6

PREPARATION: Dissolve the alum in boiling water. Add dye, cool, filter. Add acid to filtrate.

NOTE: A detailed description of the use of this stain before a complex contrast is given under DS 12.30 below.

11.123 Mayer 1891 *Mayer's acid hemalum—auct.* *see* DS 11.122 Mayer 1891 (note)

11.123 Mayer *test.* **1924 Langeron**   Langeron 1942, 525

NOTE: This is DS 11.122 Mayer 1896 with the addition of acetic acid. Mayer, however, recommended this addition only to his 1891 formula. The present solution is, therefore, Langeron's variant.

11.123 Sass 1929   20540b, **4**:127

FORMULA: water 100, ammonium alum to sat., hematoxylin 1, sodium iodate 1, acetic acid 3

11.123 Watson 1943   11360, **63**:20

FORMULA: water 32, abs. alc. 32, glycerol 32, acetic acid 3, ammonium alum 0.064, hematoxylin 0.64, potassium permanganate 0.032

PREPARATION: Dissolve the alum and permanganate in water. Add dye dissolved in alc. and then other ingredients.

NOTE: This formula stains as well as DS 11.123 Ehrlich 1886, from which Watson developed it, and does not require ripening.

11.124 Formulas Incorporating Other Mordants

11.124 Alzheimer 1910 *lithium-hematoxylin*   Nissl and Alzheimer 1910, 411

FORMULA: water 90, 95% alc. 10, hematoxylin 1, lithium carbonate 0.03

PREPARATION: Add the alkali dissolved in water to the dye dissolved in alc.

11.124 Bacsich 1937 *lithium-hematoxylin*   11025, **72**:163

FORMULA: water 100, hematoxylin 1, lithium carbonate 0.1

11.124 Clara 1933 *molybdic-hematoxylin*   23632, **50**:73

STOCK SOLUTION: 1% hematoxylin 50, 10% ammonium molybdate 50, molybdic acid to excess (*circ.* 1)

WORKING SOLUTION: stock 0.1, water 100

11.124 Cook *test.* **1883 Hogg** *copper-hematoxylin*   Hogg 1883, 237

FORMULA: water 100, "extract of logwood" 15, copper sulfate 2.5, potassium alum 15

PREPARATION: Grind the dry powders in a mortar. Add enough water to make a paste. Leave two days; add rest of water. Leave 12 hours. Filter.

NOTE: The "extract of logwood" is the result of evaporating an aqueous extract of logwood to dryness; in addition to hematoxylin and hematin (about 70% of the whole) it contains tannin, glucosides, and resins.

11.124 Crétin 1925 *ferricyanide-hematoxylin*   LeMans, 93
REAGENTS REQUIRED: *A.* water 100, ferrous sulfate 4; *B.* water 100, potassium ferrocyanide 2, potassium ferricyanide 1; *C.* water 100, hematoxylin 0.5; *D.* water 100,
ferric alum 5
METHOD: Distilled water → *A*, 24 hrs. → running tap water, overnight → *B*, 3–6 hrs. →
distilled water, rinse → *C*, overnight → *D*, till differentiated
RESULTS: nuclei dense, opaque black

11.124 Donaggio 1904 *tin-hematoxylin*   1006, **22** :192
FORMULA: water 100, hematoxylin 0.5, stannic chloride diammine 10
PREPARATION: Dissolve the dry salts each in 50 water. Mix solutions.
NOTE: Donaggio 1940 (18208, **22** :171) substitutes stannic chloride for the diaminine
complex.

11.124 Gomori 1941 *chrome-hematoxylin*   608b, 17, 395
FORMULA: water 100, sulfuric acid 0.1, potassium dichromate 0.1, chrome alum 1.5,
hematoxylin 0.5
PREPARATION: Dissolve the alum and dye each in 50. Mix. Add 2 5% potassium dichromate and 2 5% sulfuric acid. Ripen 2 days.

11.124 Hansen 1905 *chrome-hematoxylin*   23632, **22** :64
FORMULA: water 100, sulfuric acid 0.2, hematoxylin 0.3, chrome alum 3, potassium
dichromate 0.2
PREPARATION: Boil the chrome alum in 85 water until green. Dissolve hematoxylin in
5 water. Add to alum solution. Then add successively, acid in 2 water and dichromate
in 7 water with constant stirring. Filter.

11.124 Harris 1900 *mercuric-hematoxylin* *see* DS 11.122 Harris

11.124 Heidenhain *test.* **1907 Böhm and Oppel** *vanadium-hematoxylin*
Böhm and Oppel 1907, 105
FORMULA: 0.5% hematoxylin 60, 0.25% ammonium vanadate 30

11.124 Held *test.* **1937 Gatenby and Painter** *phosphomolybdic hematoxylin*
Gatenby and Painter 1937, 374
FORMULA: water 30, 95% alc. 70 hematoxylin 1, phosphomolybdic acid 15
PREPARATION: Dissolve hematoxylin in solvents. Add acid. Leave 1 month. Decant.

11.124 Hornyold 1915 *test.* **Gatenby and Painter 1937** *iodine-hematoxylin*
Gatenby and Painter 1937, 158
REAGENTS REQUIRED: *A.* abs. alc. 25, water 75, hematoxylin 0.8, ammonium alum 0.5,
tincture of iodine USP (see note) 0.5; *B.* 0.1% acetic acid in 70% alc.
PREPARATION OF *A*: Add the alum dissolved in the water to the hematoxylin dissolved in
the alc. Ripen some days. Add iodine.
METHOD: [sections] → water → *A*, 5–10 mins. → rinse → *B*, till blue → balsam, via
usual reagents
NOTE: The tincture of iodine mentioned in the original formula is the British, which
contains $2\frac{1}{2}$% each of I_2 and KI in 90% alc. The official American tincture is double
this concentration and should be used in the preparation above.

11.124 Hueter 1911 *see* DS 11.124 Schueninoff 1908 (note) and Mallory 1891 (note)

11.124 Kleinenberg 1876 and 1879 *see* DS 11.124 Squire 1892 (note)

11.124 Liengme 1930 *iron-copper-hematoxylin*   4285a, **7** :233
REAGENTS REQUIRED: *A.* DS 11.122 Böhmer 1868 50, ADS 12.1 Morel & Bassal 1909 50;
B. 0.1% hydrochloric acid; *C.* sat. sol. lithium carbonate in 70% alc.
METHOD: 70% alcohol → *A*, 1–4 days → *B*, till differentiated → 70% alcohol, wash →
C, till blued → balsam, via usual reagents

11.124 Loyez *test.* **1938 Carleton and Leach** *lithium hematoxylin*
Carleton and Leach 1938, 259
STOCK I: abs. alc. 100, hematoxylin 10; STOCK II: water 100, sat. aq. sol. lithium carbon-
ate 4
WORKING SOLUTION: stock I 10, stock II 90

11.124 Mallory 1891   *phosphomolybdic hematoxylin*   766, **7**:375

FORMULA: water 100, hematoxylin 1, phosphomolybdic acid 1, chloral hydrate 7.5

PREPARATION: Add the acid dissolved in 10 water to the dye dissolved in 90. Add chloral hydrate to mixture.

METHOD: water → stain, 10 mins. to 1 hr. → 30% alc. till differentiated

NOTE: Phenol may be substituted for chloral hydrate. **Hueter** (*test.* **Schmorl 1928,** 173) substitutes phosphotungstic for phosphomolybdic acid; but see note under Schueninoff 1908.

11.124 Mallory 1900   *phosphotungstic hematoxylin*   11189, **5**:19

REAGENTS REQUIRED: *A.* water 100, hematoxylin 0.1, phosphotungstic acid 2, hydrogen peroxide 0.2

PREPARATION: Add the acid dissolved in 20 water to the dye dissolved in 80. Add hydrogen peroxide to mixture.

METHOD: [sections of material fixed in F 3700.0010 Zenker 1894 or similar fixative] → water, thorough wash → *A*, 12–24 hrs. → 95% alcohol, about one minute → abs. alc. till differentiation complete → balsam, via xylene

NOTE: This is a polychrome, general-purpose stain.

11.124 Mallory *test.* **McClung 1929**   *phosphotungstic hematoxylin*

McClung 1929, 288

REAGENTS REQUIRED: *A.* 0.25% potassium permanganate; *B.* 5% oxalic acid; *C.* water 100, hematoxylin 0.1, phosphotungstic acid 2, potassium permanganate 0.025

METHOD: [sections of material fixed in F 3700.0010 Zenker 1894 or similar fixative] → *A*, 5–10 mins. → water, thorough rinse → *B*, 10–20 mins. → *C*, 12–24 hrs. → 95% alc., quick rinse → abs. alc., least possible time → balsam via xylene

NOTE: This is a polychrome general-purpose stain.

11.124 Mayer 1891   *Haemacalcium—auct.*   14246, **10**:182

REAGENTS REQUIRED: *A.* water 30, alc. 70, acetic acid 1.5, hematoxylin 0.15, aluminum chloride 0.15, calcium chloride 7.5; *B.* 95% alc. 30, water 70, aluminum chloride 2

PREPARATION OF *A*: Grind the dye with the aluminum chloride in a beaker. Add solvents and warm to solution. Then add calcium chloride.

METHOD: [whole objects] → 70% alc. → *A*, till stained, usually overnight → *B*, till differentiated → balsam, via usual reagents

NOTE: **Mayer 1910** *"Haemastrontium"* (*test.* **Gatenby and Cowdry 1937,** 160) differs from above only in substitution of strontium chloride for calcium chloride, and of 0.1 citric acid for 1.5 acetic acid.

11.124 Mayer 1910   *Haemastrontium—auct.*   see DS 11.124 Mayer 1891 (note)

11.124 Police 1909   *phosphomolybdic-hematoxylin*   1949, **4**:300

FORMULA: water 70, alc. 30, chloral hydrate 10, hematoxylin 0.35, phosphomolybdic acid 0.03

11.124 Rawitz 1909   *aluminum-hematoxylin*   23632, **25**:391

FORMULA: water 50, glycerol 50, hematin 0.2, aluminum nitrate 2

PREPARATION: Add the aluminum nitrate dissolved in 25 water to the dye dissolved in 25 water. Then add glycerol.

11.124 Schröder 1930   *lithium-hematoxylin*   23430, 166, 588

FORMULA: water 100, hematoxylin 0.3, lithium carbonate 0.04

11.124 Schueninoff 1908   *phosphomolybdic hematoxylin*   23681, **18**:6

FORMULA: water 100, hematoxylin 0.9, phenol 2.5, phosphomolybdic acid 0.5

NOTE: **Hueter** 1911 (Romeis 1948, 351) differs from this only in the substitution of phosphotungstic acid; but see note under Mallory 1891.

11.124 Schweitzer 1942 *test.* **1946 Roskin**   *chrome-hematoxylin*

Roskin 1946, 200

FORMULA: water 125, chrome alum 5, hematoxylin 0.5, 10% sulfuric acid 4, potassium dichromate 0.275

PREPARATION: To the first three ingredients dissolved in 90 water add the dichromate dissolved in 10.

11.124 Squire 1892   *calcium-hematoxylin*   Squire 1892, 25
   FORMULA: water 10.5, alc. 96, hematoxylin 1, calcium chloride 8, ammonium alum 1.2
   PREPARATION: Add the alum dissolved in 6.5 water to the calcium chloride dissolved in 4
      water. Add alc., leave 1 hour, filter. Dissolve dye in filtrate.
   NOTE: In the early 1880's almost any alum-calcium chloride-hematoxylin was referred
      to as "Kleinenberg," who recommended this method of preparing an aluminum
      chloride-hematoxylin (which, in effect, this is) without recourse to the very acid salt
      in commerce in his time. The method given by **Kleinenberg 1876** (Grundsüge der
      Entwickelungsgeschichte, Leipsig) proved impractical and a revised method (17510,
      74:208) published in 1879, usually erroneously cited as the original, proved little
      better.

11.124 Thomas 1943   *phosphomolybdic hematoxylin*   4285a, **20**:49
   FORMULA: water 44, dioxane 40, ethylene glycol 11, phosphomolybdic acid 16.5, hema-
      toxylin 2.5, hydrogen peroxide 2
   PREPARATION: Dissolve the hematoxylin in the dioxane and add the hydrogen per-
      oxide. Dissolve the phosphomolybdic acid in the other solvents and filter into the
      hematoxylin.

11.2 CARMINE STAINS

As in the case of hematoxylin, carmine was widely employed in the dyeing trade prior to the introduction of stains into microtomy. The carmine itself was commonly obtained as a tin lake, prepared by boiling cochineal extracts with tin salts, usually the tartrate. Though it is customary to distinguish between those staining formulas employing carmine lakes, those employing extracts of the raw cochineal, and those employing carminic acid, there is no justification for this since those formulas employing the two latter reagents have always incorporated with them some material which will take the lake into solution.

The six divisions of the carmine formulas here employed are based entirely on the ingredients, the most widely known being the first two classes of "alcohol carmines" (DS 11.22) and "alum carmines" (DS 11.21). Considerable confusion has been occasioned by the fact that Grenacher, in 1879, published formulas for each of these two divisions and early workers almost invariably employed the alum carmine, while modern workers seem to prefer the "alcoholic borax carmine."

The early employment of carmine for staining materials before sectioning was necessitated by the fact that no method had been worked out for attaching sections to slides, so that the fewer manipulations which were undertaken in the sections, the more chance there was for preserving the whole. The straight alum carmines are best employed for direct staining from exceedingly dilute solutions, a 1% solution of ammonia alum being the customary diluent. Alcoholic carmines, particularly that of Grenacher 1879, are most employed for the preparation of wholemounts of small invertebrates. The formulas of Mayer 1881 and Mayer 1892a, are the best devised for small marine invertebrates. Though the borax-carmine of Grenacher is commonly made today by the method here given for the "working formula direct" the original method of Grenacher was to prepare the dry stock and to make up working formulas from it in various strengths of alcohol. This gives far better control of the process, since the solubility of the dry stock is a direct function of the concentration of alcohol employed. When any of the alcoholic carmines are used, they are differentiated with a .1% solution of hydrochloric acid in 70% alcohol.

The aceto-carmines, (DS 11.23) which form the next class, are more widely employed in botanical than in zoological techniques, and their most valuable applications is the staining of unfixed nuclei. They should be confined if possible to this use, for their preservation as permanent objects is difficult. Their only other use, besides the counting of chromosomes, is in the diagnostic staining of parasitic platyhelminthes.

Picro-carmines (DS 11.24) are warmly recommended to the beginner, for it is almost impossible to overstain in them. The picric acid, moreover, acts as a fixative. It is possible to take a small living invertebrate, throw it into the stain for ten minutes or so, and remove it fixed and stained. The original formula of Ranvier 1889 called for a preparation of a dry stock and the preparation of a working solution from this. Until quite recent times the dry stock could be purchased. It undoubtedly makes a better solution and keeps better than do the formulas prepared as solutions directly.

Iron carmines (DS 11.25) had a brief vogue in the first decade of the present century and then again fell into disfavor. They are nuclear stains strongly resembling the reactions of the iron hematoxylins. The formula of De Groot 1903 is the one most usually recommended. Ammonia carmines (DS 11.26) and hydrochloric carmines (DS 11.26) are no longer very well known, though the formula of Hollande 1916 gives excellent nuclear staining. The final class, which contains those formulas that cannot reasonably be fitted into the previous classes, are rarely used today. The only formula finding any great acceptance is the "lithium carmine" of Orth (1892), which was rediscovered in Germany in the 1920's. It is most warmly recommended by Spielmeyer, 1924, for counterstaining sections of the nervous system.

11.20 TYPICAL EXAMPLES

Preparation of a wholemount of a liver fluke using the carmalum stain of Mayer 1897

Though many persons will be forced to rely for their material on a supply house, better preparations can be made if the living flukes are secured from a slaughter house. In this case the flukes should be removed from the liver (where they will mostly be found crawling upon the surface if the animal has been dead for some time) to a vacuum flask containing physiological saline solution at a temperature of about 35°C. to which has been added a small quantity (approximately one tenth of a gram per liter) of gelatin. Flukes can be transported alive for relatively long distances in this solution, and every possible effort should be made to keep them alive until they have been brought to the laboratory. In the laboratory the contents of the thermos flask should be poured into a dish and the worms transferred individually to another large dish containing warm physiological saline, where the last of the blood will be washed from them. Better preparations will be secured if time be taken to anesthetize the worms before fixing them. Most of the thick and opaque mounts which one seens in laboratories result from an endeavor to fix an unanesthetized worm which has contracted during the course of fixation. Liver flukes are easy to anesthetize, the simplest method being to sprinkle a few crystals of menthol on the surface of the warm saline and leave them for about half an hour. One should not, of course, permit them to die in this solution, but should watch them carefully, terminating the process when their motions become exceedingly slow and consist only of an occasional feeble contraction rather than the active movements in which they were indulging when removed from the liver.

While the worms are being anesthetized preparations for fixing them should be made. Take two sheets of quarter-inch plate glass, each of such a size as will enable one to lay on them the number of worms which are to be fixed, and place upon the lower plate two or three thicknesses of a rather coarse filter paper or paper toweling. Blotting paper is too soft for this purpose; a good filter paper is much to be preferred to a paper towel. The selection of a fixative must, of course, rest in the hands of the operator, but the author's preference is for the mercuric-acetic-nitric mixture of Gilson 1898 (Chapter 18, F 3000.0014). This has all the advantages in sharpness of definition given by mercuric fixatives, while the addition of nitric acid appears to render the flattened worms less brittle in subsequent handling. Whatever fixative is selected, the sheet of filter paper is now saturated thoroughly with it and the anesthetized worms are removed from the physiological saline and laid out one by one about an inch apart on the blotting paper. This must be done as rapidly as possible to prevent fixation taking place before an additional layer of paper (saturated with fixative) is placed on the top, and the second sheet of glass placed on top of this. Assuming that the sheets of glass are the size of a sheet of typewriting paper, it is suggested that about a two-pound weight then be placed on the upper sheet of glass. The "sandwich" should now be left for at least 12 hours before removing the glass and upper paper. Then the worms should be picked up one by one on a glass section lifter (metal cannot be used because of the presence of mercuric chloride) and transferred to a large jar of fixative, where they may remain from another day to another week at the discretion of the technician.

At the conclusion of fixation the worms should be washed in running water for at least 24 hours. It has not been the author's experience that this fixative, followed by such washing, requires the use of iodine for the final removal of the mercury. At this stage iodine tends to render the worms brittle and the author strongly recommends its omission. After being thoroughly washed in water, the worms may be stained. The formula selected for this example is the very well-known carmalum of Mayer (DS 11.21 Mayer 1897 below). Objects of this type are better stained by the additive process than by a process of differentiation. That is, they are better placed in weak solution and allowed to absorb the stain slowly than if placed in a strong solution which will require subsequent differentiation. The best diluent for the stain is a 5% solution of potassium alum. The extent of the dilution is dependent upon the choice of the operator and the size of the object which is to be stained. In the present instance a dilution of about one part of the stain to 100 parts of 5% potassium alum would be correct. It is far worse to have the solution too strong than it is to have it too weak and, since it is an excellent preservative, the worms can remain in it indefinitely. The worms are placed in this diluted stain and left there until their internal structures have become clearly visible. It is suggested that they be examined at the end of a week and subsequently every three days, until such time as examination with a low-power binocular microscope, using a bright light from beneath, shows the testes to be darkly stained. At this point the worms are removed to a fresh solution of 5% potassium alum and rinsed for a short time until all the adherent color has left them. They will still, however, be pink on the outside. Since the purpose of the stain is to demonstrate the internal organs it is desirable to bleach this outer layer in order to produce bright scarlet internal organs against a white background. In the experience of the writer this may be done most readily with the aid of a potassium permanganate-oxalic acid bleach in the following manner. Prepare a solution of potassium permanganate so weak that it appears only a very faint pink. This is best done by adding a few drops of a strong solution to a beaker of distilled water. Each worm is then taken individually and dropped into the solution until such time as it has turned a bronzy brown on the outside. This appearance can best be detected in reflected light and just as soon as the first bronze sheen appears on the outside, the worm must be removed to fresh distilled water, where it can remain until all the other worms in the batch have been similarly treated. It will be necessary, of course, to renew the potassium permanganate from time to time by adding a few more drops of the stock solution to the beaker. The strength of oxalic acid used to bleach the worm is quite immaterial. Two or 3%, arrived at by guess work rather than by weighing, is an adequate solution. As the bleaching of the surface is not as critical as is the deposition of the potassium permanganate, all the worms may be bleached at the same time by pouring off from the beaker the distilled water in which they have been accumulated, and substituting for it the oxalic acid. One or two twists of the wrist, to rotate the worms in the beaker, will result in their turning from a bronze sheen to a dead white. The oxalic acid is then poured off without any waste of time, and the worms washed in running tap water for an hour or so, before being dehydrated in the ordinary way, cleared, and mounted in balsam (see Chapter 6).

Little trouble will be experienced with worms curling if they have been fixed and treated as described; if they do curl, they should undergo the final dehydration in 95% alcohol pressed loosely between two sheets of glass.

Preparation of a wholemount of a medusa using the alcoholic-borax-carmine stain of Grenacher 1879

The preparation of a good wholemount of a medusa, particularly of the thick-bodied type such as *Sarsia* or *Gonionemus*, is one of the most difficult operations known in microtomy and is under no circumstance, to be attempted by a beginner who is liable to be discouraged. No reference is here intended to those horrible travesties of wrinkled and crumpled medusae which are occasionally seen. A good slide of a medusa should differ from the medusa in life only in that to a transparency as great as that of the original should be added such staining as will bring out structures previously almost invisible.

The first essential in the preparation of a good wholemount is the collection and preservation of the medusa itself. It is only with extreme rarity that well-preserved specimens (from the microtomist's point of view) can be secured from biological supply houses. It is presumed in the discussion which follows, therefore, that the mounter is in a position to secure his own living material. The first, and most essential, feature is that the medusa be kept in a large volume of clean sea water from the first moment of its collection. It is no use securing an assorted plankton sample in which are swimming a few medusae and anticipating that these will remain for more than a few moments in an undamaged condition. The entire plankton sample should be tipped into a large bowl of clean sea water and each individual medusa removed from it to another bowl of clean sea water. From this clean collection there should be selected and thrown away all those medusae which show the slightest damage, together with all those which are sluggish in their movements or are beginning to turn opaque.

Subsequent processes are so laborious that it is a waste of time to start with other than perfect specimens.

Medusae need to be rather thoroughly narcotized prior to fixation and, though it is commonly stated that only cocaine will work for this purpose, the author has had considerable success either with chloral hydrate or with mixtures of menthol and chloral hydrate together. A few crystals of menthol should be placed on the surface and a few drops of a 10% solution of chloral hydrate in sea water should be added for each 100 cc. of the fluid in which the medusae are swimming. Though it would appear to be a waste of reagents at first sight, it is far better to commence the process of narcotization in a relatively large volume of sea water, for medusae actively swimming in small containers are likely continually to hit themselves on the sides of the vessel. They will not expand into that perfectly relaxed condition which is prerequisite to success in fixation. The actual fluid used for fixation is a matter of individual preference; but the author has always had such success with the mercuric-cupric mixture of Lo Bianco 1890 (Chapter 18, F 3400.0000) that he has not experimented widely with other fixatives. The technique employed in fixation is more important than the fixative, and the method of Lo Bianco (*loc. cit.*) can scarcely be improved. First, secure a large glass bowl of the type customarily used in kitchens for mixing cakes, and fill it about one-third full of clean sea water. Then transfer each narcotized medusa to this bowl of clean sea water until there have been accumulated as many medusa as can conveniently be placed in it without their actually rubbing against each other. Take the bowl in the left hand and swing it in a circle in such a manner that the contained fluid with the medusae commences to rotate within the bowl. When all the medusae are facing in the same direction with their tentacles streaming behind them through the flow of the water, then slightly increase the speed while at the same time pouring in the fixative as a steady stream from a large jug held in the right hand. Allowance should be made for twice as much fixative as there is fluid in which the medusae are swimming. The rotary movement of the left hand should on no account be discontinued until at least three or four minutes have passed after the addition of the fixative. A safe criterion is that the endodermal canals shall have become opaque through the action of the fixative before the rotary movement is discontinued. The medusae will be found to settle to the bottom of the bowl in about the same period of time as it takes the mounter to resecure the use of his left arm. The medusae may then be removed, one at a time with a *glass* spoon, to a fresh large volume of the fixative in which they should remain overnight, though a period of two or three days in this fixative, will not damage them.

There now commences, between this time and the time of the final mounting of the medusa in balsam, a continual struggle against the collapse of the delicate mesoglea with the subsequent wrecking of the mount. This collapse is produced by osmotic pressure, and it is sufficient to remove the medusae to distilled water to ensure spoiling them. It is therefore necessary to transfer the medusae first to about a gallon of clean, filtered, sea water, to commence the process of washing, and then, through a quite finely drawn glass tube connected with the fresh water tap, to permit the sea water slowly to be replaced by fresh water.

It is now necessary to rig up some form of drip mechanism by which the water in which the medusae are resting may be replaced with increasing strengths of alcohol by a slow and continuous process. The writer himself uses a 50 milliliter wide-mouth bottle standing upon his bench with a liter aspirator bottle standing on the shelf above. A rubber tube from the aspirator bottle passes to an ordinary pipet inserted through a hole in the cork of the bottle, from which comes a second drainage tube leading to the waste. A screw-controlled pinchcock in the middle of the rubber tube leading from the aspirator bottle permits a very fine control of the flow of alcohol which is established, of course, before the cork is inserted into the 50 milliliter bottle. For replacing, in the first stage, the water used for washing

with 15% alcohol, a flow of 50 or 60 drops a minute will be found perfectly safe. The flow should be permitted to continue until the whole liter of 15% alcohol has passed out of the aspirator bottle and through the 50-milliliter bottle in which are the specimens.

For the type of process which is now being described it is better to utilize Grenacher's dry powder, the method of preparation for which is given in the abbreviated formula below (11.21 Grenacher 1879), than it is to endeavor to use the prepared solution in 70% alcohol. If this powder is obtainable, or can be made, it is recommended that about 100 milliliters of a 2% solution be prepared in 30% alcohol and run through the aspirator bottle into the specimen bottle in the manner in which the alcohol has already been used. This stain may be permitted to remain in contact with the specimens overnight or for whatever period of time is convenient to the operator. The aspirator bottle is now again filled with a liter of 30% alcohol to which has been added approximately one milliliter of hydrochloric acid. This acid alcohol is now used to flush out the stain from the specimen bottle. Unless a relatively pale pink solution alone remains after the passage of the acid alcohol, a further liter will have to be run through. The specimens may be left to differentiate in acid alcohol until inspection with the naked eye shows the mesoglea to be practically free of stain. The internal organs, however, should remain a rather bright pink. It must not be forgotten that the apparent degree of staining will increase greatly when the specimens are cleared.

The process of dehydration should now be completed using successive liter portions of 60% alcohol, 80% alcohol, and 95% alcohol run through by the slow flow method already described. To complete the process of dehydration the author prefers, on a cost basis, to use acetone in place of absolute alcohol, though there is, of course, no reason why alcohol should not be employed. However, it usually is necessary to run through at least two liters of the last dehydrating agent in order to be quite certain that the specimens are perfectly dehydrated.

As a clearing agent, the author prefers benzene, for the double reason that it can be used for the solution of balsam in the next stage and also because it leads to less hardening than almost any other reagent. The acetone or alcohol is replaced with benzene by the same slow flow process: passing through the stages of 20% benzene, 40% benzene, 60% benzene, 80% benzene, the percentage figures referring to the amount of benzene in mixture with fresh acetone or alcohol. These benzene-acetone mixtures should be run through in quantities of a liter each, but they need not, of course, be wasted, for only the first fraction passing through will be seriously diluted and the remaining material may be led from the outlet pipe of the bottle in which the specimen is to another bottle in which it may be stored for future use. Though it is perhaps pointing out the obvious, attention should be drawn to the fact that either synthetic rubber tubing or alternatively solid glass joints must be employed.

Transference of the perfectly cleared specimens to Canada balsam is a more difficult project than even the clearing and dehydrating already undertaken. The author prefers the method of evaporation, even though it is most tediously slow, because it has the advantage of complete safety. In this method the benzene in which the specimens are now resting is replaced, using the same flow method which has been used for the application of all the other reagents, by a 1% solution of Canada balsam in benzene. Unfortunately it is impossible to evaporate the benzene directly from the balsam, unless a tremendous volume of solution is employed, for even the relatively thin solution used for mounting sections should be at least 40% by weight balsam and for the mounting of wholemounts, 60 or 70% is not excessive. A solution stronger than 1%, even when applied by the drip method, will inevitably result in the collapse of the specimen; therefore one is forced to substitute increasingly stronger solutions before the final evaporation is made. The simplest way to do this is to pass the specimens as described into a 1% solution and then to transfer the specimens in this solution to a beaker of the 1% solution. The height of the 1% solution in the beaker is then measured with a millimeter scale and a red mark made halfway between the top of the liquid and the bottom of the beaker. The beaker is then placed in a large desiccator, the lid of which is removed at daily intervals to liberate the benzene, and the whole is permitted to evaporate until the halfway mark is reached. A fresh solution of 2% balsam is then taken and a drop of it placed carefully in the presumable 2% solution which is now in the beaker. If this drop shows by its refractive index that it is now of the same concentration as that in the beaker, the solution which is to be added should be adjusted, either with the addition of balsam or with the addition of benzene, until there is little or no difference between the two solutions. The beaker is then filled up with this fresh 2% solution to the original level and again permitted to evaporate down to the halfway mark. At this time an additional portion of 4% solution is added and so on until the beaker is filled with a 32% solution. This is now permitted to evaporate until it is just liquid enough to permit the removal of each medusa with a considerable portion of the balsam either to a hollow-ground slide or a deep cell. No coverslip is placed on it at this stage, but additional solution from the beaker is piled on top of the specimen as it evaporates so that a little mount of semiliquid balsam is constantly kept over the specimen. The utmost care must be taken to exclude dust during these proceedings. When the balsam has, by evaporation, been thickened to the point where it no longer flows, a coverslip should be dipped in clean benzene and placed on top of the mound of balsam and the slide slowly heated on a hotplate until it becomes sufficiently fluid for the coverslip to settle of its own accord onto the specimen. The specimen is then cooled, permitted to set for a day or two, and then cleaned up in the ordinary manner.

Though it must be admitted that the preparation of mounts of this type occupies several months, only a very few hours per week are required to look after the preparation. The results leave nothing to be desired, whether the mount is made of the medusa, which has been taken as a typical example, or of any other exceedingly delicate material that is liable to collapse in mounting.

Preparation of a smear to show chromosomes in salivary glands of Chironomus using the iron-aceto-carmine stain of Belling 1921

Aceto-carmine preparations are easy to make but their utility is limited by their short life, which rarely exceeds, even in a successful preparation, more than a week or two. They are, however, excellent for class demonstration, and the preparation which follows should be placed in the hands of every student of cytology who wants to see for himself the really startling detail which can be obtained in salivary gland chromosomes. Though this technique is simplest when the larva of the dipteran *Chironomus* is employed, there are many other small flies with which it may be used.

The larva of *Chironomus* which is recognized by the rapidity of its movements and its bright blood-red coloration, may usually be collected from any fresh-water stream. It is a waste of time to dissect out the salivary glands since they may be obtained more easily by pulling the animal apart. Take the *Chironomus* larva and strand it on a clean glass slide on which the final mount is to be prepared. If the animal is living in ordinary pond water containing much debris, it is desirable to transfer it for an hour or two to filtered water in order that the worst of the debris may be removed. Two mounted needles are all that are required to complete the technique. The first needle is pressed firmly upon the head of the larva which, for a right-handed individual, may be most conveniently directed toward the left. With the point of the second needle a very small hole should be torn in the upper integument immediately behind the junction of the head with the thorax. Though this hole is not absolutely essential it is an insurance against the animal's breaking in an undesirable place. The second needle

is then pressed firmly and horizontally across the abdomen and drawn with a slow and steady motion to the right. Nine times out of 10 the larva will break in half at the junction of the head with the thorax, and there will be drawn out of the thorax the anterior portion of the alimentary canal together with, of course, large numbers of attendant structures, including the salivary glands. The salivary glands may be recognized as a pair of flattened, transparent, pear-shaped structures in which the nuclei are so large that they may be recognized with even the low power of a microscope. Everything except the salivary glands should now be dissected away with the needles, the glands themselves being severed from their attachment either with the point of the needle or with the edge of a minute scalpel. A few drops of isotonic saline may now be employed to wash away the remainder of the adherent material, leaving the salivary glands isolated on, and usually adherent to, the surface of the slide.

It is assumed that a supply of Belling's aceto-carmine has already been secured, made up according to the directions given in the formula below (DS 11.23 Belling 1921). All that is now necessary is to place a few drops of this on top of the salivary glands and to add a coverslip. Care should be taken that sufficient is added to prevent undesirable squashing at this stage of the proceedings. The slide is now placed on one side for about five minutes, the aceto-carmine being replaced as it evaporates. Very little should normally be lost, however, unless the atmosphere is unduly dry. The specimen is then examined under the low power of the microscope and, if it appears to be too opaque, is flattened by gentle pressure from a needle. The ejected aceto-carmine is mopped up on a filter paper until such time as it is sufficiently thin. The specimen may then be examined under the high power of the microscope and the remarkable structure of the chromosomes noted.

There is no really satisfactory method of rendering permanent an aceto-carmine preparation, though they will keep for some weeks if the edge of the coverslip is cemented (see Chapters 2 and 3) with any material suitable for the purpose. Alternatively, recourse may be had to the combined mounting and staining media of Zirkel 1940 (see Chapter 26). These are considerably more stable but cannot be regarded as permanent.

11.21 ALUM CARMINES

11.21 Anderson 1926　　　　　　　　　　　　　11431, **29**:117
FORMULA: water 95, abs. alc. 10, acetic acid 5, carmine 1, ammonium alum 3.5, calcium hypochlorite 0.1
PREPARATION: To the carmine suspended in the alc., add the hypochlorite suspended in 5 water. Dissolve the alum in 90 water, bring to boil, add carmine mixture boil 1 minute, cool, filter. Add acid.

11.21 Arcangeli 1885a　　　　　　　　　　　　16977, **4**:233
FORMULA: water 100, ammonium alum 15, boric acid 2, carmine 0.25
PREPARATION: Boil 10 minutes. Filter.

11.21 Arcangeli 1885b　　　　　　　　　　　　16977, **4**:233
FORMULA: water 100, ammonium alum 15, salicylic acid 0.25, carmine 0.25
PREPARATION: As Arcangeli 1885a.

11.21 Böhm and Oppel 1907　　*see* DS 11.21 Rabl 1894 (note)

11.21 Czokor 1880　　　　　　　　　　　　　　1780, **18**:413
FORMULA: water 100, cochineal 2, potassium alum 2, phenol 0.25
PREPARATION: Suspend the cochineal and alum in 200 water. Boil till volume is reduced to 100. Leave 2 days, filter, and add phenol to filtrate.

11.21 Fyg 1928　　*see* DS 11.28 Fyg 1928

11.21 Gower 1939　　　　　　　　　　　　　　2054b, **14**:31
FORMULA: water 100, alum 5, residue from preparation of DS 11.23 Schneider 1880 (*q.v.*) 0.5
NOTE: This was originally recommended for trematodes, but is an excellent general-purpose, wholemount stain.

11.21 Grenacher 1879　　　　　　　　　　　　1780, **16**:465
FORMULA: water 100, carmine 1, ammonium alum 10
PREPARATION: Add the carmine to the boiling alum solution. Cool. Filter.
METHOD: [water] → suitable dilution of stain, till sufficiently stained → balsam, via usual reagents
NOTE: The larger the animal, the greater the dilution. For protozoans use full strength overnight; for a large leech use 1:5000 for 2 months. This stain is frequently confused with 11.22 Grenacher 1879. **Mährenthal's** carmine (Rawitz 1895, 60) is 4 parts of this solution with 1 of 95% alc.

11.21 Guyer 1930　　　　　　　　　　　　　Guyer 1930, 9
FORMULA: water 100, potassium alum 6, cochineal 6
PREPARATION: Boil 30 minutes. Dilute to 150. Boil till reduced to 100. Cool. Filter.

11.21 Kirkpatrick *test*. **1938 Carleton and Leach** *cit*. **Cappell**
　　　　　　　　　　　　　　　　　　　Carleton and Leach 1938, 105
FORMULA: water 100, acetic acid 2.5, ammonium alum 2.5, cochineal 2.5, salicylic acid 0.1
PREPARATION: Soak cochineal 20 minutes in 10 water with 2.5 acetic acid. Add 40 water and boil 1 hour. Dissolve alum in 50 water, bring to boil, and add to boiling cochineal. Boil 1 hour. Cool, make up to 100, filter, add salicylic acid.

11.21 Mährenthal　　*see* DS 11.21 Grenacher 1879 (note)

11.21 Mayer 1892　　*Carmalum—auct.*　　　　　　14246, **10**:482
FORMULA: water 100, potassium alum 5, carminic acid 0.5
USE: Full strength, usually for 1 to 10 days, on embryos prior to embedding and sectioning.

11.21 Mayer 1897   *Carmalum—auct.*   23632, **14**:29
  FORMULA: water 100, potassium alum 5, carmine 2
  PREPARATION: Boil 1 hour. Cool. Filter.
  NOTE: A detailed description of the use of this stain in the preparation of a wholemount
  is given under 11.20 above.

11.21 Partsch 1877   1780, **14**:180
  FORMULA: water 100, potassium alum 6, cochineal 3, salicylic acid 0 25
  PREPARATION: Boil alum and cochineal 2 hours. Cool. Filter. Add salicylic acid.

11.21 Rabl 1894   23632, **11**:168
  FORMULA: water 100, potassium alum 4, cochineal 4
  PREPARATION: Suspend cochineal and alum in 130 water. Boil till reduced to 100. Cool.
  Filter.
  NOTE: The formula of **Böhm and Oppel 1907**, 98 is in every way identical.

11.21 Rawitz 1895   Rawitz 1895, 61
  FORMULA: water 100, potassium alum 5, carminic acid 0.5

11.21 Rawitz 1899   766, **15**:438
  FORMULA: water 50, glycerol 50, ammonium alum 6.5, carminic acid 0.7
  PREPARATION: Dissolve the dye with heat in the alum solution. Filter. Add glycerol.

11.22 ALCOHOLIC CARMINES

11.22 Grenacher 1879   *Alcoholic borax carmine—compl. script.*
                                          1780, **16**:448
  PREPARATION OF DRY STOCK: Boil 250 water, 8 carmine, 10 sodium borate for 30 minutes.
  Cool overnight. Filter. Evaporate filtrate to dryness.
  WORKING FORMULA FROM DRY STOCK: 30%, 50%, or 70% alc. 100, dry stock to sat.
  PREPARATION WORKING FORMULA DIRECT: Boil 50 water, 1.5 carmine, 2 sodium borate
  for 30 minutes. Cool. Add 50 70% alc. Leave 2–3 days. Filter.
  REAGENTS REQUIRED: *A.* any selected working formula; *B.* 0.1% hydrochloric acid in
  70% alc.
  METHOD: [alcohol of lower concentration than selected working formula] → *A*, not less
  than 12 hrs. → *B*, till pink and translucent → balsam, via usual reagents
  NOTE: Though it is customary to prepare the working solution direct, much better results
  may be obtained from dry stock in variously concentrated alcohol. The solubility decreases very rapidly with increasing alcoholic content so that power of the stain may
  be accurately controlled. A detailed description of the use of this stain in the preparation of a wholemount is given under 11.20 above.

11.22 von Mährenthal   *see* DS 11.21 Grenacher 1879 (note)

11.22 Mayer 1881   *Alcoholic cochineal—compl. script.*   14246, **2**:14
  FORMULA: water 30, 95% alc. 70, cochineal 10
  PREPARATION: Digest 1 week. Filter.
  METHOD: [marine invertebrate larvae, formaldehyde or alcohol preserved] → stain, 1–10
  mins. → 70% alc., till differentiated → balsam, via usual reagents
  NOTE: For the material indicated this stain gives better results than other carmine
  formulas.

11.22 Mayer 1892a   *Paracarmine—compl. script.*   14246, **10**:491
  REAGENTS REQUIRED: *A.* 70% alc. 100, aluminum chloride 0.5, strontium chloride 4,
  carminic acid 1; *B.* 0.1% strontium chloride in 70% alc.
  METHOD: [small invertebrates] → 50% alc. → *A*, till required structures are stained, 5
  mins. to 1 wk. → *B*, if differentiation necessary → balsam, via cedar oil

11.22 Mayer 1892b   14246, **10**:498
  FORMULA: water 50, 95% alc. 50, nitric acid 0.3, cochineal 5, calcium chloride 5, aluminum chloride 0.5
  PREPARATION: Grind the dry ingredients to a paste with the acid. Mix solvents with
  paste, bring to boil, leave 5 days, filter.

11.22 Schwarz 1933   23632, **50**:305
FORMULA: water 50, methanol 50, carmine 2, sodium borate 2
PREPARATION: Boil the carmine and sodium borate 1 hour in 100 water. Evaporate to 25. Cool. Dilute to 50 and add 50 methanol. Leave 1 day. Filter.

11.22 Seiler 1881   Seiler 1881, 62
FORMULA: water 100, 95% alc. 50, sodium borate 1, carmine 0.6

11.22 Spuler *test.* **1907 Böhm and Oppel**   Böhm and Oppel 1907, 99
FORMULA: water 100, cochineal 10, 95% alc. *q.s.*
PREPARATION: Boil the cochineal in 100 water till reduced to 50. Add 95% alc. until ppt. appears. Filter. Evaporate to 100.

11.23 ACETO-CARMINES

11.23 Belling 1921   651, **54**:573
PREPARATION: To 50 DS 11.23 Schneider 1880 add ADS 12.2 Belling 1921 until ppt. appears. Then add 50 DS 11.23 Schneider 1880.
METHOD: [smears for chromosome counts, or fresh cestodes for diagnosis] → stain, on slide → examine
NOTE: A detailed description of the use of this stain is given under 11.20 above.

11.23 Gower 1939   *see* DS 11.21 Gower 1939

11.23 Henneguy 1887   Henneguy 1887, 88
STOCK FORMULA: water 100, potassium alum 6, carmine 2, acetic acid 25
PREPARATION OF STOCK: Boil the dye and alum in the water 1 hour. Cool. Add acid; leave 10 days, filter.
WORKING SOLUTION: *A*. water 99, stock 1
METHOD: [95% alc.] → *A*, until stained → distilled water → balsam, via usual reagents
NOTE: This is the only aceto-carmine well adopted for general staining of wholemounts.

11.23 Nickiforow *test.* **1900 Pollack**   Pollack 1900, 76
FORMULA: water 100, carmine 3, sodium borate 10, ammonia *q.s.*, acetic acid 0.5
PREPARATION: Boil dye and sodium borate 1 minute in 200 water. Add ammonia drop by drop till all carmine is dissolved. Evaporate to 100. Add acid.

11.23 Schneider 1880   23833, **3**:254
FORMULA: water 55, acetic acid 45, carmine·5
PREPARATION: Boil 15 minutes under reflux. Cool. Filter.
METHOD: as Belling 1921
NOTE: This formula is frequently (cf. Gatenby and Painter 1937, 685) attributed to Belling 1921 (*q.v.*). The residue on the filter paper may be used in the preparation of DS 11.21 Gower 1939.

11.23 Semmens 1938   *see* M 11.1 Semmens 1938

11.23 Sémichon 1924   19227a, **11**:193
REAGENTS REQUIRED: *A*. water 50, acetic acid 50, carmine 5; *B*. 70% alcohol
PREPARATION OF *A*: Digest ingredients 1 hour at 90°C. Cool. Filter.
METHOD: [living material] → *A*, till stained → *B*, till differentiated → balsam, via usual reagents

11.23 Zacharias 1894   23833, **11**:62
REAGENTS REQUIRED: *A*. water 70, acetic acid 30, carmine 0.5; *B*. 1% acetic acid; *C*. 1% ferric ammonium citrate
PREPARATION OF *A*: As Sémichon 1924.
METHOD: [whole objects to be sectioned, or sections] → water → *A*, 2–5 hrs. → *B*, rinse → *C*, 2–3 hrs. → distilled water, thorough wash → balsam, or paraffin, via usual reagents

11.23 Zirkle 1937   *see* M 12.1 Zirkle 1937 and M 13.1 Zirkle 1937

11.23 Zirkle 1940   *see* M 11.1, M 12.1, M.13.1, M 22.1 and M.31.1 Zirkle 1940

11.24 PICRO-CARMINES

11.24 Arcangeli *test. circ.* **1890 Francotte**   Francotte, 217
FORMULA: water 100, picric acid 1, carmine 0.5
PREPARATION: Boil 10 minutes. Cool. Filter.

11.24 Bizzozero *test.* **1889 Friedländer**   Friedländer 1889, 89
FORMULA: water 100, 95% alc. 20, picric acid 1, carmine 1, ammonia 6
PREPARATION: Dissolve carmine in ammonia. Add 100 water. Dissolve picric in 100
water. Add to carmine and evaporate to 100. Cool; filter. Add alc. to filtrate.

11.24 Francotte *circ.* **1890**   Francotte, 216
FORMULA: water 100, carmine 1, ammonia 5, picric acid 1, chloral hydrate 1
PREPARATION: Dissolve carmine in ammonia. Dissolve picric acid in 50 hot water and
add to carmine. Dilute to 100. Add chloral hydrate.

11.24 Friedländer 1889   Friedländer 1889, 88
FORMULA: water 50, carmine 1, ammonia 1, sat. sol. picric acid 100
PREPARATION: Dissolve carmine in ammonia. Add water and picric solution.

11.24 Gage 1880 *test. circ.* **1890 Francotte**   Francotte, 213
FORMULA: water 100, carmine 1, ammonia 50, picric acid 1
PREPARATION: Dissolve carmine in ammonia. Add picric dissolved in water. Leave 1 day.
Filter. Evaporate to dryness. Dissolve residue in 100 water.

11.24 Guyer 1906 *test.* **1930** *ips.*   Guyer 1930, 239
FORMULA: water 50, sat. aq. sol. picric acid 50, ammonia 5, carmine 1
PREPARATION: Dissolve carmine in ammonia. Add water and picric solution. Leave 2
days. Filter.

11.24 Jensen 1937   23684, **139**:333
STOCK SOLUTIONS: I. water 100, 0.1, carmine 0.5; II. water 100, picric acid 0.5, mag-
nesium oxide 2
WORKING SOLUTION: stock I 80, stock II 20

11.24 Legal 1884   14555, **8**:353
FORMULA: DS 11.21 Grenacher 1897 90, sat. aq. sol picric acid 10

11.24 Löwenthal 1892   *see* DS 13.7 Löwenthal 1892

11.24 Löwenthal *test.* **1900 Pollack**   Pollack 1900, 79
FORMULA: water 100, sodium hydroxide 0.5, carmine 2, picric acid *q.s.*
PREPARATION: Dissolve carmine and alkali in 50 boiling water. Boil 15 minutes. Dilute
to 100 and cool. Add picric acid in excess of saturation.

11.24 Malassez *test.* **1877 Frey**   Frey 1877, 96
FORMULA FOR DRY STOCK: water 100, ammonia 2, carmine 0.5, picric acid 2.5
PREPARATION FOR DRY STOCK: Dissolve carmine in ammonia and water. Add picric.
Shake; allow to settle; and decant. Evaporate supernatant to dryness.
FORMULA FOR WORKING SOLUTION: water 100, dry stock 2
PREPARATION OF WORKING SOLUTION: Mix. Leave 1 week. Filter.

11.24 Mayer 1897   23632, **14**:23
FORMULA: DS 11.28 Mayer 1897 10, 0.6% magnesium picrate 90

11.24 Neuman *test.* **1928 Schmorl**   Schmorl 1928, 120
REAGENTS REQUIRED: *A*. DS 11.21 Grenacher 1879 100, picric acid 1.25; *B*. 2% hydro-
chloric acid in glycerol; *C*. anhydrous glycerol
METHOD: [sections] → *A*, 5–10 mins. → *B*, 10 mins. → *C*
NOTE: To prepare balsam mounts, substitute a sat. sol. picric acid in abs. alc. for *C* above
and clear in clove oil.

11.24 Oppler *test.* **1928 Schmorl**   Schmorl 1928, 341
FORMULA: carmine 0.5, ammonia 0.5, picric acid 0.005, water 100

11.24 Orth *test*. **1904 Besson** Besson 1904, 255
FORMULA: DS 11.28 Orth (1892) 65, sat. aq. sol. picric acid 35
NOTE: This same formula is given by **Squire 1892** but without acknowledgment to Orth.

11.24 Ranvier 1875 Ranvier 1875, 100
PREPARATION OF DRY STOCK: Dissolve 5 carmine in 50 ammonia. Add 500 sat. sq. sol.
picric acid. Evaporate to 100. Cool 24 hours. Decant supernatant liquid which is
evaporated to dryness.
WORKING SOLUTION: water 100, dry stock 5
PREPARATION OF WORKING SOLUTION: Boil 10 minutes. Cool. Filter.
METHOD: [anything, living or dead] → stain, till done → 70% alc. till color clouds cease
→ balsam, via usual reagents
NOTE: The original formula called for a prolonged period of putrefaction in the course
of manufacture. This stain, now practically unknown, should be placed in the hands
of every beginner. A live Cyclops may be dropped into the solution and removed, fixed,
and stained 10 minutes later; so may any other object. A description of a preparation
utilizing this stain is given under DS 12.20 below.

11.24 Rutherford *test*. **1878 Marsh** Marsh 1878, 79
FORMULA: sat. sol. picric acid 100, carmine 1, ammonia 2, water
PREPARATION: Dissolve carmine in ammonia and 5 water. Raise picric solution to boiling
and add carmine solution. Evaporate to dryness. Dissolve residue in 100.

11.24 Squire 1892a Squire 1892, 34
FORMULA: ammonia 1.5, carmine 0.5, water 2.5, sat. aq. sol. picric acid 100
PREPARATION: Dissolve dye in ammonia. Add picric solution.

11.24 Squire 1892b Squire 1892, 35
FORMULA: water 100, sodium hydroxide 0.05, carmine 0.5, picric acid *q.s.*
PREPARATION: Dissolve the carmine in the boiling alkali sol. Add just enough sat. aq. sol
picric acid to redissolve the ppt. first formed.

11.24 Squire 1892c Squire 1892, 35
FORMULA: DS 11.28 Orth (1892) 25, sat. aq. sol. picric acid 75
NOTE: See also Orth (1904) note.

11.24 Vignal *test*. **1907 Böhm and Oppel** *cit*. **Henneguy** Böhm and Oppel 1907, 118
FORMULA: water 100, picric acid 2, carmine 1, ammonium hydroxide 5
PREPARATION OF DRY STOCK: Mix all ingredients. Leave 2–3 months in closed bottle.
Evaporate at room temperatures to 80. Decant and evaporate supernatant to dryness.
WORKING SOLUTION: water 100, dry stock 1

11.24 Weigert 1881 22575, **84**:275
FORMULA: sat. aq. sol. picric acid 100, carmine 1, ammonia 2, acetic acid *q.s.*
PREPARATION: Dissolve carmine in ammonia. Add picric solution and leave 24 hours.
Then add just enough acetic acid to produce permanent ppt. Filter.

11.25 IRON CARMINES

11.25 de Groot 1903 23632, **20**:21
FORMULA: water 100, hydrochloric acid 0.05, potassium alum 2.5, ferric alum 0.05, carminic acid 0.5
PREPARATION: Dissolve ferric alum in 10 water. Add dye and dilute to 100. Heat to 60°C
and add potassium alum. Cool. Filter. Add acid to cold filtrate.

11.25 Hansen 1905 23632, **22**:85
FORMULA: water 100, sulfuric acid 1, ferric alum 3, cochineal 3
PREPARATION: Boil all ingredients 10 minutes. Cool. Filter.

11.25 Lee 1902 *test*. **1905** *ips*. Lee 1905, 170
REAGENTS REQUIRED: A. ADS 12.1 Benda 1893; B. 0.5% carminic acid in 50% alcoho
METHOD: [sections] → water → A, some hrs. → rinse, 50% alc. → B, 1–2 hrs. → wash
50% alc. → balsam, via usual reagents

11.25 Peter 1904   23632, **21**:314

REAGENTS REQUIRED: *A*. water 100, cochineal 6, hydrochloric acid 0.3; *B*. 2.5% ferric alum

PREPARATION OF A: Boil cochineal in 150 water till reduced to 30. Dilute with hot water to 100. Cool. Filter. Add acid.

METHOD: [whole objects to be sectioned, or sections] → *A*, 48 hrs. at 37°C. → rinse → *B*, some hrs. → balsam, or paraffin, via usual reagents

RESULT: Said by Lee (Lee 1905, 171) to stain yolk granules red on a gray background.

11.25 Spuler 1901 *test*. **1910** *ips*.   Ehrlich, Krause, *et. al.* 1910, **1**:240

PREPARATION OF STOCK SOLUTION: Boil 20 cochineal 1 hour in 100 water. Filter, saving both residue and filtrate. Boil residue in 100 water 1 hour. Filter. Reject residue. Mix filtrates and reduce to 100. Add 95% alc. till ppt. appears. Filter. Reduce filtrate to 100. Filter.

REAGENTS REQUIRED: *A*. stock 35, 50% alcohol 65; *B*. 0.75% ferric alum

METHOD: 70% alcohol → *A*, 48 hrs. at 37°C. → wash → *B*, 24 hrs.

11.25 Wellheim 1898   23632, **15**:123

REAGENTS REQUIRED: *A*. 0.01% ferric chloride in 50% alc.; *B*. 0.5% carminic acid in 50% alc.; *C*. 0.1% hydrochloric acid in 70% alc.

METHOD: [sections] → 50% alc. → *A*, overnight → rinse, 50% alc. → *B*, 1–2 hrs. → wash, 50% alc. → *C*, till differentiated → balsam, via usual reagents

11.25 Zacharias 1894   *see* DS 11.23 Zacharias 1894

11.26 AMMONIA CARMINES

11.26 Beale 1857 *test*. **1880 Beale**   Beale 1880, 125

FORMULA: carmine 0.5, ammonia 1.5, water 44, 95% alc. 12, glycerol 44

PREPARATION: Dissolve carmine in ammonia. Add other ingredients.

11.26 Cole 1903   Cross and Cole 1903, 169

FORMULA: water 100, carmine 1, ammonium hydroxide 2, sodium borate 6

PREPARATION: As Beale 1857.

11.26 Frey 1877   Frey 1877, 94

FORMULA: water 40, glycerol 40, 95% alc. 20, carmine 4, ammonia *q.s.* to dissolve

PREPARATION: As Beale 1857.

11.26 Gerlach 1858 *test*. **1892 Squire**   Squire 1892, 31

FORMULA: water 100, ammonia 1, carmine 1

NOTE: Squire (*loc. cit.*) and Lee (Lee 1905, 172) recommended that the solution be allowed to grow mold, evaporated to dryness, and then redissolved in distilled water.

11.26 Hoyer *test*. **1900 Pollack**   Pollack 1900, 78

PREPARATION OF DRY STAIN: Dissolve 2 carmine in 4 ammonia and 16 water. Boil till smell of ammonia not apparent. Cool. Add 80 95% alc. Filter.

WORKING SOLUTION: water 100, powder from above 0.5

11.26 Meriwether 1935   4349, **14**:64

FORMULA: water 75, ammonia 25, potassium chloride 6.25, potassium carbonate 1.9. carmine 2.5

PREPARATION: Boil the salts and the dye in the water 2 minutes. Cool and add ammonia.

11.26 Smith *test*. **1903 Cross and Cole**   Cross and Cole 1903, 171

FORMULA: water 50, glycerol 25, 95% alc. 25, carmine 1, ammonia 1.5, sodium borate 1

PREPARATION: As Beale 1857.

11.26 Squire 1892   Squire 1892, 31

FORMULA: water 40, 95% alc. 20, glycerol 40, carmine 2.5, ammonia 5

PREPARATION: As Beale 1857.

11.27 HYDROCHLORIC CARMINES

11.27 Hollande 1916   *Chlorcarmin—compl. script.*   6630, **79**:662

REAGENTS REQUIRED: *A*. water 90, 95% alc. 10, carmine 7, hydrochloric acid 2.5 water *q.s.* to bring filtrate to 90, 70% alc. 10; *B*. 3% ferric alum; *C*. 1% pyridine

PREPARATION OF A: Grind the carmine with the acid. Wash out mortar while grinding with 12 doses each of 10 water. Boil washings till reduced to 70. Cool. Filter. Dilute to 90. Add alc.

METHOD: [sections] → water → A, 2 hrs. → water, rinse → B, till black, few minutes → B, fresh solution, till differentiated, ½–2 hrs. → C, thorough wash → running water, 15 mins. → balsam, via usual reagents

11.27 Kingsbury and Johannsen 1927　　　　　　Kingsbury and Johannsen 1927, 44
FORMULA: water 30, 95% alc. 70, carmine 2, hydrochloric acid 3
PREPARATION: Boil all ingredients under reflux. Cool. Filter.

11.27 Langeron 1942　　　　　　　　　　　　Langeron 1942, 517
REAGENTS REQUIRED: A. water 2.5, 90% alc. 100, carmine 2.5, hydrochloric acid 2.5; B. 0.5% hydrochloric acid in 80% alc.
PREPARATION OF A: Grind carmine, acid, and water to a paste. Leave 1 hour. Transfer to reflux flask with alc. Reflux on water bath till solution complete.
METHOD: [whole objects] → 70% alc. → A, till stained → B, till differentiated → balsam, via usual reagents

11.27 Mayer 1881　　　　　　　　　　　　　　14246, 2:1
FORMULA: 95% alc. 90, water 15, carmine 4, hydrochloric acid 1, ammonia $q.s.$ to give pH 7
PREPARATION: Heat water, carmine, and acid to 80°C. Add alc. and reflux 10 minutes. Adjust to pH 7 with ammonia.
NOTE: In 1883 (14246, 4:521) Mayer directed that the carmine, acid, and water be boiled to complete solution, cooled, and the alc. added before neutralization.

11.27 Mayer 1883　 *see* DS 11.27 Mayer 1881 (note)

11.27 Meyer 1885　　　　　　　　　　　　　　2626, 10:363
FORMULA: 90% alc. 50, carmine 1.25, hydrochloric acid 5, chloral hydrate 60
PREPARATION: Reflux the carmine with the acid and alc. for 30 minutes. Cool. Filter. Add chloral hydrate.

11.27 Schwarz 1934　　　　　　　　　　　　　23632, 50:305
PREPARATION OF DRY STOCK: Boil 1 carmine and 4 ammonium alum in 150 water until reduced to 75. Filter. Evaporate filtrate to dryness.
WORKING SOLUTION: water 60, methanol 40, hydrochloric acid 0.2, dry stock 8

11.28 OTHER CARMINE FORMULAS

11.28 Arcangeli 1885　*boric-carmine*　　　　　16977, 4:233
FORMULA: water 100, boric acid 4, carmine 0.5
PREPARATION: Boil 10 minutes. Cool. Filter.

11.28 Best 1906　*potash-carmine*　*see* DS 22.5 Best 1906

11.28 Cuccati 1886　*soda-carmine*　　　　　　23632, 3:50
FORMULA: water 90, 95% alc. 10, acetic acid 0.5, sodium carbonate 6.5, carmine 1.7 chloral hydrate 2
PREPARATION: Boil the carmine with the carbonate in 35 water. Cool. Add the alc. to cooled solution. Leave overnight; filter, and bring filtrate to 100. Add the acid and chloral hydrate.

11.28 Cuccati *test.* 1889 Friedländer　*soda-carmine*　　Friedländer, 1889, 90
FORMULA: water 100, carmine 4, sodium carbonate 13, abs. alc. 7, acetic acid 1.5, chloral hydrate 2.5
PREPARATION OF DRY STOCK: As Cuccati 1886, save that the final solution is evaporated to dryness.
PREPARATION OF WORKING SOLUTION: 80% alc. 100, powder $q.s.$

11.28 Francotte *circ.* 1890　*boric-carmine*　　　　Francotte, 209
FORMULA: water 25, 95% alc. 75, boric acid 5, carmine 0.4
PREPARATION: Boil under reflux 15 minutes.

11.28 Frey 1877   *borax-carmine*   Frey 1877, 95
FORMULA: water 35, sodium borate 3.5, carmine 0.6, 95% alc. 60
PREPARATION: Boil dye with water and borax. Cool. Filter. Add alc. to filtrate; leave
   24 hours. Filter.

11.28 Fyg 1928a   *chrome-carmine*   23632, **45**:242
FORMULA: water 100, chrome alum 6, carmine 1
PREPARATION: Add carmine to boiling alum solution. Boil 15 minutes. Cool. Filter.
NOTE: Copper alum may be substituted for chrome alum. Copper alum (Merck Index
   1940, 165) is prepared by fusing together 34% potassium alum, 32% cupric sulfate,
   32% potassium nitrate, and 2% camphor.

11.28 Fyg 1928b   *soda-carmine*   23632, **45**:242
FORMULA: water 100, sodium bicarbonate 5, carmine 0.5
PREPARATION: Boil 5 minutes. Cool. Filter.

11.28 Haug *test.* **1900 Pollack**   *ammonia-carmine*   Pollack 1900, 80
FORMULA: carmine 1, ammonium chlorate 2, water 100, ammonia 0.25, lithium car-
   bonate 0.5
PREPARATION: Boil carmine in chlorate solution 15 minutes. Cool. Add other ingredients.
   Filter.

11.28 Kahlden and Laurent 1896   *lithium-carmine*   Kahlden and Laurent 1896, 56
FORMULA: sat. aq. sol. lithium carbonate 100, carmine 3
PREPARATION: Boil 15 minutes. Cool. Filter.

11.28 Linder   *see* P 12.2 Amann 1896 (note)

11.28 Mayer 1897   *magnesia-carmine*   23632, **14**:23
FORMULA: magnesium oxide 0.2, carmine 2, water 100
PREPARATION: Boil 5 minutes. Cool. Filter.
NOTE: Magnesium oxide very readily turns to the carbonate which cannot be used for
   this preparation. Hence the insistence on fresh magnesia (*magnesia usta*—"burnt
   magnesia" in pharmacopeial Latin) in the original formula.

11.28 Mayer 1902   *aluminum-carmine*   14246, **10**:490
FORMULA: water 100 aluminum chloride 1.5, carminic acid 0.5

11.28 Orth *test.* **1892 Squire**   *lithium-carmine*   Squire 1892, 33
FORMULA: water 100, lithium carbonate 1.5, carmine 2.5
PREPARATION: Boil. Cool. Filter.

11.28 Rawitz 1899   *aluminum-carmine*   14246, **10**:489
FORMULA: water 50, glycerol 50, aluminum nitrate 2, cochineal 2
PREPARATION: Boil the cochineal with the water and nitrate 1 hour. Cool. Filter. Add
   glycerol.

11.28 Rukhadze and Blajin 1929   *see* DS 23.33 Rukhadze and Blajin 1929

11.28 Schmaus *test.* **1896 Kahlden and Laurent**   *uranium-carmine*
                                         Kahlden and Laurent 1896, 158
FORMULA: water 100, sodium carminate 1, uranium nitrate 0.5
PREPARATION: Boil 5 minutes. Cool. Filter.

11.28 Thiersch *test.* **1871 Robin**   *ammonia-carmine*   Robin 1871, 318
FORMULA: water 65, ammonium acetate 2, carmine 3, oxalic acid 3, 95% alc. 35
PREPARATION: Dissolve acetate in 15 hot water. Add carmine, heat to solution. Add
   oxalic acid dissolved in 50 water slowly and with constant stirring. Cool. Filter. Add
   alc. to filtrate.

11.28 Thiersch *test.* **1877 Frey**   *ammonia-carmine*   Frey 1877, 94
FORMULA: water 40, 95% alc. 60, carmine 1.25, ammonia 1.25, oxalic acid 2
PREPARATION: Dissolve carmine in ammonia with 5 water. Filter. Add acid dissolved in
   40 water. Add alc.; leave 1 day; filter.

11.3 Brazilin and Other Natural Stains

11.3 Bensley 1916 *brazilin*   590, **29**:37
FORMULA: water 10, brazilin 0.05, water 90, phosphotungstic acid 1
PREPARATION: Add the acid dissolved in 90 water to the dye dissolved in 10.
METHOD: water → stain, 12 to 3 hrs. → water, wash → balsam, via usual reagents

11.3 Guinard 1890 *alkanet*   11074, **6**:447
PREPARATION: Infuse 20 alkanet in 60 abs. alc. Filter. Evaporate to dryness and dissolve
residue in 10 acetic acid. Add 100 50% alc.

11.3 Hickson 1901 *brazilin*   17510, **44**:470
REAGENTS REQUIRED: *A*. 1% ferric alum in 70% alc.; *B*. 70% alc. 100, brazilin 0.5
METHOD: 70% alc. → *A*, 3 hrs. → 70% alc., quick rinse → *B*, overnight → 70% alc.
thorough wash → balsam, via usual reagents

11.3 O'Leary *see* DS 21.213 O'Leary

11.4 Synthetic Nuclear Stains

The term *synthetic nuclear stains* is here used in contrast to those stains, such as hematoxylin and carmine, which are extracted from natural sources. These synthetic dyes are widely called *aniline dyes* without very much justification, since by no means are all of them directly derived from aniline. The now obsolete term *coaltar dyes* was far more accurate. Almost any stain can be used to color nuclei differentially by the adjustment either of the pH or the chemical composition of the solution in which it is employed. Those here listed are those most widely employed for the purpose either alone or in combinations in complex contrast formulas.

The most interesting of these reagents, grouped in the first class, are the oxazine dyes, which are turned into their metallic lakes in the course of the preparation of the staining solutions. These were introduced by Becher 1921, in a book which never received a very wide circulation. In their staining reactions they strongly resemble hematoxylin, giving either black or blue nuclei, but they do so without the necessity for differentiating, and are far less liable either to fading or to alteration in color. They have been rediscovered at various intervals since 1921, and it is a matter of some astonishment to those who have employed them that they have not received wider acceptance as a substitute for hematoxylin. The author's choice among the formulas is the anonymous one, given first. Probably the one most widely employed is the formula of Proescher and Arkush, 1928 (20540b, **3**:36). The publication of this paper in the United States started a brief vogue for these materials. The original publication of Becher quoted not only the utilization of these oxazine dyes for nuclear staining, but also for the staining of the central nervous system and for some general-purpose polychrome stains. These will be found in their appropriate divisions later.

Safranin, in the English-speaking countries, is more widely employed in botanical than in zoological technique. In Europe, however, particularly in France, it remained the standard nuclear stain for many years, and has not yet been regularly supplanted by hematoxylin. Thus a standard French technique for a histological preparation will be safranin-light green, in which the corresponding British or American usage calls for hematoxylin-eosin. This safranin-light green combination has found occasional acceptance in the literature as *Benda's stain*. There is little to choose between any of the formulas, it being a matter of convention that the techniques of Chamberlain 1915, and Johansen 1940, are customarily employed for plant material, while Babès, 1887 and Böhm and Oppel 1907 are commonly employed for animal materials.

Magenta is less widely employed as a single nuclear stain than it is in combination with plasma stains in complex techniques. The formula of Ziehl 1882, though customarily confined to bacterial staining, is here included for the reason that it is just as good a nuclear stain as it is a stain for microorganisms. Indeed, it is very nearly as specific as is the Fuelgen reaction without any of the difficulties attached to the latter. The Fuelgen reaction itself, here cited from the paper of Fuelgen and Rossenbeck 1924, is not now as widely employed as was formerly the case. It is actually one of the oldest staining methods known, having been introduced by Schiff in 1866 (825, **93**:140), as a reagent for aldehydes. Its nuclear reactions appear to depend upon the selective staining of thymonucleic acid, but the stain itself is so difficult and so temperamental that it is doubtful that it has occasioned any real advance in microtomy.

The next class of synthetic nuclear stains, the thiazins, comprise methylene blue and its oxidation homologs: Lauth's violet and the azurs. These are used mostly in admixtures of unknown compositions, commonly referred to as *polychrome methylene blues*. These thiazins are in general excellent and specific nuclear stains and their use should not be confined to blood, as is customarily the case. They became unpopular at about the opening of the present century because of the difficulty at that time of securing mounting media in which they could adequately be preserved. They are liable to rapid fading when mounted in balsam, and also tend to be extracted by alcohol in the course of the dehydration period. If amyl alcohol is used for dehydration, and one of the *neutral mounting media* in place of balsam, there is no reason why the thiazins should not again become popular. The formulas given are only those in which methylene blue is employed alone. Many more formulas will be found later in the present chapter under the headings DS 13.1 and DS 13.2, with their subdivisions, which deal with the common combinations of thiazins and various eosins.

The next class, the crystal violets and gentian violets, are today almost confined to botanical microtechniques. This is unfortunate since they are very specific for nuclei and also do not stain albuminous yolk material as does hematoxylin. It is strongly recommended that those who are handling heavily yolked embryos should try the formula of Johansen 1932 in preference to the more conventional techniques.

11.40 TYPICAL EXAMPLES

Preparation of a strewn slide of pollen grains using the safranin stain of Johansen 1940

It is not intended here to give an example of the technique by which safranin is used for general nuclear staining, but only to give a method which may be employed for the demonstration of the nuclei in pollen grains, a rather difficult subject.

Pollen should be collected into a tube containing 1% acetic acid in absolute alcohol. It is simple to do this by dipping the anther under the surface of the fluid and then resealing the tube. In this manner a vast number of pollens can be collected in a surprisingly short time. Pollen grains may remain in this fluid for a day of two, but it is undesirable to leave them any longer than this before allowing them to settle. The supernatant liquid should then be poured off and replaced with fresh absolute alcohol. This change should be repeated several times or until the fluid poured off no longer smells of acetic acid. When the acetic acid has been washed out, the absolute alcohol is replaced with a mixture of equal parts of absolute alcohol and ether, and the pollen grains are left in this mixture overnight.

A solution should then be prepared from any nitrocellulose used for embedding, such as celloidin (see Chapter 13). About half of the alcohol-ether mixture should then be poured from the top of the tube containing the pollen and replaced with an equal quantity of the weak celloidin solution. After this has been allowed to penetrate the pollen grains for a few hours—(this will be definitely established by the grains falling to the bottom)—about three-quarters of the fluid is poured off and the tube again refilled with a fresh 0.5% solution of celloidin. When this has in its turn impregnated the pollen grains, they may be left in the tube for an indefinite period.

When it is desired to make mounts, it is necessary to clean as many coverslips as the number of mounts required, taking rather more than the usual amount of trouble. Each tube is now agitated until the pollen grains (but not air bubbles) are dispersed throughout the celloidin, one drop of the dispersion being then taken and allowed to run over the surface of the cover. The most critical stage of the proceedings is the next one, in which the celloidin is congealed without being permitted to evaporate to dryness. If it is allowed to evaporate to dryness, it will almost invariably become detached, either by curling in the dry state or in one of the solutions which is subsequently applied to it.

The best method of congealing the celloidin is with the aid of chloroform vapor, a high concentration of which is easily maintained at the bottom of a coplin jar by pouring a few cubic centimeters into the jar, placing the hand over the top, shaking the jar once or twice, and then setting it on the bench with a loose cover in place. Chloroform vapor is so heavy that it will remain in the jar for a long period. Each drop of the suspension of pollen should be spread uniformly over the coverslip and then waved once or twice in the air until it appears about to become dry. Each coverslip is then, while held with forceps, lowered into the chloroform vapor at the bottom of the coplin jar and held there for a few moments until it acquires a slightly opaque appearance. The coverslip is then dropped into a rack in a jar of 70% alcohol, where it may remain until sufficient have been accumulated to permit staining.

Two reagents are required for the stain of Johansen 1940, the first being the rather specially prepared solution of safranin given under the technique of Johansen 1930 (11.42 Johansen 1930) below, and the other, developed by Masson (Chapter 22, ADS 22.1 Masson 1942), a 65:35 mixture of a saturated solution of picric acid in 95% alcohol, and 95% alcohol. The coverslips carrying the dispersion of pollen are removed from 70% alcohol when is ready to stain them, transferred to distilled water until the diffusion currents have died down, and then placed in a jar filled with Johansen's safranin stain, where they may remain not less than 24 hours or until next required. Each individual coverslip is now taken separately and rinsed in the differentiating solution of Masson until examination under the low power of a microscope shows a clear differentiation of red nuclei against the yellow background of the pollen cell. Differentiation may be stopped immediately by transferring the coverslip from the picric acid to water.

Several courses are now open to the mounter. If it is desired only to show the nuclei, the slide may be dehydrated in the regular manner as far as 90% alcohol, cleared in terpineol to avoid dissolving the celloidin holding the pollen grains in place, and then mounted in balsam. If the general outline of the pollen cell is required as well as the nuclei, the material may be treated in the same manner up to the moment of its clearing and then counterstained either with a solution of light green or fast green in clove oil. If the latter course is adopted, the excess light green in clove oil should be washed off with clove oil and the oil itself subsequently washed out in xylene as a preliminary to mounting in balsam. The very common practice of passing directly from a solution of light green in clove oil to balsam itself is most unsatisfactory and results always in the gradual removal of the light green from the tissues as the clove oil diffuses through the balsam. The intermediate washing in clove oil is also itself insufficient, since it will result in the removal of additional dye, and necessitate the third step recommended, i.e. removal of clove oil with xylene.

Demonstration of chromosomes of the grasshopper in a smear preparation of the testes using magenta by the method of Henneguy 1891

The grasshopper provides unusually favorable material for the demonstration of chromosomes, for the reason that these are compact and small, usually with the sex chromosomes well differentiated. Any species of grasshopper may be employed, but the specimens should be collected during the early months of the summer, preference being given to young specimens (Baker 1945, 182) in which the wings are not yet fully grown.

The most essential precaution to be observed in the dissection of testes from small insects for cytological investigations is that the insect should be dissected under the surface of physiological saline. For this purpose the most convenient vessel is a deep dish or fingerbowl, to the bottom of which is fitted a circle of cork or linoleum weighted on the underside with lead sheet to which it is attached by rivets. It is undesirable in cytological investigations to kill an animal by an anesthetic. In the case of the grasshopper, the simplest method is to remove the head with a pair of sharp scissors before pinning the body down in place, after the removal of the wings and legs from one side, with the aid of four pins placed at the anterior and posterior margins of the body. Sufficient physiological saline is then added to cover the specimen to a depth of about a quarter of an inch, and the dissection is then conducted under a low-power binocular microscope. Before commencing the dissection it is desirable to have available the necessary fixative, which in the present instance should be the osmic-chromicacetic of Flemming 1882 (Chapter 18, F 1600.0010) or some other fixative of the same general composition. It is also necessary that the slides to be employed be rigorously cleaned and that the fixative be placed in a petri dish of a diameter sufficient to permit the slide to be laid flat. Smears of the type which are going to be prepared cannot satisfactorily be fixed in such a manner that they will adhere to the slide, if the whole of the latter is immersed in the fixative. It is therefore necessary to secure two short glass rods, the ends of which are bent at right angles to prevent them from rolling, and to place them in the bottom of the petri dish into which the fixative is poured until it just reaches the upper surface of the rods. The depth of the fixative should be tested before any dissection is undertaken by laying a clean slide across the two glass rods. The whole of the lower surface of the slide should be in contact with the fixative, which should not at any point cover the upper surface.

Three or four slides are now laid at hand and the dissection commenced by the removal of the chitinous exoskeleton from the whole side of the abdomen. It is very difficult to find the testes unless one is acquainted with the species of grasshopper under dissection, for they may either be fused into a single central mass or may be composed of a series of tubules joined together at the base and lying across the upper part of the intestine at right angles to the direction of the vas deferens. It is probably easiest first to identify the intestine, then to identify the heart, and then to look between the intestine and heart at about the central portion of the body for a series of small, curly objects attached posteriorly to a tube. These curly objects (or object, according to the species) will be the testes. They should be removed by cutting away the adherent connective tissues and trachea, and should then be thoroughly washed in the physiological saline which remains in the dish. A piece is now cut from one of the testes of about one-quarter-millimeter side and is removed with a pair of fine forceps to the surface of one of the specially cleaned slides. Excess normal saline should be removed from it with chemically clean blotting paper, and a second slide crushed down on it with a twisting movement in such a way that the smear is distributed over an area approximately equivalent to a 15-millimeter circle. The two slides are then rapidly pulled apart and each is laid face down on the glass rods in the fixative. The petri dish should be covered with the customary lid which one should remove only when adding slides to the dish to avoid inhaling the irritating vapors of the osmic acid. Usually, two or three slides can be placed in a dish at one time. The smears should not remain in contact with the fixative for more than about 30 minutes before being carefully removed and placed in distilled water. They may remain in distilled water for at least several days but must, in any case, be thoroughly washed in several changes with not less than two or three hours in each change. When all the slides have been accumulated in distilled water, and are known to be free of both chromic and osmic acids, one may then proceed to the staining technique. In the technique originally described by Henneguy (DS 11.43 Henneguy 1891) almost any of the synthetic nuclear stains listed in this section were recommended.

But the results obtained on insect material with magenta are so much better than those obtainable with any other stain that it has in the present work been confined to this dye. The only two solutions required are a 1% solution of potassium permanganate, which must be freshly prepared before each use, and a 1% solution of magenta in distilled water. Each of these can most conveniently be handled in a standard coplin jar.

The slides bearing the smears are removed from the distilled water and placed in 1% potassium permanganate for about five minutes. A word of warning is necessary at this point. The water from which the slides are passed to the permanganate must be distilled, for the least trace of a reducing agent in it will cause the potassium permanganate to be precipitated on the surface of the smear, from which it cannot subsequently be removed without great trouble. If, however, the distilled water is pure and the potassium permanganate is freshly made, the sections as they are removed from the potassium permanganate will be of a medium purple color with only a trace of brown. They must be passed very rapidly into another jar of distilled water, without giving them an opportunity to oxidize, or they will be ruined. After the briefest rinse in this second dish of distilled water, the sections are dropped directly into the 1% magenta. As the time in which they should remain in this is variable, it is desirable to take a single smear from the batch and run this through ahead of the remainder in order to establish the timing before running the remainder through in a single operation. In general, about five minutes should be sufficient, but the first slide should be removed from the magenta and rinsed briefly in water after about two minutes and examined with the naked eye against a white background. It should be a deep purple color: between the light purple (which it is likely to show after three minutes immersion) and a dense black purple (which will be almost impossible subsequently to differentiate). If it is already sufficiently stained at three minutes, another slide should be tested at one and two minutes; if it is not sufficiently stained

after three minutes, it should be returned and examined at one-minute intervals until it shows the desired coloration. It may then be transferred to a jar of distilled water and allowed to remain there until the rest of the batch have been put through, on the timing already established, and placed in the same jar.

Each slide will have to be differentiated separately, because alcohol removes the stain rapidly while clove oil removes it slowly. Each section is therefore placed in 95% alcohol when color clouds will immediately be seen to come from it. After a few minutes of rinsing in the alcohol, the slide is then removed to the stage of the microscope and examined under an eight-millimeter objective, if such is available, or under a 16-millimeter objective with a 20-X eyepiece if the eight-millimeter one cannot be used, to see if the nuclei are yet clearly differentiated from the cytoplasmic background. If the slides are left to differentiate in alcohol until the nuclei alone remain colored, it will be impossible to stop the process in time. They should therefore be carefully watched to determine the time at which the nuclei can be clearly distinguished against a lightly stained background. Each slide is then placed in clove oil in which it may be left to differentiate until the background, which now may be examined under a high-power objective, is seen to be entirely free from stain, leaving the chromosomes brilliantly colored. It must be emphasized that the differentiation in clove oil is very slow, and if insufficient differentiation in alcohol be given, it may be necessary to wait some weeks until the clove oil has completed the job. The process sounds complicated to describe, but is, as a matter of fact, very easy to learn and yields results with great certainty.

As soon as the differentiation in clove oil has proceeded to the desired degree, the slides are washed in xylene to remove the whole of the clove oil and then mounted in balsam in the ordinary manner. These preparations are remarkably permanent, and the stain is, if anything, more specific to chromosomes than is the iron hematoxylin which is more usually employed.

11.41 SOLUBLE METALLIC LAKES OF THE OXAZINES

11.41 Anonymous 1936   Catalogue of Vector Mfg. Co.,
                                                        London, n.d. (received 1936)
FORMULA: water 100, ferric alum 2.5, coelestin blue B 0.5, glycerol 14, sulfuric acid 2
PREPARATION: Boil the dye 5 minutes in alum solution. Cool. Filter. Add other ingredients.
METHOD: [sections] → water → stain, 5 mins. to 1 hr. → water, wash → [counterstain]
    → balsam, via usual reagents
NOTE: A description of the use of this stain, before a complex contrast, is given under
    DS 12.20 below. This is probably derived from DS 11.41 Lendrum 1935 (*q.v.*).

11.41 Becher 1921a   Becher 1921, 46
FORMULA: water 100, ferric alum 5, napthopurrin 0.5
PREPARATION: Boil 5 minutes. Cool. Filter.
METHOD: [sections] → water → stain, 2 hrs. → water, wash → [counterstain] → balsam,
    via usual reagents
RESULT: nuclei black

11.41 Becher 1921b   Becher 1921, 72
FORMULA: water 100, chrome alum 5, gallocyanin 0.5
PREPARATION: as Becher 1921a.
METHOD: as Becher 1921a save that 24 hrs. staining is recommended
RESULT: nuclei deep blue
NOTE: **Buzaglo 1934** (4285a, **11**:40) diminishes the gallocyanin to 0.1 and adds 1%
    formaldehyde to the filtrate.

11.41 Becher 1921c   Becher 1921, 40
FORMULA: water 100, aluminum chloride 5, napthazarin 0.5
PREPARATION: As Becher 1921a.
METHOD: as Becher 1921a save that 24 hrs. staining is recommended
RESULT: nuclei, deep blue violet
NOTES: Becher (*loc. cit.*) recommends also napthopurrin (dark red nuclei), purpurin
    (scarlet nuclei), and galloflavin (yellow nuclei) in solutions of aluminum chloride.

11.41 Buzaglo 1934   *see* DS 11.41 Becher 1921b (note)

11.41 Cole 1947   20540b, **22**:103
FORMULA: water 100, chrome alum 5, gallocyanin 1.5
PREPARATION: Boil the dye 5 minutes in the alum solution.

11.41 Einarson 1932 and 1935   *see* DS 22.3 Einarson 1932 and 1935

11.41 Lendrum 1935   11431, **40**:415
FORMULA: water 84, glycerol 14, sulfuric acid 2, ferric alum 4.2, celestin blue 0.42
PREPARATION: Boil the dye in the alum 5 minutes. Cool. Filter. Add glycerol and acid.

11.41 Lendrum and McFarlane 1940   *see* DS 11.41 Proescher and Arkush 1928 (note)

11.41 Petersen 1926   23632, **43**:355
FORMULA: water 100, aluminum sulfate 10, gallocyanin 0.05
PREPARATION: Boil 10 minutes. Cool. Filter. Make up to 100.

11.41 Proescher and Arkush 1928   20540b, **3**:36
FORMULA: water 100, ferric alum 5, coelestin blue B 0.5
PREPARATION: As Becher 1921a.
METHOD: [sections] → water → stain, till nuclei deep blue black, 3 mins. to 2 hrs. →
    water, wash → [counterstain] → balsam, via usual reagents
NOTE: Proescher and Arkush (*loc. cit.*) also recommended gallocyanin blue and gallo-
    cyanin in ferric alum solution; but for the latter see DS 13.5 Becher 1921. These solu-
    tions are less stable than coelestin blue B solutions. For coelestin blue B as a poly-
    chrome stain *see* DS 21.16 Becher 1921. **Lendrum and McFarlane 1940** (11431, **50**:381)
    add 14 glycerol to this solution.

11.42 SAFRANIN

11.42 Babes 1887   23632, **4**:470
FORMULA: water 100, aniline 2, safranin 7
PREPARATION: Heat to 60°C. for 1 hour stirring frequently. Cool. Filter.
METHOD: [sections of osmic fixed material] → water → stain, till nuclei bright red, 1 hr.
to 10 days → water, wash → balsam, via usual reagents
NOTE: This is what is usually meant by *Babes Safranin* even though Babes had pre-
viously (1883; 1780, **21**:356) recommended both alcoholic and aqueous solutions. A
slight modification of this is given by **Langeron 1934**, (100) as **"Babes-Langeron-
Dubosq."** This method with a light green counterstain is sometimes called *Benda's
stain.* See also DS 12.15 Land (1915).

11.42 Benda *see* DS 11.42 Babes (note)

11.42 Böhm and Oppel 1907a   Böhm and Oppel 1907, 209
FORMULA: water 72, ammonium carbonate 0.25, 40% formaldehyde 8, sat. alc. sol.
safranin
PREPARATION: Add the dye solution mixed with the formaldehyde to the carbonate
solution.
METHOD: [sections] → water → stain, 24 hrs. → 95% alc., quick rinse → water →
[counterstain] → balsam, via usual reagents

11.42 Böhm and Oppel 1907b   Böhm and Oppel 1907, 113
FORMULA: water 85, 40% formaldehyde 5, 95% alc. 10, phenosafranin 1

11.42 Chamberlain 1915   Chamberlain 1915, 51
FORMULA: water 100, 95% alc. 50, water soluble safranin 0.5, alcohol soluble safranin 0.5
PREPARATION: Dissolve each dye in the appropriate solvent and mix the solutions.
NOTE: For a rationalization of this procedure see Conn 1946, 109.

11.42 "Dubosq" *see* DS 11.42 Babes (note)

11.42 Johansen 1940   Johansen 1940, 62
REAGENTS REQUIRED: *A.* 95% alc. 25, water 25, methyl cellosolve 50, safranin 0.1,
sodium acetate 1, 40% formaldehyde 2; *B.* ADS 22.1 Masson (1942)
PREPARATION OF *A*: Dissolve the dye in the cellosolve. Add first alc., then water. Then
add remaining ingredients.
METHOD: [sections] → water → *A*, 24 to 48 hrs. → *B*, till differentiated → [counterstain]
→ balsam, via usual reagents
NOTE: A description of the use of this stain is given under 11.40 above.

11.42 Löwit 1891 *see* ADS 22.1 Löwit 1891
NOTE: "Löwit's method" means only the use of his differentiating solution for any
safranin-stained material.

11.42 Pfitzner 1881   14555, **7**:289
FORMULA: water 60, 95% alc. 40, safranin 0.3

11.42 Rawitz 1895   Rawitz 1895, 76
REAGENTS REQUIRED: *A.* 20% tannin; *B.* 2% potassium antimony tartrate; *C.* sat. sol.
safranin; *D.* 2.5% tannin
METHOD: [sections of chrome-fixed or mordanted material] → water → *A*, 24 hrs. → *B*,
24 hrs. → rinse, *D*, 24 hrs. → water, till no more color comes away → *D*, is further
differentiation required → balsam, via usual reagents

11.42 Roskin 1946   Roskin 1946, 152
STOCK SOLUTION: water 50, 95% alc. 50, safranin 3.3
PREPARATION: Dissolve the dye in alc., mix with water.
WORKING SOLUTION: stock 20, 50% alc. 80

11.42 Sémichon 1920 *test.* **1934 Langeron**   Langeron 1934, 500
FORMULA: water 50, 90% alc. 50, safranin 0.5, 40% formaldehyde 1
PREPARATION: Dissolve dye in alc. then add other ingredients.

METHOD: [sections] → 70% alc. → stain, 30 mins. to 2 days → absolute alcohol, till differentiated → balsam, via xylene

11.42 Zwaademaker 1887   23632, **4**:212

REAGENTS REQUIRED: *A*. 95% alcohol 50, safranin 1.5, sat. aq. sol. aniline 50; *B*. absolute alc.

PREPARATION OF *A*: Dissolve dye in alc., then add aniline.

METHOD: [sections of F 1600.0010 fixed material] → 95% alc. → *A*, overnight → *B*, till differentiated → balsam, via xylene

11.43 MAGENTA

11.431 Magenta as Dye

11.431 Albrecht *test.* **1943 Cowdry**   Cowdry 1943, 17

FORMULA: water 100, 95% alc. 20, phenol 8, magenta 4

PREPARATION: Dissolve the dye in phenol and alc., then add water.

11.431 Auguste 1932   *see* DS 11.431 Ziehl 1882 (note)

11.431 Biot 1901   *see* DS 11.431 Gallego 1919 (note)

11.431 Davalos *test.* **1894 Kahlden and Laurent**   Kahlden and Laurent 1894, 89

FORMULA: water 100, abs. alc. 1, phenol 5, magenta 10

PREPARATION: Grind the dye with the alc., wash out mortar with 10 successive portions of 5% phenol.

11.431 Duprès 1935   11425, **46**:77

STOCK FORMULA: water 80, 95% alc. 20, magenta 0.75

PREPARATION OF STOCK: Digest 48 hours at 40°C. Cool. Filter.

REAGENTS REQUIRED: *A*. sat. aq. sol. aniline 100, stock 5, acetic acid 1.5; *B*. ADS 22.1 Duprès 1936

METHOD: [sections] → water → *A*, 1–10 mins. → *B*, till differentiated, 5–10 mins. → counterstain → balsam, via usual reagents

11.431 Gallego 1919   21344, **17**:95

REAGENTS REQUIRED: *A*. DS 11.43 Ziehl 2, water 98; *B*. 0.5% formaldehyde

METHOD: [sections of formaldehyde material] → *A*, 5 mins. → wash → *B*, 5 mins. → wash → balsam, via usual reagents

RESULTS: nuclei, dark violet, cytoplasmic structures, polychrome

NOTE: This method of converting magenta to a blue-black stain was originally proposed for bacteriological purposes by **Biot 1910** (6593, Congrès de Lyon, 234).

11.431 Goodpasture and Burnett 1919   14975, **13**:177

FORMULA: water 80, 95% alc. 20, phenol 1, aniline 1, magenta 0.5

PREPARATION: Dissolve the dye in the mixture of alc. phenol and aniline. Add water.

NOTE: This solution was republished by **Goodpasture 1925** (608b, **1**:550) to which paper and date reference are frequently made. See also DS 23.12 Hertig and Wolbach 1924.

11.431 Henneguy 1891   11024, **27**:397

REAGENTS REQUIRED: *A*. 1% potassium permanganate; *B*. 1% magenta

METHOD: [sections or smears from F 1600.0010 Flemming 1882 fixed material] → water → *A*, 5 mins. → water, wash → *B*, 5 mins. → water, rinse → 95% alc., till partly differentiated → clove oil, till differentiation complete → balsam, via xylene

NOTE: **Schneider 1922,** 113 applies this method to any section by mordanting in 1% chromic acid. A description of the use of this stain for chromosomes is given under DS 11.40 above.

11.431 Huntoon 1931   591b, **1**:317

FORMULA: water 75, glycerol 25, phenol 3.75, magenta 0.6

11.431 Kinyoun *test.* **1946 Conn** *et al.*   Conn *et al.* 1946, 1 V, 6

FORMULA: water 100, 95% alc. 20, phenol 8, magenta 4

11.431 Krajian 1943 11284, **28**:1602

FORMULA: xylene 65, creosote 35, 95% alc. 5, magenta 0.3
PREPARATION: Dissolve dye in alc. Add to other solvents.

11.431 Maneval 1928 20540b, **4**:21

FORMULA: water 90, aniline 2.5, 95% alc. 7.5, acetic acid 0.2, magenta 1

11.431 Muller and Chermock 1945 11284, **30**:169

FORMULA: water 100, 95% alc. 20, phenol 8, magenta 4, wetting agent 0.1
NOTE: The original specifies "Tergitol 7" as the wetting agent.

11.431 Pottenger 1942 *test.* **Farber 1942** 20540b, **17**:183

FORMULA: water 80, 95% alc. 15, phenol 5, magenta 1.6

11.431 Schneider 1922 *see* DS 11.431 Henneguy 1891

11.431 Tilden and Tanaka 1945 *Tech. Bull.*, **9**:95

FORMULA: water 90, methanol 10, phenol 5, magenta III 0.5

11.431 Ziehl 1882 7276, **8**:451 and 1890 23632, **7**:39

REAGENTS REQUIRED: *A.* water 100, 90% alc. 10, magenta 1, phenol 5; *B.* 1% acetic acid
PREPARATION OF *A*: Grind the dye with phenol in a mortar. When dissolved add the alc. in 10 successive lots while grinding. Then use water in 10 successive lots to wash out mortar. Filter accumulated washings.
METHOD: [sections or smears] → water → *A*, 10–20 mins. → *B*, till differentiated → counterstain → balsam, via usual reagents
NOTE: For the use of this reagent for bacteria see DS **23.212 Neelsen 1883,** and DS **23.211** Ziehl. A detailed description of the former use is given under DS 23.20 (Chapter 21). The solution of **Auguste 1932** (6630, **111**:719) contains 2 magenta but is otherwise identical.

11.432 Magenta as Leucobase

11.432 Coleman 1928 20540b, **13**:123

FORMULA: water 100, magenta 1, *N*-hydrochloric acid 4, potassium metabisulfite 1, activated charcoal 0.25
METHOD: Dissolve dye in water. Add metabisulfite and then acid. Leave 24 hrs. in dark. Add charcoal, shake 1 min. Filter.

11.432 Feulgen and Rossenbeck 1924 23543, **135**:203

FORMULA: water 100, magenta 0.5, N-1 hydrochloric acid 20, 10% sodium bisulfite 5
PREPARATION: Raise water to boil. Add dye. Cool to 50°C. and filter. Add acid to filtrate and cool to room temperature. Add bisulfite solution, leave 24 hours in dark.
METHOD: see DS 22.1 Feulgen and Rossenbeck 1924
NOTE: The widely quoted method of **de Tomasi 1936** (20540b, **11**:137) differs only in adding 0.5 dry potassium metabisulfite in place of 5 10% sodium bisulfite. See comments on sodium bisulfite in note to DS 11.113 Knower 1930.

11.432 Lillie 1948 Lillie 1948, 143

NOTE: This differs from Coleman 1928 only in the substitution of sodium metabisulfite for potassium metabisulfite.

11.432 Schiff 1886 825, **140**:93

FORMULA: water 100, magenta 0.025, sulfur dioxide *q.s.* to decolorize solution

11.432 de Tomasi 1936 *see* DS 11.432 Feulgen and Rossenbeck 1924

11.44 THIAZINS

11.44 Anonymous 1946 4349, **26**:13

FORMULA: water 75, glycerol 20, abs. alc. 5, toluidine blue 1, lithium carbonate 0.5
PREPARATION: Dissolve dye and alkali in water, incubate 24 hours at 37°C. and return volume to 75. Add other ingredients.

11.44 Borrell *see* DS 11.44 Langeron 1908

11.44 Cobin 1946   *Tech. Bull.*, **7**:92
FORMULA: water 100, sodium phosphate, dibasic 2.94, potassium dihydrogen phosphate
3.68, methylene blue 0.76
PREPARATION: Heat the dye and sodium phosphate, dibasic in 30 water on a water bath
for 30 minutes. Cool and add the acid phosphate dissolved in 70 water.

11.44 Gabbett 1887   *see* DS 23.213 Gabbett 1887

11.44 Gatenby and Cowdry 1928   *see* DS 11.44 Nicolle 1871 (note)

11.44 Goodpasture *test.* **Langeron 1934**   Langeron 1934, 498
FORMULA: water 100, methylene blue 0.25, potassium carbonate 0.25, acetic acid 0.75
PREPARATION: Boil the dye with the carbonate 30 minutes under reflux. Cool. Add acid,
shake to dissolve ppt. Boil 15 minutes. Cool. Filter.

11.44 Jadassohn *test.* **1928 Schmorl**   Schmorl 1928, 156
FORMULA: water 100, methylene blue 1, sodium borate 1

11.44 Kingsbury and Johannsen 1927   Kingsbury and Johannsen 1927, 45
FORMULA: water 90, abs. alc. 10, methylene blue 0.2, potassium hydroxide 0.005

11.44 Kuhne *test.* **1904a Besson**   Besson 1904, 155
FORMULA: water 100, 95% alc. 30, sodium carbonate 1, methylene blue 0.5

11.44 Kuhne *test.* **1904b Besson**   Besson 1904, 154
FORMULA: water 100, 95% alc. 10, methylene blue 2, phenol 2

11.44 Langeron 1908   1886, **12**:135
PREPARATION: To 100 0.5% silver nitrate add 3% sodium hydroxide till no further ppt.
is produced. Wash ppt. thoroughly by decantation and add to it 100 1% methylene
blue. Boil 5 minutes. Cool. Filter.
USE: see DS 13.13 Shortt 1918.
NOTE: This is "Borrel's Blue." The method of preparation as stated by Langeron 1942,
545, differs little from that of **Laveran 1900** (6630, **52**:549).

11.44 Langeron 1934   Langeron 1934, 496
STOCK SOLUTION: water 100, phenol 0.5, azur II 1
WORKING SOLUTION: water 90, stock 10, 1% potassium carbonate 2
METHOD: [fixed smear] → stain, 1 min. → water, rinse → dry → neutral mountant
NOTE: This is also used as a mordant for some DS 13.12 techniques.

11.44 Langeron 1942   Langeron 1942, 610
REAGENTS REQUIRED: *A.* water 100, polychrome methylene blue 1; *B.* glyceric ether 25,
water 75
METHOD: [water] → *A*, 5 min. to 12 hrs. → *B*, till differentiated → water, thorough wash
→ abs. alc. least possible time → balsam, via cedar oil
NOTE: Langeron (*loc. cit.*) also recommends Beauverie and Hollande 1916 ADS 22.1 in a
1% dilution for B, above.

11.44 Largret and Aubertin 1938   *see* 23.12 Largret and Aubertin 1938

11.44 Laveran 1900   *see* DS 11.44 Langeron 1908

11.44 Löffler 1890   23684, **7**:625
FORMULA: water 80, 95% alc. 20, methylene blue 0.3, potassium carbonate 0.8
PREPARATION: Dissolve dye in alc. Add carbonate solution.
METHOD: see DS 11.423 Sahli 1885
NOTE: A description of a use for this stain in bacteriology is given under DS 23.20 in
Chapter 21.

11.44 Manson *test.* **1929 Wenrich**   McClung 1929, 408
FORMULA OF STOCK SOLUTION: water 100, sodium borate 5, methylene blue 2
PREPARATION OF STOCK SOLUTION: Stir the dye into the boiling borax solution. Cool.
Filter.

WORKING SOLUTION: water 100, stock 1
METHOD: as DS 11.44 Langeron 1934
NOTE: When used after DS 13.12 Wright, or similar stains, the term *panoptic* is some-
times applied.

11.44 Manwell 1945   11284, **30**:1078
FORMULA: water 100, methylene blue 0.1, 1% sulfuric acid 0.6, potassium dichromate
0.1, 1% potassium hydroxide 2
PREPARATION: Dissolve dye in water. Add acid and dichromate. Autoclave 2 hours at
3 pounds or till solution is blue. Add alkali drop by drop shaking till ppt. dissolved.
Leave 48 hours. Filter.
NOTE: Manwell (*loc. cit.*) states this method to be a modification of that of **Singh, Jaswant
and Bhattacharji 1944** (9943, **79**:102), and refers to it as the "JBS" (*sic*) method.

11.44 Martinotti 1910   23632, **27**:24
FORMULA: water 75, glycerol 20, 95% alcohol 5, toluidine blue 1, lithium carbonate 0.5

11.44 Michaelis 1901   23684, **29**:763
FORMULA: water 90, methylene blue 1, 0.4% sodium hydroxide 5, 0.5% sulfuric acid 5
PREPARATION: Add the alkali to the solution of the dye, boil 15 minutes. Cool. Add acid,
filter.

11.44 Moschkowsky *test*. 1946 Roskin   Roskin 1946, 287
FORMULA: water 100, sodium borate 2, methylene blue 1

11.44 Muller and Chermock 1945   11284, **30**:169
FORMULA: water 70, 95% alc. 30, potassium hydroxide 0.0007, methylene blue 0.44

11.44 Nicolle 1871   23730, **9**
FORMULA: sat. sol. thionine in 50% alc. 10, 1% phenol 90
NOTE: **Gatenby and Cowdry 1928,** p. 187 use 50% alc. and increase the phenol solution
to a 6:1 ratio. **Langeron 1942,** 539 takes 20 thionin solution to 80 2% phenol. Conn
1936 cites "Thionin, carbol-, Nicollé's" (*sic*) in the index but not in the text.

11.44 Proescher and Drueger   11284, **10**:153
FORMULA: *A*. water 100, methylene 1, sodium peroxide 0.025, hydrochloric acid *q.s.*
PREPARATION: Boil dye and peroxide for 15 minutes. Cool. Adjust to pH 7 with hydro-
chloric acid.

11.44 Roques and Jude 1940 *test*. 1949 Langeron   Langeron 1949, 621
PREPARATION: Grind 1 methylene blue with 10 anhydrous potassium sulfate. Add 100
95% alc. and shake at intervals for some hours. Filter and evaporate filtrate to
dryness.

11.44 Stoughton 1930   1025, **17**:162
FORMULA: water 95, phenol 5, thionin 0.1

11.44 Terry 1922   11284, **8**:157
FORMULA: water 100, methylene blue 0.2, potassium carbonate 0.2
PREPARATION: Boil 2½ minutes. Cool.

11.44 Raadt 1912   *see* DS 13.12 Raadt 1912

11.44 Sahli 1885   23632, **2**:14
REAGENTS REQUIRED: *A*. water 70, sodium borate 30, sat. sol. (*circ.* 4%) methylene blue 1
METHOD: [sections of chrome-fixed or mordanted material] → water → *A*, 1–3 hrs. →
abs. alc. till differentiated → balsam, via usual reagents

11.44 Singh, Jaswant, and Bhattacharji 1944   *see* DS Manwell 1945 (note)

11.44 Stévenel 1918   5310, **11**:870
FORMULA: *A*. water 100, methylene blue 1.3, potassium permanganate 2.0
PREPARATION: Dissolve the dye and permanganate each in 50 water. Mix and heat on
water bath till ppt. redissolved. Cool. Filter.
METHOD: *see* DS 13.13 Boyé 1940

11.44 Unna 1892   23632, **7**:483
PREPARATION OF DRY STOCK: water 100, 95% alc. 20, methylene blue 1, potassium carbonate 1.
PREPARATION: Simmer ingredients till volume reduced to 100. Leave 24 hours. Filter. Evaporate to dryness.

11.44 Volkonsky 1933 *test.* **1942 Langeron**   Langeron 1942, 1105
FORMULA: water 50, glycerol 50, methylene violet 0.4, azur II 0.1, potassium carbonate 0.1

11.45 CRYSTAL VIOLET

11.45 Atkins 1920   11056, **5**:321
FORMULA: water 75, 95% alc. 25, aniline sulfate 0.75, crystal violet 3.8

11.45 Brown and Brenn 1931   10919, **48**:69
FORMULA: water 100, phenol 0.1, sodium bicarbonate 1.25, crystal violet 0.75

11.45 Huntoon 1931   591b, **1**:317
FORMULA: water 60, glycerol 25, 95% alc. 15, crystal violet 0.45

11.45 Johansen 1932   20540b, **7**:17
REAGENTS REQUIRED: *A*. water 100, 95% alc. 20, crystal violet 1; *B*. 1% picric acid in 95% alcohol
METHOD: [sections, perfectly freed from fixative] → water → *A*, 5 mins. → water, rinse → *B*, till no more color comes away → balsam, via usual reagents
NOTE: The author strongly recommends this for nuclei in heavily yolked material.

11.45 LaCour 1931   11360, **51**:124
REAGENTS REQUIRED: *A*. 1% gentian violet; *B*. ADS 12.2 Lugol (1905); *C*. 1% chromic acid
METHOD: [sections or smears] → water → *A*, 10 mins. → water, quick rinse → abs. alc., 2 sec. → *B*, 2 mins. → abs. alc., 2 sec. → *C*, 15 sec. → abs. alc., 5 sec. → *C*, 15 sec. → abs. alc., 15 sec. → clove oil, till clear → xylene, till clove oil removed → balsam

11.45 Nastikow *test.* **1904 Besson**   Besson 1904, 155
FORMULA: water 100, gentian violet 0.2, mercuric chloride 0.05

11.45 Newton 1927   11295, **47**:346
REAGENTS REQUIRED: *A*. 1% gentian violet 100; *B*. ADS 12.2 Lugol (1905)
METHOD: [sections or smears] → water → *A*, 3–10 mins. → water, rinse → *B*, 30 secs. → 95% alc., quick rinse → abs. alc., 5–10 secs. → clove oil, till differentiated → xylene, 3 changes, till clove oil removed → balsam

11.45 Stirling 1890 *test.* **Mallory 1938**   Mallory 1938, 90
FORMULA: water 88, 95% alc. 10, aniline 2, gentian violet 5

11.46 OTHER SYNTHETIC NUCLEAR STAINS

11.46 Lendrum 1945   11431, **57**:267
FORMULA: water 90, 95% alc. 10, dextrin 0.5, phenol 0.4, acid fuchsin 1
PREPARATION: Mix the dye with the molten phenol and add the alc. Add to this the dextrin dissolved at 80°C.

12 PLASMA STAINING TECHNIQUES

Plasma staining techniques serve a dual role. Originally intended only to act as a contrast to the nuclear staining of the color selected, they may also be adapted to a wide range of differential tissue staining. Indeed, there is a very poor case to be made for their use unless they are so employed, for a good hematoxylin or oxazine nuclear stain requires no contrast which cannot be more simply and readily provided by a color screen between the lamp and the microscope than by staining the section examined. The techniques here given are divided into two main divisions: first, those which give only a single color irrespective of the material on which they are employed, and second, those which give a double contrast from a single solution. As the latter are no more difficult to apply than are the single contrast materials, there seems to be no reason for the retention of the former group save custom. The third division contains those complex stains which are designed to provide a differential staining of the cytoplasmic elements present.

12.1 SINGLE-CONTRAST FORMULAS

The division of solutions designed to produce a single contrast to the nuclear staining has been based entirely on the solvent employed. It is unnecessary, in most cases, to list references, since the majority of them are recommended by so many persons that it would be a waste of time to secure the original recommendation. The difference between the aqueous solutions and the weak alcohol solutions is very slight, since the alcohol in the latter is almost certainly designed as a biostatic agent. Almost any antiseptic can be used for this purpose, alcohol being retained as a matter of convenience. The strong alcohol solutions are either of dyes insoluble in water or of materials so readily extracted by alcohol that their use must be left to the very last stage of dehydration if they are not to be lost. Clove oil solutions are widely used both in zoological and botanical techniques, but it is a pity that more attention has not been paid to the formula of Johansen 1940, given under 12.16, which combines all the desirable characters of an alcohol and a clove oil solution. The phenol solutions are necessitated either through the desirability of having an acid solution, or by the difficulty of securing a solution of the dye without the special technique employed, or by the impossibility of preserving the solution without a biostatic reagent being included. They are far more widely employed in bacteriology than in either zoology or botany. The few stains given in the last division, other than Johansen 1940 which has already been noticed, are unusual formulas specifically designed to take part in a more complex technique given later in the work.

12.11 AQUEOUS SOLUTIONS, *compl. script.*

FORMULA: water 100, acid fuchsin 0.2 *or instead of acid fuchsin either* Bordeaux red 1, *or* Congo red 0.5, *or* erythrosin 1, *or* methyl green 1, *or* orange G 1, *or* orange II 1, *or* ponceau 2R 1

METHOD: [sections, with desired nuclear staining] → water → stain, ½ to 2 mins. → water, wash → balsam, via usual reagents

NOTE: Congo red and acid fuchsin are very alkali-sensitive and not safe after hematoxylin stains which have been "blued" in alkalis. Erythrosin is practically confined to botanical techniques, as orange II and ponceau 2R are confined to animal procedures. The writer considers the latter the best general-purpose counterstain to blue. Methyl green tends to be fugitive.

12.12 WEAK ALCOHOL SOLUTIONS, *compl. script.*

FORMULA: water 90, 95% alcohol 10, benzopurpurin 0.5 *or instead of benzopurpurin either* anilin blue 1, *or* Biebrich scarlet 1, *or* eosin B 0.5, *or* eosin Y 0.2, *or* methyl blue 1, *or* phloxin 0.2, *or* rose bengal 0.5

METHOD: as 12.11

NOTE: The use of alcohol is either to assist in forming a smooth suspension (as in Biebrich scarlet) or to discourage the growth of molds (as in the eosins). The "Magdala Red" commonly specified in botanical techniques is actually phloxine (Conn 1946, 112).

12.13 STRONG ALCOHOL SOLUTIONS, *compl. script.*

FORMULA: 95% alc. 100, aurantia 0.5 *or instead of aurantia, either* chromotrope 2R 2.0 *or* ethyl eosin 0.5 *or* light green 0.5 *or* fast green FCF 0.5 *or* spirit blue 0.5

METHOD: [sections, with desired nuclear staining] → 70% alc. → stain, ½ to 2 mins. → 95% alc., rinse → balsam, via usual reagents

12.14 CLOVE OIL SOLUTIONS, *compl. script.*

FORMULA: oil of cloves 100, light green to sat. *or, instead of light green, either* fast green FCF, *or* orange G, *or* safranin O

METHOD: [sections, or smears, with desired prior staining] → 95% alc. → stain, usually dropped on slide, till sufficiently colored → clove oil, dropped on slide, till excess stain removed → xylene, several changes → balsam

NOTE: The reputation for rapid fading, which stains applied in this manner enjoy, is largely due to imperfect removal of clove oil before mounting.

12.15 PHENOL SOLUTIONS, *compl. script.* (but probably originated by **Ziehl 1882** 7276, **8**:451)

FORMULA: water 100, phenol 2, 95% alc. 10, cresyl violet 1 *or instead of cresyl violet, either* gentian violet 1 (= "Gram's violet"—*auct.*) or methylene blue 1.5, *or* magenta 1 (see also DS 11.43 Ziehl 1890), *or* thionin 1.5 (see also DS 11.46 Nicolle), *or* isamine blue 1 (see DS 23.11 Nicolau 1939), *or* crystal violet 1 (see DS 23.213 Carpano 1916), *or* crystal violet 2 (see DS 23.213 August 1932), *or* rose bengal (see DS 23.211 Conn 1928)

PREPARATION: Grind the dye with the phenol and alc. in a mortar. Wash out the mortar while grinding with 10 successive portions of water. Filter the accumulated washings after 24 hours.

12.16 OTHER SOLUTIONS

12.16 Bensley 1916   590, **29**:37
FORMULA: water 100, anilin blue 0.2, phosphomolybdic acid 1
METHOD: [sections with red nuclei] → water → stain, 5 mins. → water, quick rinse → → abs. alc., till differentiated → balsam, via xylene
NOTE: This was originally designed by Bensley (*loc. cit.*) to follow his DS 11.3 brazilin.

12.16 Donaldson 1917   *iodine-eosin*   11995, **192**:571
FORMULA: ADS 12.21 Lugol 1905, 50, sat. aq. sol. eosin Y 50
METHOD FOR PROTOZOANS IN FECES: Mix 10 parts stain with 1 feces → place under coverslip → seal
NOTE: This method is also applicable to many marine invertebrate larvae.

12.16 Fraenkel *test.* **1948 Romeis**   *tannin-fuchsin*   Romeis 1948, 519
FORMULA: water 66, acid fuchsin 0.12, tannin 10, ADS 22.1 Unna (1928) 33

12.16 Jensen 1937   23684, **39**:333
FORMULA: DS 11.24 Jensen 1937 (stock II) 100, phenol 0.5, eosin B 0.05

12.16 Johansen 1940   *fast green*   Johansen 1940, 59
FORMULA: methyl cellosolve 30, clove oil 30, abs. alc. 30, fast green FCF 0.5
NOTE: Though intended for botanical histology (see DS 21.41 Johansen 1940) this solution is of wide application as a counterstain.

12.16 Kofoid (1920)   *see* DS 23.33 Kofoid (1920)

12.16 Krajian 1938   *eosinol—auct.*   1887a, **25**:376
PREPARATION OF DRY STAIN: To 0.35 eosin B dissolved in 0.7 water add 0.7 acetic acid. Mix and incubate at 36°C. until dry.
WORKING SOLUTION: xylene 75, phenol 25, all dry stain from above

12.16 Maneval 1936   20540b, **11**:9
FORMULA: water 80, acetic acid 20, anilin blue 0.01 (*or, instead of anilin blue,* acid fuchsin 0.1) ferric chloride 0.6

12.16 McClean 1934a   *New Phytologist*, **33**:316
PREPARATION OF DRY STOCK: To 50 1% eosin add 1.75 10% hydrochloric acid. Leave 24 hours, filter, dry ppt.
WORKING SOLUTION: xylene 100, all ppt. from above
NOTE: Erythrosin may be substituted for eosin.

12.16 McClean 1934b   *New Phytologist*, **33**:316
PREPARATION OF DRY STOCK: To 50 1% nile blue sulfate add 12.5 10% sodium hydroxide. Leave 24 hours, filter, dry ppt.
WORKING SOLUTION: xylene 100, all ppt. from above

12.16 Nuttall 1908   16035, **1**:162
FORMULA: xylene 100, picric acid to sat. (*circ.* 10%)
NOTE: Originally intended for potash-cleared arthropod endoskeletons.

12.16 Pearson 1941   *Tech. Bull.*, **3**:16
    PREPARATION: To 100 0.5% eosin Y add, drop by drop, 4 hydrochloric acid. Wash ppt.
    by decantation, dry, and dissolve in 40 95% alc.

12.16 Smith 1926 *see* DS 21.14 Smith 1926

12.16 Tonkoff 1900 *test.* **1907 Böhm and Oppel**   Böhm and Oppel 1907, 120
    FORMULA: abs. alc. 100, spirit blue 0.1, ADS 12.1 Gram 1884 0.03

12.16 Unna 1895 *orange G-tannin*   14352, **21**:540
    FORMULA: water 100, tannin 33, orange G 2
    USE: see DS 13.22 Langeron 1942b and DS 22.2 Volkonsky 1928.

12.2 DOUBLE CONTRASTS FROM ONE SOLUTION

Double contrasts from one solution are just as easy to use as are single contrasts. In those cases in which there is no histological or cytological difference between the elements which it is desired to stain, they present no improvement over the more conventional techniques, but unless one is dealing with homogenous organs, or with a very young embryo, there seems to be no possible reason why the double-contrast material should not be employed. The division of these stains into two groups is based entirely on the color of the nucleus which they are designed to set off. The first group, contrasting with red nuclei, can therefore be used either after magenta, carmine, or safranin, the picro-contrasts being by convention more commonly employed after carmine than after the other reagents. The picro-indigo-carmine of Cajal 1895 is the oldest and best known of these mixtures, but it is probably less effective than the formula of Masson used for the same purpose. The formula of Grosso 1914 was originally developed for staining blood, but it is of much wider application. The picro-spirit blue of Smith 1912, if used after magenta as a nuclear stain, is, in the opinion of the present writer, undoubtedly the best technique which has yet been developed for staining sections of heavily yoked material. The non-picric formulas, which are included in the next division of contrasts for red nuclei, contain two of the best counterstains (Chatton 1920 and Kostowiecki 1932) which have ever been developed. The formula of Kostowiecki in particular has all the advantages of the better known Mallory-Masson polychrome stains, but may be applied from a single solution. Roux's blue here given in Roux's formula of 1894 was at one time well known but has now fallen into disuse.

Contrasts for blue nuclei present more difficulties than do those for red since nuclei for these techniques are customarily stained by hematoxylin, which is very sensitive to acid. Though many of the picro-contrasts can be employed with hematoxylin, it is strongly recommended that one of the oxazine nuclear stains given above under DS 11.42 be employed in its place. The best known of these picro-contrasts is van Gieson 1896. The non-picric contrast formulas, given under DS 12.222 below, may be safely employed after either hematoxylin or methylene blue stains. Probably the best known, and certainly one of the easiest to use, is the saffron-erythrosin of Masson 1911.

12.20 TYPICAL EXAMPLES

Preparation of a transverse section of a Squalus embryo using the picro-carmine stain of Ranvier 1899 followed by the picro-indigo-carmine of Cajal 1905

This simple little preparation is very old-fashioned, but it may well be placed in the hands of a beginning student as his introduction to the art of section cutting and staining. Moreover, it utilizes the embryos of *Squalus acanthus*, which are frequently found in elementary laboratories where this form is dissected. There is often grave doubt as to what shall be done with such embryos and they are usually lost. It is presumed, of course, that we are dealing with an inland laboratory in which preserved specimens are brought from a biological supply house, so that the small embryos themselves will already have been fixed, if the term can properly be used in this case, in formaldehyde for a considerable period. Each embryo, after removal from the oviduct, should be thoroughly washed, using soap if necessary to remove the mucus from the outside, rinsed thoroughly to remove the last traces of soap, and then thrown into a gallon jar of picro-carmine prepared by the method given under DS 11.24 Ranvier 1899. The quantity of picric acid in this solution causes it to act as fixative and preservative, as well as a nuclear stain, and it has the additional advantage that it is quite impossible to overstain in it. Embryos may therefore be thrown into such a jar of picro-carmine during the course of the first half of the year's work and utilized during the second half of the year when microtechnique is usually taught.

When it is desired to cut sections, the embryos are removed from the large jar of picro-carmine and washed in running water until no further color comes away from them. Though it is immaterial how long they have remained in stain, it must be added that some weeks are usually required to secure a sufficient impregnation. The picric acid in a properly prepared Ranvier solution is usually sufficient to have decalcified the placoid scales of a young dogfish. These should be tested by rubbing a steel needle against the direction of the skin. A hard irregularity will indicate that the calcium of the placoid scales has not been removed. In this case recourse must be had to one of the methods for decalcification given in Chapter 19 under AF 20.

The specimens are then embedded and sectioned in the customary manner, it being perfectly possible for even a moderately skilled operator to cut a reasonable hand section from the paraffin block containing embryos of this size. It is, of course, preferable to use a microtome if one is available. The sections are then accumulated and attached to the slide in the ordinary manner, deparaffinized, and run down through the customary reagents until they reach 70% alcohol where the slides may be accumulated. A brief check under the low power of the microscope will now establish whether or not the nuclei have been satisfactorily stained scarlet throughout the body of the preparation. If they have not, it is no use proceeding further, for one must devote some other staining technique to these sections. Nine times out of 10, however, it will be found that the nuclei are clearly stained and quite reasonably differentiated. If the tissues other than the nuclei are stained a dark red rather than the light pink which is inevitable, each section should then be briefly differentiated in a 0.1% solution of hydrochloric acid in 70% alcohol. This, however, will very rarely be necessary.

The sections are now run down to water before being stained in picro-indigo-carmine (DS 12.211 Cajal 1895), which is the easiest, simplest, and most foolproof of all double staining methods. The slides bearing the sections are placed in the solution from three to five minutes, withdrawn from the stain, rinsed briefly in water, and then placed directly in absolute alcohol, and left until a naked-eye examination shows that the connective tissues are clear blue. This clear blue is in distinction to the bright green of the muscles or the red of such other tissues as have retained the carmine. The moment that this change from green to blue, which is clearly and sharply seen, takes place the slide is placed in xylene which stops the differentiation and permits subsequent mounting in balsam.

The results obtained by this method are not, of course, to be compared for brilliance with the more complex methods using acid fuchsin and some of the phosphotungstic reactions. But this is undoubtedly the first double-staining method which should be tried by any beginner— to whom encouragement is probably of more value than the actual colors to be obtained.

Preparation of a transverse section of the tongue of a rat using coelestin blue B followed by picro-acid fuchsin

The chief difficulty in preparing a transverse section of the tongue is to avoid hardening of the muscle which tends to become brittle, either if imperfectly fixed or if handled with undesirable reagents in any stage of the proceedings. It is therefore recommended that the following description be followed rather closely, for it can be adapted almost without variation to any other heavily muscularized tissue which it is desired to stain.

As this preparation is intended to show only the gross histological elements present, it is unnecessary to specify the manner in which the rat should be killed; but, the sacrificed animal may be used also for the staining of taste buds in the posterior lobe of the tongue by the method described in some detail in Chapter 23, "Demonstration of the nerve ending in taste buds by the method of Bielschowsky 1914," in which case the rat had better be killed by a blow on the head rather than by an anesthetic.

The tongue may be easily removed by severing the articulation of the lower jaw and by removing this together with the adherent tongue which may be detached with a short scalpel or cartilage knife. A portion of the tongue approximately 5 mm. in length is now cut off and placed in a large volume of the selected fixative.

Though opinions vary widely as to the most desirable fixative to use for muscularized tissues, it may be said at once that no alcoholic solution and no solution containing picric acid or osmic acid can be recommended. The author's choice would be for the cupric-acetic-phenol formula of Behrens 1898 (Chapter 18 F 4000.0010), which he has employed most successfully on a variety of heavily muscularized tissues. This formula would also provide an excellent prior-mordanting for the staining techniques which follow. Whatever formula is selected, however, a large volume (about 100 cc. for the piece of rat tongue described) should be employed and permitted to act for no longer than is necessary to secure the complete impregnation of the tissues. When the piece has been successfully fixed it must be washed overnight in running water and then dehydrated. The process of dehydrating, clearing, and embedding is the point at which most muscularized tissues become unmanageable. Nothing, of course, can counteract the effect of improper fixation,

but even with good fixation the utmost attention must be paid to the selection of dehydrating agent and clearing agent, and to the temperature at which the embedding takes place. It has been the experience of the writer that the newer substitutes for alcohol in dehydrating tend to harden or render brittle muscular tissue to a greater extent than does the more old-fashioned method of using ethanol. There is little choice in the matter of clearing prior to embedding, for it has been found by numerous workers that benzene has a less hardening effect on muscular tissue than have other agents.

Unless it is desired to cut very thin sections, a wax of no higher melting point than 52°C. should be employed. It may be stated categorically that should the temperature be permitted to rise above 56°C., it would be better to throw the preparation away than to waste time endeavoring to section it. Paraffin sections are now cut from the block by the standard method, then flattened and attached to a slide by either gelatin or egg albumen. It is recommended that as soon as the sections are flattened, they should be pressed to the slide with a piece of wet filter paper, rolled into position with a rubber roller, and dried with the maximum possible speed.

As soon as they are dried, the sections are deparaffinized by the usual techniques and taken down to distilled water, where they may remain until one is ready to stain them. Coelestin blue B as the nuclear stain is selected in this instance because the contrast of muscularized tissues is better brought out with the aid of a picro-contrast than by any other method. These picro-contrasts are, however, so acid that hematoxylin-stained nuclei are often decolorized in the course of counterstaining. Any of the oxazine formulas (DS 11.41 above) may be chosen, the writer's preference being for the first (DS 11.41 Anonymous 1936). The solution presents no difficulties of preparation and need not be rejected if it shows a slight precipitate at the bottom. The sections are passed directly into it from the distilled water and allowed to remain until an examination under the low power of the microscope shows the nuclei to be clearly and deeply stained. It is very difficult to overstain in this solution and, though the time specified in the formula given is from five minutes to one hour, no damage will be occasioned should the sections remain overnight in the staining solution. After removal from the staining solution they are rinsed in distilled water and accumulated in a jar either of distilled or tap water, until it is desired to counterstain them.

Any of the formulas given under DS 12.221 below may be used for counterstaining, but that of van Gieson (DS 12.221 van Gieson 1896), though old, is still one of the best. Its only disadvantage is that it has a tendency to remove hematoxylin from stained nuclei, an effect which the present method avoids. The stain requires little or no differentiation, so that the sections may be placed in it and examined from time to time until the muscles are seen to be stained yellow against a red connective-tissue back-

ground. If a small quantity of yellow is picked up by the connective tissues it will be removed in the process of differentiation. The time is not critical, but that given in the formula cited (from two to 10 minutes) will be found to cover the range normally necessary.

A slight difficulty will be occasioned in dehydration through the tendency of the picric acid to leave the tissues in the various alcohols employed. This may either be prevented by dehydrating them in a series of 1% solutions of picric acid in the various alcohols, or it may be ignored completely, according to the depth of yellow color which it is required to retain. If, on the contrary, it is desired to have them a very pale yellow, they may have to spend a period of time beyond that necessary for dehydration in 95% alcohol to remove the unwanted picric acid. The sections are then cleared in xylene in the normal manner and mounted in balsam.

12.21 CONTRASTS FOR RED NUCLEI

12.211 Formulas Containing Picric Acid

12.211 Borrel 1901   see DS 12.211 Cajal 1895 (note) and also DS 23.11 Borrel 1901

12.211 Cajal 1895 test. **1905 Lee**   picro-indigo-carmine   Lee 1905, 20
   FORMULA: water 100, picric acid 1, indigo-carmine 0.25
   METHOD: [sections with red nuclei] → water → stain, 3–5 mins. → water, quick rinse → abs. alc., till connective tissue clear blue
   RESULT: muscle, green; most connective tissues, blue.
   NOTE: See also DS 22.12 Hruby 1933. A detailed description of the use of this stain is given under 12.20 above. This stain is referred to **Borrel** (without reference) by Besson 1904, 751; see, however, DS 23.11 Borrel 1901. **Calleja** (Cajal and de Castro 1933, 87) specifies prior staining of nuclei in DS 11.28 Orth (1892).

12.211 Calleja   see DS 12.211 Cajal 1895 (note)

12.211 Curtis 1905   picro-naphthol black   6630, **57**:1038
   STOCK SOLUTIONS: I. sat. aq. sol. picric acid; II. water 80, glycerol 20, naphthol blue black 1
   WORKING SOLUTION: stock I 90, stock II 10
   METHOD: [red, preferably safranin-stained, nuclei] → stain freshly prepared, flooded on slide, 10–15 mins. → abs. alc. till differentiated → toluene to stop differentiation → balsam
   RESULT: nuclei, red; cartilage, blue; other structures, yellow.

12.211 Curtis 1905b   picro-naphthol black   1863, **17**:603
   FORMULA: water 100, glycerol 2, acetic acid 0.01, picric acid 0.9, naphthol blue black 0.1
   METHOD, ETC.: as Curtis 1905a

12.211 Domagk test. **1948 Romeis**   picro-thiazin red   Romeis 1948, 168
   FORMULA: water 100, picric acid 1, thiazin red 0.01

12.211 Dubreuil 1904   picro-methyl blue   6593, **6**:62
   FORMULA: water 100, methyl blue 0.1, picric acid 0.9

12.211 Grosso 1914   *picro-methyl green*   8545, **18**:71
PREPARATION OF DRY STOCK: Add a sat. aq. sol. picric acid to a sat. aq. sol. methyl green
till no further ppt. is formed. Wash and dry ppt.
PREPARATION OF STOCK SOLUTION: methanol 100, dry stock 0.5
PREPARATION OF WORKING SOLUTION: stock solution 15, water 65
METHOD: [sections with red nuclei] → stain, 5–10 mins. → water, quick rinse → abs.
alc., till red color clouds cease → balsam, via xylene

12.211 Grosso 1914   *see* DS 21.3 Grosso 1914

12.211 Hruby 1933   *see* DS 22.12 Hruby 1933

12.211 Krause 1911 *test.* **1948 Romeis**   *picro-indigo-carmine*
                                                Romeis 1948, 169
FORMULA: water 100, picric acid 1, indigo-carmine 0.3

12.211 Lillie 1945   *picro-blue*   11571b, **25**:1
FORMULA: water 100, picric acid to sat., methyl blue 0.1 *or* anilin blue 0.1
NOTE: Lillie 1948 p. 191 recommends this as a contrast for blue nuclei.

12.211 Lillie 1948   *picro-naphthol black*   Lillie 1948, 191
FORMULA: water 100, picric acid *q.s.* to sat., naphthol blue black 0.02 to 0.04

12.211 Masson *test.* **1934 Langeron**   *picro-indigo-carmine*
                                                Langeron 1934, 552
REAGENTS REQUIRED: *A.* 1% acetic acid; *B.* sat. aq. sol. picric acid 100, indigo-carmine
0.25; *C.* 0.2% acetic acid
METHOD: [nuclei red, preferably by some DS 11.43 method] → *A*, thorough rinse → *B*,
10 mins. → water, quick rinse → *C*, till connective tissue clear blue, about 2 mins. →
abs. alc. shortest time to complete dehydration → balsam, via xylene
RESULT: very like Cajal 1895 but with a greater range of shades.

12.211 Minchin *test.* **1928 Goodrich**   *picro-light green*   Gatenby and Cowdry 1928, 432
FORMULA: 90% alc. 100, picric acid 5, light green 1
METHOD: [red nuclei] → 90% alc. → stain, 10 mins. → abs. alc. till differentiated →
balsam, via xylene
RESULT: similar to Smith 1912.

12.211 Neubert 1922   *picro-thiazin red*   23418(1), **66**:424
REAGENTS REQUIRED: *A.* water 100, 95% alc. 10, thiazin red 0.15, picric acid 0.03;
B. sat. 95% alc. sol. picric acid
METHOD: [sections with hematoxylin-stained nuclei] → water → *A*, till collagen deeply
stained → rinse → *B*, thorough wash → balsam, via usual reagents

12.211 Pfitzer 1883   *picro-nigrosin*   2626, **1**:44
FORMULA: sat. sol. picric acid 100, nigrosin 0.2

12.211 Pol 1908 *test.* **1948 Romeis**   *picro-indigo-carmine*
                                                Romeis 1948, 169
FORMULA: water 100, picric acid 1, indigo-carmine 0.4

12.211 Roskin 1946   *see* DS 13.43 Roskin 1946

12.211 Shumway 1926   *picro-indigo-carmine*   *see* DS 13.5 Shumway 1926

12.211 Smith 1912   *picro-spirit blue*   11373, **23**:94
FORMULA: sat. alc. sol. (*circ.* 1%) spirit blue 100, picric acid 1
METHOD: [sections of material bulk stained in carmine] → abs. alc. → stain, 2 mins. →
abs. alc., till differentiated → balsam, via xylene
RESULT: nuclei, red; yolk, yellow green; yolk-free cytoplasm, clear blue.

12.211 White *test.* **1905 Hall and Herxheimer**   *picro-erythrosin*
                                                Hall and Herxheimer 1905, 63
FORMULA: water 100, sat. alc. sol. erythrosin 4, picric acid 0.6, calcium carbonate to
excess

12.212 Other Formulas

12.212 Chatton 1920   *eosin Y-light green*   1915, **59**:21
REAGENTS REQUIRED: *A*. 95% alc. 100, light green 1, eosin Y 2; *B*. 5% acetic acid in
abs. alc.
PREPARATION OF A: Dissolve with occasional agitation over period of some days. Filter.
METHOD: [sections with red nuclei] → 95% alc. → *A*, 5 mins. → *B*, till connective tissue
clear green → balsam, via usual reagents
RESULT: on arthropod material, for which the stain was designed, chitin is green on a
red background. On vertebrate material the picture is similar to DS 12.32 Patay 1934.

12.212 Kostowiecki 1932   *orange G-anilin blue*   23632, **49**:337
FORMULA: water 100, anilin blue 0.06, orange G 0.2, phosphomolybdic acid 1
PREPARATION: Boil dyes with water 3 minutes. Add acid to hot solution. Cool. Filter.
METHOD: [sections with red nuclei] → water → stain, till dark colored, ½ to 12 hrs. →
water, rinse → 95% alc., 1 min. → balsam, via usual reagents
RESULT: procartilage, light blue; cartilage, dark blue; muscle, orange; other connective
tissues, blue green.

12.212 Roux 1894   *dahlia-methyl green*   766, **9**:248
FORMULA: water 90, abs. alc. 20, dahlia violet 0.5, methyl green 0.5
PREPARATION: Grind each dye separately in 10 abs. alc. Wash out each mortar with
50 water in small successive doses. Collect washings; leave 24 hours; filter. Mix
filtrates; leave 24 hours filter.
METHOD: [red nuclei] → water → stain, 5–15 mins. → blot → abs. alc., till differentiated
→ balsam, via usual reagents
NOTE: The dahlia violet used by Roux may have been almost any mixture of pararo-
saniline derivatives. Cheap samples of gentian violet work admirably. The result is
an excellent polychrome counterstain wherever reproducibility of research results is
of less importance than classroom clarity of demonstration. The working solution
has been evaporated to dryness and sold as **Roux's blue**. (See DS 13.5 Böhm and
Oppel 1907.)

12.212 Unna *test.* **1928 Hill**   *anilin blue-orcein*   Gatenby and Cowdry 1928, 280
REAGENTS REQUIRED: *A*. 0.1% acetic acid; *B*. water 50, abs. alc. 25, acetic acid 2.5,
glycerol 10, orcein 0.5, anilin blue 0.5
PREPARATION OF *B*: Dissolve blue in water with gentle heat. Filter. Dissolve orcein in
alc. and add to it the acid and glycerol. Add this mixture to the blue.
METHOD: [red nuclei → *A*, few minutes → *B*, 1 to 10 hrs. → *A*, till differentiated →
balsam, via usual reagents
RESULT: bone and elastic fibers red-brown against a blue background.
NOTE: This reaction is more usually applied by the method of Pasini (1928) (DS 12.31).

12.22 CONTRASTS FOR BLUE NUCLEI

12.221 Formulas Containing Picric Acid

12.221 Curtis 1905   *picro-ponceau*   1863, **17**:603
FORMULA: water 100, ponceau S 0.1, picric acid 1, acetic acid 0.04

12.221 Fite 1939   *picro-fuchsin*   11284, **25**:743
FORMULA: water 100, picric acid 0.5, acid fuchsin 0.1

12.221 van Gieson 1896   *picro-fuchsin*   23632, **13**:344
FORMULA: sat. sol. (*circ*. 1.2%) picric acid 100, acid fuchsin 0.05
METHOD: [blue nuclei] → water → stain, 2–10 mins. → water, quick rinse → balsam,
via usual reagents
NOTE: A detailed description of the use of this stain is given under 12.20 above.

12.221 Gnanamuthu 1931   *picro-congo red*   11360, **51**:401
FORMULA: sat. sol. (*circ*. 1.2%) picric acid 50, ammonia 50, congo red 2
PREPARATION: Add the ammonia to the picric solution. Dissolve the dye in mixture and
boil till no odor of ammonia is apparent. Cool. Add sufficient water to redissolve ppt.
formed on cooling.

METHOD: [blue nuclei (DS 11.123 Ehrlich 1886 specified in original)] → water → stain, 1–2 mins. → blot → abs. alc., minimum time for dehydration → balsam, via usual reagents
RESULT: muscle, red; other tissues, yellow and orange. Good for most heavily muscularized tissues.

12.221 Hansen 1898   *picro-fuchsin*   766, **15**:152
REAGENTS REQUIRED: *A*. sat. sol. (*circ.* 1.2%) picric acid 100, acetic acid 0.3, acid fuchsin 0.1; *B*. water 98, A. 2
METHOD: [blue nuclei] → water → *A*, some hrs. → *B*, wash → balsam, via xylene
RESULT: selective red stain on white fibrous connective tissue.

12.221 Lillie 1948   *picro-fuchsin*   Lillie 1948
FORMULA: water 100, picric acid 1, acid fuchsin 0.1, hydrochloric acid 0.25
NOTE: Lillie (*loc. cit.*) also recommends his DS 12.211 solution as a contrast for hematoxylin-stained nuclei.

12.221 Ohlmacher 1897   *picro-fuchsin*   11189, **2**:675
FORMULA: sat. sol. (*circ.* 1.2%) picric 50, water 50, acid fuchsin 0.5

12.221 Schaffer 1899   *picro-fuchsin*   23635, **66**:214
FORMULA: sat. aq. sol. picric acid, acid fuchsin 0.15, acetic acid 0.05

12.221 Thompson 1945   *see* DS 21.3 Thompson 1945

12.221 Unna *test.* **Lillie 1948**   *picro-fuchsin*   Lillie 1948, 190
FORMULA: water 90, acid fuchsin 0.25, nitric acid 0.5, glycerol 10, picric acid *q.s.* to sat.

12.221 Weigert 1904   *picro-fuchsin*   23632, **21**:3
FORMULA: sat. sol. (*circ.* 1.2%) picric acid 100, acid fuchsin 0.1
METHOD: as van Gieson above

12.221 Wilhelmini 1909   *picro-fuchsin*   8338, **22**:18
FORMULA: water 90, 95% alc. 10, ammonium picrate 0.8, acid fuchsin 0.2
METHOD: as van Gieson above

12.222 Other Formulas

12.222 Delèphine *test. circ.* **1938 Wellings**   *fuchsin-orange*
                                              Wellings 1938, 104
FORMULA: water 100, acid fuchsin 0.04, orange G 0.2

12.222 Gray 1952   *ponceau-orange*   Gray 1952, 24
FORMULA: water 100, orange II 0.6, ponceau 2R 0.4
METHOD: [blue nuclei] → water → stain, 1–2 mins. → blot → abs. alc., till differentiated → balsam, via usual reagents

12.222 Gregg and Puckett 1943   *eosin-orange*   20540b, **18**:179
FORMULA: 95% alc. 100, eosin 0.2, orange G 0.01

12.222 Guyler 1932   *indigo-carmine-eosin Y*   11977, **18**:314
FORMULA: water 100, indigo-carmine 0.25, eosin Y 1, thymol trace
METHOD: [blue nuclei (original specifies 11.122 Delafield 1885)] → water → stain, overnight → water, quick rinse → abs. alc., till differentiated → balsam, via usual reagent

12.222 Hayem *test.* **1896 Kahlden and Laurent**   *eosin-aurantia*
                                              Kahlden and Laurent 1896, 117
FORMULA: 1% eosin W, 1% aurantia, *a.a. q.s.* to give rose-colored solution

12.222 Kingsbury and Johannsen 1927   *orange-acid fuchsin*
                                              Kingsbury and Johannsen 1927, 76
FORMULA: water 100, glycerol 7, orange G 1, acid fuchsin 2

12.222 Langeron 1942   *see* DS 12.222 Masson 1911 (note)

12.222 Male 1924 *fuchsin-martius yellow*   11035, **42**:455
   FORMULA: water 80, 95% alc. 20, acid fuchsin 0.6, martius yellow 0.8

12.222 Masson 1911 *saffron-erythrosin*   6630, **70**:573
   REAGENTS REQUIRED: *A*. 1% erythrosin; *B*. water 100, saffron 2, 5% tannin 1, 40%
     formaldehyde 1
   PREPARATION OF *B*: Extract the saffron in the water 1 hour 90°C. Filter. Add other
     ingredients to filtrate.
   METHOD: [blue nuclei] → water → *A*, 5 mins. → water, quick rinse → 70% alc., few
     sec. → water, thorough wash → *B*, 5 mins. → blot → abs. alc., flooded over slide,
     till dehydrated → balsam, via xylene
   NOTE: **Langeron 1942** (p. 596) substitutes eosin B for erythrosin in the above.

12.222 Semichon 1920 *methyl blue-eosin-victoria yellow*
                                       5401, **45**:73
   REAGENTS REQUIRED: *A*. water 100, methyl blue 0.04, eosin Y 0.2, victoria yellow 0.1
   METHOD: [blue nuclei] → water → *A*, overnight → drain → abs. alc., till differentiated
     → xylene → balsam
   RESULT: horn, hair, chitin, yellow; cartilage, blue; other tissues, orange.

12.222 Squire 1892 *fuchsin-orange*   Squire 1892, 42
   FORMULA: water 80, 95% alc. 20, acid fuchsin 0.3, orange G 2.0
   METHOD: as Gray 1952 above

12.222 Szütz 1912 *polychrome alizarin*   23632, **29**:289
   REAGENTS REQUIRED: *A*. 5% aluminum acetate; *B*. sat. alc. sol. alizarin red S 1, water 100
   METHOD: [hematoxylin-stained sections of F 2300.1000 Szütz 1912 fixed material] →
     water → *A*, 5 hrs. → rinse → *B*, 5 hrs. → wash → balsam, via usual reagents
   RESULT: nuclei, blue; cytoplasm, varying shades of red, cytoplasmic inclusions being
     generally very darkly stained.

12.3 COMPLEX CONTRAST FORMULAS

These complex contrast formulas are specifically designed to differentiate the cytoplasm into various histological components. They are more widely used in embryology than in general histology, and the first two classes, here given, are all developed from the original discovery of Mallory 1904 (11189, **5**:15) that a solution of phosphomolybdic or phosphotungstic acid will remove acid fuchsin from collagen while allowing it to remain either in the muscle or in the nuclei. Mallory's original method, however, involves staining the nuclei with acid fuchsin as an inherent part of the technique, and is therefore given under the subheading DS 13, in which combined nuclei and plasma staining techniques are dealt with. The group here discussed is commonly associated with the name of Masson, and the term "Masson's Trichromic" is widely applied. These methods require prior staining of the nuclei with hematoxylin and the subsequent staining of the connecting and supporting tissues in accordance with Mal-

lory's principle. This stains nuclei a color from blue to deep purple, and they are thus distinguished far more clearly from the background cytoplasm than are those stained by the original method. All of these phosphotungstic and phosphomolybdic methods are excellent.

The second class of complex contrast formulae are those employing phosphomolybdic or phosphotungstic acid reaction with other dyes than fuchsin, while at the same time retaining the differential nuclear stain. Of these, Patay 1934 is a very nearly fool-proof and brilliant method of triple staining. Indeed the whole class of stains, with the exception of Fleming 1891, are of recent origin, and at the present time are the most popular group of counterstains which have yet been developed. Though they are customarily employed in zoological technique, no one who has tried them in botanical technique has ever regretted it.

The final class of complex contrast formulas contains only those mixtures which cannot otherwise be classified. Among them only the techniques of Margolena in 1933 and de Winwarter and Saimonte 1908 can be regarded as having any wide application.

Preparation of a transverse section of an earthworm, using the iron-hematoxylin stain of Régaud 1910, followed by the acid fuchsin-anilin blue of Masson 1912

Considering that almost every student of biology studies a transverse section of the earthworm, it is really surprising that sections commonly available from biological supply houses should have been prepared with little thought for their ultimate use. Quite apart from any considerations of staining, it may be pointed out that the average field of view of the 3.5X objective, commonly used in elementary biological laboratories, is about 4 mm., so that a worm larger than 4 mm. in diameter cannot be got into the field of view of this low power at one observation. It is undoubtedly a technical feat of some skill to cut a transverse section of a large earthworm, but it is also extraordinarily difficult for a beginning student to envisage the relationships of the whole by successive examinations of a variety of fields. It may be taken, therefore, as the first prerequisite to a useful preparation that one should select an earthworm of approximately the right size. Though this may prove an arduous labor, it may be pointed out that at least 100,000 sections may be obtained from a single worm. Further, the majority of sections which one sees in elementary classes have been stained by a standard hematoxylin-eosin technique which gives students very little chance of envisaging the relationships of the muscles; whereas if one employs a technique of the kind here recommended, the muscles will be stained a brilliant scarlet and the connective tissues to which they are attached will be stained a bright blue. There is also a much better differentiation of the various layers of the intestine and of the nervous tissue.

Once the earthworm has been collected and selected, it then becomes necessary to remove from it the grit with which the intestine is filled. The classic method of doing this, to which the writer strongly adheres, is to place the earthworm in an environment of old coffee grounds. It is not, however, sufficient, to take coffee grounds from which a single drink has been extracted. Grounds left over from the preparation of coffee should be taken, boiled for a considerable period in water, filtered, and again boiled, until little or no coloring matter remains to be extracted from them. The earthworm may be eclectic in its diet, but its constitution does not enable it to survive the glucosides and alkaloids of a partially extracted coffee bean. These depleted grounds should then be placed in a layer an inch or two thick in a clean glass jar, the selected earthworms placed on the surface, lightly sprinkled with coffee grounds, and permitted to live undisturbed for a period of about a week. The only critical factor is the degree of humidity of the grounds. This should be such that water cannot be pressed from them when they are squeezed in the hand, yet each grain should present the appearance of being moist.

After a week on a diet of coffee grounds the worms will have voided most of their grit content and may now be narcotized prior to fixation. Though it is not as necessary to narcotize them for section cutting as it is for dissection, it is nevertheless desirable, since it appears that muscles fixed after narcotization (at least those of the Annelida) are not nearly as liable to become brittle as are those fixed in the violent state of contraction which results from dropping the worm directly into the fixative. Earthworms may be satisfactorily narcotized under the surface of water containing almost any known narcotic agent, and the choice between chloroform, chloral hydrate, or cocaine and its substitutes must rest largely upon the availability of the reagents. The worm may be considered adequately narcotized when it does not react rapidly when placed on a flat surface of filter paper and slowly stretched with the fingers. If it does not contract at all, and particularly if its outer surface presents an opaque white appearance, the worm may be considered dead and only fit to be thrown away. If it contracts strongly and develops lateral twistings, it is insufficiently narcotized. Any stage between these two may be considered sufficient.

It is much more convenient if the worm be killed in an extended condition. The simplest way to do this is with the aid of two blocks of glass lying on top of each other. Capillary attraction will hold a small worm quite satisfactorily into the angle of these two blocks, or it may be forced against the angle by a heavy piece of glass rod, if capillary attraction proves insufficient. The selection of the fixative is a matter of some dispute; the author himself prefers the antique picro-sulfuric acid of Kleinenberg 1879 (Chapter 18, F 5000.0050) which was developed for the purpose of fixing earthworms and is admittedly worthless for any other purpose. It lends itself excellently, however, to afterstaining, and leaves the embedded worm less brittle than any other fixative which the writer has ever tried, with the possible exception of the irrational chromic-nitric mixture of Perenyi (F 6000.-0040 Perenyi 1882). This also has the advantage of preventing the worm from becoming brittle. Whichever fixative is chosen, the worm should now be immersed in it to just about its own depth, until such time as it has partially hardened, i.e. enough to hold it straight, and should then be placed in a large volume of the fixative for whatever period is desired. If Kleinenberg is employed, 24 hours will be sufficient, but the solution of Perenyi should be allowed to act for from one to three days. Kleinenberg's fixative should be washed out in large volumes of 70% alcohol until no more color comes away. If Perenyi's fixative is employed, running water may be used for the washing process. In either case, mercuric fixatives should be avoided, since considerable tampering with the specimen with steel instruments remains to be done, and this cannot be satisfactorily conducted after mercuric fixatives.

After it is washed, the worm should be divided into pieces about three-eighths of

an inch long. It is usually desirable to retain about half an inch of the anterior region for sagittal sections. The reproductive regions need only be saved in the unlikely event that they may be required for advanced classes. The segments should now be dehydrated in alcohol, or any other selected reagent, in the customary manner and cleared in oil of cedar. This reagent is selected because it does not render the segments brittle, yet does make them sufficiently transparent for examination by transmitted light with a dissecting microscope (to disclose such sand particles as may still remain in the intestine). These show up clearly as brightly refractive objects, and must be removed by being pushed out of position with the bent end of a sharp needle. The experienced technician does not need to be told that the retention of a single one of these sand grains within the body of the worm will result in the destruction not only of the microtome knife but of a considerable volume of material which might otherwise be used for good sections. If any considerable mass of sand grains remains on the inside, it may often be removed by filling a hypodermic syringe with cedar oil and directing the jet of cedar oil against the inside of the intestine. If this is done, several changes of cedar oil should be used to make sure that the particles of sand dislodged from the inner surface of the intestine do not become reattached to the epidermis. The cedar oil should now be thoroughly removed in benzene (xylene tends to render the muscles brittle) since cedar oil itself tends to dilute the wax or to require too long a period of embedding for such muscularized tissues as those of the earthworm.

The pieces are then embedded in paraffin and cut into 10-micron sections, which may then be mounted, either individually or in such groups as may be desired on clean slides, and then flattened and dried. When the sections are dried they are deparaffinized as usual and taken down through the various reagents to water, in which they may be accumulated in batches to be stained together.

The selection of the iron hematoxylin of Régaud (DS 11.111 Régaud 1910) in preference to any other is based only on the fact that it is a quicker process. If the operator does not mind waiting the required 24 hours, there is no reason why he should not employ the solution of Heidenhaim or any other of the iron mordant techniques. The solutions required for this staining method consist first of a 5% solution of ferric alum, second, of a glycerol-alcohol-hematoxylin solution, and third of a picric alcohol differentiating solution recommended by Masson himself for use before his trichrome methods.

The first step is to raise both the ferric alum and the hematoxylin solutions to approximately 50°C. This temperature is not critical, but the rate of staining is dependent on temperature and decreases rapidly as the temperature drops below 50°C. Temperatures above 50°C. may cause the sections to fall off the slide. The first batch of sections is now taken from water and placed in the heated ferric alum solution for a period of 30 minutes. It is then removed from the ferric alum solution, rinsed very rapidly in distilled water, and transferred to the heated hematoxylin solution for a further period of at least 30 minutes. On removal from the hematoxylin solution the sections should be blue-black. If they are not deeply stained enough, it is necessary to return them to the hematoxylin. The slides may now be rinsed briefly in distilled water and transferred to tap water prior to differentiation. If relatively large runs are being taken through, it will usually be desirable to bring all the sections through their nuclear staining before proceeding either with the differentiation or the counterstain.

The picric alcohol of Masson (ADS 21.1 Masson 1912), which is used for differentiating, is a relatively slow medium in comparison with the ferric alum differentiation frequently recommended for iron hematoxylin stains. As, however, a somewhat acid afterstain is being employed in this instance, care should be taken that differentiation does not proceed too far. It will be quite sufficient to differentiate the background to a pale straw color (it will, of course, become blue in tap water) rather than to the absolutely colorless

background which would be desirable were one using this technique to demonstrate chromosomes. As soon as the required degree of differentiation has taken place, the sections are returned to tap water and washed until no further picric acid leaves the specimen. It will be convenient for this purpose to have a fairly large dish in the sink through which a current of tap water is running continuously. A certain amount of differentiation will take place while this washing is going on, and the washing should not be discontinued until the nuclei are deep blue-black and the differentiated background has changed again from the very pale straw color to which it was turned by the picric differentiator to a pale blue. Failure to undertake this second bluing after differentiation is responsible for many of the failures to retain hematoxylin in the nucleus.

The acid fuchsin-anilin blue stain, which is here selected as a counterstain, is one of the easiest to apply, provided the instructions are followed closely. The solutions required are given under DS 12.31 Masson 1912a below; and it will be observed from the technique described that an acid environment must be retained throughout, even to the mounting medium. The first solution required is a mixture of acetic acid and acid fuchsin in water, to which the sections may be passed directly from the tap water, and in which they should not remain longer than five minutes. Each batch of sections to be stained by this method must be taken through individually, for there is no stage of the proceedings between the original staining with acid fuchsin till the sections are dehydrated in xylene at which a pause may be made for the accumulation of separate batches. After removal from the acidfuchsin solution the sections will be seen to be stained deeply red, and they require only the quickest rinse in tap water before being placed in 1% phosphomolybdic acid where considerable quantities of red dye will be removed. The time in this solution is not as critical as in many of the others, and the five minutes specified may be varied from, say, three to eight minutes without any great damage to the specimen. On removal from the phosphomo-lybdic acid it must be emphasized that no water rinse may be given. Each slide must be taken separately, drained, and the very deep blue "C" solution poured onto the surface of the slide where it may remain from two to five minutes. It may be mentioned in parenthesis that this deep-blue stain has just as great an affinity for the human skin as for any other protein material, and that it is far more difficult to remove from the skin than it is from any section. Rubber gloves or forceps are most warmly recommended to the operator. The D solution (1% acetic acid) should be available in two vessels, one containing a fairly large volume (a 500-ml. beaker is admirable) and the other a standard coplin jar or whatever vessel is customarily employed for slide staining. The section is rinsed rapidly in the large container to remove the adherent blue, and then is placed in the smaller container until such time as no further color is seen to leave it. One of the best features of this triple stain of Masson is that one does not require to control differentiation, for if the technique has been followed properly to this stage, the blue will not leave the connective tissues in the acid solution. Modifications in which it is recommended to differentiated in alcohol should be avoided, since this reagent can remove the whole of the blue color. Even when the 1% aqueous acetic acid is used at this stage of the proceedings, it is undesirable to leave the slide for too long a period after the blue color has ceased to be liberated from it, because there is a tendency to remove the hematoxylin from the nuclei, and it is for this reason that the slides cannot be accumulated in this reagent. The only delicate portion of the preparation now follows: the dehydration of the sections without the loss of the blue. Even after mordanting in phosphomolybdic acid, the blue is likely to be removed from the tissues with alcohol, and dehydration should be undertaken directly in absolute alcohol to which has been added 1% acetic acid. Either amyl alcohol with 1% acetic acid, or acetone with 1% acetic acid, may be substituted for absolute alcohol and will render the dehydration of the speci-

men much more easy without loss of the blue. There seems to be, however, a tendency to adhere to absolute alcohol on the part of histologists; and the alternative reagents are only mentioned for the benefit of those who might be prepared to break with tradition. The least possible time should be employed in dehydration; preferably the slide should be dipped up and down in the alcohol and transferred to xylene at intervals to see whether or not it is sufficiently dehydrated to clear. After they have been cleared in xylene, the slides may be accumulated in this reagent until the whole of the batch is ready for mounting.

Many workers have specified that salicylic acid be dissolved in the xylene to render it acid, but this is a precaution really only necessary if large quantities of alcohol are carried over into it. The normal provision of two or three changes of xylene will render the addition of salicylic acid unnecessary. Each slide is now mounted; the most strongly acid balsam which can be obtained is used; or one may employ *salicylic balsam*. This does not necessitate making up a special mounting medium, since the easiest method of adding the acid to the balsam is from the coverslip. A saturated solution of salicylic acid is made in xylene and each coverslip is dipped in this and permitted to dry in air so as to become coated with a thin film of salicylic acid. Ordinary xylene balsam, or any other resin dissolved in xylene, is then placed on the sections and one of the salicylic-acid-treated coverslips is placed on the surface. Within a moment or two the salicylic acid will have dissolved in and dispersed through the mounting medium; that remaining on the upper surface can easily be wiped off after the slide is dry.

Preparations prepared in this manner, with due attention to the maintenance of an acid environment, will be found to be quite permanent enough for use for many years in class, and will be such a great improvement over the sections of earthworm usually supplied for class teaching purposes as more than to warrant the slight additional trouble which is required for their preparation.

Preparation of a transverse section of
the head of a mouse using an acid-
alum hematoxylin stain (Masson
1934) followed by ponceau
2R-light green (Patay 1934)

A large section of this type is required
not so much for the demonstration of histological detail as for the demonstration to
classes of the morphological relationship
of the various parts of the head region. For
this reason the fixative to be employed
should be selected more on the basis of its
ability to penetrate large structures than
in the hope that it will permit fine histological differentiation of detail. It is, moreover, less necessary that the fine detail of
histological structures be preserved by immediate fixation than that the mouse be
so arranged as to permit the penetration of
fixative to all parts. These considerations
must therefore dictate both the manner in
which the mouse is killed and that in
which it is fixed. If there are available to
the worker only the cruder methods of
killing, the mouse should be left until *rigor
mortis* has passed off before the different
parts are arranged. Or alternatively, and
far more satisfactorily, the mouse may
be killed by the injection of sodium bar-
bitol or some such reagent, in order that
it may die in a perfectly relaxed condition. The author has already expressed
in several places his conviction that a
mounter should experiment for himself
with fixatives, rather than follow already
established recommendations. But in the
present case his own preference is very
strongly for the mercuric-dichromate-acetic mixture of Zenker 1894 (Chapter 18,
F 3700.0010). It must be remembered that
this specimen will have to be decalcified
and the use of the mercuric-dichromate is
therefore to render the tissues as hard as
possible and to prevent, as far as possible,
the hydrolysis of the softer parts by the
acids used for decalcification.

If it is desired to secure the transverse
section through the region of the eyes, the
head should be severed from the body as
soon as the mouse is dead, and about
three-quarters of the lower jaw, the anterior end of the tongue, and the anterior
end of the snout should be removed with a
pair of sharp scissors. A series of holes
should then be drilled, or driven with a
sharp point, into the skull in as many
places as possible, leaving free from holes
only a band approximately one-quarter of
an inch wide in the exact region of the eye
where the section is required. A band of
thread should then be tied tightly around
both the anterior and posterior cut surfaces so as to hold the skin in position.
Otherwise the differential contraction of
the latter while in the fixative will cause it
to become torn loose and to give a most
unsightly appearance to the section. The
more (and the more deeply) the holes are
drilled the better will the fixative penetrate and the subsequent section appear.
Previous to these operations one should
have prepared at least a liter of the required fixative and to have placed this in a
tall narrow jar. A liter-measuring cylinder,
with a cork to fit, is excellent, for the purpose, although tall museum jars of approximately the same shape are frequently
available. A staple or bent pin, should be
driven into the underside of the cork, to
which a thread or piece of string may be
attached, on the end of which is hung the
prepared head in a cheese cloth, or any
loosely-woven bag. Fixation with a dichromate solution is always best conducted in the dark, so the jar with the suspended head may now be placed in a dark
cupboard and forgotten for a period of two
or three weeks. The exact time of fixation
is unimportant; several months could be
allowed to elapse without any great risk
of damaging the piece. Nothing, however,
can be done with the piece if it is underfixed, and even if there are a relatively
large number of holes in it, two weeks is
not too long a period for the fixative to
penetrate.

The head is now removed from the fixative and taken out of its bag, and then
washed in running water for at least 48
hours. If this can be done in the dark it
will prevent the possibility of the chromium being deposited as a dark-green layer
over the outside, an event which would
render after-staining difficult.

One is now faced with the problem of
decalcification, for which purpose any of
the formulas given in Chapter 19 under

AF 20 may be employed. The writer has a strong preference for a simple solution of picric acid, provided that the specimen has, as in this case, been prior-fixed in a dichromate or a mercuric mixture. The specimen may remain in a saturated solution of picric acid for as long as is necessary to secure complete decalcification. Decalcification may be conducted in the same jar used for fixation, with precisely the same technique of suspending the object in a small loosely-woven cloth bag about one-third of the way down the bottle. It is only necessary to place an excess of picric acid in the bottom of the jar, to fill it up with water, and shake it a few times to produce saturation before inserting the cork bearing the specimen. In the case of the mouse, at least two months will be required to decalcify the skull, the test object being the inner ear, the bony protection of which is thicker than that of any other part of the cranium. This may be tested at intervals by removing the object from the decalcifying reagent and probing delicately in the region of the inner ear with a fine needle. It is very easy to distinguish between the tough nature of a decalcified bone and the hard, sharp reaction which one obtains from endeavoring to press the point of a pin into an actual calcified structure. It is to be recommended, however, in the interest of safety, that a period of at least one additional week in the decalcifying reagent be allowed between the time when one imagines the head to be perfectly decalcified and the time when one decides to embed and section it. The great advantage of picric acid as a decalcifying agent is that one cannot leave the specimen in it for too long a period; no harm whatever can be occasioned to the head of the mouse if it be left for even a year or two in the reagent.

After removal from the picric acid, the head is washed in running water for two or three days until it ceases to liberate any yellow color. It cannot be made entirely white, because compounds will be formed between the picric acid and the protoplasm. Three days' washing, for an object of the size described, should be ample. The specimen is then dehydrated, embedded, and sectioned. No special precautions are necessary save to remember that the dehydrating agent, the clearing agent, and the wax will penetrate slowly through so large and so tough an object. It is therefore desirable in embedding first to impregnate the object thoroughly with a saturated solution of wax in the selected clearing agent and then to evaporate the clearing agent off slowly, thus gradually increasing the concentration of the wax. A low-melting-point wax is better than a high melting point for preventing the hardening of the tissues, since it may be presumed that a 12- to 15-micron section will be cut. It is unwise to loosen the string holding the skin in place until at least the last change has been made in the clearing reagent. At this point, a section for final embedding, about a quarter to three-eights of an inch thick may be cut through the object with a fine saw, although the writer prefers to leave the final trimming of the object until it is in the paraffin block.

When the paraffin block has been prepared, it should be trimmed down roughly with a knife until such time as one can clearly see the eyes and thus distinguish the region of which it is desired to cut a section. The whole front end to within a millimeter or two of this can now be cut off with a fine saw. It is almost impossible to trim off these large masses with a knife without either cracking the paraffin block or so dragging the object within the paraffin that the hold of the embedding agent is loosened.

Section cutting presents no special difficulty, the more so as it is not anticipated that one intends to mount ribbons, but only to select individual sections. If these large sections have a tendency to roll up on the knife, wet the blade of the knife with 70% alcohol in order to hold down the beginning of the ribbon, and then cut as many sections as are desired. The closer one trims the block to the region which one desires to section, the less necessity will there be to substitute a freshly sharpened knife before taking off the sections from the actual regions required. Sections are flattened as usual, though it is recommended that they be rolled into position on the slide to avoid the almost inevitable curling which will result from the absorption of water by sections of this very large area and their subsequent swelling within the bounds of the paraffin which retains them.

The sections are then dewaxed in the ordinary manner and passed to water to await staining.

The stains which are required in the present instance are the acid alum hematoxylin of Masson (DS 11.123 Masson 1934) and the three solutions specified by Patay 1934 for his triple staining method (DS 12.32 Patay 1934). A description has already been given (DS 11.10 typical preparations) of the method by which an acid alum hematoxylin of this kind can be utilized to secure a sharp and clear differential staining of nuclei. In the present instance, however, a diffuse blue stain, particularly of cartilaginous areas, is preferred to a sharp definition of nuclei. One need, therefore, have no hesitation in placing the sections directly into this stain where they may remain overnight or for such period of time as is convenient to the operator. They will usually be satisfactorily stained within an hour and sometimes in less time; though this depends so much upon the time which they have spent in previous solutions, that it cannot be forecast with accuracy. When the sections are removed from hematoxylin they should be differentiated in a 0.1% solution of hydrochloric acid in 70% alcohol until the nuclei and the matrix of the cartilage, which will be clearly visible in large areas, alone remain blue. It is more damaging to over-differentiate than to under-differentiate.

When differentiation is complete, the sections should be accumulated in a jar of alkaline tap water (rendered alkaline when necessary by the addition of sodium bicarbonate) until they have turned from dull purple to clear blue. The sections are now taken from the water and passed to the 1% solution of ponceau 2R for a period of two minutes, briefly rinsed in water, passed into 1% phosphomolybdic acid for approximately two minutes, or until such time as the cartilage is freed from the red stain, rinsed again briefly in water, and then dipped two or three times in 90% alcohol to remove the excessive water before being placed for about 30 seconds in the $\frac{1}{2}$% solution of light green in 90% alcohol, which constitutes the final stain of the series. The section should then be passed into absolute alcohol until such time as no further green color comes away before being passed to xylene and mounted in balsam.

This method of triple staining is one of the most foolproof and satisfactory of any known to the author, and it is particularly applicable to those structures which contain bone as well as cartilage.

12.31 TECHNIQUES EMPLOYING THE PHOSPHOTUNGSTIC (-MOLYBDIC-) REACTION WITH ACID FUCHSIN

12.31 Brillmeyer 1929 *acid fuchsin-anilin blue-orange G*

11571b, **12**:122

REAGENTS REQUIRED: A. 0.2% acid fuchsin; B. water 100, phosphomolybdic acid 1, anilin blue 0.5, orange G 2.0

METHOD: [blue nuclei (original specifies DS 11.122 Delafield 1885)] → A, 1 min. → drain → B, 2–3 hrs. → water, quick wash → balsam, via usual reagents

NOTE: Weiss 1932 (20540b, **7**:131) differs only in the dilution of A to 0.04% and in the substitution of 4 minutes for 3 hours immersion in B. DS 11.122 Mayer 1901 is recommended for prior staining of sections from picric fixed or mordanted material.

12.31 Crossmon 1937 *acid fuchsin-orange G-light green (or -anilin blue)*

763, **69**:33

REAGENTS REQUIRED: A. water 100, acetic acid 1, acid fuchsin 0.3, orange G 0.13, thymol 0.06; B. 1% phosphomolybdic acid; C. *either* water 100, acetic acid 1, light green 1 *or* water 100, acetic acid 2, aniline blue 2; D. 1% acetic acid

METHOD: [sections, nuclei hematoxylin-stained] → water → A, 1 min. → rinse → B, till collagen decolorized → quick rinse → C, 5 mins. → rinse → D, till differentiated → rinse → abs. alc. → balsam, via xylene

12.31 Goldner 1938   *acid fuchsin-ponceau 2R-orange G-light green*
608b, **14**:237

REAGENTS REQUIRED: *A*. water 100, ponceau 2R 0.07, acid fuchsin 0.03, acetic acid 0.2; *B*. 1% acetic acid; *C*. water 100, phosphomolybdic acid 4, orange G 2; *D*. water 100, light green 0.2, acetic acid 0.2

METHOD: [sections with nuclei stained by DS 11.121 Weigert 1904] → thorough wash → *A*, 5 mins. → *B*, wash → *C*, till collagen decolorized → *B*, rinse → *D*, 5 mins. → *B*, 5 mins. → blot → abs. alc., least possible time → balsam, via xylene

RESULT: general cytoplasm, red; erythrocytes, orange; collagen, green.

NOTE: Other color combinations may be obtained by substituting for *A* above *either* water 100, azophloxin 0.5, acetic acid 0.2 *or* water 100, acid fuchsin 0.025, ponceau 2R 0.075, azophloxine 0.01, acetic acid 0.2. For a further modification see DS 13.7 Romeis 1948.

12.31 Haythorne 1916   *acid fuchsin-orange G-anilin blue*
4349, **6**:61

REAGENTS REQUIRED: *A*. water 100, hydrochloric acid 0.06, 95% alc. 4, orange G 0.8, ferric alum 5; *B*. 0.5% acid fuchsin; *C*. sat. aq. sol. phosphomolybdic acid 100, anilin blue 2.5, orange G 2.5

PREPARATION OF *A*: Dissolve the orange G in 70 water with the alc. and acid. Dissolve the alum in 25 water and add to the dye solution. Filter.

METHOD: [sections of F 3700.0010 Zenker 1894 fixed material after 30 mins. staining in DS 11.122 Böhmer 1868] → water → *A*, 2 mins. → water, 5 mins. → *B*, 3 mins. → blot → *C*, 20 mins. → blot → 95% alc., quick rinse → abs. alc., from drop bottle, till differentiated → balsam, via xylene

RESULT: nuclei, reddish black; cartilage, white fibrous tissue, blue; keratin, chitin, erythrocytes, bright orange; muscle, red.

12.31 Laidlaw   *see* DS 23.11 Laidlaw (1936)

12.31 Lendrum and McFarlane 1940   *picro-orange G-acid fuchsin-ponceau 2R-anilin blue*
11431, **50**:381

REAGENTS REQUIRED: *A*. water 20, 95% alc. 80, picric acid 1, orange G 0.2; *B*. water 99, acetic acid 1, acid fuchsin 0.5, ponceau 2R 0.5, sodium sulfate 0.25; *C*. 1% acetic acid; *D*. 1% phosphomolybdic acid; *E*. water 99, acetic acid 1, anilin blue 2

METHOD: [sections with nuclei stained by DS 11.41 technique] → water → *A*, 2 mins. → overnight → rinse → *B*, 1–5 mins. → *C*, rinse → *D*, till collagen not quite decolorized → *E*, 2–10 mins. → *C*, rinse → balsam, via usual reagents

NOTE: Fast green FCF may be substituted for anilin blue in *E* above.

12.31 Lillie 1940   *Biebrich scarlet-fast green*
20540b, **15**:21

REAGENTS REQUIRED: *A*. water 99, acetic acid 1, Biebrich scarlet 1; *B*. water 100, phosphotungstic acid 2.5, phosphomolybdic acid 2.5; *C*. water 97.5, acetic acid 2.5, fast green FCF 2.5; *D*. 1% acetic acid

METHOD: [sections with blue nuclei (original specifies DS 11.121 Weigert 1903)] → water → *A*, 2 mins. → rinse → *B*, 1 min. → *C*, 2 mins. → *D*, 1 min. or till differentiated → balsam, via acetone and xylene

12.31 Masson 1912a   *acid fuchsin-anilin blue*
4956, **87**:290

REAGENTS REQUIRED: *A*. water 100, acetic acid 0.5, acid fuchsin 0.5; *B*. 1% phosphomolybdic acid; *C*. water 100, acetic acid 2.5, anilin blue to sat.; *D*. 1% acetic acid; *E*. 0.1% acetic acid in abs. alc.

METHOD: [sections (original required prior staining in DS 11.111 Régaud 1910)] → water → *A*, 5 mins. → water, quick rinse → *B*, 5 mins. → drain → *C*, poured on slide, 2–5 mins. → *D*, till differentiated 5–30 mins. → *E*, till dehydrated → salicylic-xylene → salicylic balsam

RESULT: nuclei, black (if prior stained in Régaud) or deep red; collagens, light blue; bone, dark blue; epithelia, muscle, some glands, light red; erythrocytes, orange; nervous tissues, violet.

NOTE: A detailed description of the use of this stain is given under 12.30 above.

12.31 Masson 1912b *acid fuchsin-ponceau 2R-anilin blue*
4956, 87:290
REAGENTS REQUIRED: *A.* water 100, acetic acid 1, acid fuchsin 0.35, ponceau 2R 0.65; *B, C, D, E* as Masson 1912a above
METHOD: as Masson 1912a above

12.31 Masson 1912c *acid fuchsin-metanil yellow*   4956, 87:290
REAGENTS REQUIRED: *A.* water 1, acetic acid 1, acid fuchsin 100; *B.* 1% phosphomolybdic acid; *C.* sat. sol. (*circ.* 6%) metanil yellow; *D.* 1% acetic acid
METHOD: [sections (original required prior staining in DS 11.111 Régaud 1910)] → water → *A*, 5 mins. → water, quick rinse → *B*, 5 mins. → drain → *C*, poured on slide, 5 mins. → *D*, 5 mins. → salicylic balsam, via usual reagents

12.31 Masson 1912 *see also* DS 12.32 Masson 1912 and DS 13.41 Masson 1912

12.31 McFarlane 1944a *picro-acid fuchsin-anilin blue*   20540b, 19:29
REAGENTS REQUIRED: *A.* water 98, acetic acid 2, picric acid 0.2, phosphotungstic acid 1, acid fuchsin 1, anilin blue 2; *B.* 2% acetic acid; *C.* water 90, 95% alc. 10, picric acid 0.25, phosphotungstic acid 2.5
METHOD: [sections with blue nuclei] → water → *A*, 5 mins. → *B*, rinse → *C*, till differentiated → *D*, 1 min. → *B*, wash → balsam, via usual reagents

12.31 McFarlane 1944b *picro-acid fuchsin-anilin blue*   20540b, 19:23
REAGENTS REQUIRED: *A.* water 98, acetic acid 2, acid fuchsin 0.8, picric acid 0.2; *B.* 2% acetic acid; *C.* water 60, 95% alc. 40, picric acid 1, phosphotungstic acid 10; *D.* water 97.5, acetic acid 2.5, anilin blue 2.5; *E.* water 90, 95% alc. 10, picric acid 0.25, phosphotungstic acid 2.5
METHOD: [sections with DS 11.121 stained nuclei] → water → *A*, 5 mins. → *B*, rinse → *C*, 5 mins. → rinse → *D*, 5–10 mins. → *B*, rinse → *E*, 5 mins. → *B*, wash → balsam, via usual reagents

12.31 McFarlane 1944c *picro-orange G-acid fuchsin-ponceau 2R-anilin blue*
20540b, 19:23
REAGENTS REQUIRED: *A.* water 20, 95% alc. 80, picric acid 1, orange G 0.25; *B.* water 99, acetic acid 1, acid fuchsin 0.25, ponceau 2R 0.25; *C.* 2% acetic acid; *D.* water 20, 95% alc. 80, picric acid 1, phosphotungstic acid 10; *E.* water 97.5, acetic acid 2.5, anilin blue 2.5; *F.* water 80, 95% alc. 20, picric acid 0.5, phosphotungstic acid 5
METHOD: [sections, stained but not differentiated, in DS 11.111 Régaud 1910] → rinse → *A*, till nuclei differentiated → wash, till only erythrocytes yellow → *B*, 5–10 mins. → *C*, rinse → *D*, 5 mins., till differentiated → *C*, rinse → *E*, 10 mins. → *C*, rinse → *F*, till differentiated → *C*, wash → balsam, via usual reagents

12.31 Papanicolaou 1941 *see* DS 23.4 Papanicolaou 1941

12.31 Pasini *test.* **1928 Hill** *eosin B-acid fuchsin-anilin blue-orcein*
Gatenby and Cowdry 1928, 280
REAGENTS REQUIRED: *A.* 2% phosphotungstic acid; *B.* 50% alc. 35, glycerol 40, eosin B 0.7, DS 12.216 Unna (1928) 35, sat. aq. sol. acid fuchsin 4
PREPARATION OF B: Dissolve the eosin in 35 50% alc. Add, in order, the Unna's stain, fuchsin solution, and glycerol.
METHOD: [sections with blue nuclei (original specifies DS 11.123 Ehrlich 1886)] → water → *A*, 10 mins. → water, quick rinse → *B*, 15–20 mins. → 70% alc. quick rinse → abs. alc., 20 secs. → *A*, 5 secs. → abs. alc. till differentiated → balsam, via xylene
RESULT: collagen, blue; elastic fibers, purple; erythrocytes, bright orange.
NOTE: See also DS 13.42 Walter 1930.

12.31 Pollak 1944 *orange G-light green-ponceau 2R-acid fuchsin*
1887a, 37:294
REAGENTS REQUIRED: *A.* water 50, 95% alc. 50, acetic acid 1, phosphotungstic acid 0.5, phosphomolybdic acid 0.5, orange G 0.25, light green SF 0.15, ponceau 2R 0.33, acid fuchsin 0.17; *B.* 0.2% acetic acid

PREPARATION OF *A*: Mix water, alc., and acetic acid. Divide into four portions. In first dissolve phosphomolybdic acid with heat; in second dissolve phosphotungstic acid and Orange G; in third dissolve light green; in fourth dissolve acid fuchsin and ponceau 2R. Mix and filter.

METHOD: [sections with blue nuclei] → water → *A*, 3–7 mins. → *B*, till differentiated → 95% alc., till dehydrated → balsam, via usual reagents

12.31 Wallart and Honette 1934   *acid fuchsin-fast yellow*

4285a, **10**:404

REAGENTS REQUIRED: *A*. 1% acid fuchsin in 1% acetic acid 30, 3% fast yellow in 1% acetic acid 30, 1% phosphomolybdic acid 30; *B*. 1% acetic acid; *C*. 1% acetic acid in abs. alc.

METHOD: [sections with nuclei stained in DS 11.121 Weigert 1903] → tap water → *A*, 5 mins. → quick rinse → *B*, 5 mins. → *C*, dropped on from pipet, 30 secs. → abs. alc. → xylene → balsam

RESULT: black nuclei, red cytoplasm, yellow collagen, pink elastin.

12.31 Weiss 1932   *see* DS 12.31 Brillmeyer 1929 (note)

12.32 TECHNIQUES EMPLOYING THE PHOSPHOTUNGSTIC (-MOLYBDIC-) REACTION WITH OTHER DYES

12.32 Duprès 1935   *toluidine blue-orange G*   14425, **46**:46

REAGENTS REQUIRED: *A*. 1% phosphomolybdic acid; *B*. water 100, toluidine blue 0.25, orange G 4, oxalic acid 4

METHOD: [red nuclei (original specifies DS 11.43 Duprès 1935)] → *A*, 10 mins. → water, thorough wash → *B*, 2–5 mins. → drain → 95% alc. till differentiated → balsam, via usual reagents

RESULT: nuclei, red; collagens, blue; bone, dark green; muscle, light green; erythrocytes, bright orange; epidermis, blue; layer of Malpighi, orange; hair, etc., bright red.

NOTE: Duprès 1935 (*loc. cit.*) also recommends methyl green in place of toluidine blue in *B* above.

12.32 Gomori 1950   *chromotrope-fast green*   *Tech. Bull.*, **20**:77

REAGENTS REQUIRED: *A*. water 100, acetic acid 1, chromotrope 2R 0.6, fast green FCF 0.3, phosphotungstic acid 0.6; *B*. 0.2 acetic acid

METHOD: [smears, or sections not more than 5 μ thick, prior stained in hematoxylin] → water → *A*, 5–20 mins. → *B*, rinse → balsam, via usual reagents

NOTE: Wheatley 1951 (*Tech. Bull.*, **21**:92) recommends this technique for protozoans in intestinal smears.

12.32 Hollande 1912   *magenta-orange G-light green*   1915, **10**:62

REAGENTS REQUIRED: *A*. 1% magenta in 70% alc.; *B*. 0.1% hydrochloric acid in 70% alc.; *C*. 1% phosphomolybdic acid; *D*. sat. sol. (*circ.* 11%) orange G; *E*. 0.2% light green

METHOD: [blue nuclei (Langeron 1942, 606 recommends DS 11.122 methods)] → water → *A*, 6–12 hrs. → water, 5 mins. → *B*, till color clouds cease, few seconds → water, thorough wash → *C*, 5 mins. → water, rinse → *D*, 5 mins. → *E*, poured on slide ½ to 1 min. → 95% alc., few secs., till differentiated → balsam, via amyl alc. and benzene

RESULT: resting nuclei, blue; mitotic figures, red; cartilage, purple; fibrous tissue, light green; erythrocytes and keratin, bright orange.

12.32 Koneff 1936   *see* DS 13.7 Koneff 1936
12.32 Lillie 1940   *see* DS 12.31 Lillie 1940

12.32 Masson 1912   *ponceau 2R-anilin blue*   4956, **87**:290

REAGENTS REQUIRED: *A*. water 100, acetic acid 1, ponceau 2R 1; *B*; *C*; *D*; *E*, as DS 12.31 Masson 1912a

METHOD: as DS 12.31 Masson 1912a

12.32 Patay 1934   *ponceau 2R-light green*   4285a, **11**:408

REAGENTS REQUIRED: *A*. 1% ponceau 2R; *B*. 1% phosphomolybdic acid; *C*. 0.5% light green in 90% alc.

METHOD: [blue nuclei (original recommends DS 11.123 Masson (1934) insufficiently differentiated)] → water → *A*, 2 mins. → water, brief rinse → *B*, 2 mins. → water, brief rinse → *C*, 30 secs. → balsam, via usual reagents

RESULT: cartilage, blue (from hematoxylin); other collagens, light green; bone, brilliant green; epithelia and muscle, orange; erythrocytes, yellow; nervous tissue, gray.

NOTE: In the opinion of the author this is the finest triple stain yet described. A detailed description of the use of this stain is given under 12.30 above.

12.33 OTHER COMPLEX CONTRASTS

12.33 Blank 1942 *see* DS 13.22 Blank 1942

12.33 Flemming 1891 *gentian violet-orange G*   1780, **37**:249

REAGENTS REQUIRED: *A*. 1% gentian violet; *B*. sat. sol. (*circ.* 11%) orange G

METHOD: [sections of Flemming 1882 or other F 1600.0000 or F 1600.0010 fixed material nuclei stained by DS 11.42 method] → water → *A*, 3 hrs. → quick wash → *B*, few moments → abs. alc., till no more color comes away → balsam, via clove oil

NOTE: **Johansen** (Johansen 1940, 84) substitutes a saturated solution of orange G in clove oil for *B*, above. For *Stockwell's Variation* see DS 13.5 Stockwell 1934.

12.33 Hubin 1928 *eosin Y-orange G-safranin*   1825, **37**:25

REAGENTS REQUIRED: *A*. 0.1% acetic acid; *B*. abs. alc. 70, water 30, eosin Y 0.1, orange II 0.2, safranin 0.2; *C*. 0.1% hydrochloric acid in 70% alc.

PREPARATION OF B: Dissolve the eosin in 50 alc. and 10 water. Add to this the orange dissolved in 10 water. To this add the safranin dissolved in 20 alc. and 10 water.

METHOD: [blue nuclei (original specifies DS 11.122 Carazzi 1911 used on sections of F 5000.1040 Hollande 1911 fixed and F 5000.1010 Bouin 1897 mordanted material)] → *A*, 4-5 secs. → 70% alc., 5 mins. → *B*, 1-3 mins. → *C*, till differentiated, 2 to 10 secs. → balsam, via usual reagents

RESULT: nuclei, cartilage, bone, blue; nerves and blood vessels, yellow; muscles and ganglia, brown.

12.33 Johansen 1940 *see* DS 12.33 Flemming 1891 (note)

12.33 Lendrum 1939 *GEEP stain—auct.*   11431, **49**:590

REAGENTS REQUIRED: *A*. water 50, 95% alc. 50, eosin Y 0.2, erythrosin 0.2, phloxine 0.2, gallic acid 0.5, sodium salicylate 0.5; *B*. sat. sol. tartrazine N.S. in ethylene glycol monoethyl ether

PREPARATION OF A: Add the dyes dissolved in the alc. to the other ingredients dissolved in water.

METHOD: [sections with hematoxylin-stained nuclei] → *A*, 2 hrs. → 95% alc., rinse → *B*, on slide, till color balance satisfactory

12.33 Lendrum 1947   11431, **59**:394

REAGENTS REQUIRED: *A*. water 100, calcium chloride 0.5, phloxine 0.5; *B*. sat. sol. tartrazine in ethylene glycol monoethyl ether

METHOD: [sections with blue nuclei] → *A*, 30 mins. → rinse → *B*, from drop bottle, till differentiated → balsam, via usual reagents

12.33 Lillie 1940 *Biebrich scarlet-picro-anilin blue*   1789, **29**:705

REAGENTS REQUIRED: *A*. water 99, acetic acid 1, Biebrich scarlet 0.1; *B*. water 100, picric acid 1, anilin blue 0.1; *C*. 1% acetic acid

METHOD: [sections, nuclei stained in hematoxylin] → water → *A*, 4 mins. → rinse → *B*, 4 mins. → *C*, 3 mins. → salicylic balsam, via usual reagents

12.33 Lillie 1948 *see* DS 13.7 Lillie 1948

12.33 Margolena 1933 *phloxine-orange G*   20540b, **8**:157

REAGENTS REQUIRED: *A*. 0.5% phloxine in 20% alc.; *B*. 0.5% orange G in 95% alc.

METHOD: [blue nuclei] → water → *A*, 1-5 mins. → 70% alc., thorough rinse → *B*, dropped on slide, ½ to 1 min. → abs. alc., till no more color comes away → balsam via usual reagents

12.33 Masson 1929 *metanil yellow-picro-fuchsin*   11571b, **12**:75

REAGENTS REQUIRED: *A*. water 100, acetic acid 0.5, metanil yellow 0.5; *B*. 0.2% acetic acid; *C*. 3% potassium dichromate; *D*. DS 11.221 van Gieson 1896; *E*. 1% acetic acid

METHOD: [sections with blue nuclei (original requires DS 11.111 Régaud 1910)] → water → *A*, 5 mins. → *B*, rinse → *C*, 5 mins. → *D*, poured on slide still wet with *C*, 2 mins. → *E*, till yellow clouds cease → salicylic balsam, via usual reagents
RESULT: collagens, clear red.

12.33 Masson 1911   *erythrosin-saffron*   6630, **70**:573
REAGENTS REQUIRED: *A*. water 100, erythrosin 1, 40% formaldehyde 0.25; *B*. water 100, saffron 2, 40% formaldehyde 1, 5% tannic acid 1
PREPARATION OF B: Boil saffron 1 hour in water. Cool. Filter. Add other ingredients.
METHOD: [blue nuclei] → *A*, 5 mins. → water, quick rinse → 70% alc., till collagens colorless → water, quick rinse → *B*, 5 mins. → water, rapid rinse → abs. alc., minimum time possible → balsam, via xylene
RESULT: nuclei, blue; collagens, yellow; muscle, red.

12.33 Maximow 1909   *eosin Y-azur* II   23632, **26**:177
STOCK FORMULAS: I. 0.1% eosin Y; II. 0.1% azur II
WORKING SOLUTION: water 100, stock I 10, stock II 10
METHOD: [sections with chromatin stained in very dilute DS 11.122 formula] → water, 24 hrs. → stain, 12–24 hrs. → 95% alc., quick rinse → abs. alc., till differentiated → neutral balsam, via xylene

12.33 Millot 1926   *acid fuchsin-martius yellow*   4285a, **3**:2
REAGENTS REQUIRED: *A*. 5% acid fuchsin in 40% alc.; *B*. 5% martius yellow in 40% alc.
METHOD: [blue nuclei] → *A*, 5 mins. at 30°C. → 40% alc., till no more color comes away → *B*, 5 mins. → balsam, via usual reagents
NOTE: This method was developed for insect histology, for which it is excellent.

12.33 Pianese 1896   *malachite green-acid fuchsin-martius yellow*
                                 2526, **1**:193
FORMULA: water 75, 95% alc. 25, malachite green 0.25, acid fuchsin 0.05, martius yellow 0.005

12.33 Reinke 1894   *gentian violet-orange G*   1780, **44**:262
FORMULA: *A*. sat. sol. (*circ*. 1%) gentian violet 25, sat. sol. (*circ*. 11%) orange G 0.2, water 75
NOTE: Use after safranin nuclear staining (DS 11.421) and differentiate with clove oil

12.33 Scriban 1924   *picro-fuchsin-brilliant green*   6630, **90**:531
REAGENTS REQUIRED: *A*. water 100, picric acid 0.5, acid fuchsin 0.1; *B*. 60% alc. 100, picric acid 0.2, brilliant green 0.1.
METHOD: [sections with DS 11.111 stained nuclei] → thorough wash → *A*, 3–4 secs. → abs. alc., wash → *B*, 3–4 secs. → abs. alc., wash → balsam via usual reagents

12.33 Stockwell 1934   *see* DS 13.5 Stockwell 1934

12.33 de Winiwarter 1923   *see* DS 12.33 de Winiwarter and Sainmont 1908

12.33 de Winiwarter and Sainmont 1908   *crystal violet-orange G*
                                 23632, **25**:157
REAGENTS REQUIRED: *A*. 1% crystal violet; *B*. sat. sol. (*circ*. 11%) orange G; *C*. 0.1% HCl in abs. alc.
METHOD: [sections of F 1600.0000 or F 1600.0010 fixed material; nuclei stained by 11.42 method] → water → *A*, 24 hrs. → brief rinse → *B*, 1 min. → *C*, 2 to 3 hrs. → clove oil, till differentiated → balsam
NOTE: de **Winiwarter 1923** (1825, **32**:329) recommends a process which differs only in the substitution of 0.2% orange G for *B*, above.

13 COMPLEX TECHNIQUES INVOLVING BOTH NUCLEAR AND PLASMA STAINING

This is a large class of staining techniques, involving those methods in which, by a series of successive and interlocking operations, both the nuclei and all the elements of the background are differentially stained. They are divided broadly, for purposes of this work, into seven classes, of which the first two (DS 13.1

and 13.2) employ the thiazins and their related compounds either in combination with eosin, or in the next class, with such other dyes as have been employed. The next class (DS 13.3) takes up the methyl green combinations and is followed by the group (DS 13.4) of complex formulas in which the Mallory reaction is employed. This is followed by a small group (DS 13.5), largely of French origin, in which safranin is employed as the nuclear stain, and another small group (DS 13.6) in which hematoxylin is employed. This still leaves for the last class (DS 13.7) a considerable miscellaneous group.

Most of these complex techniques are better employed for class demonstration than for research purposes. This does not apply with any force to the methylene blue-eosinates, so widely employed in blood staining, in which the material to be stained is customarily an unfixed, heat-dried smear, the staining reactions of the constituents of which can be controlled by the accurate adjustment of the pH of the staining solution. When, however, as in the other classes, the staining method is intended to operate on materials which have been fixed and sectioned, there is the greatest difficulty in securing a reproducibility of results, and the utmost attention should be paid to the recommendations of the original author with regard to the fixative to be employed. When, as in the case of the methylene blue-eosinates, the entire staining materials are usually applied from a single solution, there is nothing save the isoelectric point of the proteins on which they act which controls the differential staining. This factor of lack of reproducibility of results tends to render dangerous a publication of research observations based only on these staining methods for the slightest variation in the material, source of material, or fixative, and would cause anyone endeavoring to check the results to come to conclude that the method described is not applicable to his case. There is no finer group of stains which may be employed for class teaching purposes, particularly in sections of embryos and the like where a great range of tissues are available. Even in this instance, however, care should be taken that the entire batch of sections required is prepared at the same time, or students may become confused by the apparent abnormalities presented by successive batches of material.

13.1 TECHNIQUES EMPLOYING THE "EOSINATES" OF THE THIAZINS WITHOUT OTHER ADMIXTURE

The *eosinates* of methylene blue and its oxidation products are compound dyes which are usually utilized in solution in methanol. They may, however, be prepared either directly in solution or in the form of the dry powder, and in the latter state are at present widely found in commerce. For the purposes of the present work these techniques are divided into three classes. First (DS 13.11) are the straight methylene blue-eosinates, among which the original formulas of Jenner 1899 and May-Grünwald 1902 are the best known. These two techniques are not very widely used today, save as a preliminary to staining with other mixed polychrome methylene blue-eosinates. An interesting variation of these is the method of Sabrazès 1911, in which the stain is prepared in actual contact with the object to be colored.

The next class of these stains (DS 13.12) is usually incorrectly identified as *Giemsa stains*, though to the parasitologist the formulas of Leishman 1901 and Romanowski are possibly better known. These formulas are irrational, for they contain the eosinates of polychrome methylene blue, which is itself a mixture of varying composition, and which often widely varies in nature even though the method of preparation is specified. Giemsa 1902 prepared his mixture from ingredients of known composition. His formula is therefore given in the next section.

The most logical stains to use are those of the third class (DS 13.13), which are the eosinates of methylene blue and its varying oxidation products. They are prepared, however, from reagents of known composition. The formula of Giemsa 1902 is the best known of these, but the name has unfortunately been used to describe almost any azur-eosinate without specific reference to the exact azur intended. The original formula by Giemsa is no more than a two-line footnote to a paper in a somewhat obscure journal, and both the dry powder in commerce and the solutions recommended by subsequent writers vary enormously from the original proportion specified by Giemsa. A combination of Giemsa 1902 and May-Grünwald 1902 was published by Pappenheim 1908 and has become widely disseminated through the literature as the *panoptic* method. Two other modifications of the same technique, published by Pappenheim four years later, are still widely referred to in the literature as *panoptic*, though the majority of those using this term refer actually to the 1908 formula. Some of these techniques have been rationalized, particularly one by MacNeal 1922 which has become so widespread that the dry stains in the proportion given for MacNeal's solution have appeared in commerce under the name *MacNeal's Tetrachrome*. This is the more unfortunate as there are only three stains involved. The most completely rationalized of all these processes is that of Kingsley 1935. He specifies not only the ingredients to be used but also the pH to which the solutions should be buffered. He has, moreover, provided techniques whereby these same solutions can be applied either to smears, paraffin sections, or frozen sections, and has thus permitted for the first time the complete correlation of the temporary results obtained from a frozen section hurriedly produced in the course of an operation and a permanent paraffin section which may be secured from postmortem material.

13.10 TYPICAL EXAMPLES

Preparation of a blood smear using the methylene blue-azur A-methylene violet-eosin Y stain of Kingsley 1935

All of the azur-eosin techniques are designed primarily to differentiate cell types one from another rather than to differentiate gross histological structures. There is, therefore, very little need for detailed instructions to be given. A blood film is as good an object on which to practice as any other. In spite of the numerous formulas which are given in this section it cannot be too strongly recommended that the method of Kingsley (DS 13.13 Kingsley 1935) be used exclusively, unless one is endeavoring only to follow a diagnostic method given by a previous writer, or endeavoring to understand how some previous author has secured a result which one is unable to duplicate by a more rational method. The only difficulty in the method of Kingsley here given is the preparation of the necessary solutions: these *must* be made with chemically pure reagents. The two stock formulas are quite stable, but they must be prepared accurately. The figures for the dye contents of the solutions, which are given in terms of milligrams, should be adhered to and should be weighed on an accurate balance. Both the formulas are, however, liable to a certain degree of biological degradation from molds, and it is, therefore, not desirable to prepare very large quantities at one time. The reference to a buffer at pH 6.9 does not specify the buffer salts to be used. Kingsley (*loc. cit.*) specifies phosphate buffers, but the writer has used phthalate buffers with equal success. The very small quantity of the buffer required and the necessity for having it at an accurate pH suggests that (unless very considerable facilities are at the disposal of the preparator) he purchase this buffer solution ready-prepared rather than prepare it himself. The methanol, acetone, and glycerol specified as staining ingredients should be of a reagent grade. Since the working solution C requires only half a milligram of eosin Y to be added to it, and since it is improbable that the majority of people have the facilities for weighing this accurately, 1% solution of eosin Y in acetone can be prepared as a stock solution and a 1% dilution of acetic acid in acetone may be prepared as another stock solution. A moment of calculation will illustrate how these can be diluted with acetone to give the required staining reagent.

Blood films are simple to make, provided one has chemically clean glassware and remembers, if he has never made such a preparation before, that the smear must be *pushed* across the lower slide, not pulled across it. That is, one should lay one chemically clean slide on the bench, place a small drop of blood on it, and place a second slide in contact with the first at an angle of about 45° so that the blood is drawn out by the capillary attraction into the angle. The upper slide is now pushed *forward* (Fig. 29, Chapter 7) leaving behind it a thin smear of blood which is then air dried. The blood film is fixed either by placing it in chemically pure methanol for from one-half to one minute, or by pouring two or three doses of chemically pure methanol over it. After removal from methanol, the slide is dried, and the stock staining solution A (DS 13.13 Kingsley 1935, below) is then poured on it and left for a period of from five to eight minutes. This time is, of course, too long for ordinary rapid diagnostic work, but has the advantage that slides may be accumulated in a long line. Then one may continue the process on the first slide, when one has spent five minutes in preparing the series. After the required time has elapsed, the stain is washed off with a jet of distilled water directed on it from a wash bottle in such a manner as to float off the scum which has gathered on the surface as well as to rinse off the superfluous stain. The film may then either be air dried for examination, or it may be mounted in a neutral mounting medium (see Chapter 26) after dehydration through direct drying. Provided the staining solution has been accurately made and pure reagents used, a perfect stain will in every instance result from this treatment. The methods given for paraffin sections are just as easy to follow and need not be elaborated here.

13.11 METHYLENE BLUE-EOSINATES

13.11 Assmann 1906a *test.* **1928 Schmorl**　　　　　Schmorl 1928, 241

REAGENTS REQUIRED: *A*. DS 13.11 May-Grünwald 1902 (working sol.); *B*. water 100, DS 11.44 Unna 1892

METHOD: [dried smear] → *A*, 1 ml. poured on slide lying in petri dish, 3 mins. → *B*, 15 ml. poured into dish around slide, 3–4 mins. → wash → dry

13.11 Assmann 1906b *test.* **1928 Schmorl**　　　　　Schmorl 1928, 246

REAGENTS REQUIRED: *A*. DS 13.11 May-Grünwald 1902 (working sol.); *B*. 0.001% acetic acid

METHOD: [sections of F 7000.0000 Müller 1859 or F 3700.0010 Zenker 1894 fixed material] → *A*, several hrs. → *B*, till color changes to clear eosin → wash → balsam, via usual reagents

13.11 Chenzinsky 1894　　　　　　　　　　　23632, **11**:269

FORMULA: sat. sol. (*circ.* 4.5%) methylene blue 40, 0.5% eosin Y in 70% alc. 20, water 20

METHOD: [fresh smear] → stain, 5 mins. → water, rinse → dry

13.11 Ellerman 1919　　　　　　　　　　　23632, **36**:56

REAGENTS REQUIRED: *A*. water 100, 40% formaldehyde 5, eosin Y 1; *B*. DS 13.11 May-Grünwald 1902 (working sol.) 50, water 50

METHOD: [5 μ paraffin sections of F 3700.1000 Ellerman 1919 fixed material] → water → *A*, 15 mins. → wash, 2–4 mins. 45°C. → *B*, 30 mins. → wash, 5–10 mins. → blot → abs. alc. till differentiated → M 32.1 mountant via usual reagents

13.11 Held (1900)　　*see* DS 22.21 Held (1900)

13.11 Jenner 1899　　　　　　　　　　　11995, **6**:370

PREPARATION OF DRY EOSINATE: Mix equal parts 1.25% eosin Y and 1% methylene blue. Leave 24 hours. Filter. Wash and dry filtrate.

WORKING SOLUTION: dry powder 0.5, methanol 100

METHOD: [fresh smear] → stain, 3 mins. → water, rinse → dry

NOTE: The most usual employment of this formula is as a fixative before such methods as DS 13.13 Slider and Downey (1929).

13.11 Jenner *test.* **1905 Lee**　　　　　　　　Lee 1905, 385

FORMULA: 0.5% methylene blue 50, 0.5% eosin Y in methanol 62.5

METHOD: as Jenner 1899

13.11 Lim 1919   17510, **63**:542
REAGENTS REQUIRED: *A.* 1% ethyl eosin in abs. alc.; *B.* 1% methylene blue
METHOD: [sections or smears] → abs. alc. → *A*, on slide, 1 min. → water, thorough wash
  → *B*, on slide, 1 min. → blot → abs. alc., flooded on slide, 2–3 secs. → benzene →
  neutral mountant *or* → dry

13.11 May-Grünwald 1902   23720, **11**:265
PREPARATION OF DRY EOSINATE: Mix equal parts of 0.5% eosin Y and 0.5% methylene
  blue. Filter. Dry filtrate. Wash dried filtrate and redry.
WORKING SOLUTION: methanol 100, dry powder from above to sat.
METHOD: [air-dried smear] → stain, on slide, 3 mins. → add equal volume distilled
  water, leave 1 min. → wash → dry
NOTE: See note under Jenner 1899 with which this technique is nearly, but not quite,
  identical. **Zieler** (*test.* **Schmorl 1928,** 246) stains paraffin sections 2–3 minutes and de-
  hydrates in acetone; for another application of this stain to sections see DS 13.11
  Assmann 1906b above.

13.11 Michaelis 1901   7276, **27**:127
FORMULA: water 40, abs. alc. 25, acetone 35, methylene blue 0.25, eosin 0.15
PREPARATION: Dissolve the methylene blue in 25 water, 25 alc. Dissolve the eosin in 15
  water, 35 acetone. Mix. Filter.

13.11 Müller *test.* **1928 Schmorl**   Schmorl 1928, 239
REAGENTS REQUIRED: *A.* 0.5% eosin Y in 70% alc.; *B.* A 60, 0.25% methylene blue 30
METHOD: [blood smear fixed 3 mins. in methanol] → *A*, 3–5 mins. → distilled water,
  wash → blot → *B*, ½–1 min. → distilled water, wash → dry

13.11 Nocht *test.* **1903 Ehrlich**   Ehrlich, Krause, *et al.* 1903, 784
FORMULA: water 65, acetone 17, 0.1% thiazin 10, 0.1% eosin 10, buffer pH 4.6
NOTE: This is not a specific technique, though it is often quoted as such; it is a general
  direction for experiments with any thiazins and any eosin.

13.11 Sabrazès 1911   6630, **70**:247
REAGENTS REQUIRED: *A.* 30% eosin Y in 95% alc.; *B.* 0.2% methylene blue
METHOD: [smear] → place 1 drop *A* on smear and 1 drop *B* on coverslip → seal with wax
  for temporary examination → *or* water, quick rinse → dry

13.11 Willebrand 1901   7276, **27**:57
FORMULA: water 65, abs. alc. 35, eosin 0.25, methylene blue 0.5, 1% acetic acid *q.s.*
PREPARATION: Dissolve the eosin in 35 alc., 15 water. Dissolve the methylene blue in 50
  water. Mix the solutions and add acid drop by drop till solution turns red. Filter.
METHOD: [fresh smear] → stain 5 mins. → rinse → dry

13.11 Zieler   *see* DS 13.11 May-Grünwald 1902 (note)

13.12 POLYCHROME METHYLENE BLUE-EOSINATES

13.12 Brice 1930   *see* D. DS 22.8 Brice 1930

13.12 Diercks and Tibbs 1947   11056, **53**:479
REAGENTS REQUIRED: *A.* water 100, DS 13.13 MacNeal 1922 6
METHOD: [moist smear] → methanol 3 to 5 mins. → *A*, 15–20 mins. → acetone, till no
  more color comes away → blot → dry

13.12 Gordon 1939   11284, **24**:405
REAGENTS REQUIRED: *A.* 10% ammonia; *B.* ADS 12.2 Gordon 1939; *C.* water 100, eosin
  Y 0.25, phloxine 0.75; DS D. 11.44 Löffler 1890
METHOD: [sections of formaldehyde material] → *A*, 1 min. → wash → *B*, 3 mins. →
  wash → *C*, 2 mins. → wash → *D*, 4 mins., 37°C. → wash → abs. alc., till differentiated
  → balsam, via xylene

13.12 JSB stain   *see* DS 11.44 Manwell 1945 (note)

13.12 Langeron 1934   *see* DS 11.44 Langeron 1934

13.12 Leishman 1901   3579, **2**:757

PREPARATION OF DRY EOSINATE: To 100 0.5% methylene blue add 0.25 sodium carbonate Digest 12 hours at 65°C. followed by 10 days at 15°C. Filter. Add 50 0.5% eosin B to filtrate. Leave 12 hours. Filter. Wash and dry filtrate.

WORKING SOLUTION: methanol 100, dry stain 0.15

METHOD: [air-dried smear] → stain, on slide, 5–10 mins. → water, 1 min. → blot dry

NOTE: This method is stated by Leishman (*loc. cit.*) to be a modification of a stain proposed by **Rowmanowski 1891** (*St. Petersburg Med. Wschr.*, **16**:297) to the original of which the writer has never had access.

13.12 Lillie and Pasternack 1936   4349, **15**:65

PREPARATION OF DRY STOCK: Dissolve 0.25 silver nitrate in 12.5 water. Add 1–2 5% sodium hydroxide, wash ppt. five times by decantation. Add 50 1% methylene blue to wet ppt. Shake at intervals for 11 days. Filter and add 45 1% eosin. Leave overnight, filter, and dry ppt.

FORMULA OF STOCK SOLUTION: methanol (acetone-free) 75, glycerol 25, dry stock 0.6

WORKING SOLUTION: citric acid-sodium phosphate, dibasic buffer (see note) 70, acetone 6, methanol 6, stock solution 4

NOTE: The buffer must be so adjusted that after the addition of the other ingredients the pH is 5.3.

13.12 Mallory *test.* **Langeron 1942**   Langeron 1942, 614

REAGENTS REQUIRED: *A.* water 100, eosin Y 5; *B.* water 85, DS 11.44 Sahli 1885 15; *C.* ADS 22.1 Wolbach 1911

METHOD: [water] → *A*, 20 mins. → rinse → *B*, 5 mins. → *B*, fresh solution, 15 mins. → *B*, fresh solution, 30 mins. → wash → *C*, till differentiated → abs. alc. least possible time → balsam, via cedar oil

RESULT: nuclei, blue; other structures, polychrome.

13.12 Manwell 1945   11284, **30**:1078

REAGENTS REQUIRED: *A.* DS 11.44 Manwell 1945; *B.* water, adjusted to pH 6.5 with acetic acid; *C.* 0.2% eosin Y

METHOD: [methanol fixed smear] → dry → *A*, 30 secs. → *B*, wash → *A*, 30 secs. → dry → neutral mountant

13.12 Marie and Raleigh 1924   11284, **10**:250

PREPARATION OF DRY STOCK: Dissolve 1 methylene blue in 100 0.5 sodium bicarbonate and expose to U.V. arc 30 mins. in shallow dish. Cool and add 500 0.1% eosin Y. Filter, wash, and dry ppt.

WORKING SOLUTION: methanol 100, dry stock 0.16

13.12 Michelson 1942   11284, **27**:551

PREPARATION OF DRY STOCK: Dissolve 1 methylene blue in 100 N/100 sodium hydroxide. Heat 2½ hours, 55°C. shaking for 1 minute at half-hour intervals. Add 1 sodium bromide, continue heating 2½ hours. Cool. Filter. Add 60 1% eosin Y and mix. Add further eosin in doses of 5 till solution is reddish. Leave 24 hours. Filter. Dry filtrate.

WORKING SOLUTION: 0.017% dry stock in methanol

13.12 Raadt 1912   23632, **29**:236

STOCK SOLUTION: water 100, methylene blue 1, lithium carbonate 0.5

REAGENTS REQUIRED: *A.* stock 10, water 90; *B.* DS 13.11 Jenner 1899 25, water 75

METHOD: [methanol fixed smears] → *A*, on slide, 5–10 mins. → rinse → blot → *B*, 5–10. mins. → wash → dry

13.12 Roques and Jude 1940 *test.* **1949 Langeron**   Langeron 1949, 621

FORMULA OF STOCK SOLUTION: methanol 50, glycerol 50, eosin B 0.2, methylene blue 0.2, DS 11.44 Roques and Jude 1940 0.5

PREPARATION OF STOCK SOLUTION: Dissolve dyes in methanol, leave 24 hours, filter, and add glycerol.

WORKING SOLUTION: water 95, stock 5

13.12 Rowmanowsky 1891   *see* DS 13.12 Leishman 1901 (note)

13.12 Schmorl 1928   *see* DS 23.33 Schmorl 1928

13.12 Senevet 1917   5310, **10**:540
STOCK SOLUTIONS: I. methylene blue 1, sodium borate 3, water 100; II. eosin Y 1, water 100
WORKING SOLUTION: water 100, stock II 0.2, stock I 0.25 to 0.4
METHOD: [methanol-fixed smears] → *A*, 2–3 hrs. → wash → dry

13.12 Stafford 1934   10919, **55**:229
REAGENTS REQUIRED: *A*. water 100, potassium dichromate 1, eosin 1; *B*. DS 11.44 Goodpasture (1934); *C*. acetone 100, abs. alc. 10
METHOD: [frozen sections of formaldehyde-alc. material] → water → *A*, 1 sec. → wash → *B*, 30 secs. → wash → blot on slide → *C*, dropped on section till dehydrated → balsam, via xylene

13.12 Singh, Jaswart, and Bhattacharji 1944   *see* DS 11.44 Manwell 1945 (note)

13.12 Wright 1910   *Rep. Mass. Gen. Hosp.*, **3**:1
FORMULA OF METHYLENE BLUE STOCK: water 100, methylene blue 1, sodium bicarbonate 0.5
PREPARATION OF STOCK SOLUTION: Digest at 100°C. 1½ hours.
WORKING SOLUTION: methanol 80, eosin B, 0.16, stock blue 24
METHOD: [smear] → stain, on slide 2 mins. → add water, drop by drop, till green scum forms on surface, leave 2 mins. → water, thorough wash → [dry] *or* → neutral mountant, via acetone
NOTE: **Wright 1910** also recommended (17510, **57**:783) the dilution of the working solution with an equal volume of water to be used for 10 minutes. It is nowadays universal practice to substitute a phosphate buffer at pH 6.4 for the water used to dilute the stain on the slide.

13.13 OTHER THIAZIN EOSINATES

13.13 Agulhon and Chavennes 1919   *see* DS 13.13 Pappenheim 1908

13.13 Böhm and Oppel 1907   *methylene blue-thionin-eosin*
Böhm and Oppel 1907, 114
REAGENTS REQUIRED: *A*. water 96, 40% formaldehyde 4, methylene blue 0.3, thionin 0.15; *B*. 1% acetic acid; *C*. 1% eosin B
METHOD: sections → *A*, some mins. → *B*, till no more color comes away → *C*, few secs. → balsam, via usual reagents

13.13 Boye 1940   5310, **33**:248
REAGENTS REQUIRED: *A*. water 100, eosin Y 0.1; *B*. DS 11.44 Stevenel 1918
METHOD: [methanol-fixed smears] → *A*, 15–20 secs. → *B*, flooded on slide, 45 secs. → *A*, till differentiated → rinse → dry

13.13 Endicott 1945   20540b, **20**:5]
PREPARATION OF DRY STOCK: To 250 ml. 0.8% toluidine blue add 250 0.4% eosin B. Filter, wash, and dry ppt.
WORKING SOLUTION: methanol 50, glycerol 50, dry stock 0.3

13.13 Field 1941   *see* DS 23.33 Field 1941

13.13 Geschickter, Walker, Hjort, and Moulton 1931   20540b, **6**:3
REAGENTS REQUIRED: *A*. water 60, glycerol 20, 95% alc. 20, sodium hydroxide 1.47, potassium acid phosphate 0.675; *B*. ethylene glycol 75, 95% alc. 25, acetic acid 0.2, thionine-eosinate 0.75, barium-eosinate 0.25, azur A 0.25; *C*. 20% glycerol in 95% alc.; *D*. diethylene glycol monobutyl ether; *E*. n-butyl phthalate
PREPARATION OF B: Dissolve the barium-eosinate with heat; raise solution to boiling, add thionine-eosinate. Filter solution hot.
METHOD: [frozen sections of fresh tissue] → *A*, till required → *B*, 20–30 secs. → *C*, 10 secs. → *C*, fresh solution, 3 secs. → *D*, 10–15 secs. → *E*, 20 secs. → dammar
NOTE: Solution *A* should be adjusted, if necessary, to pH 7.

13.13 Giemsa 1902   23684, **31**:429

FORMULA: 0.05% eosin 95, 0.8% azur 5

NOTE: This is the original formula for Giemsa's stain, given in a footnote to the paper cited. From this time on almost any eosin-azur mixture has been referred to as *Giemsa*. The formulas of **Slider and Downey 1929** and Gatenby and Cowdry 1928 are referred to by their publishers as *Giemsa's stain*. When reference is made in the present work to DS 13.13 Giemsa 1902 the solution of Slider and Downey 1929 should be employed unless dry powder is specified. **Kopel 1945** (4349, **25**:61) substitutes ethanol for methanol in preparing the working solution.

13.13 Giemsa   *see also* DS 13.13 Langeron 1942, Slider and Downey 1928, Gatenby and Cowdry 1928

13.13 Grosso 1914   *see* DS 21.3 Grosso 1914

13.13 Haynes 1926a   20540b, **1**:68

REAGENTS REQUIRED: *A.* 1.5% azur II or azur C; *B.* sat. sol. ethyl eosin in clove oil

METHOD: [water] → *A*, 5 mins. → abs. alc. quick rinse → *B*, 30 secs. → balsam, via xylene

13.13 Haynes 1926b   20540b, **1**:107

REAGENTS REQUIRED: *A.* 2.5% phloxine; *B.* 0.1% azur I; *C.* ADS 22.1 Wolbach 1911

METHOD: [sections] → water → *A*, 15 mins. → water, thorough wash → *B*, 30 mins. → water, thorough wash → *C*, from drop bottle, till differentiated → abs. alc., minimum possible time → balsam, via xylene

13.13 Kingsley 1935   20540b, **10**:127

STOCK SOLUTIONS: I. water 50, methanol 10, glycerol 10, buffer pH 6.9 30, methylene blue 0.130, azur A 0.020; II. acetone 70, methanol 20, glycerol 10, methylene violet 0.026, eosin Y 0.090

REAGENTS REQUIRED: *A.* stock I 50, stock II 50; *B.* 0.015% acetic acid; *C.* acetone 60, acetic acid 0.005, eosin Y 0.0005; *D.* n-butyl alc. 60, eosin Y 0.001

METHOD FOR SMEARS: [air-dried smear] → methanol ½ to 1 min. → dry → *A*, 5–8 mins. → water, thorough wash → dry

METHOD FOR PARAFFIN SECTIONS: water → *A*, flooded on slide, 9–10 mins. → water, thorough wash → *C*, rinse → *D*, rinse → balsam, via xylene

TEMPORARY METHOD FOR FROZEN SECTIONS: [blot section to slide] → *A*, flooded on slide, 2–3 mins. → wash → [examine]

PERMANENT METHOD FOR FROZEN SECTIONS: [blot section to slide] → *A*, 4–5 mins. (fresh) or 8–10 mins. (fixed) → [thence as for paraffin sections]

NOTE: The application of this stain to a blood smear is described under DS 13.10 above. See also DS 21.42 Kingsley 1937. **Ritchie 1941** (*Tech. Bull.*, **2**:157) prefers, for smears, to dilute the *A* stain 8:5 with water.

13.13 Kingsley 1937   *see* DS 21.42 Kingsley 1937

13.13 Langeron 1942a   *Giemsa for wet smears—auct.*   Langeron 1942, 583

REAGENTS REQUIRED: *A.* water 100, potassium iodide 2, ADS 12.2 Lugol (1905) 3; *B.* 0.5% sodium thiosulfate; *C.* water 97, DS 13.13 Giemsa 1902 3; *D.* 1% monosodium phosphate

METHOD: [smears fixed in F 3000.0000 Schaudinn 1893 or F 3700.0010 Zenker 1894, 24 hrs.] → rinse → *A*, 5 to 10 mins. → rinse → *B*, 10 mins. → running water 5 mins. → distilled water → *C*, 30 mins. → *C*, fresh solution, 12 hrs. → *D*, if differentiation required → neutral mountant, via graded acetone-xylene mixtures

13.13 Langeron 1942b   *Giemsa for sections—auct.*   Langeron 1942, 583

REAGENTS REQUIRED: *A.* 70% alc. 97, ADS 12.2 Lugol (1905) 3; *B.* 0.5% sodium thiosulfate; *C.* water 97, DS 13.13 Giemsa 1902 3

METHOD: [5 μ paraffin section of F 3000.0000 Schaudinn 1893 or F 3700.0010 Zenker 1894 material, dewaxed and brought to water] → *A*, 20–30 mins. → rinse → *B*, 10 mins. → tap water 5 mins. → distilled water → *C*, 30 mins. → *C*, fresh solution, 2 to 12 hrs. → balsam, via graded acetone-xylene mixtures

NOTE: Langeron (*loc. cit.* p. 751) also refers to this as *Wolbach's method;* but see DS 13.13 Pappenheim 1908 (note) and DS 23.12 Wolbach 1919.

13.13 Groat 1936   11284, **21** :978

PREPARATION OF DRY STOCK: Dissolve 1.2 eosin Y in 100 water. Dissolve 1 methylene blue, 0.2 methyl violet 2 B, 0.04 thionine in 10 water. Mix solutions, heat to 50°C. and hold at 37°C., 24 hours. Filter. Wash and dry filtrate.

FORMULA OF WORKING SOLUTION: methanol 100, dry stock 0.5

METHOD: [blood smears] → stain, on slide, 5 mins. → plunge in distilled water till smear rosy-pink → dry

13.13 Kingsley 1937   11284, **22** :524

STOCK SOLUTIONS: I. water 80, phosphate buffer pH 6.920, methylene blue 0.070, methylene azur A 0.025, II. acetone 70, methanol 20, glycerol 10, methylene violet 0.018, eosin Y 0.065

WORKING SOLUTION: stock I 50, stock II 50

13.13 Kuhn 1933   19764d, **7** :758

PREPARATION OF DRY STOCK: Mix 9 ammonia with 6 2% copper sulfate. Add this to 200 0.5% methylene blue and leave 24 hours at 18°–20°C. Then add, in small amounts and with continuous agitation, 40 2% eosin Y. Filter, wash ppt. with 4% ammonia, and dry.

STOCK SOLUTION: methanol 60, glycerol 30, dry stock 0.36

WORKING SOLUTION: stock solution 25, methanol 75

13.13 Lillie 1948   *azur-eosin*   Lillie 1948, 82

PREPARATION OF DRY STAIN: Dissolve 1 azur A or C in 60 water. Add 0.8 eosin B or Y dissolved in 10 water. Mix solutions. Filter. Wash and dry ppt.

PREPARATION OF STOCK SOLUTION: glycerol 50, methanol 50, dry stock 1

PREPARATION OF STOCK BUFFERS: I. water 75, methanol 25, sodium phosphate, dibasic 2.84; II. water 75, methanol 25, citric acid 9.12

PREPARATION OF WORKING SOLUTION: stock stain 0.5, acetone 5, mixed buffers I and II 2, water to make 40

METHOD: [sections] → water → stain,   1 hr. → rinse → acetone,   till   dehydrated → balsam, via xylene

NOTE: The ratio of buffers I and II in the working stain must be adjusted to suit the fixative used and the color balance desired. Lillie, *loc. cit.*, recommends from 0.7 I : 1.3 II to 1 : 1. This is a slight modification of **Lillie 1941** (20540b, **16** :1).

13.13 MacNeal 1922   *azur I-methylene violet-eosin Y*   11006, **78** :1122

FORMULA: methanol 100, eosin Y 1, azur I 0.6, methylene violet 0.2

METHOD: [air-dried smears] → flood with stain, 2 mins. → add water, drop by drop, till green scum forms on surface → leave 1 min. → water, thorough wash → neutral mountant, via acetone

NOTE: The dry dyes, mixed in the proportion indicated, have appeared in commerce under the name *MacNeal's Tetrachrome.*

13.13 Maximow 1909   *see* DS 12.37 Maximow 1909

13.13 Maximow 1924   *azur-eosin*   11250, **34** :549

REAGENTS REQUIRED: *A*. water 100, DS 11.122 Delafield 1885 0.1; *B*. 0.1% eosin Y 10, water 100, 0.1% azur II 10

METHOD: [sections from F 3700.1010 fixed material] → water → *A*, 24 hrs. → water → *B*, 24 hrs. → 95% alc., till differentiated → balsam, via xylene

13.13 Medalia, Kahaner, and Singer 1944   *see* DS 23.33 Medalia *et al.* 1944

13.13 McNamara 1933   11284, **18** :752

REAGENTS REQUIRED: *A*. water 90, ADS 12.2 Lugol (1905) 10; *B*. 0.5% sodium thiosulfate; *C*. water 100, DS 13.13 Slider and Downey 1929 10, acetone 10, methyl alc. 10, 0.5% sodium carbonate 2; *D*. ADS 22.1 Wolbach 1911

METHOD: [4 μ sections of F 3700.0010 Zenker 1894 material] → *A*, 30 mins. → 95% alc. wash → water, wash → *B*, 10 mins. → wash → *C*, 15 mins. → *D*, till differentiated → balsam, via acetone and xylene

13.13 Pappenheim 1908   *panoptic stain—compl. script.*

                                                               13172, **4** :1244

REAGENTS REQUIRED: *A*. DS 13.11 May-Grünwald 1902; *B*. water 97, DS 13.13 Giemsa 1902 3

METHOD: [dry smear] → A, flooded on slide, 3 mins. → add 10 drops distilled water, mix well, leave 1 min. → drain → B, 10–15 mins. → wash off with jet of distilled water → wash, till differentiated → drain, dry

NOTE: **Agulhon and Chavannes 1919** (6630, **82**:149) differentiate with 1% boric acid or 1% monosodium phosphate. Otherwise the technique is identical. **Wolbach 1911** (11006, **56**:345) uses his resin alcohol (ADS 22.1, Wolbach 1911) for differentiation. Langeron 1942, p. 751 refers to his "method for sections" as *Wolbach's technique*.

13.13 Pappenheim 1912a   766, **42**:525

REAGENTS REQUIRED: A. water 75, DS 13.11 May-Grünwald 1902 25; B. water 95, DS 13.13 Giemsa 1902; C. 0.2% acetic acid

METHOD: [5 μ paraffin sections of F 7000-1000 Orth 1896 or F 3700.1000 Helly 1903 material, dewaxed and brought to water] → A, 15 mins., 37°C. → B, 40 mins., 37°C. → rinse → rinse → C, till differentiated → balsam via acetone

13.13 Pappenheim 1912b   8545, **13**:340

REAGENTS REQUIRED: A. water 75, DS 13.11 May-Grünwald 1902; B. water 97, DS 13.11 Pappenheim 1911 3; C. 0.1% picric acid

METHOD: [water] → A, 15 mins. at 37°C. → B, 30 mins. at 37°C. → wash → C, till differentiated → balsam, via graded acetone-xylene mixtures

13.13 Shortt 1918   9940, **6**:124

REAGENTS REQUIRED: A. DS 11.44 Langeron 1908 10, water 90; B. eosin Y 0.01, water 100

METHOD: [methanol-fixed smears] → 1 A mixed with 1, 2, or 3 B (proportion established by trial) → quick rinse → abs. alc., till differentiated → water, to stop differentiation → dry → balsam

NOTE: The original calls for a 0.1% solution of *Borrel's blue*. A above is identical in composition to such a solution.

13.13 Slider and Downey 1929   *azur-eosin*   McClung 1929, 246

FORMULA: glycerol 50, azur II 0.16, azur II-eosin 0.6, methanol 50

METHOD: [smears, treated with methanol *or* DS 13.11 Jenner 1899 *or* DS 13.11 May-Grünwald 1902] → equal parts stain and water (or pH 6.4 buffer), 15 mins. → water, till differentiated → blot → dry

NOTE: **Gatenby and Cowdry 1928,** 490 specify 75 methanol to 25 glycerol.

13.13 Svihla 1924   11006, **83**:2093

PREPARATION OF DRY STOCK: To 50 water add 0.69 methylene blue, 0.44 silver oxide, 0.38 sodium bicarbonate. Boil 1 hour and decant supernant liquid which is added to 50 0.62% eosin. Mix thoroughly, filter, wash, and dry ppt.

WORKING SOLUTION: methanol 100, sodium phosphate, dibasic 0.125, potassium dihydrogen phosphate 0.080, potassium hydroxide 0.004

13.13 Ugruimov 1928   *see* DS 21.3 Ugruimov 1928

13.13 Villain and Comte 1933   *see* DS 23.3 Villain and Comte 1933

13.13 Wolbach   *see* DS 13.13 Langeron 1942b (note)

13.13 Wolbach 1911   *see* DS 13.13 Pappenheim 1908

13.13 Wolbach 1919   *see* DS 23.12 Wolbach 1919

13.2 TECHNIQUES EMPLOYING THE THIAZINS AND THEIR EOSINATES IN COMBINATION WITH OTHER DYES

The combination of the thiazin-eosinates with orange G (DS 13.21) is almost as old as the utilization of the thiazin-eosinates themselves. The first and still the best known formula is that of Mann 1894, though in French literature it has largely been replaced by the method of Dominici 1902. The preoccupation of the French school with the work of Dominici has led to the production of such almost incredibly complex methods as those of Gausen 1929 and Houcke 1928. Complex methods of this type have proved of some value in the investigation of pathology, but are not to be recommended to the routine worker.

The combination of the thiazin-eosinates with other dyes than orange G (DS 13.22) have not been very successful, the main exception being the technique of Kull 1914 which, though originally designed for the demonstration of mitochondria, is one of the best and surest triple staining methods yet developed. The formula of Rhamy 1930 is of great interest in the staining of blood smears, and yields pictures which are not only of as great diagnostic value but also far more readily preserved than are the standard eosin-methylene blue mixtures.

13.21 IN COMBINATION WITH ORANGE G

13.21 Arnold 1909   *methylene blue-safranin-orange G*   1820, **3**:434
REAGENTS REQUIRED: *A*. ADS 12.2 Lugol (1905); *B*. sat. sol. safranin in 70% alc.; *C*. water 100, methylene blue 7, sodium carbonate 0.5; 1% orange G
METHOD: [sections of chromic or dichromate material] → *A*, 5 mins. → wash → *B*, 4 hrs. → wash → *C*, 4 hrs. → abs. alc., till dehydrated → *D*, till differentiated → balsam, via usual reagents
RESULT: nucleoli, centrosomes, red; many cell inclusions, blue; other structures, orange

13.21 Cowdry 1943   *phloxine-orange G-azur A*   Cowdry 1943, 69
REAGENTS REQUIRED: *A*. water 100, phloxine 0.12, orange G 0.3; *B*. 0.1% azur A
METHOD: As Dominici 1902 below
NOTE: See also note on Cowdry 1943 modification under Dominici 1902.

13.21 Dominici 1902   *eosin Y-orange G-toluidine blue*   6630, **54**:221
REAGENTS REQUIRED: *A*. water 100, eosin Y 0.5, orange G 0.5; *B*. 0.5% toluidine blue
METHOD: [water] → *A*, 5–10 mins. → water, quick rinse → *B*, 20–30 secs. → water, quick rinse → 95% alc., till differentiated → balsam, via xylene
NOTE: **Cowdry 1943** p. 69 recommends the substitution of 0.5% acid fuchsin for the eosin Y in *A* above. See also Cowdry 1943 above and Mann 1894 below.

13.21 Gausen 1929   *methylene blue-orange G-magenta*   6630, **97**:1658
FORMULA OF METHYLENE BLUE SOLUTIONS: 80% alc. 150, lactic acid 3, methylene blue 2.5
FORMULA OF ORANGE G SOLUTION: 80% alc. 100, lactic acid 2, orange G 2
PREPARATION OF COMPLEX: Add blue to orange. Heat to 80°C. Cool. Filter. Save both ppt. and filtrate.
PURIFICATION OF PRECIPITATE: Dissolve ppt. from above in 30 80% alc. Heat to 80°C. Cool. Filter. Save filtrate. Reject ppt.
PREPARATION OF WORKING SOLUTION: Mix both filtrates with 50 methylene blue solution. Filter.
REAGENTS REQUIRED: *A*. DS 11.43 Ziehl 1890; *B*. working solution
METHOD: [sections] → water → *A*, 5 mins. → water, thorough wash → *B*, 4 mins. → abs. alc., till differentiated → neutral mountant, via usual reagents
RESULT: nuclei, red; cartilage, blue; muscle, yellow; bone, green.

13.21 Houcke 1928   *toluidine blue-orange G-thionin-eosin-azur II*
                                        6630, **99**:784
PREPARATION OF STOCK SOLUTIONS: I. Mix 10 1% toluidine blue with 5 1% orange G. Dilute to 100. Leave 24 hours. Decant and leave ppt. dry. Dissolve dried ppt. in 10 methanol. II. Add 17 1% eosin Y to 100 sat. sol. (*circ.* 25%) thionine. Leave 24 hours. Decant. Dry ppt. Prepare 0.5% solution ppt. in methanol. III. Add 11 1% eosin B to 10 1% methylene blue. Thence as in II. IV. Add 1.25 1% eosin Y to 40 0.08% azureosin. Filter. Dry ppt. on filter paper. Cut in strips and extract with 10 methanol. V. Add 8 1% eosin Y to 10 1% toluidine blue.
WORKING SOLUTION: water 100, stock I 0.5, stock II 1.5, stock III 1.5, stock IV 1.5, stock V 1.5, 0.1% acetic acid 1.0

METHOD: [water] → stain, 24 hrs. → abs. alc., minimum possible time → balsam, via xylene

NOTE: Houcke (*loc. cit.*) recommends varying the acidity of the working solution by experiment to adapt it to use after various fixatives.

13.21 Holmes and French 1926   *azur C-eosin Y-orange II*

20540b, **1**:25

REAGENTS REQUIRED: *A.* 1.5% azur C; *B.* abs. alc. 99, acetic acid 1, eosin Y 0.025, orange II 0.025

METHOD: [water] → *A*, 5 mins. → methanol, till color clouds cease, 5–10 secs. → *B*, till no more blue comes away → abs. alc., quick rinse → balsam, via xylene

RESULT: nuclei, and some bacteria, blue; cell inclusions and blood, as Giemsa; collagens, bright orange; muscle, pink.

13.21 Kedrovsky 1931   *see* DS 22.12 Kedrovsky 1931

13.21 Mann 1894 *test.* 1942 Langeron *cit.* Masson   *erythrosin-orange G-toluidine blue*

Langeron 1942, 613

REAGENTS REQUIRED: *A.* ADS 12.2 Lugol (1905); *B.* 5% sodium thiosulfate; *C.* water 100, orange G 1, erythrosin 0.2; *D.* 1% toluidine blue; *E.* 0.2% acetic acid

METHOD: [sections] → water → *A*, ½ hr. → water, rinse → *B*, till bleached → water, thorough wash → *C*, 15 mins. → water, rinse → *D*, on slide, 1–2 mins. → water, rinse → *E*, till differentiated → balsam, via usual reagents.

NOTE: Langeron (*loc. cit.*) says "*Ce procédé, dit de Dominici, jouit en France d'une assez grande vogue—etc.*" See, however, DS 13.21 Dominici 1902, above.

13.22 IN COMBINATION WITH OTHER DYES

13.22 Bauer and Leriche 1934   *methylene blue-eosin Y-cresyl blue*

16550, **42**:1385

REAGENTS REQUIRED: *A.* water 100, brilliant cresyl blue 0.25; *B.* DS 13.11 Jenner 1899 (working sol.)

METHOD: Mix 4 parts blood with 1 *A*, as drop on slide, 2 mins. → smear → dry → *B*, 2 mins. → water, rinse → dry → neutral mountant.

13.22 Blank 1942   *mercurochrome-azur-eosin*   11284, **27**:1342

STOCK SOLUTIONS: I. water 82, 40% formaldehyde 9, abs. alc. 5, DS 13.13 Geimsa 1902 2.25, methylene blue 0.25, sodium borate 0.5

REAGENTS: REQUIRED: *A.* 0.1% mercurochrome 220 in 25% methanol; *B.* stock I 5, water 95

METHOD: [sections (nuclei may be hematoxylin stained)] → water → *A*, 1 min. → wash → *B*, 2 mins. → 90% alc., till no more color comes away

13.22 Geschickter 1930   *azur-erie garnet*   20540b, **5**:81

FORMULA: water 100, azur A 0.8, erie garnet B 0.1

PREPARATION: To the azur dissolved in 80 water add, very rapidly, the garnet dissolved in 20. Filter.

METHOD: [frozen sections of fresh tissue] → stain, 15–20 secs. → wash → M 10 mountant

13.22 Houcke 1928a   *methylene blue-toluidine-thionin-fuchsin*

6630, **99**:786

PREPARATION OF STOCK FORMULAS: I. Mix, without agitation, in a small graduate, 14 1% acid fuchsin with 22 1% methylene blue. Leave 24 hours. Pour liquid from viscous ppt. which adheres to side of graduate. Dry ppt. and dissolve in 20 methanol. II. Add 0.5 1% acid fuchsin to 10 sat. sol. thionine. Leave 1 hour. Centrifuge. Decant and drain. Dry ppt. in tube. Dissolve in 10 methanol. III. Mix 11 1% toluidine blue with 5 1% acid fuchsin. Then treat as II.

WORKING FORMULA: water 100, stock I 2.5, stock II 2.5, stock III 2.5, 1% acetic acid 1

METHOD: [sections] → water → stain ½ to 2 hrs. → abs. alc., shortest possible time → balsam, via xylene

NOTE: Houcke (*loc. cit.*) comments that the pH of the working solution is critical, but the optimum, which varies both with types of tissue and fixatives employed, can only be established empirically.

13.22 Houcke 1928b   *methylene blue-rhodamine B*   6630, **99**:788
FORMULA: sat. sol. (*circ.* 5%) methylene blue in 95% alc. 3, sat. sol. aniline 27, 0.5%
rhodamine B 70
METHOD: [section] → water → stain, 2–3 hrs. → abs. alc., minimum possible time →
dammar via xylene
RESULT: chromatin, blue violet; nucleoli, red; collagens, orange; muscle, deep orange;
erythrocytes, bright red.
NOTE: For tissues recently fixed Houcke recommends that the aniline solution be diluted
1:1 with water.

13.22 Langeron 1942a   *polychrome methylene blue-orcein*
Langeron 1942, 612
REAGENTS REQUIRED: *A.* water 100, polychrome methylene blue 1; *B.* 70% alcohol 100,
orcein 0.25
METHOD: Distilled water → *A*, 5 mins. → wash → *B*, 5 mins. → abs. alc., least possible
time → balsam, via xylene
RESULT: nuclei, blue; connective tissue, red; other structures, polychrome.

13.22 Langeron 1942b   *polychrome methylene blue-tannin-orange*
Langeron 1942, 612
REAGENTS REQUIRED: *A.* water 100, polychrome methylene blue 1; *B.* DS 11.44. Unna
1892
METHOD: Distilled water → *A*, 5–15 mins. → wash → *B*, till no further blue removed →
rinse → balsam via usual reagents
RESULT: nuclei in mitosis, bacteria, some connective tissues, blue; resting nuclei, most
other structures, orange.

13.22 Kull 1913   *toluidine blue-aurantia-acid fuchsin*   766, **45**:153
REAGENTS REQUIRED: *A.* sat. sol. aniline 100, acid fuchsin 20; *B.* 0.5% toluidine blue;
C. 0.5% aurantia in 70% alc.
METHOD: [sections] → water → *A*, 1 min. warmed to steaming → cool → water, quick
rinse → *B*, 1–2 mins. → water, quick rinse → *C*, till sufficient red extracted, 20–30
secs. → 95% alc., till differentiation complete → balsam, via usual reagents
NOTE: Though originally intended for the demonstration of mitochondria, this is an
excellent general-purpose stain. For the mitochondria technique see DS 22.2 Kull 1914.

13.22 Masson *test.* **Langeron 1942**   *thionin-picric acid*   Langeron 1942, 613
REAGENTS REQUIRED: *A.* DS 11.44 Nicolle (1942); *B.* 0.2% acetic acid; *C.* sat. sol. picric
acid in toluene
METHOD: water → *A*, 15 mins. → wash → *B*, till differentiated → abs. alc. till de-
hydrated → toluene → *C*, till green → balsam, via toluene
RESULT: nuclei, bacteria blue; other tissues, yellow, blue, or green.

13.22 Rhamy 1930   *methylene blue-eosin Y-magenta*   11284, **15**:490
STOCK FORMULAS: I. sat. sol. (*circ.* 6%) magenta in abs. alc.; II. sat. sol. (*circ.* 45%)
eosin Y in water; III. sat. sol. (*circ.* 1.5%) methylene blue in abs. alc.
WORKING FORMULA: 30% alc. 100, stock I 4, stock II 5, stock III 15
METHOD: [sections] → 70% alc. → stain, 5 mins. → abs. alc., till differentiated → bal-
sam, via usual reagents

13.22 Unna *test.* **1928 Schmorl**   *methylene blue-orcein*   Schmorl 1928, 76
REAGENTS REQUIRED: *A.* DS 11.44 Unna 1892; *B.* 1% orcein in 95% alc.
METHOD: [celloidin sections of alc. fixed material] → water → *A*, 10 mins. → thorough
wash → blot → *B*, 15 mins. → balsam, via bergamot oil

13.3 TECHNIQUES EMPLOYING METHYL GREEN AS THE NUCLEAR STAIN

Methyl green in combination with pyronin has been long recognized as an excellent stain for smears, but, like all other
methyl green combinations, it has the disadvantage of being very sensitive to alka-
lies—so much so that extreme care must
be taken either to provide a perfectly
neutral mounting or to use some acid
mountant such as salicylic balsam. The

formula of Pappenheim 1901 has been adapted for use with bacteria by Saathof 1905, and is now widely used for this purpose. The combination of methyl green with other dyes is best known from the Ehrlich 1898 (or Heidenhein 1888) "triacid" mixtures. These mixtures and their variations continue to occur from time to time in the literature, but it is difficult to justify their employment today. Far better methyl green-acid fuchsin combinations are the two triple stains of Foley, 1930 and 1931, which will give all the staining reactions of the earlier mixtures without their manifest disadvantages. Most of the other formulas in this class are various modifications of the "triacid" mixtures.

13.30 TYPICAL EXAMPLES

Staining a section of the suprarenal body in the methyl green-acid fuchsin-orange G stain of Foley 1939

The method of staining here described is the most rational of all the variants of the old Ehrlich's "triacid" stain. These stains are largely designed to differentiate cell types, and should be employed only on organs in which so many cell types are present that many varieties of shade are desired to differentiate between them. The suprarenal bodies fulfill this requirement and are best obtained from a young mammal. A rabbit is excellent for class demonstration; a two-third-grown male should be selected, killed in the customary manner, eviscerated, and the suprarenal bodies removed from under the peritoneum before being rinsed in physiological saline solution.

There is considerable discussion in the literature as to the best fixative to select for these materials, but a combination of dichromate and osmic acid will provide excellent fixation of the chromaffin material (which will be retained in paraffin sections) and will thus differentiate at least this cellular material with a reasonable degree of certainty. Numerous fixatives of this general composition have been suggested; that of Altmann 1890 (Chapter 18, F 1700.0000 Altmann 1890) is well suited for this particular preparation. No fixative containing osmic acid has much penetrating power, so that the suprarenal body, having been rinsed in physiological saline, should be cut with a sharp scalpel into at least three pieces before being immersed in about 50 milliliters of the selected fixative. Fixation is permitted to continue in the dark for about 24 hours before the specimen is removed and washed in running water for at least a further 12 hours. If, after this washing, the outer surface of the specimens are unduly blackened (they will in any case be a light brown color), a few drops of hydrogen peroxide may be applied in distilled water; but the pieces should not be left in this mixture for longer than it takes the black stain to disappear. They should then be washed in several changes of distilled water before being rewashed in running water for at least three or four hours. The hydrogen peroxide does not destroy the osmic hydroxides precipitated on the surface, but only causes them to revert to the water soluble tetraoxide. The soluble tetraoxide must therefore be removed by prolonged washing unless the blackening is to recur.

Dehydrating, embedding, and sectioning should present no difficulty whatever with an object of this type, though it is recommended that sections no thicker than 5 microns should be employed. These sections are attached to a slide in the customary manner, dewaxed, and brought down through the customary dehydrating agents to distilled water, in which the slides may be accumulated until they are required for staining.

The only difficulty lies in the preparation of the stain itself (DS 13.32 Foley 1930) which, if prepared imperfectly, will contain a precipitate. The addition of the acid fuchsin and the orange G solutions to the glycerol occasions no difficulty; but the greatest care should be taken to have these completely mixed together before the methyl green is added. The methyl green should be added as slowly as possible in small drops and each drop should be thoroughly mixed in before the next is added. The stain should then be allowed to remain for at least 12 hours at room temperature before being filtered immediately before each use.

Sections are passed directly from dis-tilled water into the stain, in which they may remain from overnight to about 24 hours. Overstaining does not normally occur.

Each slide must be removed separately from the stain and rinsed briefly and rapidly in 95% alcohol. It will be observed that in the alcohol color clouds rise from the sections, and that there is then a brief period when these color clouds cease. If the slide is then left for a longer period in alcohol, further stain will commence to leave it. To secure satisfactory slides, it is essential that the slide be passed from alcohol to the carbon-xylene, which is recommended for clearing, at the exact moment when the primary color clouds cease to leave. The purpose of the carbol-xylene is to permit complete dehydration, even though the length of time in alcohol has not been sufficient to remove the whole of the water from the section. The carbol-xylene must be thoroughly re-moved with pure xylene before the slide is mounted in balsam, or the latter will inevitably turn brown.

13.31 METHYL GREEN IN COMBINATION WITH PYRONIN

13.31 Flinn 1939   *see* DS 23.219 Flinn 1939

13.31 Grosso 1912   16059, **4**:41
> FORMULA: water 100, sat. sol. (*circ.* 9%) pyronin 5, sat. sol. (*circ.* 5%) methyl green 3.5, sat. sol. (*circ.* 11%) orange G 3.5
> METHOD: water → stain, 30 secs. → abs. alc., till differentiated → n-propyl alc., if de-hydration insufficient → neutral mountant
> RESULT: nuclei, green; plasma, red, orange, and yellow.

13.31 Langeron 1942   Langeron 1942, 615
> STOCK SOLUTIONS: I. water 100, methyl green 4, phenol 5; II. water 100, pyronin 4, phenol 5
> REAGENTS REQUIRED: *A.* stock I 50, stock II 50; *B.* alc. 50, acetone 50; *C.* amyl alcohol
> METHOD: distilled water → *A*, 15 mins. at 50°C. → distilled water, rinse → *B*, till differ-entiated → *C*, till dehydrated → balsam, via toluene
> RESULT: good differential staining of blood cells and glandular cell inclusions.

13.31 Lipp 1940   *see* DS 23.214 Lipp 1940c

13.31 Pappenheim 1901   1780a, **155**:427
> STOCK SOLUTIONS: I. water 100, phenol 0.25, methyl green 1; II. water 100, phenol 0.25, pyronin 1
> WORKING FORMULA: stock A 30, stock B 70
> METHOD: water → stain, 5–10 mins. → water, quick rinse → neutral mountant, via acetone
> RESULT: nuclei, violet; lymphocytes and plasma cells, red; other tissues, orange and green.
> NOTE: For bacteria see DS 23.221 Saathof 1905.

13.31 Sandiford 1937   11431, **45**:467
> FORMULA: water 75, glycerol 20, 95% alc. 5, phenol 1.5, methyl green 0.15, pyronin 0.5

13.31 Scott and French 1924   13685, **55**:337
> FORMULA: water 80, glycerol 16, abs. alc. 4, phenol 1.6, methyl green 0.8, pyronin 0.2

13.31 Unna 1910 *test.* **1928 Gatenby and Cowdry** *cit.* **Gandletz**
                                        Gatenby and Cowdry 1928, 176
> FORMULA: water 100, phenol 0.5, glycerol 20, abs. alc. 2.5, pyronin 0.25, methyl green 0.15
> PREPARATION: Grind the dyes with the alc. in a mortar. Heat glycerol to 50°C. and add to mortar in small portions while grinding. Dissolve phenol in water and use this to wash out mortar with small successive doses.
> METHOD: water → stain, 10 mins. 30°C. → water, rinse → abs. alc. till differentiated → balsam, via usual reagents
> NOTE: For adaptation for bacterial staining, see DS 23.221 Saathof 1905; for staining fungi in skin sections see DS 23.32 Unna 1929.

13.31 Walton 1939 *see* DS 23.219 Walton 1939

13.32 METHYL GREEN IN COMBINATION WITH OTHER DYES

13.32 Auerbach *test.* **1930 Guyer**   *acid fuchsin-methyl green*

Guyer 1930, 230

STOCK SOLUTIONS: I. 0.1% acid fuchsin; II. 0.1% methyl green
WORKING SOLUTION: stock I 40, acetic acid 0.005, stock II 60
METHOD: [3 λ sections of mercuric fixed material] → water → stain, 15 mins. → 95% alc.,
till green clouds cease → abs. alc. rinse → balsam, via xylene

13.32 Biondi *test.* **1888 Heidenhain**   *orange G-acid fuchsin-methyl green*

16155, **63** (suppl.): 40

STOCK SOLUTION: mix 100 sat. sol. (*circ.* 11%) orange G with 20 sat. sol. (*circ.* 13%) acid
fuchsin. Add slowly and with constant agitation 50 sat. sol. (*circ.* 5%) methyl green
WORKING FORMULA: water 100, stock 1–2
METHOD: [sections] → water → stain, 6–24 hrs. → balsam, via usual reagents
NOTES: This stain is variously attributed to Ehrlich, Ehrlich-Biondi, and Ehrlich-
Biondi-Heidenhain. Heidenhain (*loc. cit.*) explains quite clearly *"—welche dieselben
Ingredientien enthält, wie die von Babes empfohlene Ehrlich'sche Mischung (Berhend's
Ztschr f. Mikroskopie, Bd IV, S 232) aber in anderen Verhältnissen."* This would seem
to dispose of the "Ehrlich" in the name of the mixture. These new proportions, how-
ever, were stated (*loc. cit.*) as *"nach Versuchen von Biondi"* and the mixture was later
referred to (p. 43) as *Biondi'sche Flussigkeit.*

13.32 Cooper 1931 *see* DS 22.11 Cooper 1931

13.32 Ehrlich 1888   *Ehrlich's Triacid—compl. script.* *see* DS 13.32 Biondi (1888) (note)

13.32 Ehrlich 1898 *test.* **Lee 1905**   *orange G-acid fuchsin-methyl green*

Lee 1905, 212

PREPARATION: Mix 16 sat. sol. (*circ.* 11%) orange G with 7.5 sat. sol. (circ. 13%) acid
fuchsin. Dilute mixture with 40 50% alc. Add slowly and with constant agitation 15
sat. sol. (*circ.* 5%) methyl green. Then add 10 each 95% alc. and glycerol.

13.32 Foley 1930   *methyl green-acid fuchsin*   763, **45**:340

REAGENTS REQUIRED: *A.* 2% methyl green 80, 0.1% acid fuchsin 20; *B.* 0.1% hydro-
chloric acid
METHOD: [sections of osmic fixed, or mordanted, material] → running water, overnight →
A, 24 hrs. → blot → *B*, till differentiated → balsam, via carbol-xylene
RESULT: chromatin, green; muscle, brick red; other tissues, pink.

13.32 Foley 1931   *methyl green-acid fuchsin-orange G*   763, **49**:15

PREPARATION: To 10 glycerol and 20 0.1% acid fuchsin and 30 0.1% orange G, add
drop by drop, with constant agitation, 30 0.25% methyl green.
METHOD: [water] → stain, 12–24 hrs. → blot → 95% alc., till differentiated, 5–30 secs. →
balsam, via carbol-xylene
NOTE: A detailed description of the use of this stain is given under 13.30 above.

13.32 Grosso 1914 *see* DS 12.211 Grosso 1914

13.32 Guinard 1889   *methyl green-acid fuchsin*   19076, **1**:19

PREPARATION: Mix 1% methyl green with 1% acid fuchsin in such proportion as give a
violet solution. Add acetic acid to pH 3.

13.32 Heidenhain 1888 *see* DS 13.32 Biondi (1888) (note)

13.32 Kahlden and Laurent 1896 *see* DS 21.3 Kahlden and Laurent 1896.

13.32 Kardos 1911 *see* DS 21.3 Kardos 1911

13.32 Krause 1893   *methyl green-acid fuchsin-orange G*   1780, **42**:59

FORMULA: sat. sol. (*circ.* 13%) acid fuchsin 0.4, sat. sol. (*circ.* 11%) orange G 0.7, sat.
sol. (*circ.* 5%) methyl green 0.8, water 100

13.32 Krause 1911 *test.* **1948 Romeis**   *methyl green-acid fuchsin-orange G*

Romeis 1948, 169

FORMULA: water 100, methyl green 3.4, acid fuchsin 4.2, orange G 3
PREPARATION: Grind the dry dyes together to a fine powder. Dissolve in water.
METHOD: As Biondi (1888)

13.32 Maresch 1905   *see* DS 13.43 Maresch 1905

13.32 Mayer 1901 *test.* **1901 Lee and Mayer**   *methyl green-acid fuchsin-orange G*

Lee and Mayer 1901, 197

FORMULA: water 60, glycerol 15, 95% alc. 25, orange G 2.6, acid fuchsin 4, methyl green 1.3
PREPARATION: Grind dyes together and dissolve in mixed solvents.

13.32 Moore 1882   *see* DS 21.3 Moore 1882

13.32 Morel and Doleris 1902   6630, **54**:1255

FORMULA: DS 13.32 Ehrlich 1898 50, 8% formaldehyde 50, acetic acid 0.1

13.32 Oppell *test.* **1895 Rawitz**   *methyl green-acid fuchsin-picric acid*

Rawitz 1895, 71

REAGENTS REQUIRED: *A.* 1% methyl green 60, 1% eosin 1, 1% acid fuchsin 20, abs. alc. 20; *B.* sat. sol. picric acid 80, abs. alc. 20
METHOD: [sections] → *A*, 15 mins. → *B*, 30 secs. → abs. alc., minimum possible time → balsam, via usual reagents

13.32 Squire 1892   *methyl green-acid fuchsin*   Squire 1892, 37

PREPARATION: Mix 30 0.5% methyl green with 10 1.5% acid fuchsin.

13.32 Stropeni 1912   *methyl green-acridine red*   23632, **29**:302

REAGENTS REQUIRED: *A.* water 100, sodium borate 1; *B.* water 100, glycerol 20, methanol 30, phenol 2, methyl green 0.05, acridine red 0.25
PREPARATION OF B: Grind each dye with 1 phenol and wash out each mortar with 50 water. Mix washings and add other ingredients.
METHOD: water → *A*, 10 mins. → rinse → *B*, 30 mins. → abs. alc. till differentiated → balsam via xylene

13.32 Thome 1898   *methyl green-acid fuchsin-orange G*   1780, **52**:820

FORMULA: sat. sol. (*circ.* 13%) acid fuchsin 0.15, sat. sol. (*circ.* 11%) orange G 0.35, sat. sol. (*circ.* 5%) methyl green 0.6, water 100

13.4 TECHNIQUES EMPLOYING ACID FUCHSIN AS THE NUCLEAR STAIN

Within this subdivision of the complex staining techniques lie the majority of the methods which are understood today whenever the term *triple stain* is used. Originated by Mallory in 1901, they depend for the most part upon the fact that phosphomolybdic acid will extract acid fuchsin from collagens and leave it in muscle and nuclei. Various mixtures are then used differentially to stain the decolorized tissues. The original method of Mallory used methyl blue and orange G and has been widely copied. So numerous have these formulas become that it is necessary in the present instance to divide them into those using phosphomolybdic acid (DS 13.41), and those using phosphotungstic acid (DS 13.42), though in point of fact the results of the stains can scarcely be distinguished. Mallory himself (1936;

20540b, **11**:101) prefers phosphotungstic acid. No one formula in either of these two groups can be singled out as better than another, and only one of them (Heidenhain 1905) has become sufficiently well known to acquire a popular name. This stain is frequently referred to as *Heidenhain's azan* because azocarmine is used as the first solution.

13.40 TYPICAL EXAMPLES

Preparation of a transverse section of Amphioxus using the acid fuchsin-anilin blue-orange G stain of Mallory 1901

Amphioxus is a difficult subject from which to prepare satisfactory sections, the more so as it is almost impossible nowadays to secure supplies of living amphioxus and to fix them oneself, or to prevent the supplier from whom one secures the fixed material from using Bouin's picro-acetic-formaldehyde fixative (Chapter 18, F 5000.1010 Bouin 1897) in their preparation. If it is possible to secure the living lancelets, they should be fixed by one of the methods recommended for fixing very heavily muscularized material, for it is otherwise almost impossible to secure unbroken sheets of muscle in the transverse section unless one is prepared to sacrifice histological detail to the interests of morphological demonstration. It is also to be regretted that popular demand has forced the biological supply houses to sell only large specimens, because these are too large to be viewed at one time in even the lowest power commonly available on a student microscope. If any selection can be exercised, care should be taken to pick a specimen of not more than 2.5 mm. greatest thickness in order that it may be seen as a whole.

If, however, one is forced to use a Bouin-fixed specimen, it may be sectioned without too much difficulty provided that it first be soaked overnight in 1% nitric acid. This treatment destroys much of the fine cytological detail and should not be applied to any specimen in which it is desired to demonstrate, say, the detailed structure of the endostyle. The writer, however, is always prepared to sacrifice such detail as this in a section desired for class demonstration, in order to avoid endless questioning as to what is this and that cavity which will be seen in a section of Bouin-fixed amphioxus handled by routine methods.

Apart from this question of fracturing the muscular layers, no difficulty will present itself in sectioning. As many 10-micron sections as are required should be accumulated. If it is desired to place on the same slide a collection of sections from different regions of the animal, reference may be made to the description of this procedure in Chapter 12.

When the sections have been mounted on a slide, deparaffinized, and run down to water, it is recommended that they be treated overnight in a saturated solution of mercuric chloride and then washed in running water for at least six hours. This process, though it takes a day, improves the vividness of Mallory's stain almost beyond belief when it is applied to a section of Bouin-fixed material. The actual staining procedure is simplicity itself and, though the original stain of Mallory (DS 13.41 Mallory 1900) has been selected for demonstration, there is no reason why any of the other stains in the same section should not be employed. The solutions present no difficulty in their preparation, though it is recommended that 1% phosphotungstic acid be substituted for the 1% phosphomolybic acid specified in the original method. After the sections have been thoroughly washed from the mordanting in mercuric chloride, they are placed in the 1% solution of acid fuchsin for a period of about two minutes. This time is not critical, it being desired only to make sure that the entire section is thoroughly stained. On removal the sections are rinsed rapidly in water, to remove the surplus stain, and are then placed in the 1% phosphotungstic acid until such time as the red stain has been removed entirely from the connective tissues. This may be judged partly by the cessation of the color clouds which rise from the section or by an examination under the low power of the microscope to make sure that the septa between the myotomes are free from color. The specified time of two minutes is usually sufficient, but the sections will not be damaged however long they may be left. On removal from this solution they are again quickly rinsed in water, and then placed in the acid-methyl blue-orange G solution where they should remain for at least 15 minutes. The mistake is often made of leaving them for too short a time in this stain, for they will have the appearance of being deeply stained after an immersion of only a few moments. It does not matter how long they remain in the solution; it is the writer's experience that soaking for at least 15 minutes discourages the subsequent removal of the blue from the tissues. After they are removed from this rather thick staining mixture the slides are thoroughly washed in water. The wash is designed to remove not only the whole of the adherent stain from the slide, but to permit the oxalic acid also to leach out of the tissues. No differentiation of the stain should take place in water, because such differentiation as is necessary is produced by the absolute alcohol used in the next stage for dehydration. It is difficult to take sections stained by this method up through the usual graded series of alcohols, nor will any grave damage be occasioned by the omission of this step. If, however, the preparator is one who insists that his sections should pass through a graded series, mixtures of acetone and water should be substituted for alcohol and water. When the sections reach absolute alcohol, they should be watched very closely while being moved continuously up and down in the alcohol. The blue will leave them in great clouds and these clouds will taper off quite rapidly, leaving a terminal point at which no color leaves for a moment or two before a slow stream again starts to appear in the alcohol. As soon as the initial color clouds are seen to cease, the sections should be placed in xylene which stops the differentiation.

If the preparator is uncertain of this method, or is trying it for the first time, it is recommended that the slides be thoroughly washed in absolute alcohol but removed to xylene before the color clouds have ceased to leave. Examination under the low power of the microscope will now show these preparations to have a dull purple muscle and an intensely blue connective tissue. A few trial sections should now be returned to absolute alcohol for a few moments and then back into xylene and reexamined. It is possible by this means to exercise perfect control over the differentiation, which should be stopped when the muscles and nuclei are clear red, and the connective tissues a clear light blue. No attention should be paid, while differentiating, to any of the structures (such as the gonad) which by this method acquire a violet coloration. The process should be controlled only by apparent contrast between the pure blues and pure reds in the section.

The stains used in this preparation are alkali-sensitive, and it is a customary procedure in Europe to mount them in as acid a medium as possible. If one is using one of the synthetic resins, which are neutral, it is strongly recommended that the coverslip, before being applied to the resin, be dipped briefly in a strong solution of salicylic acid in xylene. This salicylic acid will then dissolve in the resin and provide a permanently acid environment.

13.41 METHODS EMPLOYING THE ACID FUCHSIN-PHOSPHOMOLYBDIC REACTION

Waterman 1937 (20540b, **12**:21) recommends that dioxane be substituted for alc. in the dehydration of sections stained by these techniques. **Kernohan 1934** (4349, **13**:82) mordants formaldehyde material 4 days in ADS 12.1 Weigert 1896 followed by 2 days in ADS 12.1 Weigert 1891.

13.41 Bensley *test.* **1938 Mallory** *cit.* **Warren**   Mallory 1938, 210
    REAGENTS REQUIRED: *A.* DS 22.21 Altmann 1890 (sol. *A*); *B.* 1% phosphomolybdic acid; *C.* water 100, orange G 2, anilin blue 0.5
    METHOD: [sections] → water → *A*, 10 mins. → rinse → *B*, 10 mins. → quick rinse → *C*, 1 hr. → 95% alc. till color clouds cease → balsam, via usual reagents

13.41 Duprès 1935   14425, **46**:77
    REAGENTS REQUIRED: *A.* DS 11.43 Gallego 1919; *B.* water 50, acetic acid 25, 40% formaldehyde 20; *C.* 1% phosphomolybdic acid; *D.* water 100, oxalic acid 4, toluidine blue 0.25, orange G 4
    METHOD: [sections of F 3670.0010 Ruffini 1927 material] → *A*, 1–10 mins. → *B*, wash → rinse → *C*, 10 mins. → wash → *D*, 1–2 mins. → blot → 95% alc., till differentiated → balsam, via usual reagents.
    NOTE: For toluidine blue in *D* above there may be substituted *either* methylene blue 0.3 *or* malachite green 0.2 *or* methyl green 0.3.

13.41 Kricheski 1931   10540b, **6**:97

REAGENTS REQUIRED: *A*. 0.25% acid fuchsin; *B*. 2% methyl blue 30, 1% orange G 30, 1% phosphomolybdic acid 30

METHOD: water → *A*, 1–3 mins. → water, thorough rinse → *B*, 3–5 mins. → water, quick rinse → 70% alc., 2 or 3 dips → 95% alc., 2 or 3 dips → abs. alc. till differentiated 1–3 mins. → balsam, via xylene

RESULT: as Mallory 1901.

13.41 Ladewig 1938   *see* DS 13.6 Ladewig 1938

13.41 Lee-Brown 1929   *see* DS 13.41 Mallory 1901 (note)

13.41 Lewis and Miller 1938   *see* DS 21.421 Lewis and Miller 1938

13.41 Mallory 1901   11189, **5**:15

REAGENTS REQUIRED: A. 1% acid fuchsin; *B*. 1% phosphomolybdic acid; *C*. water 100, methyl blue 0.5, orange G 2, oxalic acid 2

METHOD: [water] → *A*, 2 mins. → water, thorough rinse → *B*, 2 mins. → water, quick rinse → *C*, 15 mins. → water, thorough wash → abs. alc., till differentiated → balsam, via xylene

RESULTS: nuclei, red; collagens, blue; nerves and glands, violet; muscle, red; erythrocytes and keratin, orange.

NOTE: **Mallory 1936** (20540b, **11**:101) substituted 1% phosphotungstic acid in *B*. A detailed description of the application of this stain is given under DS 13.40 above. **Lee-Brown 1929** (11597, **21**:259) differs only in using sol. *C* before sol. *B*. **Rexed and Wohlfart** 1939 (23632, **56**:212) recommend that *A* above be buffered to pH 3.3 with citrate.

13.41 Masson 1912   4956, **14**:291

REAGENTS REQUIRED: *A*. 4% ferric alum at 50°C.; *B*. 1% hematoxylin at 50°C.; *C*. 2% ferric alum; *D*. 0.1% acid fuchsin; *E*. 1% phosphomolybdic acid; *F*. 1% anilin blue 50, 1% phosphomolybdic acid 50

METHOD: [water] → *A*, 5 mins., 50°C. → water, 50°C. rapid rinse → *B*, 10–15 mins., 50°C. → *C*, till nuclei alone colored → running water, 15 mins. → *D*, 10 mins. → tap water, if overstaining has occurred → *E*, 5–10 mins. → *F*, 20 mins. to 1 hr. → water, quick rinse → 95% alc., quick rinse → abs. alc. till dehydrated → balsam, via xylene

13.41 Maxwell 1938   *see* DS 21.421 Maxwell 1938

13.41 Milligan 1946   *Tech. Bull.*, **7**:57

REAGENTS REQUIRED: *A*. water 75, 95% alc. 25, potassium dichromate 2.25, hydrochloric acid 2.5; *B*. 0.1% acid fuchsin; *C*. 1% phosphomolybdic acid; *D*. 2% orange G in 1% phosphomolybdic acid; *E*. 1; acetic acid; *F*. 0.1% *either* fast green FCF *or* anilin blue in 0.2% acetic acid

METHOD: [sections of formaldehyde material] → water → *A*, 5 mins. rinse → *B*, 5 mins. → rinse → *C*, 1–5 mins. → *D*, 5–10 mins. → rinse → *E*, 2 mins. → *F*, 5–10 mins. → *E*, 3 mins. → 95% alc. → balsam, via usual reagents

13.41 Rexed and Wohlfart 1939   *see* DS 13.41 Mallory 1901 (note)

13.41 Schneidau 1937   21400a, **56**:260

REAGENTS REQUIRED: *A*. 1% acid fuchsin; *B*. 10% phosphomolybdic acid; *C*. 0.1% thionine

METHOD: [whole objects] → *A*, 2–4 mins. → wash → *B*, 1 min. → rinse → *C*, 2–4 mins. → wash → balsam, via usual reagents.

RECOMMENDED FOR: double stained wholemounts.

13.42 METHODS EMPLOYING THE ACID FUCHSIN-PHOSPHOTUNGSTIC REACTION

13.42 Cason 1950   20540b, **25**:225

FORMULA: water 100, phosphotungstic acid 0.5, orange G 1, anilin blue 0.5, acid fuchsin 1.5

METHOD: [6μ sections] → water → stain, 5 mins. → water, rinse → balsam, via usual reagents

13.42 Heidenhain 1905   *Heidenhain's Azan—compl. script.*

23632, **22**:339

REAGENTS REQUIRED: *A.* water 100, azocarmine 2, acetic acid 1; *B.* 0.1% aniline in 95% alc.; *C.* 0.1% hydrochloric acid in abs. alc.; *D.* 5% phosphomolybdic acid; *E.* water 100, orange G 2, anilin blue 0.5, acetic acid 7.5

METHOD: water → *A*, 1 hr., 50°C. → water, quick rinse → *B*, till nuclei well marked dip in *C*, before examining → *C*, thorough rinse → *D*, 2 hrs. → *E*, 2–3 hrs. → water, rinse → balsam, via usual reagents

RESULT: nuclei, scarlet; muscle, orange; collagens, blue.

13.42 Kohashi 1937   8542a, **15**:175

REAGENTS REQUIRED: *A.* water 100, azocarmine 0.1, acetic acid 1; *B.* 90% alc. 100, aniline 0.1; *C.* 1% acetic acid in 95% alc.; *D.* 5% phosphotungstic acid; *E.* DS 12.31 Pasini (1928) (sol. *B*)

METHOD: [sections] → water → *A*, 12–15 mins. 60°C. → wash → *B*, till nuclei differentiated → *C*, ½–1 mins. → rinse → *D*, ½–1 hr. → rinse → *E*, 15–20 mins. → 95% alc. till differentiated → balsam, via carbol-xylene

13.42 Walter 1930   23632, **46**:458

REAGENTS REQUIRED: *A.* 2.5% ferric alum; *B.* 2% phosphotungstic acid; *C.* DS 12.31 Pasini (1928) sol. *B*

METHOD: water → *A*, 24 hrs. → water, quick rinse → *B*, 10 mins. → water, quick rinse → *C*, 15–20 mins. → 95% alc., till color clouds cease → abs. alc., 1 min. → balsam, via usual reagents

RESULT: nuclei and elastic fibers, purple; collagens, blue; erythrocytes, orange.

13.43 METHODS USING NEITHER PHOSPHOTUNGSTIC NOR PHOSPHOMOLYBDIC ACID

13.43 Auerbach   *see* DS 13.32 Auerbach (1930)

13.43 Böhm and Oppel 1907   Böhm and Oppel 1907, 115

STOCK FORMULAS: I. water 100, orange G 0.05, acid fuchsin 0.05, acetic acid 1, 40% formaldehyde 1; II. water 90, methanol 10, 0.25% brilliant cresyl blue 0.25, 40% formaldehyde 1

WORKING SOLUTION: stock I 50, stock II 50

METHOD: water → stain, 20–30 mins. → abs. alc., till differentiated → balsam, via xylene

RESULT: nuclei, red-purple; cartilage, blue; bone, orange; muscle, red.

13.43 Buchholz 1931   *see* DS 21.41 Buchholz 1931

13.43 Delamare 1905   *see* DS 13.7 Delamare 1905

13.43 Maresch 1905   23681, **16**:41

REAGENTS REQUIRED: *A.* sat. methanol sol. methyl green 50, sat. methanol sol. picric acid 50; *B.* 0.75% acid fuchsin

METHOD: [sections] → abs. alc. → *A*, 10 mins. → water, rinse → *B*, 5–10 secs. → blot → → abs. alc. dropped on slide, till color changes from dark violet to blue gray → balsam, via xylene

13.43 Roskin 1946   Roskin 1946, 154

REAGENTS REQUIRED: *A.* 0.1% indigocarmine in sat. sol. picric acid; *B.* sat. aq. sol. magenta

METHOD: [sections] → *A*, 10–30 mins. → *B*, poured on slide, left till greenish scum appears → abs. alc., till differentiated

13.43 Waterman 1937   20540b, **12**:21

PREPARATION OF STOCK SOLUTION: water 100, phenol 5, magenta 3

REAGENTS REQUIRED: *A.* water 100, acetic acid 0.6, 40% formaldehyde 0.6, stock 10; *B.* water 100, picric acid 1, acetic acid 2, indigocarmine 0.25

METHOD: [sections of material fixed in F 4000.0040 Watermann 1937] → water → *A*, 5 mins. → rinse, 2 secs. → *B*, 90 secs. → rinse, 2 secs. → 50% dioxane, 2 secs. → balsam, via dioxane and xylene

RESULT: nuclei, red; collagen, blue; other tissues, yellow and green.

13.5 Techniques Employing Safranin as the Nuclear Stain

Safranin is scarcely employed in the English-speaking countries as a histological nuclear stain, and no current staining technique for animal tissues which requires such a procedure is known to the author. Most of the stains placed in this class were developed for plant purposes and there is no doubt that few finer botanical stains can be produced.

13.50 typical example

Preparation of a transverse section of a Ranunculus stem using the safranin-crystal violet-fast green-orange II stain of Conant (1940)

The inexperienced microtomist must clearly distinguish between those methods of staining plant tissues, such as the present, which are designed to stain both the cytoplasm and the cell walls, and those such as the example given in the next chapter, which are designed to stain only the cell walls. The latter are much simpler and may be advantageously employed for class-demonstration purposes. The present technique, which is one of the simplest of the many quadruple stains which have been suggested for plant tissues, may be used as a general-purpose stain for all plant material, and the selection, in the present instance, of a Ranunculus stem as a demonstration object is designed solely because of its relative commoness and because of the ease with which it may be prepared. This staining method has the disadvantage that it does not always yield reproducible results, hence it is better for demonstration than for research purposes. If it is of primary importance that sections show identical staining when prepared at different times from slightly different material, it is recommended that the technique of Johansen 1940 (DS 13.5 Johansen 1940) be substituted.

The species of Ranunculus selected for demonstration purposes is not of great importance, but it must be remembered that the fame which the stem of this plant enjoys for teaching purposes is based upon the structure of *Ranunculus acris*, the commonest European buttercup, which is, however, so widely dispersed in the northeastern United States that it may be gathered without trouble. So many textbook diagrams are based on the section of this species that it is well worth the trouble to collect it.

The choice of fixative is far less critical in botanical than in zoological microtechniques, and it will be quite sufficient for the present purpose to use any of those fixatives, known to botanists as AAF fixatives, which will be found in Chapter 18 under the heading of F 0000.1010. These alcohol-acetic-formaldehyde mixtures keep indefinitely, and no two botanists have ever agreed as to what are the best concentrations to be employed.

Stems should be collected, so far as possible, toward the middle of the summer, when the structural detail will be found at its best, and the fixative should be taken into the field. The fresh stem should be severed from the plant, and about the lower ¾ of an inch cut off a few moments later to get rid of the air which will have been drawn into the vessels by the turgidity of the specimen. The remainder of the stem is then cut into about ½-inch lengths and placed in a 250 cc. bottle of the fixative. It should remain in this fixative, which may be changed as rapidly as it becomes discolored, until the chlorophyll has been thoroughly removed, and should then be washed in 70% alcohol until the washings no longer smell of acetic acid. The specimens may then be stored in 70% alcohol, though it has been suggested that slightly better preservation of detail may be secured by the addition of 1% glycerol to the preserving fluid. This is not, however, a matter of any importance provided less than a year elapses between the time of the collection of the material and the cutting of sections.

The stem presents no difficulties in embedding either by the dioxane technique or by the more conventional routine of alcohol-xylene. It is suggested that sections be cut at about 15 microns in thickness, since these rather thicker than normal sections give a much better idea of general structures when used for teaching purposes. The sections are attached to the slide, deparaffinized in the usual manner, and brought down through the customary graded alcohols to 70% alcohol. Plant material is far more likely to become distorted through insufficient attention being paid to grading alcohols than is animal material.

When all the slides have been accumulated in 70% alcohol, they may be transferred to the first stain, which is of 1% safranin in 50% alcohol, and may remain in this for any time desired by the mounter. The customary limits are from 2 to 24 hours. On removal from the safranin, the slides should be checked under the low power of the microscope to make sure that the nuclei of the cells are densely stained. Provided these are stained, all other structures will have acquired the necessary safranin coloration. On removal from the safranin, the slides should be washed in distilled water until no more color comes away.

A single slide is then withdrawn, and a saturated solution of crystal violet is poured over the section on the slide and left for about one minute. After being stained with crystal violet, the sections should be rinsed in water until no more color comes away, and then dehydrated as rapidly as possible through two changes of absolute alcohol. This is a rather critical stage in the staining, since the alcohol will remove the violet very readily and one is, in effect, engaged in a race between the minimum time required for dehydration and the minimum time in which the stain will be lost. As soon as the slides are judged to be dehydrated, they are dipped briefly in 1% fast green dissolved in absolute alcohol in a coplin jar. Now place the slide in a saturated solution of

orange II in clove oil. It is essential that the alcohol from the dehydration and from the fast green stain be removed as rapidly as possible so that it is desirable to have at least two coplin jars of the orange II-clove oil solution. The first of these is used exclusively for rinsing the slide backward and forward until all the adhering alcohol has left it. The slide may then be transferred to the next coplin jar of orange II-clove oil, in which it may be left, while the remaining slides of the batch are brought from 70% alcohol through the successive stages of the technique and accumulated in their turn in the orange II-clove oil.

The orange II-clove oil acts as a differentiating agent and the slides may now be observed at intervals, and, if differentiation is insufficient, allowed to remain till the required structures can be clearly seen. As soon as differentiation is judged to be complete, the slides are transferred to a fresh jar of clove oil. Here the orange II-clove oil is thoroughly washed from them and they are then taken to xylene in which the clove oil is removed. The omission of the last clove-oil wash is a cause of frequent failure, since any adherent orange-II-clove-oil solution which is carried over into xylene will lose the orange II by precipitation, producing a veil over the finer structures. The slides may be left in xylene for as long as required before being mounted in balsam in the customary manner.

It must again be emphasized that this method is not intended for the class demonstration of skeletal structures, but only to bring out the finer details of the cytoplasmic and nuclear constituents of any plant material.

13.51 OTHER TECHNIQUES

13.51 Conant *test.* **1940 Johansen**   *safranin-crystal violet-fast green-orange II*
Johansen 1940, 87

REAGENTS REQUIRED: *A.* 1% safranin in 50% alc.; *B.* sat. sol. (*circ.* 1%) crystal violet; *C.* 1% fast green in abs. alc.; *D.* sat. sol. orange II in clove oil

METHOD: [sections] → 70% alc. → *A*, 2–24 hrs. → water, rinse → *B*, 1 min. → water, rinse → abs. alc. till dehydrated → *C*, 5–10 dips → *D*, till alcohol removed → *D*, fresh solution, till differentiated → balsam, via xylene

NOTE: A detailed description of the use of this stain is given under DS 13.50 above.

13.51 Foley 1929   *safranin-orange G-crystal violet*   763, **43**:171

REAGENTS REQUIRED: *A.* 1% safranin O; *B.* N/40 hydrochloric acid; *C.* 0.3% crystal violet in 70% alc.; *D.* ADS 12.2 Lugol (1905); *E.* 1% mercuric chloride; *F.* sat. sol. orange G in clove oil

METHOD: [sections of osmic-fixed, or mordanted, material] → wash → *A*, overnight → *B*, till outline of nuclei distinct → *C*, 20 mins. → *B*, till outline of nuclei distinct → *D*, till sections deep black, 1–3 mins. → running water, till iodine removed → *E*, till sections bright blue, 1–3 mins. → water, thorough wash → blot → 95%, rinse 5 secs. → carbol-xylene till differentiated, ¼ to 5 mins. → xylene, 2 mins. → *F*, 1–2 mins. → clove oil wash → balsam, via xylene

13.51 Henneguy 1898 *test.* 1907 Böhm and Oppel　*safranin-methyl violet-orange G*
Böhm and Oppel 1907, 111

REAGENTS REQUIRED: *A.* water 100, ammonium thiocyanate 1, methyl violet 0.1, orange G 0.1; *B.* DS 11.42 Zwaademaker 1887

METHOD: [sections] → *A*, 10 mins. → rinse → *B*, 15 mins. → rinse → *A*, 15 mins. → abs. alc., minimum possible time → balsam, via clove oil

RESULT: nuclei, red; cytoplasm, various shades of blue and blue gray.

13.51 Johansen 1940　*safranin-methyl violet-fast green-orange G*
Johansen 1940, 88

REAGENTS REQUIRED: *A.* DS 11.42 Johansen 1940; *B.* 1% methyl violet; *C.* 95% alc. 30, ethylene glycol monomethyl ether 30, tert. butyl alc. 30; *D.* clove oil 6, ethylene glycol monomethyl ether 6, fast green FCF *q.s.* to sat., 95% alc. 36, tert. butyl alc. 36, acetic acid 12; *E.* 95% alc. 50 tert. butyl alc. 50, acetic acid 0.5; *F.* sat. sol. orange G in ethylene glycol monomethyl ether 30, ethylene glycol monomethyl ether 30, 95% alc. 30; *G.* clove oil 30, ethylene glycol monomethyl ether 30, 95% alc. 30; *H.* clove oil 30, abs. alc. 30, xylene 30

METHOD: [sections] → 70% alc. → *A*, 1–2 days → water, rinse → *B*, 10–15 mins. → water, rinse → *C*, 15 secs. → *D*, 10–15 mins. → *E*, quick rinse → *F*, 3 mins. → *G*, rinse → *H*, rinse → balsam, via xylene

RESULT: (plant tissues) dividing chromatin, red; resting nuclei, purple: lignified and suberized tissues, red; cellulose, green-orange; cytoplasm, bright orange; starch grains, purple; fungal mycelia, green.

13.51 Kalter 1943　*safranin-crystal violet-fast green-orange II*
11284, **28**:995

REAGENTS REQUIRED: *A.* water 50, 95% alc. 50, 40% formaldehyde 4, sodium acetate 0.5, safranin 0.2; *B.* 0.5% crystal violet; *C.* clove oil 100, fast green FCF and orange II, each to sat.; *D.* sat. sol. orange II in clove oil

METHOD: [sections] → water → *A*, 24 hrs. → rinse → *B*, 1–2 mins. → wash → 95% alc. → *C*, 5 mins. → clove oil, till connective tissue green → *D*, 10 mins. → clove oil → xylene, thorough wash → balsam

RESULT: nuclei, red; cytoplasm, pink or light green; muscle, tan; collagen, bright green.

13.51 Laguesse 1901 *test.* 1907 Böhm and Oppel　*safranin-crystal violet-orange G*
Böhm and Oppel 1907, 154

REAGENTS REQUIRED: *A.* 2% potassium sulfite; *B.* DS 11.42 Babes 1887; *C.* sat. aq. sol. crystal violet 50, sat. aq. sol. orange G 2

PREPARATION OF *C*: Mix the solution. Add just enough water to redissolve ppt.

METHOD: [sections] → *A*, 12–24 hrs. → wash → *B*, 6–12 hrs. → wash → *C*, 24 hrs. → blot → abs. alc. minimum possible time → clove oil, till differentiated → balsam, via xylene

13.51 Stockwell 1934　*safranin-gentian violet-orange G*　19938, **80**:121

REAGENTS REQUIRED: *Aa.* ADS 12.1 Stockwell 1934 *or Ab.* 1% chromic acid; *B.* 1% crystal violet 20, 1% safranin O 40, water 40; *C.* AFS 12.1 LaCour 1931; *D.* 1% picric acid in 95% alc.; *E.* 95% alc. 100, ammon. hydroxide 0.3; *F.* 0.2% orange G in clove oil

METHOD: [sections] → water → *Aa*, if bleaching required (or *Ab* if not chromic fixed) overnight → water, thorough wash → *B*, 1–6 hrs. → water, rinse → *C*, 30 secs. → 70% alc., quick rinse → *D*, few secs. → *E*, few secs. → abs. alc., few secs. → *F*, few secs. → balsam, via xylene

13.51 Unna 1928 *test.* 1928 Schmorl　*safranin-orcein-anilin blue-eosin*
Schmorl 1928, 343

STOCK SOLUTIONS: I. water 50, abs. alc. 25, glycerol 10, acetic acid 2.5, orcein 0.5, anilin blue 0.5; II. 80% alc. 100, ethyl eosin 1; III. 1% hydroquinone

REAGENTS REQUIRED: *A*. stock I 50, stock II 15, stock III 15; *B*. 1% safranin; *C*. 0.5% potassium dichromate

METHOD: [sections] → water → *A*, 10 mins. → wash → *B*, 10 mins. → thorough wash → *C*, 10–30 mins. → wash → balsam, via usual reagents

RESULT: nuclei, black with red granules; protoplasm violet; collagen, blue; elastic fibers, red

RECOMMENDED FOR: skin.

13.51 Unna *test*. **1928 Schmorl**   *safranin-anilin blue*   Schmorl 1928, 176

REAGENTS REQUIRED: *A*. 1% safranin; *B*. water 100, tannin 15, anilin blue 0.5

METHOD: [sections] → *A*, 10 mins. → thorough wash → *B*, 10–15 mins. → thorough wash → abs. alc. minimum possible time → balsam, via xylene

13.6 Techniques Employing Hematoxylin as the Nuclear Stain

Hematoxylin is, of course, the commonest nuclear stain to be employed before any of the plasma techniques (DS 12). The formulas here given are those in which the nuclear staining is an integral portion of a complex technique which cannot be employed in combination with any other nuclear stain.

13.6 Barbrow 1937   11284, **22**:1175

STOCK SOLUTIONS: I. 1% hematoxylin in 95% alc. (well "ripened"); II. water 99, ferric chloride 2, hydrochloric acid 1; III. water 100, picric acid 1, acid fuchsin 1

WORKING SOLUTION: stock I 25; stock II 10; stock III 50

METHOD: [frozen sections of unfixed tissues] → stain, 1 min. → wash → balsam, via usual reagents.

13.6 Brown and Brenn 1931   *see* DS 23.221 Brown and Brenn 1931

13.6 Delamare 1905 *test*. **1907 Böhm and Oppel**   Böhm and Oppel 1907, 131

STOCK SOLUTIONS: I. abs. alc. 100, hydrochloric acid 2, orcein 2; II. sat. aq. sol. picric acid 100, sat. aq. sol. acid fuchsin 0.5, DS 11.123 Ehrlich 1886 1

REAGENTS REQUIRED: *A*. stock I 50, stock II 50; *B*. 0.1% hydrochloric acid

METHOD: [sections] → water → *A*, 30 mins. → *B*, rinse → tap water, to "blue" hematoxylin → balsam, via usual reagents

RESULT: nuclei, violet; muscle and general cytoplasm, yellow; collagens, red; elastic fibers, black.

13.6 Friedländer 1889   Friedländer 1889, 94

FORMULA: abs. alc. 30, hematoxylin 0.5, glycerol 30, sat. sol. potassium alum 30, 1% eosin 10

PREPARATION: Dissolve the hematoxylin in the alc. Add the glycerol and alum. Leave 1 week. Filter. Add the eosin sol. to filtrate.

13.6 Galiano 1928 *test*. **1928 Findlay**   11360, **48**:314

REAGENTS REQUIRED: *A*. 3% ferric alum; *B*. water 80, acetic acid 20, hematoxylin 0.2; *C*. 95% alc. 75 m acetic acid 25, eosin 1.5; *D*. 0.1% ammonia in 95% alc.

METHOD: [sections] → water → *A*, 15 mins. → *B*, till nuclei darkly stained → wash, 15 mins. → 70% alc., 1 min. → *C*, till differentiated → *D*, wash → balsam, via usual reagents

13.6 Kefalas 1926   11360, **46**:277

REAGENTS REQUIRED: *A*. DS 11.121 Kefalas 1926; *B*. sat. sol. Biebrich scarlet in acetone

METHOD: [sections] → acetone → *A*, till slightly overstained → *B*, till counterstained and differentiated → acetone → balsam, via xylene

13.6 Koneff 1936   763, **66**:173

REAGENTS REQUIRED: *A*. 5% ferric alum; *B*. DS 11.122 Harris 1900; *C*. water 100, anilin blue 0.03, phosphomolybdic acid 5, oxalic acid 0.6

13.6 Ladewig 1938   23632, **55**:215

REAGENTS REQUIRED: *A*. DS 11.121 Weigert 1903; *B*. 1% phosphotungstic acid; *C*. water 100, methyl blue 0.5, orange G 2, oxalic acid 2, acid fuschin 1

METHOD: [sections of formaldehyde material] → water → *A*, 3–5 mins. rinse → *B*, 2 mins. → rinse → *C*, 4 mins. → quick rinse → 95% alc., till dehydrated → balsam, via xylene

13.6 Lillie 1945　　　　　　　　　　　　　　　　　　　　　　4349, **25**:33

REAGENTS REQUIRED: *A*. sat. 95% alc. sol. picric acid; *B*. DS 11.121 Weigert 1903; *C*. 1% Biebrich scarlet in 1% acetic acid; *D*. 3% ferric chloride; *E*. water 99, acetic acid 1 *and either* anilin blue 1 *or* methyl blue 1 *or* wool green S 1; *F*. 1% acetic acid

METHOD: [sections] → 95% alc. → *A*, 2 mins. → thorough wash → *B*, 6 mins. → wash → *C*, 4 mins. → *D*, 2 mins. → *E*, 3–5 mins. → rinse → *F*, 2 mins. → balsam, via acetone and xylene

RESULT: nuclei, brown black; muscle and cytoplasm, red; connective tissue, blue or green.

13.6 Lillie 1948　　　　　　　　　　　　　　　　　　　Lillie 1948, 149

REAGENTS REQUIRED: *A*. DS 11.121 Weigert 1904; *B*. 0.02% fast green FCF; *C*. 1% acetic acid; *D*. 0.1% Bismarck brown Y in 1% acetic acid

METHOD: [sections] → water → *A*, 6 mins. → wash → *B*, 3 mins. → *C*, wash → *D*, 4–6 mins. → balsam, via usual reagents

RESULT: nuclei, black; general cytoplasm, gray green; mucus, cartilage, cell granules, brown.

NOTE: Magenta, or new magenta, may be substituted for Bismarck brown in *D*. Eosin Y may be substituted in *B*, in which case crystal violet or malachite green should be substituted in *D*.

13.6 Löwenthal 1892 *test.* **1907 Böhm and Oppel**　　　Böhm and Oppel 1907, 119

PREPARATION OF STOCK SOLUTIONS: I. Dissolve 0.4 carmine in 100 0.05% sodium hydroxide. Add 0.25 picric acid; II. to 0.5 hematoxylin dissolved in 50 abs. alc. add 50 1: ammonium alum.

WORKING SOLUTION: stock I 100, stock II 20, acetic acid 2.5

PREPARATION OF WORKING SOLUTION: Mix the stock solutions slowly and with constant agitation. Leave 24 hours. Filter. Ripen 4 weeks.

METHOD: [sections] → water → stain, 24 hrs. → wash → balsam, via usual reagents

13.6 Mollier 1938　　　　　　　　　　　　　　　　　23632, **55**:472

REAGENTS REQUIRED: *A*. DS 21.12 Unna-Tänzer (1896); *B*. DS 11.121 Weigert 1904; *C*. 1% hydrochloric acid in 70% alc.; *D*. water 100, azocarmine 2, acetic acid 1; *E*. 5% phosphotungstic acid; *F*. water 100, naphthol green B 1, acetic acid 1

METHOD: [sections] → 70% alc. → *A*, 12 hrs. → wash, till no more color comes away → *B*, 1–3 mins. → rinse → *C*, till nuclei well differentiated → wash, 15 mins. → *D*, 15–30 mins. → rinse → *E*, 3 changes, 2–6 hrs., till collagen decolorized → rinse → *F*, 15–30 mins. → 95% alc., 30 secs. with constant agitation → balsam, via usual reagents

RESULT: nuclei, deep blue; general cytoplasm, purple; elastic fibers, black; collagen, green; erythrocytes, scarlet.

13.6 Möllendorf *test.* **1946 Roskin**　　　　　　　　Roskin 1946, 158

REAGENTS REQUIRED: *A*. DS 11.121 Hansen 1905; *B*. 1% eosin in 0.3% acetic acid; *C*. 2% phosphomolybdic acid; *D*. 1% methyl blue

METHOD: [sections] → water → *A*, 5 mins. → distilled water, rinse → running water, wash → *B*, 20 mins. → rinse → *C*, 10 secs. → rinse → *D*, 1–2 mins. → rinse → 95% alc. till color clouds cease → abs. alc. balsam, via xylene

13.6 Paquin and Goddard 1947　　　　　　　　　　4349, **27**:198

REAGENTS REQUIRED: *A*. DS 11.121 Paquin and Goddard 1947; *B*. 0.5% picric acid in 95% alc.; *C*. water 100, phosphotungstic acid 0.1; eosin 0.07, phloxine 0.03, orange G 0.1; *D*. 0.2% phosphotungstic acid; *E*. 0.4% acetic acid; *F*. 0.04% anilin blue in 1% acetic acid

METHOD: [sections of F 5600.1000 Masson (1947) material] → water → *A*, 5 mins. → wash, 5 mins. → *B*, 15–20 secs. → wash → *C*, 5 mins. → *D*, 5 mins. → *E*, double rinse → *F*, 5 mins. → *E*, double rinse → *D*, 5 mins. → *E*, 30 mins. → 95% alc., 3 dips → balsam, via isoamyl alc. and toluene

RESULT: nuclei, black; elastic tissue, cherry red; other connective tissues, blue; general cytoplasm, pink.

13.6 Papanicolaou 1941　　*see* DS 23.4 Papanicolaou 1941

13.6 Petragnani 1928   *see* DS 23.13 Petragnani 1928

13.6 Rénaut *test.* **1889 Friedländer**   Friedländer 1889, 94
FORMULA: sat. sol. potassium alum in glycerol 65, sat. sol. eosin Y 15, sat. alc. sol. hematoxylin 20

13.6 Reeve 1948   20540b, **23**:13
REAGENTS REQUIRED: *A.* water 90, DS 11.122 Delafield (1885) 10; *B.* water 40, 95% alc. 60, safranin 0.01, sodium acetate 0.01; *C.* xylene 75, abs. alc. 25, sat. sol. fast green FCF in 50:50 clove oil—abs. alc. 2–5
METHOD: [sections] → water → *A*, 5–15 mins. → wash → *B*, 5–15 mins. → rinse → 95% alc., till no more color comes away → *C*, 1–3 mins. → balsam, via xylene
RECOMMENDED FOR: general plant histology.

13.6 Reynolds 1936   *see* DS 23.34 Reynolds 1936

13.6 Romeis 1948   Romeis 1948, 364
REAGENTS REQUIRED: *A.* DS 21.13 Weigert 1898 (working sol.); *B.* DS 11.121 Weigert 1903; *C.* water 100, azophloxine 0.5, acetic acid 0.2; *D.* 1% acetic acid; *E.* water 100, phosphomolybdic acid 4, orange G 2; *F.* water 100, light green 0.2, acetic acid 0.2
METHOD: [sections] → 80% alc. → *A*, 15 mins. → wash → *B*, 2–3 mins. → thorough wash → *C*, 5 mins. → *D*, wash → *E*, till collagen decolorized → *D*, rinse → *F*, 5 mins. → *D*, 5 mins. → abs. alc., least possible time → balsam, via xylene
RESULT: nuclei, black; muscles and general cytoplasm, red; collagen, green; elastic fibers, black.
NOTE: The *C, D, E, F* solutions are from DS 12.31 Goldner 1938.

13.6 Slater and Dornfeld 1939   20540b, **14**:103
REAGENTS REQUIRED: *A.* DS 11.123 Harris 1900; *B.* 1% safranin O in sat. aq. sol. aniline; *C.* 0.5% fast green in 95% alc.
METHOD: [sections by dioxane technique of amphibian embryos from F 5000.1010 Puckett 1937] → *A*, 5 mins. → *C*, 2–5 mins., till yolk granules red on green cytoplasm → balsam, via usual reagents

13.7 OTHER COMPLEX TECHNIQUES OF GENERAL APPLICATION

This is the final division of complex staining techniques in which it has been necessary to place all those miscellaneous techniques which do not fall into the preceding classifications. Few of them are well known, and the three techniques of Becher 1921 should receive wider attention than they have received. People have become accustomed to regarding the soluble lakes of the oxazines, when they are used at all, as nuclear stains, hence no attention appears to have been given to those other formulas published by Becher in which these dyes are used with varying mordants for the purpose of providing a single-solution polychrome stain. These stains can quite safely be used for research purposes, since their results are reproducible and they are stable to light and acid. Attention should also be drawn to the formula of Shumway 1926, which is a rather unusual triple stain involving magenta as the nu-

clear stain and picric-indigo-carmine as the contrast. This gives magnificent pictures on embryonic material and is so easy to use that it is safe even in the hands of beginning classes. The mixture of Twort, of neutral red and light green, was at one time even more popular for staining blood films than the conventional methylene blue-eosonates; it is now rarely heard of, and then only for staining of blood parasites. It would be an excellent general-purpose tissue stain if it were not for the extreme sensitivity of both of its ingredients to variations in the pH of the final mounting media. The methods of Lonnberg 1891 and Lynch 1930 are of interest only in that they provide methods of double-staining wholemounts. There is no justification for this from a research point of view, but they make the most amusing mounts, which can be used for popular display very effectively.

13.7 Alzheimer 1910   *see* DS 13.7 Mann 1894a (note)

13.7 Becher 1921a   *polychrome gallamin blue*   Becher 1921, 70
FORMULA: water 100, sodium alum 5, gallamin blue 0.5
PREPARATION: Boil 5 minutes. Cool. Filter.
METHOD: [sections] → water → stain, 24 hrs. → water, wash → balsam, via usual reagents
RESULT: nuclei, black; cartilage, violet.

13.7 Becher 1921b   *polychrome quinalizarine*   Becher 1921, 55
FORMULA: water 100, chrome alum 5, quinalizarin 0.5
PREPARATION: Boil 5 minutes. Cool. Filter.
RESULT: nuclei, blue; muscle and nerves, red.

13.7 Becher 1921c   *polychrome coelestin blue*   Becher 1921, 73
FORMULA: water 100, chrome alum 5, coelestin blue 0.5
PREPARATION: Boil 5 minutes. Cool. Filter.
METHOD: [sections] → water → stain, 24 hrs. → water, wash → balsam, via usual reagents
RESULT: blue black nuclei, with a violet to red polychrome staining of connective tissues. For coelestin blue as a nuclear stain, *see* DS 11.41.

13.7 Bensley and Bensley 1938   *acid fuchsin-crystal violet*
     Bensley and Bensley 1938, 97
PREPARATION OF DRY STAIN: Add a sat. sol. acid fuchsin to a sat. sol. crystal violet till no further ppt. produced. Filter. Wash and dry ppt.
PREPARATION OF STOCK SOLUTION: abs. alc. 100, dry stain from above to sat.
REAGENTS REQUIRED: *A.* water 72, abs. alc. 18, stock solution 10; *B.* clove oil 75, abs. alc. 25
METHOD: [sections] → water → *A*, 5 mins. → blot → acetone, till dehydrated → benzene → *B*, till differentiated → benzene → balsam

13.7 Böhm and Oppel 1907   *Bismarck brown-dahlia violet-methyl green*
     Böhm and Oppel 1907, 127
REAGENTS REQUIRED: *A.* Sat. sol. (*circ.* 1.5%) Bismarck brown: *B.* 12.212 Roux 1894
METHOD: water → *A*, 10 mins. → water, quick rinse → *B*, 1 min. → abs. alc. till differentiated, few secs. → carbol-xylene → balsam, via xylene
RESULT: as 12.212 Roux 1894 but with black nuclei and brown cartilage.

13.7 Bonney 1908   *methyl violet-orange G-pyronin*   22575, **193**:547
REAGENTS REQUIRED: *A.* water 100, methyl violet 0.25, pyronin 1; *B.* acetone 100 2% orange G *q.s.*
PREPARATION OF B: To 100 acetone add 2% orange G till ppt. first formed just redissolves.
METHOD: [sections, mercuric-fixed, or mordanted] → water → *A*, 2 mins. → *B*, flooded on drained slide, 1 min. → balsam, via acetone and xylene
RESULT: nuclei, purple; plasma, red and yellow.

13.7 Borrel 1901   *see* DS 23.33 Borrel 1901

13.7 Buzaglo 1934   *quinalizarin-acid alizarin blue-alizarin viridine*
     4285a, **11**:40
REAGENTS REQUIRED: *A.* DS 11.41 Becher 1921b; *B.* 70% alc. 100, hydrochloric acid 1, orcein 1; *C.* water 100, aluminum sulfate 10, acid alizarin blue 5; *D.* 5% phosphomolybdic acid; *E.* water 100, hydrochloric acid *q.s.* to make pH 5.8, alizarin viridine 0.2
PREPARATION OF C: Boil 10 minutes. Cool. Filter.
METHOD: [sections] → water → *A*, 24 hrs. → rinse → *B*, 3 changes, 5 mins. in each → rinse → *C*, 7 mins. → rinse → *D*, till muscles differentiated → wash → *E*, 7 mins. → blot → abs. alc. minimum possible time → balsam, via carbol-xylene and xylene
RESULT: nuclei, dark blue; elastic fibers, brown; muscle, blue; cartilage, green.

13.7 Calleja 1897   *carmine-picro-indigocarmine*   23632, **15**:323
REAGENTS REQUIRED: *A*. sat. sol. lithium carbonate 100, carmine 2; *B*. 0.1% hydrochloric acid; *C*. sat. sol. picric acid 100, indigocarmine 0.25; *D*. 0.2% acetic acid
METHOD: [sections] → *A*, 5–10 mins. → *B*. 20–30 secs. → wash → *C*, 5–10 mins. → *D*, few secs. → balsam, via usual reagents

13.7 Canon 1937   14900, **139**:549
FORMULA: 70% alc. 100, chlorazol black E 1
METHOD: [sections, plant or animal tissue] → stain, 15–30 mins. → wash → balsam, via usual reagents
RESULT: a very pleasing, and well-differentiated series of gray tones with some green.
NOTE: This stain is often attributed to Darrow 1940 (20540b, **15**:67) who introduced it into American literature.

13.7 Castroviejo 1932   *magenta-picro-indigo carmine*   591b, **2**:135
REAGENTS REQUIRED: *A*. water 100, 40% formaldehyde 0.6, DS 11.43 Ziehl 1882 5; *B*. DS 12.221 Cajal 1895 100, acetic acid 0.6
METHOD: [sections of formaldehyde material] → water → *A*, till nuclei well stained → wash → *B*, till stained → wash → balsam, via usual reagents

13.7 Darrow 1940   *see* DS 13.4 Canon 1937

13.7 Dobell 1919   *methyl blue-eosin Y-orange G*   Dobell 1919, 7
REAGENTS REQUIRED: *A*. DS 13.5 Mann 1894; *B*. 70% alc. 90, sat. sol (*circ.* 0.2%) orange G in abs. alc. 10
METHOD: [smears] → water → *A*, 12 hrs. → *B*, applied from drop bottle, till differentiated → abs. alc., minimum possible time → balsam, via xylene

13.7 Drew-Murray 1919   *picro-acid fuchsin-nile blue*   1200, **6**:77
REAGENTS REQUIRED: *A*. DS 12.221 van Gieson 1896; *B*. 2% nile blue sulfate
METHOD: [water] → *A*, 1–3 mins. → water, thorough rinse → *B*, 2–24 hrs. → water, wash → *A*, 1–5 mins. → wash → abs. alc., minimum possible time → xylene → clove oil till differentiated → xylene → balsam
RESULT: nuclei and some cell inclusions, blue black; keratin, orange-yellow: collagens, red.

13.7 Ehrlich *test.* **1905 Lee** *cit.* **Grubler**   *indulin-aurantia-eosin Y*
                                         Lee 1905, 218
FORMULA: glycerol 90, aurantia 6, indulin 6, eosin Y 6
PREPARATION: Digest at 40°C. till completely dissolved.
METHOD: [smears] → stain, 4–5 hrs., 40°C. → water, thorough rinse → balsam, via acetone and xylene
RESULT: nuclei, deep blue; some cytoplasmic inclusions, violet; plasma in general, orange.

13.7 Fraenkel   *see* DS 21.13 Fraenkel (1928)

13.7 Freeborn 1888   *picro-nigrosin*   645, **9**:231
FORMULA: water 100, nigrosin 0.05, picric acid 0.4
METHOD: [sections] → stains, 5–10 mins. → wash → balsam, via usual reagents
RESULT: nuclei, black; collagens, blue; other tissues, yellow.

13.7 Gomori 1946   *see* DS 21.423 Gomori 1946

13.7 Hruby 1933   *see* DS 22.12 Hruby 1933

13.7 Koneff 1938   *see* DS 21.421 Koneff 1938

13.7 Kornhauser 1943   *Quad Stain—auct.*   20540b, **18**:95
REAGENTS REQUIRED: *A*. 95% alc. 90, water 10, nitric acid 0.4, orcein 0.4; *B*. water 100, aluminum sulfate (cryst.) 10, ferric chloride 0.8, acid alizarin blue 2 B 0.35; *C*. 5% phosphotungstic acid; *D*. water 100, acetic acid 2, orange G 2, fast green FCF 0.2
PREPARATION OF B: Boil the dye in the sulfate solution 10 minutes. Add the ferric chloride dissolved in a little water.

METHOD: [sections of mercuric, or mercuric-chromic, fixed material after removal of mercury by iodine treatment] → 85% alc. → *A*, 2–24 hrs. → 85% alc., thorough wash → water, via graded alcs. → *B*, 5–10 mins. → rinse → *C*, till collagen destained → rinse → *D*, 10 mins. → 50% alc., wash → balsam, via usual reagents

RESULT: elastic fibers, brown; nuclei, blue; cytoplasm and muscle, violet; collagen, green; erthyrocytes, orange.

13.7 Kornhauser 1945   20540b, **20**:33

REAGENTS REQUIRED: *A*. as Kornhauser 1943 above; *B*. water 100, acetic acid 0.475, sodium acetate 0.023, acid alizarin blue 2 B 0.35, ammonium alum 5; *C*. water 100, phosphotungstic acid 4, phosphomolybdic acid 1; *D*. as Kronhauser 1943 above

METHOD: [material as for Kornhauser 1943 above] → 85% alc., → *A*, 2–24 hrs. → 85% alc., thorough wash → water, via graded alcs. → *B*, 5–10 mins. → rinse → *C*, 10–30 mins. → quick rinse → *D*, 10 mins. → 50% alc. wash → balsam, via usual reagents

RESULT: As Kornhauser 1943 above.

13.7 Krugenberg and Thielman 1917   23632, **34**:234

REAGENTS REQUIRED: *A*. water 108, anilin blue 0.45, eosin *B*. 0.22, phloxine 0.45

PREPARATION OF A: The eosins are each dissolved in 45 water and mixed with the blue dissolved in 18.

METHOD: [sections of alcohol-fixed material] → *A*, 2–10 mins. → rinse → abs. alc., minimum possible time → balsam, via usual reagents

13.7 Lillie 1945a   4349, **25**:27

REAGENTS REQUIRED: *A*. water 99, acetic acid 1, brilliant purpurin R 0.6, azofuchsin G 0.4; *B*. 1% acetic acid; *C*. water 100, picric acid 1, naphthol blue black 1

METHOD: [sections, nuclei stained by DS 11.121 Weigert 1903] → water → *A*, 5 mins. → *B*, rinse → *C*, 5 mins. → *B*, 2 mins. → balsam, via usual reagents

RESULT: collagen, reticulum, basement membranes, dark green; muscle and glands, brown; erythrocytes, brownish red.

13.7 Lillie 1945b   4349, **25**:28

REAGENTS REQUIRED: *A*. either 0.1% fast green FCG in 1% acetic acid or 0.3% wool green FCF in 1% acetic acid; *B*. 1% acetic acid; *C*. either 0.2% acid fuchsin or 0.2% violamine R

METHOD: [sections, nuclei stained in DS 11.122 Lillie 1948] → water → *A*, 4 mins. → *B*, wash → *C*, 10–15 mins. → *B*, 2 mins. → balsam, via usual reagents

RESULT: connective tissue, red; erythrocytes, green; muscle and cytoplasm, gray-green.

13.7 Lillie 1945c   4349, **25**:32

REAGENTS REQUIRED: *A*. 1% eosin Y; *B*. 3% ferric chloride; *C*. 1% naphthol green B; *D*. 1% acetic acid

METHOD [sections, nuclei stained by DS 11.121 Weigert 1903] → water → *A*, 3 mins. → rinse → *B*, 4 mins. → rinse → *C*, 5 mins. → *D*, 2 mins. → balsam, via acetone and xylene

RESULT: general cytoplasm, pink; collagen, green.

13.7 Lillie 1945d   4349, **25**:32

REAGENTS REQUIRED: *A*. 1% Biebrich scarlet in 1% acetic acid; *B*. 1% acetic acid; *C*. 0.5% methyl blue in 0.3% hydrochloric acid

METHOD: [sections, nuclei stained by DS 11.121 Weigert 1903] → water → *A*, 5 mins. → *B*, 2 mins. → *C*, 5 mins. → balsam, via usual reagents

13.7 Lillie 1945e   4349, **25**:41

REAGENTS REQUIRED: *A*. 1% phloxine B; *B*. 1% acetic acid; *C*. water 100, hydrochloric acid 0.25, methyl blue 0.1, orange G 0.6

METHOD: [sections with nuclei stained by DS 11.121 Weigert 1903] → water → *A*, 10 mins. → *B*, 2 mins. → *C*, 10 mins. → *B*, 5 mins. → balsam, via acetone and xylene

13.7 Lonnberg 1891   *carmine-spirit blue*   20796, **6**:1

REAGENTS REQUIRED: *A*. Any DS 11.22 formula; *B*. 0.1% hydrochloric acid in 70% alc.; *C*. sat. 60% alc. sol. spirit blue 100, hydrochloric acid 1 drop; *D*. 85% alc. adjusted with ammonia to pH 8

METHOD: [whole objects] → *A*, till stained → *B*, till differentiated → 70% alc., wash → *C*, 15 mins. → *D*, till violet → balsam, via usual reagents

RECOMMENDED FOR: double staining wholemounts.

13.7 Lopez 1946   *Tech. Bull.*, **7**:53

REAGENTS REQUIRED: *A*. water 100, DS 11.43 Ziehl 1882 10, acetic acid 0.2; *B*. water 100, 40% formaldehyde 4, acetic acid 0.2; *C*. water 100, phosphomolybdic acid 1, anilin blue WS 0.5, methyl orange to sat.

PREPARATION OF C: Dissolve the acid with gentle heat. Add the anilin blue. After complete solution, add an excess of orange. Warm a few minutes. Filter.

METHOD: [sections of formaldehyde material] → water → *A*, 1 min. → wash → *B*, 3 mins. → wash → *C*, ½–1 min. → quick rinse → abs. alc., least possible time → balsam, via xylene

13.7 Lynch 1930   *carmine-indulin*   23632, **46**:465

REAGENTS REQUIRED: *A*. DS 11.22 Grenacher 1879; *B*. hydrochloric acid; *C*. 0.5% hydrochloric acid in 70% alc.; *D*. sat. sol. indulin in 80% alc.

METHOD: [whole objects, preferably mercuric-fixed] → *A*, till thoroughly saturated → add *B*, drop by drop, till brick red ppt. formed; leave 12 hrs. → *C*, till object clear pink → add *D*, drop by drop till solution faint blue, leave till blue round edges → 95% alc., 1 hr. → balsam, via usual reagents

RESULT: thick or dense, structures, red; thin or diffuse structures, blue.

RECOMMENDED FOR: double-staining wholemounts.

13.7 Mallory 1900   *see* DS 11.124 Mallory 1900

13.7 Mann 1892   *see* DS 13.7 Mann 1894a (note)

13.7 Mann 1894a   *methyl blue-eosin*   23632, **11**:490

REAGENTS REQUIRED: *A*. water 55, 1% methyl blue 20, 1% eosin 25; *B*. 0.005% potassium hydroxide in abs. alc.; *C*. 1% eosin

METHOD: [smears or sections] → water → *A*, 24–48 hrs. → water, rinse → abs. alc., till dehydrated → *B*, till red → abs. alc., thorough wash → water → *C*, till differentiated → balsam, via usual reagents

NOTE: **Alzheimer 1910** (Nissl and Alzheimer 1910, 409) gives *A* as water 150 to 35 of each of the dye solutions. Langeron 1942, 598, attributes this formula, without reference, to "1892." **Perdrau 1939** (11431, **48**:609) recommends mordanting in 2% ammonium molybdate before this method.

13.7 Mann 1894b   *toluidine blue-erythrosin*   23632, **11**:489

REAGENTS REQUIRED: *A*. water 100, erythrosin 0.1; *B*. water 100, toluidine blue 1.0; *C*. 0.2% acetic acid

METHOD: [water] → *A*, 1–2 mins. → rinse → *B*, on slide, 1–2 mins. → *C*, till differentiated → balsam, via usual reagents

RESULT: nuclei, cartilage, blue; other structures, polychrome red and violet.

13.7 Masson *test.* **1942 Langeron**   *erythrosin-toluidine blue-orange G*
                                                            Langeron 1942, 613

REAGENTS REQUIRED: *A*. ADS 12.2 Lugol (1905); *B*. 5% sodium thiosulfate; *C*. water 100, erythrosin 0.2, orange G 1; *D*. water 100, toluidine blue 1; *E*. 0.2% acetic acid

METHOD: [sections of F 3700.1000 Helly 1903, F 7000.1000 Orth 1896. or F 3700.0010 Zenker 1894 fixed material] → water → *A*, 30 mins. → *B*, 2 mins. → thorough wash → *C*, 1–2 mins. → rinse → *D*, on slide, 1–2 mins. → *E*, till differentiated → balsam, via usual reagents

RESULT: as 13.7 Mann 1894b but with bacteria deep blue.

13.7 Matsura 1925   *polychrome neutral red*   8542a, **3**:107

REAGENTS REQUIRED: *A*. 1% congo red in 95% alc.; *B*. 1% phosphomolybdic acid in abs. alc.

METHOD: [sections] → *A*, 12–24 hrs. → abs. alc., rinse → *B*, 5 mins. → abs. alc., till differentiated → neutral mountant, via oil of thyrne

RESULT: nuclei, red; elastic fibers, red violet; collagen, green; white blood cells, violet; other tissues, brown.

13.7 Merbel 1877   *carmine-indigo carmine*   645, **1**:242
STOCK SOLUTIONS: I. water 100, sodium borate 7, carmine 1.7; II. water 100, sodium borate 7, indigocarmine 7
PREPARATION OF STOCK SOLUTIONS: Boil 15 minutes. Cool. Filter.
REAGENTS REQUIRED: A. stock I 50, stock II 50; B. sat. sol. oxalic acid
METHOD: [sections of F 7000.0000 Müller 1859 material] → water → A, 15–20 mins. → B, till differentiated → wash → balsam, via usual reagents

13.7 Norris and Shakespeare *test.* **1895 Rawitz**   *carmine-indigocarmine*
                                                          Rawitz 1895, 67
FORMULA: water 130, sodium borate 8, carmine 1, indigocarmine 4
PREPARATION: Boil the carmine in 65 water with 4 borax for 15 minutes. Cool. Filter. Boil indigocarmine in 65 water with 4 borax 5 minutes. Cool. Filter. Mix filtrates. Filter.

13.7 Petersen 1924 *test.* **1946 Roskin**   Roskin 1946, 230
REAGENTS REQUIRED: A. water 100, aluminum sulfate 10, acid alizarin blue 0.5; B. 5% phosphotungstic acid; C. water 100, acetic acid 8, orange G 2, anilin blue 0.5
METHOD: [sections] → water → A, 5 mins. → rinse → B, several minutes → distilled water, rinse → C, 2 mins. → rinse → abs. alc., till dehydrated → balsam, via xylene

13.7 Plehn *test.* **1896 Kahlden and Laurent**   *methyl blue-eosin*
                                                  Kahlden and Laurent 1896, 126
FORMULA: water 20, sat. aq. sol. methyl blue 60, 0.5% eosin in 70% alc. 20, 20% sodium hydroxide 0.5

13.7 Proescher, Zapata and McNaught 1946   *Tech. Bull.*, **7**:50
STOCK SOLUTIONS: I. 0.1% azophloxine; II. DS 11.4 anonymous 1936
WORKING SOLUTION: stock I 60, stock II 30
METHOD: [frozen sections of hot-formaldehyde-fixed materials] → stain, 10–30 secs. → abs. alc., least possible time for dehydration → M 23.1 mountant
RECOMMENDED FOR: rapid staining for diagnosis.

13.7 Roskin 1946   Roskin 1946, 231
REAGENTS REQUIRED: A. 70% alc. 100, hydrochloric acid 1, orcein 1; B. any DS 11.122 formula; C. DS 12.221 van Gieson 1896 100, acetic acid 0.3; D. water 100, C (preceding) 4
METHOD: [sections] → water → A, 1 hr. → wash, 3 mins. → B, till thoroughly overstained → distilled water, 3 mins. → running water, 3 mins. → distilled water, 3 mins. → C, 5 mins. → D, quick rinse → blot → abs. alc., minimum possible time → balsam, via xylene

13.7 Schleicher 1943   *Tech. Bull.*, **4**:35
REAGENTS REQUIRED: A. 0.1% azocarmine B in 5% acetic acid; B. 5% phosphotungstic acid; C. water 100, acetic acid 0.3, orange G 0.13, anilin blue 0.07
METHOD: [sections of F 3700.1000 Helly 1903 fixed material with mercury removed by iodine treatment] → A, 15–30 mins., 56°C. → rinse → B, 15–30 mins. till nuclei deep carmine in pink cytoplasm → rinse → C, 15–30 mins. → rinse → 95% alc., till color clouds cease → balsam, via usual reagents

13.7 Schmorl 1928   *see* DS 21.13 Schmorl 1928

13.7 Shumway 1926   *magenta-picro-indigocarmine*   20540b, **1**:37
REAGENTS REQUIRED: A. sat. sol. (*circ.* 1%) magenta; B. sat. sol. (*circ.* 0.2%) indigo carmine 50, sat. sol. (*circ.* 1.2%) picric acid 50
METHOD: [sections] → water → A, 20 mins. → B, 5 mins. → 70% alc. till pink, few secs. → abs. alc., till blue green, several secs. → balsam, via xylene
RESULT: resting nuclei, dark blue; mitotic figures, dark red; cartilage, pink; procartilage, light blue; bone, dark blue; muscle, bright green; nerves, purple.

13.7 Twort *test.* **Minchin 1909**   *neutral red-light green*   17510, **53**:755
PREPARATION OF DRY STOCK: Dilute 50 sat. sol. (*circ.* 3%) neutral red to 100. Dilute 50 sat. sol. (*circ.* 20%) light green to 100. Mix at 50°C. Cool. Filter. Wash and dry ppt.

WORKING SOLUTION: water 70, propanol 30, dry stock 0.5
METHOD: [sections from F 0000.0010 or F 7000.1000 fixed material] → water → A, 40°C.,
   10 mins. → distilled water, rinse → abs. alc., till differentiated → balsam, via xylene
RESULT: nuclei, purple; blood, green; connective tissues, blue green.
NOTE: *see also* DS 23.3 Twort 1924. Langeron 1942, 565 recommends the addition of 1%
   phenol to the working solution.

13.7 Volkman and Strauss 1934   *azocarmine-naphthol green-crystal violet*
23632, 51:244

REAGENTS REQUIRED: A. DS 21.13 Volkman and Strauss 1933 (*see* DS 21.13 Weigert
   1898—note); B. 0.1% azocarmine in 1% acetic acid; C. 0.1% aniline in 95% alc.; D.
   5% phosphotungstic acid; E. 1% naphthol green B in 1% acetic acid
METHOD: [sections] → water → A, 1–2 hrs. → 70% alc., rinse → wash → B, 30 mins. →
   → C, quick wash → D, till collagen decolorized → wash → E, 15 mins. → wash →
   abs. alc., least possible time → balsam, via xylene
RESULT: nuclei and muscles, red; collagen, green; elastic fibers, black.

13.7 Westphal 1880 *test.* Böhm and Oppel   *carmine-crystal violet*
Böhm and Oppel 1907, 193

FORMULA: water 40, abs. alc. 40, glycerol 20, acetic acid 4, ammonium alum 0.4, carmine 0.4, phenol 0.4, crystal violet 5
PREPARATION: Boil the carmine and alum in the water 15 minutes. Filter. Dissolve the
   crystal violet in the alc. Add to cooled filtrate. Leave overnight. Filter; add the
   glycerol and acid.

13.7 Williams 1935   11284, **20**:1185

PREPARATION OF STAIN: Dissolve 1 cresyl violet and 1 potassium carbonate (anhyd.) in
   95 water and 5 40% formaldehyde. Shake for 30 minutes. Add slowly and with constant agitation, 3 acetic acid. Shake 30 minutes. Filter and add 5 iospropyl alc.
METHOD: [frozen sections of unfixed tissues] → stain, 6 secs. → wash → examine
RESULT: nuclei and muscle, blue; fat, yellow; other tissues, pink.

21

Formulas and Techniques for Dye Stains of Special Application

Decimal Divisions Used in Chapter

DS 20   Dye-Staining Techniques of Special Application

The phrase *dye-staining techniques of special application* is here used in contradistinction to the *dye-staining techniques of general application* which were given in the last chapter. It must not be thought that general techniques are incapable of showing clearly any of the structures or organisms, the special methods for which have been transferred to the present chapter. This chapter has only been organized for the inclusion of those techniques which are so specialized that they cannot justifiably be employed for any other purpose than those recommended for each. It has been felt that, by the removal of these techniques to a special chapter, it would be possible to avoid concealing what are generally considered to be the techniques of wide utility within a mass of special methods. It will be emphasized again and again, in the remarks under the various headings below, that if one desires, say, to stain chitin or plant skeletal tissues one should look first among the generalized techniques; and only when it has been found that these are unsuitable, should recourse be had to those in the present chapter.

These specialized techniques have been divided into three large groups. The first of these (DS 21) includes the techniques for such histological elements as may be required to be stained differentially. This is followed by a section on cytological elements (DS 22), which are defined for the purposes of the present work as cell inclusions not known to be organisms. From time to time a confusion has arisen between mitochondria and bacteria, and there is undoubtedly at present some disagreement as to whether some of the small unidentified bodies—smaller than bacteria—which occur in certain invertebrate cells are actually organisms or cell inclusions of an unidentified function. The third great division (DS 23) comprises selective stains for specific organisms, the majority of which are naturally bacteria and their immediate allies; there are, however, a few other parasites, particularly the fungi, the methods for the selective demonstration of which are too specialized for general use. To preserve continuity of cross reference the dye stains in this chapter are subdivided from DS 20, those in the last chapter having been subdivided from DS 10.

21 SELECTIVE DYE STAINS FOR HISTOLOGICAL ELEMENTS

The justification for this section is that it is occasionally required, for purposes of research or class demonstration, that some special structure should be specifically stained. The techniques given are not intended as general-purpose stains and their use should be confined to those cases in which the demonstration of the particular tissue must outweigh all other considerations. The three histological elements which it is most commonly desired to differentiate are: skeletal tissues (DS 21.1), both plant and animal, nervous tissues (DS 21.2), commonly studied by techniques inapplicable to other purposes, and, to a lesser extent, certain special stains for specific conditions in blood (DS 21.3), which should be separated from the more generally employed blood stains. These three divisions have, however, left a necessity for a fourth division, known here as "special stains for other tissues" (DS 21.4), in which are grouped some highly specialized techniques.

21.1 SPECIAL STAINS FOR SKELETAL TISSUES

The term *skeletal tissue* is here taken in its broadest sense to cover the supporting structures of both plants and animals. The supporting structures of vertebrates are covered in the first three sections, those of invertebrates in the fourth section, and those of plants in the fifth section. This leaves a small division at the end for certain formulas which do not easily fall into any division.

21.10 TYPICAL EXAMPLES

Preparation of a wholemount of a small salamander with the skeleton stained by the alizarin technique of Gray 1929

Though this technique lies on the borderline between the making of microscope slides and the making of museum preparations, the results are sufficiently interesting to warrant inclusion. The technique about to be described deals with the entire skeleton of a small salamander—say Triturus—which is, of course, far too large to mount as a microscope specimen. An exactly similar method of operation, however, applies to the preparation of the skeleton of the hand or arm of a salamander, which can be justifiably regarded as an object for microscopic mounting. The method consists essentially in the deposition of a calcium-alizarin lake on the surface of the bones of the specimen, the muscles and skin of which are subsequently rendered translucent by alkaline hydrolysis, and the replacement of the alkali with glycerol, both to increase the transparency and to render the preparation permanent.

Any small salamander may be used. This is an excellent method of turning experimental animals which die into useful class-demonstration specimens. Each salamander should be permitted to lie untouched after death until it is entirely limp. It must then be mounted on a glass slide to hold it in position through subse-

quent operations. An ordinary $3'' \times 1''$ microscope slide serves excellently for Triturus, but the operator will naturally have little difficulty in adapting this technique to any other amphibian. The specimen is placed flat on the slide and the legs and tail maneuvered into a natural position. Soft silk thread, of the type once used for surgical ligatures, is used to tie the specimen to the glass slide in as many places as possible, so that it will not shift during the hardening operation. These ligatures need not be made too tight, since the object should always be hardened in a horizontal position.

The specimen is now hardened in an iodine solution in alcohol, the exact concentration of which is of little importance. It should be considerably weaker than the solution specified for microscopical preparation, and the suggestion given in the technique below (DS 21.11 Gray 1929) of a 10% dilution of Lugol's iodine in 95% alcohol is approximately correct. The concentration is not critical, and the degree of dilution may be comfortably made by eye rather than by measurement. At least 500 milliliters of this solution should be used for a single salamander, and the author has found it convenient to lay the salamander, or as many salamanders on slides as will fit the dish, in the bottom of a square glass dish of the type commonly known as a refrigerator jar. This jar is then filled with the iodine-alcohol and placed in a dark spot overnight, or until next required. The author has invariably found that if the iodine-alcohol is not used in the dark, the specimen will fall to pieces during the course of subsequent hydrolysis. Though there is no rational basis at present for this observation, he has made it often enough to recommend that it be followed; and he is sure that objections which have been raised to his technique are based on failure to follow this specific instruction. After the specimens have remained in the iodine-alcohol at least overnight they will be found to be so hardened that they may be stood in a vertical position without becoming distorted. They should now (still in the dark) be placed in 95% alcohol for about 24 hours, the alcohol being changed at least once in this period. It is not necessary to remove all of the iodine from the specimen, but this additional hardening in alcohol makes staining easier, and prevents the break-up of the specimen.

Considerable quantities of 5% potassium hydroxide should now be prepared, and about 100 milliliters of this taken for each specimen. To each 100 milliliters add 1 milliliter of a saturated solution of alizarin red S in absolute alcohol. Place the specimens directly from alcohol into this potassium hydroxide-dye mixture to allow the rapid diffusion currents to carry the stain into the bones. The time of exposure to the stain is not very important, though at least 24 hours should be allowed to elapse in the case of Triturus; but the time should be greatly increased if only slightly larger specimens are attempted. *Rana tigrina*, for example, should be left for at least a week in the solution. It must be remembered that the stain will be deposited nowhere save on the bones, but that, unless a thorough impregnation takes place, some of the deeper bones may not become sufficiently pigmented. As the entire process takes some months, it is a pity to find at the conclusion of the period that an additional day in the stain would have avoided wasting the whole lengthy period of preparation.

When the specimens are removed from the staining solution, they will be found to be a dull red all over, and, on examination by transmitted light, the small bones of the limbs will be clearly visible as a darker shadow within the reddish flesh. Now place the specimens in fresh 5% potassium hydroxide, changed as often as it becomes colored pink or brown, until the pink color has been removed from the flesh. This is a dual process, for the hydroxide both hydrolizes the skin and muscle, and removes at the same time the absorbed stain. The muscle under this treatment does not become white but remains a yellowish brown. Care must be taken to distinguish between this inevitable residual yellowish brown color, which is removed in the next treatment, and the pinkish color which results from incomplete removal of the stain. The time for this removal of the excess stain varies with specimens, and it is only a rough estimate to say that about two months will be required for a Triturus and from three to four months for a frog. No harm will result to the specimen should it remain as long as six months in this solution and, if a number are being prepared, they may well be forgotten for this time rather than watched closely.

The next stage is the removal of the residual brownish color from the muscles. No further translucency is imparted during this process of decolorization, which is conducted in equal parts of 5% potassium hydroxide and 1% ammonia. The solution needs to be changed as often as it becomes discolored, and this changing must be continued until the muscles and skin are bleached to a pure white color. The time for this is again variable, but rarely takes more than about two or three months for a frog or five or six weeks for a Triturus.

When the flesh has been bleached, the specimen is placed in 5% potassium hydroxide, which must be changed daily until the smell of ammonia is no longer apparent, and then transferred to 5% potassium hydroxide containing 5% glycerol. After the animal has become thoroughly penetrated by this solution, which may be determined by the fact that no further diffusion currents rise from the specimen, it may be placed in 10% glycerol until diffusion currents cease, and so on through increasing concentrations of glycerol, 10% apart from each other, until it is finally in pure glycerol, of which at least two changes should be used. The specimen is now almost glass-clear and shows bright red bones in a glasslike flesh. It is all too frequently discovered at this stage that one or another of the processes has not been continued long enough. If the bones finally disclosed in the thickest portions of the flesh are found to be insufficiently stained, there is nothing to be done but to throw the specimen away. If, however, nothing is wrong save too much residual brownish color, it is only necessary to wash out the glycerol by immersion in running water overnight and then to replace the specimen in the potassium hydroxide-ammonia mixture.

The specimens are difficult to mount as microscope slides unless one uses glycerol jelly (see Chapter 5). The glycerol-impregnated specimen should be transferred to molten glycerol jelly in a sealed capsule, and kept in it for about a month or until it is completely impregnated. By this time it is probable that the residual alkalis will, however, have hydrolized the glycerol jelly to the point at which it will no longer set; but it is possible, by using a fresh batch of glycerol jelly as a mountant, to secure a fairly permanent preparation. If, of course, one is prepared to take the trouble involved in sealing a glycerol mount (see Chapter 3) the specimen may be mounted in a deep cell in glycerol.

If the specimen is required as a museum preparation it may be sealed in the customary manner in a museum jar of pure glycerol.

Preparation of an embryo salamander to show the cartilagenous skeleton by the method of van Wijhe 1902

Unlike the preparation of a wholemount stained for bone, which has just been described, the present method lends itself better to microscope-slide preparation than it does to museum jar preparation. A salamander larva has been selected for demonstration purposes for the reason that it is convenient to secure, but the same technique may be used with any embryonic material, and it is surprising that so few of these preparations, by which the development, for example, of a chrondrocranium can be so perfectly shown, find their way into the hands of classes.

It does not very much matter what size salamander larva is selected, but a 20-mm. larva of Triturus is not only easy to secure, but is also very generally useful for demonstration purposes. The chief difficulty is in the selection of the fixative,

and though it is stated that alcohol-hardened specimens are satisfactory, the author much prefers to use a mercuric-acetic fixative of the type of Woltereck (Chapter 18, F 3000.0010 Wolterek (1910)). A specimen of the size described should be left in fixative for about 24 hours and should then be washed in a dozen changes of 70% alcohol. It is very important that all the mercuric chloride be removed from the specimen; therefore, it should be transferred from the last wash alcohol to a solution of iodine prepared by adding about 2 milliliters of Lugol's iodine (Chapter 22, ADS 12.2 Lugol 1905) to 100 milliliters of 70% alcohol. The specimen remains in this iodine wash overnight and is then again washed in 70% alcohol until the last trace of color is removed from it. It cannot be too strongly emphasized that a specimen which has been fixed in a picric mixture can never under any circumstances be used for a van Wijhe preparation.

The staining solution (DS 21.12 van Wijhe 1902) contains 0.1% each of toluidine blue and hydrochloric acid in 70% alcohol. The specimen should remain in this solution until it is completely saturated with the color. For the specimen under discussion a period of 24 hours is probably sufficient, but as overstaining cannot occur, a period longer than this may be employed. The subsequent process of differentiation and dehydration is a long one, and it is better to start with a thoroughly stained specimen than to complete a lengthy preparation with the discovery that an additional day's time in the beginning would have saved wasting the whole period. Differentiation consists merely in washing with 0.1% hydrochloric acid in 70% alcohol until no more color comes away. Repeated changes of 70% alcohol can be avoided by taking about a liter for a specimen of the size under discussion, and placing this in a tall, narrow, cylindrical museum jar fitted with a cork from which is suspended a loosely woven cloth bag containing the small embryo. Streams of color will at once start falling from the stained specimen, and when these color streams have ceased, it will be necessary to place the specimen in fresh acid alcohol, of which two changes of a smaller volume may be used to remove the last traces of the toluidine blue. The total time required for differentiation will be from one to two weeks for a specimen of the size indicated, or from three to eight months for a rabbit embryo two inches long.

As soon as differentiation is presumed to be complete, the specimen may be dehydrated, cleared, and mounted. Nothing is necessary to render these specimens permanent other than the maintenance of an acid environment, and it is therefore recommended that 0.1% of hydrochloric acid be added to all the alcohols used for dehydration. The present specimen, which can be prepared as a microscope slide, may then be dehydrated in xylene and mounted in any acid mounting medium, such as an old batch of Canada balsam or one of the synthetic resins to which salicylic acid has been added.

Preparation of cleared museum specimens is a great deal more difficult. The mounting medium employed is usually benzyl benzoate to which has been added 1% of methyl salicylate. The objection to this medium is its sensitivity to water; even a small specimen will require dehydration in many changes of absolute alcohol before it can be mounted.

Preparation of a transverse section of a root using the acid fuchsin-iodine green technique of Chamberlain 1915

This is the simplest of all the preparations described in the present section of the work, and can be unhesitatingly recommended to the beginner who has never previously prepared a section of any type. This preparation is designed only to show the skeletal outlines of the cells, the cytological contents of which are removed in the course of the preparation. If cytological detail in a botanical section specimen is required, reference should be made to the typical preparation of a plant stem described in the last chapter.

It does not matter from what source the root is obtained, but the beginner should select some soft root of about ⅛ inch, or rather less, in diameter. If the root is collected from a living plant, it should be thoroughly washed to remove any adherent sand grains, which would spoil the edge of the cutting knife, and then preserved in 95% alcohol until required. The 95% alcohol should be changed as it becomes discolored, but with this precaution the specimens may be preserved indefinitely.

It is even possible to make preparations of this type from dried roots which have been preserved in a herbarium. The best method of swelling and softening these dried preparations is that recommended by Langeron (Langeron 1942, 1263) which requires a 10% solution of phenol in lactic acid. The lactic acid employed is the ordinary commercial solution, in which the phenol should be dissolved immediately before it is required. Pieces of the dried root are then placed in a reasonably large volume of this material and heated over a low flame to a temperature of about 50°C. Within 10 or 15 minutes a completely dried herbarium specimen will have become swollen out to its normal size and softened to the extent that sections may readily be cut from it.

The method of sectioning does not particularly matter, but since the sections cannot in any case be subjected to the first process while they are attached to the slide, there is no real advantage in embedding in paraffin and cutting in this medium if an ordinary hand microtome is available. Sections can be taken from this microtome by (see Chapter 9) holding them either in pieces of pith or between the cut halves of a carrot. If the sections are cut by hand, they may be transferred immediately after they are cut to a dish of 20% alcohol, and from there to water; if they are cut in paraffin they should be at least 20 microns in thickness, and the ribbon, as it is removed from the microtome, should be dropped directly into a watch glass of xylene in which the paraffin will dissolve. The individual sections are then removed from the xylene with a section lifter, passed through absolute alcohol for the removal of the xylene, and thence downgraded through alcohols until they reach water. By whatever method the sections are produced, they are accumulated in a small dish of distilled water. These sections will, of course, retain the cell contents, which must be removed in order that the section may be turned into a true skeleton.

The best reagent to use for skeletonizing a section of plant tissue is either potassium or sodium hypochlorite; the ordinary bleaching solutions sold for household purposes under various trade names are not suitable, since they contain considerable quantities of calcium hypochlorite. If, however, the pure salts are not available, the household solution may be employed by adding to it enough of a solution of potassium or sodium carbonate to precipitate the calcareous contents, and then filtering the solution before use. If the pure salts are available, a 1% solution may conveniently be employed.

The sections are removed from the distilled water on a section lifter and transferred to a watch glass of the sodium or potassium hypochlorite solution. If the sections are made from material which has been preserved in alcohol, this solution should be used cold, but it must usually be warmed if it is to have the desired effect on materials which have been resurrected from a dried condition. In either case the operation should be watched very carefully under a low power of the microscope, and the action of the hypochlorite should be discontinued as soon as the cells are free of their contents. If the mounter is completely inexperienced in this field, and is unable to determine the point at which the operation should be stopped, it is recommended that a single section should be taken and the skeletonizing followed under a microscope while it is timed. When the operation has gone too far, the finer of the cell walls present will be dissolved by the solution. If the period at which the first of the cell walls dissolves is carefully recorded, and one-half of this time taken for the subsequent sections, they will be perfectly cleaned without the slightest risk of damage to their walls. After they are removed from the hypochlorite solution, the sections should be thoroughly washed in several changes of distilled water and then passed into 1%

acetic acid in which they are rinsed several times. They are then rewashed in ordinary water until the wash water no longer smells of acetic acid. The skeletonized sections from as many roots as it is desired to cut at one time should be accumulated in water until one is ready to stain them, or they may be preserved indefinitely in alcohol.

The stain which is recommended in the present case (DS 21.15 Chamberlain 1915a) is freshly prepared when required by mixing equal parts of a 0.2% acid fuchsin solution and a 0.2% iodine green solution. The mixed stains do not remain usable for much longer than one day, but the separate stock solutions may be kept indefinitely. The differentiating solution, which is 1% acetic acid in absolute alcohol containing 0.1% iodine, is also stable. The staining solution should be placed in a small capped vial or stoppered bottle, and the sections transferred to it from the water. They should remain in stain for about 24 hours, and it is recommended that they should not be left longer than 36 hours or they may suffer from a precipitate over the surface. For this reason it is desirable to accumulate as many sections as possible before starting the process. When the staining period is concluded the contents of the vial should be tipped out into a large watch glass. Usually some of the sections will remain stuck to the side of the vial from which they are removed. Under no circumstances should the vial be rinsed with anything except the staining solution, which should be poured back from the watch glass (the sections will have settled to the bottom), swirled around, and returned to the watch glass. A second watch glass, or even a small crystallizing dish, is now filled with the differentiating solution. Each section is removed individually with a section lifter from the stain and placed into the differentiating solution, where it may be watched under the low power of a microscope as the dish is rocked gently from side to side. Differentiation will usually take place within two or three minutes and is terminated when the lignified tissues are a bright, clear green, leaving a bright red in the nonlignified tissues. This process of differentiation is also one of dehydration, hence the sections may now be removed with a section lifter from the differentiating solution and placed in a clearing agent. The writer's preference in this method is for terpineol, which has all the advantages of clove oil without the disadvantage of tending to make the sections brittle so that they crack on mounting. All the sections may be passed through the differentiating solution and accumulated in terpineol, where they may remain until removed to a slide. Here they are covered with balsam and a coverslip is added.

Sections prepared in this manner are permanent, and the process is so simple that it can be most warmly recommended as an introduction to plant section-staining techniques for an elementary class. The sections are, however, clearly enough differentiated to be used for instructing a class at any rank, and they will generally be found much better for this purpose than complex quadruple-stained sections in which the cytological detail all too often tends to obscure the clarity of morphological detail, which is the chief requirement in this type of teaching.

21.11 BONE AND CALCIFIED TISSUES

The techniques in the present section and in the section immediately following, comprise a rather miscellaneous group, for they include both the methods intended for the staining of skeletons in wholemounts, and methods developed differentially to stain skeletal structures in serial sections intended for reconstruction.

None of these methods need be employed in those cases in which it is desired to provide a good general stain of a section, the other tissues of which should appear in contrast. Most of the methods in sections DS 12.3, DS 13.2, and DS 13.4 in the last chapter give clear differentiation of bone from cartilage in general sections. The writer's choice is for the technique of Patay 1934 (Chapter 20—DS 12.32) in which decalcified bone is stained a brilliant green in contrast to the blue of the cartilage.

21.11 Bechtol 1948   20540b, **23**:3
REAGENTS REQUIRED: A. 0.01% Biebrich scarlet; B. water 100, citric acid 2.1, methylene blue 0.001; C. 2.1% citric acid
METHOD: [formaldehyde-fixed and hydrogen-peroxide-bleached, specimens] → water → A, 24 hrs. → 95% alc., till no more color comes away → B, 24 hrs. → C, till differentiated → balsam, via usual reagents
RECOMMENDED FOR: differentiation of bone (red) and cartilage (blue) in wholemounts.

21.11 Bock 1924a   23632, **40**:318
REAGENTS REQUIRED: A. DS 11.121 Hansen 1905; B. glycerol 50, acetic acid 50; C. 1% eosin B in 95% alc.
METHOD: [sections of material fixed in F 7000.1000 Bock 1924 and decalcified in AF 21.1 von Ebner (1891)] → water → A, 12–18 hrs. → thorough wash → B, till bone alone remains stained, 5–30 mins. → running water, 1 hr. → C, ½–2 mins. → balsam, via usual reagents

21.11 Bock 1924b   23632, **40**:318
REAGENTS REQUIRED: A. F 7000.1000 Bock 1924; B. AF 21.1 von Ebner 1890; C. 5% potassium alum; D. DS 11.124 Hansen 1905; E. glycerol 50, acetic acid 50; F. 0.4% eosin Y in 95% alc.
METHOD: [fresh tissues] → A, 1 wk. to 1 month → B, till decalcified → rinse → C, 24 hrs. → running water, 1–2 days → [10 μ celloidin sections] → D, 18 hrs. → E, till differentiated 5–20 mins. → running water 1 hr. → F, 5 mins. → 95% of alc., wash → balsam, via usual reagents
RECOMMENDED FOR: demonstration of osteogenesis in decalcified tissues.

21.11 Crétin 1937   4285a, **14**:163
REAGENTS REQUIRED: A. ADS 12.2 Crétin 1937; B. water 100, hematoxylin 1.2, alizarin red S 6, phosphomolybic acid 0.04
METHOD: [sections of decalcified bone fixed in F 5000.1020 Crétin 1937] → water → A, 36 hrs. → wash → B, 1–24 hrs. → wash → balsam, via usual reagents

21.11 Dawson 1926   20540b, **1**:123

REAGENTS REQUIRED: *A.* 1% potassium hydroxide; *B.* water 100, potassium hydroxide 1, alizarin red S 0.01; *C.* P 13.1 Mall 1902

METHOD: [alc. fixed embryos] → *A*, till bones clearly visible → *B*, till bones red → *C*, till impregnated → glycerol, via graded series

RECOMMENDED FOR: staining bones in whole mammalian embryos.

21.11 Erös 1928   23681, **42**:97

REAGENTS REQUIRED: *A.* water 100, acid fuchsin 1, potassium alum to sat.; *B.* 3% nitric acid in 95% alc.

METHOD: [sections] → water → *A*, 10–15 mins. → rinse → *B*, till differentiated, 1–12 hrs. → balsam, via usual reagents

RECOMMENDED FOR: selective staining of once calcified areas in sections of decalcified material.

21.11 Grandis and Magnini 1900   1852, **34**:73

REAGENTS REQUIRED: *A.* sat. alc. sol. purpurin; *B.* 0.5% sodium chloride

METHOD: [sections] → 95% alc. → *A*, 5–10 mins. → *B*, 3–5 mins. → 70% alc., till no more color comes away → balsam, via usual reagents

RECOMMENDED FOR: differential staining of decalcified bone.

21.11 Gray 1929a   14706, **9**:341

FORMULA: sat. sol. sodium borate in 70% alc. 100, sat. sol. (*circ.* 0.5%) alizarin red S in abs. alc. 1

METHOD: [material, fixed and stored in neutralized formaldehyde] → running water, 24 hrs. → 70% alc., till saturated → stain, till calcified structures clearly differentiated, $\frac{1}{2}$ to 12 hrs. → graded alcs., each saturated with sodium borate → benzene → neutral mountant

RECOMMENDED FOR: bony skeletons in wholemounts of material too delicate for Gray 1929b.

21.11 Gray 1929b   14706, **9**:341

REAGENTS REQUIRED: *A.* ADS 12.2 Lugol (1905) 10, 95% alc. 90; *B.* 5% potassium hydroxide 100, potassium hydroxide 50, 1% ammonium hydroxide 50

METHOD: [freshly killed material] → *A*, 24 hrs. at least, in dark → 95% alc., 24 hrs., in dark → *B*, 24 hrs. → *C*, changed as frequently as it becomes colored, till red bones distinctly visible through yellowish translucent muscle (roughly dissected fish vertebra, 24 hrs.; whole frog 3 to 4 months) → *C*, till muscle pure white, 6 hrs. to 1 month → glycerol mixtures when shrinkage must be avoided

RESULT: as gray 1929a.

NOTE: Omission of step *A* is invariably fatal. A detailed description of a preparation by this method is given under DS 21.10 above.]

21.11 Grieves *test. circ.* **1938 Wellings**   Wellings *circ.* 1938, 160

REAGENTS REQUIRED: *A.* water 99, DS 23.213 Carpano 1916 1; *B.* acetone

METHOD: [ground section of balsam embedded (see Chapter 10) formaldehyde fixed tooth] → 20% alc., 15 mins. → *A*, 12–24 hrs. → rinse → *B*, till differentiated → dammar, via oil of bergamot

RECOMMENDED FOR: structure of dentine.

21.11 Hanazava 1917   7141, **59**:125

REAGENTS REQUIRED: water 10, DS 11.43 Ziehl 1882 10

METHOD: [ground sections of teeth] → water → stain, 10 mins. → 95% alc. till differentiated → balsam, via usual reagents

RECOMMENDED FOR: dentine.

21.11 Juge 1940   19288, **47**:65

REAGENTS REQUIRED: *A.* water 30, 95% alc. 70, acetic acid 0.06, methyl green 3; *B.* abs. alc. 100, acetic acid 0.2, alizarin red S 0.003

METHOD: [formaldehyde-fixed pieces] → 70% alc., 1 day → *A*, 1–3 hrs. → 70% alc., till cartilage alone stained → abs. alc., till dehydrated → *B*, 12–24 hrs. → abs. alc., till no more color comes away → balsam, via usual reagents

RECOMMENDED FOR: differential staining of bone (red) and cartilage (green) in wholemounts.

21.11 Klaatsch *test.* **1896 Kahlden and Laurent**   Kahlden and Laurent 1896, 178

    REAGENTS REQUIRED: *A*. water 100, hematoxylin 1, picric acid 1; *B*. 1% acetic acid
    METHOD: [sections] → *A*, 1–2 mins. → *B*, 30 secs. → balsam, via usual reagents
    RESULT: cartilage, blue; bone, yellow.

21.11 Kölliker *test.* **1928 Schmorl**   Schmorl 1928, 263

    REAGENTS REQUIRED: *A*. acetic acid; *B*. sat. aq. sol. indigo-carmine
    METHOD: [sections of decalcified bone] → *A*, till transparent → *B*, 15–60 secs. → wash,
    till differentiated → balsam, via usual reagents

21.11 von Korff 1907   1780, **69**:515

    REAGENTS REQUIRED: A, water 100, glycerol 7, acid fuchsin 2, orange G 1
    METHOD: [sections of chrome, or dichromate, fixed materials] → water → *A*, 1 min. →
    95% alc., till differentiated → balsam, via usual reagents
    RECOMMENDED FOR: histogenesis of bone and teeth.
    RESULT: osteoblasts and odontoblasts, orange; fibrils in degenerating cartilage, red;
    other tissues, yellow.

21.11 Lundvall 1927a   766, **62**:353

    REAGENTS REQUIRED: *A*. 1% ammonia; *B*. 4% formaldehyde; *C*. 0.02% alizarin red S in
    90% alc.
    METHOD: [embryos, or small vertebrates, fixed and bleached in AF 31.1 Lundvall 1927]
    → *A*, 24 hrs. or till all acid neutralized → *B*, 24 hrs. or till all ammonia removed →
    95% alc., till formaldehyde removed → *C*, 1–2 days → 95% alc., till no more color
    comes away → [benzyl benzoate, via abs. alc. and benzene for museum mounts] *or*
    → balsam, via usual reagents, for microscope slides
    RECOMMENDED FOR: demonstration of bone and calcified structures in wholemounts.

21.11 Lundvall 1927b   766, **62**:353

    STOCK SOLUTIONS: I. 0.1% toluidine blue in 95% alc. II. water 30, 95% alc. 69, acetic
    acid 1, alizarin red S 0.02
    REAGENTS REQUIRED: *A*. 1% ammonia; *B*. 4% formaldehyde; *C*. water 15, 95% alc. 35,
    acetic acid 0.5, stock I 10, stock II 40; *D*. 0.01% acetic acid
    METHOD: [embryos, or small vertebrates, fixed and bleached in AF 31.1 Lundvall 1927]
    → *A*, 24 hrs., or till all acid neutralized → *B*, 24 hrs., or till all ammonia removed →
    A, 1 day, 40°C. → *D*, till no more color comes away → 70% alc., till no more color
    comes away → 95% alc. thorough wash → [benzyl benzoate, via abs. alc. and ben-
    zene, for museum specimens] *or* → balsam, via usual reagents, for microscope slides
    RECOMMENDED FOR: demonstration of both cartilage (blue) and bone (red) in whole-
    mounts.

21.11 Morpugo 1908 *test.* **1928 Schmorl**   Schmorl 1928, 269

    REAGENTS REQUIRED: *A*. sat. sol. lithium carbonate; *B*. 0.025% thionin 100, ammonia
    0.1; *C*. sat. sol. phosphotungstic acid; *D*. sat. sol. picric acid
    METHOD: [celloidin sections of F 7000.0000 Müller 1859 fixed, and nitric acid decalcified,
    bone] → water, thorough wash → *A*, 1 min. → *B*, 3–5 mins. → wash → *C*, 5 mins. →
    D, 2–3 mins. → rinse → 95% alc. → balsam, via usual reagents

21.11 Nollister 1934   20540b (abstr. 1935), **10**:37

    STOCK SOLUTION: water 96.5, glycerol 13, acetic acid 3.5, chloral hydrate 0.8, alizarin
    red S to sat.
    REAGENTS REQUIRED: *A*. 1 to 4% potassium hydroxide; *B*. 1–4% potassium hydroxide
    100, stock 0.1
    METHOD: [whole fish] → *A*, till translucent → *B*, till bones stained → *A* + increasing
    quantities of glycerol under UV light till bleached and clear → pure glycerol

21.11 Rait 1935   11139b, **19**:80

    FORMULA: 70% alc. 100, 1% acetic acid 1, sat. sol. alizarin in abs. alc. 5
    METHOD: [material, fixed and stored in 10% formaldehyde, adjusted with sodium
    borate to pH 9] → running water, 24 hrs. → 70% alc., till saturated → stain, 12–24
    hrs. → 70% alc., wash → neutral mountant, via usual reagents

21.11 von Recklinghausen *test.* **1928 Schmorl**   Schmorl 1928, 266
REAGENTS REQUIRED: *A.* 0.1% thionine; *B.* sat. sol. phosphomolybdic acid in glycerol
C. 2% hydroquinone in glycerol; *D.* 3% phenol in sat. sol. potassium alum.; *E.* sat.
sol. hydroquinone; *F.* anhydrous glycerol; *G.* toluene 60, abs. alc. 30
METHOD: [hand or ground sections of nondecalcified bone preserved in P12.3 Kaiserling
1897] → *A*, till deep blue → rinse → *B*, overnight → *C*, till no more color comes away
→ *D*, 1–2 hrs. → thorough wash → *E*, thorough wash → wash → *F*, till dehydrated
→ *G*, till glycerol removed → balsam, via toluene
RECOMMENDED FOR: general bone structure.

21.11 Roehl *test.* **1933 Cajal and de Castro**   Cajal and de Castro 1933, 314
REAGENTS REQUIRED: *A.* copper tetramine solution (see note below); *B.* DS 11.121
Weigert 1904; *C.* ADS 21.1 Weigert 1885 50, water 50
METHOD: [paraffin sections] → *A*, 5 mins. → wash → *B*, 15 mins. → rinse → *C*, till
differentiated → wash → balsam, via usual reagents
RECOMMENDED FOR: pathological calcareous deposits.
NOTE: Copper tetramine is prepared by adding sufficient ammonium hydroxide to a
solution of a copper salt to redissolve the ppt. first formed; neither Cajal and de
Castro (*loc. cit.*) nor Schmorl 1928, 196 specify the strength of the solution.

21.11 Schmorl 1928a   Schmorl 1928, 265
REAGENTS REQUIRED: *A.* 0.1% thionin; *B.* sat. sol. phosphotungstic acid; *C.* 20%
formaldehyde
METHOD: [paraffin sections of decalcified bone] → water, thorough wash → *A*, 5 mins.
→ wash → 95% alc., 1–2 mins. → wash → *B*, till differentiated, few moments →
wash → *C*, 1–2 mins. → 95% alc. → balsam, via usual reagents
RECOMMENDED FOR: general bone structure.

21.11 Schmorl 1928b   Schmorl 1928, 266
REAGENTS REQUIRED: *A.* 0.1% thionin; *B.* sat. sol. phosphotungstic acid; *C.* 5% potas-
sium alum
METHOD: [paraffin sections of bone fixed in formaldehyde, hardened in F 7000.0000
Müller 1850 and decalcified in AF 21.1 Schmorl] → water, thorough wash → *A*, 10–
30 mins. → wash → 95% alc., 1–3 mins. → wash → *B*, 10–25 mins. → wash, 2 hrs.
→ *C*, 1–2 hrs. → running water, 3–12 hrs. → balsam, via usual reagents
RECOMMENDED FOR: demonstration of lamellae.

21.11 Schmorl 1889   23681, **10** :745
REAGENTS REQUIRED: *A.* DS 11.44 Nicolle 1871; *B.* sat. sol. picric acid
METHOD: [celloidin sections] → water → *A*, 5–10 mins. → wash → *B*, ½–1 min. →
thorough wash → 70% alc. till no more color comes away → balsam, via usual
reagents
RESULT: pro-cartilage, yellow; cartilage, blue; bone, brown black.

21.11 True 1947   20540b, **22** :107
REAGENTS REQUIRED: *A.* water 100, potassium hydroxide 5, hydrogen peroxide (3%)
0.1; *B.* 0.01% alizarin red S in 2% hydroxide
METHOD: [vertebrate embryos] → *A*, till bones clearly visible → *B*, till bones red →
glycerol, via graded series
RECOMMENDED FOR: bones in wholemounts.

21.11 Weil *test. circ.* **1938 Wellings**   Wellings *circ.* 1938, 156
REAGENTS REQUIRED: *A.* sat. aq. sol. mercuric chloride; *B.* 0.1% iodine in 90% alc.; *C.*
DS 11.22 Grenacher 1879; *D.* 1% hydrochloric acid in 70% alc.; *E.* 40% dried Canada
balsam in chloroform
METHOD: [1 mm. slices of tooth] → *A*, 6–8 hrs. → wash → 70% alc. via graded alcs. →
B, 12 hrs. → abs. alc., till decolorized → water, till rehydrated → *C*, 3–7 days → *D*,
24 hrs. → abs. alc., via graded alcs., till dehydrated → chloroform, 24 hrs. → *E*, till
impregnated → evaporate till hard → [grind section (see Chapter 10)]
RECOMMENDED FOR: structure of dentine.

NOTE: The method of **Must and Rose** (Wellings, *op. cit.* 158) differs only in that whole teeth, ground on each side to expose the pulp, are used. The method of **Choquet** (Wellings, *op. cit.*, 158) substitutes formaldehyde fixation for mercuric fixation.

21.11 Williams 1941   20540b, **16**:23

REAGENTS REQUIRED: A. 0.1% ammonia; B. water 30, 95% alc. 70, hydrochloric acid 0.05, toluidine blue 0.25; C. 2% potassium hydroxide; D. 2% potassium hydroxide 100, sat. sol. (*circ.* 0.5%) alizarin red S in abs. alc. 0.5; E. 1% sulfuric acid in 95% alc.
METHOD: [formaldehyde-fixed pieces] $\rightarrow$ A, 24 hrs. $\rightarrow$ B, 1 wk. $\rightarrow$ 95% alc. changed daily, 3 days $\rightarrow$ C, till bones visible $\rightarrow$ D, 24 hrs. $\rightarrow$ E, till soft tissues colorless $\rightarrow$ balsam, via usual reagents
RECOMMENDED FOR: demonstration of cartilage (blue) and bone (red) in wholemounts.

21.11 Williams 1946   20540b, **21**:55

REAGENTS REQUIRED: A. 3% potassium hydroxide; B. 2% potassium hydroxide 100, alizarin S $q.s$ to color red; C. 1% sulfuric acid in 95% alc.
METHOD: [pieces of formaldehyde-fixed skin] $\rightarrow$ A, 3 days $\rightarrow$ B, 24 hrs. $\rightarrow$ C, (if differentiation required) $\rightarrow$ wash $\rightarrow$ balsam, via usual reagents
RECOMMENDED FOR: placoid, ctenoid, and cycloid scales.

21.12   CARTILAGE

21.12 Bechtol 1948   *see* DS 21.11 Bechtol 1948

21.12 Becher 1921   *see* DS 13.5 Becher 1921a

21.12 Curtis 1905   *see* DS 12.21 Curtis 1905

21.12 Johansen 1932   *see* DS 11.45 Johansen 1932

21.12 Juge 1940   *see* DS 21.11 Juge 1940

21.12 Klaatsch (1896)   *see* DS 21.11 Klaatsch (1896)

21.12 LaCour 1931   *see* DS 11.45 LaCour 1931

21.12 Lundvall 1927   766, 62, 353

REAGENTS REQUIRED: A. water 30, 95% alc. 70, hydrochloric acid 1, toluidine blue 0.25; B. 0.25% hydrochloric acid in 70% alc.
METHOD: [embryos or small vertebrates fixed and bleached in AF 31.1 Lundvall 1927] $\rightarrow$ 95% alc., wash $\rightarrow$ A, 1 day, 40°C. $\rightarrow$ B, changed when necessary, 40°C., till no more color comes away $\rightarrow$ 95% alc., thorough wash $\rightarrow$ [benzyl benzoate, via abs. alc. and benzene for museum specimens] *or* $\rightarrow$ balsam, via usual reagents, for microscope slides
RECOMMENDED FOR: demonstration of cartilage in wholemounts.

21.12 Miller 1921   *see* DS 21.12 van Wijhe 1902 (note)

21.12 Newton 1927   *see* DS 11.45 Newton 1927

21.12 Semichon *test.* 1934 Langeron   Langeron 1934, 999

FORMULA: water 100, phenol 1, 95% alc. 1, Bismarck brown 0.1
PREPARATION: grind the dye in a mortar with the phenol. Add alc. while grinding. Wash out with 10 successive doses of water.
METHOD: [water] $\rightarrow$ stain, 10 mins. $\rightarrow$ 95% alc., till differentiated $\rightarrow$ balsam, via cedar oil
RESULT: cartilage, dark brown.
NOTE: Langeron (*loc. cit.*) recommends preliminary staining in hemalum and counterstaining in light green. This defeats the purpose of the technique, which is to render easier the reconstruction from serial sections, of cartilaginous skeletons.

21.12 van Wijhe 1902   16592, **31**:47

REAGENTS REQUIRED: A. 70% alc. 100, hydrochloric acid 0.1, toluidine blue 0.1; B. 0.1% hydrochloric acid in 70% alc.; C. 0.1% hydrochloric acid in abs. alc.; D. benzyl benzoate 99, methyl salicylate 1

METHOD: [whole embryos] → running water, 24 hrs. → 70% alc., till saturated → A, 24 hrs. → B, till no more color comes away → C, till dehydrated → salicylic balsam, via benzene *or* [(large embryos) → D, till cleared]

RECOMMENDED FOR: cartilage in wholemounts.

NOTE: Mercuric-fixed embryos, perfectly washed, are best. Picric-fixed material is worthless. A detailed description of the application of this stain is given under DS 21.10 above. **Miller 1921** (763, **20**:415) first bleaches in alcoholic peroxide and uses specially purified alcohol.

21.12 Williams 1941   *see* DS 21.11 Williams 1941

21.13 ELASTIC FIBERS

Much attention has been paid to the differential staining of elastic elements. Most of the techniques rely on the mordanting power of resorcinol, to which attention was originally drawn by Weigert in 1898. These methods stain even the finest fibers of elastic tissue a relatively dense black, and are thus primarily intended for the display of individual elastic fibers running through cartilage and similar structures. The technique of Krajian 1934, on the contrary, is designed to distinguish large masses of elastic tissue from other connective tissues through the differential staining of the elastic fibers in red against blue. The early method of Pfitzner 1887 also deserves retention, since it can be employed after chrome fixatives, when resorcinol techniques do not take well. The method of Pasini (1928) (Chapter 20, DS 12.32) is also used for this purpose, particularly in the sections destined for class demonstration, though the differentiation of fibers is not as good as the methods here given.

21.13 Argaud 1923   6630, **891**:373

FORMULA: 95% alc. 100, orcein to sat, hydrochloric acid 5

METHOD: [sections] → 95% alc. → stain, few moments → abs. alc., wash → balsam, via xylene

21.13 Delamare 1905   *see* DS 13.7 Delamare 1905

21.13 Fraenkel *test.* **1928 Schmorl**   Schmorl 1928, 70

STOCK SOLUTION: 95% alc. 60, water 30, nitric acid 3, orcein 0.75

REAGENTS REQUIRED: A. 3% nitric acid 90, stock 10; B. DS 12.211 Cajal 1895; C. 3.5% acetic acid

METHOD: [sections] → water → 80% alc., till differentiated → B, 10–15 min. → C, rinse → 95% alc., rinse → abs. alc. → balsam via xylene

21.13 French 1929   20540b, **4**:11

FORMULA OF DRY STOCK: water 100, crystal violet 0.5, magenta 0.5, dextrin 0.25, resorcinol 2, 30% ferric chloride 12.5

PREPARATION OF DRY STOCK: Boil together everything except the ferric chloride which is added to boiling solution. Continue boiling 2–5 minutes. Cool. Filter. Wash and dry ppt.

FORMULA OF WORKING SOLUTION: 95% alcohol 100, dry stock 3, hydrochloric acid 2

PREPARATION OF WORKING SOLUTION: Boil the powder 5 minutes in alc. Cool. Filter. Add acid and make up to 100 with alc.

METHOD: [sections] → water → stain ½ to 3 hrs. → 95% alc. till differentiated → balsam, via usual reagents

RESULT: elastin, dark bluish green.

21.13 French 1940   *see* DS 22.4 French 1940

21.13 Gallego-Garcia 1936 *test.* **1936 Findlay**   11360, **56**:160

REAGENTS REQUIRED: A. 0.5% anilin blue; B. 1% eosin Y

METHOD: [frozen sections of formaldehyde material] → A, 10 mins. → wash → B, 10 mins., wash → M 11.1 Apathy 1892

21.13 Goldmann *test.* **1896 Kahlden and Laurent**   Kahlden and Laurent 1896, 144
REAGENTS REQUIRED: *A.* sat. alc. sol. crystal violet; *B.* 0.01% potassium hydroxide in
95% alc.
METHOD: [sections] → *A*, 24 hrs. → 95% alc., rinse → *B*, till differentiated → balsam,
via usual reagents

21.13 Gomori 1950   *aldehyde-fuchsin—auct.*   *Tech. Bull.*, **20**:665
FORMULA: water 30, 95% alc. 70, magenta 0.5, hydrochloric acid 1, paraldehyde 1
METHOD: [paraffin sections] → 95% alc. → stain (aged at least 24 hrs.) 5–10 mins. → 95%
alc., wash → balsam, via usual reagents
NOTE: This stain will also differentiate mast cells, cells of the pancreas (15–20 minutes
in stain), certain cells in the pituitary (30 minutes–2 hours in stain).

21.13 Hart 1908   23681, **19**:1
REAGENTS REQUIRED: *A.* DS 11.28 Orth (1892); *B.* water 30, 95% alc. 70, DS 21.13
Weigert 1898 (working sol.) 5, hydrochloric acid 1
METHOD: [sections] → water → *A*, 2–5 mins. → *B*, 12–15 hrs. → wash → balsam, via
usual reagents

21.13 Hart 1908   23681, **19**:1
REAGENTS REQUIRED: *A.* 0.25% potassium permanganate; *B.* 5% oxalic acid; *C.* water
75, 95% alc., 25, DS 21.13 Weigert 1898 (working sol.) 5, hydrochloric acid 1
METHOD: [sections] → *A*, 10 mins. → wash → *B*, 20 mins. → wash → *C*, overnight →
95% alc., rinse → wash → counterstain, if desired → balsam, via usual reagents

21.13 Herxheimer 1886   8645, **4**:785
REAGENTS REQUIRED: *A.* abs. alc. 50, hematoxylin 2.5, water 50, lithium carbonate 0.04;
B. 20% ferric chloride
METHOD: [sections] → water → *A*, 5 mins. to 1 hr. → rinse → *B*, till fibers differentiated
→ wash → balsam, via usual reagents

21.13 Krajian 1934   1789a, **18**:378
REAGENTS REQUIRED: *A.* 2% aluminum chloride; *B.* water 80, sodium citrate 4, neutral
red 3, glycerol 20; *C.* ADS 12.2 Lugol (1905); *D.* water 100, anilin blue 1.5, orange G
2.5, resorcinol 3, phosphomolybdic acid 1
METHOD: [sections of formaldehyde-fixed material] → *A*, 10 mins. → water, rinse → *B*,
30 mins. → water, rinse → *C*, 30 secs. → water, rinse → *D*, 30 mins. → water, rinse
→ abs. alc., minimum possible time → balsam, via oil of thyme and xylene
RESULT: elastic fibers, bright red; other connective tissues, dark blue.

21.13 Kultschitzky 1895   1780, **46**:675
FORMULA: 95% alc. 100, water 5, potassium carbonate 0.05, magdala red 2, methylene
blue 1
USE: elastic fibers in sections of F 7000.0000 Müller 1859 fixed material
NOTE: Conn 1946, p. 112 points out that Kultschitzky (*loc. cit.*) may have used phloxine
rather than magdala red.

21.13 Mallory 1938   *see* DS 22.8 Mallory 1938

21.13 Manchot *test.* **1896 Kahlden and Laurent**   Kahlden and Laurent 1896, 144
REAGENTS REQUIRED: *A.* sat. aq. sol magenta; *B.* water 100, sucrose 100, sulfuric acid 2
METHOD: [sections] → water → *A*, 30 secs. → rinse → *B*, till differentiated M 11 or 12
mountant

21.13 Pfitzner 1887   23632, **4**:82
FORMULA: abs. alc. 100, safranin 10
METHOD: [sections of chrome-fixed material] → stain, 48 hrs., 40°C. → water, wash →
balsam, via usual reagents
RESULT: elastic fibers black on gray.
NOTE: This may be used only after chrome fixation.

21.13 Pranter *test.* **1905 Hall and Herxheimer**   Hall and Herxheimer 1905, 86
FORMULA: water 30, 95% alc. 70, nitric acid 2, orcein 0.1
METHOD: as Unna-Taenzer (1896)

21.13 Romeis 1948 *see* DS 13.7 Romeis 1938

21.13 Roskin 1946 *see* DS 13.7 Roskin 1946

21.13 Rubens-Duval *test.* **1938 Carleton and Leach**   Carleton and Leach 1938, 220
FORMULA: water 70, 95% alc. 30, nitric acid 10, orcein 0.1
METHOD: water → stain, 24 hrs. → wash → balsam, via usual reagents

21.13 Schmorl 1928a   Schmorl 1928, 168
REAGENTS REQUIRED: *A.* DS 21.13 Weigert 1898 (working sol.); *B.* DS 11.121 Weigert 1904; *C.* DS 12.221 Weigert 1904
METHOD: [sections] → water → *A*, ½–1 hr. → 95%, till differentiated, ½–1 hr. → water → *B*, 5–10 mins. → wash → *C*, till differentiated → balsam, via usual reagents

21.13 Schmorl 1928b   Schmorl 1928, 168
REAGENTS REQUIRED: *A.* DS 11.28 Orth (1892); *B.* DS 21.13 Weigert 1898 (working sol.) *C.* DS 21.41 Weigert 1887 (*A* solution); *D.* 0.6% hydrochloric acid; *E.* ADS 11.1 Gram 1880; *F.* aniline 60, xylene 30
METHOD: [sections] → water → *A*, 2–5 mins. → 95% alc., wash → *B*, 10–30 mins. → 95% alc. till differentiated → wash → *C*, 5–10 mins. → *D*, wash → *E*, 5 mins. → blot → *F*, till differentiated → balsam, via xylene
RECOMMENDED FOR: differentiation of elastic fibers in tissues containing Gram-positive bacteria.
NOTE: Bismarck brown may be substituted for magenta in the preparation of *B* above.

21.13 Schmorl 1928c   Schmorl 1928, 168
REAGENTS REQUIRED: *A.* DS 11.43 Ziehl 1882; *B.* DS 21.13 Weigert 1898 (working sol.); *C.* 1% methylene blue
METHOD: [sections] → water → *A*, 1 hr., 37°C. → 70% alc., wash → *B*, 20–30 mins. → abs. alc. till differentiated → water → *C*, 5–10 mins. → wash → balsam, via usual reagents
RECOMMENDED FOR: differentiation of elastic fibers in tissues without destaining acid-fast bacteria.

21.13 Schmorl 1928d   Schmorl 1928, 169
REAGENTS REQUIRED: *A.* DS 11.28 Orth (1892); *B.* 1% hydrochloric acid in 70% alc.; *C.* sat. sol. crystal violet in sat. sol. aniline; *D. Vesuvelin* (*see* DS 21.13 Weigert 1898, note)
METHOD: [sections] → water → *A*, 10–20 mins. → *B*, till differentiated, 10–20 mins. → wash → *C*, 1 hr., 37°C. → 95% alc., till no more color comes away → *D*, 20–30 mins. → 95% alc., wash → abs. alc., till differentiated → balsam, via xylene
RECOMMENDED FOR: differentiation of elastic fibers in tissues without destaining acid-fast bacteria.

21.13 Sheridan 1929   11571b, **12**:103
FORMULA OF DRY STOCK: water 100, crystal violet 1, resorcinol 2, 30% ferric chloride 9
PREPARATION: as French 1929
WORKING SOLUTION: Prepare from ppt. exactly as for French 1929 above.
METHOD: [sections] → 90% alc. → stain, 1–2 hrs. → abs. alc. till differentiated → balsam, via xylene
RESULT: as French 1929 but much paler.

21.13 Unna *test.* **1896 Kahlden and Laurent**   Kahlden and Laurent 1896, 143
REAGENTS REQUIRED: *A.* sat. aq. sol. Bismarck brown; *B.* 50% alc. 100, magenta 1, nitric acid 5; *C.* 25% nitric acid; *D.* 0.01% acetic acid
METHOD: [sections] → water → *A*, some hours to overnight → wash → *B*, 24 hrs. → *C*, quick dip → *D*, till differentiated → balsam, via usual reagents

21.13 Unna-Taenzer *test.* **1896 Kahlden and Laurent**   Kahlden and Laurent 1896, 144
REAGENTS REQUIRED: *A.* 50% alc. 100, orcein 0.8, hydrochloric acid; *B.* 0.1% hydrochloric acid in 80% alc.
METHOD: sections → water → *A*, 6–12 hrs. → *B*, till differentiated → balsam, via usual reagents

21.13 Verhoeff 1908　　　　　　　　　　　　　　　11006, **50**:876

REAGENTS REQUIRED: *A*. abs. alc. 60, hematoxylin 3, 10% ferric chloride 0.25, ADS 12.2 Lugol (1905) 25; *B*. 2% ferric chloride

PREPARATION OF A: Dissolve hematoxylin in alc. Add ferric chloride. Filter. Add iodine solution to filtrate.

METHOD: [sections] → water → *A*, till black, 10–20 mins. → *B*, till differentiated, 2–10 secs. → water, thorough wash → 95% alc., till no more iodine comes away → balsam, via usual reagents

RESULT: elastic fibers, black.

NOTE: Verhoeff (*loc. cit.*) recommends a 2% solution of eosin Y if counterstaining is required.

21.13 Volkman and Strauss 1934　*see* DS 21.13 Weigert 1898 (note) and DS 13.7 Volkman and Strauss 1934

21.13 Weigert 1898　　　　　　　　　　　　　　　23681, **9**:290

FORMULA OF DRY STOCK: water 100, magenta 1, resorcinol 2, 30% ferric chloride 12.5

PREPARATION OF DRY STOCK: as French 1929

WORKING SOLUTION: 95% alc. 100, dry stock 0.75, hydrochloric acid 2

PREPARATION OF WORKING SOLUTION: as French 1929

METHOD: [sections] → 95% alc. → stain, 2–24 hrs. → 95% alc., till no more color comes away → balsam, via usual reagents

RESULT: elastic fibers, blue black.

NOTE: **Fischer** (*test.* **Schmorl** 1928, 167) suggested the substitution of safranin or Bismarck brown for magenta and designated such solution by the suffix *-elin*. Hence, the names *fuchselin* (with magenta), *vesuvelin* (with Bismarck brown) and *safranelin* which add confusion to the literature. **Volkman and Strauss 1934** use crystal violet.

21.13 Unna　*see* DS 12.216 Unna (1928)

21.13 Zieler　*see* DS 23.221 Zieler 1903

21.14 STAINS FOR CHITIN

The few methods recorded in this section are not intended for the general staining of sections of arthropods, for which purpose any of the better-known triple stains can be employed. Bethe 1895 is based on a standard microchemical test for chitin and is designed principally to assist in the reconstruction from serial sections of portions of the endoskeleton which cannot well be made out in cleared specimens. The formulas of Gage, Racovitza, and Smith are intended only for wholemounts and should be used in those cases in which a valuable specimen has, through carelessness, been left in potash for so long that it has become too transparent. Such specimens are difficult to stain and the formula of Smith is invaluable for this purpose.

21.14 Bethe 1895　　　　　　　　　　　　　　　23831, **8**:544

REAGENTS REQUIRED: *A*. water 100, aniline hydrochloride 10, hydrochloric acid 1; *B*. 7.5% potassium dichromate

METHOD: [sections] → water → *A*, 5 mins. → water, quick rinse → *B*, 1 min. → tap water, till color changes from green to blue → balsam, via acetone

RECOMMENDED FOR: demonstration of chitin in sections.

21.14 Chatton 1920　*see* DS 12.212 Chatton 1920

21.14 Gage 1919　　　　　　　　　　　　　　　7871, **30**:142

FORMULA: water 100, hydrochloric acid 1, acid fuchsin 0.2

RECOMMENDED FOR: potash-cleared chitinous skeletons.

21.14 Nuttall 1908　*see* DS 12.16 Nuttall 1908

21.14 Racovitza *test.* **1942 Langeron**　　　　　　Langeron 1942, 924

REAGENTS REQUIRED: *A*. 1% pyrogallic acid; *B*. 0.5% hydrochloric acid

METHOD: [potash-cleared exoskeletons of arthropods] → water, thorough wash → *A*, ½ to 1 hr. → 70% alc., in strong light, till darkened → *B*, if differentiation required → balsam, via usual reagents

NOTE: **Vaulx 1920** (5401, **65**:214) mordants for 15 minutes in a sat. sol. ferric sulphate before this treatment.

21.14 Semichon 1920   *see* DS 12.222 Semichon 1920

21.14 Smith 1926   9940, **14**:171
    FORMULA: phenol 100, sat. alc. (*circ.* 1.5%) ethyl eosin 12.5
    METHOD: [potash-cleared skeletons of arthropods] → stain, 15 mins. at 60°C. → balsam,
    via clove oil

21.14 Vaulx 1920   *see* DS 21.14 Racovitza (1942) (note)

<h3 style="text-align:center">21.15 PLANT SKELETAL TISSUES</h3>

There is a general confusion among beginners unaccustomed to botanical microtechniques between those destined to show only the skeletal structures and those which
are designed to show the nuclei and cytoplasmic constituents of plant material. For the
latter purpose any nuclear stain and any counterstain employed for zoological purposes
can equally well be used, and many of the triple staining methods common in zoological
techniques give admirable results. The staining methods discussed in this section are
those which are used to differentiate (usually for teaching purposes) between cellulose,
callose, lignified, and suberized tissues. These tissues should be freed from protoplasmic
material before being stained, and the customary method of doing this is to immerse
them, after sectioning, in a solution of sodium or potassium hypochlorite. They should
remain in this solution until the cellular contents have been leeched away, and should
then be thoroughly washed in distilled water before staining techniques are applied to
them.

In general these techniques may be divided into two sections. First, there are those
which are destined to distinguish between lignified and cellulose tissues, which is the
purpose of almost all the formulas here given; second, there are the few genuine botanical
triple stains in which some fat-staining constituent is employed for the purpose of
bringing the suberized tissues into contrast. For the former purpose the only choice
between the different methods rests in the color in which it is desired to differentiate the
elements. It is interesting to note that the stain universally referred to as "Benda's
Stain" in zoology is equally employed in botanical microtechnique as "Land's Stain."
The best technique, if it is desired to include the suberized tissues, is that of Bugnon
1919. A good method for class-demonstration purposes in Langeron 1902, in which
advantage is taken of the relative densities of the schlerenchyma and parenchyma in
order to distinguish between the two. For those who prefer a single solution, there are
the methods of Darrow 1940 and Chamberlain 1915a. The stain of Petit 1903, though
obsolete, is included for its interest and for the reason that it gives more permanent
results than other staining methods for plant skeletal tissues.

21.15 Bugnon 1919   *light green-Sudan III-hemalum*   4999, **66**:919
    REAGENTS REQUIRED: *A*. 70% alc. 100, light green to sat, Sudan III to sat.; *B*. 11.122
    Delafield 1885
    METHOD: [sections] → 70% alc. → *A*, 10 mins. → water, rinse → *B*, 10 mins. → water,
    wash → balsam, via usual reagents
    RESULT: lignified tissues, green; suberized tissues, red; other tissues, blue.
    NOTE: **Langeron 1942, 1269** suggests the substitution of Petit 1903 (sols. *C* and *D*) for
    B above.

21.15 Chamberlain 1915a   *acid fuchsin-iodine green*   Chamberlain 1915, 62
    STOCK SOLUTIONS: I. 0.2% acid fuchsin, II. 0.2% iodine green
    WORKING SOLUTIONS: *A*. stock I 50, stock II 50; *B*. abs. alc. 100, acetic acid 1, iodine 0.1
    METHOD: [sections] → water → *A*, 24 hrs. → *B*, till differentiated → balsam, via xylene
    RESULT: lignified tissues, green; cellulose tissues, red.
    NOTE: A detailed description of the use of this stain is given under DS 21.10 above.

21.15 Chamberlain 1915b   *cyanin-erythrosin*   Chamberlain 1915, 61
    REAGENTS REQUIRED: *A*. 1% cyanin in 50% alc.; *B*. 1% erythrosin
    METHOD: [sections] → water → *A*, 5–10 mins. → 50% alc., rinse → *B*, ½ to 1 min. →
    abs. alc., least possible time → balsam, via xylene

RESULT: lignified tissue, blue; cellulose tissue, red.

NOTE: **Emig 1941, 56** states that the less expensive Capri blue may be substituted for cyanin.

21.15 Cole 1903 Cross and Cole 1903, 171

REAGENTS REQUIRED: *A.* DS 11.26 Cole 1903; *B.* 20% hydrochloric acid in 95% alc.; *C.* 2% acid green in 95% alc.

METHOD: [sections] → water → *A*, 5–10 mins. → *B*, till differentiated, 1–2 mins. → 95% alc., till acid free → *C*, 30 mins. → 95% alc., rinse → balsam, via clove oil

21.15 Conant *see* DS 13.5 Conant

21.15 Conn and Darrow 1946 *cit. compl. script. et litt.* Sharp. *Iron alum-safranin*
Conn and Darrow 1946, 11A-9

REAGENTS REQUIRED: *A.* 3% ferric alum; *B.* 0.1% hematoxylin; *C.* 3% safranin O in 90% alc.

METHOD: [sections of woody tissues, preferably cut from living material] → *A*, 10–30 mins. → water, thorough wash → *B*, till stained sufficiently → water, rinse → *C*, 1–5 mins. → water, wash → 90% alc., till dehydrated → balsam, via benzene

RESULT: lignified walls, red; unlignified walls, black.

21.15 Darrow 1940 *chlorazol black E* 20540b, **15**:67

FORMULA: 70% alc. 100, chlorazol black *E* 1

METHOD: [sections] → 70% alc. → stain, 5–10 mins. → balsam, via usual reagents

RESULT: differentiation of cell walls in black and varying shades of brown; cytoplasm, brown, yellow, and green.

21.15 Emig 1941 *see* DS 21.15 Chamberlain 1915b (note)

21.15 Foster 1934 *tannin-safranin* 20540b, **9**:81

REAGENTS REQUIRED: *A.* water 100, tannic acid 1, sod. salicylate 1; *B.* 3% ferric chloride; *C.* 1% safranin in 50% alc.

METHOD: [sections] water → *A*, 10 mins. → water, wash → *B*, 5 mins. → repeat *A* → water → *B*, if necessary, until cell walls sufficiently dark → 50% alc., 5 mins. → *C*, 48 hrs. → 70% alc., till differentiated → balsam, via usual reagents

21.15 Jackson 1926 *crystal violet-erythrosin* 20540b, **1**:33

REAGENTS REQUIRED: *A.* 1% crystal violet; *B.* sat. sol. erythrosin in clove oil; *C.* 50% xylene in abs. alc.

METHOD: [sections] → water → *A*, 15 mins. → water, rinse → 95% alc., till dehydrated → *B*, 1–5 mins. → *C*, 1–2 mins. → balsam, via xylene

RESULT: lignified tissues, violet; other tissues, red.

21.15 Johansen 1940 *safranin-picro-anilin blue see* DS 21.15 Smith 1924 (note)

21.15 Johansen 1940 *acid fuchsin-iodine green see* DS 21.15 Langeron 1942 (note)

21.15 Johansen 1940 *acid fuchsin-fast green see* DS 21.411 Johansen 1940

21.15 Johansen 1940 *see also* DS 13.5 Johansen 1940

21.15 Land *test.* **1915 Chamberlain** *safranin-light green*
Chamberlain 1915, 86

REAGENTS REQUIRED: *A.* DS 11.42 Babes 1887 *or* Conn 1915; *B.* sat. sol. light green in clove oil

METHOD: [sections] → water → *A*, 2–24 hrs. → 50% alc., till differentiated → abs. alc., till dehydrated → *B*, 3–30 mins. → balsam, via xylene

RESULT: lignified tissues, red; other tissues, green.

NOTE: This method is widely known in zoological literature as "Benda's Stain"; see DS 11.42 Babes 1887 (note).

21.15 Langeron 1942 *carmine-iodine green* Langeron 1942, 1266

REAGENTS REQUIRED: *A.* DS 11.21 Grenacher 1879; *B.* 0.01% iodine green

METHOD: [sections] → water → *A*, 1–3 hrs. → water, rinse → *B*, 5–20 secs. → balsam, via usual reagents

RESULT: lignified tissues, green; other tissues, red.

NOTE: Langeron (*loc. cit.*) refers to this as *la méthode classique.* **Johansen 1940,** 93, uses 1% acid fuchsin as the red counterstain in this technique; this modification is essentially the method of Chamberlain 1915a.

21.15 Langeron 1902 *test.* **1942** *ips.* *methylene blue-ruthenium red*
                                                          Langeron 1942, 1267
REAGENTS REQUIRED: *A.* water 100, potassium alum 10, methylene blue 1; *B.* 0.2% ruthenium red
METHOD: [sections] → water → *A*, 5–10 mins. → water, wash → *B*, 5–10 mins. → water, wash → balsam, via usual reagents
RESULT: suberized tissues, green; sclerenchyma, violet; lignified tissues, blue; parenchyma, deep rose.

21.15 Langeron   *see also* DS 21.15 Bugnon 1919 (note)

21.15 Margolena 1934   *Bismarck brown-fast green*   20540b, **9**:71
REAGENTS REQUIRED: *A.* 0.5% Bismarck brown; *B.* 0.3% fast green FCF in clove oil
METHOD: [sections of F 5000.1010 Bouin 1897 fixed buds] → *A*, 10 mins. → rinse → dehydrate → *B*, till differentiated → balsam, via xylene
RECOMMENDED FOR: Differentiation of walls of developing pollen grains.

21.15 Northen 1936   *safranin-tannin-crystal violet*   20540b, **11**:23
REAGENTS REQUIRED: *A.* 1% safranin in 50% alc.; *B.* 0.5% tannin in 50% alc.; *C.* 1% ferric chloride in 70% alc.; *D.* 0.5% crystal violet in clove oil
METHOD: [sections] → water → *A*, 24 hrs. → 50% alc., rinse → *B*, 30 secs. → 70% alc., two rinses → *C*, 10–20 secs. → abs. alc., minimum possible time → *D*, 30–60 secs. balsam, via xylene
RESULT: lignified tissue, red; other tissues, black and purple.

21.15 Petit 1903   *alkanet-iodine green-chrome yellow*   6630, **55**:507
REAGENTS REQUIRED: *A.* DS 11.3 Guinard 1890; *B.* 0.01% iodine green in 95% alc.; *C.* sat. sol. lead acetate; *D.* sat. sol. potassium dichromate
METHOD: [sections] → water → *A*, till suberized tissue red → 95% alc., rinse → *B*, till lignified tissues green → 70% alc., rinse → *C*, 5 mins. → water, thorough wash → *D*, few moments → water, thorough wash → balsam, via usual reagents

21.15 Popham, Johnson and Chan 1948   20540b, **23**:185
REAGENTS REQUIRED: *A.* 1% safranin O; *B.* 2% tannic acid; *C.* water 60, DS 11.122 Delafield (1885); *D.* 0.01% hydrochloric acid; *E.* 0.5% lithium carbonate; *F.* sat. sol. anilin blue in methyl cellosolve
METHOD: [sections] → water → *A*, 24 hrs. → rinse → *B*, 2 mins. → rinse → *C*, 2 mins. → *D*, wash → *E*, 5 mins. → dehydrate → *F*, 5–10 mins. → balsam, via usual reagents
RECOMMENDED FOR: cell walls in stem apex.

21.15 Sharman 1943   20540b, **18**:105
REAGENTS REQUIRED: *A.* 2% zinc chloride; *B.* 0.004% safranin O; *C.* water 100, hydrochloric acid 0.15, tannic acid 5, orange G 2; *D.* 5% tannic acid; *E.* 1% iron alum
METHOD: [sections] → water → *A*, 1 mm. → rinse → *B*, 5 mins. → rinse → *C*, 1 min. → rinse → *D*, 5 mins. → quick rinse → *E*, 2 mins. → balsam, via usual reagents
RECOMMENDED FOR: cell walls of stem apex.

21.15 Smith *test.* **1903 Cole**   *acid green-carmine*   Cross and Cole 1903, 170
REAGENTS REQUIRED: *A.* water 75, glycerol 25, acid green 0.1; *B.* DS 11.26 Smith (1903)
METHOD: [sections] → water → *A*, 5–10 mins. → wash → *B*, 10–15 mins. → 96% alc., wash → balsam, via clove oil

21.15 Smith 1924   *safranin-picro-anilin blue*   19938, **59**:557
REAGENTS REQUIRED: *A.* DS 11.42 Chamberlain 1915; *B.* sat. sol. (*circ.* 1.2%) picric acid 78, sat. sol. (*circ.* 5%) anilin blue WS 22
METHOD: [sections] → *A*, 2–6 hrs. → water, thorough wash → 95% alc., till differentiated → *B*, 2 hrs. → abs. alc., quick rinse → balsam, via clove oil and xylene
NOTE: **Johansen 1940, 82** substitutes his DS 11.42 Johansen 1940 for *A* above and cites the technique without reference to Smith, as do Conn and Darrow 1946, IIa-11.

21.16 OTHER SKELETAL AND CONNECTIVE TISSUES

21.16 Baird 1935 20540b, **10**:35

REAGENTS REQUIRED: *A*. 1% trypan blue; *B*. 2% neutralized formaldehyde; *C*. 1% methylene blue; *D*. 1% acid fuchsin

METHOD: [inject (for rat) 1 ml. *A* daily for 4 days] → [spread piece of subcutaneous connective tissue on slide: dry till edges adhere] → *B*, ½ to 1 hr. → wash → *C*, 1 min. → wash → *D*, 30 secs. → wash → balsam, via acetone and xylene

RECOMMENDED FOR: connective tissue spreads for class instruction.

21.16 Bowell *test.* **1948 Verdcourt** 20540b, **23**:145

REAGENTS REQUIRED: *A*. water 99, acetic acid 1, potassium permanganate 16; *B*. sat. aq. sol. (*circ.* 10%) oxalic acid; *C*. 0.1% Hoffman's violet

METHOD: [radulae isolated by potassium hydroxide treatment] → wash → *A*, 100 ml., till black → *B*, till decolorized → wash → *C*, till stained, 30 mins. → balsam, via usual reagents

RECOMMENDED FOR: radulae of mollusca.

21.16 Daniel 1927 11360, **47**:253

REAGENTS REQUIRED: *A*. 0.05% quinone in abs. alc.; *B*. abs. alc. 50, methyl salicylate 50

METHOD: [crustacea in 70% alc.] → abs. alc., till dehydrated → *A*, overnight → *B*, till diffusion currents no longer visible → methyl salicylate

RECOMMENDED FOR: demonstration of muscles in wholemounts of crustacea.

21.16 Dietrich *test.* **1928 Schmorl** Schmorl 1928, 273

REAGENTS REQUIRED: *A*. 1% brilliant black 3B in 0.1% acetic acid; *B*. 1% safranin; *C*. methanol

METHOD: [3–4 μ sections of mercuric chloride fixed material] → *A*, 1–5 mins. → rinse → *B*, 3–10 mins. → drain → abs. alc., till differentiated → *C* → balsam, via xylene

RECOMMENDED FOR: structure of heart muscle.

21.16 Hueter 1911 *test.* **1948 Romeis** Romeis 1948, 351

REAGENTS REQUIRED: *A*. 10% phosphotungstic acid; *B*. DS 11.124 Hueter 1911

METHOD: [sections] → water → *A*, 15–20 secs. → quick wash → *B*, 3–5 mins. → 50% alc., till differentiated → balsam, via usual reagents

RECOMMENDED FOR: collagen fibers.

21.16 Jasswoin 1932 23632, **49**:191

REAGENTS REQUIRED: *A*. 5% ferric alum 75, 1% hematoxylin 25

METHOD: [sheets of neutralized formaldehyde-fixed material] → thorough wash → spread on slide → 95% alc., till dehydrated → water, till rehydrated → *A*, 15–20 secs. → tap water, wash → [counterstain if desired] → balsam, via usual reagents

RECOMMENDED FOR: collagen fibers in wholemounts.

NOTE: *See also* DS 11.121 Yasvoin (1946).

21.16 Karlson 1924 6630, **90**:1122

REAGENTS REQUIRED: *A*. water 100, eosin 0.7, gallic acid 0.15; *B*. 3% pyrogallic acid; *C*. 5% methylene blue

METHOD: [sections] → water → *A*, 5–20 mins. → 70% alc., till no more color comes away → *B*, 24 hrs. → wash → *C*, 15 mins. → 70% alc., till no more color comes away → balsam, via usual reagents

RECOMMENDED FOR: differentiation of muscle (red) from other connective tissues.

21.16 Miller 1933 11431, **37**:127

REAGENTS REQUIRED: *A*. DS 22.21 Altman 1898 (sol. *A*); *B*. 0.5% aurantia in 70% alc.; *C*. 0.25% toluidine blue

METHOD: [sections of F 3700.1000 Helly 1903 material] → water → *A*, on slide, warmed to steaming, 2–4 mins. → quick wash → *C*, 10–20 secs. → rinse → blot → *C*, 10 secs. → methanol, till differentiated → balsam, via usual reagents

RECOMMENDED FOR: striae in striated muscle.

21.16 Perdrau 1921 *see* MS 33.1 Perdrau 1921

21.16 Unna 1910 *safranin-anilin-blue-tannin*   Ehrlich, Krause, *et al.* 1910, 247
 REAGENTS REQUIRED: *A*. 1% safranin; *B*. water 50, anilin blue 0.5, water 50, tannin 15
 METHOD: [sections of alc. fixed material] → *A*, 10 mins. → water, thorough wash → *B*, 15
  mins. → water, rinse → abs. alc., till color clouds cease → balsam, via xylene
 RECOMMENDED FOR: demonstration of collagen fibers in alcohol-fixed material.
 RESULT: collagen, blue.

21.16 Verocay 1908 *test.* **1948 Romeis**   Romeis 1948, 351
 REAGENTS REQUIRED: *A*. 1% chromic acid; *B*. DS 11.122 Delafield 1885
 METHOD: [paraffin sections] → water → *A*, 24 hrs., 46°C. → wash → *B*, 1–2 hrs. →
  wash → counterstain, if desired → balsam, via usual reagents
 RECOMMENDED FOR: collagen fibers.

21.2 SPECIAL STAINS FOR NERVOUS TISSUES

It has become so customary today for all nervous tissues to be stained by one of the metal-staining techniques that it is a surprise to many histologists to learn that excellent methods exist for dye-staining these structures besides those of the classic "Weigert" methods given in division 21.212 below. These stains for nervous tissues are divided into those destined to stain the neuroglia, which, though they cannot, of course, properly be called nervous tissues, are so closely associated with them that the staining technique must be kept in the same place.

21.20 TYPICAL EXAMPLES

Preparation of a transverse section of the brain of a frog using the stain of Bethe 1896

The method of Bethe (DS 21.211 Bethe 1896) for the preparation of class-teaching material or demonstration slides from the brains of the lower vertebrates is one of the best arguments against rejecting a technique for the mere reason that it is obsolete. The process is rapid and simple, yet it yields as good images as can be obtained by many of the metal-staining techniques, which would involve weeks of work, and which are capricious and unreliable in the extreme. The technique depends essentially upon the fact that solutions of methylene blue are differentially absorbed, in a living animal, into the nerve cells and processes of the brain. The dye is fixed in this position with the aid of ammonium picrate, used also as a fixative of the tissues, and finally precipitated in place with the aid of either sodium or ammonium molybdate. A frog is an easy

animal on which to experiment, not only because it is readily available, but also because of the simplicity with which the brain may be removed from the cranium.

It is necessary to start with a saturated solution of methylene blue in any standard physiological saline solution, but it need not be sterile since the animal is going to be sacrificed shortly after the application. It is simpler and pleasanter to work on an anesthetized frog, and though any anesthetic may be used for this purpose, the writer's choice for all amphibian anesthetization is tricaine methanosulfonate, more frequently known under its trade designation of *M2.2.2*. This should be prepared as a 0.2% solution in physiological saline, and the frog placed in about a liter of the solution. The frog will become nonreceptive to stimuli after about ten minutes and is unlikely to die even upon an exposure of some hours.

As soon as the frog is thoroughly anesthetized, fill a 5-milliliter hypodermic syringe with the saturated solution of methylene blue in physiological saline, and inject about 1 milliliter into the abdominal cavity. Take care not to damage the internal structures. It is simplest to pick up a fold of the frog's skin with the fingers and to insert the hypodermic syringe into the length of the fold, parallel to the main axis of the body. The point of the syringe should be watched carefully at the beginning of the injection to make sure that it has not merely slipped under the skin, but has actually penetrated through the muscular layers into the coelom. The needle is then withdrawn and the frog returned to its anesthetic saline. After three or four minutes a slight blue coloration begins to spread over the skin. Leave the frog for about ten minutes and then inject another milliliter of stain into the abdominal cavity. An hour later, check to see if the nervous system has picked up the methylene blue. This can be done by dissecting the hind leg to disclose the sciatic nerve, which is easily found by slipping the handle of a scalpel between the gastrocnemius and the posterior tibialis muscles to disclose the nerve lying alongside the bone. If the preparation has been a successful one, the nerve will be stained light blue, and as a final check the nerve may be severed and the cut end examined under a hand lens. If the cut end has a darker stain than does the outer sheath, the impregnation may be considered successful, and one may proceed with preparations to remove and fix the brain. Pin the frog belly down in the bottom of a dissecting pan. Remove the skin from the whole of the head, and scrape the frontoparietals clear of their attached muscles. Break away the posterior portion of the cranium so as to leave the way clear for the removal of the upper half to expose the brain. The brain can be removed by inserting the sharp point of a scalpel under the nasal bone, which is then lifted up and pulled away. This leaves the end of the frontoparietal hanging free so that it may be lifted very carefully with the edge of a scalpel. Do not permit it to break away, or the other end will drive down and destroy the cerebellum. As soon as it has been lifted, however, it may be grasped in a pair of blunt-nosed forceps and twisted with a rotary motion toward the center of the skull. This will result in its coming away free without damaging the brain. The same technique may now be employed on the other frontoparietal, thus leaving clear the whole anterior region of the brain. The brain will now be exposed save for those portions which are covered by the prootic bones, or by such parts of the frontoparietal as remained attached to the prootic bone when they broke. Both the prootic and the remains of the frontoparietal may be lifted off carefully and the upper surface of the brain fully exposed.

It is almost impossible to remove the brain from its bed without damaging it. A pair of heavy scissors should now be used to cut through the remains of the nasal and vomer bones, to sever the connection of the parasphenoid bone from the premaxillae, and to cut through the prootic bones at the point of attachment of the squamosals and the pterygoids. The entire brain may now be lifted out, resting, as it were, on a platter consisting largely of the parasphenoid bone.

It will be seen by reference to the technique under discussion (DS 21.211 Bethe 1896) that six alternative fixative solutions are suggested. There is no doubt that the solution which contains osmic acid and phosphomolybdic acid is the best, but the very high cost of osmic acid, and the danger of working with this irritating reagent, may lead the operator to choose in preference alternative formula No. 2, which contains ammonium molybdate and chromic acid. The results are nearly, but not quite, as good with this reagent as with the osmic-sodium-phosphomolybdate mixture. Ammonium phosphomolybdate can, of course, be substituted for sodium phosphomolybdate in the solution selected.

The first fixation is in a saturated aqueous solution of ammonium picrate, which is prepared by taking a saturated solution of picric acid in water and adding to it a considerable excess of undissolved picric acid. Ammonia is now added drop by drop, with constant shaking, until the surplus picric acid at the bottom of the container starts to dissolve. Further ammonia should now be added until the solution smells of free ammonia, and it may then be shaken once or twice to complete the saturation. A very emphatic warning must be given at this point that ammonium picrate is a highly explosive compound which can be detonated without difficulty by vibration alone. Under no circumstances whatever should dry ammonium picrate ever be allowed in a laboratory, and the fixative solution under discussion should be prepared immediately before use, and then thoroughly washed down the sink as soon as the period of fixation is finished. To leave the vessel containing the ammonium picrate about until such a time as the dry crust of the salt collects around the lip of the vessel is to invite a serious accident. Like all other picric compounds, however, this material cannot explode in solution, and is therefore perfectly safe provided that the necessary precautions are observed.

Now lift the brain on its bed of the parasphenoid bone and place it in a considerable quantity of the ammonium picrate solution for about five minutes. It should then be sufficiently hardened on the outside for it to be safe to tip the bone sideways, and to detach the brain from the parasphenoid bone with a sharp scalpel. After another five minutes in the fixative, cut the brain into small pieces (about two or three millimeters long, depending upon the region which it is desired to section) and return to the fixative for 15 to 30 minutes.

Now transfer the small pieces, without washing, to the molybdate fixative selected and leave for a period of from about four hours to overnight. A more prolonged immersion will not hurt them, but may tend to make the brain tissue very brittle during section cutting. As soon as the small pieces have been placed in the molybdate fixative, the dish containing the ammonium picrate must be thoroughly washed and the residual picrate solution washed down the sink.

On their removal from the molybdate fixative the pieces are washed thoroughly in running water and then embedded in paraffin. Do not be alarmed that during the course of dehydration in alcohol a certain amount of blue will come from the pieces. The blue which is liberated during the process of dehydration is that which is not fixed in the nerve cells; this period of dehydration therefore serves to differentiate as well as to dehydrate the tissues. Paraffin sections are now cut in the normal manner and mounted on a slide, a process which should present no difficulty with the present material. It is recommended that sections of about 15 to 20 microns in thickness be used if only the nerve cells are desired, or that sections about ten microns thick be used if it is intended to counterstain the sections to show nuclei.

If it is only desired to show the brain cells and their processes, the sections may be dewaxed, and then mounted directly in balsam. It is usually better, however, to counterstain these sections with some carmine formula, and it is conventional to use for this purpose one of the alum carmines given in Chapter 20 (DS 11.2). The author's preference is for the formula of Mayer (DS 11.21 Mayer 1892) in which the sections are stained in the following manner. After dewaxing, pass the sections down through the customary alcohols to distilled water and place them in the carmine solution. This is a slow acting, but very safe reagent, and the sections may without danger remain in it overnight. They must, however, be watched to make sure that no overstaining takes place, or the process of differentiation may remove the blue from the nerve tissues at the same time as it removes the carmine. On removal from the carmine stain the sections should be rinsed briefly in a 5% solution of potassium alum to remove the adherent stain, then washed thoroughly in tap water until they are free from potassium alum. They are then dehydrated, cleared, and mounted in balsam.

Preparation of a section of spinal
cord using the "Weigert-Pal"
stain of Anderson 1922

All of the methods given under section DS 21.212 below may loosely be referred to as "*Weigert-Pal*" techniques, and that of Anderson 1922 is selected as the example for the reason that in the author's hands it has always given the most satisfactory results. The principle difficulty which will be encountered is the preparation of the staining solutions, and this must first be briefly described before passing to a description of the technique itself. First it is necessary to prepare Weigert's primary mordant, the formula for which will be found in Chapter 22 (ADS 12.1 Weigert 1896). Raise 100 milliliters of distilled water to the boil and throw in 5 grams of reagent grade potassium dichromate, and dissolve it with rapid stirring. While the fluid is still boiling vigorously, add 2 grams of chromium fluoride, a little at a time, with brisk stirring between each addition. When the whole two grams have been added, cool the solution, leave overnight, and filter. This primary mordant of Weigert may be kept indefinitely. When required for use in the method of Anderson, convert it to Anderson's mordant (ADS 12.1 Anderson 1922) by adding 10 milliliters of a 2% solution of calcium hypochlorite to 90 milliliters of primary mordant; this mixed solution is not stable and must be prepared immediately before use. Weigert's primary mordant, as such, is also required in the technique. Anderson's hematoxylin stain (DS 21.212 Anderson 1922) is easily prepared. Take 10 milliliters of absolute alcohol and dissolve in it 0.5 gram of hematoxylin. When the hematoxylin is in solution, add three milliliters of 2% calcium hypochlorite and then shake the vessel vigorously for about two minutes. Filter the mixture and make the filtrate up to 100 milliliters before adding three milliliters of acetic acid; the solution is then ready for use. The technique also calls for the dichromate-sodium sulfate fixative of Müller (Chapter 18, F 7000.0000 Müller 1859). Differentiation requires the differentiating solutions of Pal (Chapter 22, ADS 21.1 Pal 1887). These are a freshly prepared 0.25% solution of potassium permanganate, and a solution containing 0.5% each of potassium sulfite and oxalic acid. Both solutions are relatively unstable and should be prepared immediately before use.

With these solutions on hand for the staining process, it is necessary to consider the fixative which will be used for the spinal cord. Opinions are widely divergent as to the best fixative to employ, the majority of authors preferring merely to use a 5% solution of potassium dichromate. Kultschitsky 1898 (766, **4**:223) recommends the cupric-dichromate mixture of Erlitzky (F 4700.0000 Erlitzky 1877). The writer does not consider the cupric addition necessary, since sufficient copper mordanting occurs in Weigert's primary mordant.

Having selected the fixative, it remains only to secure the spinal cord, which may be taken from any animal available to the investigator. Though the rabbit is widely used, it is somewhat small for demonstration purposes. If access can be had to a slaughterhouse it is very much better to secure a piece of the spinal cord of a pig, though this latter is almost invariably destroyed in the process of pithing with which the commercial killing of pigs is accompanied. It does not matter in the present instance that considerable time should elapse between the killing of the animal and the fixation of the cord, since postmortem changes in the myelin sheaths, which are shown by this process, are generally very slow. Whatever cord is finally selected should be cut into pieces about twice as long as they are broad, and suspended in a loosely woven cloth bag in a very large volume of the fixing solution. If, for example, 5% potassium dichromate has been selected, it is by no means unreasonable to use a liter of the solution for three or four half-inch lengths of the spinal cord of the pig. The time of fixation does not matter and should be determined by the physical condition of the spinal cord. A simple method of judging fixation in the dichromate (which will not be applicable to the copper-dichromate mixture) was suggested by Pal 1887 (23632, **6**:92), who took pieces from the fixative from time to time and cut them with a sharp knife in order to view the surface. If they are underfixed, the white matter of the cord will be lighter than the gray matter; fixation and hardening are complete when the white matter is a darker brown than the gray matter. Overfixation is not particularly harmful but underfixation will result in unsuccessful preparations. When fixation is complete the specimens are washed in running water until no further dichromate comes away, and may then be stored in 70% alcohol in the dark. If they are to be used immediately they must be dehydrated and embedded in celloidin (Chapter 18) before being cut into sections of from 15 to 20 microns in thickness by any of the techniques there given.

The sections are accumulated in distilled water, and when a sufficient number have been obtained, are transferred to Anderson's mordant (about 50 milliliters for a couple of sections) in a glass-stoppered bottle, and kept at 37°C. The exact temperature is not critical, 37° being quoted because ovens at that temperature are common in most biological laboratories. After three or four days at 37°C., the sections are transferred, without washing to Weigert's primary mordant. To avoid curling, it is recommended that the mordant be heated to about 20°C. and allowed to cool while the sections are in it, i.e. for a period of 10 to 30 minutes. Neither of the two mordanting processes are critical as to time, nor is there any method of discovering what is the best time for the particular batch, save by trial and error. After the second mordant bath, the sections are washed in several changes of distilled water. Anderson's hematoxylin is then raised, in a beaker or other container, to a temperature of about 50°C. The sections are dropped into this stain and allowed to remain for one hour. Each section is then taken from the stain (it should be a deep purple) and transferred without washing to Müller's fixative for a period of 10 to 20 minutes. This is necessary to ensure the presence of dichromate, without which differentiation cannot be controlled. This dichromate bath is peculiar to Anderson's technique; other "Weigert-Pal" methods depend on the retention of dichromate from the fixing and mordanting solutions. The sections are then transferred from Müller's solution to distilled water, and washed until no further color comes away. If the sections are now a deep blue, they may be differentiated, but if, through some error of technique, they are more brown than blue, it is desirable to transfer them briefly to a weak (0.5%) solution of sodium bicarbonate until they acquire a deep blue color. Differentiation is the most critical part of the entire method, and the inexperienced worker should proceed by short steps rather than endeavor to conduct one operation. The sections are taken one at a time and placed in the potassium permanganate solution for about 30 seconds. Each section is then removed, rinsed rapidly in distilled water, placed in the potassium sulfite-oxalic acid solution, and watched under the microscope. After two or three minutes the white matter will be differentiated from the gray matter, but it is presumed that the differentiation will not have proceeded far enough in this brief period. The section is now returned to the potassium permanganate solution, left for a further period of 20 seconds, removed, placed in the bleaching solution, and again watched. The process should be stopped just before the tracts are clearly differentiated, for the differentiation will continue while the sections are being finally washed. This is the next stage of the process. Each section, when differentiation is complete, should be passed rapidly through two or three changes of water, then dehydrated, cleared, and mounted in balsam in the customary manner.

Demonstration of the neuroglial cells of the white matter of the cerebral cortex using the crystal violet stain of Galescu 1908

Many methods for the demonstration of neuroglia are described in Chapter 23. The method of Galescu 1908 (DS 21.22 Galescu 1908) is among the more satisfactory of the dye-staining techniques, and has the advantage over the metal-staining techniques that it requires less vigorous attention to detail to secure a passable result. It is not, however, a method which can be recommended for research purposes, though it might well prove a useful and interesting demonstration in the hands of a class in microtechnique.

It is unimportant what animal is used, though a rabbit is a convenient form from which to obtain the brain. In demonstrations of neuroglial structures the animal should not be killed by anesthetics, but by a sharp blow on the head, and then tied face downward on a board while the skin is removed from the top of the cranium. The nasal bones should then be broken out with a hammer and chisel, and the free end of the frontal bone thus exposed gripped in a pair of blunt-nosed pliers. A sharp upward jerk, with an inwardly directed twist of the hand at the same time, will cause the frontal bone to break away cleanly without damage to the underlying brain structures. The parietal bone is then removed piecemeal and the process repeated on the other side of the brain. The membranes are now dissected away from the freshly exposed brain, preferably with forceps rather than with a knife. A sharp scalpel is then used to remove pieces of the cerebral cortex of about three- or four-millimeter side. As these pieces will inevitably adhere to the knife, it is not possible to transfer them directly to the 6% mercuric chloride, which is used as a fixative, because this reagent will destroy the surface of the blade. They are, therefore, best washed from the knife into a tube of normal saline, which is poured off as soon as they have sunk to the bottom and replaced with 6% mercuric chloride. The tube of fixative with its contained piece of brain is then tipped into a large vessel (at least 500 milliliters) of 6% mercuric chloride, which is agitated gently at intervals for the next five hours. When the pieces have thus been fixed, the mercuric chloride is poured off and the brain pieces, without handling, are tipped with the last of the solution into a vial of about 20-milliliter capacity. The last of the mercuric chloride is then poured off and replaced with Galescu's osmic-mercuric-chromic-acetic fixative (Chapter 17, F 1360.0010 Galescu 1918) which serves both to harden them completely and to render insoluble certain of the fatty substances present. This solution is used at a temperature of 37°C., or such approximation of this temperature as can be maintained in an available oven, for about 12 hours. A convenient time schedule is to kill the rabbit in the morning, to commence the fixation in mercuric chloride immediately, to transfer the pieces to the osmic-mercuric-chromic-acetic mixture in the evening, and continue the process the next day. The next morning the osmic-mercuric-chromic-acetic mixture is poured off, replaced with a fresh solution, and returned to the oven. In the evening the solution is again replaced, and this time the specimens are left in the oven for a whole day. The next evening, therefore, the pieces are transferred to running water for an overnight wash.

It is an integral part of Galescu's process that alcohol not be used in any stage of the technique, and the pieces are therefore next treated with an acetone-iodine solution to remove the mercury from the tissues. This solution is prepared by adding one milliliter of Lugol's iodine (Chapter 19, ADS 12.2 Lugol) to 100 milliliters of acetone. The specimens are treated for 24 hours, and about 100 milliliters should be used for half a dozen small pieces of brain. The bottle containing the pieces should be gently tipped from side to side at intervals to prevent the accumulation of depleted solution at the bottom.

The specimens are then dehydrated in pure acetone until no further iodine comes away, and embedded in paraffin, preferably by the dioxane techniques. A high-melting-point paraffin should be used, since Galescu's process depends on cutting very thin sections, 5 microns being about as thick as can be conveniently handled, and three microns being very much better if the skill of the technician permits.

The sections are mounted on a slide, dewaxed with xylene, and then transferred to acetone for the removal of the xylene. They are next placed in Galescu's crystal violet-oxalic acid stain (DS 21.22 Galescu 1908) for ten minutes, or until examination shows they have acquired a dense violet color. They are then transferred to a beaker of fresh Galescu's stain, and warmed gently on a hot plate, or in a water bath, for about five minutes or until the temperature has reached about 50°C. Each slide is then removed individually, drained, and flooded from a drop bottle with Lugol's iodine. They should under no circumstances be washed between their removal from the staining solution and their treatment with iodine. The iodine is in its turn drained from the slide and the section blotted gently with a rather stiff grade of filter paper. Each slide is then transferred to a mixture of equal parts of xylene and aniline, in which it remains until examination under the high power of a microscope shows that the required neuroglial structures are clearly differentiated. This may take from 5 minutes to 2 hours, according to the treatment which the pieces have previously received. As soon as they are found to be differentiated, the xylene-aniline mixture is washed off with xylene and the sections mounted in balsam.

21.21 NERVE CELLS AND PROCESSES

Nerve cells and processes are stained more easily by the dye-staining techniques, than they are by metal-staining techniques. It must be admitted that most of the techniques are not so specific, but they are certainly adequate for class demonstrations; and it must not be forgotten that much of the classical research was done by these methods rather than by metal stains. These techniques can be divided into three groups: first, the thiazin (methylene blue and toluidine blue) methods (DS 21.211) which were among the first to be employed; second, the great division of hematoxylin stains (DS 21.212) with which the name Weigert is linked; third, other dye-staining methods (DS 21.213) which have from time to time occurred in the literature.

21.211 Methylene Blue and Toluidine Blue Methods

The thiazin nerve-staining techniques, once far more numerous and of wider employ-ment than is today the case, can be broadly divided into two divisions: those which are customarily applied to sections of fixed material, and those which are applied to living tissues for subsequent fixation. In the latter case, some phosphomolybdate or picrate salt is applied to precipitate the blue stain which has been differentially absorbed into the nerve cells. Both methods depend for their success on accurate timing, for if the stain is permitted to act too long, other tissues than nerves become deeply stained; if too short a time is allowed for their absorption, a most disappointing result will be obtained. The classic technique for injection into the living animal is that of Bethe 1896, who published in the journal cited below no less than five separate formulas for materials designed to fix the blue in the living tissues. It is still a method which should not be ignored, since successful preparations are certainly as good as those to be obtained by the metal-staining techniques. The second type of technique for living materials is that of Cajal 1893, now practically forgotten, in which solid methylene blue is sprinkled upon a freshly cut surface of brain and allowed to absorb for such time as is considered necessary. The stain is very capricious, but the results obtained when it is used suc-cessfully are of great beauty. The technique of Betsa 1910, though slow, is one of the surest methods by which a good demonstration of Purkinje cells may be provided for class-teaching purposes.

21.211 Alzheimer 1910   Nissl and Alzheimer 1910, 409
REAGENTS REQUIRED: *A*. ADS 12.1 Weigert 1891; *B*. sat. aq. sol. phosphomolybdic acid;
   C. DS 13.7 Alzheimer 1910
METHOD: [10 μ sections by freezing technique] → water → *A*, 6 hrs. → wash → *B*, 2–12
   hrs. → rinse → *C*, till sufficiently stained → wash → balsam, via usual reagents

21.211 Bacsich 1937   11025, **72**:163
REAGENTS REQUIRED: *A*. ADS 12.1 Bacsich 1937; *B*. DS 11.124 Bacsich 1937; *C*. abs.
   alc. 50, ether 50
METHOD: [celloidin sections of formol material, attached to slide with V 21.1 Mayer 1884
   and varnished with celloidin] → water → *A*, 2 hrs. 36°C. → thorough wash → *B*, 2
   hrs. 37°C. → thorough wash → 95% alc., till dehydrated → *C*, to remove varnish →
   balsam, via usual reagents

21.211 Besta 1910   766, **36**:477
REAGENTS REQUIRED: *A*. 0.1% thionin; *B*. 20% creosote in 95% alc.; *C*. creosote
METHOD: [sections of F 0000.1200 Besta 1910 fixed material] → water → *A*, 2–3 hrs. →
   B, until differentiated → *C*, till clear → balsam, via xylene
NOTE: This method was originally recommended for the demonstration of Purkinje cells
   but is of wider application.

21.211 Bethe 1896   766, **12**:438
REAGENTS REQUIRED: *A*. sat. sol. (*circ.* 4.5%) methylene blue; *B*. sat. sol. (*circ.* 1.2%);
   ammonium picrate; *C*. water 100, sodium phosphomolybdate 5, osmic acid 0.25,
   hydrochloric acid 0.2

METHOD: [A, by copious injections into the living animal] → [small pieces of brain] → B, 15 mins. → C, 4–12 hrs. → wash → [paraffin, via usual reagents] → sections → any DS 11.21 formula if counterstain required

NOTE: Bethe, *loc. cit.*, gives the following alternative formulas for C.: I. water 100, ammonium molybdate 5, hydrochloric acid 0.2; II. water 100, ammonium molybdate 5, chromic acid 1, hydrochloric acid 0.2; III. water 100, ammonium molybdate 5, osmic acid 0.25, hydrochloric acid 0.2; IV. water 100, sodium phosphomolybdate 5, osmic acid 0.25, hydrochloric acid 0.2; V. water 100, sodium phosphomolybdate 5, hydrochloric acid 0.2. Cole 1933 (20450b, 9, 89) prefers: water 50, glycerol 50, hydrochloric acid 0.5, ammonium molybdate to excess. A detailed description of the use of this technique is given under DS 21.20 above.

21.211 Bethe *test*. 1933 Cajal and de Castro — Cajal and de Castro 1933, 169

REAGENTS REQUIRED: A. 5% nitric acid; B. 65% alc. 90, ammonium, hydroxide 10; C. 70% alc. 90, hydrochloric acid 10; D. 4% ammonium molybdate; E. 0.03% toluidine blue

METHOD: [small fragments of fresh tissue] → A, 24 hrs. → 95% alc., 24 hrs. → B, 1 wk. → 95% alc., thorough wash → C, 24 hrs. → 95% alc., thorough wash → water, wash → D, 24 hrs. → [5–8 μ paraffin sections] → water, 10–12 mins., 60°C. → E, 1–10 mins. → water, till differentiated → abs. alc., till dehydrated → balsam, via xylene

RECOMMENDED FOR: neurofibrillae.

21.211 Bethe and Mönckeberg *test*. 1933 Cajal and de Castro

Cajal and de Castro 1933, 335

REAGENTS REQUIRED: A. 0.25% osmic acid; B. water 100, sodium bisulfite 2, hydrochloric acid 1; C. 2.5% ammonium molybdate; D. 0.1% toluidine blue

METHOD: [pieces of nerve] → A, 24 hrs. → wash, 6 hrs. → 96% alc., 24 hrs. → wash, 4 hrs. → B, 18 hrs. → wash, 2–4 hrs. → [2 μ–3 μ paraffin sections] → water → B, 5–10 mins. 20°–30°C. → rinse → C, 5 mins. 50°–60°C. → rinse → balsam, via usual reagents

RECOMMENDED FOR: neurofibrillae in medullated fibers.

21.211 Bing and Ellerman 1901 — 1739, **3**:260

REAGENTS REQUIRED: A. sat. sol. (*circ.* 4.5%) methylene blue; B. sat. sol. (*circ.* 1.2%) picric acid

METHOD: [hand sections of Bing and Ellerman 1901, F 0000.1300 fixed material] → A, 5–10 mins. → B, 1 to 2 mins. → acetone, till dehydrated → balsam, via xylene

21.211 Cajal 1893 *test*. Pollack 1900 — Pollack 1900, 133

REAGENTS REQUIRED: A. methylene blue (solid powder); B. 0.1% hydrochloric acid; C. water 100, ammonium molybdate 10, hydrochloric acid 0.3; D. F 2000.1000 Cajal 1893; E. 0.3% platinic chloride; F. 0.3% platinic chloride in abs. alc.

METHOD: [small pieces of fresh, or living, tissue] → A, dusted over surface, 45 mins. → B, quick wash → C, 2 to 3 hrs. → rinse → D, 3–4 hrs. → wash briefly → E, 15 mins. → F, till dehydrated → [paraffin sections] → balsam, via usual reagents

21.211 Chang 1936 — 763, **65**:437

FORMULA: water 90, 40% formaldehyde 10, thionin 0.3

METHOD: [fresh brain tissue] → stain, few days to few months → wash → [paraffin sections] → balsam, via usual reagents

RESULT: fiber tracts, red; cell bodies, blue.

21.211 Cole 1933 *see* DS 21.211 Bethe 1896 (note)

21.211 Donaggio *test*. 1933 Cajal and de Castro — Cajal and de Castro 1933, 72

REAGENTS REQUIRED: A. pyridine; B. water 100, ammonium molybdate 4, hydrochloric acid 0.2; C. 0.01% thionin 7

METHOD: [small fragments] → A, 5–6 days → wash, 24 hrs. → B, 8 days → wash → [5 μ paraffin sections] → C, till sufficiently stained → quick rinse → B, 5 mins. → balsam, via usual reagents

RECOMMENDED FOR: neurofibrillae.

21.211 Feyrter 1936   22575, **296**:645
REAGENTS REQUIRED: *A*. water 100, tartaric acid 0.5, thionin 1.0
METHOD: [frozen sections of formaldehyde material] → *A*, 5 mins. → [add coverslip] →
cement with V 12.2 Noyer 1918
RECOMMENDED FOR: myelin sheaths.

21.211 Harris 1898   16185a, **1**:897
REAGENTS REQUIRED: *A*. 5% potassium dichromate; *B*. water 100, sodium borate 1,
toluidine blue 1; *C*. sat. sol. (*circ.* 75%) tannic acid
METHOD: *A*, till white matter dark brown → [15 μ sections] → wash → *B*, 1–2 hrs. →
rinse → *C*, till differentiated → balsam, via usual reagents

21.211 Heller, Thomas, and Davenport 1947   20540b, **22**:111
REAGENTS REQUIRED: *A*. water 90, M/15 phosphate buffer pH 5.6 5, M/2 sodium lactate
5, sodium chloride 0.6, sodium acetate 0.03, dextrose 0.2, methylene blue 0.01; *B*.
water 100, ammonium molybdate 8, potassium dichromate 1
METHOD: [thin, fresh tissues from pentobarbital-killed mammal] → *A*, 37.5°C. with pure
oxygen bubbled through solution, till nerves stained, 2–4 hrs. → *B*, 1 or more days,
→ balsam, via usual reagents [*or* paraffin sections]

21.211 Landau 1934   4285a, **11**:44
REAGENTS REQUIRED: *A*. abs. alc. 50, chloroform 50; *B*. 1% toluidine blue; *C*. 1%
toluidine blue in creosote; *D*. 1% toluidine blue in chloroform
METHOD: [pieces of formaldehyde-fixed material] → wash → drain → *A*, via graded alcs.
→ *B*, 2 days → drain and blot → *C*, 2 days → drain and blot → chloroform →
[paraffin sections]
RECOMMENDED FOR: general neurology.

21.211 Nissl *test*. **1896 Kahlden and Laurent**   Kahlden and Laurent 1896, 155
REAGENTS REQUIRED: *A*. 0.5% methylene blue; *B*. 10% aniline in 90% alc.
METHOD: [sections] → *A*, on slide, heated to steaming → alc., quick rinse → *B*, till
differentiated → balsam, via clove oil

21.211 Schabadasch 1936   4285a, **13**:137
FORMULA: water 100, sodium chloride 0.8, sodium pyruvate 0.032, magnesium bromide
0.15, glucose 0.2, methylene blue 0.025
METHOD: perfuse freshly killed animal
RECOMMENDED FOR: nerve endings in fresh tissue.

21.212 Hematoxylin methods

The literature of the hematoxylin staining techniques for nerve cells and their processes is
almost as confused as the literature of the metal-staining techniques for the same purpose.
The method is customarily and loosely referred to Weigert, who published several of the
techniques and formulas involved, and who is also responsible for the original mordant used.
His name is often coupled with that of Pal, though the latter contributed to the literature
only a method of differentiation, and not of staining. What has rendered the situation so obscure, however, is the habit of authors of referring to any of these hematoxylin techniques as
"Weigert-Pal methods," irrespective of the author to whom they are assigned. Thus Gatenby
and Cowdry 1937, say casually that the technique of Wolters 1890 is to be considered "the
standard Weigert-Pal technique," even though it differs very appreciably from any of the
methods recommended either by Weigert or Pal. At least, however, Gatenby and Cowdry
have given their reference, but the majority of authors in this field use and recommend the
most diverse techniques under the name of "Weigert-Pal." If an author says only that he
stained a nervous structure by a "Weigert-Pal" technique, it is safe only to assume that he
utilized some hematoxylin stain, which was subsequently differentiated by some method
involving a bleaching reagent. It is not quite as safe an assumption, but still very probable,
that some form of mordant was used before staining. It will have been understood from what
has been said that these techniques involve in general a mordant, usually chromic acid, or
chromium fluoride, followed by a hematoxylin stain, which is subsequently differentiated
either by another mordant (Meyer 1909) or by a bleach, usually the potassium permanganate
sodium sulfite mixture of Pal 1887. These methods tend to make sections brittle, but Miller

1926 (20540b, **1**:72) states that this can be avoided by leaving the sections for 12 hours in 80% alcohol between the staining and differentiating processes. In the technique of Olivecrona 1917, however, the mordant is incorporated with the staining mixture. In spite of the numerous modifications which have been made, the methods of Weigert 1885 and Weigert 1894 are probably the easiest and simplest to employ, though the rationalization of Anderson 1922 is now almost universal in Europe. The numerous techniques which are given below are offered less as suggestions to be followed than in the hope that they may tend to diminish the confusion by assigning to the correct author the technique which he has invented.

21.212 Anderson 1922   11977, **5**:65

REAGENTS REQUIRED: *A*. ADS 12.1 Anderson 1922; *B*. ADS 12.1 Weigert 1891; *C*. water to make 100, acetic acid 3, abs. alc. 10, hematoxylin 0.5, 2% calcium hypochlorite 3; *D*. F 7000.0000 Müller 1859; *E*. ADS 21.1 Pal 1887 (*A & B* sols.)

PREPARATION OF C: Dissolve dye in alc. Add hypochlorite. Shake well. Dilute with water and add acid.

METHOD: [15–20 μ celloidin sections] $\rightarrow$ *A*, 48 to 72 hrs. 38°C. $\rightarrow$ *B*, 10–30 mins. $\rightarrow$ wash $\rightarrow$ *C*, 1 hr., 50°C. $\rightarrow$ *D*, 10–20 mins. $\rightarrow$ wash $\rightarrow$ *E*, till differentiated $\rightarrow$ balsam, via usual reagents

RECOMMENDED FOR: myelin sheaths.

NOTE: A detailed description of the use of this technique is given under DS 21.20 above.

21.212 Anderson 1929   *see either* DS 11.121 Anderson 1929 *or* DS 11.123 Anderson 1929.

21.212 Anderson 1942   11431, **54**:258

REAGENTS REQUIRED: *A*. ADS 21.1 Anderson 1942; *B*. DS 11.113 Kultschitsky 1889; *C*. 2.5% potassium dichromate; *D*. ADS 21.1 Pal 1880 (*A* and *B* sols.); *E*. DS 11.21 Anderson 1926

METHOD: [30 μ frozen sections] $\rightarrow$ *A*, 1 hr., 50°C. $\rightarrow$ wash $\rightarrow$ *B*, 30 mins., 50°C $\rightarrow$ *C*, 2–3 mins. $\rightarrow$ wash $\rightarrow$ *D* (*A* sol.), 2 mins. $\rightarrow$ *D* (*B* sol.), 1 min. $\rightarrow$ [repeat *D* (*A*) $\rightarrow$ *D* (*B*) cycle till differentiated] $\rightarrow$ wash $\rightarrow$ *E*, 45–60 mins., 50°C. $\rightarrow$ rinse $\rightarrow$ 80% alc. $\rightarrow$ balsam, via usual reagents

21.212 Bolton 1898   11025, **32**:245

REAGENTS REQUIRED: *A*. 1% osmic acid; *B*. DS 11.113 Kultschitzky 1889; *C*. ADS 21.1 Pal 1887 (*A & B* sols.)

METHOD: [15 μ sections of formaldehyde-fixed material] $\rightarrow$ distilled water $\rightarrow$ *A*, few mins. $\rightarrow$ rinse $\rightarrow$ *B*, 3 to 24 hrs. $\rightarrow$ rinse $\rightarrow$ *C*, till differentiated $\rightarrow$ balsam, via usual reagents

RECOMMENDED FOR: myelin sheaths.

21.212 Clark and Ward 1934   20540b, **9**:34

REAGENTS REQUIRED: *A*. 4% ferric alum; *B*. DS 21.212 Weigert 1885 (sol. *C*); *C*. ADS 21.1 Pal 1887 (*A* and *B* sols.); *D*. sat. sol. lithium carbonate

METHOD: [sections] $\rightarrow$ *A*, 2–24 hrs. $\rightarrow$ quick wash $\rightarrow$ *B*, 1–2 hrs. $\rightarrow$ quick wash $\rightarrow$ *A*, till gray and white matter just distinguishable $\rightarrow$ *C* (*A* sol.), till brown $\rightarrow$ rinse $\rightarrow$ *C* (*B* sol.) till gray matter bleached $\rightarrow$ wash $\rightarrow$ *D*, 5 mins. $\rightarrow$ wash $\rightarrow$ balsam, via usual reagents

21.212 Donaggio 1939   1820, **22**:171

REAGENTS REQUIRED: *A*. ADS 12.2 Lugol; *B*. DS 11.124 Donaggio 1904; *C*. ADS 21.1 Pal 1880 (*A* and *B* solutions)

METHOD: [20 μ sections from F 3700.0010 Zenker 1894 material] $\rightarrow$ water $\rightarrow$ *A*, few moments $\rightarrow$ 90% alc., 1 hr. $\rightarrow$ water, via graded alcs. $\rightarrow$ *B*, six hrs. $\rightarrow$ *C*, (*A* sol.), 1 min. $\rightarrow$ *C* (*B* sol.), 1 min. $\rightarrow$ [repeat *C* (*A*) $\rightarrow$ *C* (*B*) cycle till differentiated] $\rightarrow$ wash $\rightarrow$ balsam, via usual reagents

RECOMMENDED FOR: differentiation of anesthetized nerves (stained) from normal nerves (unstained).

21.212 Fajerstajn 1901   16341, **1**:189

REAGENTS REQUIRED: *A*. 0.5% chromic acid; *B*. 1% hematoxylin; *C*. ADS 21.1 Pal 1887 (*A* and *B* sols.)

METHOD: [frozen sections of formaldehyde-fixed material] → water → A, 24 hrs. → wash → B, 24 hrs. → wash → C (B sol.), till decolorized → [repeat C (A) → C (B) till differentiated] → balsam, via usual reagents

RECOMMENDED FOR: myelin sheaths.

21.212 Gudden 1897   15058, **16**:24

REAGENTS REQUIRED: A. 0.5% chromic acid; B. water 90, 95% alc. 10, hematoxylin 1, 10% nitric acid 0.5; C. ADS 21.1 Pal 1887 (A & B sols.)

METHOD [20 μ celloidin sections of formalin-hardened material] → A, 10 hrs. rinse → 80% alc., till no more color comes away → B, 6–24 hrs. → wash → C, (sol. A), 15–20 secs. → C, (sol. B) few secs. → [repeat C (A) → C (B) cycle till sufficiently differentiated] → balsam, via usual reagents

RECOMMENDED FOR: myelin sheaths.

21.212 Hadjioloff 1928   *see* DS 21.212 Pal 1887 (note)

21.212 Howden 1936   *see* DS 21.212 Bolton 1898 (note)

21.212 Kaiser 1893   15058, **12**:364

REAGENTS REQUIRED: A. F 7000.0000 Müller 1859; B. F 1700.0000 Marchi 1886; C. water 50, 95% alc. 50, ferric chloride 25; D. DS 21.212 Weigert 1885 (sol. C); E. ADS 21.1 Pal 1887 (sols. A & B)

METHOD: [whole brains or pieces] → A, till hardened (some methods) → 15 mm. slices → B, 1 wk. → [25 μ sections] → C, 5 mins. → wash → D, 2 to 12 hrs. → E, till differentiated → balsam, via usual reagents

RECOMMENDED FOR: myelin sheaths.

21.212 Knower 1930   *see* DS 11.113 Knower 1930

21.212 Kozowsky 1904   *see* DS 21.212 Pal 1887 (note)

21.212 Kultschitsky 1890   766, **6**:519

REAGENTS REQUIRED: A. DS 11.113 Kultschitsky 1889; B. 1.5% lithium carbonate; C. ADS 21.1 Kultschitsky 1889

METHOD: [15–20 μ celloidin sections of F 4700.0000 Erlitzky 1877 hardened material] → A, 1–24 hrs. → B, till no more color comes away → C, till differentiated → wash → balsam, via usual reagents

RECOMMENDED FOR: myelin sheaths.

21.212 La Manna 1937   23632, **54**:257

REAGENTS REQUIRED: A. 30% ferric chloride; B. 0.5% ferric chloride; C. DS 11.121 La Manna 1937

METHOD: [paraffin sections of F 7800.1000 La Manna 1937 fixed material] → water → A, 1 hr. → B, quick rinse → C, 1 hr. → running water, overnight → B, till differentiated → thorough wash → balsam, via usual reagents

RECOMMENDED FOR: myelin sheaths.

21.212 Landau *test.* **1924 Spielmeyer**   Spielmeyer 1924, 97

REAGENTS REQUIRED: A. 3.5% ferric alum; B. 1% hematoxylin; C. "weak" hydrogen peroxide

METHOD: [celloidin sections of formaldehyde fixed material] → water → A, 12–24 hrs. → rinse → B, 12–24 hrs. → tap water, 1 hr. → C, till differentiated → balsam, via usual reagents

21.212 Landau 1938   4285a, **15**:181

REAGENTS REQUIRED: A. ADS 12.1 Landau 1938; B. 10% ferric alum; C. 1% hematoxylin D. ADS 21.1 Landau 1938

METHOD: [large pieces of formaldehyde fixed brain tissue] → thorough wash → A, 24 hrs., 25°–30°C. → thorough wash → [15 μ paraffin sections] → water → B, 3–6 hrs., 25°–30°C. → quick rinse → C, several hrs., 25°–30° → thorough wash → D, till differentiated → thorough wash → balsam, via usual reagents

21.212 Liber 1937   1887a, **24**:230

REAGENTS REQUIRED: *A*. ADS 12.1 Weigert 1896; *B*. DS 11.113 Kultschitsky 1889; *C*. 1% lithium carbonate; *D*. ADS 22.1 Pal 1887 (*A* and *B* sols.)

METHOD: [paraffin sections of formaldehyde material] → water → *A*, 12 hrs. → rinse → *B*, 1 hr. → rinse → *C*, till blue → thorough wash → *D* (*A* sol.), few seconds → *D*, (*B* sol.), till differentiated → balsam, via usual reagents

21.212 Lillie 1948a   Lillie 1948, 171

REAGENTS REQUIRED: *A*. 4% ferric alum 50, 1% hematoxylin in 95% alc. 50; *B*. 0.5% ferric alum; *C*. ADS 21.1 Lillie 1948; *D*. 0.1% safranin in 1% acetic acid

METHOD: [sections of dichromate fixed or mordanted material] → 80% alc. → *A*, 40 mins., 50°–60°C. → rinse → *B*, 1 hr. → *C*, till blue → wash → *D*, 5 mins. → balsam, via usual reagents

RECOMMENDED FOR: myelin sheaths.

21.212 Lillie 1948b   Lillie 1948, 160

REAGENTS REQUIRED: *A*. 2.5% potassium dichromate; *B*. DS 21.212 Weil 1928 (sol. *A*) *C*. 0.5% ferric alum; *D*. ADS 21.1 Lillie 1948; *E*. working solution of Sudan I prepared as in DS 22.4 Lillie 1948

METHOD: [frozen sections of formaldehyde-fixed material] → *A*, 2–4 days → wash → *B*, 45 mins. 55–60°C. → wash → *C*, till decolorized → wash → *D*, 10 mins. → wash → *E*, 10 mins. → wash → M.11 mountant

21.212 Loyez *test.* **1929 Anderson**   Anderson 1929, 65

REAGENTS REQUIRED: *A*. 4% ferric alum; *B*. abs. alc. 10, hematoxylin 1, water 90, sat. aq. sol. lithium carbonate 2; *C*. 0.1% hydrochloric acid in 70% alc.

PREPARATION OF REAGENT *B*: Dissolve hematoxylin in water. Add alc. Then add carbonate solution.

METHOD: [15–20 μ sections] → water → *A*, 24 hrs. → rinse → *B*, 2–4 hrs. 50°C. → wash → *C*, till differentiated → balsam, via usual reagents

21.212 MacConaill *test.* **1951 Gurr**   Gurr 1951, 36

STOCK SOLUTIONS: I. water 92, acetic acid 8, lead nitrate 2, acid fuchsin 0.5; II. water 96, acetic acid 4, hematoxylin 1

REAGENTS REQUIRED: *A*. stock I 50, stock II 50; *B*. water 100, ammonium molybdate 14, ammonium acetate 0.4

METHOD: [6–12 μ sections of formaldehyde-fixed material] → 30% alc. → *A*, 5 mins. → wash → *B*, 1–2 mins. → thorough wash → balsam, via usual reagents

21.212 Mallory 1936   608b, **12**:569

REAGENTS REQUIRED: *A*. sat. aq. sol. (*circ.* 1%) lead chloride; *B*. water 90, ADS 12.2 Lugol 10; *C*. 0.05% hematoxylin

METHOD: [3 mm. slices of formaldehyde-fixed material] → *A*, 6 wks. room temperature *or* 1 wk. 37°C. → wash, 24 hrs. → 80% alc., till required → [8 μ sections] → water → *B*, 1 min. → 95% alc., till color removed → *C*, ½ to 1 hr. → tap water, till blue

NOTE: All solutions must be freshly prepared immediately before use.

RECOMMENDED FOR: general neurological staining.

21.212 Mitrophanov 1896   23632, **13**:470

REAGENTS REQUIRED: *A*. ADS 12.1 Mitrophanov 1896; *B*. DS 11.113 Kultschitsky 1889; *C*. ADS 21.1 Weigert 1885

METHOD: [15–20 μ celloidin sections] → *A*, 24 hrs. 45°C. → rinse → *B*, 10 mins. → rinse → *C*, till differentiated

RECOMMENDED FOR: myelin sheaths.

21.212 Nelson *test.* **1930 Guyer**   Guyer 1930, 104

REAGENTS REQUIRED: *A*. 1% potassium hydroxide; *B*. water 75, acetic acid 12, glycerol 12, chloral hydrate 0.75; *C*. water 75, glycerol 12, DS 11.123 Ehrlich 1886 12, chloral hydrate 0.75

METHOD: [alcohol-hardened small vertebrates] → *A*, till translucent → *B*, 3 days → *C*, 7 days → *B*, till differentiated → glycerol

RECOMMENDED FOR: staining nerves in wholemounts of small vertebrates.

21.212 Neumen 1915   4349, **5**:71
REAGENTS REQUIRED: *A*. water 100, chromic acid 5, potassium dichromate 4; *B*. 3%
ferric chloride; *C*. sat. aq. sol. (*circ.* 7.5%) cupric acetate; *D*. sat. alc. sol. (*circ.* 35%)
hematoxylin; *E*. water 100, potassium ferrocyanide 7, sodium borate 0.5; *F*. sat. sol.
lithium carbonate
METHOD: [celloidin sections] → water → *A*, 2–5 mins. → wash → *B*, 2–5 mins. → wash
→ *C*, 2–5 mins. → wash → *D*, 2–5 mins. → wash → *C* (fresh sol.), till copious color
clouds are produced → wash → *D*, till differentiated → wash → *F*, 2 mins. → wash
→ balsam, via usual reagents

21.212 Olivecrona 1917   23681, **28**:521
REAGENTS REQUIRED: *A*. water 30, 95% alc. 60, hematoxylin 0.6, ferric chloride 0.15,
hydrochloric acid 0.3; *B*. water 100, ferric chloride 0.8, hydrochloric acid 1.0; *C*. sat.
sol. lithium carbonate
PREPARATION OF A: Add the dye dissolved in alc. to the iron and acid dissolved in water.
METHOD: [sections by freezing technique] → 70% alc. → *A*, 1 hr. → wash → *B*, till
differentiated → wash → *C*, till blue → balsam, via usual reagents
RECOMMENDED FOR: myelin sheaths.

21.212 Pal 1887   *Weigert-Pal—compl. script.*   23632, **6**:92
REAGENTS REQUIRED: *A*. 5% potassium dichromate; *B*. DS 21.212 Weigert 1885 (sol. *C*)
C. ADS 21.1 Pal 1887 (*A & B* sols.)
METHOD: [pieces of brain] → *A*, till white matter dark brown (some wks.) → wash → 80%
alc., till required → [section 15 μ to 20 μ] → water → *B*, 2 hrs. to 1 day → wash → *C*
(sol. *A*), 15–20 secs. → rinse → *C* (sol. *B*), few secs. → [repeat *C* (*A*) → *C* (*B*) cycle
till sufficiently differentiated] → balsam, via usual reagents
RECOMMENDED FOR: myelin sheaths.
NOTE: **Tschernyschew and Karusin 1897** (23632, **13**:354) substitute Kultschitsky 1889
DS 11.113 for *B* above. **Kozowsky 1904** (15058, **23**:1041) substitutes his ADS 21.1 for
C above. **Hadjioloff 1928** (4285a, **5**:431) counterstains in a sat. alc. sol. light green.

21.212 Schröder 1930   23430, **166**:588
REAGENTS REQUIRED: *A*. ADS 12.1 Schröder 1930; *B*. DS 11.124 Schröder 1930; *C*. 0.25%
potassium permanganate; *D*. water 100, oxalic acid 0.5, potassium sulfite 0.5; *E*. 0.02%
lithium carbonate
METHOD: [20–30 μ frozen sections of formaldehyde-fixed material] → *A*, 1 day, 37°C. →
rinse → *B*, 12 hrs., 37°C. → wash → *C*, 30 secs. → rinse → *D*, 1 min. → thorough
wash → [repeat *C* → *D* cycle if differentiation insufficient] → *E*, 15 mins. → wash →
balsam
RECOMMENDED FOR: myelin sheaths.
NOTE: **Schröder 1939** (23430, **166**:588) does not differ significantly from the above.

21.212 Schultze *test*. **1933 Cajal and de Castro**   Cajal and de Castro 1933, 234
REAGENTS REQUIRED: *A*. 1% osmic acid; *B*. 1% potassium dichromate; *C*. 0.5% hematoxylin in 70% alc.
METHOD: [small blocks of brain tissue] → *A*, overnight → *B*, in dark, 3 or 4 changes in
24 hrs. → 50% alc., 24 hrs. in dark → *C*, till stained throughout → [celloidin or
paraffin sections]
RECOMMENDED FOR: myelin sheaths.

21.212 Seidelin 1911   *see* DS 11.121 Weigert 1904 (note)

21.212 Sihler *test*. **1907 Böhm and Oppel** *cit.* **Gad**   Böhm and Oppel 1907, 268
REAGENTS REQUIRED: *A*. water 75, glycerol 12, acetic acid 12, chloral hydrate 0.75;
B. water 75, DS 11.123 Ehrlich 1886 12, glycerol 12, chloral hydrate 0.75; *C*. 0.1%
acetic acid in glycerol
METHOD: [pieces of fresh muscle] → *A*, 18 hrs. → *B*, 3 to 10 days → *C*, till differenti-
ated → glycerol

21.212 Smith and Quiegley 1937   608b, **13**:491
REAGENTS REQUIRED: *A*. 4% ferric alum; *B*. water 97, acetic acid 3, hematoxylin 1;
C. 0.5% lithium carbonate
METHOD: [sections] → water → *A*, 15 mins. → 70% alc., short wash → *B*, 30–60 mins.,
55°C. → rinse → *C*, till blue → wash → balsam, via usual reagents

21.212 Spielmeyer 1930 *test.* **1938 Mallory**   Mallory 1938, 237
REAGENTS REQUIRED: *A.* 2.5% ferric alum; *B.* water 100, 10% ripened hematoxylin in abs. alc. 5
METHOD: [20–30 μ frozen sections of formaldehyde-fixed material] → *A*, 6 hrs. → rinse → 70% alc. 10 mins. → rinse → *A*, till differentiated → balsam, via usual reagents
RECOMMENDED FOR: myelin sheaths.

21.212 Tschernyschew and Karusin 1896   *see* DS 21.212 Pal 1887 (note)

21.212 Vassale 1889   *see* DS 21.212 Weigert 1885 (note)

21.212 "Weigert-Pal" see almost any method in this section. Gatenby and Cowdry 1937, 526, state Wolters 1890 to be "the standard 'Weigert-Pal' technique."

21.212 Weigert 1885   8645, **3**:236
REAGENTS REQUIRED: *A.* 5% potassium dichromate; *B.* 3.5% copper acetate; *C.* water 90, 95% alc. 10, hematoxylin 1, sat. aq. sol. lithium carbonate 1; *D.* ADS 21.1 Weigert 1885
METHOD: [pieces of brain] → *A*, till white matter dark brown (some wks.) → [embed in celloidin] → *B*, 55°C., 2 days → 80% alc., till required → section 15–20 μ → water → *C*, 2 hrs. to 1 day → wash → *D*, till differentiated → wash → balsam, via usual reagents
RECOMMENDED FOR: myelin sheaths.
NOTE: **Vassale 1889** (19460, **15**:102) uses *B* after *C* but it is otherwise identical. **Weigert 1886** (7936a, **6**:10) substitutes for *A* his F 6700.0000 fixative.

21.212 Weigert 1904   *see* DS 11.121 Weigert 1904

21.212 Weil 1928a   *method for thin sections—auct.*   1879, **20**:392
REAGENTS REQUIRED: *A.* water 100, ferric alum 2, hematoxylin 0.5; *B.* 4% ferric alum; *C.* ADS 21.1 Weil 1928a; *D.* 0.1% ammonia
PREPARATION OF *A*: Add 50 1% hematoxylin to 50 4% ferric alum.
METHOD: [sections less than 30 μ thick] → 70% alc. → water → *A*, 20–30 mins., 55°C. → *B*, 5 mins. → *C*, till differentiated → wash → *D*, till blue → balsam, via usual reagents
RECOMMENDED FOR: myelin sheaths.

21.212 Weil 1928b   *method for thick sections—auct.*   1879, **20**:32
REAGENTS REQUIRED: *A.* 3% potassium dichromate; *B.* (see Weil 1928a, sol. *A*, above); *C.* 4% ferric alum; *D.* ADS 21.1 Weil 1928a; *E.* ADS 21.1 Weil 1928b *A* & *B* sols.; *F.* 0.1% ammonia
METHOD: [sections more than 30 μ thick] → 70% alc. → water → *A*, overnight → wash → *B*, 20–30 mins., 55°C. → *C*, 10 mins. → *D*, till differentiated → *E* (*A*), 10 mins. → *E* (*B*), till bleached → [repeat *E* (*A*) → *E* (*B*) till background sufficiently bleached] → wash → *F*, till blue → balsam, via usual reagents

21.212 Wharton 1937   763, **67**:467
REAGENTS REQUIRED: *A.* water 76, acetic acid 12, glycerol 12, chloral hydrate 0.75; *B.* water 76, DS 11.123 Ehrlich 12, glycerol 12, chloral hydrate
METHOD: [thin organs stranded on paper] → *A*, 18 hrs. → *B*, 24 hrs. → *either* glycerol *or* → balsam, via carbol-xylene
RECOMMENDED FOR: demonstration of nerves in wholemounts.

21.212 Wolters 1890   23632, **7**:466
REAGENTS REQUIRED: *A.* DS 11.113 Wolters 1890; *B.* F 7000.0000 Müller 1859; *C.* ADS 21.1 Pal 1887 (*A* & *B* sols.)
METHOD: [15–20 μ celloidin sections of Erlitzky 1877 F 4700.0000 hardened material] → *A*, 24 hrs., 45°C. → *B*, rinse → rinse → *C*, till differentiated → water, wash → balsam, via usual reagents
RECOMMENDED FOR: myelin sheaths.

21.212 Wolters *test.* **1896 Kahlden and Laurent**   Kahlden and Laurent 1896, 172
REAGENTS REQUIRED: *A.* water 100, vanadium chloride 2, ammonium acetate 6; *B.* water 100, acetic acid 3, hematoxylin 2; *C.* 0.1 hydrochloric acid in 80% alcohol

METHOD: [celloidin sections of F 4700.0010 Wolters (1896) fixed material] → water → A, 24 hrs., 50°C. → wash → B, 24 hrs., 50°C. → C, till differentiated → balsam, via usual reagents

RECOMMENDED FOR: myelin sheaths.

NOTE: Solution A, above, is not Wolters' original mordant for which see ADS 12.1 Wolters 1891.

21.212 Wright *test.* 1938 Mallory   Mallory 1938, 236

REAGENTS REQUIRED: A. 10% ferric chloride; B. 0.02% hematoxylin

METHOD: [frozen sections varnished to slide with collodion] → A, 5 mins. → blot → B, poured on slide, 30 mins. → A, till differentiated → balsam, via usual reagents

RECOMMENDED FOR: myelin sheaths.

21.213 Other Methods

So deeply have the hematoxylin methods, given in the last section, become embedded in the literature, that it is almost impossible for an author today to suggest the use of any other dye in the staining of nervous elements after mordanting. Particular attention should therefore be drawn to the formula of Becher 1921, which is permanent, easy, and simple, and which gives an admirable picture of the nervous elements in a general brain structure. It does not give so sharp a differentiation, either as a silver method, or a well-differentiated hematoxylin one, but it has at least the advantage of providing a permanent, simple, one-solution method which can with safety be placed in the hands of a beginner. Attention must also be drawn to the formula of Romeis 1922, which is designed to stain specifically the nervous elements in wholemounts of small invertebrates. The stain is certain, and completely specific, but it has the unfortunate disadvantage that no method has yet been found by which it can be rendered permanent. It should, however, be placed in the hands of any class studying small invertebrates, particularly fresh-water oligochaetes, for it is fascinating to a student to watch the development of the nervous structures as they become clearer and clearer. It is also, of course, of immense value in cases in which the morphology of the nervous system plays any part in the taxonomy of an invertebrate.

21.213 Adamkiewicz *test.* 1896 Kahlden and Laurent   Kahlden and Laurent 1896, 165

REAGENTS REQUIRED: A. 0.01% nitric acid; B. sat. aq. sol. safranin O; C. 0.01% nitric acid in abs. alc.

METHOD: [sections] → A, rinse → B, 6–12 hrs. → abs. alc., rinse → C, rinse → clove oil, till differentiated → balsam

RECOMMENDED FOR: general neurological staining.

21.213 Alzheimer 1910   Nissl and Alzheimer 1910, 410

REAGENTS REQUIRED: A. 4% formaldehyde; B. F 1600.0010 Flemming 1882; C. sat. aq. sol. acid fuchsin; D. 0.6% picric acid; E. sat. aq. sol. light green

METHOD: [fresh tissue] → A, 24 hrs. → B, 8 days → wash → [2–3 μ paraffin sections] → 95% alc. → C, 1 hr. at 60°C. → wash till no more color comes away → D, 15–20 secs. → rinse twice → E, 20–50 mins. → balsam via usual reagents

RECOMMENDED FOR: general neurological staining.

NOTE: *See also* DS 22.8 Alzheimer 1910.

21.213 Aronson 1890   23730, **28**:577

REAGENTS REQUIRED: A. F 7000.0000 Müller 1859; B. 2% copper acetate; C. water 85, 95% alc. 15, sodium carbonate 0.03, gallein to sat.; D. ADS 21.1 Weigert 1885

METHOD: [whole brains] → A, till hardened → [15 mm. slices] → B, 1 wk. → wash → [12–25 μ sections] → C, 24 hrs. → rinse → D, till differentiated → balsam, via usual reagents

NOTE: Erlitzky 1877 F 4700.0000 may replace A, with the consequent omission of B.

21.213 Becher 1921   *see* DS 13.5 Becher 1921c

21.213 Boissezon 1941   4285a, **18**:90
REAGENTS REQUIRED: A. acetone; B. sat. 70% alc. sol. Sudan black B
METHOD: [frozen sections] → A, 15 mins. → 70% alc., 10 mins. → B, 5 mins. → 60%
alc., till differentiated → M 12.1 mountant
RECOMMENDED FOR: myelin of peripheral nerves.

21.213 Bretschneider 1914   10899, **52**:271
REAGENTS REQUIRED: A. 1% eosin; B. DS 11.122 Delafield (1885); C. 1% phosphomolybdic acid; D. DS 13.41 Mallory 1901 (sol. C)
METHOD: [sections of formaldehyde-fixed material] → water → A, 20 mins. → wash →
B, 30 secs. → wash → C, 2–3 mins. → wash → D, 10 secs. → wash → balsam, via
usual reagents
RECOMMENDED FOR: insect brains.

21.213 Campbell 1929   *see* DS 23.223 Campbell 1929

21.213 Chilesotti *test.* **Böhm and Oppel** *cit.* **Schmaus**   Böhm and Oppel 1907, 289
REAGENTS REQUIRED: A. sodium carminate 1, uranium nitrate 100, water 100, hydro-
chloric acid 0.03; B. 0.5% hydrochloric acid; C. F 7000.0000 Müller 1859
METHOD: [sections of chrome, or dichromate, fixed material] → water → A, 1 hr. → B,
till differentiated → wash → C, 1 hr. → wash → balsam, via usual reagents
RECOMMENDED FOR: axis cylinders.

21.213 Eberspache 1936   *see* ADS 22.1 Eberspache 1936

21.213 Gross 1952   *Tech. Bull.*, **22**:234
STOCK SOLUTIONS: I. 4% magenta in 95% alc.; II. 6% phenol; III. 1.5% methylene blue
in 95% alc.
REAGENTS REQUIRED: A. stock I 25, stock II 75, tergitol 7 0.1; B. 3% hydrochloric acid
in 95% alc.; C. water 100, stock III 30, potassium hydroxide 0.01
METHOD: [smears] → A, 5–10 mins. → rinse → B, ½ to 1 min. with agitation → rinse
→ C, 3–5 mins. → rinse → dry

21.213 Lison and Dagnelle 1935   4285a, **12**:85
REAGENTS REQUIRED: A. sat. 70% alc. sol. Sudan black B
METHOD: [30 μ frozen sections of formaldehyde-fixed material] → water → 70% alc. →
→ A, 1–12 hrs. → 50% alc., till differentiated → water → M 12.1 mountant
RECOMMENDED FOR: myelin sheaths.

21.213 McManns 1946   *see* DS 22.21 McManns 1946

21.213 Menner 1935   23822, **110**:200
STOCK SOLUTION: water 100, oxalic acid 2, potassium antimony tartrate 0.5, azoacid
blue B 1. Boil; cool. Filter.
REAGENTS REQUIRED: A. 0.005% chromic acid; B. water 96, stock solution 4
METHOD: [pieces of fresh spinal cord] → A, 2–8 days → rinse → B, 24 hrs. → rinse →
glycerol, via graded glycerol-water series
RECOMMENDED FOR: ganglion cells in wholemounts.

21.213 Nikiforoff *test.* **1896 Kahlden and Laurent**   Kahlden and Laurent 1896, 166
REAGENTS REQUIRED: A. sat. sol. safranin in sat. sol. aniline; B. 0.2% gold chloride
METHOD: [sections of chrome-fixed materials] → A, 24 hrs. → 95% alc., till gray matter
begins to differentiate from white → B, till violet → thorough wash → 95% alc., till
gray matter clearly differentiated from white → balsam, via clove oil
RECOMMENDED FOR: general neurological staining.

21.213 Nissl *test.* **1896 Kahlden and Laurent**   Kahlden and Laurent 1896, 156
REAGENTS REQUIRED: sat. aq. sol. magenta
METHOD: [sections] → stain, on slide, heated to steaming, few moments → abs. alc., till
color clouds cease → oil of cloves, till differentiated → balsam, via xylene
RECOMMENDED FOR: nerve cells and processes.

21.213 Obersteiner *test.* **1896 Kahlden and Laurent**   Kahlden and Laurent 1896, 175

REAGENTS REQUIRED: *A.* 20% ferric chloride; *B.* sat. sol. dinitroresorcinol in 75% alc.

METHOD: [pieces of nerve trunks] → *A*, 1 to 2 days → wash, till wash water iron-free → *B*, several wks. → [paraffin sections]

RESULT: axis cylinders bright green.

21.213 O'Leary *test.* **1943 Cowdry**   Cowdry 1943, 144

REAGENTS REQUIRED: *A.* 3% potassium dichromate *or* F 7000.0000 Müller 1859; *B.* water 100, acetic acid 0.2, abs. alc. 10, brazilin 1; *C.* 0.25% potassium permanganate; *D.* ADS 21.1 Weil 1928b

PREPARATION OF B: Dissolve the dye in alc. Allow to "ripen" 1–6 months. Add other ingredients.

METHOD: [celloidin sections of F 7000.0000 Müller 1859 fixed tissue] → water → *A*, 12–24 hrs. → *B*, till deeply stained → water, wash → *C*, till differentiated, 1–5 mins. → *D*, till permanganate decolorized → water, wash → balsam, via usual reagents

21.213 Prince 1952   4349, **11**:55

FORMULA: sat. aq. magenta 6, 1% erythrosin 17.5, sat. aq. sol. methyl orange 47, sat. aq. sol. anilin blue 29.5

METHOD: [sections of formaldehyde-fixed material] → water → stain, 10–30 secs. → wash → abs. alc. → balsam, via xylene

21.213 Romeis 1922   6628, **175**:455

REAGENTS REQUIRED: *A.* water 100, benzidine 1, acetic acid 0.1; *B.* "12 vol." hydrogen peroxide

METHOD: [small invertebrates, either living or alcohol-fixed] → *A*, ½ to 1 hr. → *B*, dropped directly on animal on slide → examine

RECOMMENDED FOR: demonstration of nervous system of small invertebrates.

NOTE: The stain is specific but fugitive.

21.213 Schrotter 1902   15058, **21**:338

REAGENTS REQUIRED: *A.* water 100, alizarin red S 5, oxalic acid 0.01; *B.* water 100, sodium carbonate 0.3

METHOD: [sections] → *A*, 2–3 hrs. → *B*, till no more color comes away → balsam, via usual reagents

21.213 Tress and Tress 1935   20540b, **10**:105

REAGENTS REQUIRED: *A.* water 100, acetic acid 0.01, cresyl violet 0.5; *B.* chloroform 75, abs. alc. 12.5, ether 12.5; *C.* 0.0025 hydrochloric acid in 95% alc.; *D.* 0.01% sodium bicarbonate in 95% alc.

METHOD: [celloidin sections of formaldehyde-fixed material] → water → *A*, 30 mins. 50°C. → wash → 70% alc., till celloidin stain-free → *B*, 2–5 mins. *C*, till differentiated → *D*, till neutralized → 95% alc., wash → balsam, via n-butyl alc.

21.213 Verne 1928   4285a, **5**:223

REAGENTS REQUIRED: *A.* DS 11.44 Schiff 1866; *B.* water 100, sodium metabisulfite 0.5, hydrochloric acid 5

METHOD: [frozen sections of mercuric or platinic fixed nerves] → 90% alc., 10 mins. → *A*, till deep red → *B*, wash in several changes → rinse → M 11.1 Apáthy 1892

RECOMMENDED FOR: selective staining of myelin.

21.22 METHODS FOR NEUROGLIA

The crystal violet and victoria blue methods for staining the supporting elements of the nervous system are less specific than are the metal stains. They still occur with some frequency in the literature, however, and are warmly advocated by many technicians.

21.22 Alzheimer 1910a *test.* **1938 Mallory**   Mallory 1938, 245

REAGENTS REQUIRED: *A.* F 1600.0010 Flemming 1882; *B.* sat. aq. sol. acid fuchsin; *C.* 3% picric acid in 30% alc.; *D.* 10% light green

METHOD: [thin slices of formaldehyde-fixed material] → *A*, 8 days in dark → wash → [2–4 μ paraffin sections] → *B*, 1 hr., 60°C. → wash → *C*, few secs. to 2 mins. → wash → *D*, ½ to 1 hr. → wash → 95% alc., till violet → abs. alc., minimum possible time → balsam, via xylene

. 21.22 Alzheimer 1910b *test.* **1938 Mallory**   Mallory 1938, 245

REAGENTS REQUIRED: *A.* ADS 12.1 Weigert 1891 90; *B.* sat. sol., (*circ.* 60%) phosphomolybdic acid, 40% formaldehyde 10; *C.* DS 13.7 Mann 1892a

METHOD: [slices of fresh tissue] → *A*, 2 wks. → wash → [10 μ frozen sections] → *B*, 2–12 hrs. → quick wash → *C*, 1–5 hrs. → water, till color clouds cease → 95% alc., till gray matter blue and white matter pink → abs. alc. minimum possible time → balsam, via xylene

21.22 Alzheimer 1910c *test.* **1938 Mallory**   Mallory 1938, 245

REAGENTS REQUIRED: *A.* ADS 12.1 Weigert 1891; *B.* 0.5% acetic acid; *C.* DS 11.124 Mallory 1891 3, water 97

METHOD: [slices of fresh tissue] → *A*, 2 wks. → wash → [10–12 μ frozen sections] → *B*, 2 mins. → *C*, 2 mins. → rinse → balsam, via usual reagents

21.22 Anderson 1923   11431, **26**:431

REAGENTS REQUIRED: *A.* F 5000.1010 Bouin 1897; *B*, ADS 12.2 Anderson 1923 stock A 65, stock B 35; *C*, ADS 21.1 Pal 1887 (*A & B* sols.); *D.* 1.5% Victoria blue; *E.* ADS 12.2 Lugol (1905); *F.* aniline 50, xylene 50

METHOD: [frozen sections of formaldehyde-fixed material] → *A*, overnight → 70% alc., wash → *B*, 10–30 mins. → wash → *C*, (*A* sol.), 5 mins. → *C* (*B* sol.), 5 mins. or until next required → [sections attached to slide] → *D*, flooded on slide while boiling, 5 mins. → drain → *E*, dropped on slide 1 min. → *F*, 15 secs. → xylene, till clear → *F*, till differentiated → balsam, via xylene

NOTE: Anderson later (Anderson 1929, 133) recommended equal parts stock A and stock B for mixture *B* above.

21.22 Anglade and Morel 1901   19219, **9**:137

REAGENTS REQUIRED: *A.* 6% mercuric chloride; *B.* F 1360.0010 Galescu 1908; *C.* sat. sol. (*circ.* 4%) Victoria blue; *D.* ADS 12.2 Lugol (1905); *E.* xylene 35, aniline 65

METHOD: [pieces of tissue] → *A*, 5 hrs. → *B*, 12 hrs., 37°C. → *B*, (fresh sol.), 12 hrs. 37°C. → *B*, (fresh sol.) 24 hrs. 37°C. → wash → [paraffin sections] → water → *C*, poured on slide and heated to steaming → *D*, used to wash *C* from slide → *E*, till differentiated → balsam, via xylene

21.22 Bailey 1923   11343, **44**:73

FORMULA OF DRY STOCK: water 100, orange G 0.5, ethyl violet 1

PREPARATION DRY STOCK: Digest 1 day 40°C. Filter. Wash and dry filtrate.

PREPARATION OF STOCK SOLUTION: 95% alc. 100, dry powder from above to sat.

REAGENTS REQUIRED: *A.* ADS 12.2 Gram 1884; *B.* 3% potassium dichromate; *C.* water 60, 96% alc. 15, stock solution 25; *D.* clove oil 75, 95% alc. 25

METHOD: [paraffin sections of F 3700 or F 5000 fixed material] → *A*, few mins. → 95% alc., wash → *B*, 3 days → wash → *C*, 12 hrs. → acetone, wash → toluene, few mins. → clove oil, till toluene removed → *D*, till differentiated → balsam, via toluene

21.22 Bauer 1941   1799, **114**:71

REAGENTS REQUIRED: *A.* 5% ferric alum; *B.* DS 11.124 Held (1937) 10, water 100; *C.* ADS 21.1 Weigert 1885; *D.* 5% sodium phosphate, dibasic

METHOD: [paraffin sections of F 3700.0010 Zenker 1894 fixed material] → water → *A*, 20 mins., 40°C. → rinse → *B*, 12 hrs., 40°C. → rinse → *C*, till differentiated → *D*, wash → wash → balsam, via usual reagents

21.22 Benda *test.* **1933 Cajal and de Castro**   Cajal and de Castro 1933, 241

REAGENTS REQUIRED: *A.* 10% nitric acid; *B.* 2% potassium dichromate; *C.* 1% chromic acid; *D.* 4% ferric alum; *E.* "amber yellow" solution of alizarin red S; *E.* 0.1% toluidine blue; *F.* 1% acetic acid; *G.* creosote

METHOD: [pieces of 5 mm. side] → 95% alc., 2 days or longer → *A*, 24 hrs. → wash → *B*, 24 hrs. → *C*, 24 hrs. → wash → [paraffin sections] → water → *D*, 24 hrs. → rinse → *E*, 2 hrs. → rinse → blot → *E*, warmed to steaming, 15 mins. → *F*, wash → abs. alc., till dehydrated → *G*, till differentiated → balsam, via xylene

RECOMMENDED FOR: macroglia.

21.22 Beyer 1940 591b, **4**:65

REAGENTS REQUIRED: *A*. F 7000.0000 Müller 1859; *B*. DS 11.121 Hansen 1905; *C*. 2% hydrochloric acid, in 70% alc.; *D*. 0.1% ammonia; *E*. water 100, acetic acid 0.3, ponceau 2R 0.07, acid fuchsin 0.03; *F*. water 100, phosphotungstic acid 3, orange *G*. 2; G 0.5% anilin blue

METHOD: [5 μ sections of formaldehyde-fixed material] → *A*, 3–12 hrs. → thorough wash → *B*, 5 mins. → wash → *C*, till differentiated → wash → *D*, till blue → wash → *E*, 5 mins. → wash → *F*, 5 mins. → quick rinse → *G*, 10–15 mins. → abs. alc., least possible time → balsam, via xylene

RECOMMENDED FOR: astrocytes.

21.22 Brand 1941 *see* DS 21.22 Holzer 1921 (note)

21.22 Eisath 1911 14370, **20**:3

REAGENTS REQUIRED: *A*. 2% formaldehyde; *B*. 0.2% mercuric chloride; *C*. water 70, DS 11.124 Mallory 1891 30; *D*. ADS 21.1 Eisath 1911

METHOD: [sections by freezing technique of F 7000.1000 Eisath 1911 fixed material] → *A*, till required → *B*, 30 secs. → wash → *C*, on slide, few minutes → wash → *D*, till differentiated → wash → balsam, via usual reagents

21.22 Galescu 1908 6630, **65**:429

REAGENTS REQUIRED: *A*. 6% mercuric chloride; *B*. F 1360.0010 Galescu 1908; *C*. acetone 100, ADS 12.2 Lugol 1; *D*. water 80, 95% alc. 20, crystal violet 5, oxalic acid 0.2; *E*. ADS 12.2 Lugol; *F*. xylene 50, aniline 50

METHOD: [pieces of brain] → *A*, 5 hrs. → *B*, 12 hrs. 37°C. → *B* (fresh sol.), 12 hrs. 37°C. → *B* (fresh sol.), 24 hrs. 37°C. → wash → *C*, 24 hrs. → [3 μ paraffin sections, via acetone] → acetone → *D*, 10 mins. → *D*, (warmed till steaming) 5 mins. → *E* (poured on slide), few moments → blot → *F*, till differentiated → balsam

NOTE: A detailed description of the use of this technique is given under DS 21.20 above.

21.22 Hadjioloff 1929 6630, **102**:789

REAGENTS REQUIRED: *A*. sat. alc. sol. (*circ.* 0.2%) acid fuchsin; *B*. sat. aq. sol. (*circ.* 20%) light green

METHOD: [5 μ paraffin sections of F 1600.0010 Flemming 1884 fixed material] → water → *A*, 5–15 mins., 60°C. → wash → *B*, 10–20 mins. → wash → balsam, via usual reagents

21.22 Held 1909 *test.* **1933 Cajal and de Castro** Cajal and de Castro 1933, 245

REAGENTS REQUIRED: *A*. 1% sodium hydroxide in 80% alc.; *B*. 5% ferric alum; *C*. to 100 1% hematoxylin add an excess of molybdic acid: dilute to an "intense violet" color for use; *D*. DS 12.221 van Gieson 1896

METHOD: [celloidin sections of material fixed in F 3700.1010 Held 1909] → *A*, 5 mins. → wash → *B*, 1 min. → wash → *C*, 24 hrs., 50°C. → rinse → *B*, till connective tissues decolorized → wash → *D*, 15 secs. → abs. alc., till no more color comes away → balsam, via usual reagents

RECOMMENDED FOR: macroglia.

21.22 Holzer 1921 23430, **60**:354

REAGENTS REQUIRED: *A*. water 30, 95% alc. 60, phosphomolybdic acid 0.2; *B*. chloroform 80, abs. alc. 20; *C*. chloroform 80, abs. alc. 20, crystal violet 5; *D*. 10% potassium bromide; *E*. choroform 60, aniline 40, hydrochloric acid 0.3

METHOD: [sections by freezing technique of formaldehyde-fixed material] → *A*, 30–90 secs. → float to slide, blot with paper soaked in *B* → *C*, on slide, 3–5 mins. → *D*, wash → blot with filter paper soaked in *E* → *E*, till differentiated → balsam, via xylene

NOTE: Holzer 1921 (23632, **37**:508) differs only in substituting aniline for *E* above. Brand 1912 (23430, **172**:531) recommends counterstaining in his DS 12.221.

21.22 Jakob 1913 *test.* **1937 Gatenby and Painter** Gatenby and Painter 1937, 542

REAGENTS REQUIRED: *A*. ADS 12.1 Weigert 1891, 90, 40% formaldehyde 10; *B*. 0.1% acid fuchsin; *C*. sat. aq. sol. (*circ.* 60%) phosphomolybdic acid; *D*. DS 13.41 Mallory 1901, sol. C

METHOD: [frozen sections of material fixed in A] → water → B, 3–10 mins. → wash → C, 1–24 hrs. → rinse → D, 30 mins. → 95% alc., till differentiated → balsam, via usual reagents

21.22　Lehrmitte and Guccione 1909　　　　　　20080, **19**:205
REAGENTS REQUIRED: A. 7% mercuric chloride; B. F 1600.0010 Lehrmitte and Guccione 1909; C. 1.5% Victoria blue; D. ADS 12.2 Lugol; E. aniline 50, xylene 50
METHOD: [sections of formaldehyde-fixed material by freezing technique] → A, 2 hrs. → B, 2 days → wash → strand section on slide → C, poured on slide, warmed to steaming → drain → D, 1 min. → drain → E, till differentiated → balsam, via xylene

21.22　Mallory 1938　　　　　　　　　　　　Mallory 1938, 241
REAGENTS REQUIRED: A. sat. sol. lead chloride; B. 5% oxalic acid; C. DS 11.124 Mallory 1900
METHOD: [2–3 mm. slices of formaldehyde-fixed material] → A, 6 wks. → wash → [celloidin sections] → B, 30–60 mins. → rinse → 95% alc. → balsam, via usual reagents

21.22　Merzbacher 1909　　　　　　　　　11392, **12**:1
REAGENTS REQUIRED: A. 95% alc. 70, water 30, sodium hydroxide 2; B. sat. aq. sol. Victoria blue; C. ADS 12.2 Lugol; (1905); D. aniline 50, xylene 50
METHOD: [10–15 μ sections] → A, 2–5 mins. → rinse alc. → water → B, 24 hrs. → C, rinse → D, till differentiated → balsam, via xylene

21.22　Meyer 1909　　　　　　　　　　　15058, **28**:353
REAGENTS REQUIRED: A. 5% potassium dichromate; B. ADS 12.1 Weigert 1891 at 37°C.; C. DS 11.121 Weigert 1904; D. water 70, ADS 21.1 Weigert 1885 30
METHOD: [pieces of brain] → A, till white matter dark brown → [50 μ sections by celloidin technique] → water → B, 24 hrs., 38°C. → wash 70% alc. → C, 24 hrs. → D, till differentiated → balsam, via usual reagents

21.22　Peers 1941　　　　　　　　　　　　1887a, **32**:446
REAGENTS REQUIRED: A. 6% mercuric chloride; B. AMS 12.2 Lugol; C. 5% sodium sulfite; D. 0.025% potassium permanganate; E. 5% oxalic acid; F. DS 11.124 Mallory 1900
METHOD: [sections of formaldehyde-fixed material] → A, 3 hrs., 57°C. → rinse → B, 5 mins. → rinse → C, 5 mins. rinse → D, 5 mins. → rinse → E, 5 mins. → thorough wash → F, overnight → wash → balsam, via usual reagents

21.22　Potter 1910　　　　　　　　　　　23632, **27**:238
REAGENTS REQUIRED: A. ADS 12.1 Weigert 1891; B. DS 21.22 Weigert 1903; C. 0.5% potassium permanganate; D. ADS 21.1 Weigert 1885
METHOD: [15 mm. slices of formaldehyde-fixed material] → A, 14 days → alc. wash → [15 μ celloidin sections] → water → B, 2–3 hrs. → wash → C, till differentiation well started → D, till differentiation completed → balsam, via usual reagents
RECOMMENDED FOR: macroglia.

21.22　Rubaschkin 1904　　　　　　　　　1780, **63**:577
REAGENTS REQUIRED: A. sat. aq. sol. (circ. 3%) methyl violet; B. ADS 12.2 Gram 1884; C. aniline
METHOD: [celloidin sections of F 4700.0010 Rubaschkin 1904 fixed material] → A, on slide, 6–12 hrs. → B, on slide, ½ to 1 min. → C, till differentiated → balsam, via xylene

21.22　Sokolansky 1935　　　　　　　　　23632, **51**:378
REAGENTS REQUIRED: A. 6% potassium dichromate; B. DS 11.113 Kultschitsky 1889; C. F 7000.0000 Müller 1850; D. ADS 21.1 Pal 1887 (A and B sols.)
METHOD: [5–8 μ frozen sections] → A, 24 hrs., 37°C. → rinse → B, 4–6 hrs., 50–60°C. → C, 2–3 mins. → rinse → D (A sol.), few mins. → rinse → D (B sol.), till decolorized → [repeat D (A) → D (B) cycle if insufficiently differentiated] → balsam, via usual reagents

21.22 Weigert 1891   *see* DS 21.22 Weigert 1894 (note)

21.22 Weigert 1894   7276, **17**:1184

REAGENTS REQUIRED: *A.* 5% potassium dichromate; *B.* ADS 12.1 Weigert 1891; *C.* water 46, 95% alc. 64, sat. alc. sol. lithium carbonate 4, hematoxylin 1; *D.* ADS 21.1 Weigert 1885

PREPARATION OF C: Add the dye dissolved in alc. to the water and alkali.

METHOD: [pieces of brain] → *A*, till white matter dark brown (some wks.) → [embed in celloidin] → *B*, 24 hrs., 55°C. → [section, 15–20 μ] → water → *C*, 4–24 hrs. → wash, 90% alc. → wash → *D*, till differentiated → balsam, via usual reagents

RECOMMENDED FOR: neuroglia.

NOTE: **Weigert 1891** (7276, **17**:1184) omits *D*. **Weigert 1903** (Ehrlich, Krause, *et al.* 1910, 942) substitutes for *C* the following: To 50 0.4% ferric chloride add 50 1% hematoxylin in 95% alc.

21.22 Weigert 1895 *test.* **1937 Gatenby and Painter**   Gatenby and Painter 1937, 337

This method involved the use of a proprietary reagent of secret composition and cannot therefore be further noticed. Any of the Victoria blue or crystal violet methods recorded in this section may be substituted.

21.22 Weigert 1903   *see* DS 21.22 Weigert 1894 (note)

21.22 Windle, Rhines, and Rankin 1943   *see* DS 22.3 Windle, *et al.* 1943 (note)

21.23 METHODS FOR OTHER NERVOUS ELEMENTS

21.23 Koinikow *test.* **1933 Cajal and de Castro**   Cajal and de Castro 1933, 320

REAGENTS REQUIRED: *A.* F 7000.1000 Orth 1896; *B.* F 7000.0000 Müller 1859; *C.* F 1700.-0000 Marchi 1886; *D.* sat. aq. sol. phosphomolybdic acid; *E.* DS 13.7 Mann 1894a (*A* sol.); *F.* 0.1% sodium hydroxide in abs. alc.; *G.* 0.01% acetic acid in abs. alc.

METHOD: [piece of nerve] → *A*, 24 hrs. → *B*, till required → *C*, 8–10 days → [teased preparations *or* celloidin sections] → *D*, 1 hr. → wash → *E*, 24 hrs. → rinse → abs. alc., till dehydrated → *F*, till color changes from blue to red → wash, abs. alc. → *G*, till color changes from red to blue → wash, abs. alc. → xylene → white petroleum *or* "neutral mountant"

RECOMMENDED FOR: Schwann cells.

21.23 Fieandt *test.* **1933 Cajal and de Castro**   Cajal and de Castro 1933, 265

REAGENTS REQUIRED: *A.* 10% iodine in 95% alc.; *B.* 0.25% sodium thiosulfate; *C.* DS 11.124 Mallory 1900; *D.* 10% ferric chloride in abs. alc.

METHOD: [5 μ sections of 2 mm. slices fixed in F 3000.0012 Heidenhain 1909] → water → *A*, few mins. → 95% alc. till no more color comes away → *B*, 1 hr. → wash → *C*, 10–14 hrs. → blot → *D*, till differentiated, some hrs. → blot → quick rinse → abs. alc., 24 hrs. → balsam, via oil of thyme

RECOMMENDED FOR: gliosomes.

21.23 Nageotte *test.* **1933 Cajal and de Castro**   Cajal and de Castro 1933, 325

REAGENTS REQUIRED: *A.* 30% alc.; *B.* 0.1% nitric acid; *C.* DS 11.122 Cajal and de Castro 1933; *D.* DS 12.211 Cajal 1895

METHOD: [fresh piece of nerve] → *A*, 1 day → *B*, till fibers dissociated → [tease on slide] → *C*, till deep blue → wash → *D*, till differentiated → balsam, via usual reagents

RECOMMENDED FOR: syncytium of Schwann cells.

21.23 Nageotte *test.* **1933 Cajal and de Castro**   Cajal and de Castro 1933, 319

REAGENTS REQUIRED: *A.* 2.5% ferric alum; *B.* 1% hematoxylin

METHOD: [pieces of nerve, fixed in F 3900.1000 Dominici 1905 and teased on a slide] → *A*, some hrs. → *B*, some hrs. → *C*, till differentiated → wash → balsam, via usual reagents

RECOMMENDED FOR: selective staining of Schwann cells.

21.23 Reich   *see* DS 22.8 Reich (1933)

21.3 Special Stains for Blood

Nowhere is the purpose of the present writer in his classification of staining techniques more likely to be misunderstood than in this division. At least a hundred methods for staining blood have been advocated, and it is today conventional to utilize only the methods given in Chapter 20 (DS 13.1, 13.2, and to a less extent 13.3). Those techniques are, however, of far wider application, for they may be used for sections, for staining parasites in blood, and for many other purposes. Moreover, blood films themselves may be excellently stained by almost any triple-staining method, though it usually is a surprise to the hematologist who has seen nothing but a methylene blue-eosin preparation to observe the magnificent differentiation which can be secured by many of the DS 12.3 or DS 13.4 techniques. Under these circumstances the writer has included in the present section only those methods of staining blood which are useless for any other purpose.

21.3 Brice 1930   *see* DS 22.8 Brice 1930

21.3 Bruner and Edwards 1940   *see* DS 23.219 Bruner and Edwards 1940

21.3 Bacsich 1936   11025, **70**:267
> REAGENTS REQUIRED: *A*. water 20, 95% alc. 80, phenol 2.5, Sudan III 0.5; *B*. DS 11.121 Weigert 1903; *C*. 0.5% hydrochloric acid in 40% alc.
> PREPARATION OF A: Boil the dye 5 minutes in 100 95% alc. Add phenol and filter hot. Cool to 4°C., 24 hours. Filter. Add water drop by drop till alc. concentration reduced to 80%.
> METHOD: [air-dried smears] → *A*, on slide, 5 mins., 56°C. → thorough wash → *B*, 30–60 secs. → rinse → *C*, till differentiated → wash → dry → M 12.1 Zwemer 1933

21.3 Baillif and Kimbrough 1947   11284, **32**:155
> REAGENTS REQUIRED: *A*. sat. sol. Sudan black B in 70% alc.; *B*. DS 13.11 May and Grunwald 1902; *C*. DS 13.13 Giemsa 1902 2, water 98
> METHOD: [alc.-formaldehyde-fixed smears] → *A*, 30–60 mins. → rinse → *B*, on slide, 3 mins. → add water, 1 min. → drain → *C*, on slide, 15 mins. → wash → dry

21.3 Buzard 1930   4285a, **7**:264
> REAGENTS REQUIRED: *A*. 1% acid fuchsin; *B*. 0.8% bromine water; *C*. 1% hydrochloric acid in 95% alc.
> METHODS: [fixed smears] → *A*, 30 secs. → *B*, 4–5 mins. → wash → *C*, till mauve → balsam, via usual reagents

21.3 Campbell and Alexander *test*. 1938 Mallory   Mallory 1938, 257
> REAGENTS REQUIRED: *A*. acetic acid 0.5, benzidine 0.1, sodium nitroferricyanide 0.1; *B*. water 100, 30% hydrogen peroxide 0.1
> PREPARATION OF A: Dissolve benzidine in acetic acid and dilute to 20. Dissolve nitroferricyanide in 20 water and add to benzidine. Dilute mixture to 100. Filter.
> METHOD: [200 to 300 μ frozen sections of formaldehyde-fixed material] → *A*, 30 mins. 37°C. with frequent shaking → rinse → *B*, 30 mins., 37°C. with frequent shaking → balsam, via usual reagents
> RECOMMENDED FOR: capillaries in brain.
> RESULT: capillaries black against colorless background.

21.3 Crossmon 1940   20540b, **15**:155
> REAGENTS REQUIRED: *A*. water 100, acetic acid 1, chromotrope 2R 0.25; *B*. 5% phosphotungstic acid in 95% alc.; *C*. water 100, acetic acid 1, methyl blue 0.5; *D*. 2% acetic acid
> METHOD: [sections from formaldehyde-fixed material] → water → *A*, 1–5 mins. → rinse → *B*, till erythrocytes alone stained → *C*, 2–5 mins. → *D*, till differentiated → balsam, via usual reagents
> RECOMMENDED FOR: differential staining of erythrocytes in sections.

21.3 Cunningham 1920   1845, **26**:405
REAGENTS REQUIRED: *A*. 0.3% brilliant cresyl blue in 95% alc.; *B*. DS 13.12 Wright 1910
METHOD: [dip coverslip in *A* and dry] → make smear on clean cover → press to *A* →
separate → dry → *B*, full technique → dry
RECOMMENDED FOR: reticulocytes.

21.3 Dekhuyzen 1901   766, **19**:536
FORMULA: water 100, osmic acid 1.8, acetic acid 0.6, methylene blue 0.1
METHOD: blood drop on slide → stain, mixed with drop → smear → dry

21.3 Doherty, Suk and Alexander 1938   1879, **40**:158
REAGENTS REQUIRED: *A*. water 50, abs. alc. 50, benzidine 0.5, sodium nitroferricyanide
0.1; *B*. water 50, abs. alc. 50, acetic acid 2, hydrogen peroxide 0.5, sodium nitroferricyanide 0.1
PREPARATION OF REAGENT A: Dissolve the benzidine in the abs. alc. Dissolve the nitro-
ferricyanide in 10 water. Mix and dilute to 100.
METHOD: [200–300 μ sections of formaldehyde fixed material] → wash → *A*, with frequent agitation 10 mins. → rinse → *B*, with frequent agitation, till capillary net
stained → wash → balsam, via usual reagents
RECOMMENDED FOR: differential staining of blood in capillaries in sections.

21.3 Dubuscq 1899   1915, **6**:481
FORMULA: water 250, copper chloride 0.6, copper acetate 0.6, osmic acid 0.6, acetic acid
0.6, thionin 0.6
METHOD: Mix equal parts stain and arthropod blood. Leave 5 mins. Make smear.

21.3 Ellermaner 1919   23633, **36**:56
REAGENTS REQUIRED: *A*. water 100, eosin B 1, neutralized formaldehyde 5; *B*. DS 13.13
Maximow 1924
METHOD: [5 μ sections of F 3700.1000 Maximow 1909 material] → water → drain → *A*,
15 mins. → wash, 2 mins., 45°C. → *B*, 30 mins. → wash → blot → abs. alc., till sec-
tion blue → balsam, via xylene

21.3 Epstein *test.* **1946 Roskin**   Roskin 1946, 243
REAGENTS REQUIRED: *A*. water 100, citric acid 1, toluidine blue 1; *B*. sat. aq. sol. (*circ.*
1%) picric acid
METHOD: [dried smears] → *A*, 20–30 mins. → rinse → *B*, 1–2 secs. → wash → dry

21.3 Fiessinger and Laur 1930 *test.* **1942 Langeron**   Langeron 1942, 1023
FORMULA: sat. alc. sol. cresyl blue 75, sat. alc. sol. (*circ.* 2.5%) neutral red 25
METHOD: Mix equal parts blood and stain → smear → dry
NOTE: Recommended for reticulocytes.

21.3 Flinn 1939   *see* DS 23.219 Flinn 1939

21.3 Freifeld 1931 *test.* **1950 Jones**   Jones 1950, 225
FORMULA: water 100, DS 11.43 Ziehl 1882 1, 1% methylene blue 0.7
METHOD: [methanol-fixed smears] → stain, 1 hr. → dry
RECOMMENDED FOR: toxic neutrophiles.

21.3 Graham 1916   11343, **35**:231
REAGENTS REQUIRED: *A*. 95% alc. 90, 40; formaldehyde 10; *B*. water 60, 95% alc. 40,
α-naphthol 1, hydrogen peroxide 0.2; *C*. water 60, 95% alc. 40, pyronin 0.1, aniline 4;
D. 0.5% methylene blue
METHOD: [air-dried smears] → *A*, 1–2 mins. → wash → *B*, 4–5 mins. → wash → *C*, 2
mins. → wash → *D*, ½ to 1 min. → wash → blot → dry
RECOMMENDED FOR: demonstration of oxidase granules.

21.3 Graham 1918   11343, **39**:15
REAGENTS REQUIRED: *A*. 95% alc. 90, 40% formaldehyde 10; *B*. water 60, 95% alc. 40,
hydrogen peroxide 0.2, benzidine *q.s.* to sat. immediately before use; *C*. DS 11.44
Löffler 1890
METHOD: [air dried smears] → *A*, 1–2 mins. → wash → *B*, 5–10 mins. → wash → *C*, 3
secs. → wash → blot → dry
RECOMMENDED FOR: demonstration of oxidase granules.

21.3 Groat 1936   *see* DS 13.13 Groat 1936

21.3 Grosso 1914   16059, **6**:235
PREPARATION OF DRY STOCK: Add a sat. sol. picric acid to a sat. sol. methylene blue until no further ppt. forms. Filter. Wash and dry ppt.
WORKING SOLUTION: methanol 100, dry stock 0.5
METHOD: [dry smear] → 10 drops, placed on slide, 3–4 mins. → 10 drops water, added to stain on slide, 5 mins. → wash → dry

21.3 Hayem 1889   23632, **6**:335
FORMULA: water 100, mercuric chloride 0.25, sodium sulfate 2.5, sodium chloride 0,5. eosin 0.05
METHOD: Mix 1 blood with 100 stain. Make smear.

21.3 Kahlden and Laurent 1896   Kahlden and Laurent 1896, 134
FORMULA: sat. aq. sol. orange G 25, sat. 20% alc. sol. acid fuchsin 25, 95% alc. 15, sat. aq. sol. methyl green 25
PREPARATION: Mix in order given. Leave 24 hours. Decant supernatant stain (do not filter).
METHOD: [dry smear] → stain 5–10 mins. → wash → dry → balsam

21.3 Kardos 1911   8545, **12**:39
PREPARATION OF DRY STAIN: Mix equal parts 2% orange G and sat. sol. methyl blue. Filter. Wash and dry ppt.
REAGENTS REQUIRED: *A.* DS 13.11 May-Grünwald 1902; *B.* water 95, DS 13.13 Giemsa 1902 3, sat. sol. above ppt. in methanol 2
METHOD: [smear] → *A*, 3 mins. on slide → add water to *A* on slide, 1 min. → drain → *B*, on slide, 15 mins. → rinse → dry

21.3 Kuhn 1933   *see* DS 13.13 Kuhn 1933

21.3 Liebmann 1942   20540b, **17**:31
REAGENTS REQUIRED: *A.* DS 13.12 Wright 1910; *B.* 0.01% acetic acid
METHOD: [smears fixed in F 1700.1000 Maximow 1909] → *A*, 24 hrs. → *B*, 1–1½ mins. → balsam, via acetone and xylene
RECOMMENDED FOR: invertebrate blood.

21.3 Liebmann 1945   20540b, **20**:83
REAGENTS REQUIRED: *A.* water 100 azur II 0.005, eosin Y 0.0075
METHOD: [fix smears 10 mins. in formaldehyde vapor: flame 5 times] → *A*, 6 hrs. → 95% alc., 1–2 mins. → abs. alc., 30–60 secs. → balsam, via xylene
RECOMMENDED FOR: amphibian blood.

21.3 Lightwood, Hawksley and Bailey 1935   16916, **28**:405
FORMULA: abs. alc. 100, neutral red 0.04, Janus green B 0.3
METHOD: Dip clean slides in stain. Let dry. Make smear on slide.

21.3 McCullough and Dick 1942   *see* DS 23.219 McCullough and Dick 1942

21.3 Michaelis 1899   *see* DS 13.11 Michaelis 1899

21.3 Moore 1882 *test.* **1884 Cole**   Cole 1884, vol. 1, 12
REAGENTS REQUIRED: *A.* water 50, 95% alc. 50, eosin W 1; *B.* 0.3% methyl green
METHOD: [dried smear of amphibian blood] → *A*, on slide, 2 mins. → rinse → *B*, on slide, 2 mins. → wash → dry → balsam

21.3 Okajima 1917   763, **11**:295
REAGENTS REQUIRED: *A.* 10% phosphomolybdic acid; *B.* water 100, alizarin red S 6, phosphomolybdic acid 2.5
METHOD: [sections of material (not picric-fixed)] → *A*, 1 min. → water, quick rinse → stain, 1–24 hrs. → balsam, via usual reagents
RESULT: erythrocytes, orange yellow; other tissues, colorless.
RECOMMENDED FOR: specific staining of erythrocytes in sections.

21.3 Oliver 1934   *see* DS 22.8 Oliver 1934

21.3 Osgood and Wilhelm 1934   11284, **19**:1129
REAGENTS REQUIRED: *A.* 1% brilliant cresyl blue in 0.85% sodium chloride
METHOD: Mix 5 ml. each *A* and oxalated blood. Prepare and dry smear.
RECOMMENDED FOR: reticulocytes.

21.3 Pappenheim 1917   8545, **22**:15
REAGENTS REQUIRED: *A.* DS 13.11 May and Grünwald 1902; *B.* DS 13.13 Slider and
   Downey (1929)
METHOD: [dry smears] → *A*, 3 mins. on slide → add equal vol. water to *A* on slide, 1 min.
   → drain → *B*, on slide, 15 to 30 mins. → water till differentiated, about 1 min. → dry

21.3 Pickworth 1934   11025, **69**:62
REAGENTS REQUIRED: *A.* water 75, acetic acid 0.5, benzidine 0.125, sodium nitroprusside
   0.1; *B.* water 100, hydrogen peroxide (3%) 0.5
METHOD: [250 µ sections of formaldehyde-fixed brain, sectioned by E 11.1 Pickworth
   1934] → thorough wash → *A*, 1 hr., 37°C. with continuous shaking → wash →
   balsam, via usual reagents
RECOMMENDED FOR: blood vessels in thick sections of brain.

21.3 Price-Jones 1933 *test.* **1937 Gatenby and Painter**   Gatenby and Painter 1937, 397
FORMULA: water 90, sodium chloride 0.7, 40% formaldehyde 10, gentian violet 0.01
USE: Use as blood diluent. Make smear.

21.3 Pryce 1939   11284, **49**:594
REAGENTS REQUIRED: *A.* sat. sol. brilliant cresyl blue in abs. alc.; *B.* DS 13.12 Leishman
   1901
METHOD: [dip slides in *A* and air dry. Make smear on coated slide and prevent evaporation by laying another slide not quite in contact with smear. Leave 5 mins. Remove
   cover. Dry] → *B*, on slide, 5 mins. → dilute stain on slide, leave 5 mins. → wash till
   smear changes from blue to red → dry
RECOMMENDED FOR: demonstration of reticulocytes.

21.3 Pugsley 1940 *test.* **1944 Randall**   20540b, **19**:150
REAGENTS REQUIRED: *A.* water 100, potassium oxalate 0.2; brilliant cresyl blue 1; *B.*
   any DS 13.12 mixture
METHOD: [mix equal parts *A* and blood, leave 1 min.] → make smear → *B*, till counter-
   stained
RECOMMENDED FOR: reticulocytes.

21.3 Raadt 1912   *see* DS 13.12 Raadt 1912

21.3 Rossi 1889   23632, **6**:475
FORMULA: water 100, osmic acid 0.5, methyl green 5
METHOD: [blood, drop on slide] → stain, mixed with drop → make smear → dry → glyc-
   erol, via graded glycerol water mixtures

21.3 Sabin 1923   10919, **34**:277
FORMULA: abs. alc. 100, neutral red 0.1, Janus green 0.05
METHOD: Dip clean slide in stain. Let dry. Make smear on slide.

21.3 Sato 1928   11284, **13**:1058
REAGENTS REQUIRED: *A.* 0.5% copper sulfate; *B.* benzidine 0.1, water 100, hydrogen
   peroxide 0.2; *C.* 1% safranin
METHOD: [dry smears on coverslips] → *A*, floated on solution, 1 min. → rinse → *B*, 2
   mins. → wash → *C*, 20 secs. → wash → blot → dry
RECOMMENDED FOR: demonstration of peroxidase granules.
RESULT: peroxidase granules, blue; basophilic granules and nuclei, red.

21.3 Saye 1943   *Tech. Bull.*, **4**:12
REAGENTS REQUIRED: *A.* 0.25% eosin Y in 95% alc., 0.05% thionine in 80% alc.
METHOD: [air-dried smear] → *A*, 1 min. → drain briefly → *B*, 1 min. → wash → dry

21.3 Schmorl 1928 *see* DS 22.8 Schmorl 1928

21.3 Sheehan 1939 11431, **49**:58

REAGENTS REQUIRED: *A*. sat. sol. Sudan black B; *B*. sat. sol. ethyl eosin in 70% alc.; *C*. sat. sol. methylene blue

METHOD: [methanol-fixed smear] → *A*, 30 secs. → wash → 70% alc., 1 min. → *B*, 30 secs. → wash → *C*, 3 mins. → rinse → blot → dry

RECOMMENDED FOR: lipoid granules in leukocytes.

21.3 Sheehan and Storey 1947 11431, **59**:336

STOCK SOLUTIONS: I. 0.3% Sudan black B in abs. alc.; II. water 100, abs. alc. 30, phenol 16, sodium phosphate, dibasic (cryst.) 0.3

PREPARATION OF B: Add the phenol dissolved in alc. to the phosphate dissolved in water.

REAGENTS REQUIRED: *A*. stock I 60, stock II 40; *B*. DS 13.13 Giemsa 1902 1, water 100; *C*. 0.2% potassium dihydrogen phosphate

METHOD: [smear fixed in formaldehyde vapor] → *A*, 10–60 mins. → 70% alc., rinse → wash → *B*, 5 mins. → *C*, till differentiated → wash dry

RECOMMENDED FOR: fat granules in leukocytes.

21.3 Simpson 1922 11343, **40**:77

FORMULA: 95% alc. 100, neutral red 1, Janus green 0.5

METHOD: Dip clean slide in stain. Leave dry. Make smear on slide.

21.3 Slominski and Cunge *test.* **1948 Romeis** Romeis 1948, 470

PREPARATION OF STAIN: To 100 1% benzidine add 10 of 10% hydrogen peroxide (3%).

METHOD: [120 *μ* frozen sections of material fixed in F 8000.1000 Slominski and Cunge (1948)] → water → *A*, till sufficiently stained → balsam, via usual reagents

RECOMMENDED FOR: differential staining of capillaries in sections.

21.3 Steil 1936 20540b, **11**:99

REAGENTS REQUIRED: *A*. DS 13.12 Wright 1910

METHOD: [dry smears] → *A*, on slide, 1–2 mins. → equal amount water added to stain, 3 mins. → drain → flood with water till smear pink → drain → methanol, 1–2 mins. → water, till smear pink → abs. alc. → balsam, via clove oil

21.3 Strumia 1936 11284, **21**:930

PREPARATION OF STOCK SOLUTIONS: I. DS 13.13 Giemsa 1902 (dry powder) 0.2, glycerol 12, methanol acetone 44; II. DS 13.11 May-Grünwald 1902 (dry powder) 0.04, methanol 50, acetone 50.

REAGENTS REQUIRED: *A*. stock I 65, stock II 35; *B*. 0.2% sodium carbonate

METHOD: [air-dried smear] → 1 ml. *A*, on slide, 2 mins. → add 1 ml. *B*, leave 3 mins. → wash → dry

21.3 Thompson 1945 1887a, **38**:49

REAGENTS REQUIRED: *A*. 4% ferric alum; *B*. sat. sol. picric acid 87, 1% acid fuchsin 13

METHOD: [sections or smears, with nuclei prior stained in DS 11.122 Mallory 1938] → wash → *A*, 1 min. → rinse → *B*, 15 mins. → 95% alc., till differentiated → balsam, via usual reagents

RESULT: structures or pieces containing hemoglobin, green; other structures, yellow, red, brown, and gray.

RECOMMENDED FOR: differentiation of erythrocytes, and pieces of erythrocytes, in smears and sections.

21.3 Ugruimow 1928 23632, **45**:191

REAGENTS REQUIRED: 0.1% azur II in phosphate buffer pH 6.3 15, 0.1% eosin BA in phosphate buffer pH 6.3 16, water 100

METHOD: [heat-fixed smear] → stain, 10–12 hrs. → acetone, till differentiated → acid balsam

21.3 Westphal *test.* **1896 Kahlden and Laurent** Kahlden and Laurent 1896, 134

FORMULA: A DS 11.21 Grenacher 1879 30, sat. alc. sol. crystal violet 30, glycerol 30, phenol 25, acetic acid 5

METHOD: [dry smear] → stain, 20–30 mins. → wash → balsam, via usual reagents

21.3 Willebrand 1901   *see* DS 13.11 Willebrand 1901

21.3 Ziegler 1945 *test.* **1945 Riley**   20504b, **21**:37
REAGENTS REQUIRED: *A.* water 50, abs. alc. 50, benzidine 0.5, sodium nitroprusside 0.1;
B. water 47, abs. alc. 50, acetic acid 3, hydrogen peroxide (30%) 0.5, sodium nitro-
prusside 0.1; *C.* 2% acetic acid in 70% alc.; *D.* 2% acetic acid in 90% alc.
METHOD: [formaldehyde-fixed cornea] → thorough wash → *A*, 20 mins. → brief wash
→ *B*, 15 mins. → *B*, fresh solution, 45 mins., 37°C. wash → *C*, 10 mins. → *D*, 10
mins. → abs. alc. → M 23.1 mountant
RECOMMENDED FOR: demonstration of capillaries in wholemounts of cornea.

21.4 SPECIAL STAINS FOR OTHER TISSUES

21.41 DESIGNED TO DIFFERENTIATE TYPES OF TISSUES NOT COVERED UNDER 21.1, 21.2 OR 21.3

21.411 Plant Tissues

21.411 Buchholz 1931   20540b, **6**:13
REAGENTS REQUIRED: *A.* 1% acid fuchsin 80, 1% light green in 90% alc. 20; *B.* 80%
lactic acid
METHOD: [cortex dissected from pistil killed in formalin-alcohol] → *A*, 6 hrs. → rinse →
B, till cleared and differentiated → [seal in *B* under coverslip]
RECOMMENDED FOR: staining wholemounts to show pollen tubes.

21.411 Chandler 1931   20540b, **6**:25
REAGENTS REQUIRED: *A.* DS 11.23 Schneider 1880; *B.* sat. aq. sol. (*circ.* 0.3%) magenta
METHOD: [cortex dissected from pistil killed in formalin-alcohol] → *A*, on slide, few
secs. → *B*, dropped on *A* on slide, 1 drop, few secs. → bolt → dehydrate by drop
method → balsam, via xylene
RECOMMENDED FOR: staining wholemounts to show pollen tubes.

21.411 Gardiner 1888   ·   *Arb. bot. inst. Würz,* **3**:52
REAGENTS REQUIRED: *A.* 50% sulfuric acid; *B.* water 50, 95% alc. 50, picric acid to sat.,
anilin blue 1
METHOD: [sections] → water → *A*, 2–10 secs. → wash → *B*, 10 mins. → wash, till no
more color comes away → glycerol
RECOMMENDED FOR: demonstration of protoplasmic connections between plant cells.

21.411 Johansen 1939   20540b, **14**:125
REAGENTS REQUIRED: *A.* DS 11.42 Johansen 1940; *B.* 1% methyl violet 2B; *C.* 95% alc.
30, methyl cellosolve 30, tert. butyl alc. 30; *D.* sat. sol. fast green FCF in equal parts
clove oil and methyl cellosolve 15, 95% alc. 40, tert. butyl alc. 40, acetic acid 1.5; *E.*
DS 12.16 Johansen 1940; *F.* clove oil 30, abs. alc. 30, methyl cellosolve 30
METHOD: [sections] → 70% alc. → *A*, 1–2 days → rinse → *B*, 10–15 mins. → rinse → *C*,
5 secs. → *D*, 10 mins. → *C*, 5 secs. → *E*, 5 mins. → *F*, rinse → balsam, via usual
reagents
RECOMMENDED FOR: plant histology and cytology.

21.411 Johansen 1940   Johansen 1940, 93
REAGENTS REQUIRED: *A.* 1% acid fuchsin in 70% alc.; *B.* DS 12.16 Johansen 1940 fast
green; *C.* DS 13.5 Johansen 1940 (solution H)
METHOD: [sections] → 95% alc. → *A*, 20 mins. → water, rinse → 95% alc., rinse → *B*,
on slide, few secs. → *C*, till clear → balsam, via xylene
RECOMMENDED FOR: differentiation of reproductive structures in marine Phaeophyta.

21.411 Meyer *test.* **1915 Chamberlain**   Chamberlain 1915, 130
REAGENTS REQUIRED: *A.* ADS 12.2 Gram 1884; *B.* water 75, sulfuric acid 25, iodine to
sat.; *C.* 3% methyl violet
METHOD: [sections] → water → *A*, 3–5 mins. → *A*, under coverslip → *B*, run under
coverslip → *C*, run under coverslip, 3 mins. → wash → glycerol
RECOMMENDED FOR: demonstration of protoplasmic connections between plant cells.

21.411 Nebel 1931   20540b, **6**:27
REAGENTS REQUIRED: *A*. water 100, martius yellow 0.05, resorcin blue 0.05, ammonium hydroxide *q.s.* to give pH 8
METHOD: [sections of styles, or crushed styles, or cortices dissected from styles fixed in F 0000.0010 Carnoy 1887] → wash, till acid-free → *A*, 2–5 mins. → balsam, via graded alcs. containing resorcin blue at pH 8
RECOMMENDED FOR: staining pollen tubes.

21.411 Strasburger *test*. **1915 Chamberlain**   Chamberlain 1915, 130
REAGENTS REQUIRED: *A*. 1% osmic acid; *B*. ADS 2.2 Gram 1884 60, water 30; *C*. 25% sulfuric acid; *D*. 25% sulfuric acid 100, iodine to sat., 3% methyl violet 0.1
METHOD: [sections of fresh material] → *A*, 5 mins. → wash → *B*, 20–30 mins. → *C*, 24 hrs. → *D*, 5 mins. → glycerol
RECOMMENDED FOR: demonstration of protoplasmic connections between plant cells.

21.411 Watkin 1925   11211, **15**:340
REAGENTS REQUIRED: *A*. water 25, glycerol 25, lactic acid 25, phenol 25, methyl blue 0.1
METHOD: Fix, stain, and mount style in *A*.
RECOMMENDED FOR: demonstration of pollen tubes in flowers of Gramineae.

21.412 Animal Tissues

21.412 Badertscher 1940   20540b, **15**:29
REAGENTS REQUIRED: *A*. DS 22.4 Herxheimer 1901
METHOD: [thick, freehand sections of formaldehyde-fixed skin] → 70% alc., till formaldehyde-free → *A*, 12–24 hrs. → 70% alc. till glands differentiated → glycerol → M12 mountant (Chapter 26)
RECOMMENDED FOR: differential staining of sebaceous glands in wholemounts.

21.412 Behrens 1898   23328, **3**:76
FORMULA: *A*. ADS 12.2 Merkel (1898); *B*. 1% potassium permanganate; *C*. 1% sodium sulfite; *D*. 0.5% formic acid; *E*. 1% methyl violet
METHOD: [sections of formaldehyde-fixed material] → *A*, 4 or 5 days → *B*, 10 mins. → wash → *C*, 5 mins. → *D*, few secs. → [repeat *C*, *D* cycle till bleached] → wash → *E*, 2 mins. → 95% alc., till no more color comes away → balsam, via xylene
RECOMMENDED FOR: bile capillaries.

21.412 Bloom 1925   *see* DS 21.412 Eppinger 1902 (note)

21.412 Buzzi 1898   14352, **8**:149
REAGENTS REQUIRED: *A*. sat. sol. picric acid; *B*. 1% nigrosin
METHOD: [sections of formaldehyde-fixed material] → water → *A*, 5 mins. → rinse → *B*, 1 min. → rinse → 95% alc., minimum possible time → balsam, via origanum oil
RECOMMENDED FOR: differentiation of keratin from eleidin in skin sections.
RESULT: eleidin, blue-black; keratin, yellow.

21.412 Clara 1933   23639b, **17**:698
REAGENTS REQUIRED: *A*. ADS 11.1 Clara 1903; *B*. DS 11.113 Kultschitzky 1889; *C*. ADS 21.1 Weigert 1885
METHOD: [celloidin sections of formaldehyde-fixed material] → water → *A*, 1 day, 40–50°C. → rinse → *B*, 1 day, 37°C. → wash → *C*, till differentiated → wash → balsam, via usual reagents
RECOMMENDED FOR: differential staining of bile capillaries.

21.412 Clara 1934   23507a, **35**:1
REAGENTS REQUIRED: *A*. water 100, potassium dichromate 3.2, chrome alum 1.6, chromic acid 0.125, ammonium molybdate 0.25; *B*. DS 11.113 Kultschitzky 1889
METHOD: [sections of alc.-formaldehyde-fixed material] → *A*, 24 hrs., 50°C. → rinse → *B*, till sufficiently stained → wash → balsam, via usual reagents
RECOMMENDED FOR: demonstration of bile capillaries.

21.412 Dahlgren 1929   McClung 1929, 306

REAGENTS REQUIRED: *A*. sat. sol. picric acid 100, nigrosin 2

METHOD: [sections fixed, or mordanted, in picric acid] → water → *A*, 5 mins. → 95%
alc., till color clouds cease → balsam, via usual reagents

RECOMMENDED FOR: to distinguish muscle from other connective tissues.

RESULT: muscle, yellow; other connective tissues, brown.

21.412 Dublin 1944 *see* MS 32.1 Dublin 1944

21.412 de Galantha *test.* **1934 Wilbur**   1887a, **18**:157

REAGENTS REQUIRED: *A*. F 3700.0010 Zenker 1894; *B*. ADS 12.2 Lugol; *C*. 2% sodium
thiosulfate; *D*. ADS 12.1 Weigert 1896; *E*. ADS 12.1 Weigert 1891; *F*. 1% azocarmine
in 1% acetic acid; *G*. 1% aniline in 95% alc.; *H*. 1% hydrochloric acid in 95% alc.; *I*.
5% phosphotungstic acid; *J*. water 100, acetic acid 8, orange G 2, anilin blue 0.5

METHOD: [paraffin sections of formaldehyde-fixed material] → water → *A*, 1 hr. → wash
→ *B*, 5 mins. → wash → *C*, till bleached → wash → *D*, 4 hrs. → wash → *E*, 2 hrs. →
running water, 1 hr. → *F*, 40 mins. → *G*, till nuclei differentiated → *H*, wash → rinse
→ *I*, 2 hrs. → rinse → *J*, 5 mins. → rinse → abs. alc., till differentiated → balsam,
via xylene

RECOMMENDED FOR: histological differentiation of kidney.

21.412 Eppinger 1902   2526, **31**:230

REAGENTS REQUIRED: *A*. 4% formaldehyde; *B*. ADS 12.1 Weigert 1891; *C*. 1% hematoxylin; *D*. 5% cupric acetate; *E*. ADS 21.1 Weigert 1885; *F*. 1.5% lithium carbonate

METHOD: [small pieces] → *A*, 5–10 days → *B*, 10 days → wash → celloidin sections → *C*,
24 hrs. → rinse → *D*, 5 mins. → wash → *E*, till sections differentiated → wash → *F*,
till celloidin decolorized → balsam, via usual reagents

RECOMMENDED FOR: demonstration of bile capillaries in liver.

NOTE: **Bloom 1925** (590, **36**:455) uses B 1 week at 37.5°C. and *C* for only a few moments.

21.412 Forsgren 1928   23639b, **6**:647

REAGENTS REQUIRED: *A*. 3% barium chloride; *B*. 4% formaldehyde; *C*. 0.1% acid
fuchsin; *D*. 1% phosphomolybdic acid; *E*. DS 13.41 Mallory 1900 (*C* sol.)

METHOD: [3–4 mm. slices of liver] → *A*, 6–12 hrs. → *B*, 12–18 hrs. → 95% alc., quick
wash → [5 μ paraffin sections] → water → *C*, 1–3 mins. → wash → *D*, ½–1 min. →
rinse → *E*, 3–5 mins. → wash → balsam, via usual reagents

RECOMMENDED FOR: differential staining of bile duct.

21.412 Hansen 1898 *see* DS 12.221 Hansen 1898

21.412 Heidenhain 1903   23632, **20**:179

REAGENTS REQUIRED: *A*. 1% thiazin red; *B*. 1% thionin

METHOD: [sections of trichloroacetic-fixed material] → water → *A*, 1–6 hrs., till deeply
stained → rinse → *B*, 1–12 hrs. → 95% alc. till differentiated → balsam, via usual
reagents

RECOMMENDED FOR: contraction bands on striped muscle.

21.412 Holmer 1927 *test.* **1948 Romeis**   Romeis 1948, 495

REAGENTS REQUIRED: *A*. 30% ferric chloride; *B*. 0.5% hematoxylin; *C*. 0.1% ferric
chloride; *D*. sat. sol. lithium carbonate

METHOD: [sections of formaldehyde-fixed material] → water → *A*, 3–5 mins. → short
wash → *B*, 5–10 mins. → rinse → *C*, till differentiated → wash → *D*, till blue → balsam,
via usual reagents

RECOMMENDED FOR: differential staining of bile capillaries.

21.412 Kockel 1899   23681, **10**:749

REAGENTS REQUIRED: *A*. 1% chromic acid; *B*. DS 21.212 Weigert 1885 (sol. *C*); *C*. 10%
ammonium alum; *D*. ADS 21.2 Weigert 1885 50, water 50

METHOD: [paraffin sections] → water → *A*, 5–10 mins. → quick rinse → *B*, 15–20 mins.
→ wash → *C*, till dark blue → wash → *D*, till differentiated → wash → *C*, till background decolorized → counterstain with any DS 11.21 formula if required → balsam,
via usual reagents

RECOMMENDED FOR: fibrin in sections.

21.412 Kramer 1948   19938, **108**:141

REAGENTS REQUIRED: *A.* 0.5% eosin in 95% alc.; *B.* methyl salicylate
METHOD: [Bouin 1897 F 5000.1010 fixed material] → 50% alc., 10 mins. → 70% alc.,
1 hr. → 95% alc., 10 mins. → *A*, 6–8 hrs. or until specimen uniform pink color → 95%
alc., 30 mins. → *B*, drops added to alc., at such intervals as will prevent collapse of
specimen → *B*
RECOMMENDED FOR: differential staining of muscles in insect wholemounts.
RESULT: muscles pink; other tissues greenish.
NOTE: Times cited are for 4-day-old housefly larvae.

21.412 Kromayer 1892   1780, **39**:141

REAGENTS REQUIRED: *A.* sat. sol. methyl violet 6 B. 50, sat. sol. aniline 50; *B.* ADS 11.1
Lugol (1905) 30, water 60; *C.* xylene 60, aniline 30
METHOD: [5 μ sections] → water → *A*, 10–15 mins. → thorough wash → *B*, 1–30 secs.
→ drain → blot → *C*, 50°C., till differentiated → balsam, via xylene
RECOMMENDED FOR: epithelial fibers in skin.

21.412 Kultschitzky 1875   1780, **46**:675

REAGENTS REQUIRED: *A.* water 100, acetic acid 3, acid fuchsin 0.5; *B.* 2% acetic acid; *C.*
water 100, acetic acid 3, anilin blue WS 0.5
METHOD: [sections of F 7000.0000 Müller 1859 material] → *A*, 3–5 mins. → *B*, till no
more color comes away → *C*, till differentiated → balsam, via usual reagents
RECOMMENDED FOR: reticulum fibers.

21.412 Lillie 1948   Lillie 1948, 189

REAGENTS REQUIRED: *A.* water 100, nitric acid 0.5, sodium periodate 1; *B.* DS 11.44
Schiff 1866; *C.* 0.5% sodium bisulfite; *D.* DS 11.121 Weigert 1903; *E.* 1% orange G
METHOD: [sections] → water → *A*, 10 mins. → wash → *B*, 3–5 mins. → *C*, 3 successive
baths, 1½ mins. each → wash → *D*, 1–2 mins. → wash → *E*, till plasma sufficiently
stained → balsam, via usual reagents
RECOMMENDED FOR: reticulum fibers.

21.412 Long 1948   *see* MS 33.44 Long 1948

21.412 Mall *test.* **1950 Hall and Herxheimer**   Hall and Herxheimer 1950, 83

REAGENTS REQUIRED: *A.* water 100, sodium bicarbonate 10, pancreatin 5; *B.* water 90,
95% alc. 10, picric acid to sat.; *C.* water 65, 95% alc. 35, acid fuchsin, 10
METHOD: [sections by freezing technique] → *A*, 24 hrs. → wash, with agitation → strand
sections on slide and dry → *B*, dropped on slide and allowed to dry → *C*, 30 mins. →
balsam, via usual reagents
RECOMMENDED FOR: reticulum fibers.

21.412 Neubert 1940   23418(1), **110**:709

REAGENTS REQUIRED: *A.* DS 11.41 Petersen 1926; *B.* 5% phosphotungstic acid
METHOD: [sections] → water → *A*, 5–30 mins. → *B*, till differentiated → wash → bal-
sam, via usual reagents
RECOMMENDED FOR: smooth muscle in sections.

21.412 Pinkus 1944   1829, **49**:355

REAGENTS REQUIRED: *A.* water 30, 95% alc. 70, hydrochloric acid 0.6; orcein 1; *B.* 0.3%
hydrochloric acid in abs. alc.; *C.* DS 13.13 Giemsa 1902 0.6, water 100; *D.* 0.001%
eosin Y in 95% alc.
METHOD: [sections] → 70% alc. → *A*, ½–1 hr. → rinse → 95% alc., few dips → abs.
alc., till decolorized to pale brown → *B*, till almost completely decolorized → wash
→ *C*, 2–12 hrs. → blot → D, till dehydrated → balsam, via usual reagents
RECOMMENDED FOR: sections of skin.

21.412 Unna 1928 *test.* **1928 Schmorl**   Schmorl 1928, 343

REAGENTS REQUIRED: *A.* water 100, ammonium alum 10, crystal violet 1.5; *B.* ADS 12.2
Lugol (1905) 2, water 98, *C.* aniline 20, xylene 80; *D.* aniline 50, xylene 50
METHOD: [[celloidin sections of alc. fixed material] → water → *A*, 1 hr. → wash → *B*,
30 secs. → *C*, ½–1 min. → *D*, dropped on slide, till differentiated → xylene → balsam
RECOMMENDED FOR: fibers in skin.

21.412 Weigert 1887   8645, **5** :228

STOCK SOLUTIONS: I. abs. alc. 82, aniline 22, methyl violet to sat.; II. sat. aq. sol. methyl
violet
REAGENTS REQUIRED: *A*. stock I 9, stock II 81; *B*. 0.6% hydrochloric acid; *C*. ADS 12.2
Gram 1880; *D*. aniline 60, xylene 30
METHOD: [sections] → water → *A*, 5–10 mins. → *B*, wash → *C*, 5 mins. → blot → *D*,
till differentiated → blot → xylene → balsam
RECOMMENDED FOR: fibrin.
NOTE: **Mallory 1938,** 193 substitutes equal parts aniline and xylene for *D* above; he
further suggests prior staining of nuclei with carmine. Both Mallory (*loc. cit.*) and
Schmorl 1928, 158 recommend avoiding chrome or dichromate fixation. **Unna** (*test.*
1928 Schmorl, *op. cit.*, 160) substitutes 1.5% gentian violet in 10% alum for *A* above.

21.42 DESIGNED TO DIFFERENTIATE TYPES OF CELLS

21.421 In Pituitary

21.421 Berblinger and Bergdorf 1935   7802, **15** :381

REAGENTS REQUIRED: *A*. 1% cresofuschin; *B*. DS 11.21 Grenacher 1879; *C*. water 100,
phosphomolybdic acid 1, orange G 2; *D*. 5% phosphomolybdic acid; *E*. 0.2% anilin
blue
METHOD: [sections of formaldehyde-fixed material] → *A*, 12 hrs. → water, quick rinse
→ *C*, 5 mins. → water, quick rinse → *D*, 2 mins. → blot, or wipe around sections →
E, 15 mins. → water, quick rinse → 70% alc., till no more color comes away → bal-
sam, via usual reagents
RECOMMENDED FOR: pregnancy cells in hypophysis.
RESULT: pregnancy cells, blue with yellow granules; basophil cells, blue with purple
granules.

21.421 Biggart 1935   7599, **81** :42

REAGENTS REQUIRED: *A*. 0.5% eosin Y 50, 0.3% isamine blue 50; *B*. 95% alc. 80, 5%
sodium carbonate 20
METHOD: [sections of F 3700.1010 fixed material] → water → *A*, 50°C., 30 mins. → rinse
→ *B*, till differentiated → neutral mountant, via usual reagents
RECOMMENDED FOR: differentiation in cell types in the pituitary.
RESULT: basophil cells, blue; chromophobe cells, light blue; acidophile cells, red.

21.421 Cleveland and Wolfe 1932   763, **51** :410

REAGENTS REQUIRED: *A*. DS 11.123 Ehrlich 1886; *B*. 5% potassium dichromate; *C*. 5%
erythrosin; *D*. water 100, phosphomolybdic acid 1, orange G 2; *E*. 1% anilin blue
METHOD: [2 to 3 μ sections of material fixed in F 7000.1000 Régaud 1910] → *A*, 3 mins.
→ water, quick rinse → *B*, in dark, 3 days, changed daily → water, rinse → *C*, 20–30
secs. → water, rinse → *E*, 30–60 secs. → balsam, via usual reagents

21.421 Colin 1923a   6630, **89** :1230

FORMULA: sat. aq. sol. aniline 100, acid fuchsin 12, light green 6
METHOD: [sections of formol material] → water → *A*, 2 mins. at 40°C. → water, till
differentiated → balsam, via usual reagents

21.421 Colin 1923b   6630, **89** :1230

FORMULA: water 100, aniline to sat., acid fuchsin 16, methyl blue 2.8
METHOD: as Colin 1923a

21.421 Crook and Russel 1935   11431, **40** :256

REAGENTS REQUIRED: *A*. water 100, potassium dichromate 2.4, acetic acid 4.75; *B*.
ADS 12.2 Lugol (1905); *C*. 1% acid fuchsin; *D*. DS 13.41 Mallory 1901, sol. *C*
METHOD: [sections] → water → *A*, 12–18 hrs. → wash → *B*, 3 mins. → 95% alc., till
decolorized → *C*, 15 mins. → wash → *D*, 20 mins. → wash → 95% alc., till differentiated → balsam, via usual reagents

21.421 Dawson and Friedgood 1938   20540b, **13** :17

REAGENTS REQUIRED: *A*. 3% potassium dichromate; *B*. water 99, acetic acid 1, azocarmine 0.2; *C*. 1% aniline in 95% alc.; *D*. 1% acetic acid in 95% alc.; *E*. 5% phosphotungstic acid; *F*. water 100, acetic acid 8, anilin blue 0.5, orange G 2

METHOD: [sections from F 3000.1000 Dawson and Friedgood 1938] → *A*, 12 hrs. → rinse → *B*, 1 hr., 55°C. → rinse → *C*, till "carmine cells" only remain red → *D*, rinse → rinse → *E*, 2 hrs. → rinse → *F*, 12–36 hrs. → rinse → 95% alc., balsam, via usual reagents

RECOMMENDED FOR: differentiation of two classes of acidophile cells in the pituitary.

21.421   Koneff 1938   20540b, **13**:49

REAGENTS REQUIRED: *A*. 0.1% aniline in 90% alc.; *B*. 1% acetic acid in 90% alc.; *C*. water 100, acetic acid 1, azocarmine 1; *D*. 0.06% aniline in 90% alc.; *E*. 5% phosphotungstic acid; *F*. water 100, phosphotungstic acid 0.05, oxalic acid 2, orange G 2, anilin blue 0.5; *G*. 1% acetic acid

METHOD: [3–4 μ cellulose sections of F 3700.1000 fixed material, attached to slide and cellulose dissolved away] → 70% alc. → *A*, 45 mins. → *B*, 1–2 mins. → *C*, 2 hrs. 56°C. → wash → *D*, till nuclei red, cytoplasm pink → *B*, 1–2 mins. → *E*, 4 hrs. → rinse → *F*, 4 hrs., till basophils blue → wash → *E*, 3–5 mins. → wash → *G*, rinse → wash → neutral mountant, via usual reagents

RECOMMENDED FOR: differentiation of basophils (blue), acidophils (orange red) and chromophobes (light gray).

21.421   Kraus 1912   2526, **54**:520

REAGENTS REQUIRED: *A*. 5% potassium dichromate; *B*. DS 11.113 Kultschitzky 1889; *C*. ADS 21.1 Weigert 1885

METHOD: [5 μ paraffin sections of formaldehyde-fixed material] → *A*, overnight, 37.5°C. → thorough wash → *B*, 24 hrs. → wash → *C*, till β-cells decolorized → DS 12.221 counterstain, if desired → balsam, via usual reagents

RECOMMENDED FOR: differential staining of α-cells (black) in hypophysis.

21.421   Lewis and Miller 1938   20540b, **14**:111

This is identical with DS 13.41 Kricheski 1931, save that the time in the A and B solutions is increased to 30 minutes and 24 hours respectively. The authors make the common error of referring to Kricheski's formula for the B solution as "Mallory's stain."

21.421   Lillie 1948   Lillie 1948, 99

FORMULA: water 90, citric/phosphate buffer, pH 8.5, safranin O 0.05, eriocyanine A 0.05

METHOD: [sections] → water → stain, till differentiated → rinse → acetone, till dehydrated → balsam, via xylene

RESULT: acidophile cells, blue; basophiles, red.

21.421   MacCallum, Futcher, Duff, and Ellsworth 1935   10919, **56**:350

REAGENTS REQUIRED: *A*. sat. sol. cupric acetate; *B*. 0.4% ripened hematoxylin; *C*. 3% potassium dichromate; *D*. ADS 21.1 Weigert 1885

METHOD: [paraffin sections of F 3700.1000 Helly 1903 material] → water → *A*, 5 mins. → wash → *B*, 1 min. → wash → *C*, 1 min. → wash → *D*, till differentiated → wash → balsam, via usual reagents

RECOMMENDED FOR: differentiation of anterior lobe from pars intermedia cells in the pituitary.

RESULT: anterior lobe cells with black granules; granules unstained in pars intermedia cells.

21.421   Martins 1933   6630, **113**:1275

REAGENTS REQUIRED: *A*. DS 11.123 Harris 1900; *B*. 0.1% acid fuchsin; *C*. 1% phosphomolybdic acid; *D*. 0.5% methyl blue

METHOD: [sections of F 3700.1000 Helly 1903] → water → *A*, 2–3 mins. → wash → *B*, 10 secs. → rinse → *C*, 1–2 mins. → drain → *D*, 2–3 mins. → balsam, via usual reagents

21.421   Maurer and Lewis 1922   11189, **36**:141

REAGENTS REQUIRED: *A*. 1.7% acid fuchsin 70, sat. aq. sol. "acid violet" 30; *B*. clove oil 75, abs. alc. 25

METHOD: [sections from F 3600 fixed material] → water → stain, 20–30 secs. → blot → acetone → benzene → *B*, till differentiated → benzene → balsam

RECOMMENDED FOR: differentiation of cell types in pars intermedia of pituitary.

21.421 Maxwell 1938   20540b, **13**:93
REAGENTS REQUIRED: *A*. 1% acid fuchsin; *B*. 0.02% ammonia; *C*. 0.1% hydrochloric acid;
D. 0.5% phosphomolybdic acid; *E*. water 100, anilin blue, orange G 2, phospho-
molybdic acid 1
METHOD: [3–5 μ sections in E 21.1 Maxwell 1938 of F 3700.1010 Heidenham 1916 fixed
material] → water → *A*, 30 mins. → rinse → *B*, till differentiated → *C*, few moments
→ *D*, 3 mins. → *E*, 1 hr. → rinse → 95% alc., till differentiated → abs. alc. → bal-
sam, via S 41.1 Maxwell 1938

21.421 Perry and Lochead 1939   4349, **19**:101
REAGENTS REQUIRED: *A*. 3% potassium dichromate; *B*. 0.1 aniline in 90% alc.; *C*. 1%
acetic acid in 90% alc.; *D*. 1% azocarmine in 1% acetic acid; *E*. 90% alc. 30, *B* (above)
60; *F*. 5% phosphotungstic acid; *G*. water 100, oxalic acid 2, phosphotungstic acid
0.05, orange G 2, anilin blue 0.5
METHOD: [4 μ sections of F 3700.1010 Heidenhain 1916 fixed material] → water → *A*, 12
hrs. → rinse → *B*, 4 hrs. 56°C. followed by 14 hrs. room temperature → wash → *C*,
till nuclei differentiated → *D*, 1–2 mins. → *E*, 4 hrs. → rinse → *F*, 4 hrs. → wash →
G, 5–10 mins. → wash → *C*, 1–2 mins. → wash → abs. alc., till differentiated →
balsam, via xylene
RECOMMENDED FOR: pituitary of mouse.

21.421 Pearse 1950   20540b, **25**:97
REAGENTS REQUIRED: *A*. ADS 11.1 Hotchkiss 1948 (*A* and *B* sols.); *B*. DS 11.43 de
Tomasi 1936; *C*. DS 11.41 Lendrum and McFarlane 1940; *D*. DS 11.122 Mayer 1896;
E. 2% hydrochloric acid in 70% alc.; *F*. water 100, phosphotungstic acid 5, orange
G 2
PREPARATION OF F: Mix ingredients. Stand 48 hours and decant.
METHOD: [4–4 μ sections F 3700.1000 Helly 1903 fixed material] → 70% alc. → *A* (*A*
sol.), 5 mins. → 70% alc., rinse → *A* (*B* sol.), 1 min. → 70% alc., rinse → *B*, 10–30
mins. → thorough wash → *C*, ½–3 mins. → rinse → *D*, ½ to 3 mins. → *E*, 10–20
secs. → thorough wash → *F*, 10 secs. → wash, till differentiated, 5–30 secs. → balsam,
via usual reagents

21.421 Romeis 1940 *test.* **1948** *ips.*   Romeis 1948, 511
REAGENTS REQUIRED: *A*. DS 21.13 Weigert 1898; *B*. 0.1% aniline in 95% alc.; *C*. water
100, acetic acid 1, azocarmine 0.1; *D*. 1% acetic acid in 95% alc.; *E*. 5% phospho-
molybdic acid; *F*. water 100, acetic acid 3, anilin blue 0.2
METHOD: [5 μ sections of formaldehyde, or sublimate-formaldehyde, material] → water
→ *A*, till δ-cells dark blue-black → 95% alc., till background decolorized → *B*, 15
mins. → *C*, 1 hr. 58°C. → leave cool, 30 mins. → *B*, till connective tissues decolorized
→ *D*, quick wash → wash → *E*, 4 mins. → drain and blot → *F*, 40 mins. → quick
rinse → 95% alc., till no more color comes away → balsam, via usual reagents
RESULT: α-cells pink; β-cells dark brown violet; γ-cells light violet; δ-cells cobalt blue.

21.421 Severinghaus 1932   763, **53**:1
REAGENTS REQUIRED: *A*. F 1670.0000 Severinghaus 1932; *B*. water 65, pyroligneous acid
35, chromic acid 0.6; *C*. 3% potassium dichromate; *D*. DS 22.1 Altmann 1890 sol. *A*.;
E. 1% picric acid in 30% alc.; *F*. 1% phosphomolybdic acid; *G*. water 85, 95% alc. 15,
methyl green 0.4, "acid violet" 0.3; H.25% alc., 75% clove oil
METHOD: [small pieces] → *A*, 24 hrs. → wash → *B*, 24 hrs. → wash → *C*, 3 days → wash
→ [3 μ paraffin sections] → *D*, on slide heated to steaming 2–3 changes → wash → *E*,
till differentiated → wash → *F*, 1 min. → wash → *G*, 1 min. → wash → blot → 95%
alc., 5 secs. → *H*, till differentiated → balsam, via xylene

21.421 Spark 1935   11284, **20**:508
REAGENTS REQUIRED: *A*. 0.25% anilin blue; *B*. DS 11.122 Mayer 1891; *C*. DS 12.221
van Gieson 1890
METHOD: [sections of F 7000.1000 material] → *A*, 1–1½ mins. → wash, 30 secs. → *B*,
10 mins. → wash 2–3 mins. → *C*, 1–1½ mins. → wash 1 min. → balsam, via usual
reagents
RESULT: β-granules, blue; α-granules, green.
RECOMMENDED FOR: differentiation of cell types in pituitary.

21.421 Wallraff 1939   23507a, **45**:631

REAGENTS REQUIRED: *A*. ADS 12.2 Salazar 1923; *B*. 3% ferric alum; *C*. 0.5% hydrochloric acid in 70% alc.; *D*. water 100, acetic acid 1, azocarmine 0.1; *E*. 0.1% aniline in 95% alc.; *F*. 1% acetic acid in 95% alc.; *G*. 0.5% toluidine blue

METHOD: [5 μ sections of F 5000.1000 Bouin 1897 fixed material, washed free of fixative] → water → *A*, 2–3 mins. → wash → *B*, 30 secs. → wash → *C*, till β-cells differentiated → wash, 70% alc. → *D*, ½–1 hr. 58°C. → *E*, till connective tissues decolorized → *F*, rinse → *G*, 1–3 mins. 95% alc., 24 hrs. → balsam, via usual reagents

RECOMMENDED FOR: differentiation of β-cells (black) in hypophysis.

21.422 In Other Glands

21.422 Baley 1937a   11431, **44**:272

PREPARATION OF DRY STOCK: Mix equal parts saturated solutions of magenta and orange G. Filter. Wash till pale yellow. Dry.

REAGENTS REQUIRED: *A*. ADS 12.2 Lugol (1905); *B*. DS 11.123 Ehrlich 1886; *C*. 0.1% hydrochloric acid in 70% alc.; *D*. water 50, sat. sol. dry stock in abs. alc. 50

METHOD: [sections of F 3700.1000 Baley 1937 fixed material] → abs. alc. → *A*, 2 mins. → abs. alc., wash → *B*, 20 mins. → wash → *C*, till pink → tap water, till blue → *D*, on slide, warmed to steaming, 1 min. → blot → abs. alc. rinse → *A*, till red, 10 secs. → blot → abs. alc. → balsam, via xylene

RECOMMENDED FOR: zymogen granules (red) in pancreas.

21.422 Baley 1937b   11431, **44**:272

PREPARATION OF DRY STAINS: I. Mix equal parts saturated solutions of magenta and methylene blue. Filter. Wash ppt. till wash-water pale blue. Dry. II. As I, substituting "acid violet" for methylene blue.

REAGENTS REQUIRED: *A*. ADS 12.2 Lugol (1905); *B*. water 50, sat. sol. either I or II in abs. alc. 50

METHOD: [sections of F 3700.1000 Baley 1937 fixed material] → abs. alc. → *A*, 2 mins. → abs. alc., wash → *B*, on slide, warmed to steaming, 1 min. → blot → abs. alc., rinse → *A*, till red, 10 secs. → blot → abs. alc. → balsam, via xylene

RECOMMENDED FOR: differentiation of β-cells (red with I, violet with II) from α-cells (blue with I, unstained with II) in islets of Langerhans.

21.422 Baley 1937c   11431, **44**:272

REAGENTS REQUIRED: *A*. ADS 12.2 Lugol (1905); *B*. 1% eosin; *C*. 1% acetic acid; *D*. water 100, acetic acid 0.5, anilin blue 0.375, orange G 0.625, resorcin 0.75

METHOD: [sections of F 3700.1000 Baley 1937 fixed material] → abs. alc., → *A*, 2 mins. → abs. alc., wash → *B*, 10 mins. → blot → *C*, 2 mins. → *D*, 1 min. → blot → abs. alc., rinse → *A*, 10 secs. → blot → abs. alc. → balsam, via xylene

RECOMMENDED FOR: differentiation of zymogen granules (bright red); granular cells of acini (dark red); β-cells (red); α-cells (blue) in pancreas.

21.422 Bensley 1916   590, **19**:37

REAGENTS REQUIRED: *A*. 1% ammonium chlorostannate; *B*. DS 11.3 Bensley 1916; *C*. DS 12.16 Bensley 1916

METHOD: [sections of F 3700.1000 fixed thyroid] → water → *A*, 2 mins. → water, quick rinse → *B*, 1–3 hrs. → water, wash → *C*, 1–5 mins. → water, quick rinse → abs. alc. → balsam, via xylene

RECOMMENDED FOR: differentiation of glandular elements of thyroid.

21.422 Bowie 1925   763, **29**:57

PREPARATION OF DRY STOCK: Mix 60 sat. sol. ethyl violet with 30 sat. sol. Biebrich scarlet. Filter. Wash and dry ppt.

REAGENTS REQUIRED: *A*. water 80, alc. 20, dry stock 0.001; *B*. clove oil 75, abs. alc. 25

METHOD: [3 μ sections of F 3700.0010 Bowie 1925 fixed material] → water → *A*, 24 hrs. → acetone, rinse → *B*, till differentiated → acetone → toluene → balsam

RECOMMENDED FOR: differentiation of cell types in pancreas.

RESULT: α-cells, blue; γ-cells, red; β-cells purple.

21.422 Fujiware 1939   1887a, **27**:1030
STOCK SOLUTIONS: I. 1% ponceau 2R in 1% acetic acid; II. 1% acid fuchsin in 1% acetic acid
REAGENTS REQUIRED: *A*. stock I 60, stock II 30; *B*. sat. aq. sol. picric acid
METHOD: [sections of F 3700.1010 Heidenhain 1916 material] → *A*, 5 mins. → rinse → *B*, 5 mins. → balsam, via usual reagents
RECOMMENDED FOR: androgenic cells in adrenal cortex.

21.422 Gomori 1939   763, **74**:439
REAGENTS REQUIRED: *A*. water 100, azocarmine 0.1, acetic acid 2; *B*. 1% aniline in 90% alc.; *C*. 5% ferric alum; *D*. water 100, orange G 0.2, anilin blue 0.6
METHOD: [sections of F 5000.1010 Bouin 1897 fixed material] → water → *A*, 45–60 mins., 55°C. → rinse → blot → *B*, till acinous cells decolorized → rinse → *C*, 5 mins. → rinse → *D*, till collagen deep blue → abs. alc., till differentiated → balsam, via xylene
RECOMMENDED FOR: differentiation cell types in islets of Langerhans.
RESULT: α-cells, orange; β-cells, red; δ-cells, blue.

21.422 Gomori 1941   608b, **17**:395
REAGENTS REQUIRED: *A*. F 5000.1010 Bouin 1897; *B*. water 100, sulfuric acid 0.3, potassium permanganate 0.3; *C*. 3% sodium bisulfite; *D*. DS 11.124 Gomori 1941; *E*. 1% hydrochloric acid in 70% alc.; *F*. 0.5% phloxine; *G*. 5% phosphotungstic acid
METHOD: [sections of F 5000.1010 Bouin 1897 fixed material] → water → *A*, 1 day → thorough wash → *B*, 1 min. → *C*, till bleached → wash → *D*, 10–15 mins., till cells deep blue → *E*, 1 min. → tap water, till blue → *F*, 5 mins. → rinse → *G*, 1 min. 95% alc., till differentiated → balsam, via usual reagents
RECOMMENDED FOR: differentiation of α, β and δ cells of pancreas.

21.422 Lane *test.* **1937 Duthie**   Gatenby and Painter 1937, 420
PREPARATION OF DRY STOCK: Mix 50 1.5% crystal violet and 50 1.25% orange G. Filter, wash, and dry ppt.
PREPARATION OF STOCK SOLUTION: abs. alc. 100, dry powder from above to sat.
REAGENTS REQUIRED: *A*. water 90, stock solution from above 10; *B*. clove oil 75, abs. alc. 25
METHOD: [3 μ sections of material fixed in either F 3700.0000 Lane (1910) (for α-cells) or F 3700.0000 Lane (1937) (for β-cells)] → water → *A*, 24 hrs. → blot → acetone, till dehydrated → toluene → *B*, till differentiated → balsam, via toluene
RECOMMENDED FOR: differentiation of α and β cells in islets of Langerhans.

21.422 Launoy 1904a *test.* **1907 Böhm and Oppel**   Böhm and Oppel 1907, 355
REAGENTS REQUIRED: *A*. DS 11.122 Launoy 1904; *B*. 0.1% hydrochloric acid in 70% alc.; *C*. DS 11.43 Ziehl 1882; *D*. 0.1% light green in 70% alc.
METHOD: [sections of osmic, chrome, or platinic fixed material] → *A*, 15 mins. → wash → *B*, till nuclei alone colored → wash → *C*, on slide, warmed to steaming, 5–10 mins. → wash, till no more color comes away → *D*, few moments → *B*, till differentiated → balsam, via usual reagents
RECOMMENDED FOR: cellular differentiation in pancreas.

21.422 Launoy 1904b *test.* **1907 Böhm and Oppel**   Böhm and Oppel 1907, 357
REAGENTS REQUIRED: *A*. DS 11.122 Launoy 1904; *B*. 0.1% hydrochloric acid in 70% alc.; *C*. DS 11.42 Zwaademaker 1887; *D*. sat. aq. sol. orange G
METHOD: [sections] → *A*, 15–20 mins. → *B*, ½ to 1 hr. → *C*, 48 hrs. → wash till no more color comes away → *D*, few moments → 95% alc., wash → *B*, till differentiated → balsam, via usual reagents
RECOMMENDED FOR: cellular differentiation in pancreas.

21.422 Lillie 1948   *see* DS 21.422 Wiesel 1903 (note)

21.422 Müller 1950   *Mikroskopie*, **6**:245
REAGENTS REQUIRED: *A*. water 100, potassium permanganate 0.125, sulfuric acid 0.25, *B*. 2% oxalic acid; *C*. water 100, zinc acetate 0.5, Bismarck brown 0.5; *D*. 0.6 acetic acid; *E*. 0.5% light green

METHOD: [3–5 μ sections of F 5000.1010 Bouin 1896 fixed material] $\rightarrow$ water $\rightarrow$ A, 2 mins. $\rightarrow$ wash $\rightarrow$ B, till white $\rightarrow$ wash $\rightarrow$ C, 2 mins. $\rightarrow$ rinse $\rightarrow$ D, till differentiated $\rightarrow$ wash $\rightarrow$ E, 2 mins. $\rightarrow$ wash $\rightarrow$ balsam, via usual reagents

RECOMMENDED FOR: differentiation of α (green) and β (brown) cells in islets of Langerhans.

21.422 Wiesel 1902   764, **19**:481

REAGENTS REQUIRED: A. 1% toluidine blue; B. 1% safranin

METHOD: [sections of F 7000.1000 Wiesel 1902 material] $\rightarrow$ water $\rightarrow$ A, 20 mins. $\rightarrow$ wash, 5 mins. running water $\rightarrow$ B, 20 mins. $\rightarrow$ 95% alc., till again blue $\rightarrow$ balsam, via carbol-xylene

RECOMMENDED FOR: demonstration of chromaffin cells in adrenal.

RESULT: nuclei, red; chromaffin cells, green; other cells, blue.

NOTE: Lillie **1948** (p. 104) cites Schmorl (no reference) in substituting anilin blue for toluidine blue in A above and in specifing "chromate fixed material."

21.422 Williamson and Pearse 1923   11025, **57**:193

REAGENTS REQUIRED: A. ADS 12.1 Lugol (1905); B. 0.25% potassium permanganate; C. 5% oxalic acid; D. DS 11.124 Mallory 1900

METHOD: [sections of F 3670.0000 Williamson and Pearse 1923 fixed material] $\rightarrow$ water $\rightarrow$ A, 30 mins. $\rightarrow$ 95% alc., wash $\rightarrow$ B, 10 mins. $\rightarrow$ rinse $\rightarrow$ C, till decolorized $\rightarrow$ wash $\rightarrow$ D, 24 hrs. $\rightarrow$ wash $\rightarrow$ balsam, via usual reagents

RECOMMENDED FOR: differentiation of cell types in thyroid.

21.423 In Other Structures

21.423 Coutelin 1931   899a, **9**:188

REAGENTS REQUIRED: A. 0.5% acid fuchsin; B. 1% phosphomolybdic acid

METHOD: [20 μ sections from formaldehyde-fixed material] $\rightarrow$ water $\rightarrow$ A, 5–10 mins. $\rightarrow$ water, wash $\rightarrow$ B, 10–20 secs. $\rightarrow$ balsam, via usual reagents

RECOMMENDED FOR: differentiation of flame cells.

RESULT: nuclei, and cilia, of flame cells, red.

21.423 Downey 1913   *see* DS 21.423 Wright 1910 (note)

21.423 Endicott 1945   20540b, **20**:5

REAGENTS REQUIRED: A. water 60, DS 11.122 Delafield (1885) 30; B. 1% hydrochloric acid in 95% alc.; C. 1% sodium phosphate dibasic; D. water 96, citric acid 0.212, sodium phosphate, dibasic (cryst.) 0.241, DS 13.13 Endicott 1945 (working sol.) 4

METHOD: [nitrocellulose sections of F 7000.1000 Orth 1896 fixed, and formic acid decalcified, material] $\rightarrow$ water $\rightarrow$ A, 5 mins. $\rightarrow$ B, rinse 95% alc., quick wash $\rightarrow$ C, till blue $\rightarrow$ wash $\rightarrow$ D, 1 hr. $\rightarrow$ E, till differentiated $\rightarrow$ balsam, via usual reagents

RECOMMENDED FOR: differentiation of cell types in bone marrow.

21.423 Fuller 1943   11284, **28**:1475

REAGENTS REQUIRED: A. water 50, DS 11.123 Ehrlich 1886 50; B. water 99, acetic acid 1, ponceau 2 R 0.5, acid fuchsin 0.5; C. water 100, phosphomolybdic acid 1, orange G 2

METHOD: [alc. fixed smears] $\rightarrow$ water $\rightarrow$ A, 2 mins. $\rightarrow$ wash, 4 mins. $\rightarrow$ B, 2 mins. $\rightarrow$ rinse $\rightarrow$ C, 2 mins. $\rightarrow$ balsam, via usual reagents

RECOMMENDED FOR: vaginal smears.

21.423 Gomori 1946   *Tech. Bull.*, **7**:45

REAGENTS REQUIRED: A. 0.05% azocarmine in 1% acetic acid; B. 1% aniline in 95% alc.; C. 3% phosphotungstic acid; D. water 100, oxalic acid 2, methyl blue 0.5, tartrazine 2

METHOD: [sections of material after other than dichromate fixation] $\rightarrow$ water $\rightarrow$ A, 1–1½ hrs., 60°C. $\rightarrow$ rinse $\rightarrow$ blot $\rightarrow$ 95% alc., rinse $\rightarrow$ B, till chromaffin cells deep pink $\rightarrow$ rinse $\rightarrow$ C, 20 mins. $\rightarrow$ quick wash $\rightarrow$ D, 15–40 mins., till collagen deep blue $\rightarrow$ rinse $\rightarrow$ balsam, via usual reagents

RECOMMENDED FOR: demonstration of chromaffin granules (purple to ruby-red).

21.423 Hamazaki 1935   22575, 295:703

REAGENTS REQUIRED: *A*. water 95, abs. alc. 5, phenol 2.8, magenta 0.5; *B*. 1% hydrochloric acid; *C*. ADS 12.2 Lugol (1905); *D*. 1% sodium thiosulfate; *E*. 3% hydrochloric acid

METHOD: [6 μ sections of F 3700.1010 Hamazaki 1935 fixed material] → water → *A*, 1 hr. → wash → *B*, 10 mins. → *C*, 30 mins. → rinse → *D*, till iodine-free → wash → *E*, 30 mins. → wash → balsam, via usual reagents

RECOMMENDED FOR: demonstration of wandering cells (red) in smooth muscle.

21.423 Hoecke and Sebruyns 1952   20540b, 27:263

REAGENTS REQUIRED: *A*. sat. sol. Bismarck brown in 70% alc.; *B*. sat. sol. anilin blue in 2.5% acetic acid; *C*. 0.1% methyl violet; *D*. water 30, 95% alc. 70, aluminum chloride 0.1, hematein 0.2; *E*. 95% alc. 100, saffron 2; *F*. 0.1% acetic acid in abs. alc.

PREPARATION OF E: Digest 6 hours at 60°C. Filter.

METHOD: [sections] → 70% alc. → *A*, 3 mins. → 70% alc., rinse → water, wash → *B*, 2 hrs. → *C*, dropped on slide, 2 mins. → 70% alc., wash → *D*, 30 mins. → 70% alc., rinse → *E*, till differentiated → *F*, 30 secs. → balsam, via usual reagents

RECOMMENDED FOR: differential staining of gastric glandular cells.

21.423 Kingsley 1937   8545, 57:87

REAGENTS REQUIRED: *A*. DS 13.13 Kingsley 1935 (sol. *A*); *B*. 0.008% acetic acid; *C*. acetone 100, eosin Y 0.001, acetic acid 0.04

METHOD: [sections of F 3500.1000 Kingsley 1937 fixed material] → water, via butyl alc. → *A*, 8–10 mins. → rinse → *B*, wash → rinse → blot → *C*, rinse → "neutral mountant," via butyl alc. and xylene

RECOMMENDED FOR: demonstration of megakaryocytes in sections of bone marrow.

21.423 Levine 1928   11284, 14:172

REAGENTS REQUIRED: *A*. 1% thionin; *B*. sat. sol. orange G in clove oil

METHOD: [5 μ sections] → water → *A*, 5 mins. → water, till no more color comes away → blot → *B*, few moments → clove oil, till differentiated → balsam, via xylene

RECOMMENDED FOR: mast cells in connective tissue of parathyroid.

RESULT: mast cells blue; other structures orange.

21.423 Novak 1910   766, 36:217

REAGENTS REQUIRED: *A*. DS 12.212 Unna 40, 1% eosin in 80% alc. 40, 1% hydroquinone 12, orcein 0.4; *B*. 1% safranin; *C*. 0.5% potassium dichromate

METHOD: [sections] → water → *A*, 5–10 mins. → *B*, 10 mins. → wash → *C*, 30 mins. → wash → balsam, via usual reagents

RECOMMENDED FOR: demonstration of corpuscles of Herbst.

21.423 Ralston and Wells 1939   591b, 3:72

REAGENTS REQUIRED: *A*. water 100, azocarmine 1, acetic acid 1; *B*. 0.15% aniline in 95% alc.; *C*. 0.07% acetic acid in 95% alc.; *D*. 0.5% toluidine blue

METHOD: [4 μ sections of bone decalcified in AF 21.1 Ralston and Wells 1939] → water → *A*, 20 mins., 56°C. → *B*, till color clouds cease → *C*, till rose red → wash → *D*, 10–15 secs. → abs. alc., least possible time for dehydration → balsam, via xylene

RECOMMENDED FOR: differential staining of bone marrow.

21.423 Shoor 1941   19938, 94:545

FORMULA: water 50, 95% alc. 50, Biebrich scarlet 0.5, orange G 0.25, fast green FCF 0.075, phosphotungstic acid 0.5, phosphomolybdic acid 0.5, acetic acid 1

METHOD: [alcohol-ether-fixed smears] → stain, 1 min. → 70% alc., rinse → dammar, via usual reagents

RECOMMENDED FOR: vaginal smears.

21.423 Papanicolaou 1941   11284, 26:1200

REAGENTS REQUIRED: *A*. DS 11.123 Ehrlich 1886; *B*. water 100, phosphotungstic acid 0.112, phosphomolybdic acid 0.225, anilin blue W.S. 0.06, orange G 0.125, acid fuchsin 0.1, eosin Y 0.21

METHOD: [alcohol-fixed smears] → water → *A*, 2 mins. → rinse → "blue" in tap water → rinse → *B*, 2–5 mins. → rinse → balsam, via dioxane

RECOMMENDED FOR: vaginal smears.

21.423 Papanicolaou 1942　　　　　　　　　　19938, **95**:438

REAGENTS REQUIRED: *A*. DS 11.123 Ehrlich 1886; *B*. 0.5% hydrochloric acid; *C*. 95% alc. 100, orange G 0.5, phosphotungstic acid 0.015; *D*. *either* 95% alc. 100, light green SF 0.225, Bismarck brown 0.05, eosin Y 0.225, phosphotungstic acid 0.2, lithium carbonate 0.0005 *or* 95% alc. 100, light green SF 0.22, Bismarck brown 0.06, eosin Y 0.22, phosphotungstic acid 0.17, lithium carbonate 0.0005

METHOD: [ether-alcohol-fixed vaginal smears] → water, via graded alcs. → *A*, 5–10 mins. → *B*, till differentiated → "blue" → 95% alc., via graded alcs. → *C*, 1 min. → 95% alc., rinse → *D*, 2 mins. → 95% alc., rinse → balsam, via usual reagents

RECOMMENDED FOR: vaginal smears.

NOTE: The two alternatives under D above were named respectively EA 36 and EA 25 by their inventor.

21.423 Pfaff and Williams 1942　　　　　　　20540b, **17**:165

STOCK SOLUTIONS: I. water 100, acetic acid 2.5, benzedine 0.5, II. 0.5% sodium nitro-ferricyanide

REAGENTS REQUIRED: *A*. stock I 20, stock II 20, water 60; *B*. water 100, hydrogen per-oxide (30%) 0.2

METHOD: [pieces of formaldehyde-fixed material] → *A*, 30–45 mins., 37°C. → wash, 37°C. several mins. → *B*, 30 mins., 37°C. → wash, 37°C. → balsam, via usual reagents

RECOMMENDED FOR: demonstration of blood vessels in wholemounts.

21.423 Schleicher 1942　　　　　　　　　　　20540b, **17**:161

REAGENTS REQUIRED: *A*. methanol 100, DS 13.12 Wright 1910 (dry powder) 0.17; *B* water 100, methanol 5, acetone 0.5

METHOD: [air-dried smear of mixed plasma and myeloid-erythroid layer produced by centrifugation of heparinized bone marrow] → 0.5 ml. *A*, on smear, 2 mins. → add 2 ml. water, 5–10 mins. → *B*, 1–5 secs. → rinse → dry

RECOMMENDED FOR: cells of bone marrow.

21.423 Wright 1910　　　　　　　　　　　　　11373, **21**:263

REAGENTS REQUIRED: *A*. DS 13.12 Wright 1910 (*A* sol.) 75, 0.2% eosin Y in methanol

METHOD: [sections of mercuric-fixed marrow] → stain, 10 mins. → wash → resin in turpentine, via acetone and turpentine

RECOMMENDED FOR: demonstration of megakaryocytes in sections of bone marrow.

NOTE: **Downey 1913** (8545, **15**:25) specifies fixation in his F 3000.1000 solution.

21.423 Zimmerman 1925　　　　　　　　　　　7962, **24**:281

REAGENTS REQUIRED: *A*. any DS 11.122 formula; *B*. 1% hydrochloric acid in 70% alc. *C*. DS 22.7 Mayer 1896a (working sol.); *D*. sat. sol. aurantia in 50% alc.

METHOD: [sections] → water → *A*, till deeply stained → *B*, till connective tissues des-tined → wash → *C*, 24 hrs. → wash → *D*, till deeply stained → 50% alc. till differ-entiated → balsam, via usual reagents

RESULT: superficial epithelium, red; parietal cells, red; chief cells, gray blue; other tissues, yellow.

RECOMMENDED FOR: differentiation of cell types in stomach.

22 DYE STAINS FOR CYTOLOGICAL ELEMENTS

It has been very difficult to determine which techniques should lie in the present section and which should have been referred to section DS 23.1. The term *cell inclusion* is all embracing and might be held to cover the result of almost any technique which has been used to demonstrate the existence of a small particle, the nature of which has never been disclosed or the existence of which has subsequently been doubted. As the term is employed here, the nature of the research for which the technique was designed, rather than the results obtained, has been used as a guide. It is, therefore, very possible that many, if not all, of the techniques designed to show cell inclusions would show these same cell inclusions if the techniques given under DS 23.1 below were to be substi-tuted for them.

In the division of cytological elements there has been followed, in general, the usual classification. The first class, con-taining nuclear techniques, is quite seexplanatory, though it must be emphasized that only those techniques are included in this division which are intended for the specific staining of nuclear elements. General nuclear stains are given under the headings DS 11 in Chapter 20. Probably much annoyance will be caused to cytologists by the grouping together, in the second class, of mitochondria and Golgi apparatus. It is not intended, of course, by this grouping to suggest that these are in any way related to each other. They are, however, the chief preoccupation of the cytological cytologist, and the techniques intended for their display may therefore be justifiably included in the same place. The next four sections deal with a variety of cell inclusions too well known to need further explanation at this point; the final class has been erected to contain all those miscellaneous techniques which have been designed to show not only cell inclusions, but also such cell extrusions as cilia, flagella, and the like.

22.1 NUCLEI

For staining nuclei in cells any of the techniques given in the last chapter (DS 11) may be satisfactorily employed. These nuclear stains are, however, by no means the best when it is desired to bring out for the interest or information of students the various portions of a mitotic figure other than the chromosomes themselves or when, for one reason or another, it is desired to stain the chromosomes in a manner which leaves them relatively transparent. The majority of these techniques have been developed by botanists, but they may be applied equally well to sections of animal material, and are designed throughout to demonstrate clearly all the elements, including the spindle fibers, of a mitotic division. Most research workers would prefer, probably, to retain the iron-hematoxylin techniques to which they are accustomed, but it is sincerely to be hoped that the manufacturers of slides for class purposes will learn of the existence of other methods and will cease to supply the now inevitable iron-hematoxylin-stained mitotic figure, which rarely shows more than the chromosomes themselves.

22.10 TYPICAL EXAMPLES

Demonstration of mitosis in an onion root tip using the rose bengal-orange G-toluidine blue stain of Kedrovsky 1931

Nobody who has prepared onion root tip for class demonstration by this method will ever be likely to revert to the iron hematoxylin method formerly employed, for nothing is more attractive to an elementary class than a polychrome-stained specimen.

Though the term *onion root* is usually applied to these preparations, there are several members of the genus Allium which will give better class-demonstration material. The author's preference is for the root tip of the leek (*Allium porrum*), which can be obtained just as readily as the root tip of an onion. Excellent demonstration material can be obtained from a leek seedling about a month old. These can be cultured in the laboratory, for there is no objection to the etiolation which results from the growing of such material in improperly lighted surroundings. The high temperatures at which most laboratories are maintained is also an advantage, since it causes a more rapid growth and a greater variety of stages to be obtainable in a single section. The writer does not think that there is much choice in fixative for these specimens, as the mercuric-acetic-nitric fixative of Petrunkewitsch (Chapter 18, F 3000.0014) gives uniformly successful preparations. The leek seedling, upon being removed from the soil, should be very, very thoroughly washed in normal saline solution to remove adherent particles of fine grit which would blunt the knife and the tip of the seedling, with the roots attached, is then dropped into a considerable volume of Petrunkewitsch's fixative. It may remain here overnight before being removed and thoroughly washed in several changes of 50% alcohol.

This material will present no difficulties in sectioning. It is customary to cut a longitudinal section; and a section thickness of from five to eight microns should be employed rather than the conventional ten microns. The sections are then attached to the slide in the usual way, dewaxed, and run down through the customary alcohols to water.

An alternative technique, which is not nearly as widely used but is really most successful, is to employ smears rather than sections of the root tip. Though these do not give, of course, a clear picture of the relations of the cells to each other, they at least insure that the majority of mitotic figures will be so oriented on the slide as to occasion no difficulty to the students studying them. These smears may be prepared by taking the tip of the root, placing it on the slide, taking a sharp scalpel, and smearing, quite literally, the root onto the glass with the pressure of the flat side of the knife and a rotary motion of the hand. These smears are then fixed by being placed face down, resting across two glass rods, in a petri dish of fixative. The depth of the fluid must be such that the lower surface of the slide bearing the smear is in contact with the fixative, which must not, however, be permitted to rise up until the upper surface of the slide is wetted by it. After fixation by this method the slides are removed and washed in several changes of 50% alcohol until the fixative is removed.

Two solutions are required for staining. First is DS 21.11 Kedrovsky 1931. To prepare this, dissolve 0.3 gram of rose bengal in 50 milliliters of water; add one milliliter of 1% phosphomolybdic acid to the boiling solution, one drop at a time, with constant stirring. Cool and add 50 milliliters of a 1.2% solution of orange G. The only other stain required is a 1% solution of toluidine blue.

Whether sections or smears are being employed, the slides are transferred from distilled water to the rose bengal-phosphomolybdic acid stain for from 20 to 30 minutes. The time is not particularly critical, and a period of as long as one hour may be employed if it is more convenient. Each slide is then taken separately, rinsed very briefly in distilled water, and transferred to 1% toluidine blue for 5 minutes. It is transferred directly from toluidine blue to 70% alcohol, in which it is waved backward and forward for about one minute to remove the excess stain from the section, and then transferred to 95% alcohol, in which differentiation proceeds relatively slowly. If differentiation in 95% alcohol is too slow, the specimen may be returned to 70% alcohol for a brief period, and then put back in 95% alcohol. The sections must be examined under a high power of the microscope to determine when they are properly differentiated, and it is not safe to do this if they have been removed directly from alcohol. Before being examined, therefore, each section should be dipped in bergamot oil (specified by Kadrovsky) or in clove oil, which is equally safe. The oil should be wiped from the back of the slide and the slide then examined. The differentiation should not be watched with regard to the chromosomes themselves, but with regard to the spindle fibers, which are far better shown by this than by any other method. In a properly differentiated specimen the spindle fibers will be a clear pink against a blue background, and when this condition has been reached the bergamot oil should be washed off thoroughly in xylene, and the specimen mounted in balsam. If the spindle fibers are properly differentiated the chromatin will be a clear dark blue, very readily differentiated from the blue background of the cytoplasm, and the students' attention will clearly be drawn to the nucleoli in the resting nuclei, which are stained a bright red.

22.11 OTHER TECHNIQUES

22.11 Backman 1935   20540b, **10**:83
> This method, recommended by Gatenby and Painter 1937, 691, calls for a "saturated solution of anthraquinone"; anthraquinone is not soluble in water and it is not apparent which soluble derivative was employed by Backman.

22.11 Balbiani *test.* **1895 Maggi**   Maggi 1895, 174
> REAGENTS REQUIRED: *A.* 1% osmic acid; *B.* water 100, acetic acid 1, methyl green 1; *C.* 0.2% ammonia
> METHOD: [protozoans] → *A*, 1 min. *B*, 3 mins. → *C*, till differentiated
> RECOMMENDED FOR: nuclear detail in ciliates.

22.11 Barrett 1932   20540b, **7**:63
FORMULA: water 25, 95% alc. 25, acetic acid 50, hematoxylin 0.06, ferric alum 0.5
METHOD: [smear preparations] → stain, under coverslip, till chromosomes clear → seal cover
RECOMMENDED FOR: pollen mother cells.

22.11 Bradley 1948   20540b, **23**:29
REAGENTS REQUIRED: *A*. F 0000.0010 Bradley 1948; *B*. 4% ferric alum; *C*. 50% hydrochloric acid; *D*. DS 11.23 Belling 1921
METHOD: [plant ovaries] → *A*, 2 days → *B*, 75°C., 3 mins. → water, 75°C. 2 mins. → fresh water, 75°C., 2 mins. → cold water, 2–3 mins. → *C*, 10 mins. → thorough wash → [scrape ovules from placenta to slide] → [apply cover and top to separate cells] → heat to steaming → jar filled with alc. vapor, 24 hrs. → abs. alc., 1 drop run under cover → spread M 23.1 mountant round edge of cover, leave in jar with slight alc. vapor content 24 hrs. → dry

22.11 Bizzozero-Vassale *test.* **1894 Kahlden and Laurent**
                                    Kahlden and Laurent 1894, 71
REAGENTS REQUIRED: *A*. DS 23.211 Ehrlich 1882; *B*. ADS 12.2 Gram 1884; *C*. 1% chromic acid
METHOD: [sections] → *A*, 10 mins. → abs. alc., rinse → *B*, 2 mins. → abs. alc., 30 secs. → *C*, 30 secs. → abs. alc., 30 secs. → *C*, 30 secs. → abs. alc., 30 secs. → clove oil, till no more color comes away → balsam, via usual reagents

22.11 Conn 1943   20540b, **18**:189
REAGENTS REQUIRED: *A*. 1% chlorazol black E
METHOD: [sections of root tips] → water → *A*, 2 hrs. → balsam, via usual reagents

22.11 Cooper 1931   591, **18**:337
REAGENTS REQUIRED: *A*. 1% methyl green; *B*. 1% acid fuchsin; *C*. 1% erythrosin
METHOD: [sections] → water → *A*, 1 hr. → water, rinse → *B*, 1 min. → water, quick rinse → *C*, few secs. → abs. alc., minimum possible time → balsam, via xylene
RESULT: chromatin, green; linin, red.

22.11 Dalton *test.* **1948 Lillie**   Lillie 1948, 87
REAGENTS REQUIRED: *A*. water 55, acetic acid 1, orcein 45; *B*. 0.15% fast green FCF in abs. alc.
PREPARATION OF A: Dissolve dye in hot acid. Cool. Dilute to 100 with water.
METHOD: [pieces for chromosomes] → *A*, 48 hrs. → fragments crushed under coverslip on slide coated with V 21.1 Mayer 1884 → alc. vapor, 48 hrs. → 95% alc., few moments → *B*, few secs. → balsam, via usual reagents

22.11 Darrow 1944   20540b, **19**:65
REAGENTS REQUIRED: *A*. 1% safranin O; *B*. sat. sol. (*circ.* 1%) anilin blue W S in 95% alc.
METHOD: [sections from F 6000.1010 fixed material] → water → *A*, 15 mins. → rinse → *B*, 2 mins. → balsam, via usual reagents
RECOMMENDED FOR: chromosomes in root tips.

22.11 Geither 1940 *test.* **1948 Romeis**   Romeis 1948, 223
REAGENTS REQUIRED: *A*. 2% osmic acid; *B*. F 1600.0010 Benda 1901; *C*. 3% hydrogen peroxide; *D*. 1% safranin; *E*. 0.2% light green
METHOD: [fresh smears] → *A*, 10–20 secs. → *B*, 10 mins. → thorough wash → *C*, 10 mins. → thorough wash → *D*, 10 mins. → rinse → *E*, ¼–1 min. → 95% alc. → balsam, via usual reagents
RESULT: chromatin, nucleoli, red; centrosome, spindle fibers, green.

22.11 Hancock 1942   20540b, **17**:79
REAGENTS REQUIRED: *A*. 1% chromic acid; *B*. 0.1% crystal violet; *C*. 1% iodine and 1% potassium iodide in 80% alc.
METHOD: [10 μ sections of F 6000.1010 Belling 1928 fixed material] → water → *A*, 20 mins. → 95% alc., rinse → abs. alc., least possible time → clove oil, till clear → xylene, 2 hrs. → balsam
RECOMMENDED FOR: minute plant chromosomes.

22.11 Hermann 1893 *test.* **1905 Böhm and Davidoff**   Böhm and Davidoff 1905, 76

REAGENTS REQUIRED: *A.* 1% safranin; *B.* sat. sol. gentian violet in sat. sol. aniline; *C.* ADS 12.2 Lugol (1905)

METHOD: [sections from F 1200.0010 Hermann 1889 fixed material] → water → *A*, overnight → *B*, 3–5 mins. → rinse → *C*, till uniform black → 95% alc. till violet → clove oil → examine → [repeat 95% alc. if insufficiently differentiated] → balsam, via xylene

RESULT: chromosomes, bluish violet; nucleoli, aster, spindle fibers, red.

22.11 Hruby 1933   19938, 77:352

REAGENTS REQUIRED: *A.* sat. sol. (*circ.* 1%) magenta; *B.* sat. sol. (*circ.* 1.2%) picric acid 50, sat. sol. (*circ.* 2%) indigo-carmine 50

METHOD: [sections] → water → *A*, 5–20 mins. → water, thorough wash → *B*, 5–10 mins. → 70% alc., rinse → abs. alc., till green → balsam, via usual reagents

RESULT: chromosomes, red; nucleoli, blue; spindle fibers, dark blue.

22.11 Johansen 1932   20540b, 7:17

REAGENTS REQUIRED: *A.* 1% methyl violet 2B; *B.* sat. sol. (*circ.* 1.2%) picric acid in 95% alc.; *C.* 0.1% ammonia in 95% alc.; *D.* abs. alc. 50, clove oil 50, erythrosin to sat.

METHOD: [sections] → water → *A*, 15 to 30 mins. → water, quick rinse → *B*, till differentiated, about 15 secs. → *C*, 15 secs. → 95% alc., thorough rinse → *D*, 5–10 secs. → clove oil, 15 secs. → balsam, via xylene

RESULT: chromatin purple, plastin red.

22.11 Kedrovsky 1931   23632, 47:433

REAGENTS REQUIRED: *A.* water 100, orange G 0.6, rose bengal 0.3, phosphomolybdic acid 0.01; *B.* 1% toluidine blue

PREPARATION OF A: Dissolve the rose bengal in 50 boiling water. Add 1 1% phosphomolybdic acid slowly and with constant agitation. Cool and add orange G dissolved in 50 water.

METHOD: [sections or smears] → *A*, 20–30 mins. → water, rinse → *B*, 5 mins. → 70% alc., 1 min. → 95% alc., till differentiated → balsam, via bergamot oil

RESULT: chromatin, dark blue; nucleoli, bright red; spindle fibers, pink against blue.

NOTE: A detailed description of the use of this stain is given under DS 22.10 above.

22.11 Kurnick and Ris 1948   20540b, 23:17

FORMULA: water 55, 95% alc. 9, acetic acid 36, orcein 0.8, fast green 0.1, sodium chloride 0.4

METHOD: [fresh smears, or mounted sections, taken to water] → stain, few moments → balsam, via usual reagents

RESULT: chromatin, red brown; cytoplasm, nucleoli, green.

22.11 Kurnick and Ris 1948   20540b, 23:17

FORMULA: water 55, acetic acid 36, 95% alc. 9, orcein 0.8, fast green FCF 0.1 sodium chloride 0.4

METHOD: [smears and squashes] → *A*, under cover, few mins. → remove cover → balsam, via usual reagents → replace cover

RESULT: chromatin, brownish red; nucleoli, green.

22.11 La Cour 1941   20540b, 16:169

REAGENTS REQUIRED: *A.* water 55, acetic acid 45, orcein 1; *B.* 10% acetic acid

METHOD: [fresh smear] → *A*, under coverslip, 2–3 mins. → invert slide in *B* till cover falls off → balsam, via usual reagents

22.11 Maneval 1934   19938, 80:292

REAGENTS REQUIRED: *A.* DS 11.43 Maneval 1928; *B.* 0.01% hydrochloric acid in 95% alc. *C.* clove oil 100, light green 0.075, orange G 0.025

METHOD: [sections] → water → *A*, 3–5 mins. → wash → *B*, till differentiated → abs. alc., till dehydrated → *C*, till stained → balsam, via xylene

RECOMMENDED FOR: mitosis in plant cells.

22.11 McClintock 1929   20540b, **4**:53
REAGENTS REQUIRED: *A*. 25% acetic acid in abs. alc.; *B*. DS 11.23 Belling 1921; *C*. 10%
acetic acid; *D*. 50% acetic acid in abs. alc.; *E*. 10% acetic acid in abs. alc.; *F*. abs. alc.
50, xylene 50
METHOD: [fresh anthers] → *A*, till required → squeeze contents of anther onto slide,
cover with *B*, crush → warm to steaming → cool → repeat warming 3 or 4 times →
C, in petri → *E*, 2 mins. → abs. alc., 2 mins. → *F*, 2 mins. → xylene, 2 mins. → [re-
combine slide and cover] → balsam
RECOMMENDED FOR: plant chromosomes.

22.11 Meyer 1885 *see* DS 11.28 Meyer 1885

22.11 Mitter and Bartha 1948   20540b, **23**:27
REAGENTS REQUIRED: *A*. water 55, acetic acid 45, brilliant cresyl blue 0.75; *B*. 45%
acetic acid
METHOD: [whole salivary glands of Drosophila] → *A*, in vial, 30–45 mins. → transfer
glands to slide → drain → blot → cover and tap cover to break nuclei → *B*, under
cover, if differentiation necessary → seal cover
RECOMMENDED FOR: salivary gland chromosomes of Drosophila.

22.11 Nissl 1894 *see* DS 11.113 Nissl 1894

22.11 Rawitz *see* DS 11.42 Rawitz 1895

22.11 van Rosen 1947   14900, **160**:121
REAGENTS REQUIRED: *A*. 30% acetic acid in 95% alc., *B*. 30% hydrochloric acid in 95%
alc.; *C*. water 50, acetic acid 50, nigrosin, alc. soluble 4
METHOD: [fresh tissue] → *A*, 24 hrs. (cooled for roots) → *A*, 1–10 mins. 4°C. → wash,
15–30 mins. → *B*, on slide, 1–2 mins. → blot
RECOMMENDED FOR: plant chromosomes.
NOTE: the dye used was probably indulin, alc. sol.

22.11 Sax 1931   20540b, **6**:117
REAGENTS REQUIRED: *A*. 1% crystal violet; *B*. water 20, 95% alc. 80, iodine 1, potassium iodide 1
METHOD: [smears fixed 1–2 hrs. in F 6000.1010 Navashin 1912] → 15% alc., thorough
wash → *A*, 1–5 mins. → rinse → *B*, 30 secs. → abs. alc., till differentiated → balsam,
via usual reagents
RECOMMENDED FOR: pollen mother cells.

22.11 Schmorl 1928   Schmorl 1928, 140
REAGENTS REQUIRED: *A*. DS 11.122 Böhmer 1868; *B*. 1% safranin; *C*. water 100, picric
acid 0.1, tannin 25
METHOD: [celloidin sections of alc. fixed material] → water → *A*, 5 mins. → tap water,
till blue → *B*, 20 mins. → wash → *C*, till differentiated, 2–5 mins. → thorough wash
→ balsam, via usual reagents
RESULT: *sauren Kerne*, red; *gewöhnlichen Kerne*, blue.

22.11 Semmens and Bhaduri 1939   20540b, **14**:1
REAGENTS REQUIRED: *A*. 5% sodium carbonate; *B*. water 98, 95% alc. 12, aniline 0.1,
light green 0.5; *C*. sat. sol. sodium carbonate in 70% alc.
METHOD: [sections, chromatin stained by DS 11.43 de Tomasi 1936] → *A*, 1 hr. → wash,
30 mins. → *B*, 10 mins. → *C*, rinse → 95% alc., 10 mins. → repeat *C* → alc. cycle
till cytoplasm free of green → balsam, via usual reagents
RECOMMENDED FOR: differential staining of nucleoli (green) and chromosomes (purple).

22.11 Smith 1934   20540b, **9**:95
REAGENTS REQUIRED: *A*. ADS 12.2 Lugol (1905); *B*. 1% crystal violet; *C*. sat. sol. (*circ*.
1.2%) picric acid in abs. alc.
METHOD: [sections or smears] → 70% alc., → *A*, 10–20 mins. → water, rinse → *B*, 15
mins. → 95% alc., rinse → *C*, few secs. → abs. alc., till yellow removed → clove oil,
till differentiated → xylene, till clove oil removed → balsam

22.11 Togby 1942   20540b, **17**:171

REAGENTS REQUIRED: *A*. 95% alc. 50, hydrogen peroxide (3%) 50; *B*. 1% chromic acid; *C*. 1% crystal violet; *D*. 1% iodine and 1% potassium iodide in 50% alc.; *E*. sat. sol. picric acid in 95% alc.; *F*. 0.1% ammonia in 95% alc.

METHOD: [sections of F 1670.0010 La Cour 1931a fixed material] → water → *A*, 30 mins. → rinse → *B*, 30 mins. → rinse → *C*, 1 hr. → rinse → *D*, 30 secs. → 70% alc., rinse → *E*, rinse → *F*, rinse → abs. alc., till dehydrated → clove oil, till differentiated → xylene, thorough wash → balsam

RECOMMENDED FOR: chromosomes of Crepis.

22.11 Unna *test.* **1928 Schmorl**   Schmorl 1928, 139

REAGENTS REQUIRED: A. DS 11.44 Unna 1892; *B*. 25% tannin

METHOD: [sections of F 7000.0000 Müller 1859 or F 1600.0010 Flemming 1882 fixed material] → water → *A*, 2 mins. → wash → *B*, 10–15 mins. → wash → balsam, via usual reagents

22.11 Wing 1930   23639b, **10**:699

REAGENTS REQUIRED: *A*. ADS 12.2 Wing 1930; *B*. 1% gentian violet

METHOD: [thin sections] → *A*, 5–30 mins. → momentary rinse → *B*, 5–15 mins. → quick rinse → *A*, 20–30 secs. differentiation → abs. alc., least possible time for dehydration → clove oil, till differentiated → balsam, via xylene

22.2 MITOCHONDRIA AND GOLGI APPARATUS

The techniques designed for the demonstration of mitochondria in sections so closely resemble those intended for the demonstration of bacteria under the same conditions (see DS 23.22 below), that it is not surprising that for many years there was confusion in the literature as to whether or not mitochondria existed. The now universal acceptance of the existence of mitochondria has, however, unfortunately permitted students to become careless, and it must never be forgotten that the bacteria which frequently grow in the egg albumen, with which sections are attached to a slide, will stain in the same colors and be of much the same size and shape as mitochondria. The original technique, for example, of Altmann 1890, could be employed very readily for staining acid-fast bacteria in almost any section of tissue.

The next development in the staining of mitochondria, after Altmann, was the demonstration by Kull in 1914 that the dye, aurantia, could satisfactorily be substituted for picric acid, to which it is chemically closely related, in the differentiation of Altmann's stain. It may be remarked at this point, parenthetically, that aurantia is even more explosive than picric acid, and is so dangerous to manufacture that its supply has been discontinued by many firms. If it is handled in the laboratory, it should be treated with the respect which is accorded to any high-explosive material. Kull also substituted the fixative of Champy 1913 for the fixative specified by Altmann in 1890. On the somewhat slender basis that Champy invented this fixative for another purpose, the technique has been commonly known as the *Champy-Kull technique*, and this term is now generally adopted in English-speaking countries. In France and Germany, however, most of what are called Champy-Kull techniques in this country are replaced by the so-called "Parat techniques," in which material is "pre-dichromated" before being stained with a hematoxylin stain. The name *Parat*, however, has tended to be applied to almost any method of staining mitochondria after treatment with dichromate, just as the term *Champy-Kull* has come to be transferred to any technique in which acid fuchsin is used as the primary stain. The two methods were brought together in 1928 by Volkonsky, who combined the pre-dichromating of Parat with the acid-fuchsin-aurantia technique of Kull, and followed these with a double-staining technique using hematoxylin, orange G, and aniline blue by a method closely resembling those of the Masson techniques described in sections DS 12.31 and DS 12.32 above.

22.20 TYPICAL EXAMPLES

Demonstration of mitochondria in the pancreas using the acid fuchsin-toluidine blue-aurantia stain of Kull 1914

There are so many modifications of the method of demonstrating mitochondria here described, that it seems desirable to give a fairly detailed description of the original technique, and to leave to the reader the task of determining by subsequent experimentation which of the numerous modifications he would prefer to employ. The method here described, which is most commonly referred to in the literature as *Champy-Kull*, has the advantage that it permits considerable experimentation under standardized conditions, and yields reproducible results, once the timing on any particular batch of material has been established. The method involves overstaining in acid fuchsin, which is strongly absorbed by the nuclei, the mitochondria, and any bacteria present. The acid fuchsin is then differentiated in a solution of toluidine blue, which removes the acid fuchsin from the nuclei. These remain stained blue, and finally differentiation is conducted in aurantia which removes the unwanted toluidine blue from all parts of the cytoplasm except the mitochondria.

A word of warning may be inserted at this point relative to the use of aurantia. This dye is produced from diphenylamine, to the derivatives of which many persons are exceedingly sensitive. Those who have suffered from dermatitis in the handling of photographic developers should under no circumstances handle solutions of aurantia, for the dermatitis produced is difficult to get rid of and the sensitivity of the worker to this reagent appears to be increased by every exposure to it. The dry dye itself is explosive and should always be kept in solution.

Pancreas has been selected as a demonstration object because it is both readily obtainable, and also normally contains very large and clear mitochondria. Baker 1933, 189 recommends the intestinal mucosa of the white mouse for the same

reason. The writer prefers the pancreas because it is so much more easily fixed than the mucosa of the mouse; if the intestine is used it must be split up, and the piece pinned out flat, to enable the fixative to reach the epithelium.

It does not matter which particular animal is taken, but if mitochondria are to be well demonstrated, it should be in good health and should be killed by a blow on the head rather than by narcotic drugs. The pancreas is most readily obtained in the following manner.

Tie or pin out the animal on its back, remove the whole of the skin from the abdomen without breaking through the muscular wall of the abdominal cavity, and then remove the wall of the abdominal cavity by an incision made round its periphery. The very considerable loss of blood which results from this may be ignored. Now spread the pancreas on a piece of glass by the following method. Hold the glass by the edges in the right hand, and lift the stomach and upper portion of the small intestine with the left hand, the intestine being spread away from the stomach with the fingers. This leaves the pancreas stretched in the mesentery. Now lay the sheet of glass flat against the mesentery, with the pancreas spread on the surface, and then pass the stomach and intestine from left to right, while tipping the glass slide upward, so that the weight of the stomach and of the intestine hanging down keep the mesentery stretched over the surface. Run a sharp knife round the edge of the slide so as to cut through the mesentery, leaving the pancreas exposed on the glass surface. It is, naturally, necessary to lower the right hand to prevent the weight of the stomach and intestine from dragging the mesentery off the glass when the first cut is made, but a little practice will enable one to obtain the material spread cleanly on the glass slide with little trouble. Place the slide, with its adherent mesentery flat in a glass dish (naturally with the pancreas on its upper surface) and flood with the fixative. The classical technique of Kull requires the osmic-chromic-dichromate-pyroligneous fixative of Champy 1913 (Chapter 18, F 1670.0080), which is applied in three separate stages. The first solution contains 3 grams of potassium dichromate, 1.15 grams of chromic acid, and 1.25 grams of osmic acid in 250 milliliters of water. This is poured over the pancreas on the slide and placed in a dark cupboard for about 24 hours. At the conclusion of this period the fixative is poured off (it may be used many times), the dish filled with distilled water, and rocked gently backward and forward for about half an hour. The pancreas and mesentery will usually become detached from the glass at this stage, and the glass may be withdrawn. The distilled water is then replaced with the second solution of Champy, which contains 2.5 grams of chromic acid dissolved in a mixture of 35 milliliters of pyroligneous acid and 175 milliliters of water. Pyroligneous acid, it may be said, is the product of the dry destructive distillation of wood, and contains a mixture of various creosotes and tars in a weak solution of acetic acid. It is unfortunately not at present known which of its various constituents exercise the required effect, but it may be stated quite categorically that weak solutions of acetic acid cannot be substituted for it. This solution should be allowed to act for about 20 hours and the specimen again washed in distilled water for about 30 minutes.

At this point the pancreas may be cut into small pieces with a pair of sharp scissors. Pieces of about 3-millimeter side should be selected and removed from the distilled water in which the cutting is done to another vial of distilled water. After enough pieces have been selected, the distilled water is poured off and replaced with 3% potassium dichromate for three or four days before being washed in running water for 24 hours. Fixation is now complete. Many of the modifications which have been suggested are for the purpose of diminishing the time in the dichromate bath, by using various dichromate fixatives at higher temperatures. The method of Champy, however, is reliable, and though it is slow and cumbrous, it yields far more certain results than many of its modern, more complicated variants.

After washing in running water for 24 hours, the specimens are dehydrated and embedded in paraffin in the customary manner before being sectioned. It is recommended that sections about five microns in thickness be employed, and that these be mounted on the slides in the customary manner.

It is now necessary to make the acid fuchsin stain of Altmann 1890 (DS 22.2 Altmann 1890) about which there has been considerable controversy. This solution is prepared by dissolving 20 grams of acid fuchsin in 100 cc. of "aniline water," which is itself a saturated solution of aniline in water. It is better that the solution be made when a little free aniline is present, since the solubility of acid fuchsin in aniline is far higher than in water. Take, therefore, 100 grams of water, add to it about five milliliters of aniline, and shake vigorously for a few moments. Throw in 20 grams of acid fuchsin, shake vigorously for a few moments, and lay on one side in a warm place. Shake the bottle at intervals during the next 24 hours, at the end of which time the acid fuchsin (despite statements to the contrary in the literature) will be found to have dissolved. The failure of some investigators to cause more than a few grams of acid fuchsin to go into solution (see for example the remarks of Gatenby and Painter 1937, 305) is probably due to the fact that they first prepared a saturated solution of aniline in water, and then endeavored to dissolve the acid fuchsin into it. A mixture of aniline and water will dissolve, possibly by a process of mutual solubility, the required quantity of acid fuchsin. This point must be insisted upon, since the entire success of the preparation depends upon the maintenance of a very high concentration of acid fuchsin in the solution first used for staining. The other staining solutions required in this method are a 0.5% solution of toluidine blue in water and a 0.5% solution of aurantia in 70% alcohol; neither present any difficulty of preparation.

Now take one of the slides, drain off the water so far as possible, and blot round the section with filter paper before flooding the slide with acid fuchsin. The draining and blotting are necessary, since the high concentration of acid fuchsin will not be maintained if it is poured onto a slide over which are gathered films and droplets of water. Lay the slide on a support of some kind and wave a bunsen flame backward and forward underneath it, until steam rises from the surface of the stain; no bubbles must be permitted to form. Neither the time of staining nor the exact temperature are in any way critical; as soon as the slide has started to steam, the flame is removed and the slide left until it is cool enough to handle. Then use a jet of water from a wash bottle to remove the excess acid fuchsin. The sections will now be stained a dense purple red, and are transferred to the solution of toluidine blue in a coplin jar for one to two minutes. The purpose of the toluidine blue is to remove the acid fuchsin from the nuclei and to replace it with the blue stain. After one or two minutes pick out the slide, rinse it in distilled water, and place it in the aurantia until the mitochondria are differentiated through the removal of the acid fuchsin from the cytoplasm around them, and the substitution of the clear yellow color of the aurantia for this pink color. This process may only with difficulty be controlled under the microscope. It is better to leave a trial slide in the aurantia for two minutes, to remove it, dehydrate it in absolute alcohol for the minimum time possible, and then to transfer it to xylene before examining it under the high power of the microscope. If the timing in the toluidine blue and aurantia solutions has been correct, the nuclei will be a vivid, bright blue, the cytoplasm clear yellow, and the mitochondria vivid scarlet. If the nuclei are still purple, and the mitochondria are not clearly differentiated in scarlet, the next trial slide should be left longer in toluidine blue. If, however, the only defect is that the cytoplasm remains a clear pink, the time in aurantia should be increased. By thus juggling the times in the toluidine blue and the aurantia (it is a waste of time to try to control the timing in the acid fuchsin or in the alcohols), it is possible to arrive at a schedule which yields perfect preparations. Once this schedule has been established, it is possible to prepare a long series of slides, in each which there is clear differentiation of nuclei, mitochondria, and cytoplasm. It must be pointed out that the staining technique of Altmann, which has been used, can also be used to stain bacteria, and that if the sections are mounted on the slide with an excess of either gelatin or egg albumin, and are then permitted to remain damp and warm for 24 hours, bacteria will undoubtedly be found, and also that these bacteria have given rise to certain inaccurate observations. This can be avoided, however, either by using an adequate quantity of a biostatic agent in the adhesive used for the sections, or by avoiding leaving them under conditions which will encourage bacterial growth.

22.21 OTHER TECHNIQUES

22.21 Altmann 1890 *test*. **1928 Gatenby and Cowdry**   Gatenby and Cowdry 1928, 333

REAGENTS REQUIRED: *A*. sat. sol. aniline 100, acid fuchsin 20; *B*. water 65, sat. sol. picric acid in 95% alc. 35

METHOD: [sections of F 1700.0000 Altmann 1890 fixed material] → water *A*, on slide, heated to steaming, 1 min. → *B*, on slide, heated to steaming, till differentiated → blot → abs. alc., minimum possible time → balsam, via xylene

RESULT: mitochondria red on yellow.

NOTE: This method is sometimes erroneously referred to **Zimmerman**. For a slight modification of this procedure see **DS 21.421 Severinghaus 1932. Kiyono 1914** (23681, **25**:481) states that formaldehyde-fixed material can be stained by this technique if the sections are treated 2–3 days at 37°C. in AMS 12.2 Kiyono 1914. For an adaptation of this technique to blood smears see **DS 2.28 Schmorl 1928. Baker 1932** (19400, **30**:134) recommends heating tissues intended for this technique with 0.05% to 0.5% parabenzoquinone in isotonic saline for 1 hour prior to fixation. For a detailed description of the preparation of the *A* sol. see under DS 22.20 above.

22.21 Bailey 1920   11343, **42**:353

REAGENTS REQUIRED: *A*. DS 22.21 Altmann 1890 (sol. *A*); *B*. water 100, acid˙violet 1, 10% sulfuric acid *q.s.*

PREPARATION OF B: Add the acid drop by drop to the dye solution until no further increase in intensity of color takes place.

METHOD: [sections of F 7000.1000 Régaud 1910 fixed material] → A, on slide warmed to steaming, 6 mins. → drain → water, quick rinse → B, on slide, 5 secs. → drain → abs. alc., till differentiated, few secs. → carbol-xylene → xylene → balsam

22.21 Baker 1933   *see* DS 22.21 Kull 1914

22.21 Baker 1944   17510, **85**:1

REAGENTS REQUIRED: A. water 90, 40% formaldehyde 10, cadmium chloride 1; B. 25% gelatin; C. 2.5% gelatin; D. sat. sol. Sudan black in 70% alc.; E. DS 11.21 Mayer 1892

METHOD: [fresh tissues] → A, 3 days → wash → B, 24 hrs., 37°C. → [cast as block] → A, 24 hrs. → wash → [15 μ frozen sections, fixed on slide with C] → A, till required wash → 70% alc. → D, 5–10 mins. → 50% alc., rinse → E, till nuclei stained → wash → M 11 mountant (Chapter 26)

RECOMMENDED FOR: Golgi bodies.

22.21 Baker and Thomas 1933   Baker 1933

REAGENTS REQUIRED: A. DS 22.21 Altmann 1890, sol. A; B. water 65, alc. 35, picric acid 2; C. water 65, alc. 35, picric acid 2

METHOD: [5 μ sections of F 1700.0000 Baker and Thomas 1933 fixed material] → water → A, flooded on slide and heated till steaming, 1 min. → cool, 5 mins. → B, 30 secs. → C, till differentiation complete → wash → balsam, via usual reagents

22.21 Benda 1903   7936a, **12**:752

REAGENTS REQUIRED: A. 4% ferric alum; B. water 100, sat. sol. alizarin in abs. alc. 1; C. water 55, sat. sol. aniline 25, hydrochloric acid 0.025, 95% alc. 7.5, sat. sol. crystal violet in 70% alc. 12.5; D. 30% acetic acid

METHOD: [sections from material fixed in F 1670.0018 Benda 1903, F 1670.0080 Champy 1913, or F 7000.1000 Régaud 1910] → water → A, 2–5 hrs. → water, quick rinse → B, poured on slide, heated to steaming, 1 min. → C, poured on slide, heated to steaming, 1 min. → water, quick rinse → D, till nuclei well defined → running water, 10 mins. → blot → abs. alc., quick rinse → carbol-xylene → balsam, via xylene

RESULT: cell inclusions purple on yellow.

22.21 Bensley 1911   *see* DS 22.21 Cowdry 1918 (note)

22.21 Benoit 1922   *see* DS 22.21 Cowdry 1918 (note)

22.21 Cain 1948   17510, **89**:229

REAGENTS REQUIRED: A. 0.5% iodine in 70% alc.; B. 5% sodium thiosulfate; C. DS 22.21 Altmann 1890 (sol. A); D. 0.1% sodium carbonate; E. 1% hydrochloric acid; F. 1% methyl blue

METHOD: [3 μ sections of F3700.1000 Helly 1903 fixed material] → water → A. 5 mins. → rinse → B, 5 mins. → wash → C, on slide, heated to steaming, 1 min. → E, few secs. [repeat D → E cycle if insufficiently differentiated] → wash → F, till counterstained → wash → E, brief dip → balsam, via usual reagents

22.21 Cansey 1925   21400a, **44**:156

REAGENTS REQUIRED: A. 5% ferric alum; B. DS 11.111 Régaud 1910 (sol. B)

METHOD: [osmic-fixed protozoans] → A, 30 mins. → rinse → B, 45 mins. → A, till differentiated → balsam, via usual reagents

RECOMMENDED FOR: mitochondria in protozoans.

22.21 Champy-Kull   *see* DS 22.21 Kull 1914

22.21 Cowdry 1918   6816, **8**

REAGENTS REQUIRED: A. DS 22.21 Altmann 1890, A sol.; B. 1% methyl green

METHOD: [sections of F 7000.1000 Régaud 1910 material] → water → A, poured on slide, warmed to steaming, 6 mins. → wipe round sections → water, quick rinse → B, on slide, 5 secs. → drain → abs. alc., till differentiated → balsam, via toluene

RESULT: mitochondria, purple-red on green.

NOTE: The method of **Benoit 1922** (6630, **86**:1101) differs only in specifying prior fixation in his F 1379.0000 fixative; that of **Bensley 1911** (590, **12**:297) in requiring his F 1700.0010. **Gough and Fulton 1929** (11431, **32**:765) treat sections of formaldehyde-fixed material with their ADS 12.2 mordant before this technique.

22.21 Champy 1911   *see* DS 22.21 Kull 1913

22.21 Drew 1920   11360, **40**:295
REAGENTS REQUIRED: *A*. Drew 1920 ADS 12.1; *B*. 3% ferric alum; *C*. 0.5% hematoxylin; *D*. 2% pyridin
METHOD: [sections by freezing technique of Drew 1920 F 9000.1000 material] → wash → *A*, 15 mins. to 1 hr. 50°C. → rinse → *B*, 15 mins. 50°C. → quick rinse → *C*, 15 mins. 50°C. → *B*, till differentiated, room temperature → *D*, 2 mins. → balsam via usual reagents

22.21 Dufrenoy 1929   *see* DS 22.11 Milovidov 1928 (note)

22.21 Fain and Wolfe 1939   *see* DS 11.421 Fain and Wolfe 1939

22.21 Fieandt   *see* DS 21.23 Fieandt (1933)

22.21 Gough and Fulton 1929   *see* ADS 12.2 Gough and Fulton 1929

22.21 Held *test*. **1900 Pollack**   Pollack 1900
REAGENTS REQUIRED: *A*. water 100, acetic acid 0.1, erythrosin 0.7; *B*. water 50 DS 22.3 Nissl 1898 47, acetone 3; *C*. 0.1% potassium alum
METHOD: [sections] → water → *A*, 2 mins. on slide while warming → cool → water, quick rinse → *B*, on slide, warmed till no further smell of acetone → cool → *C*, till sections turn reddish → water, quick rinse → blot → neutral mountant, via propyl alc.
RESULT: nuclei, red; nucleoli, nissl granules, mitochondria, blue; plasma, reddish.

22.21 Hirsch and Bretschneider 1938 *test*. **1948 Romeis**
                                          Romeis 1948, 233
REAGENTS REQUIRED: *A*. 3% ferric alum; *B*. 0.5% hematoxylin
METHOD: [sections of F 7000.1000 Régaud fixed 1910 material] → water → *A*, ½–1 hr. 60°C. → quick wash → *B*, 10–20 mins. 60°C. → thorough wash → *A*, till differentiated

22.21 Hollande 1930   6630, **104**:473
REAGENTS REQUIRED: *A*. DS 22.21 Altmann 1890, sol. *A*; *B*. 0.5% phosphomolybdic acid; *C*. 1% methylene blue
METHOD: [5 μ sections of F 3790.1000 Bénoit 1922 fixed material, varnished on slide with 5% collodion] → water → *A*, 30 mins. → brief wash → *B*, 5 mins. → *C*, 10–20 mins. → rinse → abs. alc., 1 min. → amyl alc. till differentiated → balsam, via xylene

22.21 Kull 1913   *see* DS 13.22 Kull 1913

22.21 Kull 1914   766, **45**:153
REAGENTS REQUIRED: *A*. DS 21.21 Altmann 1890, sol. *A*; *B*. 0.5% toluidine blue; *C*. 0.5% aurantia in 70% alc.
METHOD: [sections of F 1670.0090 Champy 1913 fixed material] → *A*, on slide, heated to steaming, 1 min. → water, quick rinse → *B*, 1–2 mins. → water, quick rinse → *C*, till mitochondria differentiated → abs. alc., minimum possible time → balsam, via xylene
NOTE: This technique is often called *Champy-Kull*. **Baker 1933** (p. 189) recommends fixation in F 3700.1000 Helly 1903, followed by "post-chroming" by the method of Parat 1926a below. A detailed description of the application of this technique is given under DS 22.20 above.

22.21 McManns 1946   11431, **58**:93
REAGENTS REQUIRED: *A*. sat. sol. Sudan black in 70% alc.
METHOD: [sections of material fixed 1 month in F 8000.1000 McManns 1946] → 70% alc. → *A*, 30 mins. → M 11.1 mountant
NOTE: This also stains myelin and some fat granules.

22.21 Martinotti 1910   23632, **27**:24

REAGENTS REQUIRED: *A.* water 75, lithium carbonate 0.5, toluidine blue 1.0, glycerol 20
95% alcohol 5; *B.* 1% acetic acid

PREPARATION: Dissolve in order given and ripen 1 month.

METHOD: [distilled water] → *A*, overnight → *B*, till required inclusions differentiated.

22.21 Milovidov 1928   6630, **98**:555

REAGENTS REQUIRED: *A.* DS 22.21 Altmann (1920); *B.* 0.5% aurantia in 70% alc.; *C.*
water 100, phosphomolybdic acid 1, sodium hydroxide 0.1; *D.* DS 11.44 Unna 1892
25, water 75

METHOD: [paraffin sections of F 3700.1000 Milovidov 1928 fixed material] → abs. alc. →
[varnish in thin collodion] → water → *A*, 80°C., 1–3 mins. → wash → *B*, few secs. →
wash → *D*, few mins. → rinse → *D*, few mins. → wash → balsam, via usual reagents

RESULT: mitochondria red; bacteria blue.

RECOMMENDED FOR: differentiation of mitochondria and bacteria in root nodules of
legumes.

NOTE: This was reprinted in English by **Dufrenoy 1929** (20540b, **4**:13) to whom it is
often attributed.

22.21 Parat 1926   4285a, **3**:222

REAGENTS REQUIRED: *A.* DS 11.113 Kultschitzky 1889; *B.* ADS 21.1 Weigert 1885

METHOD: [sections of F 3700.1000 fixed, and Parat 1926a (below) mordanted material]
→ *A*, 24 hrs. 37°C. → *B*, till mitochondria differentiated

22.21 Parat 1926a   4285a, **3**:220

Any method is commonly referred to as *Parat* in which small pieces of fixed material
are treated with a sat. sol. potassium dichromate for 24–48 hours at 40°C. before being
sectioned and stained.

22.21 Volkonsky 1928   4295a, **5**:220

REAGENTS REQUIRED: *A.* DS 22.21 Altmann 1890, *A* sol.; *B.* 0.5% aurantia in 70% alc.;
C. 1% phosphomolybdic acid; *D.* DS 11.44 Unna 1892; *E.* DS 12.16 Unna 1895

METHOD: [sections of F 3700.1000 Helly 1903 fixed and Parat 1926a treated material] →
water → *A*, on slide, heated to steaming, 1 min. → *B*, till mitochondria differentiated
→ *C*, 1 min. → water, wash → *D*, 5–10 mins. → water, rinse → *E*, till nuclei differentiated → balsam, via usual reagents

22.21 Volkonsky 1933 *test.* **1942 Langeron**   Langeron 1942, 1105

REAGENTS REQUIRED: *A.* Altmann 1890, *A* sol.; *B.* water 55, N/1 sodium hydroxide 10,
phosphomolybdic acid 1, 95% alc. 35, aurantia 0.25; *C.* DS 11.44 Volkonsky 1933; *D.*
DS 12.16 Unna 1895

PREPARATION OF B: Dissolve the acid in 30 water. Add the hydroxide. Dissolve the dye in
25 water 35 alc. Add this solution to the first.

METHOD: [sections prepared as for Volkonsky 1928 above] → water → *A*, on slide,
heated to steaming, 1 min. → water, rinse → *B*, till mitochondria differentiated →
water, rinse → *C*, 10–15 mins. → water, rinse → *D*, till nuclei differentiated → abs.
alc., minimum possible time → balsam, via xylene

22.21 Zimmermann 1896 *see* DS 22.5 Zimmermann 1896

22.3 NISSL GRANULES

Nissl bodies were originally described by Nissl 1894, who used an alkaline solution of
methylene blue for their display. His formula has generally been followed save that
toluidine blue has been substituted by most of the recent workers. Deipolli and Pomerri
1938 have substituted magenta for the blue dye in a method which will show mitochondria and bacteria as well as Nissl bodies. Attention should also be drawn to the
methods of Einarson 1932 and 1935 which use two of the oxazine dyes. The best method
for demonstration is, however, that of Windle, Rhines, and Rankin 1943 who have
worked out the satisfactory pH at which staining will take place after a series of given
fixatives.

22.3 Addison 1929 *cit. compl. script.*   McClung 1929, 326
FORMULA: 1% thionin (*or* toluidine blue *or* methylene blue *or* cresyl violet)
METHOD: [sections of material fixed in 5% acetic in 95% alc.] → stain, 6–12 hrs. →
water, quick rinse → abs. alc. till differentiated → balsam, via xylene
NOTE: **Spielmeyer 1924,** 69, recommends a 0.1% dye solution, used hot.

22.3 Anderson 1929   ·   Anderson 1929, 42
REAGENTS REQUIRED: *A.* 1% toluidine blue; *B.* ADS 21.1 Gothard 1898
METHOD: [10 μ sections] → water → *A*, 10–20 mins., 50°C. → wash → *B*, till differentiated → abs. alc. till dehydrated → xylene → [repeat *B* → abs. → xylene, until required picture secured] → cedar oil

22.3 Bean 1926   20540b, **1**:56
REAGENTS REQUIRED: *A. either* 1% neutral red *or* 1% methylene blue; *B. either* 0.5%
methyl orange *or* 0.5% eosin in 50% alc.
METHOD: [12 μ sections of F 0000.1010 Bean 1926 fixed material] → water → *A*, 90°–
100°C., in water bath, 20 mins. → 50% alc., till differentiated → *B*, few secs. →
balsam, via usual reagents

22.3 Clark and Sperry 1945   20540b, **20**:23
REAGENTS REQUIRED: *A.* 0.05% lithium carbonate; *B.* 0.25% thionin in 0.05% lithium
carbonate
METHOD: [celloidin sections] → *A*, 5 mins. → *B*, till grossly overstained → rinse → 80%
alc., till differentiated → balsam, via butyl alc. and xylene

22.3 Deipolli and Pomerri 1938   14425, **49**:123
REAGENTS REQUIRED: *A.* water 100, DS 11.43 Ziehl 1882 2.5, acetic acid 0.5; *B.* water
100, 40% formaldehyde 1, acetic acid 1
METHOD: [sections of alcohol or formaldehyde-fixed material] → water → *A*, 3–4 mins.
→ water, quick rinse → *B*, till Nissl bodies differentiated → water, wash → balsam,
via usual reagents

22.3 Einarson 1932   608b, **8**:295
FORMULA: water 100, chrome alum 5, gallocyanin 0.15
PREPARATION: Boil 20 minutes. Cool. Filter.
METHOD: [50 μ celloidin sections of F 3700.0010 Zenker 1894 fixed material] → water
→ stain, 12–24 hrs. → water, wash → 80% alc., wash → 95% alc., 1 hr. → abs. alc.,
till dehydrated → abs. alc. and ether, till celloidin removed → abs. alc., wash →
→ balsam, via oil of Cretan thyme

22.3 Einarson 1935   11135, **61**:105
FORMULA: water 100, gallamin blue 0.2
PREPARATION: Boil 5 minutes. Cool. Filter.
METHOD: [sections] → water → stain 12–24 hrs. → water, wash → 50% alc., till differ-
entiated → 95% alc., → balsam, via usual reagents

22.3 Gothard 1898   6630, **5**:530
REAGENTS REQUIRED: *A.* DS 11.44 Unna 1892; *B.* ADS 21.2 Gothard 1898
METHOD: [celloidin sections of alcohol-fixed material] → *A*, 24 hrs. → 80% alc., quick
rinse → *B*, till differentiated → balsam, via usual reagents

22.3 Hansburg 1935   19938, **81**:364
REAGENTS REQUIRED: *A.* DS 13.12 Wright 1910 100, DS 13.13 Giemsa 1902 20
METHOD: [10 μ paraffin sections] → water → *A*, on slide, 2 mins. → dilute *A* on slide to
3 times volume, leave 2 mins. → wash, 1 min. → 80% alc., 15 secs. → abs. alc., least
possible time → balsam, via xylene
RECOMMENDED FOR: Nissl granules in spinal cord.

22.3 Held 1900   *see* DS 22.21 Held 1900

22.3 Huber *test.* **1943 Cowdry** *cit.* **Addison**   Cowdry 1943, 95
REAGENTS REQUIRED: *A.* 0.1% toluidine blue; *B.* 0.05% lithium carbonate
METHOD: [sections of F 3000.0020 Huber (1943) fixed material] → *A*, 15–18 hrs. →
water, wash → *B*, 2 hrs. → 70% alc., till differentiated → balsam, via usual reagents

22.3 Johnson 1916 *see* DS 22.3 Kirkman 1932 (note)

22.3 King 1910   763, **4**:213
FORMULA: 1% phenol 100, thionin to sat.
METHOD: [sections] → stain, 2–3 mins. → water, quick rinse → 95% alc., till differ-entiated → balsam, via usual reagents

22.3 Keller 1945   4349, **25**:77
REAGENTS REQUIRED: *A*. 0.5% cresyl violet; *B*. 50% Canada balsam in xylene
METHOD: [sections] → *A*, 3–5 mins. → wash → xylene, via graded alcs. → *B*, 2 mins. → xylene → [repeat abs. alc. → *B* → xylene cycle till differentiation complete] → balsam

22.3 Kirkman 1932   763, **51**:323
FORMULA: water 100, neutral red 0.2, acetic acid 0.4
METHOD: [sections stained by DS 21.212 Weigert, or similar technique] → water → stain, 10–20 mins. → water, wash 95% alc., till differentiated → balsam, via usual reagents
NOTE: The technique of **Johnson 1916** (763, **11**:297) was essentially the same, with the additional provision that the neutral red be diluted from a 1% solution which has been "ripened" 1–4 years.

22.3 Lugaro 1905   19219, **3**:339
REAGENTS REQUIRED: *A*. 0.05% toluidine blue; *B*. 4% ammonium molybdate
METHOD: [sections of alcohol, or acetic alcohol, fixed material] → *A*, 1–3 hrs. → water, rinse → *B*, 15 mins. abs. alc. till differentiated → balsam, via benzene

22.3 Nissl 1894   15058, **13**:507
REAGENTS REQUIRED: *A*. water 100, castile soap 0.2, methylene 0.4; *B*. 10% aniline in 95% alc.
PREPARATION OF A: Dissolve soap in water. Add dye. "Ripen" some months.
METHOD: [sections of alcohol-fixed material] → stain, in watch glass, heated till bubbles form → *B*, in watch glass, till no more color comes away → transfer to slide and blot → oil of cajeput, till clear → balsam
NOTE: The original calls for *venetianische Seife* which was presumably the *Sapo venetus* of the Austrian pharmacopeia of the period. This is identical in composition with the *sapo durus* of the current pharmacopeia, commonly known as *castile soap. Venetian soap*, specified by most texts, is a meaningless term in English.

22.3 Roussy and Lehrmitte *test.* **1938 Carleton and Leach**
    Carleton and Leach 1938, 243
REAGENTS REQUIRED: *A*. 1% thionin, *B*. ADS 21.2 Gothard 1898
METHOD: [sections of formaldehyde-fixed material] → water → *A*, 6 mins. → rinse → 95% alc., 1 min. → *B*, till differentiated → abs. alc. → balsam, via xylene

22.3 Sadorsky *test.* **1900 Pollack**   Pollack 1900, 100
REAGENTS REQUIRED: *A*. 1% methylene blue; *B*. 1% acetic acid
METHOD: [sections of formaldehyde-fixed material] → *A*, overnight → *B*, till differenti-ated

22.3 Snider 1943   20540b, **18**:53
FORMULA: water 15, 95% alc. 20, dioxane 65, toluidine blue 1
PREPARATION: Dissolve dye in water and alc. Add dioxane.
METHOD: [1 cm. thick slabs of fresh brain] → stain, 3–5 days → [50 μ sections by freezing technique, fixed to slide with albumen] → 95% alc., till differentiated → balsam, via usual reagents

22.3 Spielmeyer 1924 *see* DS 22.3 Addison 1929 (note)

22.3 Tsiminakis 1928   23632, **45**:50
REAGENTS REQUIRED: *A*. 0.3% potassium permanganate; *B*. water 100, oxalic acid 0.5, sodium sulfite 0.5; *C*. 0.5% toluidine blue; *D*. 30% aniline in 95% alc.
METHOD: [sections of chrome-fixed material] → water → *A*, 5 mins. → *B*, 10–15 mins. → wash → *C*, 4 mins. → wash, 10 mins. → *D*, till differentiated → balsam, via terpineol and xylene

22.3 Windle, Rhines, and Rankin 1943   20540b, **18**:77
  STOCK SOLUTIONS: I. acetate-veronal buffer, pH 3.65. II. 1% thionin
  WORKING SOLUTION: stock I 100, stock II 5
  METHOD: [sections from formaldehyde or F 0000.0010 Carnoy 1887 fixed material] →
    water → stain, 10–20 mins. → water, till no more color comes away → 70% alc. till
    no more color comes away → balsam, via usual reagents

22.4 YOLK AND FAT GRANULES

  Techniques for staining fat granules may be broadly divided into two classes. In the
first of these, fat-soluble stains such as Sudan II, or Sudan black B, are applied to sections obtained by the freezing technique, in which the fat is left in its original condition.
The other class consists of those in which fixation has taken place with a chromate- or
dichromate-formaldehyde mixture, with the result that certain of the unsaturated fatty
acids are rendered insoluble in the solvents used for paraffin sectioning, and may thus
be stained by almost any method which will bring out small objects. None of the techniques given here are intended to be microchemical tests for the various classes of fat.
They are strictly histological methods to be used by those who desire to demonstrate
the existence of granules rather than to demonstrate the nature of the materials of
which the granules are composed.

22.4 Arndt 1925   *see* DS 22.6 Arndt 1925

22.4 Bacsich 1936   *see* DS 21.3 Bacsich 1936

22.4 Bell 1914   11431, **19**:105
  REAGENTS REQUIRED: DS 22.4 Daddi 1896
  METHOD: [paraffin sections of F 7000.0010 Tellyesniczky 1898 fixed material] → 70% alc.
    → stain 10 mins. → 50% alc. till differentiated → water → M11 mountant (Chapter
    26)
  NOTE: **Mulon 1914** (6593, **6**:12) differs from above in specifying F 5000.1010 Bouin 1897
    fixation and DS 22.4 Herxheimer 1904 stain.

22.4 Benda *test.* **1911 Mallory and Wright**   Mallory and Wright 1911, 386
  REAGENTS REQUIRED: *A.* sat. sol. hematoxylin in 60% alc.; *B.* ADS 21.1 Weigert 1885
  METHOD: [frozen sections of material fixed in F 4600.1010 Benda (1911)] → water → *A*,
    6 hrs. → water, wash → *B*, till differentiated → [balsam, via usual reagents] *or* →
    water → M11 mountant.

22.4 Burdon, Stokes, and Kimbrough 1942   *see* DS 23.219 Burdon, *et al.* 1942

22.4 Clark 1947   11431, **59**:337
  REAGENTS REQUIRED: *A.* 95% alc. 50, acetone 50, Sudan IV to sat.; *B.* DS 11.123
    Ehrlich 1886; *C.* 0.1% hydrochloric acid in 70% alc.
  METHOD: [sections by E 11.1 Clark 1947 (Chapter 27)] → rinse → 70% alc. → *A,* 3–5
    mins. → 70% alc., wash → rinse → *B*, 10 mins. → wash → *C*, till differentiated →
    tap water, till blue → M 12.2 Moore 1933

22.4 Daddi 1896   1852, **26**:143
  FORMULA: 70% alc. 100, Sudan III to sat (*circ.* 0.2%)
  METHOD: [sections by freezing technique] → water → stain, 5–10 mins. → water, wash
    → M11 mountant (Chapter 26)
  NOTE: **Rosenthal 1900** specifies fixation in his F 3000.1000 before this technique.

22.4 Dietrich 1910   22264, **14**:263
  REAGENTS REQUIRED: *A.* 5% potassium dichromate; *B.* DS 11.113 Kultschitzky 1889; *C.*
    ADS 21.1 Weigert 1885
  METHOD: [frozen sections of formaldehyde-fixed material] → *A*, 1–3 days, 37°C. →
    water, wash → *C*, till differentiated (overnight) → water, wash → M11 mountant
    (Chapter 26)

22.4 Fischler 1904   23681, **15**:913

REAGENTS REQUIRED: *A.* 12.5% cupric acetate; *B.* DS 21.212 Weigert 1885 (sol. *C*); *C.* ADS 21.1 Weigert 1885 5, water 95

METHOD: [sections by freezing technique of formaldehyde-fixed material] → water → *A*, 2–24 hrs. → wash → *B*, 20 mins. → rinse → *C*, till differentiated → M11 or 12 mountant (Chapter 26)

22.4 French 1940   1887a, **30**:1243

REAGENTS REQUIRED: *A.* 4% formaldehyde; *B.* water, 10 DS 21.13 Weigert 1898 50, sat. sol. Sudan III in equal parts acetone and 70% alc. 40; *C.* any DS 11.122 stain

METHOD: [gelatin sections of formaldehyde-fixed material] → *A*, 1 day → wash → 70% alc., rinse → *A*, 15 mins. → 70% alc., rinse → water, rinse → *C*, 1–2 mins. → wash → M 12.1 mountant

RECOMMENDED FOR: simultaneous demonstration of fat and elastic tissue.

22.4 Galesesco and Bratiano 1928   6630, **99**:1460

PREPARATION OF STAINING SOLUTION: Digest 50 Gm. fragments of cortical zone of carrots in 100 ml. 95% alc. 2 hours on water bath. Cool. Digest in dark at room temperature 8–10 days. Filter. Dilute to 80% alc. content.

REAGENTS REQUIRED: *A.* staining solution from above; *B.* DS 11.122 Böhmer 1868

METHOD: [frozen sections of formaldehyde-fixed material] → 70% alc. → *A*, 6–24 hrs. → 70% alc. till no more color comes away → water → *B*, till nuclei blue → wash → M 12.1 mountant (Chapter 26)

22.4 Gros 1930   23632, **47**:64

REAGENTS REQUIRED: *A.* water 50, diacetin 50, scarlet R 0.6

PREPARATION: Heat to 60°C. Cool. Filter.

METHOD: [frozen sections] → water → *A*, 10 mins. 60°C. → wash → M11 mountant (Chapter 26)

22.4 Herxheimer 1901   23681, **14**:891

FORMULA: 80% alc. 100, sodium hydroxide 2, Sudan IV 0.1

METHOD: [sections by freezing technique of formaldehyde-fixed material] → 70% alc. → stain, 2–4 mins. → DS 11.122 counterstain, if desired → M12 mountant (Chapter 26)

NOTE: **Herxheimer 1904** (23632, **21**:57) substituted a mixture of equal parts 70% alc. and acetone for the alkaline alcohol; this is the more usually cited formula. In the place cited above he also recommends a sat. sol. indophenol (probably indophenol blue—Conn 1946, 87) in 70% alc.

22.4 Herxheimer 1904   *see* DS 22.4 Herxheimer 1901

22.4 Kionka 1894   764, **1**:414

REAGENTS REQUIRED: *A.* DS 11.22 Grenacher 1879; *B.* water 70, 95% alc. 30, orange G 0.05, hydrochloric acid 0.1

METHOD: [paraffin sections of alc. fixed chicken blastoderms] → *A*, overnight → quick rinse → *B*, till differentiated → balsam, via usual reagents

RECOMMENDED FOR: yolk granules in embryonic cells.

22.4 Leach 1938   11431, **47**:635

REAGENTS REQUIRED: *A.* 50% diacetin; *B.* water 50, diacetin 50, Sudan black B to excess

PREPARATION OF B: Digest 2 days at 55°C. Cool. Filter.

METHOD: [sections by freezing technique of F 1670.0000 Zweibaum (1943) fixed material] → *A*, 30 secs. → *B*, 2 hrs. → *A*, 30 secs. → DS 11.21 counterstain, if desired → M11 or 12 mountant (Chapter 26)

22.4 Lillie 1945   20540b, **20**:7

REAGENTS REQUIRED: *A.* sat. sol. oil blue N in 60% isopropyl alc. 85, water 15; *B.* 0.1% Bismarck brown R; *C.* 5% acetic acid

METHOD: [frozen sections of formaldehyde-fixed material] → *A*, 5–10 mins. → water, rinse → *C*, till differentiated, 1 min. → water → M12 mountant

NOTE: The dilution of *A* should be made immediately before use.

22.4 Lillie 1948a   Lillie 1948, 159

PREPARATION OF STOCK SOLUTION: water 40, isopropyl alc. 60, oil blue N to sat.
REAGENTS REQUIRED: *A*. stock 60, water 30; *B*. 0.1% Bismarck brown; *C*. 5% acetic acid
METHOD: [frozen sections] → *A*, 5–10 mins. → wash → *B*, 5 mins. → rinse → *C*, 1 min.
→ wash → M11 mountant

22.4 Lillie 1948b   Lillie 1948, 159

PREPARATION OF STOCK SOLUTION: *A*. isopropyl alc. 100, Sudan brown *or* oil red 4B *or*
oil red O 1.5
REAGENTS REQUIRED: *A*. stock 60, water 40; *B*. water 80, acetic acid 1.6, DS11.122
Lillie 1941 20; *C*. 1% sodium phosphate, dibasic
METHOD: [frozen sections] → water → *A*, 10 mins. → wash → *B*, 5 mins. → rinse → *C*,
till blue → wash → M11 or 12 mountant (Chapter 26)

22.4 Lillie and Ashburn 1943   1780a, **36**:432

FORMULA: sat. sol. Sudan IV in isopropyl alc. 50, water 50
METHOD: [frozen sections of formaldehyde-fixed material] → water → *A*, 10 mins. →
water, wash → DS 11.123 counterstain if desired → balsam, via usual reagents

22.4 Martinotti 1914   23543, **91**:425

REAGENTS REQUIRED: *A*. 1% chrysoidin; *B*. 1% potassium dichromate
METHOD: [frozen sections of formaldehyde-fixed tissue] → water → *A*, some hrs. → water,
rinse → *B*, 1 min. → water, wash → balsam, via usual reagents

22.4 McManus 1946   *see* DS 22.21 McManus 1946

22.4 Mulon 1914   *see* DS 22.4 Bell 1914 (note)

22.4 Peter 1904   *see* DS 11.25 Peter 1904

22.4 Proescher 1927   20540b, **2**:60

REAGENTS REQUIRED: *A*. 50% pyridine; *B*. water 30, pyridine 70, oil red O 4; *C*. 60%
pyridine
PREPARATION OF B: Add dye to mixed solvents. Leave 1 hour with occasional agitation.
Filter.
METHOD: [frozen sections of formaldehyde-fixed material] → *A*, 3–5 mins. → *B*, 3–5
mins. → *C*, till differentiated → water → M11 or 12 mountant (Chapter 26)

22.4 Rosenthal 1900   *see* DS 22.4 Daddi 1896 (note)

22.4 Schaffer 1926 *test.* **1933 Cajal and de Castro**   Cajal and de Castro 1933, 305

REAGENTS REQUIRED: *A*. 5% potassium dichromate; *B*. DS 11.121 Weigert 1904; *C*.
ADS 21.1 Pal 1887 (sol. *B*); *D*. sat. aq. sol. lithium carbonate; *E*. DS 12.221 van
Giesen 1896
METHOD: [paraffin sections of dichromate-fixed material] → water → *A*, 1 wk., 37°C. →
thorough wash → *B*, 1–2 days, 37°C. → wash → *C*, till differentiated → *D*, 37°C.,
till dark blue → thorough wash → *E*, till sufficiently counterstained → balsam, via
usual reagents

22.4 Sheehan 1939   *see* DS 21.3 Sheehan 1939

22.4 Sheehan and Storey 1947   *see* DS 21.3 Sheehan and Storey 1947

22.4 Smith 1907   11431, **12**:1

REAGENTS REQUIRED: *A*. sat. sol. (*circ.* 0.2%) Nile blue; *B*. 1% acetic acid
METHOD: [frozen sections of fresh or formaldehyde-fixed material] → *A*, 10–24 hrs. →
water, wash → M11 or 12 mountant

22.4 Smith and Mair 1911   20214, **25**:247

REAGENTS REQUIRED: *A*. sat. sol. Nile blue 100, sulfuric acid 0.5; *B*. 2% acetic acid
PREPARATION OF A: Boil under reflux 1–2 hours. Cool. Filter.
METHOD: [frozen sections of fresh tissue] → water → *A*, overnight → *B*, till differenti-
ated → water, wash → M11 mountant (Chapter 26)
RESULT: fatty acid, blue. Neutral fats, red.

NOTE: The reflux boiling should continued until a xylene extract of a sample shows strong red fluorescence. The chemical validity of this separation has been sharply queried by **Kaufmann and Lehmann 1926** (22575, **261**:623). For a discussion of the arguments for and against see Gatenby and Cowdry 1937, 280 and Cowdry 1943, 136. The fact remains that fatty cell inclusions are differentiated in red and blue, on a reproducible basis.

22.4 Smith and Rettie 1924   11431, **27**:115
REAGENTS REQUIRED: *A*. ADS 12.1 Smith and Rettie 1924; *B*. water 99.5, acetic acid 0.5, hematoxylin 1; *C*. ADS 21.1 Smith and Rettie 1924
METHOD: [frozen sections of formaldehyde-fixed material] → *A*, 1–2 days, 37°C. → wash → *B*, 6–18 hrs. → *C*, till differentiated → wash → M 12.1 mountant

22.4 Vrtis 1931   23632, **47**:443
REAGENTS REQUIRED: *A*. 4% formaldehyde; *B*. sat. sol. Sudan III in 70% alc.
METHOD: [pieces of skin] → *A*, overnight → wash → 50% alc., ½ to 1 hr. → *B*, ½–1 hr. → 50% alc., till differentiated → glycerol *or* M/10 mountant.
RECOMMENDED FOR: fat glands in wholemounts of rodent skin.

22.4 Wilson 1950   4349, **31**:216
REAGENTS REQUIRED: *A*. DS 22.4 Lillie and Ashburn 1943; *B*. DS 11.124 Gomori 1941; *C*. 1% acetic acid; *D*. 0.5% light green
METHOD: [5 μ frozen sections, mounted on slide] → *A*, 10 mins. → thorough wash → *B*, 4 mins. → tap water, till blue → *C*, rinse → *D*, quick dip → *C*, rinse → M 12.1 Kaiser 1880

22.5 PLASTIDS

Plastids are commonly demonstrated in sections of plant tissue by a hematoxylin staining technique, or by any other technique which is customarily employed in the histological examination of vegetable structures. The two methods given below are those which distinguish (if distinction is possible) between proplastids and mitochondria. The method of Milovidov 1928 is merely a modification of the standard Altmann acid fuchsin-aurantia mitochondrial staining technique, while the technique of Nemeč 1906 relies on prior mordanting in tannin before the use of gentian violet.

22.5 Milovidov 1928   1823, **24**:9
REAGENTS REQUIRED: *A*. DS 22.2 Altmann 1890 (*A*. sol.); *B*. 5% aurantia in 95% alc.; *C*. 2% tannin; *D*. 1% methyl green
METHOD: [sections of F 7000.1000 Régaud 1910 (or any F 6700.1000 fixative) fixed material] → *A*, poured on slide and warmed till steaming, 1 min. → *B*, till mitochondria alone remain red → 70% alc., rinse → *C*, 20 mins. → *D*, 5–10 mins. → 95% alc., till starch grains sharply differentiated → balsam, via usual reagents
RESULT: mitochondria and proplastids, red; starch, green.

22.5 Nemeč 1906   2626, **24**:528
REAGENTS REQUIRED: *A*. 2% tannin; *B*. 1.5% antimony potassium tartrate; *C*. 1% gentian violet
METHOD: [paraffin sections of F 5000.0015 Nemeč 1899 fixed material] → water → *A*, 1 hr. → water, wash → *B*, 5–15 mins. → water, wash → *C*, ½ to 2 hrs. → water, wash → 95% alc., till starch granules well differentiated → balsam, via usual reagents
NOTE: **Schneider 1922, 351** recommends fixation in F 1600.0010 Flemming 1882, with subsequent bleaching in hydrogen peroxide.

22.5 Schneider 1922   *see* DS 22.5 Nemeč 1906 (note)

22.6 STARCH, GLYCOGEN, AND AMYLOID GRANULES

Starch and glycogen are both most commonly stained by the application of iodine, which turns the former blue and the latter brown. These iodine techniques, however, do not leave permanent stains, though endeavor has been made by Reilhes 1941 to provide a degree of permanence in a resin mount. These preparations do not last, at their best, more than a few months. The original method for the differential staining of glycogen was that of Best 1906, and it has not yet been surpassed. One of the most satisfactory methods for the differentiation of starch granules in plant tissues is that of Milovidov 1928, which is given in section 12.5 above for the reason that it is also intended for the demonstration of the differentiation of the proplastids. An endeavor to adapt the Feulgen 1924 technique to the demonstration of starch was made by Crétin 1941, and has only the disadvantage that it requires mounting in liquid petrolatum with the subsequent difficulty of cementing the coverslip in place. In cases in which it is desired to give general differential stain, as well as a stain for glycogen, the technique of Vastarini-Cresi 1907 can be confidently recommended.

22.6 Arndt 1925   23681, **35**:545
    REAGENTS REQUIRED: *A.* sat. sol. glucose in 4% formaldehyde; *B.* sat. sol. glucose; *C.* DS 22.6 Best 1906 (sol. *A*); *D.* DS 22.6 Best 1906 (sol. *B*); *E.* any DS 11.122 formula, saturated with glucose; *F.* 70% alc. 50, acetone 50, chlorophyll to sat.
    METHOD: [pieces of fresh tissue] → *A*, 24 hrs. → frozen sections → *B*, till required → *C*, ¾–1 hr. → *D*, till differentiated → *E*, till nuclei stained → *B*, thorough wash → 70% alc., 1 min. → *F*, 15–20 mins. → 70% alc., 1 min. → *B*, 1 min. → levulose syrup
    RESULT: glycogen, red; fat, green.

22.6 Bennhold 1922   14674, **2**:1537
    REAGENTS REQUIRED: *A.* 1% Congo red; *B.* 1% lithium carbonate; *C.* any DS 11.122 formula
    METHOD: [paraffin sections] → water, thorough wash → *A*, 15–30 mins. → *B*, rinse → 80% alc., till color clouds cease → wash → [*C*, if counterstain required] → balsam, via usual reagents
    RECOMMENDED FOR: amyloid.

22.6 Bensley 1939   *see* DS 22.6 Best 1906 (note)

22.6 Best 1906   1780, **23**:520
    STOCK SOLUTION: water 75, potassium carbonate 1.2, carmine 2.5, ammonia 25
    PREPARATION OF STOCK: Boil dye with salts 15 minutes. Cool. Filter. Add ammonia to filtrate.
    REAGENTS REQUIRED: *A.* stock solution 25, ammonia 35, methanol 35; *B.* water 50, 95% alc. 40, methanol 20
    METHOD: [sections of alcohol-fixed material, stained by any DS 11.12 method] → water → *A*, overnight → water, rinse → *B*, till glycogen granules differentiated → balsam, via usual reagents
    NOTE: **Bensley 1939** (20540b, **14**:47) recommends pure methanol for *B*, with subsequent dehydration in acetone. See Neukirch 1909, below, for another way of using these solutions. **Zieglwallner 1911** (*test.* Schmorl 1928, 218) stains fat in his F 1300.0010 mixture before following Best's technique; **Schmorl 1928,** 218 recommends his F 1600.0010 for the same purpose.

22.6 Birch-Hirschfeld 1887 *test.* **1928 Schmorl**   Schmorl 1928, 210
    REAGENTS REQUIRED: *A.* sat. sol. Bismarck brown; *B.* 0.5% crystal violet; *C.* 1% acetic acid
    METHOD: [frozen sections] → *A*, 5 mins. → 95% alc., wash → distilled water, wash → *B*, 5 mins. → *C*, till differentiated → thorough wash → levulose syrup
    RECOMMENDED FOR: amyloid.

22.6 Crétin 1941   6630, **135**:355
    REAGENTS REQUIRED: *A.* methanol 100, phenyl hydrazine 1, hydrochloric acid 1; *B.* DS 11.43 Feulgen 1924; *C.* water 100, sodium bisulfite 2, hydrochloric acid 0.2
    METHOD: [sections of F 5000.0020 Crétin 1941 fixed materials] → *A*, overnight → *B*, few mins. → *C*, several hrs. → liquid petrolatum, via usual reagents
    NOTE: Solution *A* may also be used to mordant the tissues before sectioning.

22.6 Edens   *see* DS 22.6 Schmorl 1928a (note)

22.6 Highman 1946a   1887a, **41**:559
REAGENTS REQUIRED: *A*. 0.5% Congo red in 50% alc.; *B*. 0.2% potassium hydroxide in 80% alc.
METHOD: [sections of formaldehyde or alc. fixed material] → *A*, 1–5 mins. → *B*, 1–3 mins. till differentiated → wash → counterstain, if desired → balsam, via usual reagents
RECOMMENDED FOR: demonstration of amyloid

22.6 Highman 1946b   1887a, **41**:559
REAGENTS REQUIRED: *A*. DS 11.121 Weigert 1904; *B*. 0.1% crystal violet in 2.5% acetic acid
METHOD: [sections of formaldehyde or alc. fixed material] → water → *A*, 5 mins. → wash → *B*, 1–30 mins. → wash → MS 11.1 Highman 1946
NOTE: **Lieb 1947** (591b, **17**:413) substitutes a 0.3% solution of crystal violet in 0.3% hydrochloric acid for *B*, above.
RECOMMENDED FOR: demonstration of amyloid.

22.6 Klein 1906   590, **5**:323
REAGENTS REQUIRED: *A*. sat. aq. sol. orange G 50, sat. aq. sol. acid fuchsin 50; *B*. sat. aq. sol. toluidine blue
METHOD: [sections of F 3700.1000 Klein 1906 fixed material] → water → *A*, 1 min. wash → *B*, 1 min. → wash → balsam, via usual reagents
RESULT: chromatin and prozymogen, blue; zymogen, red.
RECOMMENDED FOR: granules in Paneth cells.

22.6 Krajian 1952   Krajian 1952, 169
REAGENTS REQUIRED: *A*. DS 11.123 Harris 1900; *B*. water 80, glycerol 20, Congo red 3.2; *C*. 2% sodium cyanide
METHOD: [unmounted sections by freezing technique] → *A*, 15 secs. → tap water, wash → *B*, 15 mins. → wash → *C*, till differentiated, few secs. → strand on slide and drain → M 12.1 mountant
RECOMMENDED FOR: amyloid.
NOTE: Stated by author (*loc. cit.*) to be modification of DS 22.6 Bennhold 1922.

22.6 Langhans 1890   22575, **120**:28
REAGENTS REQUIRED: *A*. DS 11.22 Mayer 1881; *B*. ADS 12.2 Gram 1884; *C*. 2.5% iodine in abs. alc.
METHOD: [celloidin sections of alc. fixed material] → *A*, 10–15 mins. → *B*, 5–10 mins. → → *C*, till dehydrated → oil of origanum
RECOMMENDED FOR: demonstration of amyloid.

22.6 Lieb 1947   *see* DS 22.6 Highman 1946b (note)

22.6 Lillie 1948   Lillie 1948, 143
REAGENTS REQUIRED: *A*. water 100, nitric acid 0.5, sodium periodate 1; *B*. DS 11.432 Lillie 1948; *C*. 0.52% sodium bisulfite; *D*. DS 11.121 Weigert 1904
METHOD: [sections of formaldehyde-fixed material, varnished on slide with collodion] → water → *A*, 10 mins. → wash → *B*, 15 mins., with occasional agitation → *C*, 3 changes, 1½ mins. in each → wash → *D*, 2–5 mins. → tap water, till blue → balsam, via usual reagents

22.6 Lubarsch *test*. **1905 Hall and Herxheimer**   Hall and Herxheimer 1905, 112
FORMULA: water 20, DS 11.122 Delafield (1885) 40, ADS 12.2 Gram 1884 40
METHOD: [sections to water] → stain, 5 mins. → abs. alc., least possible time for dehydration → balsam, via xylene
RECOMMENDED FOR: glycogen.

22.6 Mayer *test*. **1938 Mallory**   Mallory 1938, 134
REAGENTS REQUIRED: *A*. 0.5% crystal violet; *B*. 1% acetic acid; *C*. 7.5% potassium alum
METHOD: [paraffin sections, *without removal of paraffin*] → *A*, 40°C., 5–10 mins. → wash → *B*, 10–15 mins. → wash → *C*, few minutes → wash → [fix to slide] → balsam, via xylene
RECOMMENDED FOR: demonstration of amyloid.

22.6 Milovidov 1928 *see* DS 22.5 Milovidov 1928

22.6 Neukirch 1909   23681, **20**:531

REAGENTS REQUIRED: *A*. sat. sol. glucose in sat. sol. mercuric chloride; *B*. sat. sol. glucose in 80% alc.; *C*. ADS 11.1 Lugol; *D*. DS 22.6 Best 1906 (sol. *A*) *E*. DS 22.6 Best 1906 (sol. *B*)

METHOD: [pieces of fresh tissue] → *A*, 6–12 hrs. → *B*, wash → *C*, 6 hrs. → 95% alc., 24 hrs. or till required → celloidin sections → water → [hematoxylin nuclear stain, if required] → *D*, overnight → rinse → *B*, till differentiated → balsam, via usual reagents

NOTE: Neukirch (*loc. cit.*) also recommends glucose-saturated 40% formaldehyde in place of *A*, above, in which case steps *B* and *C* are omitted. **Schmorl 1928**, 216 finds this better for large pieces.

22.6 Reilhes 1941   6630, **135**:554

FORMULA: *A*. abs. alc. 100, iodine 8, ammonium iodide 2

METHOD: [paraffin sections of alcohol-fixed material] → abs. alc. → stain, dropped on slide, several minutes → abs. alc., quick rinse → dry → Venice turpentine, direct

22.6 Schmorl 1928a   Schmorl 1928, 210

REAGENTS REQUIRED: *A*. 0.5% crystal violet; *B*. 1% acetic acid; *C*. 7% ammonium alum

METHOD: [paraffin sections, or ribbons, *not deparaffinized*] → *A*, floated on surface, 5–10 mins. 40°C. → wash, floating on surface → *B*, floating on surface, till differentiated → wash, floating on surface → *C*, floating on surface, till required → wash, floating on surface → strand on slide, dry with gentle heat → xylene till deparaffinized → balsam

RECOMMENDED FOR: amyloid.

NOTE: **Edens** (*test.* Schmorl *loc. cit.*, 211) uses 0.1% methyl violet in 0.3% hydrochloric acid for 24 hours and omits steps *B* and *C*, above.

22.6 Schmorl 1928b   Schmorl 1928, 211

REAGENTS REQUIRED: *A*. DS 11.44 Unna 1891; *B*. 0.5% acetic acid; *C*. 7.5% ammonium alum.

METHOD: [paraffin sections] → water → *A*, 10–15 mins. → rinse → *B*, quick rinse → *C*, 2–5 mins. → abs. alc., minimum possible time → balsam, via xylene

RECOMMENDED FOR: amyloid.

22.6 Schmorl 1928c *see* DS 22.6 Best 1906 (note)

22.6 Schmorl 1928d   Schmorl 1928, 209

REAGENTS REQUIRED: *A*. 1% methyl violet; *B*. 2% acetic acid

METHOD: [frozen sections] → *A*, ½–1 min. → *B*, 2–3 mins. → thorough wash → glycerol

RECOMMENDED FOR: amyloid.

22.6 Vastarini-Cresi 1907 *test.* **1942 Langeron**   Langeron 1942, 1173

REAGENTS REQUIRED: *A*. DS 21.13 Weigert 1898 (working solution) 150, resorcin 6, cresofuchsin 3, 95% alc. 150, hydrochloric acid 6; *B* 1% orange G in 95% alc.

METHOD: [paraffin sections] → 95% alc. → *A*, 2 hrs. 35°C. → 95% alc., thorough wash → *B*, 1 min. → balsam, via usual reagents

RESULT: elastic fibers, blue; glycogen, red; plasma, pale orange.

22.6 Zieglwallner 1911 *see* DS 22.6 Best 1906 (note)

22.7 MUCIN

22.7 Highman 1945   20540b, **20**:85

FORMULA: water 75, 95% alc. 25, new methylene blue N 0.1, citric acid 0.2

METHOD: [sections] → water → stain, 3–10 mins. → rinse → balsam, via acetone and xylene

22.7 Hoyer 1900   1780, **36**:310

REAGENTS REQUIRED: *A*. sat. aq. sol. mercuric chloride; *B*. 0.005% thionin

METHOD: [sections of mercuric chloride-fixed material] → water → *A*, 30 secs. → 95% alc., wash → *B*, 5–15 mins. → balsam, via S 22.1 Minot (1928)

22.7 Lillie 1928   23632, **45**:381
REAGENTS REQUIRED: 0.2% toluidine blue
METHOD: [sections] → water → stain, 1 min. → quick rinse → acetone, till dehydrated
→ balsam, via xylene
NOTE: This method was republished by **Lillie 1929** (4349, **12**:120) to which later paper
reference is most frequently made.

22.7 Mallory 1938   Mallory 1938, 131
REAGENTS REQUIRED: *A*. DS 11.122 Mallory 1938, 10, 95% alc. 9, tap water 81; *B*.
0.1% magenta
METHOD: [paraffin sections alcohol-fixed material] → water → *A*, 5–15 mins. → thorough
wash → *B*, 5–10 mins. → 95% alc., till no more color comes away → balsam, via
xylene

22.7 Masson 1910 *test*. **1948 Romeis**   Romeis 1948, 481
REAGENTS REQUIRED: *A*. Any DS 11.122 formula; *B*. 5% metanil yellow in 0.2% acetic
acid; *C*. DS 22.7 Mayer 1896a (working sol.)
METHOD: [sections of F 5000.1010 Bouin 1896 fixed material] → water → *A*, till deeply
stained → rinse → *B*, till nuclei differentiated → wash → *C*, 5–10 mins. → wash →
balsam, via usual reagents

22.7 Mayer 1896a   *mucihaematin—compl. script.*   14246, **12**:303
REAGENTS REQUIRED: *A*. water 30, 95% alc., 70, hematin 0.2, aluminum chloride 0.1,
nitric acid 0.05
METHOD: [sections of alcohol-fixed material] → water → *A*, 10 mins. → 1 hr. → thorough
wash → balsam, via usual reagents
NOTE: **Mallory 1938**, 129 recommends this for mucin of fibroblastic origin.

22.7 Mayer 1896b   *mucicarmine—compl. script.*   14246, **12**:303
STOCK SOLUTION: Heat together for 2 minutes water 2, aluminum chloride 0.5, carmine 1.
Add with constant stirring 100 50% alc.
WORKING SOLUTION: stock 10, 70% alc. 90
METHOD: [sections of alcohol-fixed material] → stain, 10–15 mins. → rinse → balsam,
via usual reagents
NOTE: **Mallory 1938**, 130 recommends this for mucin derived from epithelial cells.

22.7 Merkel *test*. **1928 Schmorl**   Schmorl 1928, 164
REAGENTS REQUIRED: *A*. 5% cresyl violet; *B*. abs. alc. 50, toluene 50
METHOD: [5 μ–7 μ sections of alcohol-fixed material] → *A*, 10–30 mins. → 95% alc.,
rinse → *B*, controlled under microscope, till differentiated → balsam, via xylene

22.7 Unna 1894   14352, **18**:509
REAGENTS REQUIRED: *A*. DS 11.44 Unna 1892; *B*. 0.1% acetic acid; *C*. 10% potassium
dichromate; *D*. 1% hydrochloric acid in aniline
METHOD: [sections of alcohol-fixed material] → water → *A*, 10 mins. → *B*, rinse → *C*,
30 secs. → blot → *D*, till differentiated, 15–30 secs. → balsam, via usual reagents

22.7 Zimmerman 1925   *see* DS 21.4 Zimmermann 1925

22.8 OTHER CELL INCLUSIONS AND EXTRUSIONS

22.8 Alzheimer 1910   Nissl and Alzheimer 1910, 411
REAGENTS REQUIRED: *A*. sat. aq. sol. copper acetate; *B*. DS 11.124 Alzheimer 1910
METHOD: [sections prepared as in steps *A*, and *B* (DS 21.213 Alzheimer 1910)] → water
→ *A*, 1 hr. 35°C. → rinse → *B*, 30 mins. → wash → balsam, via usual reagents
RECOMMENDED FOR: demonstration of granules in nerve cell cytoplasm.

22.8 Bensley *test*. **1915 Chamberlain**   Chamberlain 1915, 134
REAGENTS REQUIRED: *A*. ADS 12.1 Gram 1884; *B*. sat. aq. sol. copper acetate; *C*. 0.5%
hematoxylin; *D*. 5% potassium dichromate; *E*. ADS 21.1 Weigert 1885
METHOD: [sections of F 3700.1000 Bensley (1915) fixed material] → water → *A*, some
hrs. → wash → *B*, 5–10 mins. → wash, 1 min. → *C*, 5–10 mins. → wash, 1 min. → *D*,
30 secs. → *E*, till differentiated → wash → balsam, via usual reagents
RECOMMENDED FOR: canaliculi in plant cells.

22.8 Beyard 1930   4285a, **7**:264
REAGENTS REQUIRED: *A*. 1% acid fuchsin; *B*. 0.8% bromine
METHOD: [sections] → water → *A*, 30 secs. → rinse → *B*, 4–5 secs. till violet → 95% alc.,
    till pale mauve → [DS 11.111 nuclear stain if required] → balsam, via usual reagents
RECOMMENDED FOR: basophilic granules in mast cells.

22.8 Bowie 1935   763, **64**:357
PREPARATION OF DRY STAIN: Add 67 0.4% ethyl violet to 33 0.4% Biebrich scarlet.
    Collect, wash and dry ppt.
STOCK SOLUTION: 1% dry stock in 95% alc.
REAGENTS REQUIRED: *A*. 95% alc. 80, water 20, stock sol. 0.1–0.5; *B*. 50:50 clove
    oil:xylene
METHOD: [sections of F 7000.1000 Régaud 1910 material] → water → *A*, 24 hrs. → blot
    → *B*, till differentiated, 20–30 mins. → balsam, via benzene
RECOMMENDED FOR: pepsinogen granules in gastric mucosa.

22.8 Brice 1930   20540b, **5**:101
REAGENTS REQUIRED: *A*. abs. alc. 100, benzidine 0.3, sodium nitroferricyanide 0.4; *B*.
    water 100, hydrogen peroxide 0.5; *C*. DS 13.12 Wright 1910, working solution
METHOD: [air-dried blood smear] → *A*, flooded on slide, 1 min. → *B*, equal in quantity
    to *A*, flooded on slide, 3 mins. → water, thorough wash → blot → dry → *C*, flooded
    on slide, 2 mins. → add water, drop by drop, till green scum forms on surface, leave
    2 mins. → water, thorough wash → [dry] *or* neutral mountant, via acetone
RECOMMENDED FOR: oxidase granules in erythrocytes.

22.8 Bujard 1930   4285a, **7**:264
REAGENTS REQUIRED: *A*. 1% acid fuchsin; *B*. 0.8% bromine; *C*. 1% hydrochloric acid
    in 95% alc.
METHOD: [sections] → water → *A*, 30 secs. → *B*, 4–5 mins. → *C*, till granules alone
    stained → DS 11.111 Régaud 1910 if nuclear staining is required → balsam, via usual
    reagents
RECOMMENDED FOR: basophilic granules in mast cells.

22.8 Ehrlich 1891 *test.* 1938 Mallory   Mallory 1938, 174
FORMULA: water 30, 95% alc. 62, acetic acid 8, Hofmann's violet to sat.
RECOMMENDED FOR: granules in mast cells.

22.8 Hall and Powell 1926   21400a, **45**:256
REAGENTS REQUIRED: *A*. 0.2% Bordeaux red; *B*. 4% ferric alum; *C*. 0.5% hematoxylin
METHOD: [flagellates fixed in F 3000.0000 Schaudinn 1893] → water → *A*, 1–2 days →
    B, 1–2 days → *C*, 1–2 days → *B*, till differentiated → balsam, via usual reagents
RECOMMENDED FOR: internal structures in euglenoid flagellates.

22.8 Harvey 1907   590, **6**:207
REAGENTS REQUIRED: *A*. sat. aq. sol. (*circ.* 7%) cupric acetate; *B*. 3% potassium di-
    chromate; *C*. sat. aq. sol. hematoxylin; *D*. ADS 21.1 Weigert 1885
METHOD: [sections of F 3700.1000 Harvey 1907 fixed material] → *A*, 1 min. → wash →
    B, 1 min. → wash → *C*, 1 min. → wash → *D*, till differentiated → balsam, via usual
    reagents
RECOMMENDED FOR: demonstration of parietal cell granules.

22.8 Hamperl 1926   22575, **259**:179
REAGENTS REQUIRED: *A*. Any DS 11.21 formula; *B*. 0.01% methyl violet
METHOD: [sections of F 0000.1000 Hamperl 1926 fixed material] → water → *A*, till
    nuclei stained → wash → *B*, till granules stained → abs. alc. least possible time →
    balsam, via usual reagents
RECOMMENDED FOR: granules in chief cells of stomach.

22.8 Heidenhain 1894   1780, **42**:665
REAGENTS REQUIRED: *A*. 0.01% aniline blue; *B*. DS 11.111 Heidenhain 1892 (both sol.)
METHOD: [sections of F 3000.0010 material] → *A*, 24 hrs. → *B*, full technique → balsam,
    via usual reagents
RECOMMENDED FOR: centrosomes in animal tissues.

22.8 Horvath 1931   23632, **47**:463

REAGENTS REQUIRED: *A*. 1% phosphotungstic acid; *B*. 0.1% toluidine blue
METHOD: [protozoa, fixed and mordanted 20 mins. in sat. aq. sol. mercuric chloride] →
water, thorough wash → *A*, 10 mins. → water, rinse → *B*, 1 min., 50°–60°C. → balsam, via usual reagents
RECOMMENDED FOR: demonstration of cilia, cirri, and basal bodies in ciliate protozoa.

22.8 Kraus 1914   22575, **218**:107

REAGENTS REQUIRED: *A*. DS 11.44 Unna 1892; *B*. 25% tannin; *C*. DS 12.16 Fraenkel
(1948); *D*. 2% acid fuchsin; *E*. 1% phosphomolybdic acid
METHOD: [3 μ–5 μ sections of formaldehyde-fixed material] → water → *A*, 6 mins. →
wash → *B*, till no more color comes away → *C*, till nuclei blue → wash → *D*, 1 min
→ rinse → *E*, 30 secs. → wash → [drain and blot] → abs. alc. least possible time →
balsam, via xylene
RECOMMENDED FOR: differentiation of tannic acid fast (red-violet), fuchsinophile (reddish yellow) and fuchsinophobe (blue) colloid in thyroid.

22.8 Lendrum 1945   11431, **57**:267

REAGENTS REQUIRED: *A*. DS 11.122 Mayer 1901; *B*. 1% fast green FCF in 0.5% acetic
C. ADS 12.2 Lugol; *D*. 2% phosphotungstic acid in 95% alc.; *E*. DS 11.46 Lendrum
1945
METHOD: [sections] → *A*, till thoroughly stained → wash → *B*, 1–2 mins. → rinse → *C*
2 mins. → 95% alc., rinse → *D*, few moments → rinse → *E*, 2–6 mins. → wash →
balsam, via usual reagents
RECOMMENDED FOR: granules in cystic breast epithelium and basement membrane o:
renal glomerulus.

22.8 MacCallum et al.   *see* DS 21.42 MacCallum *et al.*, 1935

22.8 Mallory 1938a   Mallory 1938, 136

REAGENTS REQUIRED: *A*. 0.5% magenta in 50% alc.
METHOD: [sections with nuclei prior stained by any DS 11.122 method] → water → *A*
5–20 mins. → 95% alc., till differentiated → balsam, via xylene
RECOMMENDED FOR: demonstration of hemafuchsin granules.

22.8 Mallory 1938b   Mallory 1938, 151

REAGENTS REQUIRED: *A*. 1% acid fuchsin; *B*. 0.1% potassium permanganate
METHOD: [sections from F 3700.0010 Zenker 1894 fixed material] → water → *A*, over
night → drain → *B*, 40–60 secs. → abs. alc., → balsam, via xylene
RESULT: fibroglia fibrils, bright red; collagen, reddish yellow; elastic fibrils, bright yellow
RECOMMENDED FOR: demonstration of fibroglia fibrils.

22.8 Mallory 1898 *test*. 1938 Mallory   Mallory 1938, 138

REAGENTS REQUIRED: *A*. 95% alc. 75, sat. sol. ammonium sulfide 25; *B*. water 100
hydrochloric acid 0.5, potassium ferricyanide 10; *C*. 0.5% magenta in 50% alc.
METHOD: [sections] → water → *A*, 1–24 hrs. → wash → *B*, 10–20 mins. → wash → *C*
5–20 mins. → rinse → 95% alc., till differentiated → balsam, via usual reagents
RESULT: nuclei and hemofuchsin, red; hemosiderin, blue.
RECOMMENDED FOR: differentiation of hemosiderin and hemofuchsin in sections.

22.8 Mallory 1938   Mallory 1938, 207

REAGENTS REQUIRED: *A*. DS 11.122 Mallory 1938; *B*. 0.5% phloxine in 20% alc.; *C*
0.1% lithium carbonate
METHOD: [sections of alc. or formol fixed material] → *A*, 1–5 mins. → tap water, wash →
B, 10–30 mins. → tap water, wash → *C*, ½–1 min. → tap water, wash → balsam, vi:
usual reagents
RECOMMENDED FOR: hyalin.

22.8 McJunkin 1922   763, **24**:67

REAGENTS REQUIRED: *A*. water 25, 95% alc. 75, benzidine 0.2, hydrogen peroxide 0.2
B. Any DS 11.122 solution; *C*. 0.1% eosin
METHOD: [5 μ sections of formaldehyde-fixed material] → water → *A*, 5 mins. → wash →
B, 2 mins. → wash → *C*, 20 secs. → wash → balsam, via usual reagents
RECOMMENDED FOR: peroxidase granules in bone marrow.

22.8 Oliver 1934   11250, **55**:266

REAGENTS REQUIRED: *A.* ADS 12.2 Oliver 1934; *B.* DS 11.43 Ziehl 1882
METHOD: [air-dried smear from a 1:4 dilution of blood in hirudin saline, incubated 40–50
mins. 37°C.] → *A*, 20 mins. → wash → blot → *B*, 20 mins. → wash → dry
RECOMMENDED FOR: "flagella" on erythrocytes.

22.8 Oppler *test.* **1928 Schmorl**   Schmorl 1928, 341

REAGENTS REQUIRED: *A.* DS 11.24 Oppler (1928); *B.* 0.5% picric acid in 95% alc.
METHOD: [celloidin sections of alcohol-fixed material] → water → *A*, ½–1 min. → blot
→ *B*, 1 min. → balsam, via usual reagents
RECOMMENDED FOR: demonstration of eleidin in cells of stratum lucidum of skin.

22.8 Reich *test.* **1933a Cajal and de Castro**   Cajal and de Castro 1933, 323

REAGENTS REQUIRED: *A.* 1% toluidine blue
METHOD: [15 μ celloidin sections of F 7000.0000-Müller 1890 fixed nerve] → water → *A*,
5 mins. → quick rinse → 95% alc. till differentiated → abs. alc., till no more color
comes away → balsam, via usual reagents
RECOMMENDED FOR: granules in Schwann cells.

22.8 Reich *test.* **1933b Cajal and de Castro**   Cajal and de Castro 1933, 324

REAGENTS REQUIRED: *A.* water 100, phenol 5, acid fuchsin 1; *B.* ADS 21.1 Pal 1887 (*A*
and *B* sols.); *C.* 2% toluidine blue
METHOD: [15 μ frozen sections of formaldehyde-fixed nerve] → *A*, 24 hrs. 37°C. → *B*
(*A* sol.), 30 secs. → *B*, (5 sol.), few moments → [repeat *B* (*A*) → *B* (*B*) cycle till no
more color comes away] → balsam, via xylene
RESULTS: nuclei, blue; μ granules, red; π granules, purple.
RECOMMENDED FOR: differentiation of μ and π granules in Schwann cells.

22.8 Russel *test.* **1894 Kahlden and Laurent**   Kahlden and Laurent 1894, 73

REAGENTS REQUIRED: *A.* sat. sol. magenta in 2% phenol; *B.* 1% iodine green in 2% phenol
METHOD: [sections of dichromate-fixed material] → *A*, 10 mins. → thorough wash →
abs. alc., 30 secs. → *B*, 5 mins. → balsam, via usual reagents
RECOMMENDED FOR: miscellaneous cellular inclusions.

22.8 Russell *test.* **1928 Schmorl** *cit.* **Miller**   Schmorl 1928, 219

REAGENTS REQUIRED: *A.* DS 11.43 Ziehl 1882; *B.* water 100, phenol 5, iodine green 1
METHOD: [sections] → water → *A*, 10–30 mins. → wash → abs. alc. ½–1 min. → *B*
5 mins. → abs. alc., wash → balsam, via usual reagents
RECOMMENDED FOR: hyalin.

22.8 Russell *test.* **1948 Lillie** *cit.* **Ehrlich**   Lillie 1948, 105

REAGENTS REQUIRED: *A.* sat. sol. magenta in 2% phenol; *B.* 1% iodine green in 2% phenol
METHOD: [sections of F 7000.0000 Müller 1850] → water → *A*, 10–30 mins. → wash,
5 mins. → abs. alc., 30 secs. → *B*, 5 mins. → abs. alc., till differentiated → balsam, via
usual reagents
RESULTS: nuclei, green; Russell's bodies, red.
RECOMMENDED FOR: demonstration of Russell's bodies.

22.8 Sannomiya 1927   8542a, **5**:202

REAGENTS REQUIRED: *A.* 10% hydrochloric acid; *B.* 1% acid fuchsin; *C.* sat. sol. picric
acid; *D.* 1% phosphomolybdic acid.
METHOD: [small pieces fresh pancreas] → *A*, 24 hrs. → running water, 24 hrs. → celloidin
sections → *B*, 3 mins. → water, thorough wash → *C*, 3–4 mins. → water, quick rinse
→ *D*, 1–2 mins. → water, rinse → balsam, via usual reagents
RESULTS: paranuclei, red.
RECOMMENDED FOR: demonstration of paranuclear bodies in pancreas.

22.8 Schmorl 1928   Schmorl 1928, 244

REAGENTS REQUIRED: *A.* DS 22.21 Altmann 1890 (sol. *A*); *B.* DS 22.21 Altmann 1890
(sol. *B*)
METHOD: [blood smears fixed for 1 hr. in 1% osmic acid] → quick wash → *A*, 5 mins.,
55°–60°C. → wash, till no more color comes away → *B*, 15 mins. → rinse → blot →
abs. alc. least possible time → balsam, via xylene
RECOMMENDED FOR: Schridde's granules in lymphocytes.

22.8 Wallace 1931   19938, **74**:369

REAGENTS REQUIRED: *A*. Any DS 11.122 formula; *B*. 0.5% eosin Y; *C*. water 45, aniline 45, abs. alc. 10, methyl violet to sat; *D*. ADS 12.2 Lugol (1905); *E*. aniline 30 xylene 60
METHOD: [5 μ sections of F 3700.1010 fixed material] → *A*, till nuclei lightly stained → wash → *B*, 30 secs. → thorough wash → *C*, 2 hrs. → wash → *D*, 10–15 mins. → wash → *E*, till differentiated → xylene wash → balsam
RECOMMENDED FOR: basal bodies of cilia.

23. SELECTIVE STAINS FOR SPECIFIC ORGANISMS

There are surprisingly few stains which will selectively stain a specific organism compared to the number of stains which have been proposed for that purpose. Bacteria, for example, may be very well stained by any nuclear staining technique; therefore here are given (DS 23.2) only those methods for staining them which have, by convention and custom, come to be supposed to be "bacteriological methods."

One is on even less secure ground in dealing with the first class (DS 23.1), in which are given those stains which stain virus, Rickettsiae, and Negri bodies, for it is, of course, impossible that any individual virus molecule could be stained in such a manner as to bring it within the range of an optical microscope. But the methods given in the division DS 23.11 for staining minute unidentified bodies may quite possibly represent aggregates of virus, as they were supposed to do by the inventors of the techniques.

The third division here given (DS 23.3) is for the differential staining of parasites in host tissues, to which much attention has been devoted, and for which a number of relatively specific methods have been proposed. The last two divisions (DS 23.4, DS 23.5) contain a few staining techniques of such specialized application that they cannot possibly be given elsewhere in the present work.

23.1 VIRUS, RICKETTSIAE, AND NEGRI BODIES

23.10 TYPICAL EXAMPLES

Demonstration of Rickettsiae in the scrotum of a guinea pig using the magenta-thionin stain of Macchiavello 1938

It is presumed, in the description which follows, that the technician is acquainted with the exceedingly dangerous nature of Rickettsiae and is prepared to take all those aseptic precautions through which he or she may be protected against infection. Even then it must be emphasized that Rickettsiae can only be handled in properly equipped laboratories and under the supervision of a skilled bacteriologist or pathologist.

The staining method here described (DS 23.12 Macchiavello 1938) is the basic method which has been adapted by numerous people, who usually refer to their own method as "Macchiavello." The volume of Macchiavello 1938 is, moreover, not readily available and most workers have derived their information as to the method from the publication of Cox 1939 (17302, **53**:2242) to whom this method is therefore frequently attributed. Rickettsiae are difficult to stain satisfactorily, and though it is suggested that the beginning technician attempt this original technique of Macchiavello for the first preparation, it is very probable that he will have to vary the technique to suit the materials which he is using.

The only difficulty likely to be encountered will be by technicians who are accustomed to staining bacteria by some method in which every effort is made to get these bodies free on the slide without a great deal of cell debris around them. Rickettsiae, on the contrary, cannot be satisfactorily stained and differentiated unless they are within a cell, hence the critical stage of the preparation consists in securing undamaged cells containing Rickettsiae in a layer thin enough to permit their examination with the highest powers of the microscope.

Rickettsiae may be recovered either from the walls of the blood vessels or from the subcutaneous tissues of almost any infected animal. The guinea pig has been selected for the present demonstration because it appears to be the most usually employed in laboratories. The guinea pig may be killed by any method; it is then strapped down on a board in the customary manner. Rickettsiae are most readily obtainable to the beginner from the inner surface of the scrotal sac of a male, which has the advantage of being free from hair because it lies entirely within the coelomic cavity and is free from dermal adhesions. The guinea pig is opened by a median incision and the skin stretched back. This will disclose perfectly enormous vesicula seminales, and a very large prostate gland. These are pushed to one side to disclose the testes lying within a peritoneal fold. This is washed free of extravasated blood with a jet of normal saline, and a piece about 5 mm. square is cut from the anterior surface of the sac. This piece is now removed and laid with the inner surface upwards in the center of a $3'' \times 1''$ glass slide, where it may remain while the body of the guinea pig is being disposed of with the customary precautions.

It is now necessary to cut, not to scrape, a few cells from the exposed inner surface of the material. This is best done with a freshly sharpened razor or with a changeable-blade scalpel, using a new blade, cutting parallel to the surface of the glass with short, jerky strokes. One should be careful to draw the knife as much as push it. The debris accumulated on the blade of the knife is then spread over the surface of a second chemically clean slide, which is put aside to dry. More slides are now prepared in the same manner until a dozen or two smears have been accumulated. As soon as the smears are dry, the slides are placed in a large jar of absolute alcohol, and if care is taken that the entire surface of the slide is covered, the jar may now be removed from the operating room and turned over to a technician. If the slides are, moreover, picked one at a time from the jar with sterile forceps and placed in another jar outside the operating room, it is now safe to proceed with the staining without any further aseptic precautions.

The preparation of the stain presents few difficulties, for it is a three-step process involving first, gross overstaining in a magenta solution buffered to a pH of 7.5,

followed by differentiation and counterstaining in an acid thionin solution, with a final clearing of the thionin with weak citric acid.

Each slide is removed from the absolute alcohol and waved backward and forward in the air until it is dry. The slides are then examined unstained under the low power of the microscope, and those which show more than one or two cells lying on top of each other are rejected. Normally, in a batch of about a dozen slides, one or two will be found in which the smear is so thin that numerous isolated, undamaged cells will be seen in the field of the low power. These slides alone are worth staining, and each must be treated individually. The slide is placed on a rack, or held in the hand, and flooded with the magenta-phosphate buffer stain for three minutes. The magenta is then drained off without washing, and the citric acid-thionin solution is flooded onto the surface and off again immediately. The simplest technique is to hold the slide in the left hand, to take a pipetful of the stain in the right hand, allow this to fall over the slide, moving the pipet backward and forward to insure an even distribution, and then to tip the slide immediately onto a thick layer of blotting paper so that the stain runs off. While the stain is being run from the slide in the left hand, the right hand picks up a pipetful of the citric acid solution, and squirts this against the inclined slide in such a manner as to wash off the blue dye. The slide is then passed into tap water, where it may remain while successive slides from the same batch are treated with the stain.

The slides should remain in tap water until no further color comes away, and should then be washed in distilled water and air-dried. It is usually not worth while to mount the slides under a coverslip, but to accumulate them dry and to observe them with an oil immersion objective. After each observation the immersion oil may be washed off with xylene.

A successful preparation shows deep red Rickettsiae in light blue cells. The usual error is to remove too much of the blue which, under the very high powers necessary, is a desirable background for picking out the red Rickettsial bodies. The modification of Zinsser, Fitzpatrick, and Hsi 1938 (11189, **69**:179) consists of differentiating the magenta stain with citric acid, and in staining in methylene blue for a longer period; this, however, though undoubtedly giving a better background stain, does not give as clear a differentiation of the Rickettsial bodies.

Demonstration of Negri bodies in the brain of a guinea pig using the ethyl eosin-methylene blue technique of Stovall and Black 1940

Negri bodies are usually diagnosed by the smear technique which is described in Chapter 8. The method here described is intended more for the preparation of class-demonstration material, though it may also, when time is not vital, be used for diagnostic purposes. The guinea pig has been selected as a test animal, since it is so commonly used for diagnostic infection with the virus of rabies, the presence of which in the brain causes Negri bodies to appear in the cells, particularly those of the horn of Ammon. It is presumed that the investigator is acquainted with the aseptic precautions which must be observed in handling animals infected with the virus of rabies.

The guinea pig is killed, commonly with chloroform, and tied down on its ventral surface on a dissecting board. The head is then skinned and the muscles dissected away from the surface of the cranium. Since only the anterior region of the brain is required, it is advisable to cut with a saw about $\frac{1}{4}$ inch anterior to the supra-occipital bone vertically downwards for about $\frac{2}{3}$ of the distance through the skull and brain. The supraoccipital and posterior portions of the cranium are now removed with a pair of powerful pliers which will permit the cut end of the parietal bone to be gripped and stripped off without damage to the cerebral hemispheres. It does not matter if the cerebral hemispheres are slightly damaged, since ample protection will be afforded to the horn of Ammon. The membranes of the brain should be stripped off with forceps and the back of a large blunt knife inserted in the slit between the two cerebral hemispheres. A twist of the knife to the left will push a hemisphere to one side, so that it can be gripped firmly and drawn back until a cartilage knife, or similar instrument, can be used to sever the hemisphere from the brain stem. This will leave the other cerebral hemisphere exposed so that it may in its turn be severed. These two hemispheres are now removed to a dish of physiological saline, and the carcass of the guinea pig destroyed with the customary aseptic precautions. Each hemisphere is now cut with a horizontal movement of a large knife just about through the middle, and the upper half is thrown away. This will disclose the horn of Ammon at the posterior end. A little experience may be necessary to determine the exact point at which the cut should be made. Negri bodies are most commonly found in the basal portions of the horn of Ammon, and from this portion a few pieces about $\frac{1}{4}$ centimeter in thickness and a centimeter square should be removed to the selected fixative.

Stovall and Black (DS 23.13 Stovall and Black 1940) suggest the use of their method for diagnostic purposes by using acetone as a fixative, which permits rapid dehydration. For class-demonstration purposes, however, it is better to use 5% potassium dichromate in which the pieces of brain are suspended in a loosely woven cloth bag for a week or two to harden them.

If the sections are to be cut by an inexperienced technician, it is recommended that every step of the procedure up to this point be conducted by a physician, preferably a pathologist, and the pieces of brain in potassium dichromate turned over to the technician for further treatment.

After the pieces have hardened for a week or two, they are washed in running water overnight, embedded in the customary manner, and cut into sections of about five microns in thickness. These sections are mounted on the slide, dewaxed in xylene, and run down through the alcohols to distilled water.

The great advantage of the technique of Stovall and Black is that it involves the use of buffers, and thus gives a clearly reproducible result. Stovall and Black recommend phosphate buffers, of which two will be required, one at pH 3, the other at pH 5.5. It is not known to the writer whether or not other buffers than phosphate can be substituted in this technique. One per cent of ethyl eosin is then dissolved in the pH 3 buffer, and 0.25% of methylene blue is dissolved in equal parts of the pH 5.5 buffer and absolute alcohol. The only other solution required is 0.4% acetic acid.

Sections are taken from the distilled water and placed in the buffered eosin solution for two minutes. From this they are passed to distilled water, in which they are rinsed until the whole of the eosin adherent to the slide, but not that in the sections, is removed. They are then dipped up and down in the methylene blue solution for about 30 seconds. Each slide, without washing, is next placed in acetic acid and watched. When it is taken from the blue stain it will be purple-blue, and it will be sufficiently differentiated when it has changed to brownish red. This color change is relatively sharp and is accompanied by a cessation of the clouds of blue stain, which will be seen leaving the section when it is first placed in the acetic acid. The slide is then transferred to running water and thoroughly washed to remove the acid as rapidly as possible. It is recommended that the slides be run through the technique up to this point, one at a time, and accumulated in the wash water. They may then be dehydrated in the regular manner, either in alcohol, or in any other solvent selected by the preparator, before being mounted in balsam.

23.11 METHODS OF STAINING UNIDENTIFIED ORGANISMS SMALLER THAN BACTERIA

Little can be said in favor of the methods given under this section, save that they have appeared in the literature and are certified by their discoverers to place in evidence, in sectioned material, certain particles presumed by the writers of the articles to have been living, and which cannot be, with certainty, assigned to any known group or class of organism.

23.11 Bland and Canti 1935   11431, 40:233
FORMULA: DS 13.13 Gatenby and Cowdry 1928 7, phosphate buffer pH 7 100
METHOD: [pieces of infected explant] → methanol, 5 mins. → stain, 24 hrs. → acetone, till differentiated → xylene, till acetone completely removed → balsam

23.11 Gutstein 1937   11431, 45:313
FORMULA: 1% methyl violet 50, 2% sodium bicarbonate 50
METHOD: [methanol-fixed smears] → stain, 20–30 mins., 37°C. → wash → dry

23.11 Hosokowa 1934 test. 1942 Langeron   Langeron 1942, 841
STOCK SOLUTION: methanol 50, glycerol 50, DS 13.11 Jenner 1899 (dry powder) 0.8, azur I 0.2, crystal violet 0.01
REAGENTS REQUIRED: A. 1% eosin B; B. stock 100, water 2
METHOD: [smears, fixed and dehydrated in F 0000.0101 Hosokowa 1934] → A, poured on slide and warmed to steaming, 1 min. → thorough wash → B, 30–40 mins. → dry

23.11 Laidlaw test. 1936 Pappenheimer and Hawthorne   608b, 12:627
REAGENTS REQUIRED: A. DS 11.121 Weigert 1903; B. 0.5% hydrochloric acid in 70% alc.; C. 1% acid fuchsin; D. 1% phosphomolybdic acid; E. 0.25% orange G in 70% alc.
METHOD: [3 μ sections of F 3000.0010 Laidlaw (1936) fixed material] → water → A, 5 mins. → B, till nuclei differentiated → wash → C, 5–15 mins. → rinse → D, 30 secs. → rinse → E, till inclusion bodies differentiated → balsam, via usual reagents

3.11 Nicolau and Kopciowska 1937   6628, 104:1276
REAGENTS REQUIRED: A. water 65, methanol 35, glycerol 5, oxalic acid 0.15, methyl blue 1.5; B. water 100, oxalic acid 0.06, acid fuchsin 1.5
METHOD: [thin sections of F 5000.1010 Dubsoscq and Brazil 1905 fixed material] → 95% alc. → A, ½ to 1 hr. → water, rinse → abs. alc., rinse → B, 10–20 mins. → abs. alc. → balsam, via usual reagents

23.12 METHODS FOR RICKETTSIAE

The staining of Rickettsiae in sections is relatively easy, provided that an alkaline solution be employed at some stage of the proceedings. The method of Castañeda 1930 and Macchiavello 1938, which involve the use of a phosphate buffer at a pH of 7.5, have now almost replaced the other methods, which are given here largely for their historical value, and to enable the research worker to check, if necessary, the results of the early publishers in this field. Attention must therefore be drawn to the technique of Lépine 1932, in which a definitely acid solution is employed for staining. It must, however, in all fairness, be pointed out that the technique of Lépine would equally well stain bacteria or mitochondria were they present. Indeed, the general warning must be given that the demonstration of Rickettsiae in cells is far more dependent upon the symptoms shown by the animal from which they were taken, than on any demonstration which can be made with an optical microscope. There are numerous methods for staining small particles occurring in cells, which have been given both under the cytological techniques above and in various places in the previous divisions of the work. There is no evidence of any kind that any of the techniques given in this section will stain Rickettsiae to the exclusion of any other small particle or small body.

23.12 Begg, Fulton, and van den Ende 1944 11431, **56**:109
REAGENTS REQUIRED: *A.* M/15 phosphate buffer pH 7.6 10, 0.1% magenta 90; *B.* M/50 citrate buffer pH 3.0; *C.* 1% methylene blue
METHOD: [heat-fixed impression smears] → *A,* 5 mins. → wash → *B,* ½ to 1½ mins. → wash → *C,* 30 secs. → dry

23.12 Böhner *test.* **1928 Schmorl** Schmorl 1928, 428
REAGENTS REQUIRED: *A.* 1% methyl blue 35, 1% eosin 35, water 100; *B.* 0.005% sodium hydroxide in abs. alc.; *C.* 0.1% acetic acid
METHOD: [sections of alc. or acetone, fixed material] → water → *A,* ½–5 mins. → rinse → 50% alc., rinse → *B,* 15–20 secs. → abs. alc., rinse → water, wash → *C,* 1–2 mins. → abs. alc., rinse → abs. alc. → balsam, via usual reagents

23.12 Bond *test.* **1938 Mallory** Mallory 1938, 285
REAGENTS REQUIRED: *A.* water 100, eosin 0.1, methyl blue 0.1; *B.* xylene 30, aniline 60
METHOD: [methanol-fixed smears] → wash → stain, 4–5 mins. → wash → blot → dry → *B,* till differentiated → balsam, via xylene

23.12 Castañeda 1930 11250, **47**:416
REAGENTS REQUIRED: *A.* phosphate buffer pH 7.5 100, 40% formaldehyde 5 DS 11.44 Löffler 1890 1; *B.* 0.1% safranin
METHOD: [very thin smears] → *A,* 3 mins. → drain → *B,* on slide, 2–3 secs. → water, till no more color comes away → dry

23.12 Clancy and Wolfe 1945 19938, **102**:483
REAGENTS REQUIRED: *A.* water 100, methylene blue 0.02, magenta 0.02
METHOD: [air-dried smears] → xylene, flooded on slide, few mins. → dry → *A,* 5 mins. → wash → dry

23.12 Cox 1939 *see* DS 23.12 Macchiavello 1938 (note)

23.12 Darzins 1943 23684, **151**:18
REAGENTS REQUIRED: *A.* ADS 12.2 Lugol 50, water 50; *B.* 0.1% thionin in 10% alc.
METHOD: [air-dried smears] → *A,* 30 secs. → rinse → *B,* 5 secs. → wash → dry

23.12 Goodpasture and Burnett 1919 *see* DS 23.12 Hertig and Wolbach 1924 (note)

23.12 Gracian 1942 *test.* **1943 von Brand** 20540b, **18**:150
REAGENTS REQUIRED: *A.* 7% potassium dichromate; *B.* DS 13.13 Giemsa 1902 10, water 90
METHOD: [smear] → xylene, 3 mins. → 96% alc., 1 min. → water → *A,* 3 mins. → wash → *B,* 10–20 mins. → wash → dry

23.12 Hertig and Wolbach 1924   11343, **44**:332

REAGENTS REQUIRED: *A*. DS 11.43 Goodpasture and Burnett 1919; *B*. 40% formaldehyde; *C*. sat. sol. picric acid

METHOD: [thin sections of F 3700.0000 fixed material] → *A*, poured on slide, warmed to
steaming, 5 mins. → water, quick rinse → *B*, dropped on slide till no more color comes
away → *C*, 1 min. → balsam, via usual reagents

23.12 Laigret and Auburtin 1938   5310, **31**:790

PREPARATION OF DRY "SALT": To a sat. sol. thionin add 10% sodium hydroxide until
no further ppt. is formed. Filter. Wash and dry ppt.

WORKING SOLUTION: water 100, phenol 2, ppt. from above to sat.

METHOD: [alcohol-fixed smears] → stain, on slide, 30–50 secs. → drain → abs. alc., quick
wash → balsam, via xylene

23.12 Lépine 1932   6630, **109**:1162

REAGENTS REQUIRED: *A*. water 90, phenol 3, DS 11.43 Ziehl 1890 10; *B*. sat. aq. sol.
(*circ.* 2.5%) Bismarck brown

METHOD: [smears of vaginal scrapings, fixed on slide by F 7000.1000 Régaud 1910] →
water, wash → *B*, 2–3 mins. → water, wash → dry

RESULT: Rickettsiae red in pale brown cells.

23.12 Lépine 1933   6630, **112**:17

STOCK SOLUTIONS: I. water 100, phenol 0.5, azur II 1; II. 1% potassium carbonate

REAGENTS REQUIRED: *A*. water 100, stock I 3.5, stock II 2, 40% neutralized formaldehyde 5; *B*. 0.1% safranin

METHOD: [very thin smears] → *A*, 3 or 4 mins. → water, wash → *B*, till differentiated →
water, wash → dry

23.12 Macchiavello 1938   Macchiavello 1938, 48

REAGENTS REQUIRED: *A*. sat. alc. sol. (*circ.* 4%) magenta 0.4, phosphate buffer pH 7.5
100; *B*. water 100, thionin 0.01, citric acid 0.13; *C*. 0.5% citric acid

METHOD: [thin smears] → *A*, on slide, 3 mins. → *B*, 2–3 secs. → *C*, 2–3 secs. → tap
water, thorough wash → dry

NOTE: **Zinsser, Fitzpatrick, and Hsi 1938** (11189, **69**:179) omit step *B* and stain for 1
minute in 1% methylene blue after washing off the citric acid. This modification is
commonly referred to as "Macchiavello's method." The original method was cited by
Cox 1939 (17302, **53**:2242) to whom it is sometimes referenced. A detailed description
of the use of this technique is given under DS 23.10 above.

23.12 Nyka 1944   11431, **56**:264

REAGENTS REQUIRED: *A*. 5% magenta in 90% alc.; *B*. 0.01% methyl violet; *C*. 0.007%
acetic acid.

METHOD: [3 μ sections of F 7000.0000 Müller 1859 fixed material] → 95% alc. → *A*, 5–10
mins. → rinse → 95% alc., 1–2 mins. → *B*, 1–3 mins. → rinse → *C*, till differentiated
→ balsam, via acetone and xylene

23.12 Nyka 1945   11431, **52**:317

REAGENTS REQUIRED: *A*. 0.01% methyl violet; *B*. 0.05% acetic acid; *C*. 0.01% metanil
yellow

METHOD: [sections of formaldehyde-fixed material] → water → *A*, ½ to 1 hr. → *B*, till
cytoplasm clear → rinse *C*, few secs. → balsam, via acetone and xylene

23.12 Roskin 1946   Roskin 1946, 158

REAGENTS REQUIRED: *A*. water 80, 95% alc. 20, phenol 1, aniline 1, magenta; *B*. DS 11.44
Löffler 1890

METHOD: [sections] → water → *A*, 10 mins. → wash → 95% alc. till differentiated →
wash → *B*, 15–60 secs. → wash → abs. alc., minimum possible time → balsam, via
xylene

RECOMMENDED FOR: Rickettsiae and Negri bodies.

23.12 Stutzer 1911   23454, **69**:25

REAGENTS REQUIRED: *A*. DS 11.44 Löffler 1890; *B*. 1% tannin

METHOD: [thin sections] → water → *A*, 5–15 mins. → rinse → *B*, till differentiated →
wash → blot → abs. alc., least possible time → balsam, via xylene

23.12 Wolbach 1919   11343, **41**:75

REAGENTS REQUIRED: *A*. 70% alc. 98, ADS 12.2 Lugol (1905) 2; *B*. 0.5% sodium thiosulfate; *C*. distilled water 100, sodium bicarbonate 0.001, methanol 10, DS 13.13 Giemsa 1902 2; *D*. ADS 21.2 Wolbach 1919 2; *E*. acetone 70, xylene 30

METHOD: [3 μ–5 μ sections of Wolbach F 3700.0000 material, dewaxed and brought to 90% alc.] → *A*, 20–30 mins. → 70% alc., wash → water, wash → *B*, 5 mins. → wash → *C*, 30 mins. → *C*, fresh solution, 30 mins. → *C*, fresh solution, overnight → *D*, flooded on slide, 15–30 secs. → *E*, till dehydrated → xylene → cedar oil

RESULT: nuclei and Rickettsiae, blue; cytoplasm, red.

23.12 Zinsser and Bayne-Jones 1939   Zinsser and Bayne-Jones 1939, 654

STOCK SOLUTIONS: I. phosphate buffer pH 7.5 100, 40% formaldehyde 0.5; II. 1% methylene blue in methanol

REAGENTS REQUIRED: *A*. stock I 100, stock II 0.75, 40% formaldehyde 5; *B*. water 100 safranin O 0.05, acetic acid 0.075

METHOD: as DS 23.12 Casteñeda 1930

23.12 Zinnser, Fitzpatrick, and Hsi 1939   *see* DS 23.12 Macchiavello 1938 (note)

23.13 METHODS FOR NEGRI, AND OTHER VIRUS INCLUSION, BODIES

Negri bodies are generally supposed to be aggregations of virus particles, though they may well be the breakdown products of the cell itself. The stains which have been developed for them are far more specific than the stains given for Rickettsiae in the previous section. The method of Schleifstein 1937 is in general employment in the United States today, although a far better demonstration, if speed is not of more importance than accuracy, is to be obtained from the technique of Lépine 1935. The "glyceric ether" mentioned in the technique of Manouélian is not an article of commerce in the United States, but is so readily available in Europe, where Manouélian's method is widespread, that it is here included. Particular attention should be given to the formula of Stovall and Black 1940, for it is the only one of the formulas which have been given for the staining of these minute particles in which an acid buffer is employed

23.13 Barreto 1944 *test*. **1945 Conn**   20540b, **20**:66

REAGENTS REQUIRED: *A*. *either* DS 11.121 Weigert 1903 *or* DS 11.123 Ehrlich 1886; *B*. 1% hydrochloric acid in 70% alc.; *C*. water 100, methyl blue 0.12, eosin 0.12; *D*. 95% alc. 100, picric acid 0.005, acetic acid 0.1

METHOD: [sections] → water → *A*, till stained → *B*, till differentiated → tap water, till blue → *C*, on slide, 15 mins. → rinse → *D*, till differentiated → 90% alc. → balsam via usual reagents

23.13 Carpano 1916 *test*. **1942 Langeron**   Langeron 1942, 845

REAGENTS REQUIRED: *A*. 1% eosin Y; *B*. DS 12.15 crystal violet 20, water 80; *C*. AD 12.2 Lugol (1905)

METHOD: [5 μ sections of F 3700.0010 Zenker 1894 fixed material, or smears similarly fixed] → *A*, 1 min. → 95% alc., wash → *B*, warmed to steaming, 5 mins. → *C*, used to wash *B* from slide, 1 min. → 95% alc., till differentiated → balsam, via usual reagents

23.13 Craigie 1933   11431, **36**:185

REAGENTS REQUIRED: *A*. 2% mercurochrome; *B*. water 100, sodium phosphate, dibasic (12 H_2O) 0.35, mercurochrome 0.002, azur I 0.01, methylene blue 0.25

PREPARATION OF B: Mix 1 2% mercurochrome, 57% $Na_2HPO_4.12H_2O$, 1 1% azur I. Add 75 water and 25 1% methylene blue.

METHOD: [air-dried blood smears or tissue scrapings] → methanol, 5–10 mins. → dry - rinse → blot → *A*, 5–10 mins. → rinse → blot → *B*, 5–10 mins. → quick rinse → dry

RECOMMENDED FOR: Paschen bodies.

23.13 Coles 1935   11360, **55**:249

REAGENTS REQUIRED: *A*. DS 13.13 Giemsa 1902 (dry stock) 0.75, glycerol 25, 95% alc. 75; *B*. water 100, tannic acid 5, orange G I

METHOD: [smears] → *A*, 24 hrs. → wash → dry → *B*, few moments → wash → dry

RECOMMENDED FOR: virus inclusions in general.

23.13 Dawson 1934   11284, **20**:659

REAGENTS REQUIRED: A. 2% phloxine; B. DS 11.44 Löffler 1890

METHOD: [methanol-fixed smears] → water → A, 2–5 mins. → water, wash → B, 15 secs. → 20% alc., till no more color comes away → balsam, via usual reagents

NOTE: A detailed description of the use of this technique is given on p. 75.

23.13 Frotheringham *test.* **1952 Krajian and Gradwohl**   Krajian and Gradwohl 1952, 216

FORMULA: water 100, sat. aq. sol. magenta 0.9, sat. aq. sol. methylene blue 0.6

METHOD: [smears from hippocampus or cerebellum (see Chapter 8)] → abs. alc., few moments → stain, 10–15 secs. → blot → dry

RESULT: Negri bodies red with blue granules.

23.13 Gallego 1923   23454, **25**:74

REAGENTS REQUIRED: A. water 100, ferric chloride 0.3, nitric acid 0.3; B. water 100, DS 11.43 Ziehl 1882 3, acetic acid 0.3; C. water 100, 40% formaldehyde 0.6, nitric acid 0.3; D. DS 12.211 Cajal 1895

METHOD: [sections by freezing technique of F 0000.1010 fixed material] → A, 1–5 mins. → B, poured on slide, 5 mins. → water, wash → C, 1–10 mins. → wash → D, 1 min. → → balsam, via usual reagents

23.13 Gerlach 1926 *test.* **1948 Lillie**   Lillie 1948, 226

REAGENTS REQUIRED: A. water 100, DS 11.44 Löffler 1890 12, DS 11.43 Ziehl 1890 6

METHOD: [paraffin sections of alcohol-fixed material] → A, poured on slide, heated to steaming, 1 min. → repeat 3 further times → neutral mountant, via usual reagents

23.13 Goodpasture 1925   608b, **1**:550

REAGENTS REQUIRED: A. water 80, alcohol 20, phenol 1, aniline 1, magenta 0.5; B. DS 11.43 Löffler 1890

METHOD: [thin sections of F 3700.0010 Zenker 1894 material] → water → A, 10–20 mins, → wash → blot → 95% alc., till light pink → wash → 8–15 secs. to 1 min. → abs. alc., till differentiated → balsam, via xylene

RESULT: Negri bodies red on blue.

23.13 Hamilton 1934   11587, **37**:139

REAGENTS REQUIRED: A. water 50, 95% alc. 50, ethyl eosin 0.5, eosin Y 0.5; B. sat. sol. potassium alum; C. 0.15% ammonia in 95% alc.; D. 0.5% methyl blue

METHOD: [4 μ–6 μ sections of F 3700.1000 Helly 1903 fixed material] → A, on slide, set alight and allowed to burn out → repeat → drain → B, flooded on slide → drain → B, in jar, 10 mins. → wash → C, till tissue pink → wash → D, 10 mins. → abs. alc., rinse → C, till inclusion bodies (vermilion) clearly differentiated → wash → balsam, via usual reagents

RECOMMENDED FOR: virus inclusion bodies in general.

23.13 Harris 1908   11250, **5**:566

REAGENTS REQUIRED: A. 1% ethyl eosin in 95% alc.; B. water 80, DS 11.44 Unna 1892 20

METHOD: [alcohol-fixed smears] → water → A, 1–3 mins. → water, quick rinse → B, 10 secs. → water, rinse → 95% alc., till differentiated → balsam, via usual reagents

23.13 Jordan and Heather 1929   20540b, **4**:121

REAGENTS REQUIRED: A. ADS 12.2 Lugol (1905); B. 2% sodium thiosulfate; C. water 100, eosin Y 0.5, phloxine 0.25; D. 0.1% azur B; E. clove oil 30, abs. alc. 60

METHOD: [5 μ sections by E 22.1 Jordan and Heather 1929 method of F 3800.1000 Dominici 1905 fixed tissues] → A, 10 mins. → wash → B, till decolorized → thorough wash → C, 15 mins. → wash → D, 2–5 mins. → 95% alc., wash → E, till differentiated → abs. alc., least possible time → xylene → gum elemi

23.13 Kaiser and Gherardini 1934   23684, **131**:128

REAGENTS REQUIRED: A. water 100, phloxine 0.5, aniline 1.5

METHOD: [sections] → water → A, 1 min. → wash → balsam, via usual reagents

RECOMMENDED FOR: Guarnieri bodies

23.13 Krajian 1941   *see* DS 23.221 Krajian 1942

23.13 Lenz 1907   23684, **44**:374

REAGENTS REQUIRED: *A*. 0.5% eosin Y in 60% alc.; *B*. water 100, potassium hydroxide 0.1, sat. alc. sol. (*circ.* 2%) methylene blue 30; *C*. 0.005% potassium hydroxide in abs. alc.; *D*. 0.1% acetic acid in abs. alc.

METHOD: [paraffin sections of acetone fixed and dehydrated material] → 70% alc. → *A*, 1 min. → water, wash → *B*, 1 min. → blot or drain → *C*, till yellowish → *D*, till nerve cells clear blue → balsam, via usual reagents

23.13 Lépine 1935   6630, **119**:804

REAGENTS REQUIRED: *A*. 0.5% magenta in 50% alc. 50, 0.2% safranin 50; *B*. abs. alc. 50, acetone 50; *C*. DS 11.44 Stévenel 1918

METHOD: [paraffin sections of F 3700.0010 fixed material] → *A*, 10 mins. → *B*, quick rinse → water, wash → *C*, 1 min. → *B*, till section turns blue → water, wash → *B*, quick dip → abs. alc., till section turns lilac → balsam, via xylene

23.13 Lillie 1948   Lillie 1948, 225

REAGENTS REQUIRED: *A*. abs. alc. 90, water 6, acetic acid 3.25, ethyl eosin 1; *B*. any DS 11.122 stain; *C*. 0.25% acetic acid

METHOD: [alcohol-fixed material] → *A*, 2 mins. → 95% alc., rinse → water, wash → *B*, till sufficiently stained → *C*, till differentiated → balsam, via usual reagents

23.13 McWhorter 1941   20540b, **16**:143

REAGENTS REQUIRED: *A*. any wetting agent; *B*. 0.5% phloxine; *C*. 0.9% sodium chloride; *D*. 0.5% trypan blue

METHOD: [surface shaving from virus infected leaf] → *A*, brief rinse → *B*, 3–8 secs. → *C*, brisk wash → *D*, 2–4 mins. → *C*, for observation

RESULT: viroplasts blue, red, or purple.

NOTE: Formaldehyde-fixed material may be used after 1–6 hours in 10% citric acid. **Rich 1948** (20540b, **23**:19) recommends pretreatment in water 85, sodium chloride 0.7, 95% alc. 10, ether 5.

23.13 Manouélian 1912   857, **26**:972

REAGENTS REQUIRED: *A*. acetone 100, ADS 12.2 Lugol (1905) 0.3; *B*. DS 13.7 Mann 1892 (sol. *A*); *C*. 2% glyceric ether in 95% alc.

METHOD: [fresh smears] → *A*, 5 mins. → acetone, thorough wash → *B*, 1 min. → *C*, till differentiated → balsam, via usual reagents

NOTE: **Langeron 1949, 653** states that ADS 22.1 Beauverie and Hollande 1916, diluted 50:1 with water may be used in place of glyceric ether.

23.13 Nagle and Pfau 1937   617, **27**:356

REAGENTS REQUIRED: *A*. phosphate buffer pH 7.4 90, 8% alc. magenta 0.3, sat. sol methylene blue 0.2

METHOD: [dry impression smear] → methanol, 2 mins. → wash → *B*, on slide, heated to steaming, 5 mins. → wash → dry

23.13 Neri 1909   23684, **50**:409

REAGENTS REQUIRED: *A*. water 100, iodine 0.1, potassium iodide 0.2, eosin Y 1; *B*. 1% methylene blue .

PREPARATION OF *A*: Dissolve the iodine and iodide in a few drops of water. Dilute to 50 Add dye dissolved in 50 water to iodine solution.

METHOD: [sections of acetone-fixed, or smears of alcohol-fixed material] → *A*, 10–15 mins → water, wash → *B*, 5 mins. → water, rinse → 95% alc., till differentiated → balsam via usual reagents

23.13 Petragnani 1928a *test.* **1930 Ciferri**   20540b, **5**:34

REAGENTS REQUIRED: *A*. ADS 12.2 Petragnani (1928) (working sol.); *B*. 0.5% eosin in 50% alc.; *C*. DS 11.122 Mayer 1896; *D*. 0.1% methylene blue; *E*. 0.05% sodiu hydroxide in abs. alc.

METHOD: [sections] → abs. alc. → *A*, 5–10 secs. → abs. alc., rinse → *B*, 10–20 secs. – wash → *C*, 1 min. → rinse → *D*, till violet (*not* blue) → blot → *E*, 15–20 secs. → 95% alc., till blue → balsam, via usual reagents

RESULT: Negri bodies, eosin-red; capillaries, nuclei, red; nerve cells, blue.

23.13 Petragnani 1928b *test.* **1930 Ciferro**   20540b, **5**:35
REAGENTS REQUIRED: *A.* ADS 12.2 Petragnani (1928) (working sol.); *B.* 0.5% acid fuchsin in 50% alc.
METHOD: [sections] → abs. alc. → *A*, few secs. → abs. alc., rinse → 70% alc., rinse → *B*, 30 secs. → wash → balsam, via usual reagents

23.13 Parsons 1939   4349, **19**:104
REAGENTS REQUIRED: *A.* water 94, 95% alc. 5.4, acetic acid 0.6, ethyl eosin 0.054; *B.* DS 11.44 Jadassohn (1928); *C.* 0.025% acetic acid
METHOD: [paraffin sections of formaldehyde-fixed material] → water → *A*, 2 mins. → 95% alc., till pink → *B*, 2 mins. → rinse → *C*, till pale bluish pink → 95% alc., rinse → abs. alc., least possible time → balsam, via xylene
RESULT: Negri bodies, bright orange red with blue central dot; Nissl bodies, blue.

23.13 Rich 1948   *see* DS 23.13 McWhorter 1941 (note)

23.13 Schleifstein 1937   617, **27**:1283
STOCK SOLUTION: methanol 50, glycerol 50, magenta 0.9, methylene blue 0.5
WORKING SOLUTION: stock 1.25, 0.0025% potassium hydroxide 100
METHOD: [paraffin sections of F 3700.0010 Zenker 1894 fixed material] → water → stain, poured on slide, warmed to steaming, 5 mins. → 90% alc., till pale violet → balsam, via usual reagents

23.13 Stovall and Black 1940   591b, **10**:1
REAGENTS REQUIRED: *A.* 1% ethyl eosin in pH 3.0 buffer; *B.* 0.25% methylene blue in 50% alc. at pH 5.5; *C.* 0.4% acetic acid
METHOD: [acetone-fixed material] → *A*, 2 mins. → water, rinse → *B*, 30 secs. → *C*, till brownish red → water, wash → balsam, via usual reagents
NOTE: A detailed description of the use of this technique is given under DS 23.10 above

23.13 Taniguchi, Hosokawa, Kuga, Komora, and Nakamura 1932 *test.* **1933 Findlay**
                                                            11360, **53**:43
REAGENTS REQUIRED: *A.* acetone; *B.* 1% cadmium iodide in 40% formaldehyde; *C.* water 92.5, 95% alc. 5, 40% formaldehyde 2.5, eosin 0.1; *D.* DS 11.43 Ziehl 1882
METHOD: [air-dried smear] → *A*, 1 min. → wash → *B*, 2 mins. → rinse → *C*, 30 secs. → rinse → *D*, 10 secs. → wash → dry
NOTE: Any turbidity in *B* is cleared up with a few drops of hydrochloric acid.

23.13 Turewitsch   23684, **129**:381
REAGENTS REQUIRED: *A.* 2.5% ferric alum; *B.* 5% tannic acid; *C.* 0.02% azur I; *D.* sat. sol. picric acid
METHOD: [sections] → *A*, 20–25 mins. → wash → *B*, 10 mins. → wash → *D*, 10–15 mins. → wash → balsam, via usual reagents
RECOMMENDED FOR: Paschen bodies in cornea.

23.13 Williams 1908   618, **18**:10
FORMULA: sat. alc. sol. (*circ.* 6%) magenta 1.25, sat. alc. sol. (*circ.* 3.5%) methylene blue 25, water 75
METHOD: [smears] → cover with stain, heat to steaming → wash → blot → dry

23.13 Zottner 1934   6630, **115**:593
REAGENTS REQUIRED: *A.* 30% nitric acid; *B.* DS 11.43 Ziehl 1882; *C.* water 100, picric acid 0.5, indigocarmine 0.5
METHOD: [paraffin sections] → abs. alc. → *A*, few drops on slide, 2–3 mins. → *B*, on slide, 15 secs. → rinse → *C*, 15 secs. → abs. alc., till green → balsam, via xylene

23.2 BACTERIA

Bacteria can be stained by any of the techniques which are customarily applied to nuclei, as well as the majority of techniques which are used for the demonstration of mitochondria. The grouping together of the techniques given below as "bacterial stains" is due entirely to the fact that persons skilled in the staining of zoological and botanical forms have drifted so far from bacteriological technicians as to tend to throw these bacteriological techniques into a separate branch of the science. This is very unfortunate and has given rise to many misunderstandings in the literature. Bacterial stains can be broadly divided, as they are below, into those which are applied customarily to smears, and those which are applied to the differential staining of bacteria in cells. The former class is very much the larger of the two, for the staining of bacteria in cells is rarely used for diagnostic purposes, being generally confined to demonstrations in bacteriology and pathology classes.

23.20 TYPICAL EXAMPLES

Staining a bacterial film with crystal violet by the technique of Hucker (1929)

The technique is so simple that it would be scarcely worth the trouble to describe it, were it not necessary for the benefit of those who have never previously handled bacterial material, and who may wish to attempt this for the first time.

The only tools and reagents necessary are a clean glass slide, a wire loop of the type used normally in bacteriology, a drop bottle containing crystal violet stain (DS 23.211 Hucker 1929), and a wash bottle containing distilled water.

Take a culture from which it is desired to stain the organisms, and touch the freshly flamed wire loop *as lightly as possible* either to the surface of the medium in a test tube or to the surface of the colony in an agar petri-dish culture. The loop is then touched lightly to the center of the clean slide to transfer the bacteria. The only mistakes likely to be made by the beginner is securing too great a quantity of material, or making too large an area. It must be remembered that the specimen is to be examined under an oil immersion lens so that the smallest possible smear, derived just by touching the slide with the moist platinum loop, will have an ample area for the purpose required.

If the micro-organisms have been taken from a test tube containing a liquid culture which has not yet reached a very thick stage of growth, the spot may now be allowed to dry in air; but if the bacteria were taken from a colony on the surface of agar, it is necessary to dilute them with water, taken in the same platinum loop, and touched to the same spot. The spot is then spread with the loop, and the slide is dried.

As soon as the slide has dried, which should take only a moment or two if a sufficiently small quantity of fluid has been used, it is taken and "heat-fixed" in the flame of a bunsen burner or a spirit lamp. This is done by taking the slide and passing it twice quite rapidly through the flame of the bunsen. The actual temperature should not exceed about 80°C., and it is customary to hold the slide smear downward as it passes through the flame. Care must be taken that the slide is quite dried before being thus quickly flamed, or the bacteria will burst and be worthless.

Now take the flamed and dried smear and place on it a drop of the selected stain (in this case crystal violet), leaving this in place for about 30 seconds. The time is not critical; any time between a half and one minute is satisfactory. It will be noticed that the stain frequently evaporates slightly, leaving a greenish film on the surface. It is, therefore, better to wash it off with a jet from a wash bottle than to endeavor to rinse it off. This jet should be directed from the fine orifice of the wash bottle, at an angle of about 30°, to the slide and should be intended to hit the edge of the drop. This will instantly lift off and float away the surface film, and will also wash excess stain out of the preparation. The preparation is now dried, touched with immersion oil, and examined under the oil-immersion lens.

Demonstration of Gram-positive bacteria in smear preparations by the method of Gram 1884

The name of Gram is so firmly fixed to these iodine-differential techniques, that it seems well to describe the original method without modification, leaving it to the technician to determine for himself which of the numerous modifications, proposed in section DS 23.212 below, best fits his particular problem. For the benefit of those who are not acquainted with bacteriology, it may be added that it has been customary, since the time of Gram, to utilize the reactions of bacteria to iodine mordanting as a basis of diagnostic classification. All bacteria, without reference to their nature, may be stained by the method given in the last example, but there are some bacteria from which the stain can be removed by the action of an iodine-potassium iodide solution reinforced with alcohol. The bacteria from which the stain is not removed are known as Gram-positive; those from which the stain is removed are known as Gram-negative. The solutions required are crystal violet (Gram himself used the mixture of dyes known as gentian violet) which is usually prepared as a phenol solution by the method given in Chapter 20 (DS 12.15). There is often a sharp argument between technicians as to whether or not this method of preparation is essential, but it is in customary usage and should be followed by the beginner. Gram's iodine solution, the formula for which is given as ADS 12.2 Gram 1884 (Chapter 22) is difficult to prepare unless the technique is exactly followed. Iodine is very soluble in strong solutions of potassium iodide, but is only slightly soluble in weak solutions. If the total quantities of iodine and potassium iodide shown are placed in the total quantity of water, a period as long as a week may elapse before a solution is complete; but if the dry iodine and the dry potassium iodide are mixed together, and a few drops of water are added, a solution will be produced almost instantly.

A smear is prepared as described in the last example. The same precautions as to dilution there mentioned must be taken if the material is obtained from a bacterial colony. The smear is then dried, flamed, and a drop of crystal violet poured onto it from a drop bottle, exactly as in the previous example. In this instance, however, it is not desirable to extract too much of the stain with water, hence, after the stain has been acting for two minutes or so, the entire slide is rinsed rapidly in water, and a drop or two of the iodine solution poured over it. If many slides are being stained, it is probably simpler to drop the slide into a coplin jar containing the iodine solution than to pour iodine on it. After the iodine has acted for one minute the slide is given a quick rinse to remove the excess iodine, and then placed into absolute alcohol until no more color comes away; unless the film is very thick, this will appear completely to decolorize it. It is then passed from alcohol to water, which instantly stops differentiation, and then dried. Varying types of bacteria require varying periods of differentiation, but it is better for the beginner to use absolute alcohol until no more color comes away, than to endeavor to control the differentiation under the microscope.

Though such a preparation is a Gram's preparation by the original technique, it is customary nowadays to provide a counter-stain of a contrasting color to bring clearly into evidence any Gram-negative organisms which may be mixed with Gram-positive. A 1% solution of safranin is widely employed, though Kopelloff and Beerman 1922 (DS 23.212 below) recommend a 0.1% solution of magenta for the same purpose. In either case, the second red contrasting stain is allowed to act for five to ten seconds and is then washed off with water.

Demonstration of tubercle bacilli
in sputum by the technique
of Neelsen 1883

When Neelsen published his original technique for the demonstration of tubercle bacilli (DS 23.213 Neelsen 1883), the standard magenta solution used for the staining of bacteria was that proposed in the previous year by Ziehl. Because of this Neelsen's technique was referred to as a modification of Ziehl, and to this day the hyphenated term *Ziehl-Neelsen* is applied to almost any method for the demonstration of tubercle bacilli in sputum, irrespective of the author of the technique.

It is proposed here to describe the original technique of Neelsen, leaving it to the technician to determine which of the other methods given in this section is more readily applicable to his problem. It may be said in favor of the technique of Neelsen that it gives a better differentiation of tubercle bacilli than do some of the more recent methods. These, though they give good preparation, do tend to cause certain errors of diagnosis through the ability of other bacteria to withstand the lower concentration of acids nowadays employed.

It is to be presumed that the sputum collected from the patient will have been placed at the disposal of the technician in the glass vessel in which it was secured. It should be looked over carefully to see if any small yellowish particles exist in it; if they do, one of these particles should be carefully extracted with a sterile bacteriological wire loop and utilized in making the preparation. If no such particles are visible to the naked eye, it is, of course, possible that tubercle bacilli will be present, but due consideration should be given to some method of concentrating these bacilli before making the smear. The standard method of concentration is to hydrolize the sputum to the extent necessary with the aid of a weak solution of potassium hypochlorite, which is known to be without action on tubercle bacilli. For a long time, a proprietary compound known as *antiformin*, which is a strongly alkaline solution of potassium hypochlorite, was also used for the same purpose. About an equal quantity of the selected solution and the sputum are placed in a centrifuge tube, the tube incubated in a serological water bath (37°C.) for about ten minutes, and then centrifuged rapidly. The smear is made from the denser portions which remain at the bottom of the tube.

Whichever method is employed, the quantity removed by the sterile loop should be about the size of a large pinhead. That is, a great deal more should be employed than is used for a simple bacterial smear from a known culture. This pinhead of material must be spread over the largest possible area of the slide. This is best done by pressing another slide on it and then drawing the two slides apart with a lateral motion. Both slides are then dried in air and flamed as has been described in the discussion of previous bacteriological preparations.

The solutions required for the original Neelsen technique are the phenol-magenta

solution of Ziehl (Chapter 20, DS 11.43), a 25% solution of nitric acid, and the polychrome methylene blue of Löffler (Chapter 20, DS 11.44). The slide is first flooded with the magenta solution and then placed on a metal sheet, where it should be warmed by a bunsen flame to the point at which it is steaming, but at which no bubbles have appeared. If it shows signs of drying, fresh quantities of the magenta solution should be added to it. It may either be left at this temperature for three to five minutes (Neelsen's original recommendation) or, as is customary in modern practice, it may be raised to steaming, permitted to cool, again raised to steaming, permitted to cool, and so on, until four such cycles have been completed. The slide is then washed in tap water until no further magenta comes away and placed in 25% nitric acid until it is almost completely decolorized. It cannot be decolorized too far, but there will usually be, even after prolonged exposure to the acid, a faint pink coloration of the background. The slide is now washed in running water until all the acid is removed, and then treated with a blue stain for about two minutes, to provide a contrasting coloration of any other bacteria present. It should then be washed thoroughly, dried, and examined in the customary manner.

It must be emphasized that this technique as described is specifically designed to show tubercle bacilli, and is so violent that many bacteria which are acid-fast to less strong acids will be decolorized.

Demonstration of the flagella of *Proteus vulgaris* by the method of Tribondeau, Fichet, and Dubreuil 1916

Examination of the abbreviated form of this technique (DS 23.215 Tribondeau, Fichet, and Dubreuil 1916) below would give one the impression that it was a simple matter to stain the flagella of bacteria. In point of fact it is one of the most difficult preparations known to the science of microtomy.

In the first place it is necessary to secure a culture in which the organisms are actively motile and growing; it is useless to attempt to stain flagella for demonstration purposes in any other than a culture which has been specially prepared for the purpose. It is desirable to take an actively growing culture and to check, under a dark field illuminator, that the organisms are motile. This culture is then subcultured, in the evening, into the same medium, and checked again the next morning. The temperature of the culture is then raised about ten degrees above that at which it has been maintained overnight, and left at this temperature for about an hour. A final check should be made on the motility of the organisms.

The chief difficulty in staining these organisms lies in the fact that the stain is not in any sense of the term a specific stain for flagella. It is only designed to make certain that any minute particle present on the slide will be colored so densely as to become apparent when examined under a microscope. The stain is deposited just as enthusiastically on the body of the bacteria as it is on the flagella, and, if anything, more enthusiastically on every minute speck of organic detritus which may remain on the slide. Little or nothing can be done about this organic detritus which may be present in the culture medium, and the reason for subculturing the selected culture is to make sure that only young organisms shall be present, and that numerous decomposing bodies of bacteria shall be absent.

The method employed is a mordant process, using an alum-tannic acid solution which must be prepared with some care. Take 100 milliliters of water and add to it at the same time 3.5 grams of potassium alum and 3 grams of tannic acid. These should be placed in a 250-milliliter Ehrlenmeyer flask, and warmed over a flame with constant agitation until they are boiling. The flask is now plugged with cotton, autoclaved at 20 pounds pressure for 30 minutes, and allowed to cool until it can be handled. It is filtered, and the filtrate is placed in a refrigerator until chilled. While the filtrate is cooling, prepare a 1% solution of crystal violet. The staining solution, which consists of about 10 parts of the crystal violet to 100 parts to the tannic acid solution, should be prepared immediately before use and, after mixing, should be passed through a bacterial filter to remove from it any fragments which might possibly remain and which, adhering to the dried film, would stain just as readily as would the flagella themselves.

Having secured an appropriate culture and having made up the staining solution, make a smear in the manner described in the first example of bacterial technique, dry it, flame it, and pour over it a good supply of the mixed solution. Then hold the slide over a very low bunsen flame and heat until bubbles appear. The heating should be continued for about 20 seconds beyond the time when the bubbles first appear. The slide is then washed off with water, until no more color comes away, and dried before being examined under an oil immersion objective. If everything has gone correctly the bacteria and their flagella will be stained a dense black against a background absolutely free from debris. If, however, there is a granular deposit on the background, which has not been derived from the culture, a fresh solution should be made, using, say, 7 parts of violet to 100 of the mordant. If the bacteria, but not the flagella, are stained, take 15 parts of violet to 100 of the mordant, and repeat the process again. No success is possible save by trial and error.

Demonstration of diplococci in the liver of the rabbit using the phloxine-methylene blue-azur II stain of Mallory 1938

This method of Mallory is the best of all the eosin-methylene blue methods which have from time to time been suggested for staining bacteria in sections. It has the advantage of giving a first-class histological stain, in addition to differentiating bacteria, and it might well be used as a standard procedure in place of the more customary hematoxylin-eosin, at least in pathological investigations. The liver of a rabbit is so frequently infected with diplococci that it has been selected as a type demonstration, for such infected animals will be found in ordinary laboratory investigations, making it unnecessary to go to the trouble of infecting a rabbit for the purpose of securing the necessary demonstration material.

If, then, in the course of routine dissections, a sacrificed rabbit is found to have a pneumococcal infection of the liver, which may easily be seen as yellow lesions on the surface, it is only necessary to cut the lesion and some surrounding tissue, and to place it in a suitable fixative. Mallory himself recommends fixation in Zenker 1894 (Chapter 18, F 3700.0010) for about 24 hours. As Zenker contains mercuric chloride it is undesirable that the specimen should remain in it for more than three or four days, but the actual time of fixation is not critical. As always, when dealing with dichromate fixatives, a large quantity of fixative should be used, and the object should be suspended in the fixative solution in a loose cloth bag. When fixation is complete the pieces are removed from the fixative and washed in running water overnight. They are then embedded in paraffin and sectioned in the ordinary manner. Sections of from five to eight microns are desirable if it is intended to demonstrate the bacteria, though these are quite readily seen in the ten-micron sections customarily employed for histological examinations. When the sections have been fixed on the slide, they may, if desired, be freed from the last traces of mercuric chloride by treating them with iodine and bleaching with sodium thiosulfate. The writer does not usually do this, but the treatment is insisted upon by Mallory in the description cited.

The staining solutions used in this technique are simple to prepare and relatively stable. The first solution is a 2.5% solution of phloxine in water. Two stock solutions are also required: one of 1% each of methylene blue and borax in distilled water, and the other a 1% solution of azur II in distilled water. Five milliliters of each are added to 90 milliliters of distilled water for use. Differentiation is in Wolbach's resin-alcohol (ADS 21.2 Wolbach 1911).

It is difficult to secure a sufficiently heavy stain in phloxine to withstand the alkaline thiazine solutions used for counterstaining. Mallory recommends that the sections be placed in a coplin jar of the solution in a 55°C. oven and that they remain there for at least an hour. The coplin jar is then removed from the oven and cooled before the sections are removed; they should be stained a dense orange. If they have not yet acquired this color, they should be returned to a paraffin oven for a further period. If the sections are satisfactorily stained, the solution may be poured off or the slides removed from it and briefly rinsed in water. The purpose of this rinse is not to differentiate the eosin in the section but to remove it from the glass. The slides bearing the sections are then placed in the methylene blue-azur solution in another coplin jar for 5 to 20 minutes; the exact time varies according to the specimen which one is staining and can only be determined by experiment. Mallory recommends that the solution be freshly filtered onto each slide, rather than that the solution be used in a coplin jar; but the writer has not found this nearly as convenient, nor does it appear to be in any way obligatory. After the slides have taken up sufficient methylene blue solution to appear bluish rather than pinkish, they may be accumulated in water, before being differentiated in the resin alcohol one at a time. This differentiation is best conducted in a dish which is large enough to admit the slide in a flat position. The slide is taken in a pair of angle forceps, dipped under the surface of the solution, and waved gently backward and forward for about a minute. As it is being moved backward and forward in the differentiating solution, the blue color will come off in clouds; it is much easier to overdifferentiate than to underdifferentiate.

The differentiation may be readily controlled by inspection under the microscope, though it is not necessary to observe the bacteria, since the nuclei have exactly the same staining reaction. Differentiation should be stopped when the nuclei can be seen, under the low power of the microscope, to be very deep blue, while the general background of the section is pink. After a little practice the required color may be gaged without examination under the microscope.

These specimens are not permanent unless the alcohol and resin are removed from them. It is desirable, therefore, as soon as differentiation is complete, to dehydrate them in absolute alcohol and then clear them in at least three changes of xylene, so as to make sure that no alcohol can be carried over into the mounting medium.

23.21 BACTERIA IN SMEARS

Bacterial smears are rarely, if ever, fixed. Hence, they share with blood smears the ability to be stained by a method depending not only upon the chemical composition of the material, but also upon the isoelectric point of the protein from which it is produced. Smears may be prepared either upon the slide or the coverslip, and are usually from cultures which have been heavily diluted either with the medium upon which they are grown or with an isotonic salt solution.

23.211 General Methods

It would be quite impossible to gather in one place all the stains which have, from time to time, been recommended for use with bacterial smears. Such a listing of techniques would have to include every stain recommended for staining nuclei, and the great majority of synthetic stains when adjusted to a suitable pH. Gathered here are only those solutions which are commonly found in laboratories of bacteriology, or those which involve some departure from the normally recognized techniques, such as the early stain of Claudius 1897, or its more recent modification by Spehl 1927. It must be emphasized again that the staining of a particle by any of the methods given is no voucher for the bacterial nature of the particle. Many of the techniques given are almost indistinguishable from the techniques recommended for the display of mitochondria, therefore, some other evidence than staining is required to prove the existence of bacteria.

23.211 Claudius 1897   857, **11**:332
    REAGENTS REQUIRED: *A*. DS 12.15 gentian violet; *B*. sat. aq. sol. picric acid 50, water
      50; *C*. chloroform
    METHOD: [dry smears] → *A*, flooded on slide, 2 mins. → quick rinse → *B*, 1 min. → blot
    and let dry → *C*, till no further color removed → balsam

23.211 Conn 1928   20540b, **26**:257
    FORMULA: water 100, phenol 5, calcium chloride 0.01, rose bengal 1
    METHOD: [smears of gelatin-suspended soil dried at 100°C.] → stain, on slide, heated on
    water, bath, 1 min. → water, wash → dry

23.211 Ehrlich 1882   7276:270
    FORMULA: abs. alc. 10, gentian violet 5, sat. sol. aniline 90
    PREPARATION: Add the aniline to a solution of the dye in alc.
    METHOD: As Ziehl 1882   *see also* DS 23.213 Koch 1884

23.211 Goodpasture *test*. 1938 Mallory   Mallory 1938, 274
    FORMULA: water 70, 96% alc. 30, aniline 1, phenol 1, magenta 0.6

23.211 Hucker *test*. 1929 Conn   McClung 1929, 93
    FORMULA: 95% alc. 20, crystal violet 2, water 80, ammonium oxalate 0.8
    PREPARATION: Add the oxalate dissolved in water to the dye dissolved in alc.
    METHOD: As Ziehl 1882
    NOTE: A detailed description of the use of this technique is given under DS 23.20 above.

23.211 Löffler 1890   for formula *see* DS 11.44 Löffler 1890; for method *see* DS 23.211 Ziehl
    1882

23.211 Maneval 1941   20540b, **16**:13
    FORMULA: water 95, phenol 3.9, acetic acid 5, ferric chloride 3, *either* acid fuchsin 0.01 *or*
    anilin blue 0.05 *or* fast green FCF 0.05 *or* light green 0.05
    METHOD: [air-dried or heat-fixed smear] → stain, 1 min. → wash → dry

23.211 Manson 1890   for formula *see* DS 11.44 Manson (1890); for method *see* DS 23.211, Ziehl 1882

23.211 Pick and Jacobson *test.* **1942 Langeron** *cit.* **Morax**
Langeron 1942, 1198

FORMULA: water 100, DS 11.43 Ziehl 1882 3, sat. alc. sol. (circ. 2%) methylene blue 1.5
METHOD: [heat-fixed smear] → stain, 20–30 secs. → wash → dry

23.211 Sahli 1885   for formula *see* DS 11.44 Sahli 1885; for method *see* DS 23.211 Ziehl 1882

23.211 Spehl 1927 6630, **107**:920

REAGENTS REQUIRED: *A.* DS 12.15 gentian violet; *B.* sat. aq. sol. iodine; *C.* sat. aq. sol. picric acid; *D.* chloroform; *E.* DS 12.15 magenta 10, water 90
METHOD: [dry smears] → *A*, 2 min. → quick rinse → *B*, 30 secs. → *C*, 30 secs. → dry → *D*, till no more color comes away → dry → *E*, 1 min. → wash → dry → balsam

23.211 Unna 1892   for formula *see* DS 11.44 Unna 1892; for method *see* DS 23.211 Ziehl

23.211 Volkonsky 1933   for formula *see* DS 11.44 Volkonsky 1933; for method *see* DS 23.211 Ziehl

23.211 Ziehl 1882 7276, **8**:451

REAGENTS REQUIRED: *A.* DS 11.43 Ziehl 1882, sol. *A.*
METHOD: [heat, or alc., fixed smears] → *A*, poured on slide, 30 secs. → water, wash → dry
NOTE: The same technique may be employed with DS 11.44 Löffler 1890, Manson (1929), Martinotti 1910, Sahli 1885, Unna 1892, Volkonsky 1933. *See also* DS 22.213 Neelsen 1883.

23.212 Iodine Differential Methods

The stains given in this section are commonly referred to as "Gram stains," and the organisms which retain the color after any of the techniques here given are known as Gram-positive. Certain methods, such as Burke 1922, involve after-staining, usually with safranin, in such a manner as to render those bacteria from which the stain is removed (the Gram-negative bacteria) red, or such color as will contrast well with the Gram-positive bacteria. The methods require, without exception, preliminary heavy overstaining of the smear, the removal of the stain with iodine, and usually, the removal of the iodine with acetone before the application of the counterstain.

23.212 Atkins 1920 11056, **5**:321

REAGENTS REQUIRED: *A.* DS 11.45 Atkins 1920; *B.* ADS 12.2 Atkins 1920
METHOD: [heat-fixed smear] → *A*, 1 min. → wash → *B*, 1 min. → wash → 95% alc., rinse → dry

23.212 Burke 1922 11056, **7**:159

REAGENTS REQUIRED: *A.* 1% crystal violet; *B.* 5% sodium bicarbonate; *C.* ADS 12.2 Burke 1922; *D.* ether 25, acetone 75; *E.* 2% safranin O
METHOD: [smears] → *A*, flooded on slide → add 2–3 drops *B* to *A* on slide, 2–3 mins. → *C*, rinse → *C*, fresh solution, 2 mins. → water, wash → blot → *D*, dropped on slide till no more color comes away → dry → *E*, 10 secs. → water, wash → dry
RESULT: Gram-positive, blue; Gram-negative, red
NOTE: **Kopeloff and Cohen 1928** (20540b, **3**:64) substitute equal parts acetone-alc. for *D* above.

23.212 Hucker and Conn 1923 20936, **93**:1

REAGENTS REQUIRED: *A.* DS 23.211 Hucker (1929); *B.* ADS 12.2 Gram 1884; *C.* 95% alc. 10, safranin O 0.25, water 100
METHOD: [smears] → *A*, 1 min. → water, wash → *B*, 1 min. → water, wash → blot → 95% alc. 30 secs. → blot → *C*, 10 secs. → water, wash → dry
RESULT: Gram-positive bacteria, blue; Gram-negative, red.

23.212 Gram 1884 8645, **2**:185

REAGENTS REQUIRED: *A.* DS 12.15 crystal violet; *B.* ADS 12.2 Gram 1884; *C.* absolute alc.

METHOD: [dried smears] → *A*, dropped on slide, 2 mins. → quick rinse → *B*, 1 min. →
quick rinse → *C*, till differentiated → water, to stop differentiation → dry → balsam
NOTE: A detailed description of the use of this technique is given under DS 23.210 above.

23.212 Konschegg 1940   14674, **87**:465
REAGENTS REQUIRED: *A*. water 90, 95% alc. 7, aniline 3, gentian violet 2; *B*. sat. aq.
sol. picric acid
METHOD: [heat-fixed smears] → *A*, 5 secs. → *B*, 5 secs. → 95% alc., till no more color
comes away → dry
NOTE: This stain, though not using iodine, is intended to demonstrate Gram-positive
bacteria.

23.212 Kopeloff and Beerman 1822   11250, **31**:480
REAGENTS REQUIRED: *A*. water 105, crystal violet 0.75, sodium bicarbonate 1.25; *B*. ADS
12.1 Atkins 1920; *C*. ether 25, acetone 75; *D*. 0.1% magenta
METHOD: [smears] → *A*, 5–10 mins. → *B*, rinse → *B*, fresh solution, 2 mins. → blot →
C, dropped on slide, till no more color comes away → dry → *D*, 5–10 secs. → water,
wash → dry
RESULT: Gram-positive, blue; Gram-negative, red.

23.212 Kopeloff and Cohen 1928   20540b, **3**:64
REAGENTS REQUIRED: *A*. 1% methyl violet 6B 60, 5% sodium bicarbonate 8; *B*. ADS
12.2 Kopeloff and Cohen 1928; *C*. acetone 50, 95% alc. 50; *D*. 0.1% magenta
METHOD: [heat-fixed smear] → *A*, on slide, 5 mins. → *B*, on slide, 2 mins. → drain → *C*,
drop by drop on slide till drippings colorless → dry

23.212 Mérieux *test.* 1904 Besson   Besson 1904, 247
REAGENTS REQUIRED: *A*. DS 23.212 Nicolle 1895, sol. *A*; *B*. water 100, iodine 0.5, potassium iodide 1, eosin Y 2
PREPARATION: Dissolve the iodine and iodide in a few drops of water. Add the eosin dissolved in 100 water.
METHOD: [heat-fixed smear] → *A*, on slide, 10–20 secs. → rinse → *B*, 5–10 secs. → wash
dry

23.212 Nicolle 1895   857, **9**:664
REAGENTS REQUIRED: *A*. DS 12.15 crystal violet; *B*. ADS 12.2 Nicolle 1895; *C*. absolute
alc. 85, acetone 15
METHOD: [dried smears] → *A*, flooded on slide, 2 mins. → quick rinse → *B*, 1 min. →
rinse → *C*, till differentiated → water, to stop differentiation → dry → balsam

23.212 Schmorl 1928   *see* DS 21.13 Schmorl 1928b

23.212 Weiss 1940   11284, **26**:1518
REAGENTS REQUIRED: *A*. water 80, alc. 20, gentian violet 3; *B*. ADS 12.2 Lugol (1905);
C. acetone; *D*. 2% magenta in 95% alc.
METHOD: [heat-dried smears] → *A*, 3–5 mins. → warm water, wash → *B*, 3–5 mins. →
warm water → *C*, till no more color comes away → water, wash → *D*, 15 secs. →
water, wash → dry

23.212 White and Culbertson 1945   *Tech. Bull.*, **6**:53
REAGENTS REQUIRED: *A*. 1% crystal violet; *B*. 5% sodium bicarbonate; *C*. water 100,
mercuric iodide 0.55, potassium iodide 0.45; *D*. 0.1% safranin O
METHOD: [heat-dried smears] → *A*, 1 ml. on slide → *B*, 5 drops, added to *A* on slide, leave
1 min. → drain → dry → *C*, 1 min. → wash → acetone, till no more color comes away
→ dry → *D*, 10 secs. → wash → dry
NOTE: The original calls for "a 1% solution of potassium mercuric iodide"; there is no
such salt. The pharmacopeial *liquor hydrargyri et potassii iodidi* contains mercuric
iodide and potassium iodide in the proportions given for *C* above. The same result
could be secured by diluting 55 of the pharmacopeial solution to 100. If the solution is
prepared from the dry salts, they must first be dissolved in a minimum of water, and
then diluted.

23.213 Methods for Acid-fast Organisms

"Acid-fast" bacteria were originally so identified because a solution of magenta was not removed from them by strong acid. These techniques are commonly all lumped together as "Ziehl-Neelsen techniques" for the reason that the phenol-magenta stain of Ziehl 1882 was in 1883 used for the first demonstration of acid-fast bacteria by Neelsen. It is nowadays, however, most unusual to use so violent an acid solution (25% nitric acid) as did Neelsen, and there is no justification for the blanket retention of the names of these two technicians for every acid differentiated stain which has been proposed. Many, if not indeed most, of the modern techniques do not use acid for differentiation at any stage of the proceedings, and attention should be drawn to the technique of Burke, Dickson, and Phillips 1932 by which acid-fast bacteria may be clearly differentiated from all other bacteria in the section without the use of any acid at all. Similarly, the technique of Fontès 1909 gives a similar differentiation using neutral solution. When the term "Ziehl-Neelsen" is loosely used in the literature today, the technique of Günther 1899 is the one which is most usually intended.

23.213 Alexander 1932　　　　　　　　　　　　　　19938, **75** :197

REAGENTS REQUIRED: *A.* DS 11.43 Ziehl 1882; *B.* 3% nitric acid in 70% alc.; *C.* DS 11.44 Löffler 1890; *D.* 0.05% sodium hydroxide

METHOD: [heat-fixed smears] → *A*, on slide, warmed to steaming, 5 mins. → rinse → *C*, on slide → *D*, 6–8 drops, added to *C* on slide, 2–3 mins. → wash → dry

23.213 Alexander and Jackson 1944　　　　　　　　19938, **99** :307

REAGENTS REQUIRED: *A.* DS 11.43 Ziehl 1882; *B.* 3% hydrochloric acid; *C.* DS 11.44 Löffler 1890; *D.* 4% sodium hydroxide; *E.* 0.2% sodium hydrosulfite; *F.* water 100, light green 0.5, fast yellow 0.5

METHOD: [heat-fixed smear] → *A*, 3 mins. → wash → *B*, 1–3 mins. → wash → *C*, on slide → *D*, 6 drops added to *C* on slide, 1 min. → *E*, flooded on slide → thorough wash → *F*, flooded on slide → wash → dry

23.213 Auguste 1932　　　　　　　　　　　　　　　6630, **11** :719

REAGENTS REQUIRED: *A.* DS 11.43 Ziehl 1882 50, DS 12.15 crystal violet (Auguste) 50; *B.* 95% alc. 60, acetic acid 30, picric acid to sat.; *C.* 1% methylene blue

METHOD: [heat-fixed smears] → *A*, warmed to steaming, 3 mins. → *B*, till no more color comes away → water, wash → *C*, 15 secs. → water, wash → dry

23.213 Biot 1901　*see* DS 23.213 Neelsen 1883 (note)

23.213 Burke, Dickson, and Phillips 1932　　　　　20540b, **7** :21

REAGENTS REQUIRED: *A.* DS 11.43 Ziehl 1882; *B.* sat. sol. malachite green in acetone

METHOD: [smears] → *A*, on slide, warmed to steaming, 3–5 mins. → water, rinse → *B*, flood on slide and replaced as evaporation occurs, 3–5 mins. → wash → dry

RESULT: acid-fast bacteria, red; others, green.

23.213 Doglio 1932　　　　　　　　　　20540b (abstr. 1933) **8** :76

REAGENTS REQUIRED: *A.* DS 11.43 Ziehl 1882; *B.* water 85, 95% alc. 20, sulfuric acid 10, brilliant yellow 0.15

METHOD: [heat-fixed smears] → *A*, warmed to steaming, 2–3 mins. → thorough wash → *B*, 40–50 secs. → wash → dry

23.213 Fontès 1909　　　　　　　　　　　　　　　13465, **1** :59

REAGENTS REQUIRED: *A.* DS 11.43 Ziehl 1882; *B.* DS 12.15 crystal violet; *C.* ADS 12.2 Lugol (1905); *D.* abs. alc. 60, acetone 30; *E.* 1% methylene blue

METHOD: [heat-fixed smears] → *A*, warmed to steaming 2 mins. → wash → *B*, warmed to steaming, 2 mins. → *C*, mixed with *B* on slide, 1 min. → *D*, till no more color comes away → water, wash → *E*, 15 secs. → water, wash → dry

23.213 Fraenkel 1884　　　　　　　　　　　　　　　2813, **13** :1

REAGENTS REQUIRED: *A.* DS 23.211 Ehrlich 1882; *B.* water 50, alc. 30, nitric acid 20 methylene blue to sat.

METHOD: [heat-fixed smears] → *A*, 12 hrs. → water, rinse → *B*, dipped until smear changes from blue to red → water, wash → dry

23.213 Gabbet 1887 *test.* **1928 Zinnser and Bayne-Jones**

Zinnser and Bayne-Jones 1928, 847

REAGENTS REQUIRED: *A*. DS 11.43 Ziehl 1882; *B*. water 75, sulfuric acid 25, methylene blue 2

METHOD: [heat-fixed smears] → *A*, warmed to steaming, 2 mins. → water, wash → *B*, 1 min. → water, wash → dry

23.213 Gibbe *test.* **1903 Cole**

Cross and Cole 1903, 160

FORMULA: water 45, 95% alc. 45, aniline 9, magenta 6, methyl blue 3

PREPARATION: Grind dyes together and dissolve in aniline and alc. Dilute to 100 with water.

METHOD: [heat-dried smears] → stain, heated to steaming, 4–5 mins. → 95% alc., till no more color comes away → balsam, via clove oil

23.213 Günther 1898

Günther 1898, 347

REAGENTS REQUIRED: *A*. DS 11.43 Ziehl 1882; *B*. 3% nitric acid in 70% alc.; *C*. sat. sol. (*circ.* 2%) methylene blue

METHOD: [coverslip smear] → *A*, in watch glass, heated to steaming, 1 min. → *B*, 1 min. → water, wash → *C*, on coverslip, few secs. → water, wash → dry

23.213 Herman *test.* **1904 Besson**

Besson 1904, 638

REAGENTS REQUIRED: *A*. 1% ammonium carbonate 80, 3% crystal violet 20; *B*. 10% nitric acid; *C*. 1% eosin in 60% alc.

METHOD: [heat-fixed smear] → *A*, heated to boiling, 1 min. → *B*, 4–5 secs. → abs. alc., till decolorized → *C*, 30 secs. → abs. alc., quick rinse → dry

23.213 Koch 1884

1648, **2**:10

REAGENTS REQUIRED: *A*. DS 23.211 Ehrlich 1882; *B*. 25% nitric acid; *C*. sat. sol. (*circ.* 1.5%) Bismarck brown

METHOD: [smears] → *A*, 12 hrs. → *B*, momentary dip → 60% alc., wash → *D*, 15 secs. → water, wash → dry

NOTE: Much confusion exists in the literature about this technique, which is often attributed to **Ehrlich** (*loc. cit.*, *A* above) who recommended his solution for general, not diagnostic, staining. The journal reference given above is technically incorrect for, in the two years prior to 1886, the journal was known as the *Mitteilung der Kaiserliche Gesundheitsamte*, which is, however, not recorded in the *World List of Scientific Periodicals*.

23.213 Muller and Chermock 1945

11284, **30**:169

REAGENTS REQUIRED: *A*. DS 11.43 Muller and Chermock 1945; *B*. 3% hydrochloric acid in 95% alc., *C*. DS 11.44 Muller and Chermock 1945

METHOD: [heat-stained smears] → *A*, 1 min. → *B*, 30 secs. → *C*, 1 min. → wash → dry

23.213 Neelsen 1883 *Ziehl-Neelsen—compl. script*   23730, **21**:497

REAGENTS REQUIRED: *A*. DS 11.43 Ziehl 1882; *B*. 25% nitric; *C*. DS 11.44 Löffler 1890

METHOD: [sputum smears, heat-fixed] → *A*, on slide warmed to steaming, 3–5 mins. → water, rinse → *B*, till faint pink → wash → *C*, 2 mins. → wash → dry

RESULT: acid-fast bacteria, red; others, blue.

NOTE: The *B* solution is nowadays usually replaced by a 3% solution of hydrochloric acid in 95% alc. (Cowdry 1943, 17.) The term *Ziehl-Neelsen* has come to mean any acid-differentiated magenta stain. **Biot 1901** (6539, C. Lyons, 234) recommends 40% formaldehyde in place of *C* above. A detailed description of the use of this technique is given under DS 23.20 above.

23.213 Pappenheim 1898

2813, **37**:809

REAGENTS REQUIRED: *A*. DS 11.43 Ziehl 1882; *B*. abs. alc. 100, glycerol 20, aurin 1, methylene blue to sat. (*circ.* 2)

METHOD: [heat-fixed smear] → *A*, heated to steaming, 2 mins. → *B*, on slide, drained and renewed 4–5 times → water, wash → dry

23.213 Pottenger 1942 *test.* **1942 Farber**   20540b, **17**:183
  REAGENTS REQUIRED: *A.* DS 11.43 Pottenger 1942; *B.* 3% hydrochloric acid; *C.* 0.3%
  picric acid
  METHOD: [heat-dried, fixed smear] → *A*, 15 mins. 65°C. → *B*, 30 secs. → 70% alc., till
  no more color comes away → *C*, 10 secs. → rinse → dry

23.213 Randolf and Mikele 1944   665, **49**:109
  STOCK SOLUTIONS: I. 1% magenta in propylene glycol. II. 5% phenol
  REAGENTS REQUIRED: *A.* stock I 20, stock II 80; *B.* 1% hydrochloric acid in 70% alc.
  C. 1% methylene blue
  METHOD: [heat-fixed smears] → *A*, 4 mins. → wash → *B*, till decolorized → *C*, 1 min. →
  wash → dry

23.213 Spehl 1918   *see* DS 23.213 (note) Spengler 1907

23.213 Schulte-Tigges 1920   7276, **46**:1225
  REAGENTS REQUIRED: *A.* DS 11.43 Ziehl 1882; *B.* 10% sodium sulfite; *C.* sat. aq. sol. picric
  acid
  METHOD: [heat-fixed smears] → *A*, warmed to steaming, 1 min. → wash → *B*, till decolorized → wash → *C*, few mins. → wash → dry

23.213 Spengler 1907   7276, **33**:337
  REAGENTS REQUIRED: *A.* DS 11.43 Ziehl 1882; *B.* 95% alc. 50, sat. sol. (*circ.* 1.2%) picric
  acid 50; *C.* 15% nitric acid
  METHOD: [heat-fixed smears] → *A*, warmed to steaming, 1 min. → *B*, mixed with *A* on
  slide, few secs. → 70% alc., wash → *C*, 30 secs. → 70% thorough wash → *B*, 15 secs.
  → 95% alc., quick rinse → dry
  NOTE: **Spehl 1918** (6630, **81**:248) substitutes a mixture of 3 parts DS 11.43 Ziehl 1882
  with 2 parts DS 11.44 Nicolle 1871 for *A* above.

23.213 Weiss 1942   665, **46**:199
  REAGENTS REQUIRED: *A.* ADS 12.1 Weiss 1942; *B.* 2.5% safranin; *C.* 15% acetic acid in
  acetone; *D.* DS 11.44 Löffler 1890
  METHOD: [flame-fixed smears] → *A*, on slide, heated to steaming, 5 mins. → wash →
  B, on slide, heated to steaming, 5 mins. → wash → *C*, till decolorized → wash → *D*,
  1 min. → wash → dry

23.213 Ziehl 1882   *see* DS 23.213 Neelsen 1883

23.214 Methods for Spirochetes

Spirochetes are resistant to dye-staining techniques, and are usually better demonstrated either unstained with dark ground illumination, or else with the aid of one of
the metal-staining techniques given in Chapter 23. When they are to be stained with
dyes, most of the early techniques involve the utilization of Giemsa's 1902 technique
(Chapter 20 DS 13.13), usually with the addition of a strongly alkaline differentiating
solution, with or without prior mordanting or subsequent differentiation in a solution
of tannic acid. More recently, certain techniques have appeared such as that of Noguchi
1921, in which prior mordanting is conducted in a solution buffered to pH of 7.6, with
subsequent staining in any stain desirable to the technician. A very unusual and excellent stain, which should possibly have been placed in the section on metal staining,
is that of Ono 1938. He utilized the heavy deposition of oxides of manganese from a
solution of potassium permanganate, after mordanting with formaldehyde. This method
tends to cause darkening of the background, because the oxides of manganese will be deposited on any organic detritus present, but if the culture is relatively free of organisms,
or materials other than the spirochetes, the method can be confidently recommended.

23.214 Becker 1920 *test.* **1928 Schmorl**   Schmorl 1928, 400
  REAGENTS REQUIRED: *A.* F 0000.1010 Ruge (1942); *B.* water 100, tannin 10, phenol 1;
  C. DS 11.43 Ziehl 1890
  METHOD: [smears] → 1 min. → rinse → *B*, 30 secs. 40°–50°C. → rinse → *C*, warmed to
  steaming, 30–45 secs. → wash → dry → balsam

23.214 Doutrelepont *see* DS 23.214 Giacomi (1896) note

23.214 Du 1936 *test.* **1937 Kennedy** 20540b, **12**:37
REAGENTS REQUIRED: *A*. water 96, abs. alc. 4, aniline 8, crystal violet 8; *B. either* 1%
sodium hydroxide *or* 5% potassium carbonate *or* 1% ammonia
METHOD: [air-dried smear] → 8 drops *A*, on slide → 8 drops 5% alc. added → 8 drops *B*,
added → leave 2 mins. → wash → dry
RECOMMENDED FOR: *Treponema pallida.*

23.214 Dupérié 1909 11307, **20**:1
FORMULA: water 100, DS 13.13 Giemsa 1902 5, 0.1% sodium carbonate 3
METHOD: [smears from formaldehyde-fixed organs] → dry → abs. alc., 5 mins. → dry →
stain, 5–30 mins. → wash → dry

23.214 Gelarie 1936 11284, **21**:1065
REAGENTS REQUIRED: *A*. water 100, sodium chloride 10, zirconium oxychloride 2.5; *B*.
10% citric acid; *C*. water 100, sodium lactate 1.1, crystal violet 0.25; *D*. water 100,
potassium iodide 0.5, mercuric iodide 0.5; *E*. water 100, phenol 0.2, methylene blue 0.2
METHOD: [air-dried smears] → *A*, 5 secs. → wash → *B*, 10 secs. → wash → *C*, 30 secs. →
wash → *D*, 5 secs. → wash → *E*, 5 secs. → wash → blot → dry

23.214 Giacomi *test.* **1896 Kahlden and Laurent** Kahlden and Laurent 1896, 111
REAGENTS REQUIRED: *A*. DS 11.43 Ziehl 1882; *B*. 0.001% ferric chloride; *C*. 10% ferric
chloride
METHOD: [smears] → *A*, several mins. 50°C. → *B*, wash → *C*, till differentiated → abs
alc. → balsam, via xylene
NOTE: Kahlden and Laurent (*loc. cit*) state that **Doutrelepont** substitutes a sat. sol.
methyl violet for *A* above.

23.214 Giemsa 1905 7276, **31**:1026
REAGENTS REQUIRED: *A*. water 100, DS 13.13 Giemsa 1902 1, 0.1% potassium carbon-
ate 1
METHOD: [heat-dried smear] → *A*, 10–30 mins. → water, wash → dry

23.214 Giemsa 1909 7276, **35**:1751
REAGENTS REQUIRED: *A*. water 100, DS 13.13 Giemsa 1902 1
METHOD: [heat-dried smear] → *A*, on slide, warmed to steaming, 15 secs. → drain → re-
peat 4 or 5 times → water, wash → dry

23.214 Goldsworthy and Ward 1942 11431, **54**:382
REAGENTS REQUIRED: *A*. water 47.5, methanol 50, acetic acid 2.5, Victoria blue 4R 0.2;
B. 10% copper sulfate
METHOD: [air-dried smears] → *A*, on slide, heated till alc. evaporated → *B*, to wash off
stain → blot → dry

23.214 Hoffman 1921 7177, **33**:1
REAGENTS REQUIRED: *A*. water 100, potassium carbonate 0.01, DS 13.13 Giemsa 7.5;
B. 25% tannic acid
METHOD: [osmic vapor fixed smears] → water, wash → *A*, 1–2 days → water, wash →
B, 1 min. → water, wash → dry

23.214 Harris 1930 19938, **72**:275
REAGENTS REQUIRED: *A*. 1% potassium permanganate; *B*. 2% methyl violet
METHOD: [heat-fixed smear] → *A*, 8–10 mins. → wash → *B*, 8–10 mins. → wash → dry

23.214 Keil 1929 7176, **89**:1398
REAGENTS REQUIRED: *A*. water 100, glycerol 10, 95% alc. 10, Victoria blue 3, pyronin
0.9, methyl green 0.1
METHOD: [heat-fixed smears] → *A*, 3–4 mins. → water, wash → dry

23.214 Krauss *test.* **1942 Langeron** Langeron 1942, 827
REAGENTS REQUIRED: *A*. water 100, potassium carbonate 0.005, DS 13.13 Giemsa 5
METHOD: [heat-fixed smear] → *A*, on slide, heated to steaming, 4 or 5 times → water,
rinse → *B*, 1 min. → water, wash → dry

23.214 Lipp 1940a   7676, **87**:888
REAGENTS REQUIRED: *A*. 1% potassium hydroxide; *B*. 0.5% magenta.
METHOD: [methanol-fixed smears] → *A*, on slide → *B*, added to *A* on slide, 3 mins. →
wash → dry

23.214 Lipp 1940b   7676, **87**:888
REAGENTS REQUIRED: *A*. 5% potassium permanganate; *B*. DS 11.43 Ziehl 1882 10,
water 90
METHOD: [air-dried smear] → *A*, 3 mins. → wash → *B*, 2 mins. → wash → dry

23.214 Lipp 1940c   7676, **87**:888
FORMULA: water 81, glycerol 10, abs. alc. 9, Victoria blue 4R 3, pyronin 0.9, methyl
green 0.1
METHOD: [air-dried smear] → stain, 3 mins. → wash → dry

23.214 Muhlpfordt 1924   7176, **79**:921
REAGENTS REQUIRED: *A*. 3% Victoria blue
METHOD: [heat-fixed smears] → *A*, 2–3 mins. → wash → dry
NOTE: The method of **Keil 1929** is very commonly referred to Muhlpfordt.

23.214 Noguchi 1921   11006, **78**:191
REAGENTS REQUIRED: *A*. phosphate buffer pH 7.6 90, 40% formaldehyde 10; *B*. sat. alc.
sol. (*circ.* 8%) magenta
METHOD: [smear from equal parts specimen and *A*, left 5 mins. before smearing] → dry
→ *B*, 1–5 mins. → water, wash → dry

23.214 Ono 1938 *test.* **1942 Langeron**   Langeron 1942, 830
REAGENTS REQUIRED: *A*. 4% formaldehyde; *B*. 1% potassium permanganate
METHOD: [smears] → *A*, 15 mins. → water, quick wash → *B*, 24 hrs. 60°C. wash → dry
NOTE: **Ono 1933** (abstract 1935; 20540b, **10**:112) recommended this process as a mordant
before crystal violet.

23.214 Perrin 1943   *Tech. Bull.*, **4**:28
REAGENTS REQUIRED: *A*. water 60, DS 11.43 Ziehl 1882 25, acetic acid 6, 40% formalde-
hyde 6
METHOD: [heat-fixed smears] → *A*, 6 mins. → wash → dry

23.214 Rénaux 1923   6630, **89**:420
REAGENTS REQUIRED: *A*. sat. sol. picric acid; *B*. DS 12.15 crystal violet
METHOD: [smears fixed 5 mins. in F 0000.0101 Ruge] → 95% alc., rinse → *A*, 10 mins. →
water, wash → *B*, 10 mins. → water, wash → dry

23.214 Rénaux and Wilmaers 1917   6630, **80**:55
REAGENTS REQUIRED: *A*. 5% tannin; *B*. DS 11.43 Ziehl 1882
METHOD: [alcohol-fixed smears] → *A*, warmed to steaming, 30 secs. → water, rinse →
B, warmed to steaming, 30 secs. → water, wash → dry

23.214 Sabrazès 1926   6628, **187**:875
REAGENTS REQUIRED: *A*. DS 11.43 Ziehl 1882
METHOD: [heat-fixed smears] → *A*, on slide, heated to steaming, 2 or 3 times → water,
wash → dry

23.214 Sabrazès 1928   6630, **98**:239
REAGENTS REQUIRED: *A*. water 100, tannin 5, phenol 1; *B*. DS 11.43 Ziehl 1882
METHOD: [smears fixed 2 mins. in F 0000.1010 Ruge] → 95% alc., rinse → *A*, warmed to
steaming, 30 secs. → water, wash → *B*, warmed to steaming on slide 3 or 4 times →
water, wash → dry

23.214 Sabouraud *test.* **1904 Besson**   Besson 1904, 638
REAGENTS REQUIRED: *A*. DS 11.43 Ziehl 1890; *B*. 1.5% potassium permanganate; *C*. 2%
sulfurous acid; *D*. 1% methylene blue
METHOD: [heat-fixed smear] → *A*, 1–2 hrs. → *B*, to wash off *A* → *C*, till decolorized →
wash → *D*, 1–3 mins. → wash → dry

23.214 Tunnicliff 1921   11006, **78**:191
REAGENTS REQUIRED: *A*. DS 12.15 crystal violet; *B*. ADS 12.2 Lugol 1905; *C*. 1%
safranin O
METHOD: [heat-fixed smear] → *A*, 30 secs. → water, wash → *B*, 30 secs. → water, wash →
C, 30 secs. → water, wash → dry

23.214 Weiss 1929   11284, **14**:1191
REAGENTS REQUIRED: *A*. acetic acid; *B*. ADS 12.2 Weiss 1929; *C*. sat. aq. sol. crystal
violet *or* safranin *or* magenta *or* brilliant green; *D*. 10% acid green *or* acid violet *or*
acid fuchsin in 70% alc.
METHOD: [drop material and drop *A* incubated as hanging drop, 37.5°, 15 mins.] → air-
dried smear → *B*, on slide, heated to steaming, 2–5 mins. → wash → *C*, 2–5 mins. →
wash → *D*, 8–10 mins. → wash → dry
NOTE: The selected dyes in *C* and *D* above should be of contrasting colors.

23.214 Woolman 1939 *test.* **1939 Findlay**   11360, **59**:184
REAGENTS REQUIRED: *A*. water 97, 40% formaldehyde 2, acetic acid 1; *B*. water 100
hydrochloric acid 0.7, crystal violet 0.15, copper sulfate 10
METHOD: [air-dried smears] → *A*, 3–5 mins. → wash → abs. alc., 1–2 mins. → blot →
B, 10–15 mins. → drain → dry

23.215 Flagella Stains

The term *flagella stains* is somewhat misleading because there is no known technique
which could be employed differentially to stain a flagella protruding from a bacteria
without staining every other minute particle of the protein material present. The purpose of these stains, however, is to provide so dense a deposition of dye as to assure
that these minute particles will become so covered as to be visible in an optical microscope. For this reason every possible type of mordant, usually if not always combining
tannin with iron, is used before a solution either of one of the thiazins or of magenta.
The real difficulty in the staining of flagella is not to deposit the stain, but to differentiate the subsequently stained flagella from the background. For this reason the very
utmost care must be taken in the cleanliness of the slides employed for the preparation
of a smear, and all those precautions proper to metal stains (which are given in Chapter 24) can with justice be used in the present instance. If, however, the flagellated
organisms are taken from a culture filled with small particles of organic detritus, it is
a waste of time to endeavor to stain the flagella on them. A recent method of Fisher
and Conn 1942 gives the most minute directions for the selection for the culture as well
as for staining the organisms.

23.215 Bailey 1929   16913, **27**:111
REAGENTS REQUIRED: *A*. ADS 12.2 Bailey 1929; *B*. ADS 12.2 Bailey 1929 70, DS 11.43
Ziehl 1882 10, hydrochloric acid 10, 40% formaldehyde 10; *C*. DS 11.43 Ziehl 1882
METHOD: [dry smear] → *A*, 2 mins. → *B*, 7 mins. → wash → *C*, warmed to steaming, 30
secs. → wash → dry

23.215 Bowhill 1898   23684, **23**:667
PREPARATION OF STOCK SOLUTIONS: I. water 40, 95% alc. 50, orcein 1; II. water 100,
tannin 20
REAGENTS REQUIRED: *A*. stock I 50, stock II 50; *B*. DS 23.211 Ehrlich 1882
METHOD: [heat-fixed smear] → *A*, 10 mins. at 50°C. → wash → dry → *B*, heat to steam-
ing, 30 secs. → wash → dry

23.215 Bunge 1894   8645, **12**:24
FORMULA: water 100, tannic acid 100, ferric chloride 1.4, magenta 0.25, hydrogen per-
oxide *q.s.*
PREPARATION: Dissolve the tannic acid and ferric chloride in 90 water. Add the dye dis-
solved in 10 water. Add enough hydrogen peroxide just to turn solution brown.
METHOD: As DS 23.215 Löffler 1890

23.215 Casarès-Gil *test.* **1946 Conn and Darrow**   Conn and Darrow, 1946, 111A2-14
REAGENTS REQUIRED: *A.* water 50, ADS 12.2 Casarès-Gil (1946) 50; *B.* DS 11.43 Ziehl 1890
METHOD: [heat-fixed smears] → *A,* on slide, 1 min. → water, wash → *B,* on slide, 5 mins. → wash → dry

23.215 Cerrito *test.* **1904 Besson**   Besson 1904, 171
REAGENTS REQUIRED: *A.* 25% tannin 60, 5% ferric alum 30, magenta 0.3; *B.* water 100, 95% alc. 10, phenol 5, magenta 0.25
PREPARATION OF A: Heat ingredients to 100°C. for 6 hours. Cool. Filter.
METHOD: [heat-fixed smear] → *A,* 10 mins. → wash → dry → *B,* on slide, warmed to steaming, several secs. → wash → dry

23.215 van Ermengen 1894   *see* MS 31.1 van Ermengen 1894

23.215 Fisher and Conn 1942   20540b, **17**:117
STOCK SOLUTIONS: I. water 100, tannic acid 7.2, ferric chloride 1.5; II 95% alc. 100, magenta 0.5
REAGENTS REQUIRED: *A.* stock I; *B.* stock I 54, stock II 8, hydrochloric acid 8, 40% formaldehyde 30; *C.* DS 11.43 Ziehl 1890
METHOD: [thick smears of washings, incubated 10 mins., from active cultures] → *A,* 3½ mins. → drain → *B,* 7 mins. → water, wash → *C,* warmed to steaming, 1 min. → water, wash → dry

23.215 Gemelli *test.* **1904 Besson**   Besson 1904, 172
REAGENTS REQUIRED: *A.* 0.25% potassium permanganate; *B.* water 100, calcium chloride 0.75, neutral red 0.05
METHOD: [heat-fixed smear] → *A,* 10–20 mins. → wash → *B,* 15–30 mins. → wash → dry

23.215 Gray 1926   11056, **12**:273
REAGENTS REQUIRED: *A.* ADS 12.2 Gray 1926; *B.* DS 11.43 Ziehl 1890
METHOD: [heat-fixed smears] → *A,* on slide, 10 mins. → water, wash → *B,* 5 mins. → water, wash → dry

23.215 Inouye 1924 *test.* **1942 Langeron**   Langeron 1942, 1219
REAGENTS REQUIRED: *A.* DS 23.215 Löffler 1890 (sol. *A*); *B.* water 75, potassium alum 3, sat. alc. sol. (*circ.* 10%) crystal violet 15
METHOD: [heat-fixed smears] → *A,* on slide, warmed to steaming, 1 min. → water, wash → *B,* on slide, warmed to steaming, 1 min. → wash → dry

23.215 Kendall 1902   *see* DS 23.215 Pittfield (1910)

23.215 Kulp 1926   20540b, **1**:60
REAGENTS REQUIRED: *A.* water 75, 95% alc. 5 tannic acid 10, ferrous sulfate 4, magenta 0.5; *B.* 0.6% magenta in sat. sol. aniline
PREPARATION OF A: Dissolve the tannic acid in 50 water. Add the ferrous sulfate dissolved in 25 and the dye dissolved in the alc. Leave 18–24 hours. Filter or centrifuge.
METHOD: [air-dried smears] → *A,* 15 mins. → thorough wash → *B,* 15 mins. → wash → dry

23.215 Liefson 1930   11056, **20**:203
FORMULA: water 80, 95% alc. 36, potassium alum 2, tannic acid 4, magenta 0.6
PREPARATION: To the alum dissolved in 40 water add the tannic acid dissolved in 20. Add 20 water and 30 alc. To this add the dye dissolved in 6 alc.
METHOD: [air-dried smear] → stain 10 mins. → wash → [DS 11.44 Löffler 1890, if counterstain desired] → dry

23.215 Löffler 1890a   23684, **7**:625
REAGENTS REQUIRED: *A.* water 100, tannic acid 12, ferrous sulfate 5, magenta .03; *B.* water 100, aniline and crystal violet, each to sat., sodium carbonate .001
PREPARATION OF A: To the tannic acid dissolved in 60 water, add the ferrous sulfate dissolved in 30. To this add dye dissolved in 10 water.

METHOD: [heat-fixed smears, still warm] → A, flooded on slide and warmed to steaming, 1 min. → 90% alc. till color clouds cease → B, flooded on slide and warmed to steaming, 1 min. → water, rinse → balsam, via usual reagents

NOTE: The original method recommended that either 1% sulfuric acid or 1% sodium carbonate be added to A in amounts determined empirically for each organism. **Zikes 1930** (23684, **81**:161) substitutes his ADS 12.2 for A above.

23.215 Löffler 1890b   23684, **7**:629

REAGENTS REQUIRED: A. water 80, tannin 20, ferric alum 5, sat. aq. sol. indigocarmine 10, sat. alc. sol. methyl violet 10; B. sat. aq. sol. aniline **10**0, crystal violet to sat, 10% sodium carbonate 0.1

METHOD: [heat-fixed smears] → A, flooded on slide and warmed to steaming, 1 min. → 90% alc., till color clouds cease → B, adjusted by trial and error to required pH, flooded on slide and warmed to steaming, 1 min. → wash → balsam, via usual reagents

NOTE: The formula for A above will come as a shock to those who have not consulted the original reference. Most authors quote "ferrous sulphate" from the fact that the solution of *"ferrum sulphuricum oxydulatum ammoniatum"* given on p. 629 (*loc. cit*) is casually referred to as the *ferrosulphatlösung* on p. 630. The formula for the B solution comes from Löffler 1889 (23684, **6**:213) and was there recommended for staining after a hematoxylin mordant.

23.215 Maneval 1929   20540b, **4**:21

REAGENTS REQUIRED: A. water 100, tannic acid 13, ferric chloride 1, DS 11.43 Ziehl 1882 6.5, hydrogen peroxide (3%) 12; B. water 60, 95% alc. 27.5, aniline 2.5, acetic acid 0.1, magenta 2

METHOD: [smears of distilled water, suspensions of actively motile organisms] → A, 2–4 mins. → wash → B, 2–3 mins. → wash → dry

23.215 Muir *test*. **1920 Stitt**   Stitt 1920, 56

REAGENTS REQUIRED: A. DS 23.217 Muir (1920) sol. B. 80, DS 11.43 Ziehl 1890 20; B. sat. sol. (*circ.* 4%) potassium alum 100, sat. alc. sol. (*circ.* 15%) methyl violet 20

METHOD: [heat-fixed smears] → A, steamed over bath, 1 min. → water, 2 mins. → dry → B, on slide, warmed to steaming, 1 min. → water, wash → dry

NOTE: Both A and B solutions are unstable.

23.215 Nicolle and Morax *test*. **1904 Besson**   Besson 1904, 169

REAGENTS REQUIRED: A. DS 23.215 Löffler 1890b, (sol. A); B. DS 11.43 Ziehl 1882

METHOD: [heat-fixed smear] → A, on slide, heated to steaming, 3 or 4 changes → B, on slide, heated to steaming, 3 or 4 secs. → wash → dry

23.215 Novel 1939   *see* MS 33.52 Novel 1939

23.215 Pittfield *test*. **1910 Heymann**   Ehrlich, Krause, *et al.* 1910, 2, 394

STOCK SOLUTIONS: I. 10% aluminum acetate 10, sat. alc. sol. crystal violet 100, II. 10% tannic acid

WORKING SOLUTION: stock I 50, stock II 50

METHOD: [heat-fixed smears] → stain, lightly warmed → 30% alc. till differentiated → dry

NOTES: **Wright 1928** (20540b, **3**:17) cites (with reference to **Kendall 1902**: 11032, **5**:1936) a method of Pittfield 1902 in which the mordant contains "sat. sol. alum."

23.215 Remy and Sugg *test*. **1904 Besson**   Besson 1904, 169

REAGENTS REQUIRED: A. DS 23.215 Löffler 1890 (sol. A); B. ADS 12.2 Gram 1884; C. sat. aq. sol. aniline 80, sat. alc. sol. (*circ.* 10%) crystal violet 0.2, water 20

METHOD: [heat-fixed smear] → A, 15–30 mins. → B, on slide, few moments → wash → abs. alc., wash → C, 30 mins. at 37°C. → wash → balsam, *via* usual reagents

23.215 Rossi *test*. **1904 Besson**   Besson 1904, 170

REAGENTS REQUIRED: A. ADS 12.2 Rossi (1904); B. DS 11.43 Ziehl 1882

METHOD: [heat-fixed smear] → A, 30 mins. → wash → dry → B, heated to steaming, 3–4 mins. → wash → dry

23.215 Ryo 1937 11796, **14**:218

STOCK SOLUTIONS: I. water 100, phenol 2.5, tannic acid 10, potassium alum 4, II. sat. alc. solc. (*circ.* 10%) crystal violet
WORKING SOLUTION: stock I 100, stock II 10
METHOD: [heat-fixed smear] → stain, 3–5 mins. → thorough wash → dry

23.215 Sclavo *test.* 1904 Besson Besson 1904, 172

REAGENTS REQUIRED: *A.* 1% tannin in 50% alc.; *B.* 5% phosphotungstic acid; *C.* DS 23.211 Ehrlich 1882
METHOD: [heat-fixed smears] → *A*, 1 min. → rinse → *B*, 1 min. → rinse → *C*, heated to steaming, 3–5 mins.

23.215 Shunk 1920 11056, **5**:181

REAGENTS REQUIRED: *A.* ADS 12.2 Shunk 1920; *B.* 95% alc. 80, aniline 20; *C.* DS 11.44 Löffler 1890 90, 95% alc. 8, aniline 2
METHOD: [heat-fixed smear] → *A*, on slide → *B*, added to *A* on slide, about 10% of quantity of *A* used, 15 secs. → drain → *C*, 15 secs. → water, wash → dry

23.215 Trenkmann 1890 23684, **8**:385

REAGENTS REQUIRED: *A.* ADS 12.2 Trenkmann (1904); *B.* sat. aq. sol. iodine; *C.* DS 23.211 Ehrlich 1882
METHOD: [heat-fixed smear] → water → *A*, 6–8 hrs. → wash → *B*, 1 hr. → water → *C*, 30 mins. → wash → balsam, via usual reagents

23.215 Tribondeau, Fichet, and Dubreuil 1916 6630, **79**:710

STOCK SOLUTIONS: I. water 100, potassium alum 3.5, tannic acid 3; II. 1% crystal violet
PREPARATION OF STOCK I: Mix ingredients. Autoclave, 20 lbs. for 30 minutes. Cool. Filter.
WORKING SOLUTION: stock I 100, stock II 10
METHOD: [heat-fixed smear] → stain, heated to boiling, 30 secs. → wash → dry
NOTE: If background too granular, decrease proportion of stock II. If flagella not stained, increase proportion of stock II. A detailed description of the use of this technique is given under 23.20 above.

23.215 Wright 1928 *see* DS 23.215 Pittfield 1910

23.215 Yokata 1924 6630, **90**:1303

REAGENTS REQUIRED: *A.* ADS 12.2 Yokata 1924; *B.* sat. sol. (*circ.* 3.5) aniline 100, magenta 0.03
METHOD: [heat-dried smear] → *A*, raised to boiling, 30 secs. → water, wash → *B*, on slide, raised to boiling 2 or 3 times → water, wash → dry

23.215 Zettnow 1891 *see* MS 33.1 Zettnow 1891

23.215 Zikes 1930 *see* DS 23.215 Löffler 1890 (note)

23.216 Spore Stains

The reagents here given are intended not so much to stain bacterial spores in their free condition as to differentiate a spore within a bacterium, in order that its spore-forming nature may be determined for diagnostic purposes. The majority of these methods depend on differentiating a first stain with an acid solution, and then applying a counterstain to bring into contrast the main body of the bacteria. Other methods depend upon the selective affinity of malachite green or light green for the spore itself, and thus permit the direct coloration of the spore without subsequent differentiation. Probably the surest and simplest method is that of Muzzarelli 1931, though the selection from the methods given is largely a matter of opinion.

23.216 Abbott *test.* 1920 Stitt Stitt 1920, 55

REAGENTS REQUIRED: *A.* DS 11.44 Löffler 1890; *B.* 2% nitric acid; *C.* 1% eosin
METHOD: [heat-fixed smears] → *A*, on slide, raised to boiling 3 or 4 times, 1 min. → *B*, till colorless → water, wash → *C*, 15 secs. → water, wash → dry
RESULT: spores blue on yellow.

23.216 Aladar-Anjeszky *test.* **1904 Besson**   Besson 1904, 165
> REAGENTS REQUIRED: *A*. 0.5% hydrochloric acid; *B*. DS 11.43 Ziehl 1890; *C*. 4% sulfuric acid; *D*. 1% methylene blue
> METHOD: [air-dried smear] → *A*, 3 mins. in beaker at 80°C. → wash → dry → flame → *B*, on slide, heated to steaming, 2 or 3 changes → *C*, till decolorized → wash → *D*, 1 min. → wash → dry

23.216 Anjeszky 1909   23684, 23
> REAGENTS REQUIRED: *A*. 0.5% hydrochloric acid; *B*. DS 11.43 Ziehl 1890; *C*. 3% sulfuric acid; *D*. 1% malachite green
> METHOD: [dried, but *not* flamed, smear] → *A*, heated to steaming, 3–4 mins. → wash → dry, → flame → *B*, warmed to steaming, 1–2 mins. → wash → *C*, till decolorized → thorough wash → *D*, 1–2 mins. → wash → dry

23.216 Ashby 1938   19938, **87**:443
> REAGENTS REQUIRED: *A*. 5% malachite green; *B*. 0.5% safranin
> METHOD: [heat-fixed smear] → *A*, on slide, heated over steam bath, 1 min. → water, wash → dry

23.216 Besson 1904a   Besson 1904, 164
> REAGENTS REQUIRED: *A*. 5% chromic acid; *B*. DS 12.15 gentian violet
> METHOD: [heat-fixed smears] → *A*, on slide, 4–5 mins. → wash → *B*, on slide, 15–20 mins. → wash → dry

23.216 Besson 1940b   Besson 1904, 165
> REAGENTS REQUIRED: *A*. DS 11.43 Ziehl 1882; 25% nitric acid; *C*. 1% methylene blue
> METHOD: [heat-fixed smear] → *A*, on slide, heated to steaming, 3–4 mins. → wash → *B*, few secs. → wash → *C*, on slide, 30 secs. → wash → dry
> RESULT: spores, red; bacteria, blue.

23.216 Bitter 1913   23684, **68**:227
> REAGENTS REQUIRED: *A*. 1% formaldehyde; *B*. DS 11.44 Löffler 1890; *C*. water 50, sat. alc. sol. (*circ.* 3%) safranin 50
> METHOD: [heat-fixed smears] → *A*, 10–20 mins. → water, wash → *B*, on slide, heated to boiling, 2–3 times, → water, thorough wash → *C*, 30 secs. → water, wash → dry

23.216 Botelho 1918   6630, **81**:183
> FORMULA: water 50, acetic acid 50, light green 4, acid fuchsin 2
> METHOD: [heat-fixed smears] → stain, heated to steaming, 3 to 4 times → water, wash till greenish → repeat staining cycle till color sufficiently deep → wash → dry
> RESULT: spores red on green.

23.216 Bruner and Edwards 1939   11284, **25**:543
> REAGENTS REQUIRED: *A*. 5% malachite green; *B*. 0.5% safranin
> METHOD: [heat-fixed smears] → *A*, 5 mins. → wash → *B*, 10 secs. → wash → dry

23.216 Dorner 1926   11988, **6**:8
> REAGENTS REQUIRED: *A*. DS 11.43 Ziehl 1890; *B*. 10% nigrosin
> METHOD: [suspension of organism in test tube] → add equal volume *A*, heat to 100°C., 10 mins. → place loopful of mixture on slide, add loopful of *B*, smear → dry
> NOTE: Snyder **1934** (20540b, **9**:71) applies *A* to smear under saturated blotting-paper cover and counterstains with *B*.

23.216 Dutton 1928   20540b, **3**:140
> REAGENTS REQUIRED: *A*. phosphate buffer pH 7.6; *B*. DS 13.12 Wright 1910 (0.15% in methanol)
> METHOD: Prepare thick suspension of bacteria in *A*. Add 0.1 *B*. Seal tube and heat to 100°C. for 10 mins. Cool, unseal tube, and make smear.

23.216 Fraenkel 1922   23684, **89**:106
> REAGENTS REQUIRED: *A*. 20% tannin; *B*. DS 11.43 Ziehl 1890; *C*. 5% sulfuric acid; *D*. 0.1% methylene blue.

METHOD: [heat-fixed smears] → *A*, heated to bubbling → cool → [repeat twice] → wash → blot → *B*, warmed to steaming → cool → repeat twice → *C*, till decolorized → wash → *D*, 30 secs. → wash → dry

23.216 Gray 1941   14900, **147**:329

REAGENTS REQUIRED: *A*. water 100 malachite green 0.5, magenta 0.05
METHOD: [heat-fixed smears] → *A*, heated to steaming, 1 min. → wash → dry

23.216 Kahlden and Laurent 1896   Kahlden and Laurent 1896, 101

REAGENTS REQUIRED: *A*. DS 11.43 Ziehl 1882; *B*. 5% nitric acid; *C*. DS 11.44 Löffler 1890
METHOD: [heat-fixed smear] → *A*, 20–40 mins. → *B*, 1 min. → wash → *C*, 2 mins. → wash → blot → dry

23.216 Lagerberg 1917   23684, **79**:191

REAGENTS REQUIRED: *A*. sat. sol. (*circ.* 25%) copper sulfate; *B*. 20% ammonium hydroxide; *C*. DS 11.43 Ziehl 1882; *D*. 4% sulfuric acid
METHOD: [heat-fixed smears] → *A*, flooded on slide → *B*, added drop by drop till ppt. just redissolved → warm to steaming → add several drops *A* → *B*, rinse → water, wash → *C*, on slide, heated to steaming, 1 min. → *D*, till no more color comes away → water, wash → dry

23.216 May 1926   20540b, **1**:105

REAGENTS REQUIRED: *A*. 5% chromic acid; *B*. ammonia; *C*. DS 11.43 Ziehl 1882; *D*. 1% sulfuric acid; *E*. DS 11.44 Löffler 1890
METHOD: [heat-fixed smear] → *A*, on slide, 30 secs. → *B*, added (twice as much) to *A* on slide; 2 min. → rinse → *C*, on slide, heated to steaming, 2–3 mins. → rinse → *D*, 15–30 secs. → wash → *E*, few drops added to water on slide, 10–30 secs. → rinse → blot → dry

23.216 Möller 1891   23684, **10**:9

REAGENTS REQUIRED: *A*. chloroform; *B*. 5% chromic acid; *C*. DS 11.43 Ziehl 1882; *D*. 1% sulfuric acid; *E*. 1% methylene blue
METHOD: [heat-fixed smears] → *A*, 1–2 mins. → abs. alc., rinse → water, wash → *B*, 1 min. → water, wash → *B*, 1 min. → water, wash → *C*, on slide, heated to steaming, 5 mins. → water, wash → *D*, till faint pink → water, wash → *E*, 10 secs. → water, wash → dry

23.216 Muzzarelli 1931 *test.* **1942 Langeron**   Langeron 1942, 1216

REAGENTS REQUIRED: *A*. water 75, DS 11.44 Manson 25; *B*. 10% nitric acid; *C*. 1% eosin
METHOD: [heat-fixed smears] → *A*, warmed to steaming, 30 secs. → water, wash → *B*, till no more color comes away → water, wash → *C*, 15 secs. → water, wash → dry

23.216 Neisser and Hueppe *test.* **1928 Schmorl**   Schmorl 1928, 355

REAGENTS REQUIRED: *A*. sat. sol. magenta in sat. sol. aniline; *B*. 25% sulfuric acid; *C*. 1% methylene blue
METHOD: [heat-fixed smear] → *A*, 100°C., 1–5 hrs. → *B*, 5 secs. → abs. alc., till no more color comes away → water → *C*, 3–5 mins. → wash → dry
NOTE: Schmorl (*loc. cit.*) recommends a steam chest for step *A*.

23.216 Proca 1909   6630, **68**:307

FORMULA: water 50, DS 11.44 Löffler 1890 50, DS 11.43 Ziehl 1882 4
METHOD: [heat-fixed smears] → stain, 1 min. → water, wash → dry
RESULT: live bacteria, colorless spores on blue; dead bacteria, blue spores on red.
NOTE: See also DS 23.21 Gay and Clark 1924, who have adapted this technique to general use.

23.216 Ruiz 1946 *test.* **1947 Pemander**   20540b, **22**:164

REAGENTS REQUIRED: *A*. 1% methyl violet; *B*. 0.1% eosin Y 100, normal horse serum 30
METHOD: Mix 1 drop *A* with bacterial suspension, leave 5 mins. Add 1 drop *B*, leave 3 mins. Make smear and dry.

23.216 Schaeffer and Fulton 1933   19938, **77** :194
    REAGENTS REQUIRED: *A*. 5% malachite green; *B*. 0.5% safranin O
    METHOD: [heat-fixed smears] → *A*, poured on slide, heated and reheated to steaming, 3–4
    times → water, wash → *B*, 30 secs. → water, wash → dry
    RESULT: spores green on red.

23.216 Shapiro 1944   20540b, **19** :65
    REAGENTS REQUIRED: *A*. 5% malachite green; *B*. 0.5% safranin
    METHOD: [mix 2–3 drops bacterial suspension with equal amount *A*. Heat in boiling
    water bath 15–20 mins. Make smear and heat fix.] → wash, 10 secs. → *B*, 1 min. →
    wash → blot → dry

23.216 Snyder 1934   *see* DS 23.216 Dorner 1926 (note)

23.216 Tribondeau 1917   6630, **80** :880
    REAGENTS REQUIRED: *A*. ADS 12.2 Lugol (1905); *B*. DS 12.15 crystal violet; *C*. 0.2%
    Bismarck brown
    METHOD: [heat-fixed smears] → *A*, heated to steaming, 2–3 times → blot → *B*, heated
    to steaming, 2–3 times → water, wash
    RESULT: spores violet on brown.

23.216 Zeeti 1935   20540b (abs. 1936) **11** :87
    REAGENTS REQUIRED: *A*. water 100, eosin Y 5, phenol 5, iodine 2, potassium iodide 1; *B*.
    0.075% methylene blue in 5% alc.
    METHOD: [heat-fixed smears] → *A*, heated to boiling, 5 mins. → wash → *B*, 1–2 mins. →
    wash → dry

23.217 Capsule Stains

    The standard method for staining the capsule of capsulated bacteria is still that of
Hiss 1905, though many other methods have been developed. One of the most interesting of these is that of Huntoon 1917, in which the capsule is first caused to absorb a
solution of nutrose, which is itself subsequently brought into prominence by a chemical
reaction specific to it. The other methods largely rely on mordanting with formaldehyde
and subsequently carrying out a standard Gram procedure with counterstaining for the
mordanted capsule.

23.217 Anthony 1931   *see* DS 23.207 Hiss 1905 (note)

23.217 Besson 1904   Besson 1904, 166
    REAGENTS REQUIRED: *A*. water 100, crystal violet 0.5, acetic acid 1
    METHOD: [heat-fixed smear] → *A*, 1 min. → rinse → dry

23.217 Boni *test.* **1928 Schmorl**   Schmorl 1928, 359
    REAGENTS REQUIRED: *A*. V 21.1 Mayer 1884; *B*. DS 11.43 Ziehl 1890
    METHOD: [place a drop of *A* on slide. Mix in a trace of bacterial culture. Make smear.
    Dry. Flame] → *B*, warmed to steaming, 1 min. → wash → dry

23.217 Buerger 1904 *test.* **1928 Zinnser and Bayne-Jones**
                                           Zinnser and Bayne-Jones, 1928, 847
    REAGENTS REQUIRED: *A*. ADS 12.2 Gram 1882; *B*. DS 23.211 Ehrlich 1882; *C*. 2% so-
    dium chloride
    METHOD: [F 3700.0000 fixed smear] → wash → 95% alc. → wash → *A*, 1–3 mins. →
    95% alc., wash → dry → *B*, few secs. → *C*, wash → examine in *C*

23.217 Churchman and Emelianoff 1932   16913, **29** :514
    REAGENTS REQUIRED: *A*. DS 13.12 Wright 1910; *B*. phosphate buffer pH 6.4
    METHOD: [air-dried smear] → *A*, on slide, till evaporation changes color from blue to
    pink → *B*, wash → dry

23.217 Gutstein 1926   23684, **93**:393

REAGENTS REQUIRED: *A*. sat. sol. ammonium sulfate; *B*. 5% tannin; *C*. 1% malachite
green

METHOD: [air-dried smear] → *A*, 5 mins. → rinse → *B*, 2 mins. → thorough wash → *C*,
5–60 secs. → wash → dry → balsam

23.217 Hiss 1905   11189, **6**:317

REAGENTS REQUIRED: *A*. 0.1% crystal violet; *B*. 20% copper sulfate

METHOD: [heat-fixed smears] → *A*, on slide, warmed to steaming, ½ to 1 min. → *B*, till
no more color comes away → blot → dry

RESULT: capsule blue.

NOTE: **Anthony 1931** (19938, **73**:319) substitutes 1% crystal violet for *A* above. **Tyler**
test. **1946 Conn and Darrow** *cit*. **Park and Williams 1933** (Conn and Darrow 1946,
111A2-18) adds 0.25% acetic acid to *A* above.

23.217 Huntoon 1917   11056, **2**:241

REAGENTS REQUIRED: *A*. 3% nutrose; *B*. water 100, phenol 2, lactic acid 0.5, acetic acid
0.01, magenta 0.1, DS 11.43 Ziehl 1882 1

METHOD: [smear, of culture diluted with *A*, air-dried] → *B*, 30 secs. → water, wash →
dry

NOTE: Solution *A* must be steam-sterilized (not autoclaved) and preservative added if
required to keep.

23.217 Johne *test*. **Kahlden and Laurent 1896**   Kahlden and Laurent 1896, 100

REAGENTS REQUIRED: *A*. sat. aq. sol. crystal violet; *B*. 1% acetic acid

METHOD: [smears] → *A*, 25 to 30 secs. → *B*, 5–10 secs. → dry

23.217 Kahlden and Laurent 1896   Kahlden and Laurent 1896, 104

REAGENTS REQUIRED: *A*. water 60, crystal violet 0.5, acetic acid 30; *B*. 1% acetic acid

METHOD: [smears] → *A*, 24 hrs. 37°C. → *B*, wash → balsam, via usual reagents

23.217 Klett *test*. **1928 Schmorl**   Schmorl 1928, 359

REAGENTS REQUIRED: *A*. 1% methylene blue in 10% alc.; *B*. 1% magenta in 10% alc. 7

METHOD: [heat-fixed smears] → *A*, warmed to steaming, 3–5 mins. → wash → *B*, 5 secs.
→ wash and dry

23.217 Lawson 1940   11284, **25**:435

REAGENTS REQUIRED: *A*. 5% phosphomolybdic acid; *B*. DS 13.12 Wright 1910 (working
solution) 60, glycerol 30

METHOD: [air-dried smears] → *A*, on slide, 30 secs. → wash → wash, methanol → 10–20
drops water, 10–20 mins. → rinse → dry

23.217 Muir 1916   11431, **20**:257

REAGENTS REQUIRED: *A*. DS 12.15 gentian violet; *B*. ADS 12.2 Gram 1884; *C*. water 100,
mercuric chloride 2, potassium alum 1.3, tannic acid 7; *D*. sat. sol. (*circ*. 35%) eosin;
sat. sol. (*circ*. 3.5%) potassium alum

METHOD: [mercuric-chloride-fixed, and acetone-washed, smears] → *A*, on slide, 2 mins.
→ water, rinse → *B*, on slide, 1 min. → water, wash → methanol 1 min. → clove oil,
heated to fuming, 1 min. → methanol, wash → water, wash → *C*, 5 mins. → water,
rinse → *D*, 30 secs. → water, wash → *E*, 1 min. → water, rinse → dry

23.217 Muir *test*. **1920 Stitt**   Stitt 1920, 55

REAGENTS REQUIRED: *A*. DS 11.43 Ziehl 1890; *B*. water 100, mercuric chloride 1.5, tannic acid 4, potassium alum 3; *C*. 1% methylene blue

METHOD: [heat-fixed smears] → *A*, heated to steaming, 30 secs. → 95% alc., rinse →
water, wash → *B*, 5–10 secs. → water, wash → 95% alc., 1 min. → water, wash →
C, 1 min. → dry

23.217 Raebiger *test*. **1904 Besson**   Besson 1904, 166

REAGENTS REQUIRED: 40% formaldehyde 100, crystal violet 15

PREPARATION: Heat to boiling. Cool. Filter.

METHOD: [air-dried smears] → *A*, 1 min. → wash → dry

23.217 Schmorl 1928   Schmorl 1928, 359
REAGENTS REQUIRED: *A.* 1% potassium hydroxide; *B.* 2% crystal violet
METHOD: [heat-fixed smears] → *A*, 3–5 mins. → quick rinse → *B*, 3–4 mins. → wash → dry

23.217 Tyler 1946   *see* DS 23.217 Hiss 1905 (note)

23.217 Wadsworth 1906   11250, **3**:610
REAGENTS REQUIRED: *A.* 40% formaldehyde; *B.* DS 23.211 Ehrlich 1882; *C.* ADS 12.2 Gram 1882; *D.* 0.1% magenta
METHOD: [heat-fixed smears] → *A*, 2–5 mins. → water, rinse → *B*, 2 mins. → *C*, 2 mins. → 95% alc., till no more color comes away → *D*, 30 secs. dry

23.217 Welch 1892   10919, **3**:81
REAGENTS REQUIRED: *A.* acetic acid; *B.* DS 23.211 Ehrlich 1882 (sol. *A*); *C.* 2% sodium chloride
METHOD: [dried, not heated, smear] → *A*, few secs. → *B*, drained and renewed on slide till *A* removed → *B*, fresh solution, 2 mins. → *C*, wash → examine

23.218 Diphtheria Bacilli

Diphtheria bacilli themselves are not susceptible to differential staining. Diagnosis by microscope is dependent upon bringing into prominence the granules which they uniquely have within them. These granules have much the same reactions as any other minute body, hence the methods for their demonstration most strongly resemble those given either for the demonstration of Rickettsiae, or for mitochondria and other cell inclusions. The original method of Neisser 1897 is still the most widely employed and all these techniques are occasionally referred to as *Neisser stains* even though they may bear no relation at all to the original description.

23.218 Albert 1921   11006, **76**:240
REAGENTS REQUIRED: *A.* water 100, 95% alc. 2, acetic acid 1, methyl green 0.02, toluidine blue 0.15; *B.* ADS 12.2 Gram 1882
METHOD: [heat-fixed smears] → *A*, 5 mins. → blot → *B*, 1 min. → water, rinse → blot → dry
NOTE: **Laybourn 1924** (11006, **83**:121) substitutes 0.2 malachite green for 0.02 methyl green in *A* above.

23.218 Ambrosioni 1940   988, **50**:228
REAGENTS REQUIRED: *A.* water 95, acetic acid 5, crystal violet 0.33; *B.* 2% chrysoidin; *C.* ADS 12.2 Lugol 99, lactic acid 1
METHOD: [heat-fixed smear] → *A*, 10–15 secs. → *B*, 20–30 secs. → wash → *C*, 5 secs. → wash → dry

23.218 Beauverie 1917   6630, **80**:609
REAGENTS REQUIRED: *A.* DS 11.44 Löffler 1890; *B.* ADS 12.2 Lugol
METHOD: [alcohol-fixed smears] → *A*, 2–3 mins. → wash → *B*, 2–3 mins. → wash → dry
NOTE: **Mallory 1922** (4349, **8**:110) recommends counterstaining in 1% eosin after this technique.

23.218 Cowdry 1943   Cowdry 1943, 62
REAGENTS REQUIRED: *A.* DS 23.218 Neisser 1897 (sol. *A*) 60, 0.3% crystal violet 30; *B.* 0.3% chrysoidin
METHOD: [heat-fixed smear] → *A*, on slide, ½ to 1 min. → water, wash → *B*, on slide, 30 secs. → water, wash → dry
NOTE: *See also* DS 23.218 Neisser 1897 (note).

23.218 Kinyoun 1915   617, **5**:246
FORMULA: water 120, acetic acid 1, 95% alc. 5, toluidine blue 0.01, azur A 0.01, methylene blue 0.01
PREPARATION: Dissolve dyes in alc. Add acidified water.
METHOD: [heat-fixed smears] → stain, 5 mins. → water, wash → dry
RESULT: granules red on blue.

23.218 Kemp 1931   11284, **16**:593

REAGENTS REQUIRED: *A*. ADS 12.2 Gram 1884; *B*. DS 11.44 Löffler 1890; *C*. 1% safranin

METHOD: [heat-fixed smears] → *A*, 1 min. → wash → *B*, 20–30 secs. → wash → *C*, 10–15 secs. → wash → dry

23.218 Laybourn 1924   *see* DS 23.218 Albert 1921 (note)

23.218 Ljubinsky *test.* **1946 Conn and Darrow** *cit.* **Blumenthal and Lipskerow**

Conn and Darrow 1946, 111A2-12

REAGENTS REQUIRED: *A*. water 95, acetic acid 5, crystal violet 0.25; *B*. 0.1% Bismarck brown Y

METHOD: [heat-fixed smears] → *A*, 12 to 2 mins. → water, wash → *B*, 30 secs. → water, wash → dry

RESULT: granules, blue-black on yellow.

23.218 Mallory 1922   *see* DS 23.218 Beauverie 1917 (note)

23.218 Neisser 1897   23454, **24**:448

REAGENTS REQUIRED: *A*. 95% alc. 2, methylene blue 0.1, water 95, acetic acid 5; *B*. 0.2% Bismarck brown

METHOD: [heat-fixed smears] → *A*, 1–3 secs. → water, wash → *B*, 3–5 secs. → water, wash → dry

NOTE: The timing given is that of the original paper. Modern practice calls for longer staining. **Cowdry 1943, 62,** for example, recommends ½ to 1 minute in *A* and 30 seconds in *B*.

23.218 Ponder *test.* **1920 Stitt**   Stitt 1920, 55

FORMULA: water 100, 95% alc. 2, acetic acid 1, toluidine blue 0.02

METHOD: [heat-fixed smear on coverslip] → stain, dropped on coverslip → examine as hanging drop

23.218 Ryn 1940   11796, **17**:53

REAGENTS REQUIRED: *A*. sat. aq. sol. potassium aluminate (*not* alum) 5, sat. alc. sol. methyl violet 1

METHOD: [heat-fixed smear] → stain, 2–3 mins. → wash → dry

23.218 Stottenberg 1926   7276, **20**:426

FORMULA: water 100, acetic acid 3, abs. alc. 3, malachite green 0.25, toluidine blue 0.05, hematoxylin 0.01

METHOD: [dry smear] → stain, 1 min. → wash → dry

23.218 Tribondeau and Dubreuil 1917   6630, **80**:331

REAGENTS REQUIRED: *A*. DS 11.44 Nicolle (1942); *B*. 0.2% Bismarck brown

METHOD: [alcohol-fixed smear] → *A*, 5 mins. → water, wash → 1–2 mins. → water, wash → dry

23.219 Other Methods for Bacterial Smears

23.219 Broadhurst and Paley 1939   11023, **94**:525

FORMULA: 95% alc. 62, tetrachlorethane 40, sulfuric acid 0.4, methylene blue 1, magenta 0.08

PREPARATION: Mix 50 alc. with tetrachlorethane and acid. Heat to 55°C. Add methylene blue and shake to solution. Dissolve magenta in 10 alc. and add to blue.

METHOD: [thin film of milk dried to slide] → stain, on slide, 15 secs. → drain → dry → wash till faint pink → dry

RECOMMENDED FOR: bacteria in milk.

23.219 Bruner and Edwards 1940   11284, **25**:543

REAGENTS REQUIRED: *A*. 5% malachite green; *B*. 0.5% safranin

METHOD: [heat-fixed blood smear] → *A*, 5 mins. → rinse → *B*, 10 secs. → wash → dry

RECOMMENDED FOR: demonstration of bacteria in leukocytes.

23.219 Burdon, Stokes, and Kimbrough 1942   11056, 43:717
REAGENTS REQUIRED: *A.* 0.3% Sudan black B; *B.* 1% safranin
METHOD: [emulsify bacteria from slant with *A*] → make smear → *B,* 15 secs. → wash
  → dry
RECOMMENDED FOR: demonstration of fat in bacteria.

23.219 Erb 1929   11284, 14:377
FORMULA: ether 50, methanol 50, methylene blue 0.59
METHOD: [air-dried milk smear] → stain, 1 min. → rinse → dry
RECOMMENDED FOR: bacteria in milk.

23.219 Flinn 1939   11284, 25:316
PREPARATION OF STAIN: Grind 0.15 methyl green with 0.5 pyronin and 15 95% alc.
  Add while grinding 85 3% phenol. Leave 1 week.
METHOD: [fresh blood smears] → stain, 4 mins. → wash → dry
RECOMMENDED FOR: demonstration of bacteria (deep red) in leukocytes.

23.219 Gay and Clark 1934   11056, 27:175
REAGENTS REQUIRED: *A.* DS 11.44 Löffler 1890; *B.* DS 11.43 Ziehl 1882
METHOD: [heat-fixed smears] → *A,* 3–5 mins. → rinse → *B,* 5–10 secs. → wash → dry
RECOMMENDED FOR: differentiation of living and dead bacteria.
NOTE: *See also* DS 23.216 Proca 1909.

23.219 Kahlden and Laurent 1896   Kahlden and Laurent 1896, 103
REAGENTS REQUIRED: *A.* 1% eosin in 96% alc.; *B.* 1% methyl blue
METHOD: [dry smears] → *A,* 1–2 mins. 30°C. → blot → *B,* 30 secs. → wash → dry
RESULT: cocci, blue; cellular material, red.
RECOMMENDED FOR: differentiation of cocci in smears of cellular material.

23.219 McCullough and Dick 1942   20540b, 17:153
FORMULA: water 50, methanol 50, phenol 0.5, sodium chloride 0.5, sodium phosphate,
  dibasic (12 H_2O) 0.02, methylene blue 0.02
METHOD: [smears] → methanol, 6 mins. → stain, 10–30 mins. → wash → dry
RECOMMENDED FOR: demonstration of bacteria in leukocytes.

23.219 Schwitz *test.* **1896 Kahlden and Laurent   Kahlden and Laurent 1896, 103**
REAGENTS REQUIRED: *A.* sat. sol. methyl blue in 5% phenol; *B.* 0.25% acetic acid; *C.*
  0.2% safranin
METHOD: [dried smears] → *A,* 5–10 mins. → *B,* 2–3 secs. → wash → *C,* 15–30 mins. →
  wash → dry
RECOMMENDED FOR: differentiation of cocci in smears of cellular material.

23.219 Shutt 1947   20540b, 22:1
FORMULA: ether 50, methanol 50, methylene blue 0.5, hydrochloric acid 0.35
PREPARATION: Dissolve dye in mixed solvents. Add acid to solution.
METHOD: [make smear] → stain, 5–10 secs. → dry
RECOMMENDED FOR: bacteria in milk.

23.219 Walton 1939   11284, 24:1308
FORMULA: water 100, phenol 2, glycerol 20, methanol 10, methyl green 1, pyronin 0.2
PREPARATION: Dissolve the dyes in the methanol. Add phenol and water. Shake 2 hours
  per day for 2 days. Filter. Add glycerol to filtrate.
METHOD: [heat-fixed smears] → stain, on slide, warmed till steaming → wash → dry
RESULT: gonococci, red.
RECOMMENDED FOR: specific differentiation of gonococcus.

23.219 Weiss 1929   11284, 15:170
REAGENTS REQUIRED: *A.* water 85, 95% alc. 10, acetic acid 5, methylene blue 5; *B.* 1%
  safranin
METHOD: [heat-fixed smears] → *A,* 5 mins. → wash → *B,* 1–2 mins. → wash → dry
RECOMMENDED FOR: demonstration of polar bodies (deep blue) in bacterial cells (red).

23.219 Zaribnecky 1934 2818, **50**:224

FORMULA: water 90, naphazarine 0.15, azophloxine 0.1

PREPARATION: Boil the naphazarine and alum chloride in 60 water. Cool. Filter. Add the azophloxine dissolved in 30 water.

METHOD: [dried smear of milk] → stain, 5–10 mins. → dry

RECOMMENDED FOR: staining bacteria in milk.

23.22 BACTERIA IN SECTIONS OF TISSUES

Relatively few methods are found for staining bacteria in cells for two reasons. First, these methods are rarely, if ever, used for diagnostic purposes but are confined to sections destined for research or teaching; second, the majority of methods which are used for staining bacteria in smears can also be used for staining bacteria in sectioned material. The methods given below are therefore confined to those which are used exclusively for staining sections and which cannot be used for staining smears. For staining sections of specific organisms, for which a technique in smears is recommended, the smear technique should always be tried in preference to one of the techniques here given.

23.221 General Methods

23.221 Foshay 1931 11284, **17**:193

FORMULA: water 80, sat. sol. Nile blue sulfate 12, 1% safranin 8

METHOD: [sections] → stain, overnight → rinse → balsam, via usual reagents

23.221 Fraenkel *test.* **1928 Schmorl** Schmorl 1928, 363

REAGENTS REQUIRED: *A.* DS 11.44 Löffler 1890; *B.* 0.5% acid fuchsin 30, 33% tannin 30, ADS 22.1 Unna (1928) 30

METHOD: [sections] → *A*, overnight → thorough wash → *B*, till differentiated → wash → balsam, via usual reagents

RESULT: bacilli, blue-black; nuclei, light blue; other structures, red.

23.221 Guyer 1930 Guyer 1930, 117

REAGENTS REQUIRED: *A.* DS 11.44 Löffler 1890; *B.* 0.1% acetic acid

METHOD: [sections] → water → *A*, ½ to 24 hrs. → *B*, 10–20 secs. → abs. alc., rinse → balsam, via xylene

23.221 Holmes and French 1926 *see* DS 13.21 Holmes and French 1926

23.221 Krajian 1941 1887a, **32**:825

REAGENTS REQUIRED: *A.* DS 11.123 Harris 1900; *B.* 0.1% hydrochloric acid in 70% alc.; *C.* water 100, zinc sulfate 4, copper sulfate 7; *D.* 3% brilliant green in *C*; *E.* 5% ammonium nitrate; *F.* DS 11.43 Ziehl 1882; *G.* creosote 50, xylene 50

METHOD: [7–10 μ frozen sections] → *A*, 2 mins. → tap water, till blue → *B*, 5 or 6 dips → *C*, 3 mins., on slide → *D*, 5 mins., on slide → rinse → *E*, 1 min. → rinse → *F*, 2 mins., on slide → rinse → blot → dioxane, 2 mins. → *G*, till differentiated → dammar, via xylene

23.221 Krajian 1943 11284, **28**:1602

REAGENTS REQUIRED: *A.* DS 11.44 Löffler 1890; *B.* creosote 25, xylene 75; *C.* B 100, 95% alc. 5, magenta 1.2

METHOD: [sections] → water → *A*, 3 mins. → wash → isopropyl alc., till dehydrated → *B*, till differentiated → *C*, 1 min. → *B*, till excess red removed → xylene, thorough wash → balsam

23.221 Kühne *test.* **1904 Besson** Besson 1904, 260

REAGENTS REQUIRED: *A.* DS 11.44 Kühne (1904)a; *B.* ADS 12.2 Gram 1884; *C.* sat. alc. sol. (*circ.* 2%) fluorescein

METHOD: [sections] → water → *A*, 5–15 mins. → wash → *B*, 2 or 3 mins. → wash → *C*, till differentiated → balsam, via usual reagents

23.221 Langeron 1942 *see* DS 13.22 Langeron 1942b

23.221 Mallory 1938   Mallory 1938, 86
STOCK SOLUTIONS: I. water 100, sodium borate 1, methylene blue 1; II. 1% azur II
REAGENTS REQUIRED: *A*. 2.5% phloxine; *B*. stock I 5, stock II 5, water 90; *C*. ADS 21.2
   Wolbach 1911
METHOD: *A*, 1–2 hrs., 50°C. → water, wash → *B*, 5–20 mins. → water, wash → *C*, till
   differentiated → balsam, via xylene
NOTE: A detailed description of the use of this technique is given under DS 23.20 above.

23.221 Masson   *see* DS 13.22 Masson (1942) *or* DS 13.5 Masson (1942)

23.221 Nicolle *test.* **1904 Besson**   Besson 1904, 258
REAGENTS REQUIRED: *A*. DS 11.44 Kühne (1904) a *or* b; *B*. 10% tannic acid
METHOD: [sections] → water → *A*, 2–3 mins. → wash → *B*, a few secs. → rinse → blot →
   dehydrate least possible time → balsam, via usual reagents

23.221 Nicolle   *see* DS 11.423 Nicolle (1942)

23.221 Noniewicz *test.* **1896 Kahlden and Laurent**   Kahlden and Laurent 1896, 108
REAGENTS REQUIRED: *A*. DS 11.44 Löffler 1890; *B*. water 99, acetic acid 1, tropeolin 0.1
METHOD: [sections] → water → *A*, 2–5 mins. → wash → *B*, 1–5 secs. → wash → dry

23.221 Ollett 1947   11431, **59**:357
REAGENTS REQUIRED: *A*. DS 23.211 Ehrlich 1882; *B*. ADS 12.2 Gram 1884; *C*. 2% acetic
   acid in abs. alc.; *D*. water 75, DS 13.7 Twort (1909) 25
METHOD: [3 μ sections of formaldehyde-fixed material] → *A*, 3–5 mins. → rinse → *B*,
   3 mins. → rinse → blot → *C*, till decolorized → rinse → *D*, 5 mins. → rinse → *C*, till
   no more color comes away → balsam, via xylene

23.221 Pappenheim   DS 23.221 *see* Saathof 1905

23.221 Saathof 1905   *Unna-Pappenheim method—compl. script.*
                                                     7276, **32**:2047
FORMULA: water 75, phenol 1.5, glycerol 20, 95% alc. 5, pyronin 0.15, methyl green 0.5
METHOD: [sections] → stain, 1–3 mins. → water, wash → acetone, till dehydrated → bal-
   sam, via xylene

23.221 Unna   *see* DS 23.221 Saathof 1905

23.222 Iodine Differential Methods

Staining Gram-positive bacteria sections is only another instance in which a standard
method has become so embedded in the literature that all other methods are referred
to it. In this instance it is the Gram-Weigert technique which dominates the field.
Gram, in point of fact, had nothing to do with the technique of Weigert, published in
1887, which depended entirely upon Weigert's contribution of differentiating with
aniline the crystal violet stain of Ehrlich, after mordanting with Gram's iodine. So
confused, however, has the picture become, that even Weigert's well-known resorcin-
magenta method for staining elastic fibers has been recommended for the purpose of
differentiating bacteria. Moreover, some authors (see comments under "Gram-Weigert"
below) have recommended prior nuclear staining either with carmine or hematoxylin.
Most of the techniques recommended here still rely on differentiation with aniline,
though the method of Brown and Brenn 1931 substitutes a mixture of acetone and
ether for the aniline.

23.222 Brown and Brenn 1931a   10919, **48**:69
REAGENTS REQUIRED: *A*. DS 11.123 Harris 1900; *B*. 3% hydrochloric acid in 95% alc.; *C*.
   1% ammonia; *D*. DS 11.45 Brown and Brenn 1931; *E*. ADS 12.2 Lugol; *F*. 0.005%
   rosanilin hydrochloride; *G*. 0.1% picric acid
METHOD: [sections] → water → *A*, 2–5 mins. → rinse → *B*, till pink → rinse → *C*, till
   blue → wash → *D*, 2 mins. → wash → *E*, 1 min. → wash → blot → *F*, 5 mins. →
   wash → blot → acetone, rinse → *G*, till yellowish pink → balsam, via acetone and
   xylene
RESULT: Gram-positive organisms, red; Gram-negative organisms, blue black.

23.222 Brown and Brenn 1931b 11056, 21:21

STOCK SOLUTIONS: I. water 100, gentian violet 1; II. water 100, sodium bicarbonate 5, phenol 0.5

REAGENTS REQUIRED: A. stock I 100, stock II 11; B. ADS 12.2 Lugol (1905); C. acetone 75, ether 25; D. 0.005% magenta; E. 0.1% picric acid in acetone

METHOD: [sections, nuclei stained by DS 11.122 technique] → water → A, on slide, 2 mins. → rinse → B, 1 min. → wash → blot → C, on slide, till no more color comes away → blot D, 5 mins. → wash → blot E, till color turns to yellowish pink → balsam, via acetone and xylene

23.222 Glynn 1935 1789a, 20:896

REAGENTS REQUIRED: A. DS 11.45 crystal violet; B. ADS 12.2 Gram (1884); C. acetone; D. water 100, magenta 0.05, hydrochloric acid q.s. for pH 2.5; E. sat. sol. picric acid

METHOD: [sections] → water → A, 2 mins. → drain → B, on slide, 1 min. → C, till no more color comes away → water, wash → D, 3 mins. → drain → E, on slide, 1 min. → C, 10–15 secs. → balsam, via xylene

RESULT: Gram-positive bacteria, violet; Gram-negative bacteria, red.

23.222 "Gram-Weigert"—compl. script.

The original method is Weigert 1887 (see below). Almost any technique involving the differentiation of gentian violet with iodine followed by aniline has come to bear this name. Unfortunately Weigert's 1898 (23681, 9:290) resorcin-magenta method (see DS 21.13 Weigert 1898) has also become confused with the 1887 method. Authors who state only that they "stained by the Gram-Weigert method" may have used crystal violet or magenta, with or without prior nuclear staining in carmine (Zinsser, Bayne-Jones, 1939, 860) or hematoxylin (Mallory, 1938, 272), with or without aniline differentiation.

23.222 Haythorn 1929 4349, 12:128

REAGENTS REQUIRED: A. DS 11.122 Mallory 1938; B. 0.1% hydrochloric acid in 70% alc.; C. DS 23.211 Ehrlich 1882; D. ADS 12.2 Lugol (1904); E. aniline 60, xylene 30; F. sat. alc. sol. erythrosin; G. aniline 30, xylene 60

METHOD: [sections] → water → A, 5–10 mins., or till deeply stained → B, quick rinse → tap water, wash → C, 2–5 mins. → blot → D, 2–5 mins. → E, till differentiated → F, 30–60 secs. → G, till no more color comes away → balsam, via xylene

23.222 Krajian 1943 11284, 28:1602

REAGENTS REQUIRED: A. DS 11.44 Löffler 1890; B. xylene 65, creosote 35; C. DS 11.43 Krajian 1943

METHOD: [sections] → water → A, 3 mins. → wash → abs. alc., least possible time for dehydration → B, till differentiated, 2–5 secs. → C, on slide, 2 changes, 10 secs. each → blot → B, on slide till differentiated → blot → balsam, via xylene

RESULT: nuclei, Gram-negative organisms, Negri bodies, red; Gram-positive organisms, actinomycetes, blue.

23.222 Krajian 1950 Krajian 1950, 196

REAGENTS REQUIRED: A. 5% thorium nitrate; B. DS 11.121 Krajian 1950; C. 1% hydrochloric acid in 70% alc., D. water 100, potassium iodide 5, zinc sulfate 5; E. DS 11.43 Ziehl 1882; F. 2% sodium sulfite; G. 3% acetic acid; H. 50:50 aniline xylene; I. cresote

METHOD: [5 μ to 7 μ sections] → water → A, 5 mins. → rinse → B, 3 mins. → wash → C, till no more color comes away → tap water, till blue → D, 5 mins. → rinse → E, 7–10 mins. → wash → F, 2 mins. → rinse → G, 3 mins. → blot → H, 30 secs. → I, till pink clouds cease → dammar, via xylene

RESULT: Gram-positive organisms, blue black; Gram-negative organisms, red.

23.222 Male 1924 11035, 42:455

REAGENTS REQUIRED: A. 0.5% methyl violet; B. ADS 12.2 Gram 1880; C. water 75, 95% alc. 25, light green 0.05, neutral red 0.25

METHOD: [sections] → water → A, 1–2 mins. → B, 1–2 mins. → 95% alc., till no more color comes away → C, 3–5 mins. → wash → balsam, via usual reagents

23.222 Mallory 1938   Mallory 1938, 272

REAGENTS REQUIRED: *A*. 2.5% phloxine; *B*. DS 11.45 Sterling 1890; *C*. ADS 12.2 Gram;
  D. aniline

METHOD: [sections of F 3700.0010 Zenker 1894 fixed material, prior stained by DS 11.122
  method] → *A*, 10 mins., 50°C. → water, wash → *B*, ½ to 1 hr. → water, wash → *C*,
  1–2 mins. → blot → *D*, till differentiated → balsam, via usual reagents

23.222 Verchoeff 1940   11006, **115**:1546

REAGENTS REQUIRED: *A*. DS 11.45 Sterling 1890; *B*. ADS 12.2 Gram 1880; *C*. trichlor-
  ethylene; *D*. oil of thyme

METHOD: [sections] → water → *A*, 2 mins. → wash → *B*, 1 min. → 95% alc., till color
  clouds appear → *C*, till color clouds cease → *D*, 1 min. → [examine and repeat 95%
  alc. → *C* → *D* cycle till differentiation complete] → balsam, via xylene

RECOMMENDED FOR: "Leptotriches" or Parinaud's conjunctives.

23.222 Weigert 1887   8644, **5**:228

REAGENTS REQUIRED: *A*. DS 23.211 Ehrlich 1882; *B*. 0.9% sodium chloride; *C*. ADS 12.2
  Gram, 1882; *D*. aniline.

METHOD: [sections] → water → *A*, 1 min. → *B*, wash → *C*, 1 min. → blot → *D*, till
  differentiated → xylene → balsam

NOTE: See comments under "Gram-Weigert" above.

23.222 Zeissig 1929   20540b, **4**:91

REAGENTS REQUIRED: *A*. DS 23.212 Hucker and Conn 1923; *B*. ADS 12.2 Gram 1884; *C*.
  water 95, ADS 12.2 Gram 1884 5

METHOD: [sections, with nuclei stained] → *A*, 2–3 mins. → wash → *B*, 5 mins. → wash
  → *C*, till differentiated → counterstain, if required → balsam, via xylene

23.223 Methods for Acid-fast Organisms

Techniques for staining acid-fast organisms in sections essentially follow those for
the staining of acid-fast organisms in smears. The most interesting variation is that of
Mallory 1938, in which the acid used is in such a low strength that it permits the
retention of hematoxylin stains in the nuclei while still allowing for the differentiation
of the bacteria.

23.223 Adams *test*. 1946 anonymous   4349, **26**:13

REAGENTS REQUIRED: *A*. ADS 11.121 Weigert 1903; *B*. 0.1% hydrochloric acid in 50%
  alc., *C*. DS 11.43 Goodpasture and Burnett 1919; *D*. 5% acetic acid; *E*. 0.1% light
  green in 0.2% acetic acid

METHOD: [sections] → water → *A*, 1 min. → *B*, wash → *C*, 1 min. → *D*, till no more color
  comes away → repeat *C* → *D* cycle three times → wash → *E*, 1 min. → 85% alc. →
  balsam, via usual reagents

RESULT: nuclei, black; bacteria, red; other structures, green.

23.223 Albrecht *test*. 1943 Cowdry   Cowdry 1943, 17

REAGENTS REQUIRED: *A*. DS 11.43 Albrecht (1943); *B*. 1% hydrochloric acid in 70%
  alc.; *C*. DS 11.123 Harris 1900; *D*. 0.3% hydrochloric acid in 70% alc.; *E*. 0.4%
  ammonium hydroxide

METHOD: [sections] → water → [lay filter paper saturated with *A* on slide, steam, 3 mins.
  leave 30 mins.] → *B* (removing filter paper), till sections deep pink → wash → *C*,
  10 mins. → wash → *D*, till differentiated → wash → *E*, till nuclei blue → balsam, via
  usual reagents

23.223 Baumgarten *test*. 1942 Langeron   Langeron 1942, 1212

REAGENTS REQUIRED: *A*. DS 11.43 Ziehl 1882; *B*. 10% nitric acid in 95% alc.; *C*. 1%
  toluidine blue

METHOD: [sections] → *A*, ½–1 hr. → water, wash → *B*, till no more color comes away
  → water, wash → *C*, 1–2 mins. → water, wash → balsam, via usual reagents

RECOMMENDED FOR: leprosy bacilli in sections.

23.223 Bertrand and Medakovitch 1924 *test.* **Langeron 1942**

Langeron 1942, 1204

REAGENTS REQUIRED: *A.* sat. sol. aniline 90, 95% alc. 10 magenta 5; *B.* 3% hydrochloric acid; *C.* 1% lithium carbonate; *D.* 1% malachite green

METHOD: [paraffin sections of F 1500.0010 fixed material] → water → *A*, 1 min. 60°C. → water, rinse → *B*, till no more color comes away → water, wash → *C*, 1 min. → *D*, 30 secs. → balsam, via usual reagents

RECOMMENDED FOR: acid-fast bacilli in sections.

23.223 Campbell 1929   4349, **12**:129

REAGENTS REQUIRED: *A.* DS 11.43 Kinyoun (1946); *B.* 0.5% hydrochloric acid in 35% alc.; *C.* DS 11.122 "Harris"; *D.* 1% ammonia; *E.* 1% orange G

METHOD: [paraffin sections of F 3700.0010 Zenker 1894 fixed material] → water → *A*, 30 mins. → rinse → *B*, 2 changes, till pink → *C*, 2 mins. → *B*, till nuclei differentiated → *D*, till nuclei blue → wash → *E*, till plasma orange → balsam, via acetone and xylene

RECOMMENDED FOR: demonstration of *B. leprae* (red) in sections. Myelin sheaths also stain red.

23.223 Czaplewski *test.* **1896 Kahlden and Laurent**   Kahlden and Laurent 1896, 117

REAGENTS REQUIRED: *A.* DS 11.43 Ziehl 1882; *B.* 95% alc. 100, fluorescin to sat., methyl blue to sat.; *C.* sat. alc. sol. methyl blue

METHOD: [sections] → water → *A*, 3–5 mins., 37°C. → drain → *B*, 12 dips, draining slowly between each → *C*, flooded on slide, 1 min. → rinse → dry → balsam

23.223 Doubrow 1929   4285a, **6**:142

REAGENTS REQUIRED: *A.* DS 11.43 Ziehl 1882; *B.* 4.5% picric acid in 95% alc.; *C.* 0.5% light green in 95% alc.

METHOD: [sections, nuclei stained by DS 11.111 Régaud 1910] → *A*, 45 mins., 50°C. → *B*, till only nuclei appear stained → water, till yellow stain removed → *C*, 1 min. → balsam, via usual reagents

23.223 Douglas 1932   11284, **17**:1131

REAGENTS REQUIRED: *A.* DS 11.43 Ziehl 1882 100, sodium chloride 0.3; *B.* 5% nitric acid in 95% alc.; *C.* 1% azur II 5, DS 11.44 Jadassohn (1928) 5, water 90; *D.* ADS 22.1 Wolbach 1911

METHOD: [paraffin sections] → *A*, overnight → refrigerator, 30 mins. → wash → *B*, 1 min. → wash → *C*, 10 mins. → wash → *D*, till differentiated → balsam, via usual reagents

23.223 Fite 1939   11284, **25**:743

REAGENTS REQUIRED: *A.* water 90, methanol 10, phenol 5, new magenta 0.5; *B.* 20% formaldehyde; *C.* 2% hydrochloric acid in 95% alc.; *D.* 1% potassium permanganate; *E.* 2% oxalic acid; *F.* DS 11.123 Harris 1900; *G.* DS 12.221 Fite 1939

METHOD: [sections of formaldehyde-alcohol-fixed material] → water → *A*, 12–24 hrs. → *B*, 5 mins. → *C*, 5 mins. → rinse → *D*, 2–5 mins. → *E*, 1 min. wash → *F*, 2 mins. → wash → *G*, till stained → 95% alc., → balsam, via usual reagents

23.223 Flexner *test.* **1938 Mallory**   Mallory 1938, 276

REAGENTS REQUIRED: *A.* DS 11.43 Ziehl 1882; *B.* ADS 12.2 Gram (1904); *C.* aniline

METHOD: [paraffin sections, nuclei stained by any DS 11.122 technique] → water → *A*, 1 hr. → water, wash → *B*, ½ to 1 min. → water, wash → blot → *C*, till differentiated → balsam, via xylene

23.223 Fuller 1938   11284, **23**:416

REAGENTS REQUIRED: *A.* 5% ferric alum; *B.* water 80, glycerol 10, 95% alc. 10, hematoxylin 1; *C.* 5% picric acid in 95% alc.; *D.* 1.5% magenta in sat. aq. sol. aniline; *E.* 3% nitric acid in 95% alc.; *F.* 0.01% ammonia; *G.* 1% light green

METHOD: [sections] → water → *A*, 5 mins., 50°C. → rinse → *B*, 5 mins. 50°C. → *C*, till nuclei only stained → *D*, on slide, heated to steaming 3 mins. → cool → reheat, 3 mins. → *E*, till sections pale pink → *F*, few secs. → wash, 10 mins. → *G*, 5 mins. → rinse → balsam, via usual reagents

RESULT: bacilli, red; nuclei, blue green; cytoplasm, pale green.

23.223 Haythorne 1929   4349, **12**:130
REAGENTS REQUIRED: *A.* DS 11.43 Ziehl 1882; *B.* 10% sulfuric acid; *C.* sat. abs. alc. sol.
    orange G
METHOD: [sections of F 3700.0010 Zenker 1894 fixed material with nuclei hematoxylin
    stained] → water → *A*, 1 hr., 55°C. → wash, 20°C. → wash, 8° to 10°C. → *B*, 8–10°C.,
    till sections pale violet → wash, 8°–10°C. → tap water → 95% alc., from drop bottle,
    least possible time → *C*, from drop bottle, till sections pale orange → blot → balsam,
    via xylene

23.223 Krajian 1943   *Tech. Bull.*, **4**:45
REAGENTS REQUIRED: *A.* DS 11.43 Ziehl 1882; *B.* water 40, 95% alc. 60, arsenic trioxide
    1; *C.* DS 11.44 Löffler 1890; *D.* creosote 50, isopropyl alc. 50
METHOD: [frozen sections varnished to slide with celloidin, or mounted paraffin ribbons]
    → water → *A*, heated to steaming, 3 mins.

23.223 Kühne *test.* **1904 Besson** *cit.* **Borrel**   Besson 1904, 638
REAGENTS REQUIRED: *A.* DS 11.122 Böhmer 1868; *B.* DS 11.43 Ziehl 1890; *C.* 2% aniline
    hydrochloride
METHOD: [sections] → water → *A*, 2 mins. → wash → *B*, 15 mins. → *C*, few secs. →
    abs. alc., till differentiated → balsam, via usual reagents

23.223 Langeron 1942   Langeron 1942, 1204
REAGENTS REQUIRED: *A.* DS 11.43 Ziehl 1882; *B.* 3% hydrochloric acid; *C.* 0.4% formal-
    dehyde; *D.* water 100, acetic acid 0.6, DS 11.43 Ziehl 1882 0.6; *E.* water 100, 40%
    formaldehyde 0.6, acetic acid 0.3; *F.* DS 12.211 Cajal 1895
METHOD: [sections] → water → *A*, ½ to 1 hr. → water, wash → *B*, till no more color
    comes away → *C*, 5 mins. → water, wash → *D*, 3 mins. → water, rinse → *E*, till no
    more color comes away → water, wash → *F*, 1 min. → 95% alc., till dehydrated →
    balsam, via usual reagents

23.223 Langrand 1913   *see* DS 23.32 Langrand 1913

23.223 Letulle 1894 *test.* **1894 Kahlden and Laurent**   Kahlden and Laurent 1894, 89
REAGENTS REQUIRED: *A.* DS 11.122 Böhmer 1868; *B.* DS 11.43 Ziehl 1890; *C.* water 100,
    iodine green 1, phenol 2
METHOD: [sections of F 7000.0000 fixed material] → water → *A*, 2–3 mins. → wash →
    B, 15 mins. → rinse → *C*, 5 mins. → abs. alc., till differentiated → balsam, via clove
    oil

23.223 Mallory 1938   Mallory 1938, 276
REAGENTS REQUIRED: *A.* DS 11.43 Ziehl 1882; *B.* 0.1% hydrochloric acid in 70% alc.;
    C. 0.01% ammonia
METHOD: [sections, nuclei prior stained, by any DS 11.122 method] → water → *A*, over-
    night → [*or*, *A*, 1 hr., 60°C.] → *B*, 20 secs. → *C*, wash → balsam, via usual reagents
NOTE: This is specifically recommended for tubercle bacilli.

23.223 Müller and Chermock 1945   11284, **30**:169
REAGENTS REQUIRED: *A.* DS 11.43 Müller and Chermock 1945; *B.* hydrochloric acid in
    95% alc.; *C.* water 98, 95% alc. 2, fast green FCF 0.005.
METHOD: [sections] → water → *A*, 5 mins. → rinse → *B*, till light pink → *C*, 2 mins. →
    rinse → balsam, via usual reagents

23.223 Putt 1951   *Tech. Bull.*, **21**:94
REAGENTS REQUIRED: *A.* water 90, methanol 10, phenol 5, magenta-III 1; *B.* sat. aq. sol.
    lithium carbonate; *C.* 5% acetic acid in 95% alc.; *D.* 0.5% methylene blue in abs. alc.
METHOD: [5 μ paraffin sections of formaldehyde-fixed material] → water → *A*, 5 mins. →
    B, 1 min. → *C*, 3–5 mins., till sections pale pink → abs. alc., wash → *D*, 1 min. → abs.
    alc., two changes, 30 secs. each → neutral mountant, via toluene
RECOMMENDED FOR: leprosy bacilli.

23.223 Spoerri 1933　　　　　　　　　　　　　　　20540b, **23**:133

REAGENTS REQUIRED: *A.* water 70, 95% alc. 30, cresyl violet 1, toluidine blue 0.5, thionine 0.25; *B.* 0.2% sulfuric acid

METHOD: [4 μ paraffin sections attached to slide by V 21.1 Spoerri 1939] → water → *A*, 5–10 secs., 90°C. → *B*, 1 sec. → rinse 1 sec. → 95% alc. 2 secs. → 80% alc., 1 sec. → *A*, 2 secs. → [repeat 80% alc. → A cycle till stain sufficient] → balsam, via usual reagents

23.223 Tilden and Tanaka 1945　　　　　　　　*Tech. Bull.*, **6**:95

REAGENTS REQUIRED: *A.* DS 11.43 Tilden and Tanaka 1945; *B.* 40% neutralized formaldehyde; *C.* 1% hydrochloric acid in 70% alc.; *D.* 1% potassium dichromate; *E.* 2% oxalic acid; *F.* DS 11.123 Harris 1900; *G.* DS 12.221 Fite 1939

METHOD: [sections of formaldehyde-alcohol-fixed material varnished to slide with nitrocellulose] → water → *A*, 15 mins. → wash → *B*, 5 mins. → wash → *C*, 5 mins. → wash → *D*, 2–5 mins. → wash → *E*, till brown not quite removed → wash → *F*, 2–5 mins. → wash → *G*, 3 mins. → gum damar, via usual reagents

23.224 Other Methods for Bacteria in Sections

Within the present class are grouped all those stains intended for sections which, when used for smears, lie within the classes DS 21.214 through DS 21.218. The majority of smear techniques can, in any case, be used for sections.

23.224 Lustgarten *test.* **1903 Cole**　　　　　　Cross and Cole 1903, 162

REAGENTS REQUIRED: *A*, aniline 3, 95% alc. 20, crystal violet 1, water 100; *B.* 1% potassium permanganate; *C.* 5% sulfuric acid

METHOD: [sections] → *A*, 24 hrs. → abs. alc., till color clouds cease → *B*, 10 secs. → *C*, few moments → wash → balsam, via usual reagents

RECOMMENDED FOR: spirochetes in sections.

23.224 Milovidov 1928　　*see* DS 22.21 Milovidov 1928

23.224 Nikiforoff *test.* **1916 Warthin**　　　　　　4349, **6**:56

REAGENTS REQUIRED: *A.* water 65, 95% alc. 35, propaeolin 0.35, methylene blue 1.3, potassium hydroxide 0.0005; *B.* abs. alc. 50, ether 50

METHOD: [sections of F 3700.0000 Nikiforoff 1916 fixed material] → water → *A*, 24 hrs. → wash → *B*, few dips → balsam, via usual reagents

RECOMMENDED FOR: spirochetes in sections.

23.224 Schmorl *test.* **1916 Warthin**　　　　　　4349, **6**:56

REAGENTS REQUIRED: *A.* DS 13.13 Giemsa 1902 3, water 97; *B.* 6% potassium alum

METHOD: [thin frozen sections] → *A*, 1 hr. → *A*, fresh solution, 24 hrs. → *B*, wash → rinse → [attach to slide, leave till nearly dry] → cedar oil → balsam

RECOMMENDED FOR: spirochetes in sections.

23.224 Smith *test.* **1924 Mallory and Wright**　　Mallory and Wright 1924, 289

REAGENTS REQUIRED: *A.* DS 23.211 Ehrlich 1882; *B.* ADS 12.2 Gram 1882; *C.* 40% formaldehyde; *D.* water 100, eosin Y 2.5, methyl green 0.5

METHOD: [sections of F 3700.0010-5 Zenker 1894 fixed material] → *A*, warmed to steaming, few secs. → drain → *B*, wash → *C*, wash → 95% alc., till no more color comes away → *B*, rinse → *D*, on slide, warmed to steaming, few moments → water, wash → balsam, via usual reagents

RECOMMENDED FOR: staining capsules in sections.

23.224 Stoughton 1930　　　　　　　　　　　　1025, **17**:162

REAGENTS REQUIRED: *A.* water 100, phenol 5, thionine 0.1; *B.* sat. alc. sol. (*circ.* 0.2%) orange G

METHOD: [sections] → water → *A*, 1 hr. → abs. alc., till dehydrated → *B*, 1 min. → abs. alc. till no more color comes away → balsam, via xylene

RECOMMENDED FOR: bacteria in plant tissues.

23.3 OTHER PARASITES AND COMMENSALS

The techniques here given are not only those which are specifically intended for the differentiation of parasite from host in sections, but include also those techniques which have been developed for the staining of specific parasites, and which cannot reasonably be employed for the staining of any free-living organism. The four classes which have been set up are obviously the only four into which parasites can be divided. The techniques which are given in each of the four classes are, without exception, so specific that their individual application is given under each.

23.30 TYPICAL EXAMPLES

Demonstration of mycelia of Penicillium in orange rind using the thionin-light green-orange G-erythrosin stain of Margolena 1932

The method here described is one of the easiest and most certain methods of demonstrating the penetration of the mycelia of parasitic fungi through the tissues of their plant hosts, though the example selected for demonstration is quite possibly an example of a saprophytic, rather than a parasitic, fungus. This material, however, has the advantage that it may be procured without the slightest difficulty, if it is required for class-demonstration purposes, and also that it permits a clear definition of the invading mycelia.

To secure a growth of Penicillium on orange rind it is only necessary to take an orange and to remove the wax, with which the marketer has protected and polished it, by rubbing any very fine form of grit gently onto the surface with the fingers. One of the most readily available forms of grit are the scouring powders sold for the cleaning of domestic utensils. If an orange be scrubbed with some of this scouring powder, it will not appreciably damage the surface, but will roughen it sufficiently to permit the spores of Penicillium, which are always in the air, to light directly on the damaged surface. The orange should then be placed under a bell jar on top of moist blotting paper and kept at about 85°F. After a few days, a vigorous growth of Penicillium will be seen on the surface, and a piece of about ¼-inch side should be cut from the rind and dropped into any of the alcohol-acetic-formaldehyde mixtures (Chapter 18, F 0000.1010) which may be available. It should remain in this fixative for about three days and then be placed in absolute alcohol in which it should remain, with frequent changes, until such time as the oil has ceased to leave it. The piece should then be embedded in paraffin (Chapter 12) and cut into sections of from ten to twelve microns in thickness. These sections are mounted on a slide, deparaffinized, and brought down to water. It is also possible, though not so convenient, to use this same technique on unmounted sections cut on a hand microtome.

The staining solutions required are: first, a 0.1% solution of thionin in 5% phenol; second, a 0.5% solution of light green in 95% alcohol; third, a mixture in the proportion of 1:2 of a saturated alcoholic solution of orange G with a saturated solution of erythrosin in clove oil.

The sections are taken from water and placed in the thionin solution for one hour. They are then rinsed in water to remove the excess thionin, or, if many sections are being dealt with, accumulated in water while the next stage is passed through. The sections are then dehydrated before being dipped up and down in the light green until the color changes from blue to green. They may then be returned to water until no more color comes away. All the sections are then taken together and passed to absolute alcohol, in which they remain until they are dehydrated. Several changes of absolute alcohol may be required, but graded alcohols cannot be used because they would extract the stain. The alcohol-clove-oil stain mixture is then dropped, from a drop bottle, on each individual slide and allowed to act for from one to two minutes. The excess stain is then washed off the slide with fresh clove oil, the clove oil removed with xylene, and the section mounted in balsam.

Demonstration of parasitic fungi in
tissue scrapings using the technique
of Chalmers and Marshall 1914

All the methods for the diagnostic demonstration of fungi in tissue scrapings are
very much the same, and combine partial
hydrolysis (clearing) of the removed epi-
dermal tissue in strong alkali with the
staining of the fungi by a bacterial staining method, subsequently differentiated in
aniline. The present method (DS 23.32
Chalmers and Marshall 1914) is one of the
easiest to use and has, therefore, been selected for discussion. It is to be presumed
that scrapings from the surface of the
patient's skin will be removed by the
physician, and it is recommended that
they be brought to the technician in a
watch glass. The technician should sort
over the material presented, and should
remove from it with fine forceps those
pieces which definitely present the appearance of scales. These scales are then
placed in a 25% solution of potassium hydroxide at 40°C. for a few hours. The
scales must then have the alkali removed,
for which purpose it is best to use 15%
alcohol rather than water. The washing is
most easily done by picking up the scales
with a section lifter and passing them
through half a dozen watch glasses of 15%
alcohol, rather than by pouring off the
solution and replacing it with alcohol. It
does not matter how long the specimens
remain in alcohol. It is often a useful routine procedure to accumulate all of the
day's collected scrapings in separate jars
of alcohol, and to stain them the first
thing the next morning before additional
scales are received. When it is desired to
stain the material, each separate scale is
lifted from the 15% alcohol and placed in
the center of a chemically clean slide
where it is dried. If the scales have been
so softened that they cannot be lifted from
the fluid, it is only necessary to pour the
contents of the jar into a fingerbowl of
15% alcohol, and then to maneuver the
slide under the selected scale. This scale
is then held with a needle against the
slide, which is lifted from the alcohol,
leaving the scale stranded. The objection
to the stranding technique is that it is

difficult to place more than one scale on a
slide, whereas if each scale can be lifted
and spread out, a dozen typical scales
from one patient may be stained on the
same slide. It does not matter whether
the slides are dried at room temperature
or on a warm table, but there is some risk
that, if the temperature is elevated too
far, the scale will curl off the slide as it
dries.

A drop of Ehrlich's crystal violet (DS
23.211 Ehrlich 1882) is then placed over
the scales, and allowed to remain at room
temperature for about 20 minutes. It
should be looked at from time to time and,
if it shows signs of drying, further quantities of crystal violet should be placed on
top. At the end of 20 minutes the crystal
violet is drained carefully from the scales,
which are not washed, and replaced with
several drops of Gram's iodine (Chapter
22, ADS 12.2) which is allowed to act for a
period of about 3 minutes.

Differentiation in aniline is very simple,
for it is impossible to overdifferentiate.
The slide is placed at about a 45° angle in
a glass dish, and aniline is allowed to flow
over it from a pipet. If the drops are allowed to fall from a height the scales may
become detached, therefore, the edge of
the pipet should be rested just above the
scales, and a slow and steady stream of
aniline allowed to flow over them. This
stream of aniline must be continued until
no further color comes away, by which
time the fungal hyphae will be perfectly
differentiated against a colorless background. They may be mounted in this
condition if desired, or, as suggested by
Chalmers and Marshall (DS 23.32 below),
counterstained for one minute with a 2%
alcoholic solution of eosin Y, which is
poured over the slide without removal of
the aniline. Aniline is then used exactly as
before to remove the excess eosin; the flow
of aniline is discontinued when no more
eosin comes away. The aniline is then
washed from the slide with xylene and the
specimens are mounted in balsam. Fungal
hyphae will be clearly stained bright blue
against a yellow background. The principal purpose of the background is to enable one to find the scales under a low
power of the microscope before using the

high to search for fungal filaments. Without the counterstain it is sometimes very
difficult to detect the almost perfectly
cleared scales in a balsam mount. These
slides may be filed for reference, for they
are quite permanent.

23.31 PLANTS PARASITIC IN PLANTS

23.31 Bostrøm *test.* **1896 Kahlden and Laurent**   Kahlden and Laurent 1896, 120
REAGENTS REQUIRED: *A.* DS 23.211 Ehrlich 1882; *B.* DS 11.24 Ranvier 1889
METHOD: [sections] → water → *A*, 10–15 mins. → *B*, 5–10 mins. → water, wash → abs.
alc., till differentiated → balsam, via xylene
RECOMMENDED FOR: staining actinomycetes in sections of plant tissues.

23.31 Cartwright 1929   1032, **43** :412
REAGENTS REQUIRED: *A.* 1% safranin; *B.* water 100, anilin blue 1, picric acid 1
METHOD: [sections of wood] → water → *A*, few secs. → water, wash → *B*, heated to sim-
mering, few mins. → water, till no more color comes away → balsam, via usual
reagents
RECOMMENDED FOR: hyphae in woody sections.

23.31 Cohen 1935   20540b, **10** :25
REAGENTS REQUIRED: *A.* water 97, acetic acid 3, orseillin BB to sat.; *B.* 1% crystal violet
in clove oil
METHOD: [sections from F 5600.1000 Cohen 1935 fixed material] → water → *A*, 30 mins.
→ rinse → dehydrate via graded alcs. → *B*, 5 mins. → xylene, wash → balsam

23.31 Cornwall 1937   *Microscope,* **1** :137
REAGENTS REQUIRED: *A.* water 100, picric acid 0.25, methyl blue 0.35; *B.* 0.25% safranin
O in 90% alc.
METHOD: [sections of alcohol-fixed wood] → *A*, 15–20 mins. → 50% alc., till no more
color comes away → *B*, 5 mins. → 70% alc., rinse → abs. alc., till pink
RECOMMENDED FOR: fungus hyphae (blue) in wood.

23.31 Dickson 1920   19938, **52** :63
REAGENTS REQUIRED: *A.* 2% phloxine in 85% alc.; *B.* clove oil 98, abs. alc. 2, light green 2
METHOD: [sections] → 95% alc. → *A*, 5–10 mins. → 95% alc., wash → *B*, 1–3 mins. →
clove oil, till no more color comes away → balsam, via usual reagents
RECOMMENDED FOR: staining fungus in plant tissues.
NOTE: "Phloxine" is given for solution *A* above on the authority of Conn 1946, 112, who
states that Dickson was in error in supposing his stain to be Magdala red.

23.31 Ferrari 1930   2174, **2** :81
REAGENTS REQUIRED: *A.* 0.01% ruthenium red; *B.* 10% potassium hydroxide
METHOD: [alcohol-preserved tissues] → *A*, till stained (10 mins. to several days) → *B*,
till differentiated → glycerol
RECOMMENDED FOR: staining fungi in plant tissues.

23.31 Garrett 1937 *test.* **1942 Langeron**   Langeron 1942, 1285
FORMULA: water 100, sodium hydroxide 4, bromthymol blue 0.4
METHOD: [fresh root tissue] → *A*, overnight → glycerol
RECOMMENDED FOR: staining fungi in roots.

23.31 Hutchins and Lutman 1941   20540b, **16** :63
REAGENTS REQUIRED: *A.* water 88, 95% alc. 10, aniline 2, crystal violet 5; *B.* ADS 12.2
Gram 1884
METHOD: [sections] → water → *A*, 24 hrs. → wash → *B*, 24 hrs. → abs. alc., till color
clouds cease → xylene, till no more color comes away → balsam
RECOMMENDED FOR: actinomyces in potato tuber tissue.

23.31 Israel *test.* **1940 Johansen**   Johansen 1940, 226
REAGENTS REQUIRED: *A.* sat. aq. sol. orcein in 0.1% acetic acid
METHOD: [sections] → water → *A*, several hrs. → abs. alc., till differentiated (several
hrs.) → balsam, via xylene
RECOMMENDED FOR: staining actinomycetes in sections of plant tissues.

23.31 Johansen 1940   *see* DS 13.5 Johansen 1940

23.31 Langeron 1942   Langeron 1942, 1285
REAGENTS REQUIRED: *A*. water 100, sodium carbonate 20, benzoazurine 0.2; *B*. glycerol
90, water 10, cupric sulfate 0.2
METHOD: [pieces or sections, chlorine-bleached if necessary] → *A*, 1–2 hrs. → *B*, for
preservation
RECOMMENDED FOR: staining fungus in plant tissues.

23.31 Lepik 1928   16233, **18**:869
REAGENTS REQUIRED: *A*. 95% alc. 40, phenol 20, lactic acid 40, glycerol 20; *B*. *A* (above)
100, anilin blue 0.02, safranin 0.1; *C*. DS 12.14 safranin
METHOD: [sections] → 95% alc. → *A*, 1–15 mins. → *B*, 2 hrs. → *A*, till differentiated →
abs. alc. till dehydrated → *C*, till clear → clove oil, till no more color comes away →
balsam, via xylene
RECOMMENDED FOR: staining of Peronosporales in sections.

23.31 Mangin 1895   5133, **8**:1
REAGENTS REQUIRED: *A*. 10% potassium hydroxide in 90% alc.; *B*. acetic acid 100,
orceillin BB *q.s.*; anilin blue *q.s.*
PREPARATION OF B: add enough each of sat. sols. of the two dyes to make a violet mixture.
METHOD: [pieces, if necessary chlorine-bleached] → *A*, 1–2 hrs. → *B*, till sufficiently
stained → glycerol
RECOMMENDED FOR: demonstration of Peronosporales in pieces.

23.31 Margolena 1932   20540b, **7**:25
REAGENTS REQUIRED: *A*. DS 11.44 Stoughton 1930; *B*. 0.5% light green in 95% alc.;
C. sat. alc. sol. (*circ.* 0.25%) orange G 30, sat. clove oil sol. erythrosin 60
METHOD: [sections] → water → *A*, 1 hr. → water, rinse → *B*, till sections appear green
→ water, till no more color comes away → abs. alc., till dehydrated → *C*, 1–2 mins. →
balsam, via xylene
RECOMMENDED FOR: staining fungus hyphae in plant tissues.
NOTE: A detailed description of the use of this technique is given under DS 23.30 above.

23.31 Moore 1933   19938, **77**:23
REAGENTS REQUIRED: *A*. 2% ferric alum; *B*. water 20, glycerol 40, lactic acid 20, phenol
20, phenosafranin 0.5; *C*. 0.5% ferric alum in 0.5% hydrochloric acid; *D*. 1% ammonium hydroxide
METHOD: [paraffin sections] → water → *A*, 2 hrs. → water, quick rinse → *B*, 5–15 mins.
→ water, rinse → *C*, till differentiated → *D*, 15–30 secs. → balsam, via usual reagents
RECOMMENDED FOR: staining hyphae in sections.

23.31 Ravn *test.* **1942 Langeron** *cit.* **Strasburger**   Langeron 1942, 1285
REAGENTS REQUIRED: *A*. water 100, acetic acid 3, orceillin BB to sat.; *B*. water 100,
acetic acid 3, anilin blue to sat.
METHOD: [sections of chrome fixed, or mordanted, material] → *A*, 12–24 hrs. → water,
wash → *B*, 1–2 hrs. → 95% alc., till differentiated → balsam, via usual reagents
RECOMMENDED FOR: staining fungus in plant tissues.

23.31 Vaughn 1914   1048, **1**:241
REAGENTS REQUIRED: *A*. water 75, 95% alc. 25, malachite green 0.25, acid fuchsin 0.05,
Martius yellow 0.005; *B*. 0.1% hydrochloric acid in 95% alc.
METHOD: [sections] → water → *A*, ¼ to 1 hr. → water, rinse → *B*, till differentiated →
balsam, via carbol-xylene
RECOMMENDED FOR: demonstration of hyphae in sections.

23.32 PLANTS PARASITIC IN ANIMALS

23.32 Bachman 1920   1752, **1**:50
FORMULA: water 70, 95% alc. 20, acetic acid 3, orange G 0.5, sat. sol. (*circ.* 1%) crystal
violet 7.5

PREPARATION: Dissolve orange in solvents. Add violet.

METHOD: [fresh scrapings] → water, on slide → dry → stain, on slide, 2 mins. → 95% alc., 15 secs. → water, 15 secs. → dry

RECOMMENDED FOR: staining fungi in tissue scrapings.

23.32 Bardelli and Cillé 1928 *test.* 1942 Langeron   Langeron 1942, 1251

REAGENTS REQUIRED: *A.* acetic acid; *B.* DS 11.43 Ziehl 1882; *C.* ADS 12.2 Lugol; *D.* aniline

METHOD: [thin sections] → *A*, on slide, warmed gently, 30 secs. → 96% alc., thorough wash → dry → *B*, 3 mins. → drain or blot → *C*, 5 mins. → *D*, till differentiated → balsam, via carbol-xylene

RECOMMENDED FOR: demonstration of Zymonema in sections.

23.32 Berberian 1937   1756, **36**:1171

REAGENTS REQUIRED: *A.* 50% acetic acid; *B.* ether; *C.* acetone; *D.* DS 11.44 Martinotti 1910 75, glycerol 20, 95% alc. 5; *E.* 0.5% acetic acid

METHOD: [scrapings] → *A*, on slide → dry → *B*, on slide, 20–30 secs. → *C*, 2 changes, 1 min. each → abs. alc. → [series alcs. to 70%] → *D*, 10–15 mins. → *E*, till differentiated → balsam, via acetone and xylene

RECOMMENDED FOR: fungus hyphae in skin scrapings.

23.32 Besson 1904   Besson 1904, 70

REAGENTS REQUIRED: *A.* DS 11.24 Orth (1924); *B.* DS 23.211 Ehrlich 1882; *C.* 0.7% sodium chloride; *D.* ADS 12.2 Gram 1884; *E.* aniline

METHOD: [sections] → *A*, overnight → rinse → *B*, 20 mins. → *C*, rinse → *D*, some minutes → *E*, on slide, till differentiated → balsam, via xylene

RECOMMENDED FOR: demonstration of *Aspergillus fumigatus* in sections of lung.

23.32 Bernhardt 1943   1829, **48**:533

REAGENTS REQUIRED: *A.* 10% potassium hydroxide; *B.* M 13.1 Bernhardt 1943 100, cotton blue 0.5; *C.* M 13.1 Bernhardt 1943

METHOD: [skin scrapings or nail fragments] → *A*, under cover, till clear and soft → press cover with blotter → *B*, drawn under cover, warmed → press cover with blotter → *C*, drawn under cover → seal

23.32 Bigot 1924   5310, **17**:547

REAGENTS REQUIRED: *A.* DS 12.15 crystal violet; *B.* ADS 12.2 Gram 1884; *C.* 1% erythrosin

METHOD: [smears, fixed in F 5000.1010 Duboscq and Brazil 1905 and depicrated in lithium carbonate sol.] → *A*, 6–12 hrs. → quick rinse → *B*, 1 min. → water, thorough wash → *C*, 30 secs. → water, wash → dry

RECOMMENDED FOR: demonstration of Zymonema in tissue fragments or exudates.

23.32 Boeck *test.* 1896 Kahlden and Laurent   Kahlden and Laurent 1896, 146

REAGENTS REQUIRED: *A.* DS 11.44 Sahli 1885; *B.* 0.1% resorcin; *C.* 3% dilution of 30% hydrogen peroxide

METHOD: [scales degreased in alc. and ether] → water → *A*, 1–2 mins. → *B*, ½ to 1 min. → *C*, till differentiated → wash → balsam, via usual reagents

RECOMMENDED FOR: fungi in skin scrapings.

23.32 Chalmers and Marshall 1914   11587, **17**:256

REAGENTS REQUIRED: *A.* 40% potassium hydroxide; *B.* DS 23.211 Ehrlich 1882; *C.* ADS 12.2 Gram 1884; *D.* aniline; *E.* 2% eosin Y in 95% alc.

METHOD: [scrapings] → *A*, some hrs., 40°C. → 15% alc. thorough wash → strand on slide → dry → *B*, on slide, 20 mins. → drain → *C*, 3 mins. → *D*, till no more color comes away → *E*, 1 min. → *D*, till no more color comes away → balsam, via xylene

RECOMMENDED FOR: staining fungi in tissue scrapings.

NOTE: A detailed description of the use of this technique is given under DS 23.30 above.

23.32 Curtis *test.* 1904 Besson   Besson 1904, 699

REAGENTS REQUIRED: *A.* DS 11.28 von Orth 1892; *B.* water 100, potassium hydroxide 0.01, methyl violet 6B 1.5; *C.* 1% pyrogallic acid

METHOD: [sections] → A, 10–15 mins. → wash → B, 10 mins. → wash → C, 1 min. wash → balsam, via usual reagents
RECOMMENDED FOR: Saccharomyces in sections.

23.32 Guégen 1905   5293, 21:42

REAGENTS REQUIRED: A. P 12.2 Amann 1896; B. P 12.2 Amann 1896 100, Sudan III to sat., aniline blue 0.5
PREPARATION OF B: Boil Sudan III in solvent to saturation. Cool. Filter. Dissolve blue in filtrate.
METHOD: [scrapings] → A, till clear → drain → B, added on slide → cover → seal
RECOMMENDED FOR: staining fungi in tissue scrapings.

23.32 Guégen 1906   5293, 22:224

FORMULA: lactic acid 100, Sudan III 0.1, anilin blue 0.1, ADS 12.2 Lugol 0.1
PREPARATION: Dissolve Sudan III in lactic acid with boiling. Cool. Add other ingredients.
METHOD: As Guégen 1905 above.

23.32 Kligman, Mescon, and DeLameter 1951   Tech. Bull., 21:86

REAGENTS REQUIRED: A. 1% periodic acid; B. DS 11.43 Feulgen and Rosenbeck 1924; C. 5% thionyl chloride; D. 1% light green
METHOD: [sections] → water → A, 5 mins. → thorough wash → B, 10–15 mins. → C, 5 mins. → thorough wash → D, 1 min. → balsam, via usual reagents
NOTE: This is a synthesis of the methods of Hotchkiss 1948 (Arch. Biochem., 16:131) and McManns (20540b, 23:99).

23.32 Langrand 1913   9775, 7:128

REAGENTS REQUIRED: A. DS 11.43 Ziehl 1882; B. 2% aniline hydrochloride; C. DS 12.15 crystal violet; D. ADS 12.2 Gram 1884; E. 0.2% eosin Y
METHOD: [sections] → A, on slide, warmed to steaming, 5 mins. → water, wash → B, several dips → abs. alc., till no more color comes away → water, wash → C, on slide, 3 mins. → water, rinse → D, on slide, 1 min. → water, wash → E, few secs. → balsam, via usual reagents
RESULT: Tubercle bacilli, red; actinomyces, violet.
RECOMMENDED FOR: demonstration of actinomyces and tubercle bacilli in sections.

23.32 Lemière and Bécue test. 1904 Besson   Besson 1904, 677

REAGENTS REQUIRED: A. 30% potassium carbonate; B. 5% eosin; C. 50% sodium acetate
METHOD: [dry smear] → ether, 2–3 mins. → dry → A, several mins. → B, 15 mins. → C, 5 mins. → seal in C
RECOMMENDED FOR: actinomyces in smears of pus.

23.32 Lignières 1903   1886, 7:444

REAGENTS REQUIRED: A. DS 12.15 crystal violet; B. ADS 12.2 Lugol (1905); C. abs. alc. 80, acetone 20, acetic acid 2, sat. sol. (circ. 12.5%) acid fuchsin 0.3; D. 1% acetic acid
METHOD: [sections, nuclei stained by any DS 11.11 technique] → water → A, 3 mins. → rinse → B, 1 min. → C, till section turns bright red → water, till differentiation complete → D, few dips → salicylic balsam, via carbol-xylene
RECOMMENDED FOR: demonstration of actinomyces in sections.

23.32 Mahdissan 1935   1798, 85:61

REAGENTS REQUIRED: A. 5% potassium hydroxide; B. 5% acetic acid; C. 1% acid fuchsin; D. 0.01% picric acid in xylene
METHOD: [larvae fixed in F 0000.1010 Mahdissan 1935] → water → A, till skin transparent → B, 5 mins. → C, 30 mins. → wash, till no more color comes away → [graded alcs.] → D, till clear → balsam
RECOMMENDED FOR: demonstration of symbiotic microflora in larvae of scale insects.

23.32 Mallory 1895a test. 1938 ips.   Mallory 1938, 279

REAGENTS REQUIRED: A. 2.5% phloxine; B. DS 23.211 Ehrlich 1882; C. ADS 12.2 Gram 1884; D. aniline
METHOD: [paraffin sections of alcohol- or formaldehyde-fixed material, nuclei stained by any DS 11.122 method] → water → A, 15 mins., 50°C. → water, wash → B, 5–15 mins.

→ water, wash → *C*, 1 min. → water, wash → blot → *D*, till no more color comes away → balsam, via xylene

RECOMMENDED FOR: staining actinomycetes in paraffin sections.

23.32 Mallory 1895b *test.* **1938** *ips.*   Mallory 1938, 279

REAGENTS REQUIRED: *A.* DS 23.211 Ehrlich 1882; *B.* aniline 100, magenta to sat.; *C.* aniline

METHOD: [celloidin sections of alcohol- or formaldehyde-fixed material attached to slide after nuclear staining by any DS 11.122 method] → water → *A*, 3–10 mins. → water, wash → blot → *B*, 1–3 mins. → *C*, till differentiated → balsam, via xylene

RECOMMENDED FOR: staining actinomycetes in celloidin sections.

23.32 Morel and Dulaus *test.* **1904 Besson**   Besson 1904, 677

REAGENTS REQUIRED: *A.* Any DS 11.123 formula; *B.* 1% Victoria blue in 10% alc.; *C.* ADS 12.2 Gram 1884; *D.* 1% methyl violet in 10% alc.; *E.* oil of cinnamon 50, abs. alc. 50

METHOD: [sections] → *A*, till nuclei stained → wash → *B*, 3 mins. → wash → *C*, few secs. → 95% alc., wash → *D*, several minutes → abs. alc. rinse → *E*, till differentiated → balsam, via usual reagents

RECOMMENDED FOR: staining actinomyces in sections.

23.32 Morris *test.* **1943 Cowdry** *cit.* **Mallory and Wright**
                                            Cowdry 1943, 82

REAGENTS REQUIRED: *A.* 95% alc. 50, ether 50; *B.* 5% gentian violet in 70% alc.; *C.* ADS 12.2 Gram 1882; *D.* aniline 100, nitric acid 1

METHOD: [fresh scrapings] → *A*, 5–10 mins. → dry → *B*, on slide, 5–30 mins. → *C*, 1 min. → water, rinse → *D*, till differentiated → balsam, via xylene

RECOMMENDED FOR: staining fungi in tissue scrapings.

23.32 Priestly 1917   13034, **2**:471

REAGENTS REQUIRED: *A.* P 12.2 Priestly 1917a or b.; *B.* chloroform; *C.* formic acid; *D.* DS 11.44 Sahli 1885

METHOD: [fresh scrapings] → *A*, till clear → water, wash → *B*, 5 mins. → strand on slide → dry → *C*, 2–3 mins., 100°C. → water, wash → *D*, 10–15 mins. → water, rinse → 95% alc., till differentiated → balsam, via usual reagents

RECOMMENDED FOR: demonstration of hyphae in skin scrapings.

23.32 Schleiff 1940   14674, **87**:785

REAGENTS REQUIRED: *A.* F 0000.0010 Carnoy 1887; *B.* 0.5% azur I

METHOD: [skin scrapings on slide] → *A*, 3–10 mins. → drain → dry → *B*, on slide, 2–3 mins. → wash → dry

RECOMMENDED FOR: demonstration of fungal hyphae in skin.

23.32 Schubert 1937   7176, **105**:1025

REAGENTS REQUIRED: *A.* 2% potassium hydroxide; *B.* water 50, phenol 25, lactic acid 25, anilin blue 1.25

METHOD: [fresh scrapings] → *A*, ½ to 1 hr. → water, thorough wash (at least 3 hrs.) → *B*, on slide → examine

RECOMMENDED FOR: staining fungi in tissue scrapings.

23.32 Swartz and Conant 1936   1752, **33**:291

REAGENTS REQUIRED: *A.* 10% potassium hydroxide; *B.* P 12.2 Amann 1896 100, anilin blue 0.5; *C.* P 12.2 Amann 1896

METHOD: [skin scraping] → *A*, till clear → drain → wash, on slide → *B*, 5–10 mins. → *C*, till surplus *B* removed → M 11 mountant

RECOMMENDED FOR: demonstration of hyphae in skin scrapings.

23.32 Unna 1929   7176, **88**:314

FORMULA: water 80, glycerol 10, 95% alc. 9, pyronin 0.9, methyl green 0.1, phenol 0.5.

METHOD: [10 μ sections of alcohol-fixed material] → water → stain 5–10 secs. → water, rinse → abs. alc., till dehydrated → balsam, via xylene

RECOMMENDED FOR: fungi in skin sections.

23.33 ANIMALS PARASITIC IN ANIMALS

23.33 Alli 1944   13685, **95**:317
REAGENTS REQUIRED: *A*. ADS 12.1 Alli 1944; *B*. 4% ferric alum; *C*. 1% hematein; *D*. 0.1% hydrochloric acid in 70% alc.
METHOD: [fresh smears] → *A*, 10 mins. → wash → *B*, 10 secs. → rinse → *C*, 5–10 mins. → wash → *D*, till differentiated → balsam, via usual reagents
RECOMMENDED FOR: intestinal protozoans.
NOTE: **Morrison 1946** substitutes his ADS 12.1 for *A* and omits *B*.

23.33 Anonymous 1946   4349, **26**:13
REAGENTS REQUIRED: *A*. water 100, calc. chloride 0.01, phloxine 1; *B*. DS 11.44 Anonymous 1946; *C*. acetone; *D*. 0.2% acetic acid; *E*. ADS 22.1 Anonymous 1946
METHOD: [sections] → water → *A*, 5 mins. → tap water, 1 min. → *B*, 1 min. → rinse → *C*, 2 mins. → *D*, till color clouds cease → *E*, 1–2 mins. → balsam, via acetone and xylene
RECOMMENDED FOR: malarial parasites in sections.

23.33 Bidegaray 1926   899a, **4**:385
REAGENTS REQUIRED: *A*. ADS 12.2 Lugol (1905); *B*. DS 23.212 Nicolle 1895 (dye solution)
METHOD: [fresh fecal smear] → equal parts of *A* and *B*, mixed with smear, 2–3 mins. → examine
RECOMMENDED FOR: protozoans in fecal smears.

23.33 Bignami *test*. 1896 Kahlden and Laurent   Kahlden and Laurent 1896, 126
FORMULA: 95% alc. 100, magenta, aurantia *a.a.q.s.* to sat.
METHOD: [sections of F 3000.0010 Bignami (1896) fixed material] → 95% alc. → stain overnight → abs. alc., till differentiated → balsam, via xylene
RECOMMENDED FOR: Plasmodium in sections.

23.33 Borrel 1901   857, **15**:57
REAGENTS REQUIRED: *A*. sat. aq. sol. magenta; *B*. DS 12.211 Cajal 1895
METHOD: [sections of F 1260.0030 Besson 1904 fixed material] → water → *A*, 1 hr. → *B*, till differentiated → abs. alc., minimum possible time → balsam, via clove oil
RECOMMENDED FOR: coccidia in tissues.

23.33 Corbin 1946   *Tech. Bull.*, **7**:92
REAGENTS REQUIRED: *A*. water 80; *B*. 20; *B*. water 29, glycerol 19 DS 13.13 Giemsa 1902 (dry powder) 0.29, DS 11.44 Corbin 1946 3.5, 0.5% eosin Y in 25% alc. 5.7, methanol 43
METHOD: [air-dried, thick blood smears] → *A*, 2 mins. → *B*, 15 secs. → wash → dry
RECOMMENDED FOR: malarial parasites.

23.33 Chorine 1932   5310, **25**:561
REAGENTS REQUIRED: *A*. 4% formaldehyde; pH 7.5; *B*. water 100, potassium iodide 2, ADS 12.2 Lugol (1905) 3; *C*. 5% sodium thiosulfate; *D*. water 95, DS 13.13 Giemsa 1902 5
METHOD: [thick smears, even when old] → *A*, till bleached → water, wash → *B*, 3–5 mins. → water, rinse → *C*, till colorless → water, wash → *D*, 10–30 mins. → water wash → dry
RECOMMENDED FOR: staining Plasmodium in smears.

23.33 Crough and Becker 1931   19938, **73**:212
REAGENTS REQUIRED: *A*. acetic acid; *B*. 0.01% Janus green; *C*. sat. aq. sol. eosin
METHOD: [oöcysts, separated by saline flotation, on slide under coverslip] → *A*, drawn under cover, 10 mins. 30–40°C. → *B*, drawn under cover, 10 mins. → *C*, drawn under cover, 5 mins. → wash → blot → seal coverslip
RECOMMENDED FOR: oöcysts of coccidia.

23.33 Dammin 1937   11284, **23**:192
REAGENTS REQUIRED: *A*. water 70, acetic acid 20, 40% formaldehyde 10, picric acid 1; *B*. 10% sodium hydroxide; *C*. 5% hydrochloric acid

METHOD: [short lengths compressed between bound slides] → *A*, overnight → remove slides → running water, 2–3 mins. → *B*, till partial clearing shows reproductive system orange on yellow → water, quick rinse → *C*, 1–2 hrs. → water, thorough wash → balsam, via usual reagents

RECOMMENDED FOR: diagnostic demonstration of cestode reproductive system.

23.33 Dobell 1919   Dobell 1919, 7
REAGENTS REQUIRED: *A*. water 85, 95% alc. 15, acid fuchsin 0.5; *B*. 1% acetic acid; *C*. DS 12.211 Cajal 1895; *D*. 0.2% acetic acid
METHOD: [sections] → water → *A*, 10 mins. → water, thorough wash → *B*, on slide, few secs. → drain → *C*, on slide, 10 mins. → water, rinse → *D*, till differentiated → abs. alc., till differentiated → balsam, via xylene
RECOMMENDED FOR: differential staining of *E. histolytica* in sections.

23.33 Dobell 1919   *see* DS 13.7 Dobell 1919

23.33 Dobell 1942a   16035, **34**:101
REAGENTS REQUIRED: *A*. 2% phosphotungstic acid; *B*. 0.2% hematoxylin
METHOD: [fixed smears] → *A*, 10 mins. → wash → *B*, 10 mins. → wash → balsam, via usual reagents

23.33 Dobell 1942b   16035, **34**:101
REAGENTS REQUIRED: *A*. 2% ammonium molybdate; *B*. 0.2% hematoxylin
METHOD: [fixed smears] → *A*, 10 mins. → thorough wash → *B*, 10 mins. → wash → balsam, via usual reagents
RECOMMENDED FOR: intestinal protozoans, particularly Trichomonas.

23.33 Field 1940   21671, **34**:195
REAGENTS REQUIRED: *A*. water 100, sodium phosphate (anhydr.) 1, potassium dihydrogen phosphate (anhydr.) 1.25, brilliant cresyl blue 1
METHOD: [air-dried smears] → *A*, 1 sec. → wash, 5 secs. → drain → dry
RECOMMENDED FOR: Plasmodium in thick smears.

23.33 Giemsa 1935   23684, **134**:483
REAGENTS REQUIRED: *A*. DS 13.13 Giemsa 1902; *B*. water 100, sodium phosphate, monobasic 1, eosin Y 0.01
METHOD: [dry smear] → *A*, 30 mins. → water, quick rinse → *B*, till differentiated → water, rinse → dry
RECOMMENDED FOR: staining Plasmodium in smears.

23.33 Ginrich 1941   20540b, **16**:159
REAGENTS REQUIRED: *A*. DS 13.13 Giemsa 1902 1, water 99; *B*. DS 13.11 May and Grünwald 1902
METHOD: [thick blood films] → *A*, 15 mins. → wash → dry → *B*, 30 secs. → wash → dry
RECOMMENDED FOR: permanent slides of Plasmodium.

23.33 Goldman 1952   Cowdry 1952
STOCK SOLUTIONS: I. 1% hematoxylin in 95% alc., II. water 100, sulfuric acid 0.12, acetic acid 1, ferric alum 4
WORKING SOLUTION: stock I 50, stock II 50
METHOD: [fixed smears] → stain, ½–3 mins. → wash → balsam, via usual reagents
RECOMMENDED FOR: intestinal protozoans.

23.33 Hewitt 1939   11428, **24** (suppl.):22
REAGENTS REQUIRED: *A*. 2.5% potassium dichromate; *B*. water 97, DS 13.13 Giemsa 1902 3
METHOD: [5 μ sections of F 3700.1000 Helly 1903 fixed material] → water → *A*, ½ to 1 hr. → water, quick rinse → *B*, 24 hrs. → water, rinse → 70% alc., till differentiated → balsam, via graded acetone-xylene mixtures
RECOMMENDED FOR: staining Plasmodium in sections.

23.33 Hewitt 1939   600a, **29**:115
REAGENTS REQUIRED: *A*. 2.5% potassium dichromate; *B*. water 100, DS 13.13 Giemsa 2.5, sodium bicarbonate 0.0005
METHOD: [5 μ sections of F 3700.0010 Zenker 1894 material] → water → *A*, 30–60 mins. → rinse → *B*, 24 hrs. → 70% alc., till differentiated → balsam, via acetone and xylene
RECOMMENDED FOR: avian malarial parasites in tissues.

23.33 Hobbs and Thompson 1945   *Tech. Bull.*, **6**:29
REAGENTS REQUIRED: *A*. water 100, potassium dihydrogen phosphate (anhyd.) 1.25, sodium phosphate, dibasic (anhyd.) 1, azur B 0.1, methylene blue 0.16; *B*. 1% eosin in same buffer as *A*.
METHOD: [air-dried smear] → *A*, 1 sec. → rinse, 5 secs. → *B*, 1 sec. → rinse, 5 secs. → dry
RECOMMENDED FOR: Plasmodium.

23.33 Hollande 1920   1915, **59**:75
REAGENTS REQUIRED: *A*. 1% eosin Y; *B*. 1% phosphomolybdic acid; *C*. 0.5% light green; *D*. amyl alc.
METHOD: [smears fixed in F 5000.1040 Hollande 1911 or F 4500.1010 Hollande 1918] → [nuclei stained by any DS 11.111 method and fully differentiated] → water → ½ to 1 min. → 95% alc., till differentiated → *D*, till dehydrated → balsam, via xylene
RECOMMENDED FOR: staining flagellate protozoans in fecal smears.

23.33 Jäger *test*. **1928 Schmorl**   Schmorl 1928, 432
REAGENTS REQUIRED: *A*. Any DS 11.122 formula; *B*. 0.1% eosin Y
METHOD: [fecal smears fixed in F 3000.0010 Jäger 1928] → *A*, 10 mins. → wash → *B*, 1–2 mins. → balsam, via usual reagents
RECOMMENDED FOR: parasitic amebas.

23.33 Knowles 1931   9943, **64**:271
REAGENTS REQUIRED: *A*. water 100, acetic acid 1, tartaric acid 0.8; *B*. methanol; *C*. buffer pH 7.2; *D*. DS 13.13 Giemsa 1902
METHOD: [thick smears] → *A*, till bleached → water, wash → *B*, 2–3 mins. → *C*, wash → *D*, 5–10 mins. → water, wash → dry

23.33 Kofoid *test*. **1920 Stitt**   Stitt 1920, 58
STOCK SOLUTIONS: *A*. sat. sol. eosin in normal saline; *B*. sat. sol. iodine in 5% potassium iodide in normal saline
REAGENTS REQUIRED: *A*. stock A 50, stock B 50; *B*. normal saline
METHOD: Mix 1 drop feces with *A*, another with *B*. Place on slide and cover both drops with 1 coverslip.
RECOMMENDED FOR: demonstration of protozoans in fecal smears.

23.33 Langeron 1942   Langeron 1942, 763
REAGENTS REQUIRED: *A*. DS 11.22 Grenacher 1879; *B*. water 100, picric acid 1, anilin blue 0.5
METHOD: [tissues, well washed from fixative] → *A*, 24–48 hrs. → 70% alc. thorough wash → [5 μ paraffin sections] → water → *B*, 12 hrs. → water, wash → salicylic balsam, via usual reagents
RECOMMENDED FOR: demonstration of Myxosporid parasites in sections of arthropods.

23.33 Mallory 1897 *test*. **1938** *ips.*   Mallory 1938, 297
REAGENTS REQUIRED: *A*. 0.25% thionin; *B*. 2% oxalic acid
METHOD: [sections] → water → *A*, ½ to 1 min. → *B*, till differentiated ½ to 1 min. → wash → balsam, via usual reagents
RECOMMENDED FOR: differential staining of Entamoeba in sections.

23.33 Markey, Culbertson, and Giordano 1943   *Tech. Bull.*, **4**:2
REAGENTS REQUIRED: *A*. 5% ferric alum; *B*. water 100, acetic acid 2, hematoxylin 0.1
METHOD: [smears fixed in F 3000.0000 Schaudinn 1893] → water → *A*, 2–3 mins. 56°C. → rinse → *B*, 1–2 mins., 56°C. → running water, 15–30 mins. → balsam, via usual reagents
RECOMMENDED FOR: protozoans in fecal smears.

23.33 Medalia, Kahaner, and Singer 1944   *Tech. Bull.*, **5**:68
REAGENTS REQUIRED: *A*. water 100, sodium phosphate, dibasic 0.56, dihydrogen potassium phosphate 1.70; *B*. water 100, sodium phosphate, dibasic 1.70, dihydrogen potassium phosphate 0.56, methylene blue 0.16, azur II 0.10
METHOD: [methanol-fixed smears] → water → *A*, 4 secs. → rinse → *B*, 6 secs. → rinse → dry
RECOMMENDED FOR: Plasmodium in smears.

23.33 Meriwether 1935   4349, **14**:64
REAGENTS REQUIRED: *A*. DS 11.26 Meriwether 1935 24, ammonia 36, methanol 36; *A*. water 45, abs. alc. 36, methanol 18
METHOD: [sections of formaldehyde-fixed material with nuclei hematoxylin stained] → water → *A*, 5 mins. → *B*, till differentiated → balsam, via usual reagents
RECOMMENDED FOR: differential staining of parasitic amebas in tissue sections.

23.33 Moorthy 1937   11428, **23**:100
REAGENTS REQUIRED: *A*. water 100, sodium chloride 1, mercuric chloride 0.5; *B*. water 100, methylene blue 0.06, DS 13.13 Giemsa 1902 (solution) 24
METHOD: [larvae of Dracunculus, isolated from Cyclops killed in *A*] → *A*, on slide, under coverslip → *B*, drawn under coverslip → *C*, replacing *B*, drawn under coverslip → [seal coverslip]
RECOMMENDED FOR: larvae of Dracunculus.

23.33 Moschkovsky *test.* **1946 Roskin**   Roskin 1946, 287
REAGENTS REQUIRED: *A*. water 95, DS 11.44 Moschkovsky (1946) 5; *B*. 2% tannic acid
METHOD: [thick smears] → *A*, 10–15 mins. → rinse → *B*, 1 min. → rinse → dry
RECOMMENDED FOR: blood parasites in thick smears.

23.33 Noble 1944   19938, **100**:37
REAGENTS REQUIRED: *A*. water 67.5, 40% formaldehyde 7.5, acetic acid 25, ferric alum 3; *B*. 0.5% hematoxylin
METHOD: [fresh, moist smear] → *A*, on slide, warm to steaming → drain → *B*, on slide, warm to steaming → wash → blot → balsam, via dioxane and toluene
RECOMMENDED FOR: protozoan parasites in fecal smears.

23.33 Reynolds 1936   20540b, **11**:167
FORMULA: water 70, DS 11.21 Guyer 1930 30, DS 11.122 Delafield 1885 10
RECOMMENDED FOR: nematodes in sections and wholemounts.

23.33 Rukhadze and Blajin 1929   11587, **32**:342
FORMULA: lactic acid 30, water 100, carmine 0.3
PREPARATION: Dissolve with boiling
METHOD: [living cestodes] → stain, ½ to 1 hr. → running water, ½ to 3 hrs. → balsam, via usual reagents
RECOMMENDED FOR: staining wholemounts of cestodes.

23.33 Schmorl 1928   Schmorl 1928, 421
FORMULA: sat. sol. methylene blue 60, 0.5% ethyl eosin in 70% alc. 20, water 20, 20% potassium hydroxide 0.4
METHOD: [smears] → stain, 3–5 mins. → wash → dry
RECOMMENDED FOR: Plasmodium.

23.33 Schüffner *test.* **1928 Schmorl**   Schmorl 1928, 421
REAGENTS REQUIRED: *A*. water 94, glycerol 5, 40% formaldehyde 1; *B*. any DS 11.122 formula
METHOD: [fresh blood smear] → dry in dark, 6–30 mins. → *A*, 5–10 mins. → wash → *B*, 1–10 mins. → wash → dry → balsam
RECOMMENDED FOR: Plasmodium.

23.33 Shortt 1927   9940, **14**:565
FORMULA: xylene 75, phenol 25, eosin Y 1
PREPARATION: Dissolve dye in phenol. Dilute with xylene.
METHOD: [fixed smears, either dehydrated in alc., or air dried] → stain, 1–5 mins. →
xylene, thorough wash → balsam
RECOMMENDED FOR: demonstration of parasitic Sarcodina, and their cysts, in smears.

23.33 Simons 1938   5310, **31**:100
REAGENTS REQUIRED: A. water 100, methylene blue 0.2, sodium chloride 0.6, sodium
citrate 1, saponin 0.6, 6% formaldehyde 4; B. 50% glycerol
PREPARATION OF A: Dissolve the dye and sodium salts in water with gentle heat. Cool.
Add saponin and shake till dissolved. Add formaldehyde.
METHOD: [mix on slide 1 part blood to 5 parts A] → dry → B, till differentiated → seal
coverslip
RECOMMENDED FOR: staining Plasmodium in fresh blood.

23.33 Sinton and Mulligan 1930   9940, **17**:329
REAGENTS REQUIRED: A. 0.04% sodium hydroxide in 90% alc.; B. 1% Bordeaux red;
C. 4% ferric alum; D. DS 11.111 Shortt 1923 (sol. B); E. 0.3% iron alum; F. 0.1%
eosin
METHOD: [thick smears fixed in F 0000.0010 Gilson, 1897] → 50% alc. → A, several
hours → water, via graded alcs. → B, 12–24 hrs. → rinse → C, 18 hrs. → rinse → D,
overnight → E, till differentiated → F, 3 mins. → wash → balsam, via usual reagents
RECOMMENDED FOR: Plasmodium in thick smears.

23.33 Sternberg 1905   23681, **16**:293
REAGENTS REQUIRED: A. DS 13.13 Giemsa 1902 3, water 97; B. 0.5% 5% acetic acid
METHOD: [thin paraffin sections] → water → A, 24 hrs. → wash → B, till section red →
wash → dry → abs. alc., till blue → dry → balsam
RECOMMENDED FOR: Plasmodium in sections.

23.33 Tomlinson and Grocott 1944   591b, **14**:36
REAGENTS REQUIRED: A. water 100, calcium chloride 0.01, phloxine 1; B. water 75,
lithium carbonate 0.5, toluidine blue 1, glycerol 20, abs. alc. 5; C. 0.2% acetic acid;
D. acetone 75, abs. alc. 25, rosin 3.75, orange G 0.01
METHOD: [sections] → water → A, 5 mins. → rinse → B, 45–60 secs. → rinse → acetone,
2 mins. → C, till blue clouds cease → D, 1–2 mins. → balsam, via acetone and xylene
RECOMMENDED FOR: Plasmodium in sections.
NOTE: Pigmented tissues may be bleached in 5% ammonium sulfite before this stain.

23.33 Tompkins and Miller 1947   591b, **17**:755
REAGENTS REQUIRED: A. 4% ferric alum; B. 0.5% hematoxylin; C. 2% phosphotungstic
acid.
METHOD: [smears fixed in F 3000.0000 Schaudinn 1893 after iodine treatment for removal of mercury] → water → A, 3–5 mins. → rinse → B, 1 min. → rinse → C, 2
mins. → blue in tap water or alkali → wash → dammar, via usual reagents
RECOMMENDED FOR: protozoans in fecal smears.

23.33 Tsuchiuya 1932   11284, **17**:1163
REAGENTS REQUIRED: A. 4% ferric alum; B. DS 13.12 Wright 1910
METHOD: [fecal smears fixed in F 3000.0000 Schaudinn 1893] → A, 20 mins. → wash, 3
mins. → B, on slide, 1 min. → B, diluted on slide, 5 mins. → wash → balsam, via
usual reagents
RECOMMENDED FOR: intestinal protozoans.

23.33 Villain and Comté 1933   1843, **22**:137
STOCK SOLUTIONS: I. 0.08% eosin B; II. 0.08% azur II
WORKING SOLUTION: stock I 6.5, stock II 6.5, water 87
METHOD: [alcohol-fixed smears] → stain, ½ to 1 hr. → wash → dry
NOTE: All solutions must be adjected to pH 7.4 to 7.6.
RECOMMENDED FOR: Plasmodium.

23.34 ANIMALS PARASITIC IN PLANTS

23.34 Strong 1924   624, **4**:345

REAGENTS REQUIRED: *A*. methanol; *B*. DS 13.13 Giemsa 1902

METHOD: [smears of latex, partially dried] → *A*, 5 mins. → water, wash → *B*, on slide, 10–15 mins. → water, wash → dry

RECOMMENDED FOR: demonstration of Phytomonas (the protozoan *not* the bacteria) in Euphorbia.

23.4 OTHER ZOOLOGICAL TECHNIQUES

23.5 OTHER BOTANICAL TECHNIQUES

The techniques given under this heading are so specific for the purpose and class of plant to which they are applied, that they could not be justifiably given under any other heading. These methods, moreover, are so varied that they cannot be subdivided into sections, hence the specific purpose for which each was intended is given under the individual formula.

23.5 Alcorn and Worley 1936   20540b, **11**:119

REAGENTS REQUIRED: *A*. DS 11.43 Ziehl 1882; *B*. 2% hydrochloric acid in 70% alc.

METHOD: [dried perithecia scraped from leaf] → *A*, 48 hrs. 50°C. → [place single perithecium on slide, open by tapping coverslip] → *A*, under coverslip, 15 mins. 95°C. replacing stain as it evaporates → *B*, drawn under cover, till differentiated → balsam, via usual reagents

RECOMMENDED FOR: Perithecia of Erysiphaceae.

23.5 Baumgartel 1902   1798, **41**:87

FORMULA: water 99, acetic acid 1, methylene blue 0.5, acid fuchsin *q.s.* to give violet color

METHOD: [alcohol-fixed algae] → stain, till stained → water, till no more color comes away → balsam, via usual reagents

RECOMMENDED FOR: staining wholemounts of algae, particularly Cyanophyceae.

23.5 Baumgartel 1917   2626, **64**:1138

REAGENTS REQUIRED: *A*. water 80, 95% alc. 20, picric acid 0.5, mercuric chloride 1, potassium alum 1, hematin 0.1

PREPARATION: Dissolve all ingredients except the dye in water. Add dye dissolved in alc.

RECOMMENDED FOR: staining wholemounts of algae.

23.5 Bonnet 1910   6630, **38**:103

RECOMMENDED FOR: combined fixation and staining of algae. *See* DS 24 Mennier and Vaney 1910.

23.5 Chamberlain 1915a   Chamberlain 1915, 198

REAGENTS REQUIRED: *A*. 1% eosin Y; *B*. 1% acetic acid

METHOD: [fresh material] → abs. alc., 2 mins. → *A*, 2 mins. → *B*, quick rinse → water, thorough wash → glycerol

NOTE: This method is also given by Johansen 1940, 245 without reference to source.

RECOMMENDED FOR: wholemounts of filamentous fungi.

23.5 Chamberlain 1915b   Chamberlain 1915, 110

REAGENTS REQUIRED: *A*. 1% phloxine in 90% alc.; *B*. 1% anilin blue in 90% alc.; *C*. 0.1% hydrochloric acid in 90% alc.

METHOD: [algae in 95% alc.] → *A*, 24 hrs. → 90% alc., 1 min. → *B*, 3–30 mins. → *C*, till differentiated → Venice turpentine, via usual reagents

RECOMMENDED FOR: wholemounts of filamentous algae.

NOTE: A detailed description of the use of this technique is given in Chapter 6.

23.5 Gardiner 1898 *test.* **1931 Crafts**   20540b, **6** :127

REAGENTS REQUIRED: *A.* water 100, iodine 0.5, potassium iodide 0.75; *B.* 10% sulfuric acid; *C.* water 95, sulfuric acid 5, iodine 1, potassium diodide 1.25; *D.* 5% sulfuric acid *E.* water 95, sulfuric acid 5, 0.5% gentian violet *q.s.* to give green color.
METHOD: [sections of living material] → *A*, 5 mins. → *B*, 5 mins. → *C*, 5 mins. → *D*, till iodine starts to fade → *E*, till dark → P 13.1 Gardiner 1898
RECOMMENDED FOR: demonstration of protoplasmic connections between plant cells.

23.5 Gutstein 1924   23684, **93** :233

REAGENTS REQUIRED: *A.* 1% methylene blue; *B.* 5% tannic acid; *C.* 1% safranin
METHOD: [heat-dried smear] → *A*, 2–3 mins. → water, wash → *B*, 2 mins. → water, wash → *C*, 2 mins. → water, wash → dry
RECOMMENDED FOR: demonstration of nuclei in yeasts.

23.5 Gutstein 1925   23684, **95** :1

REAGENTS REQUIRED: *A.* DS 11.43 Ziehl 1882; *B.* 5% acetic acid; *C.* 5% tannic acid; *D.* 1% safranin
METHOD: [heat-dried smears] → *A*, 2 mins. → *B*, till no more color comes away → water, wash → *C*, 2 mins. → water, wash → *D*, 2–5 mins. → water, wash → dry
RECOMMENDED FOR: demonstration of ascospores in yeast.

23.5 Johansen 1940   Johansen 1940, 270

REAGENTS REQUIRED: *A.* 1% Bismarck brown in 70% alc.; *B.* DS 12.16 Johansen 1940; *C.* clove oil 50, abs. alc. 25, xylene 25
METHOD: [sections] → water → *A*, 20 mins. → 95% alc., till no more color comes away → *B*, 5–8 secs. → *C*, till differentiated → balsam, via xylene
RECOMMENDED FOR: staining sections of Thallophyta.

23.5 Kufferath 1929 *test.* **1942 Langeron**   Langeron 1942, 1249

REAGENTS REQUIRED: *A.* DS 11.43 Ziehl 1882; *B.* 2% lactic acid in 95% alc.; *C.* 1% Nile blue sulfate
METHOD: [smear, dried at 100°C.] → *A*, on slide, warmed nearly to boiling → drain → water, wash → *B*, a few secs. → water, wash → *C*, 30 secs. → water, wash → dry
RECOMMENDED FOR: staining ascospores in yeasts.

23.5 Langeron 1942   Langeron 1942, 1239

FORMULA: water 100, acetic acid 3, anilin blue 0.5
METHOD: [dried hyphae on slide] → stain, 5 mins. → water, till no more color comes away → balsam, via usual reagents
RECOMMENDED FOR: staining fungus mycelia.

23.5 Maneval 1929   20540b, **4** :21

REAGENTS REQUIRED: *A.* 1% acid fuchsin; *B.* 5% tannic acid; *C.* 2% sulfuric acid
METHOD: [heat-dried smears] → *A*, 1 min. → *B*, 20 secs. → *C*, till differentiated → balsam, via usual reagents
RECOMMENDED FOR: demonstration of nuclei in yeasts.

23.5 Rivalier and Seydel 1932   6630, **110** :181

FORMULA: *A.* P 12.2 Amann 1896 100, anilin blue 1
METHOD: [collodion varnished coverslip preparations] → stain, 10–50 mins. → 70% alc., rinse → 90% alc., till differentiated → balsam, via graded acetone-xylene series
RECOMMENDED FOR: staining fungus mycelium in coverslip cultures.

23.5 Semmens 1937   *Microscope*, **1** :5

REAGENTS REQUIRED: *A.* P 12.2 Semmens 1937 100, osmic acid 0.04 *and either* light green 0.5 *or* anilin blue 0.5 *or* phloxine 0.5; *B.* P 12.2 Semmens 1937
METHOD: [fresh algae] → *A*, 1 hr. → *A*, another color, if required, 5–30 mins. → *B*, till required → *B*, on slide → ring cover with V 11.2 Semmens 1937
RECOMMENDED FOR: wholemounts of algae.

23.5 Taylor 1921 21400a, **40**:94
REAGENTS REQUIRED: *A*. 0.05% methylene blue; *B*. 0.1% picric acid
METHOD: [fresh material] → *A*, ½ to 1 min. → water, rinse → *B* → examine
RECOMMENDED FOR: sheath structure of desmids.

23.5 Yamanouchi *test*. **1915 Chamberlain** Chamberlain 1915, 167
REAGENTS REQUIRED: *A*. 10% alc.; *B*. 1% safranin in 95% alc.; *C*. 1% crystal violet; *D*.
1% orange G
METHOD: [dried smears] → *A*, overnight → *B*, 4 days → water, 5 mins. → *C*, 2 days →
→ water, brief rinse → *D*, 3 mins. → 95% alc., brief rinse → abs. alc. 1 min. → clove
oil, till differentiated → balsam, via xylene
RECOMMENDED FOR: wholemounts of small Chlorophyceae.

24 MISCELLANEOUS DYE-STAINING TECHNIQUES

The existence of any techniques in the present miscellaneous class must of necessity be a
criticism of the classification adopted by the author. He is, therefore, pleased that few techniques have so far evaded the classification which he has developed as to be forced into the
refuge of this miscellaneous group.

24 Francotte *test*. **1942 Langeron** Langeron 1942, 1011
FORMULA: water 55, 90% alc. 20, glycerol 20, 40% formaldehyde 5, Bismarck brown
0.05, malachite green 0.10
METHOD: Fresh or preserved plankton is mixed with stain and examined. For perma-
nence allow to evaporate under coverslip and replace with P 12.1 Francotte (1942).
RECOMMENDED FOR: staining mixed plankton collections.

24 Langeron 1942 Langeron 1942, 866
REAGENTS REQUIRED: *A*. 5% potassium hydroxide; *B*. 1% acetic acid; *C*. any DS 11.24
formula; *D*. 1% anilin blue in 1% acetic acid
METHOD: [roughly dissected radulae] → *A*, boiling, till clear → water, rinse → *B*, till
neutralized → *C*, ½ to 1 hr. → water, wash → *D*, few mins. → balsam, via usual
reagents
RECOMMENDED FOR: demonstration of radula of mollusca.

24 Meunier and Vaney 1910 6630, **68**:727
REAGENTS REQUIRED: *A*. water 100, quinone 0.3
METHOD: [fresh plankton] → *A*, equal vol., till objects settled out → 70% alc., 2 changes
→ balsam, via usual reagents
NOTE: An identical technique was applied to algae by Bonnet 1910 (6630, **38**).
RECOMMENDED FOR: staining mixed plankton collections.

22

Accessory Dye-staining Solutions

<hr>

Decimal Divisions Used in Chapter

ADS 10 Mordants and Miscellaneous Solutions

These formulas have been separated from the stains with which they are customarily associated because many of them are capable of a much wider employment than they usually receive. One might take, for example, the mordant of Casares-Gil (ADS 12.2) which was originally developed for staining the flagella of bacteria, but which can be applied admirably to revive the staining properties of sections of tissues which have been preserved so long in alcohol that they would otherwise be useless. Attention should also be paid to such formulas as those of Drew 1920 (ADS 12.1) which, by combining a chromic-acid and an osmic-acid mordant, enable one to apply stains, usually applied only to tissues fixed in such fluids, to tissues which have been fixed in picric acid, and which have therefore been rendered incapable of giving a good differentiation with many of the common triple staining methods.

11 MISCELLANEOUS

These formulas are of very wide application, and are accordingly placed before the formulas of specific application.

11.1 FORMULAS

11.1 Anderson 1929   Anderson 1929, 127
FORMULA: water 100, potassium dichromate .375, calcium hypochlorite 1.25
PREPARATION: Dissolve the dichromate and hypochlorite in separate portions of the water. Filter the hypochlorite into the dichromate.
USE: After osmic stains to prevent removal of alcohol-soluble fats.

11.1 Chura 1925   23632, **42**:59
FORMULA: water 70, acetic acid 30, picric acid *q.s.* to sat.
RECOMMENDED FOR: solution of cytoplasmic inclusions in chrome-fixed material to render chromosomes more evident.
NOTE: *See also* ADS 12.1 Chura 1925.

NOTE: The proportions of the above mixture are misquoted by **Minouchi 1928** (see ADS 12.1). Gatenby and Painter 1937, 267 assign Minouchi's formula to Chura but give the wrong reference.

11.1 Hotchkiss 1948   *Arch. Biochem.*, **16**:131
REAGENTS REQUIRED: *A.* water 30, abs. alc. 70, sodium acetate 0.8, periodic acid 0.8; *B.* water 40, abs. alc. 60, sodium thiosulfate, cryst 2, potassium iodide 2, hydrochloric acid 0.07
METHOD: [sections] → water → *A*, 2–5 mins. → 70% alc., rinse → *B*, 1 min. → 70% alc., wash
RECOMMENDED FOR: originally intended for increasing stainability of polysaccharides. Now recommended for many other purposes.

11.1 Szecsi 1913   7276, **39**:1584
FORMULA: acetone 100, benzyol peroxide 10
RECOMMENDED FOR: use as a tissue reviver.

12 MORDANTS

12.1 FORMULAS FOR USE BEFORE HEMATOXYLIN STAINS

12.1 Alli 1944   13685, **95**:317
FORMULA: water 25, 95% alcohol 65, tannic acid 10, acetic acid 10, phenol 5

12.1 Anderson 1922   11977, **5**:65
FORMULA: ADS 12.1 Weigert 1896 90, 2% calcium hypochlorite 10

12.1 Anderson 1942   11431, **54**:258
FORMULA: water 100, potassium dichromate 3.75, chromium fluoride 1.875, phospho-molybdic acid 0.64, calcium hypochlorite 0.2

12.1 Bacsich 1937   11025, **72**:163
FORMULA: water 100, chromic acid 1, ferric chloride 1

12.1 Benda 1893   22246, **7**:161
FORMULA: water 40, sulfuric acid 15, ferrous sulfate 80, nitric acid 15
PREPARATION: Dissolve the sulfate in the sulfuric acid and water. Heat to 50°C. Add nitric acid.
NOTE: This is roughly equivalent in iron content to a 70% solution of ferric sulfate. This salt, however, is so hygroscopic that it is almost impossible to prepare a solution of known concentration from the solid. The additional acids both stabilize the solution and render it more effective as a mordant. For a solution sometimes known as *Benda's Mordant see* Chapter 18, F 4600.1010 Benda (1911).

12.1 Chura 1925   23632, **42**:59
FORMULA: water 100, chromium fluoride 0.5, chrome alum 0.5, potassium dichromate 2.5
RECOMMENDED FOR: use after F 5670.1000 Chura 1925 to mordant cytoplasmic inclusions.
NOTE: *See also* ADS 11.1 Chura 1925.

12.1 Clara 1933   23639b, **17**:698
FORMULA: water 100, potassium dichromate 3, chrome alum 1.5, chromic acid 1.25, ammonium molybdate 1.25

12.1 Cole 1916   19938, **44**:452
FORMULA: 95% alc. 50, water 50, ferric chloride 5, acetic acid 10

12.1 Drew 1920   11360, **40**:295
FORMULA: water 100, chromic acid 2, osmic acid 1
RECOMMENDED FOR: tissue reviver before hematoxylin stains.

12.1 Eichhorn 1941   1887a, **31**:391
FORMULA: F 3700.0010 Zenker 1894 237.5, nitric acid 12.5

12.1 Faure 1924 6630, **90**:87
FORMULA: water 100, ferric chloride 0.2, cupric acetate 0.1, hydrochloric acid 2

12.1 Kupperman and Noback 1945 *see* F 5000.1010 Bouin (note) *or* F 0000.1010 Lavdowsky 1894 (note)

12.1 Landau 1938 4285a, **15**:181
FORMULA: water 100, ferric chloride 0.06, potassium dichromate 5

12.1 Lang 1936 20540b, **11**:149
FORMULA: water 100, acetic acid 1, sulfuric acid 0.12, ferric alum 4
RECOMMENDED FOR: use in place of simple ferric alum solutions before hematoxylin stains
NOTE: The same solution, diluted with an equal volume of water, may be used for differentiation.

12.1 Merkel *test.* **1898 Behrens** 23328, **3**:76
FORMULA: water 100, chrome alum 2.5, copper acetate 5, acetic acid 5
PREPARATION: Add the copper acetate and acetic acid to a boiling solution of the alum. Boil 5 minutes. Cool. Filter.

12.1 Minouchi 1928 10881, **1**:231
FORMULA: water 50, picric acid 0.6, acetic acid 50
RECOMMENDED FOR: as Chura 1925.
NOTE: This formula is attributed by Gatenby and Painter 1937, 267 to Chura 1925 (*q.v.*).

12.1 Mitrophanow 1896 23632, **13**:470
FORMULA: water 50, 90% alcohol 50, copper acetate 5

12.1 Morel and Bassal 1909 11024, **45**:632
FORMULA: water 100, ferric chloride 2, copper acetate 0.04, hydrochloric acid 1

12.1 Morrison 1946 *Turtox News*, **24**:66
FORMULA: water 70, 95% alcohol 30, tannic acid 10, acetic acid 10, phenol 5

12.1 Mullen and McCarter 1941 608b, **17**:289
REAGENTS REQUIRED: *A.* water 95, acetic acid 5, chromic chloride 5; *B.* 0.25% potassium permanganate; *C.* 5% oxalic acid

12.1 Smith and Rettie 1924 11431, **27**:115
PREPARATION: Dissolve 2.5 paraldehyde in 2.5 50% hydrochloric acid at 37°C. with continuous shaking. Neutralize with sodium hydroxide and adjust to pH 6 with acetic acid.

12.1 Weiss 1942 665, **46**:199
FORMULA: water 57, 95% alcohol, 40% formaldehyde 10, acetic acid 10, tannic acid 25
RECOMMENDED FOR: treatment of sections of formaldehyde-fixed tissues before staining techniques specifying chromic or dichromate fixation.

12.1 Schröder 1930 23430, **166**:588
FORMULA: water 100, potassium dichromate 3.75, chromium fluoride 1.25, sodium sulfate 0.5
NOTE: This can be prepared by mixing equal parts of F 7000.1000 Müller 1850 and ADS 12.1 Weigert 1896.

12.1 Vastarini-Cresi 1915 *see* ADS 12.1 Weigert 1896 (note)

12.1 Weigert 1896 *Weigert's primary mordant—compl. script.*
7936a, **6**:14
FORMULA: water 100, potassium dichromate 5, chromium fluoride 2.5
PREPARATION: Dissolve with boiling.
RECOMMENDED FOR: pretreatment of sections of central nervous system before hematoxylin stains. See DS 21.212 (Chapter 21).

NOTE: Vastarini-Cresi 1915 (10157, **31**:38) substitutes ammonium dichromate for potassium.

12.1 Weigert 1891 *test.*, **1910** *ips.*   *Weigert's secondary mordant—compl. script.*

Ehrlich, Krause, *et al.* 1910, **1**:231

FORMULA: water 100, chromium fluoride 2.5, acetic acid 2, copper acetate 5

PREPARATION: Add fluoride to boiling water. Boil 5 minutes. Cool to 80°–90°C. and add other ingredients.

RECOMMENDED FOR: use as a mordant before hematoxylin staining, particularly of connective tissues in the central nervous system. See DS 21.212 and 21.22 (Chapter 21).

NOTE: This was named *Gliabeize* by its inventor. Attempts to graft this word onto the English language appear, mercifully, to be failing. For an adaptation of this formula to fixative use *see* F 4600.1010 Benda (1911) (Chapter 18) and DS 21.22 Jakob 1913 (Chapter 21).

12.1 Williamson and Pearse 1923   *see* F 3670.0000 Williamson and Pearse 1923

12.1 Wolters 1891   23632, **7**:471

FORMULA: water 100, vanadium chloride 2, aluminum acetate 6.5

12.2 FORMULAS FOR USE BEFORE OTHER STAINS

12.2 Anderson 1923   11431, **26**:431

FORMULA: *A.* water 100, sodium sulfite 5, oxalic acid 2.5, potassium iodide 5, iodine 2.5, acetic acid 5; *B.* water 95, ferric chloride 5

PREPARATION OF A: Dissolve the oxalic acid and sulfite in 95 water. Dissolve iodine and iodide in 5 water. Mix and add acetic acid.

RECOMMENDED FOR: mordant before Victoria blue neuroglia stains.

NOTE: The proportions of *A* and *B* vary according to the technique employed. Equal parts are generally satisfactory.

12.2 Atkins 1920   11056, **5**:321

FORMULA: water 100, sodium hydroxide 0.4, iodine 2

PREPARATION: Dissolve the dry ingredients in 10 water. Dilute to 100.

12.2 Bailey 1929   16913, **27**:11

FORMULA: water 100, ferric chloride 2.5, tannic acid 3.75

12.2 Belling 1921   651, **54**:573

FORMULA: water 55, acetic acid 45, ferric oxide 5

RECOMMENDED FOR: use as an ingredient of, or mordant before, aceto-carmine stains.

12.2 Bethe 1896   *see* DS 21.21 Bethe 1896

12.2 Burke 1922   *see* ADS 12.2 Lugol (1905)

12.2 Casares-Gil *test.* **Anselmier**   16157b, **5**:33

STOCK SOLUTION: 70% alc. 75, water 25, tannic acid 25, aluminum chloride 45, zinc chloride 25, rosaniline hydrochloride 3.57

WORKING FORMULA: stock 20, water 80

RECOMMENDED FOR: reviving old tissues and as a general mordant.

PREPARATION: Dissolve the tannic acid and aluminum chloride in the alc. Dissolve the zinc chloride in the water and add drop by drop, with constant agitation, to first solution. Dissolve rosaniline hydrochloride in mixed solution.

12.2 Crétin 1937   4285a, **14**:163

FORMULA: water 100, aluminum chloride 0.7, ferric chloride 0.025, calcium chloride 5

PREPARATION: Dissolve each salt separately and mix in order given.

12.2 David 1934   23684, **132**:240

FORMULA: water 90, potassium alum 5, mercuric chloride 1.25, tannic acid 4

12.2 van Ermengen   *see* AMS (*not ADS*) 21.1 van Ermengen

12.2 Gordon 1939　　　　　　　　　　　　11284, **24**:405
FORMULA: water 100, copper sulfate 12, mercuric chloride 2.5, potassium dichromate 1, sodium sulfate 0.5

12.2 Gough and Fulton 1929　　　　　　　　11431, **32**:765
FORMULA: water 100, acetic acid 0.1, mercuric acetate 3
RECOMMENDED FOR: mordanting of fatty tissues prior to staining for mitochondria.

12.2 Gram 1884　*see* AF 12.1 Gram 1884

12.2 Gray 1926　　　　　　　　　　　　　11056, **12**:273
FORMULA: sat. sol. (*circ.* 6%) potassium alum 50, 20% tannic acid 20, sat. sol (*circ.* 4%) mercuric chloride 20, sat. alc. sol. (*circ.* 5%) magenta 4
RECOMMENDED FOR: use as Casares-Gil.
NOTE: This solution is unstable. It may, however, be prepared from the first three, and the last ingredients, each as a separate solution. **Liefson 1930** (11056, **20**:203) substitutes 95% alc. for the sat. sol. mercuric chloride.

12.2 Harris 1898　　　　　　　　　　　　16185, N.V., 47
FORMULA: water 250, potassium ferricyanide to sat. (*circ.* 85 Gms.), osmic acid 0.1
RECOMMENDED FOR: mordanting before DS 11.44 staining.
NOTE: Harris recommends cooling to about 0°C. before use.

12.2 Kilduffe 1923　　　　　　　　　　　11006, **81**:2182
FORMULA: water 100, iodine 0.3, potassium iodide 0.6, sodium bicarbonate 1.

12.2 Liefson 1930　*see* ADS 12.2 Gray 1926 (note)

12.2 Lugol *test.* **Lee 1905**　*see* AF 12.1 Lugol (1905)

12.2 Marquez 1933　　　　　　　　　　　3360, **112**:1056
FORMULA: water 100, chrome alum 10, potassium alum 10, potassium dichromate 10
RECOMMENDED FOR: mordanting before staining for mitochondria.

12.2 Michailow 1910　　　　　　　　　　23632, **27**:19
FORMULA: water 250, sodium molybdate 20, 40% formaldehyde 1.5
RECOMMENDED FOR: use before methylene blue nerve stains. *See* DS 21.211 (Chapter 21).

12.2 Mullen and McCarter 1941　　　　　608b, **17**:289
FORMULA: water 95, acetic acid 5, chromic chloride 5.

12.2 Muir　*see* DS 23.217 Muir

12.2 Oliver 1934　　　　　　　　　　　　11250, **55**:266
FORMULA: water 100, tannic acid 6.5, ferrous sulfate 11, acid fuchsin 0.7

12.2 Petragnani 1928 *test.* **1930 Ciferri**　　20540b, **5**:34
FORMULA OF WORKING SOLUTION: water 75, methanol 25, acetic acid 0.06
PREPARATION: Stock I. In 100 0.1% acetic acid dissolve with heat 3 potassium alum 2 and 0.5 lead acetate. Stock II. In 100 70% methanol dissolve 14 tannic acid and 4 ferric chloride
WORKING SOLUTION: Mix 2 stock I with 1 stock II. Add 100 to 300 methanol.

12.2 Ponselle 1913　　　　　　　　　　6630, **74**:1072
FORMULA: abs. alc. 100, iodine 0.6

12.2 Rossi *test.* **1904 Besson**　　　　　Besson 1904, 170
FORMULA: water 100, tannic acid 5, potassium carbonate 1

12.2 Salazar 1923　　　　　　　　　　　763, **26**:60
FORMULA: water 70, acetic acid 30, tannin 1

12.2 Semmens 1939　　　　　　　　　　*Microscope*, **3**:6
FORMULA: water 100, chromic acid 10, sodium uranate 0.5
USE: Before crystal violet nuclear stains.
NOTE: For the preparation of the sodium uranate *see* F 3800.0010 Semmens 1939b.

12.2 Shunk 1920   11056, **5**:181
FORMULA: water 100, tannic acid 200, ferric chloride 1.25

12.2 Stockwell 1934   19938, **80**:121
FORMULA: water 90, chromic acid 1, potassium dichromate 1, acetic acid 10
RECOMMENDED FOR: As a mordant prior to safranin staining, particularly for plant tissues containing much phlobaphene.

12.2 Trenkmann 1890   23684, **8**:385
FORMULA: water 100, tannic acid 2, hydrochloric acid 0.2

12.2 Weiss 1929   11284, **14**:1191
FORMULA: 95% alc. 65, tannic acid 65, 40% formaldehyde 32.5, acetic acid 2.5

12.2 Winge 1930   23639b, **10**:699
FORMULA: 96% alc. 80, water 20, iodine 1, potassium iodide 1

12.2 Yokata 1924   6630, **90**:1303
FORMULA: water 100, tannic acid 5, potassium antimony tartrate 0.5

12.2 Zikes 1930   23684, **81**:161
FORMULA: water 116, tannic acid 15, chrome alum 9, osmic acid 0.112, crystal violet 0.15
PREPARATION: Dissolve the tannic acid in 60 water. Add alum, dissolved in 37.5 and osmic acid dissolved in 11.25. Filter. Add dye dissolved in 7.5.

ADS 20 Differentiating Solutions

The principal reason for separating these differentiating solutions from the stains with which they are used is that the same formula may be used with thirty or forty stains, and will therefore have either to be given thirty or forty times in the section on dye staining, or, alternatively, be the subject of continual cross references within the section on dye staining.

It is hoped that the technician will not hesitate to experiment by applying solutions, designed for differentiating one particular technique, to quite different techniques. As an example, one may quite the formula of Pal 1887 below, the use of which is generally confined to the differentiation of hematoxylin-stained sections of nervous tissue. The author recommends its employment, in another place in this book, for the surface bleaching of parasitic flatworms which have been stained in carmine. Many other examples of this kind of double use could be given and the whole science of microtomy would greatly benefit were persons to experiment more widely with existing solutions, rather than to invent new ones every time they are faced with new problems.

Hematoxylin stains are usually differentiated with "acid alcohol" which is either 0.1% (British and American practice) or 1% (German practice) hydrochloric acid in 70% alcohol.

The "glyceric ether," used in continental Europe for the differentiation of thiazin stains, is not an article of commerce in the United States. It is prepared by the distillation of glycerol over aluminum chloride at room temperature. The distillate, in microtomic practice, is diluted with 10% glycerol in 95% alcohol according to the fancy of the supplier or user.

21 FOR DIFFERENTIATING HEMATOXYLIN

21.1 FORMULAS

21.1 Eisath 1911   14370, **20**:3
FORMULA: water 55, 95% alc. 45, tannin 12, pyrogallic acid 6

21.1 Gordon 1936   11284, **22**:294
FORMULA: water 90, 40% formaldehyde 10, ferric alum 0.25

21.1 Gouillart and Brouardel 1938 *Bull. Soc. franc. microsc.*, **7**:140
FORMULA: water 98, acetic acid 2, potassium permanganate 0.01, oxalic acid 0.01

21.1 Kozowsky 1904 15058, **23**:1041
FORMULAS: *A*. water 100, potassium permanganate 1; *B*. water 100, ferric chloride 1
RECOMMENDED FOR: differentiation, by successive immersion in *A* and *B*, of hematoxylin stains.

21.1 Kultschitzky 1889 766, **14**:223
FORMULA: water 100, potassium ferricyanide 0.1, lithium carbonate 1.0

21.1 Landau 1938 4285a, **15**:181
FORMULA: water 100, lithium carbonate 1.5, potassium ferrocyanide 2.5

21.1 Lang 1936 *see* AMS 12.1 Lang 1936

21.1 Lillie 1948 *see* ADS 21.1 Weigert 1885 (note)

21.1 Pal 1887 23632, **6**:92
FORMULAS: *A*. water 100, potassium permanganate 0.25; *B*. water 100, potassium sulfite 0.5, oxalic acid 0.5
RECOMMENDED FOR: use as a differentiator of stains, particularly D.S. 21.22 Weigert by alternate immersion in *A* and *B*, and as a general surface bleach.

21.1 Rossolino and Busch 1896 *test.* **Schiefferdecker 1897**
23632, **14**:55
FORMULA: water 100, oxalic acid 0.05, sodium sulfite 0.05
USE: Differentiation of hematoxylin stains.

21.1 Smith and Rettie 11431, **27**:115
FORMULA: water 100, potassium ferricyanide 0.5, borax 1

21.1 Weigert 1885 8645, **3**:238
FORMULA: water 100, potassium ferricyanide 2.5, sodium borate 2
RECOMMENDED FOR: use as a differentiator of hematoxylin stains, particularly those of Weigert.
NOTE: **Lillie 1948**, 161, differs only in containing half the quantity of sodium borate.

21.1 Weil 1928a 1879, **20**:392
FORMULA: water 100, potassium ferricyanide 1.25, sodium borate 1

21.1 Weil 1928b 1879, **20**:392
FORMULAS: *A*. 0.25% potassium permanganate; *B*. water 100, sodium bisulfite 0.25, oxalic acid 0.25

22 FOR DIFFERENTIATING OTHER STAINS

22.1 FORMULAS

22.1 Beauverie and Hollande 1916 6630, **79**:605
FORMULA: ethylene glycol 80, creosote 20
RECOMMENDED FOR: differentiating methylene blue stains.

22.1 Duprès 1935 14425, **46**:77
FORMULA: water 50, 40% formaldehyde 20, acetic acid 25
RECOMMENDED FOR: differentiating after nuclear staining with magenta.

22.1 Eberspächer 1936 23684, **138**:92
FORMULA: abs. alc. 90, water 10, urea 4
RECOMMENDED FOR: differentiation of smears of acid-fast bacteria in place of acid solutions.

22.1 Gothard 1898 6630, **5**:530
FORMULA: abs. alc. 50, xylol. 15, beechwood creosote 15, oil of cajeput 20
RECOMMENDED FOR: differentiation of methylene blue stains.

22.1 Kiyono 1890   23681, **25**:481
  FORMULA: water 100, potassium dichromate 5, chrome alum 2
  RECOMMENDED FOR: *see* DS 22.21 Altmann 1920.

22.1 Lenoir 1929   6630, **101**:1203
  FORMULA: abs. alc. 50, oil of cloves 50, hydrochloric acid 0.1
  RECOMMENDED FOR: differentiation of safranin stains.

22.1 Lewis *test.* **1900 Pollack**   Pollack 1900, 86
  FORMULA: 2% chloral hydrate 25, oil of cloves 25, abs. alc. *q.s.*
  PREPARATION: Shake first two ingredients till emulsified. Add alc. with constant shaking
    till emulsion clears.
  RECOMMENDED FOR: differentiation of dyes applied to neural structures.

22.1 Löwit 1891   1780, **38**:524
  FORMULA: 95% alc. 100, picric acid 1, ADS 12.1 LaCour 1931 1
  RECOMMENDED FOR: differentiation of safranin stains in plant tissues.
  NOTE: **Tuan 1930** (20540b, **5**:103) recommends the addition of picric acid to all alcohols
    used in differentiation.

22.1 Masson *test.* **1942 Langeron**   Langeron 1942, 530
  FORMULA: sat. sol. picric acid in 95% alc. 65, 95% alc. 35
  RECOMMENDED FOR: differentiation of iron hematoxylin and, particularly, safranin
    stains.

22.1 Tuan 1930   *see* ADS 22.1 Löwit 1891 (note)

22.1 Unna *test.* **1928 Schmorl**   Schmorl 1928, 154
  FORMULA: glyceric ether 10, water 90
  NOTE: *See* comment under ADS 20 above.

22.1 Wolbach 1911   11006, **56**:345
  FORMULA: 95% alc. 100, rosin 0.5
  RECOMMENDED FOR: in differentiation of thiazin stains.
  NOTE: There is no reason to refer to this as *colophonium alcohol,* even though this phrase
    occurs in the title of Wolbach's paper. The obsolete term *colophonium* has now been
    replaced by *rosin* or *colophony* in both the United States and British Pharmacopoeias.
    Moreover, in spite of his title, Wolbach used "common brown resin"—and says so, in
    just those words.

22.1 Wolbach 1919   11343, **41**:75
  FORMULA: acetone 90, rosin 15
  RECOMMENDED FOR: differentiation of thiazin stains, usually after great dilution.

23

Formulas and Techniques for Metal Stains

Decimal Divisions Used in Chapter

MS 00 General Observations

The practice of metal staining, except in neurological techniques, has in late years fallen into some disrepute, largely through the lack of success which has attended its use in the hands of the inexperienced, or of those not able to observe the very specific precautions which alone can lead to success. The most necessary of these precautions are the utilization of nothing but the purest reagents available, and the maintenance throughout of a condition of chemical cleanliness in the glassware employed.

It is difficult to justify the retention of the term *metallic impregnations* for this class of microscopic preparation. Many dyes impregnate materials, and there is certainly no justification for the retention of this term to include only those processes which are supposed to result in the deposition, on the surface of the structure to be observed, of a film of metal or metallic oxides and hydroxides. It is indeed doubtful how far a successful metal stain is ever the result of such a deposition. As will be pointed out later, metallic silver is less frequently found in a successful silver stain than is a silver proteinate, nor is it possible always to draw the line in gold staining between the absorption of gold salts by the tissues and the deposition of very finely divided colloidal gold through-out their mass. It seems, therefore, preferable to retain the old term *metal staining* for these reactions.

Many metal staining techniques should be more widely employed than is at present the case. This is particularly true of staining with osmium tetroxide or with any of the osmic-chromic fixatives found in Chapter 18. These materials will render the internal organs of a small invertebrate so sharply defined that all after-staining is unnecessary. And no one who has ever examined a properly dehydrated and cleared small crustacean, after fixation in an osmic material, will again be inclined to try to stain these forms with dyes which yield a more diffuse image.

At the present time, however, these techniques are almost confined to the cytologist searching for Golgi apparatus, or such other lipid materials as may be demonstrated by the surface deposition of osmium hydroxides, or to the neuroanatomists, the majority of whose discoveries have been made with the aid of silver impregnations. It is to be hoped, however, that the classification of stains which follows will encourage more biologists to endeavor to utilize these excellent and rapid techniques more generally than is at present the case.

MS 01 CLASSIFICATION OF METHODS AND FORMULAS

Two broad considerations necessitate the employment of a classification of metal stains different from that used for the dye stains in Chapters 20 and 21. First, none of the metal stains are of such general application that a division of "stains of general application" is possible. Second, only three metals—in contrast to several hundred dyes—are commonly used, so that "osmium," "gold," "silver," and "other metals" form convenient titles for primary divisions.

Many metal-staining methods require that the tissues shall have some special pretreatment in an *accelerator* or *mordant;* most metal-staining methods necessitate after-treatments such as *development, toning,* and the like. The solutions used in these pre- and after-treatments, however, are very much the same, whatever metal be used for staining. Much space has therefore been saved by the removal of these *accessory metal staining formulas* to Chapter 24, which should be consulted for the composition of any solution referenced "AMS" in the formulas which follow.

Each of the four primary divisions of metal stains are secondarily divided, when the variety justifies such division, according to the particular compound of the metal employed; all are further divided according to the purpose for which the technique is intended. Constant repetition of the formulas for "staining solutions," many of which are used in dozens of techniques, has been avoided by placing such formulas at the beginning of each of the subdivisions in which they are employed.

It is difficult to decide, in the case of osmic acid, which of the staining formulas given should be regarded as *fixatives*—and more properly should be removed to Chapter 18—and which should be regarded as staining solutions, which are more properly retained in the present section. The author has adopted as a criterion the question of whether or not any after-staining solutions are to be employed. When after-staining treatment is an essential part of the technique, the solution has been removed to the division on fixatives; when no after-staining is necessary, the formula has been retained in this section as a stain.

MS 10 Osmic Acid

Osmic acid is a greatly neglected stain, and there is no real justification for its present retention as a reagent which is used almost entirely for the demonstration of the Golgi apparatus. It is not denied that it does this well, but it is a pity that its one-time use as a general histological stain should have sunk into disrepute. Osmic acid is an excellent general-purpose stain, either for materials intended for subsequent sectioning with a view to demonstrating in class the relative distribution of cells, nuclei, and the like, or for the preparation of wholemounts of small invertebrates. Probably one of the most unfortunate things that has happened to the science of microtomy has been the substitution, for these clear gray and black specimens, of the standard monstrosities which are stained by convention bright red, and the fuzzy outlines of which cannot compare for simplicity with those produced by osmic staining.

The exact nature of the material laid down when tissues are exposed to osmic acid is not known; it appears fairly certain that it is not metallic osmium. Partington and Huntingford (Gatenby and Cowdry, 1928, 29) state that it is a hydrated form of one of the lower oxides. These oxides are laid down first on unsaturated fatty acids and, later, on other constituents of the cell and cell wall. Excess blackening may be removed either with hydrogen peroxide or by the standard permanganate-oxalic acid techniques, but in both cases fresh osmium tetroxide is liberated in the tissues. This osmium tetroxide must be thoroughly washed out, or it will redeposit on the places from which it has been oxidized. Osmic acid stains are, in general, permanent.

MS 11 STAINING METHODS

MS 11.0 TYPICAL EXAMPLES

Demonstration of Golgi network
in the ovary of the earthworm
by the Ludford 1925 method

In this, as in every other metal-staining technique, the first essential is to make certain that all glassware is chemically clean. In this instance two stoppered bottles of about 25-milliliter capacity will be required, though if only a single specimen is to be prepared, it will be better to use the small, straight-sided, upright type of stoppered weighing bottles. Both bottles should be soaked overnight in sulfuric-dichromate cleaning solution, thoroughly rinsed in tap water, soaked for at least an hour in two changes of large volumes of distilled water, and then dried under such conditions that dust cannot reach them. If either bottle has previously had its stopper greased for any purpose, it is better to reject it outright than to endeavor to clean it.

In the first bottle, place 10 to 15 milliliters of Mann's 1894 osmic-dichromate fixative, which will be found under the classification F 1300.0000 in Chapter 18. In the other bottle place a layer of about 3 millimeters of 2% osmic acid. Before pouring the osmic acid from the bottle in which it is kept, wipe the neck of the bottle with a rag soaked in alcohol, and then rinse off the alcohol with distilled water, which is subsequently dried off with a lintless cloth. This is necessary, since the osmic acid will become reduced on the surface of any organic material. It is also necessary to provide six small dishes of about 10- to 15-milliliter capacity, filled with triple-distilled water, for the intermediate wash between the two reagents. These dishes should be as clean as possible, but need not be chemically clean, as must those used for the fixative and for the stain. Also required are a chemically clean pipet of the eye-dropper type, a sharp scalpel, and a pair of very fine pointed forceps. If the latter can be of stainless steel, so much the better, but it is not absolutely essential in this technique.

Next, remove the ovary from the earthworm. First, identify the female genital aperture in segment fourteen. This establishes the ventral side of the earthworm. Then wrap the earthworm round the forefinger, holding its back end between the first and second fingers, so that the genital aperture is towards the tip of the finger. The worm will then be lying on its left side, provided the operator is right-handed and thus has the worm in his left hand. Next, take a sharp scalpel and make an incision covering two segments posterior, and one anterior, to the fourteenth segment about one millimeter to the left of the genital aperture. Apply considerable pressure and spread the lips of the wound. The ovary will then appear as a small,

white, pear-shaped body, which can be removed without difficulty by taking hold of it with fine forceps, just at the point of its insertion, and pulling gently. Now lay the ovary against the inside of the stoppered bottle containing the osmic-mercuric mixture, placing it against the side of the bottle, a good centimeter above the level of the liquid. Under no circumstances should the tip of the metallic forceps be brought into contact with the liquid. The ovary will adhere to the glass surface, thus permitting the withdrawal of the forceps, and it is then only necessary to shake the tube gently, so that the ovary is washed into the fixative. It should remain in this liquid from a half to one hour (the time is not critical) and should be shaken gently at intervals.

After fixation the ovary should be removed with the pipet, together with the least possible quantity of fixative, to one of the dishes of wash water. The pipet should then be used to suck water in and out rapidly, so as to mix the contents of the dish. After about five minutes the ovary is removed to the next dish, again being thoroughly rinsed backward and forward, and should remain in each dish for about 30 minutes, with occasional agitation. It is better, but not absolutely essential, that it should remain in the final wash water overnight. Remember that if any of the osmic-mercuric mixture is taken over into the osmic stain, there will be a tendency to overfixation, which will make the ovary brittle.

When the ovary has been sufficiently washed, transfer it to the osmic acid using the same technique which was used to place it in the original bottle; that is, lay it against the inner wall of the bottle and then remove the forceps. This avoids carrying over any water and thus diluting the osmic-acid solution. There should be enough osmic acid in the bottle to cover the ovary so that the outline of the tissue shows on the surface. The specimen is now placed in a cupboard in the dark for from ten days to two weeks; but it should be examined daily to make sure that no contamination is causing the reduction of the osmic acid anywhere except on the ovary. If, in any of these examinations, the osmic acid is seen to be cloudy, or if there is a black precipitate on the bottom of the bottle, the ovary should be removed to another bottle containing a fresh supply of osmic-acid solution. It is a waste of time to add fresh osmic to the existing bottle, which has demonstrated, through the reduction of the reagent, that it is already contaminated.

When the ovary is sufficiently impregnated, the bottle containing it should be filled to the brim with triple-distilled water and tilted backward and forward once or twice to mix the contents. The ovary is then allowed to settle to the bottom, and the surplus water is poured off. This should be repeated once or twice, and then only half the water removed, leaving the ovary immersed in about ten milliliters of water. The bottle with the water in it should then be placed in an oven, or on a water bath, which will maintain a temperature of about 38°C. for one or two days. The ovary is then examined under the surface of water with a binocular microscope. It should present a very dark brown, but not absolutely dead-black, appearance. If it is covered with a dead-black, amorphous deposit, it is evident that it has been too long in osmic acid. If it is light brown, it has not been in osmic long enough. In either circumstance it had better be thrown away. If, however, it has been properly impregnated, it should now be thoroughly washed, either in at least ten changes of triple-distilled water with not less than one hour in each, or overnight in slowly running, triple-distilled water.

The ovary is then embedded in paraffin by the methods described in Chapter 12, and sections are cut longitudinally at a thickness of from one to two microns. The sections are dried on a slide, the wax melted, and the slide dropped into xylene to remove the wax. Meanwhile, set up two tubes, or coplin jars, one containing anhydrous turpentine and the other oil of cedar. As soon as the wax has been dissolved, pass the slide into the cedar oil until the xylene has been removed, withdraw the slide, wipe the surplus oil from the bottom, and examine it under an oil-immersion lens. If impregnation has been successful—that is, if the Golgi apparatus and yolk granules are shown as dead-black spots against a pale brown background —return the slide to xylene until the cedar oil has been removed, and then mount it in balsam under a coverslip. If no signs of Golgi apparatus are present, the slide may be thrown away, and it must be presumed that some mistake has been made in the technique. If, however, as frequently happens, there is some evidence of Golgi apparatus as black dots, but the background is obscured by other scattered black granules, place the slide in turpentine for about two minutes, rinse it rapidly in xylene, return to cedar oil, and re-examine. Repeat these operations until the section has been properly differentiated. Some people recommend that all sections should be treated with turpentine, but this is not usually necessary in the case of so simple an object as the earthworm ovary.

If turpentine has been used, wash the slide in a jar of clean xylene in order that all turpentine may be removed from the slide before it is finally mounted.

The majority of formulas from this section have been transferred to the appropriate section of Chapter 18. Those retained were originally suggested as stains and have never been recommended as fixatives. Simple solutions of osmic acid are not listed separately, but are given with individual techniques.

11.1 STAINING SOLUTIONS

11.1 van Gehuchten 1927   *see* F 1700.0000 van Gehuchten 1927

11.1 Hamilton 1897   3464, **20**:180
    STOCK SOLUTIONS: I. Brain tissue hardened in F 7000.0000 Müller 1859 for 3 weeks 50, F 7000.0000 Müller 1859 100. (Grind to a paste and filter.) II. 1% osmic acid.
    WORKING SOLUTION: stock I 100; stock II 0.5.

11.1 Kolossow 1892   23632, **9**:39
    FORMULA: water 50, 05% alc. 50, nitric acid 2, osmic acid 1

11.1 Mann 1894   *see* F 1300.0000 Mann 1894

11.1 Orr 1900   *see* F 1000.0010 Orr 1900

11.1 Rossolino and Busch 1896 *test.* 1897 Schiefferdecker
$$23632, \textbf{14}:55$$
FORMULA: water 50, 95% alc. 50, 40% formaldehyde 0.2, osmic acid 0.2

11.1 Swank and Davenport 1924   *see* F 1000.1010 Swank and Davenport 1924

11.1 Swank and Davenport 1935   *see* F 1000.1010 Swank and Davenport 1935

11.1 Takahashi 1908   *see* F 1600.0060 Takahashi 1908

11.2 Neurological Techniques
11.21 methods for degenerative changes

These methods are commonly known as *Marchi methods*. For further information *see* **Mettler 1932** (20540b, **7**:95), **Swank and Davenport 1934** and **1935** (20540b, **9**:11 and *ibid*, **12**:45).

11.21 Anderson 1929   Anderson 1929, 68
REAGENTS REQUIRED: *A.* 2% potassium iodate; *B.* F 1800.0000 Busch 1898; *C.* ADS 11.1 Anderson 1929
METHOD: [small pieces of formaldehyde-fixed tissue] → *A*, 24 hrs. → *B*, 7 days → thorough wash → *C*, 7 days, 37°C. → thorough wash → [celloidin sections]

11.21 Busch 1898   *see* MS 11.21 Anderson 1929 for method, and F 1800.0000 Busch 1898 for formula

11.21 van Gehuchten *test.* **1927 Kingsbury and Johannsen**
                      Kingsbury and Johannsen 1927, **8**:9
REAGENTS REQUIRED: *A.* 3.7% potassium dichromate; *B.* F 1700.0000 van Gehuchten 1927
METHOD: [fresh tissue] → *A*, 3 wks. → *B*, 3 wks. 2 or 3 changes → wash → [frozen sections]

11.21 Hamilton 1897   3464, **20**:180
REAGENTS REQUIRED: *A.* F 7000.0000 Müller 1859; *B.* MS 11.1 Hamilton 1897; *C.* AMS 21.1 Hamilton 1897; *D.* 0.25% potassium permanganate; *E.* 2% potassium sulfite
METHOD: [whole brains] → *A*, till hardened, 3–5 months → [celloidin section enclosed between two coats of celloidin and stripped from the slide] → *B*, 24 hrs. 37°C. → wash → *C*, 24 hrs. 37°C. → wash → *D*, 24 hrs. → wash → *E*, till decolorized → wash → *D* → *E* cycle repeated twice → wash → *C*, fresh solution, 24 hrs., 37°C. → wash → M 32.1 mountant

11.21 Marchi 1896   19460, **12**:3
REAGENTS REQUIRED: *A.* F 7000.0000 Müller 1859; *B.* F 1700.0000 Marchi 1886
METHOD: [1 cm. slices fresh tissue] → *A*, 3–5 days → wash → *B*, 5–14 days → wash → [celloidin sections]

11.21 Mettler 1932   20540b, **7**:95
REAGENTS REQUIRED: *A.* 10% neutralized formaldehyde; *B.* 3% potassium dichromate; *C.* F 1700.0000 Marchi 1886
METHOD: [pieces] → *A*, 24 hrs. → [4 mm. slices] → *B*, 2 wks. → rinse → *C*, 5–14 days → wash → [celloidin sections]
NOTE: Sol. *B* should be "aged" 3 months. *C* should be replaced if it ceases to smell of osmic acid.

11.21 Orr 1900   11431, **6**:387
REAGENTS REQUIRED: *A.* F 7000.0000 Müller 1859; *B.* Orr 1900 F 1000.0010
METHOD: [*A*, several wks. to months] → wash → [freehand sections] → *B*, 1–2 days → balsam, via usual reagents

11.21 Stewart 1936   11431, **43**:339

REAGENTS REQUIRED: *A*. 2% potassium dichromate; *B*. 1% osmic acid

METHOD: [30 μ frozen sections of neutral formaldehyde-fixed material] → wash → *A*, 1 day, 21°C. → wash, till pale yellow → *B*, in dark, 16–36 hrs. → wash → M 30 mountant

NOTE: Sections in which the normal myelin is too deeply stained may be differentiated by ADS 21.1 Pal 1887.

11.21 Swank and Davenport 1935   20540b, **10**:88

REAGENTS REQUIRED: *A*. water 100, magnesium sulfate 5, potassium dichromate 3; *B*. 4% formaldehyde; *C*. Swank and Davenport 1935 F 1000.1010

METHOD: [animal killed with nembutal] → *A*, perfused through aorta → [central nervous system removed] → *B*, 48 hrs. → wash → [celloidin sections]

11.22 OTHER NEUROLOGICAL METHODS

11.22 Azoulay 1894   766, **10**:25

REAGENTS REQUIRED: *A*. F 7000.1000 Müller 1859; *B*. 0.002% osmic acid; *C*. 10% tannin

METHOD: *A*, some months → [sections] → *B*, 5–15 mins. → rinse → *C*, warmed till steaming → wash → balsam, via usual reagents

RECOMMENDED FOR: myelin sheaths.

11.22 Böhm and Oppel 1907   Böhm and Oppel 1907, 261

REAGENTS REQUIRED: *A*. 1% osmic acid; *B*. glycerol

METHOD: [teased fibers of muscle on slide under coverslip] → *A*, 30 mins. in moist chamber → *B*, substituted for *A* without moving coverslip → [seal coverslip]

RECOMMENDED FOR: myelin sheaths.

11.22 Champy, Coujard, and Coujard-Champy 1946   *Acta Anatomica*, **1**:233

REAGENTS REQUIRED: *A*. water 100, osmic acid 0.25, sodium iodide 2.25

METHOD: [2–3 mm. slices of fresh tissues] → *A*, 24 hrs. → running water → [paraffin sections]

RECOMMENDED FOR: sympathetic nerve endings in gland cells.

11.22 Heller-Robertson *test.* **1929 Anderson**   Anderson 1929, 64

REAGENTS REQUIRED: *A*. ADS 12.2 Weigert 1891; *B*. 1% osmic acid; *C*. 5% pyrogallic acid; *D*. ADS 21.1 Pal 1887, *A* and *B* sols.

METHOD: [frozen sections] → *A*, 24 hrs. → wash → *B*, in dark, 30 mins. → wash → *C*, 30 mins. → wash → *D* (sol. *A*), 30 secs. → wash → *D* (sol. *B*), till colorless → balsam, via usual reagents

RECOMMENDED FOR: myelin sheaths.

11.22 Rossolino and Busch 1896 *test.* **Schiefferdecker 1897**

23632, **14**:55

REAGENTS REQUIRED: *A*. 0.5% chromic acid; *B*. MS 11.1 Rossolino and Busch 1896

METHOD: [sections of formaldehyde-fixed material] → *A*, 2–3 hrs. → rinse → *B*, 24 hrs. → wash → balsam, via usual reagents

RECOMMENDED FOR: granule cells.

11.3 HISTOLOGICAL METHODS

11.3 Altmann 1878   *see* V31 Altmann 1878

11.3 Cramer 1919   1200, **6**:77

REAGENTS REQUIRED: *A*. 2% osmic acid at 37°C.

METHOD: Expose fragments to vapor from *A* in stoppered bottle for 1½ hrs. at 37°C. → [sections via usual reagents]

RECOMMENDED FOR: cell differentiation in adrenal gland.

11.3 Hamann 1885   *see* F 1000.0010 Hamann 1885

11.3 Hermann 1891   1780, **37**:4

REAGENTS REQUIRED: *A*. F 1200.0010 Hermann 1889; *B*. 90% alc.; *C*. crude pyroligneous acid

METHOD: *A*, overnight → wash *B*, 1 to 2 wks. → *C*, 12–18 wks. → wash

11.3 Hirschler 1918   *see* F 1300.0000 Hirschler 1918

11.3 Kolossow 1892   23632, **9**:39
REAGENTS REQUIRED: *A.* MS 11.1 Kolossow 1892; *B.* AMS 21.1 Kolossow 1892; *C.* 0.05%
osmic acid
METHOD: [small pieces or objects] → *A*, 15 mins. → wash → *B*, 5 mins. → *C*, wash →
balsam, via usual reagents
NOTE: **Lee 1891** (23632, **9**:185) claimed this method on the grounds that he had in 1887
(6011, **4**:110) published a description of it. **Kolossow 1892** (23632, **9**:316) pointed out
that Lee had given only a general indication of an uncontrolled method of reducing
osmic acid with tannin.
RECOMMENDED FOR: general histological staining.

11.3 Krajian 1940   1887a, **30**:766
REAGENTS REQUIRED: *A.* 1% osmic acid; *B.* 1% phloxine
METHOD: [10 μ frozen sections of formaldehyde-fixed material] → *A*, 60°C., 5 mins. →
thorough wash → *B*, 1 min. → wash → M 12.1 mountant
RECOMMENDED FOR: fat in frozen sections.

11.3 Lee 1887   6011, **4**:110
REAGENTS REQUIRED: *A.* 1% osmic acid; *B.* 0.5% pyrogallol
METHOD: *A*, 1–2 days → wash → *B*, till green-brown throughout → [paraffin sections
via usual reagents]
RECOMMENDED FOR: general histological staining.

11.3 Lee 1905   Lee 1905, 255
REAGENTS REQUIRED: *A.* F 1200.0010 Hermann 1889 or F 1600.0010 Flemming 1882;
B. 0.25% pyrogallol
METHOD: *A*, not more than 30 mins. → *B*, 24 hrs. → [sections by paraffin technique]
RECOMMENDED FOR: general histological staining.
NOTE: Lee 1905 (*loc. cit.*) states that this method has been attributed to von Maehren-
thal.

11.3 von Maehrenthal   *see* MS 11.3 Lee 1905 (note)

11.3 Sjovall 1905   764, **30**:261
REAGENTS REQUIRED: *A.* 4% formaldehyde; *B.* 2% osmic acid
METHOD: [small fragments] → *A*, 8 hrs. to 2 days → wash → *B*, 2 to 15 days → 3 μ
paraffin sections, via usual techniques

11.3 Woronin 1898 *test.* **1948 Romeis**   Romeis 1948, 304
REAGENTS REQUIRED: *A.* 1% osmic acid; *B.* sat. aq. sol. tannin
METHOD: [sections] → water → *A*, 10 mins. → *B*, 10 mins. → *A*, 20 mins. → abs. alc.,
thorough wash → balsam, via xylene
RECOMMENDED FOR: epithelial tissues.

11.4 METHODS FOR CELL INCLUSIONS

These techniques for the demonstration of the Golgi apparatus are commonly referred to
as *Mann-Kopsch techniques.*

11.4 Gatenby 1920a   17510, **64**:267
REAGENTS REQUIRED: *A.* 2% osmic acid at 37°C.; *B.* F 1700.0000 Altman 1890 or
F 1670.0000 Champy 1913
METHOD: expose fragments to vapor from *A* in stoppered bottle at 37°C. for 112 hrs. →
A, several days → or *B*, several days → wash → sections via usual reagents

11.4 Gatenby 1920b   17510, **64**:267; Langeron 1942, 646
REAGENTS REQUIRED: *A.* F 1300.0000 Mann 1894; *B.* 2% osmic acid; *C.* turpentin
METHOD: [small fragments] → *A*, 15 mins. to 3 hrs. → wash → *B*, 2 to 3 wks. in dark →
3 μ sections by paraffin technique → *C*, till differentiated
NOTE: Langeron 1942, 646 refers to this as the *Kopsch-Gatenby technique.*

11.4 Hirschler 1918   1780, **89**:271
REAGENTS REQUIRED: *A*. F 1300.000 Hirschler 1918; *B*. 2% osmic acid
METHOD: [small fragments] → *A*, 1–3 hrs. → wash → *B*, 12–16 days → wash → paraffin
via chloroform
NOTE: This was reprinted, with slight alterations in the timing, in 1924 (6630, **90**:83).

11.4 Kopsch 1902   20170, **40**:929
REAGENTS REQUIRED: *A*. 2% osmic acid
METHOD: [small fragments] → rinse → *A*, in dark, 2 wks. → wash → [3 μ paraffin
sections, via usual reagents]

11.4 Kopsch-Gatenby *test*. **Langeron 1942**   *see* MS 11.4 Gatenby 1920b (note)

11.4 Ludford 1925   11360, **45**:31
REAGENTS REQUIRED: *A*. F 1300.0000 Mann 1894; *B*. 2% osmic acid; *C*. turpentine
METHOD: [small pieces fresh tissue] → *A*, ½ to 1 hr. → wash → *B*, sufficient to cover
piece on bottom of 1 oz. stoppered bottle, 10 days to 2 wks. → water at 38°C., 1–2
days → wash → [paraffin sections by usual techniques] → xylene, till wax removed →
C, if differentiation necessary → balsam, via usual reagents

11.4 "Mann-Kopsch" *see* note under 11.4 above.

11.4 Nassanow 1923   1780, **97**:136
REAGENTS REQUIRED: *A*. F 1670.0000 Nassanow 1923; *B*. 2% osmic acid at 35°C.
METHOD: [small pieces fresh tissue] → *A*, 24 hrs. → wash → *B*, 3 to 7 days, 35°C. →
wash → [paraffin sections by usual techniques]

11.4 Newcomer 1940   20540b, **15**:89
REAGENTS REQUIRED: *A*. F 4700.0000 Zirkle 1934; *B*. 2% osmic acid; *C*. 1% potassium
permanganate; *D*. 3% oxalic acid
METHOD: [growing root tips] → *A*, 48 hrs. → wash, overnight, → *B*, changed alternate
days, 4–6 days → wash, overnight → [5 μ paraffin sections] → water → *C*, 5 mins. →
rinse → *D*, 2–3 mins. → thorough wash → balsam, via usual reagents
RECOMMENDED FOR: mitochondria in plant cells.

11.4 Weigert *test*. **McClung 1929, 208**   *see* DS 11.4 Weigl 1912 note

11.4 Weigl 1912   *Mann-Kopsch—compl. script.*   4346, **23**:1
REAGENTS REQUIRED: *A*. F 1300.0000 Mann 1894; *B*. 2% osmic acid
METHOD: [small fragments] → *A*, 30 mins. to 2 hrs. → wash → *B*, 10 days to 3 wks. →
wash → [sections via usual techniques]
NOTE: This is almost universally referred to as the *Mann-Kopsch technique* for the reason
that the former invented solution *A* for another purpose, while the latter recommended
solution *B* for the present one. McClung 1929, 208 refers to the method as *Weigert's
Mann-Kopsch*.

MS 20 Gold

Gold is used either by direct application of the chloride to partially hydrolized tissues, or in combination with mercury, either from complex solutions or by successive applications, or in combination with osmium or other metals. Techniques in which gold is used to replace silver-impregnated structures (the toning reaction of the photographer) are given under *silver staining* in MS 30 below.

MS 21 METHODS USING GOLD ALONE

These are the most primitive of all the metal-staining techniques though, when they are successful, they yield beautiful results. There is still no method as satisfactory for the demonstration of nerve endings in muscle as the classic gold-lemon-juice method of Ranvier given below. The effect is presumably produced by the reducing action exercised by the sheath of the nerve on gold chloride, but there is no evidence of the exact reaction produced, nor has it been satisfactorily established that the resultant precipitate is metallic gold. The very fugitive nature of many of the gold stains would tend to make one believe that the metal cannot be involved. It cannot be too strongly emphasized that absolute cleanliness and the rigorous control of the extent of light admitted during the reaction are two criteria of success.

MS 21.0 TYPICAL EXAMPLE

Demonstration of the termination of the fourth cranial nerve in the superior oblique muscle by the method of Ranvier 1889

This method is more than half a century old, but it is one of the simplest and best available, both for training classes in gold techniques and for demonstrating the nerve terminations in muscles. Only two prerequisites are essential to success. The first is that the lemon juice employed shall be from a relatively fresh lemon, shall have been squeezed with as little oil of lemon getting into it as possible, and that it shall then have been filtered through paper; this is tedious unless it is done with a filter pump. It is better to prepare the lemon juice immediately before use, and it is not nearly as good, even if it be left overnight. The second essential to success is that the glassware used should be chemically clean. In this particular technique four glass-stoppered bottles, or upright glass-stoppered weighing bottles, should be soaked in sulfuric-dichromate cleaning solution, thoroughly washed off in tap water, soaked in distilled water, and then dried under conditions which will leave them as dust-free as possible. In the first bottle place the freshly filtered lemon juice, in the second bottle 1% gold chloride, in the third bottle 0.2% acetic acid, and in the fourth bottle 20% formic acid. There will also be required two glass dishes of triple-distilled water which should be as clean as possible.

A rabbit is a good subject for this technique; but if a small shark or dogfish is available, it will be found to be better. In either case, the animal should be killed, the skin removed from around the orbit, and the eye taken out carefully so as to leave all the muscles intact within the orbit. The fourth nerve, leading to the superior oblique muscle, should then be identified and severed where it leaves the foramen. The muscle itself should then be cut off, leaving as much as possible in front of the nerve and about a quarter of an inch behind the nerve. Then take a surgical silk or other fine, clean fiber and tie this round the upper end of the nerve. Using this thread as a suspensor, hang the muscle by the nerve in the bottle of lemon juice. It will become transparent within a few hours, and may be passed to the next stage at any period between the time when it becomes completely transparent and about the twelfth hour of immersion. The longer period is, in general, better for mammalian tissue, and the shortest possible period for fish tissues.

As soon as the muscle has become transparent, withdraw it from the lemon juice by the thread, snip off the thread and, holding the muscle by one end in a pair of forceps, rinse it thoroughly in one of the jars of triple-distilled water. Then, after having drained off the water by touching the end of the muscle to a clean filter paper, drop the preparation into at least 60 milliliters of 1% gold chloride. Leave it in this solution, with gentle agitation at intervals, for about 20 minutes; it will darken slightly, from the transparent yellow of the lemon juice to a light brown.

One certain way to insure failure of this technique is to use metallic forceps to remove the muscle from the gold chloride and pass it to the acetic acid. It must be picked up on the end of a glass hook or with a glass spoon. The muscle is then rinsed and placed in the bottle of 0.2% acetic acid. The intensity of light is critical, for if the object be placed in direct sunlight it will become badly overstained, while in the dark it will not become stained at all. It was recommended by Ranvier originally that this technique should be carried out on days when there were clear, white clouds in the sky from which the sunlight was reflected. Though this is possibly rather an excessive view, there is no doubt that the state of the weather has more effect on the technique than any other single factor. It would perhaps be simplest to suggest that the specimen be exposed to bright daylight, that is, some intermediate condition between the dingy darkness of a winter day and bright, direct sunlight. It should remain in the acetic acid for from one to two days. The period of time is, of course, dependent upon the degree of illumination to which it is exposed.

If the technique is successful the entire muscle will change to a dull purple color. The word *dull* should be emphasized. Dark purple indicates too great a degree of reduction, and there will be no differentiation of the nervous tissues. A light mauve color indicates that the material has not been sufficiently reduced, and it is doubtful that it is worth exposing it further to daylight, since prolonged exposure to inferior illumination does not have the same effect as a correct length of exposure to the proper illumination.

The best way of determining whether or not the impregnation has been successful is to examine the muscle under a binocular microscope with the strongest possible illumination from beneath. If the beginnings of the divisions of the nerve within the muscle can be seen, the preparation is satisfactory; if, however, the material is so dark that the nerve cannot be followed beyond the point of its entry into the muscle, it is doubtful that it is worth proceeding further.

Successful impregnations should be removed from the acetic acid and placed in the formic acid for 48 hours in the dark. Then take a straight upright tube of about one inch in diameter by four inches long, and place an inch of pure glycerol in the bottom; with a pipet, very carefully place about a two-inch layer of 20% formic acid on the top of the glycerol, being careful to mix them as little as possible. The preparation is now transferred to the upper layer of formic acid, and will naturally float at the interphase between the formic acid and the glycerol. After about 24 hours

the muscle will have sunk through the glycerol, but it should not be removed until it shows no further streams of formic acid rising from it through the glycerol. The formic acid is then carefully pipetted from the top of the tube, and a fresh portion of glycerol is added. There will probably have been a considerable mixture of formic acid and glycerol by diffusion, thus the muscle will again float at the interphase between this diluted glycerol and the fresh glycerol which has been added. As soon as the muscle has again sunk, thus demonstrating that it is completely impregnated, the partially diluted glycerol should be pipetted from the surface and the muscle transferred to a watch glass or stender dish full of fresh glycerol.

This is an excellent time at which to issue the muscle and nerve to a class, and there are many methods which may subsequently be followed to secure preparations showing the nerve endings. The simplest for class purposes is to divide the muscle into a series of freehand sections taken longitudinally, each section being about $\frac{1}{10}$-millimeter thick. If each student is provided with one of these sections, he can then examine it under the microscope, and will usually without further trouble be able to see the fine terminations of the nerves. To make better and more permanent preparations, it is desirable to take these thin sections and to tease them with needles so as to separate the individual fibers, following the process under a binocular dissecting microscope. Fibers which look as though they might show endings, are then transferred to a slide and mounted permanently in glycerol jelly. In place of glycerol jelly one may also employ any of the gum-arabic-glycerol media, or probably, though the author has never tried it, some of the polyvinyl-alcohol media.

These preparations are not very permanent unless they are preserved in the dark, and no method seems to be known by which permanency can be given to them. Under no circumstances can they be mounted in anything save an aqueous medium.

MS 21.1 Staining Solutions

21.1 Jabonero 1935 *test.* **1936 Findlay**   11360, **56**:160
FORMULA: water 100, glucose 1, gold chloride 0.02

21.1 Kolossow 1888   23632, **5**:52
FORMULA: water 245, hydrochloric acid 25, gold chloride 25

21.1 Ranvier 1880   17510, **80**:456
FORMULA: water 200, formic acid 50, gold chloride 2

21.1 Stoehr 1894 *test.* **1907 Böhm and Oppel**   Böhm and Oppel 1907, 258
FORMULA: water 200, formic acid 50, gold chloride 2
PREPARATION: Dissolve the chloride in the dilute acid. Bring to boil. Cool. Repeat 3 times. Filter.

MS 21.2 Techniques

Unless specific recommendations are made, it is to be understood that all the following methods are intended for nerve endings in muscle.

21.2 Apáthy 1897   14246, **12**:718
REAGENTS REQUIRED: *A.* 1% gold chloride; *B.* 1% formic acid
METHOD: [fresh tissue] → *A*, in dark → blot → *B*, 6 to 8 hrs., evenly illuminated from all sides

21.2 Beckwith *test. circ.* **1938 Wellings**   Wellings *circ.* 1938, 130
REAGENTS REQUIRED: *A.* 1% gold chloride; *B.* 20% sodium hydroxide; *C.* 10% potassium carbonate; *D.* 10% potassium iodide
METHOD: [sections from F 4700.0000 Erlitzky 1877 or F 7000.0000 Müller 1859 fixed material] → water → *A*, 5–6 hrs. → rinse → *B*, 3 mins. → drain → *C*, 30 mins. → drain → *D*, till differentiated
RECOMMENDED FOR: nerves in teeth.

21.2 Bensley and Bensley 1935 *test.* **1952** *ips.*   Cowdry 1952, 8
REAGENTS REQUIRED: *A.* 10% gold chloride; *B.* 4% neutralized formaldehyde; *C.* 1% toluidine blue; *D.* water 100, ammonium molybdate 2.5, potassium ferrocyanide 0.5
METHOD: [inject mouse intravenously through tail with 1 ml. *A*] → [after death fix lungs in *B*] → [paraffin sections on slide] → water → *C*, 10 mins. → rinse → *D*, 5 mins. → balsam, via usual reagents
RECOMMENDED FOR: alveolar epithelium of lung.

21.2 Boccardi 1886 *test.* **Lee 1905**   *see* MS 21.2 Manfredi 1881 (note)

21.2 Böhm 1907 *test.* **1907 Böhm and Oppel**   Böhm and Oppel 1907, 437
REAGENTS REQUIRED: *A.* 50% formic acid; *B.* 1% gold chloride; *C.* AMS 21.1 Pritchard 1907
METHOD: [small fragments, fresh tissue] → *A*, 20 mins. → rinse → *B*, 20 mins. → rinse → *C*, large volumes, 24–36 hrs. in dark → paraffin sections via usual reagents
NOTE: This technique is sometimes referred to **Carrière 1882** (1780, **21**:146) who, however, attributes it without reference to Böhm as do, still without reference, most other authors including those cited.

21.2 Carrière 1882   *see* MS 21.2 Böhm 1907 (note)

21.2 Cole 1946   20540b, **21**:23
REAGENTS REQUIRED: *A.* 10% citric acid in 0.9% sodium chloride; *B.* 1% gold chloride; *C.* 20% formic acid
METHOD: [muscle pieces] → *A*, 10 mins. → *B*. 1 hr. → *C*. 10–20 hrs. → glycerol by evaporation from glycerol-alcohol mixtures

21.2 Cornheim 1867   *see* MS 21.2 Manfredi 1881 (note)

21.2 Dependorf 1913   7282, **31**:377
REAGENTS REQUIRED: *A*. 30% formic acid; *B*. 1% gold chloride; *C*. formic acid
METHOD: [small pieces of fresh teeth] → *A*, 5–10 mins. → *B*, 2–6 hrs., in dark → *A*, 1
    day, in dark → *C*, 1 day, in dark → [celloidin sections]
RECOMMENDED FOR: nerves in teeth.

21.2 Drasch 1887   23632, **4**:492
REAGENTS REQUIRED: *A*. 0.5% gold chloride; *B*. 20% formic acid
METHOD: [pieces of fresh tissue, left without preservative at 4°C. for 48 hrs.] → *A*, in
    dark, ½ to ¾ hrs. → rinse → *B*, till nerves visible → glycerol, several changes
RECOMMENDED FOR: nerve endings in alimentary canal.

21.2 Flechsig 1884 *see* MS 21.2 Ranvier 1880 (note)

21.2 Freud *test.* **1896 Kahlden and Laurent**   Kahlden and Laurent 1896, 159
REAGENTS REQUIRED: *A*. 0.5% gold chloride in 50% alc.; *B*. 5% sodium hydroxide; *C*.
    10% potassium iodide
METHOD: [small pieces, or sections, of dichromate-fixed material] → water → *A*, 3–5 hrs.
    → wash → *B*, 2–3 mins. → *C*, 5–15 mins. → wash → balsam, via usual reagents
RECOMMENDED FOR: axis cylinders.

21.2 Graven 1925   3464, **48**:380
REAGENTS REQUIRED: *A*. 25% formic acid; *B*. 1% gold chloride
METHOD: [fresh tissue] → *A*, 10–15 mins. → blot → *B*, 20 mins., in shade → blot → *A*,
    10–15 mins, → *B*, 24 hrs., in dark → blot → *A*, 10–15 mins. → blot → *B*, 24 hrs., in
    dark → wash → glycerol

21.2 Hanazawa 1917   7141, **59**:125
REAGENTS REQUIRED: *A*. 1% gold chloride in 95% alc.; *B*. 5% potassium hydroxide;
    C. 10% potassium iodide
METHOD: [embed tooth in resin, grind section to half millimeter (see Chapter 10)] → *A*,
    2–3 days, in dark → wash → *B*, 15–20 mins. → wash → *C*, 12–24 hrs. → [grind thin]
    → balsam, via usual reagents
RECOMMENDED FOR: dentine.

21.2 Henocque *test.* **1895 Rawitz**   Rawitz 1895, 81
REAGENTS REQUIRED: *A*. 1% gold chloride; *B*. sat. sol. tartaric acid
METHOD: [small pieces] → *A*, 15 mins. → rinse → *B*, till reduced

21.2 Kolossow 1888   23632, **5**:52
REAGENTS REQUIRED: *A*. MS 21.1 Kolossow 1888; *B*. 0.02% chromic acid
METHOD: [fresh tissue] → *A*, 3 hrs. → blot → *B*, 2 or 3 days in dark

21.2 Jabonero 1935 *test.* **1936 Findlay**   11360, **56**:160
REAGENTS REQUIRED: *A*. 50% glucose; *B*. MS 21.1 Jabonero 1935; *C*. 5% sodium car-
    bonate
METHOD: [frozen sections of fresh tissue] → *A*, 10 mins., 60°C. → *B*, warmed till sections
    violet → balsam, via usual reagents
RECOMMENDED FOR: myelin sheaths.

21.2 Löwit 1875   20170, **71**:1
REAGENTS REQUIRED: *A*. 50% formic acid; *B*. 1% gold chloride; *C*. 25% formic acid;
    D. formic acid
METHOD: [fresh skin] → *A*, until epidermis peels off → *B*, 15 mins. → *C*, in dark 24 hrs.
    → *D*, in dark 24 hrs. → [sections by paraffin technique] → balsam, via usual reagents
RECOMMENDED FOR: nerve endings in skin.

21.2 Manfredi 1881   1946, **5**:30
REAGENTS REQUIRED: *A*. 1% gold chloride; *B*. 0.5% oxalic acid
METHOD: [fresh tissue] → *A*, 30 mins. → rinse → *B*, until reduced → glycerol mounts
NOTE: This method is essentially that of **Cornheim 1867** (22575, **34**:606) save that
    oxalic acid has been substituted for the acetic acid of the original. **Boccardi 1886**
    (*test.* Lee 1905, 251) substituted MS 23.1 Boccardi 1886 for *B* above.

21.2 Miller 1923 763, **25**:77
REAGENTS REQUIRED: *A.* 4% citric acid; *B.* 1% gold chloride; *C.* 30% formic acid
METHOD: [fresh tissue] → *A*, 20–30 mins., in dark → rinse → *B*, 20–30 mins., in dark →
C, 2 days → wash → glycerol

21.2 Nikiforoff *see* DS 21.213 Nikiforoff 1896

21.2 Ranvier 1880 17510, **80**:456
REAGENTS REQUIRED: *A.* Ranvier 1880 MS 21.1; *B.* 20% formic acid
METHOD: *A*, 20 mins. to 2 hrs. → *B*, in dark until reduced
NOTE: **Flechsig 1884** 1739, 463 substitutes 10% sodium hydroxide for *B* above.

21.2 Ranvier 1889 Ranvier 1889, 813
REAGENTS REQUIRED: *A.* fresh filtered lemon juice; *B.* 1% gold chloride; *C.* 0.2% acetic
acid; *D.* 20% formic acid
METHOD: [fresh tissue] → *A*, until transparent → rinse → *B*, 20 mins. → rinse → *C*, in
light, 24 to 48 hrs. → examine → [if successful render permanent by] → *D*, 48 hrs. in
dark

21.2 Rufini *test.* **1933 Cajal and de Castro** Cajal and de Castro 1933, 348
REAGENTS REQUIRED: *A.* 20% formic acid; *B.* 1% gold chloride; *C.* 1% potassium ferro-
cyanide
METHOD: [fresh tissue] → *A*, till translucent → wrap in cloth → *B*, in dark, 20–30 mins.
→ *A*, in dark, 24 hrs. → *C*, if overstained, till differentiated → wash → glycerol

21.2 Stoehr 1894 *test.* **1907 Böhm and Oppel** Böhm and Oppel 1907, 258
REAGENTS REQUIRED: *A.* MS 21.1 Stoehr 1894; *B.* 20% formic acid
METHOD: [fresh muscle] → *A*, 45 mins. → wash → *B*, in light, 36 hrs.

MS 22 METHODS USING GOLD IN COMBINATION WITH MERCURY

These methods are mostly used for the demonstration of neuroglia, particularly oligodendroglia and microglia. They appear at first sight to be simple, but are actually more difficult to use than are the silver techniques developed for the same purpose. There appears to be no criterion for success, though this may be rendered the more likely by the use of pure reagents and the most rigorous attention to chemical cleanliness of the glassware employed. Nothing appears to be known of the theory lying behind these stains.

MS 22.0 TYPICAL EXAMPLE

Demonstration of protoplasmic
neuroglia in the cerebral
cortex by the method
of Cajal 1916

This is a deceptively simple technique which is unlikely, in inexperienced hands, to yield as good results as are the silver methods (MS 31.22, 33.22, 34.22) more commonly employed for this purpose. It is essential that the reagents, the distilled water, and the glassware employed be pre-

pared as though one were engaged in a critical analysis. For the first step, secure a living or freshly killed rabbit and the solution of ammonium bromide listed in Chapter 24 as AMS 11.1 Cajal 1913. This solution must be prepared with reagent quality materials throughout, including the formaldehyde; and the bottle in which it is placed must be chemically clean. It is desirable to place in the bottom of this bottle a layer of about half an inch, either of fat-free absorbent cotton or of a fine glass fiber.

The freshly killed rabbit is tied face down on a board, the upper surface of the head skinned, and the frontal and parietal bones removed with forceps, particular care being taken not to break the blood vessels of the meninges. All extraneous blood should be removed with a gentle washing in either triple-distilled water or with a normal saline made with triple-distilled water. The surface of the brain is then flooded with a relatively large quantity of the ammonium bromide-for-maldehyde solution, which acts as a hemo-static agent during the removal of the meninges. Finally, remove a series of cubes of about one-centimeter side from the cerebral cortex. Stainless steel knives may be used for this purpose, but the author has always found it more practical to employ the sharp edge of a broken coverslip. If a standard 18-by-22-millimeter coverslip be broken roughly along a diagonal, it will be found to cut the brain most satisfactorily. This avoids the risk of surface contamination from metals which will interfere with subsequent staining. Two or three blocks will be sufficient, and they should be placed in the stoppered bottle containing the fixative, of which at least 250 milliliters should be employed for two or three one-centimeter cubes; four times this volume is not an unreasonable quantity.

The blocks should be removed from the fixatives as soon as they are adequately hardened. The exact degree of hardening necessary can best be gaged by pressing gently on the surface of the block with the rounded end of a glass rod. The block should be springy but not hard, and should not be removed until it can be handled with forceps without running the risk of crushing any of the internal structures.

After removal from the fixative, the blocks are washed in running triple-distilled water for at least a day, or washed in not less than five successive changes of at least 500 milliliters each. After washing, each block is subdivided, preferably by the broken edge of a glass coverslip, into five or six smaller blocks, which form a reasonably sized portion for sectioning on the freezing microtome. One of the most fruitful sources of error of this technique is the use of crude commercial mucilages of gum arabic in the course of the sectioning, even after taking stringent precautions with the purity of the reagents employed in fixation. It is far better to employ pure sugar solutions than to rely on gum materials which may contain such impurities as will stultify subsequent work.

Sections are removed, as made, to a watch glass of triple-distilled water. Again it must be emphasized that the watch glass should be chemically clean. Before commencing to section the material, it is desirable to prepare the staining reagent,

the formula for which is given as MS 22.1 Cajal 1916 below. The very greatest care is required in making this solution. All the reagents involved, particularly the mercuric chloride, should be of the grade sold for analytical analysis; the ordinary commercial chloride found in biological laboratories is not satisfactory. Cajal does not indicate in his formulas which of the numerous types of gold chloride or mixed gold, potassium, and sodium chlorides he used in the original formula. The method of preparing the formula is, however, critical. First, the mercuric chloride is dissolved in hot triple-distilled water at from 70°C to 80°C. It should give a clear solution entirely free from opalescence, and if the faintest trace of a precipitate is seen, the solution must be rejected and a purer batch of the reagent sought. In a second chemically clean beaker dissolve the gold chloride at room temperature in triple-distilled water. The gold solution is then added to the hot mercuric chloride solution with constant stirring; the utmost care is taken to avoid the production of a precipitate, the presence of which will render the solution valueless. The solution is then brought up to 250 with triple-distilled water.

The sections are taken from the triple-distilled water and transferred to the staining solution for from four to six hours in the dark at room temperature. If time is a consideration, it is possible to warm the solution to about 25°C., which reduces the period required for staining to three hours. It is not difficult to determine when staining is sufficient; the sections should, in any case, be examined at hourly intervals and be withdrawn from the stain when they have become dark purple. A lilac color indicates understaining, and they will be spoiled if they are left until they have become brown. The successful application of this technique depends on the ability to judge the exact shade of purple which indicates a satisfactory termination of the staining process. Sections should be removed from the stain and washed for at least three hours in running triple-distilled water, or in at least three changes of a considerable volume of triple-distilled water changed at hourly intervals.

If the preparations are required only for temporary examination, they may be, at this point, dehydrated and cleared, but the stain itself is still light-sensitive and it is necessary to fix the sections if they are to be mounted in balsam. Cajal himself recommends an acid-thiosulfate solution, the formula for which is given in Chapter 24 as AMS 24.1 Cajal 1913. The sections should be treated in a large volume of this solution for five or ten minutes. The time of application is not critical, and it is better to err on the side of too long application than too short. The solution cannot be used twice and should be thrown away after each batch of sections have been passed through it. The fixing solution must, of course, itself be removed by thorough washing and Langeron (Langeron 1942, 653) recommends 40% alcohol

for this purpose. This is no better than water from the point of view of removing an excess of the fixative, but has the advantage of commencing the process of dehydration.

After the sections have been adequately washed they should be removed one by one from the washing solution, placed on a clean slide, covered with filter paper, and blotted to remove as much of the alcohol as possible. They may then be dehydrated by dropping alcohol on them from a pipet or wash bottle, and cleared in any satisfactory clearing agent before mounting in balsam.

These preparations at the best are only moderately permanent, and should never be exposed to bright light for long periods of time.

22.1 Staining Solutions

22.1 Cajal 1916   21344, **14**:155
> FORMULA: water 100, mercuric chloride 0.7, gold chloride 0.14
> PREPARATION: Dissolve mercuric chloride in 15 water at 70–80°C. Dissolve gold chloride in 15 water at room temperature and add to mercuric chloride. Dilute mixture to 100.

22.1 Raileanu 1930   6630, **104**:285
> FORMULA: water 100, mercuric chloride 1.6, gold chloride 0.16
> PREPARATION: *see* Cajal 1916 (above)

22.1 Ziehen 1891   15058, **10**:65
> FORMULA: water 100, mercuric chloride 0.5, gold chloride 0.5
> PREPARATION: *see* Cajal 1916 (above)

22.2 Neurological Methods

22.21 Nerve Cells and Processes

22.21 Apáthy 1893   23632, **10**:349
> REAGENTS REQUIRED: *A*. 1% formic acid; *B*. 1% gold chloride
> METHOD: [paraffin sections of material fixed in F 1300.0000 Apáthy 1893] → wash → *A*, 1 min. → *B*, 24 hrs. → blot → *A*, evenly illuminated from both sides, till reduction complete → balsam via usual reagents
> NOTE: **Lee 1905**, 254 substitutes 0.1% formaldehyde for the second usage of *A* above.

22.21 Lee 1905   *see* MS 22.21 Apáthy 1893 (note)

22.21 Nabias 1904   6630, **56**:426
> REAGENTS REQUIRED: *A*. ADS 12.2 Gram 1884; *B*. 1% gold chloride; *C*. sat. sol. aniline
> METHOD: [sections of material fixed in mercuric chloride] → *A*, till yellow → rinse → *B*, 5 mins. → rinse → *C*, till differentiated
> RECOMMENDED FOR: ganglia of invertebrates.

22.21 Ogawa 1913   1798, **29**:248
> REAGENTS REQUIRED: *A*. 1% gold chloride; *B*. 1% formic acid
> METHOD: [smears, fixed in F 3000.0000 or F 3000.0010 mixtures] → wash → *A*, 24 hrs. → wash → *B*, in direct sunlight, till purple → balsam, via usual reagents

22.21 Ziehen 1891   15058, **10**:65
 REAGENTS REQUIRED: *A*. MS 22.1 Ziehen 1891; *B*. ADS 12.2 Lugol 1905 20, water 80
 METHOD: [fresh tissues] → *A*, 1–6 months, till copper red → [sections by freezing tech-
   nique] → *B*, till differentiated → balsam, via usual reagents
 RECOMMENDED FOR: axis cylinders and dendrites.

22.22 NEUROGLIA

22.22 Cajal 1916   21344, **14**:155
 REAGENTS REQUIRED: *A*. AMS 11.1 Cajal 1913; *B*. MS 22.1 Cajal 1916; *C*. AMS 24.1
   Cajal 1913
 METHOD: [fresh tissue] → *A*, 2 to 10 days → wash → [sections by freezing technique] →
   rinse → *B*, 4 to 6 hrs. → wash → *C*, 6 to 10 mins. → wash, 40% alc. → balsam, via
   usual reagents

22.22 Raileanu 1930   6630, **104**:285
 REAGENTS REQUIRED: *A*. 6% neutralized formaldehyde; *B*. AMS 11.1 Raileanu 1930;
   C. MS 22.1 Raileanu 1930; *D*. AMS 24.1 Raileanu 1930
 METHOD: [fresh tissue] → *A*, 24 hrs. at 37°C. → [sections by freezing technique] → *B*,
   24 to 48 hrs. → wash → *C*, in dark, 4 to 7 hrs., till deep violet → wash → *D*, 15 mins.
   → wash, 30 mins., 50% alc. → balsam, via usual reagents

23 METHODS USING GOLD IN OTHER COMBINATIONS

23.0 TYPICAL EXAMPLE

Demonstration of the nervous
elements in spinal cord by
the method of Gerlach
1872

It is a pity that this method should
have become obsolete and that it is today
cited in so few textbooks. The method is
simple and certain, hence it is suitable
for class demonstration, and it shares with
the method of Ranvier, already described,
the distinction of being the only gold technique that may reasonably be so employed. It is not suitable for original
research, since the structures which it
displays are already well known, but it
cannot be surpassed for a method of preparing demonstration material.

Only four solutions are required, all of
which are stable indefinitely. These solutions are: first, a 1% solution of ammonium dichromate, which must, of course,
be prepared from a reagent of analytical
grade; second, a 0.01% solution of gold
chloride; third, 0.5% hydrochloric acid;
and fourth, 0.1% hydrochloric acid in
60% alcohol. These solutions, with the
exception of the gold, should be available
in relatively large volumes. In the description which follows it will be presumed that
the method is being utilized for the in-

struction of a class in an elementary technique of gold staining.

The instructor should first secure short
lengths of spinal cord from a freshly killed
mammal. The technique works equally
well on the spinal cords of fish and am-
phibia, but these are in general too small
for convenient handling by a class. The
cord should be cut into approximately
one-inch lengths and placed in a large
volume of the ammonium dichromate solution in a stoppered bottle. It is a matter
of convenience that this bottle should
have about a one-inch layer of fat-free
absorbent cotton or of glass fiber on the
bottom, to prevent the distortion of the
spinal cord through pressure against the
glass. The period of fixation should be
from two to three weeks and is not critical.
At the beginning of the week in which the
class is to be held, the lengths of spinal
cord should be removed from the reagent
and washed in running distilled water for
at least 24 hours. They may then be left
in a bottle of triple-distilled water until
required for class purposes.

A freezing microtome can be used to cut
sections for issue to the class, but the
shape and hardness of the spinal cord
makes it convenient for freehand sectioning, either between layers of the pith, or
by any other method customarily used in
the class in question. These freehand sec-

tions should be as thin as possible, though the necessary structures can be seen in sections as thick as 40 microns. These sections should be washed in several changes of triple-distilled water, after preparation by the class, and then placed, preferably in glass-stoppered, chemically clean bottles, in the gold-staining solution and left there overnight. If the class does not meet on two successive days, it is probably better for the instructor to handle the whole technique up to this point and to issue to the class the material in the gold-chloride solution. The sections are taken from the gold-chloride solution directly to the 0.5% hydrochloric acid, where they are rocked gently backward and forward in a clean watch glass for a few minutes. This will reduce the gold and will be a useful lesson to the class on the perils of over-reduction. When the outlines of individual nerve cells within the ganglia are clearly visible un-

der the low power of the microscope, it is time to remove the sections, one at a time, to 0.1% hydrochloric acid in 60% alcohol, where they may remain for a matter of ten minutes. Immersion in acid of this concentration in alcoholic dilution does not cause much further reduction. After they have been thoroughly dehydrated to the extent possible in the 60% alcohol, they should be removed and passed through other watch glasses where they are dehydrated and cleared by the ordinary reagents. The sections may then be mounted in balsam.

Beginning students of microtomy are frequently so frightened of the metal-staining techniques that they ignore them completely, and the real value of this method is to provide each student of such a class with a gold-stained permanent slide by a method which is very nearly foolproof.

23.1 STAINING SOLUTIONS
(Vacant)

23.2 NEUROLOGICAL METHODS

23.21 NERVE CELLS AND PROCESSES

23.21 Ciaccio 1880   13495, **10**:301
  REAGENTS REQUIRED: A. 0.2% acetic acid; B. water 100, gold chloride 0.1, potassium chloride 0.1; C. 0.1% osmic acid
  METHOD: [fresh amphibian tendons] → A, till transparent → B, 5 mins. → C, 1 day in dark and 3 hrs. in sunlight → C, 24 hrs. → M 11 mountant
  RECOMMENDED FOR: nerve endings in amphibian tendons.

23.21 Gerlach 1872 *test.* **Lee 1905** *cit.* **Stricker 1872**   Lee 1905, 253
  REAGENTS REQUIRED: A. 1% ammonium dichromate; B. 0.01% gold chloride; C. 0.5% hydrochloric acid; D. 0.1% hydrochloric acid in 60% alc.
  METHOD: [fresh spinal cord] → A, 15 to 20 days → wash → sections freehand, or by freezing technique → wash → B, 10 to 12 hrs. → C, wash → D, 10 mins. → balsam, via usual techniques

23.21 Golgi 1880   13497, **32**:382
  REAGENTS REQUIRED: A. 2% potassium dichromate; B. 1% arsenic acid; C. 0.5% gold chloride
  METHOD: [fresh tissue] → A, 10 to 20 mins. → wash → B, 10 to 20 mins. → rinse C, 30 mins. → wash → B, in sunlight, until completely reduced → wash → glycerol

23.21 Kerschner 1908   1780, **71**:522
  REAGENTS REQUIRED: A. F 1000.0030 Kerschner 1908; B. 1% gold chloride; C. 25% formic acid
  METHOD: [fresh tissue] → A, until brown → wash → B, 2–6 hrs. in dark → rinse → C. 12 hrs. in dark → C, fresh solution, 24 hrs. in light → glycerol or M 12 mountant

23.21 Kolossow 1888   *see* MS 21.2 Kolossow 1888

23.21 Muschenkoff *test.* **1907 Böhm and Oppel**   Böhm and Oppel 1907, 267
  REAGENTS REQUIRED: *A.* 2% potassium dichromate; *B.* 20% formic acid; *C.* 0.5% gold
  chloride; *D.* 0.1% acetic acid
  METHOD: [small pieces] → *A,* 1 month → wash → *B,* 15–20 mins. → rinse → *C,* in dark,
  30 mins. → *D,* in light, till reduced → M 10 mountant
  RECOMMENDED FOR: nerve endings.

23.21 Upson *test.* **1896 Kahlden and Laurent**   Kahlden and Laurent 1896, 160
  REAGENTS REQUIRED: *A.* 1% potassium dichromate; *B.* 1% gold chloride in 2% hydrochloric acid; *C.* 10% potassium hydroxide; *D.* water 75, sulfuric acid 10, ADS 12.2
  Lugol (1905) 15, ferric chloride 0.3
  METHOD: [fresh spinal cord] → *A,* 4–6 mnths., in dark → [2–3 mm. thick slabs] →
  rinse → 50% alc., 2–3 days → 95% alc. till green, 2–4 wks. → [celloidin sections] → *B,*
  2 hrs. → wash → *C,* 30 secs. → *D,* till reduction complete → wash → balsam, via
  usual reagents
  RECOMMENDED FOR: axis cylinders.

23.21 Viallane 1883 *test.* **Lee 1905**   Lee 1905, 250
  REAGENTS REQUIRED: *A.* 1% osmic acid; *B.* 25% formic acid; *C.* 0.02% gold chloride;
  D. 25% formic acid
  METHOD: [arthropod tissues] → *A,* until light brown → *B,* 10 mins. → *C,* 24 hrs. in dark
  → 24 hrs. in light

23.3 CYTOLOGICAL METHODS

23.3 Beams *test.* **1930 Guyer**   Guyer 1930, 150
  REAGENTS REQUIRED: *A.* water 100, gold chloride 0.2, acetic acid 0.3; *B.* 5% sodium
  thiosulfate
  METHOD: [3 μ sections of F 1360.0010 Brouba 1930 material] → water → *A,* till differ-
  entiated → wash → *B,* 2 mins. → wash → balsam, via usual reagents
  RECOMMENDED FOR: Golgi bodies in glands.

23.4 OTHER METHODS

23.4 Kupffer 1876   1780, **12**:353
  REAGENTS REQUIRED: *A.* 0.05% chromic acid; *B.* 0.01% gold chloride in 0.01% hydro-
  chloric acid
  METHOD: [sections by freezing technique of fresh tissue] → *A,* 15 mins. → rinse → *B,* in
  shade, till violet → wash → glycerol
  RECOMMENDED FOR: connective tissue in liver

23.4 Kupffer 1899   1780, **5**:219
  REAGENTS REQUIRED: *A.* 0.01% chromic acid; *B.* water 100, 40% formaldehyde 0.01,
  gold chloride
  METHOD: [frozen sections of fresh liver] → *A,* 10 mins. → *B,* 30 hrs. → wash → balsam,
  via usual reagents
  RECOMMENDED FOR: demonstration of astrocytes in liver.

MS 30 Silver

The techniques of silver staining are commonly compared to those of photography, though the analogy cannot justifiably be maintained, save in the case of the original process by Simarro (Gatenby and Painter 1937, 477). Photography consists essentially in the reduction to metallic silver of particles of silver bromide, maintained in a colloidal environment, and which have been rendered unstable through the absorption of photon energy. Simarro impregnated living forms with solutions of potassium bromide and then sensitized them, as in the photographic methods of his day, by immersion in a solution of silver nitrate. Parts of these impregnated animals were then sectioned and exposed to light; such silver bromide as may have been present was then reduced to the metallic form by a photographic developer. It is doubtful, however, whether or not metallic silver is the end product of any of the reactions employed in modern silver-staining techniques.

There is no question in photography of any intermediate condition between the bromide and the metal, the various gradations of shade being dependent on the total mass of silver present. Many of the silver-staining techniques, on the contrary, result in varying shades of brown, making it more probable that the end product is some dark colored silver proteinate, a hypothesis born out by the fact that some of these stains may be differentiated by exposure to distilled water. Thus, in the techniques of del Río-Hortega (MS 33.31 del Río-Hortega 1925) mitochondria are demonstrated by the process of washing out all impregnated material, other than mitochondria, in water.

In the absence of any accurate information as to the method by which the results are produced, it is best to divide the techniques into four great classes according to the reagents employed. In the first class, silver is applied to the tissues as a solution of silver nitrate to which, in some modifications, may be added alcohol or pyridine. Moreover, in many cases, so little pyridine is added that the amount of silver-pyridinium complex present is insignificant. The second class comprises the Bodian techniques in which silver is employed as the proteinate. The third class contains those techniques in which the application of silver nitrate is either followed, or replaced, by immersion in solutions containing silver-diammine complexes, secured usually by dissolving either silver hydroxide or silver carbonate in ammonia. The fourth class involves prior treatment of the tissues with a solution containing some other metallic ion, such as a chromate or dichromate, with which the silver subsequently applied is known to react.

The first class, designated below as MS 31, is usually referred to as the "Cajal technique," although this name is also associated with the third class. Cajal 1907 (21344, **8**:21) distinguished eleven methods by which his results could be produced, and divided the possible reactions into eight classes. In broad outline it may be said that these techniques involve either the exposure of fresh tissues to silver nitrate, and the subsequent reduction of the absorbed silver to a dark-colored complex by exposure to formaldehyde, or alternatively, the prior treatment of the tissues with a series of "accelerators," the purpose of which is to cause a greater differentiation of types of nervous structures. These techniques are used principally for the demonstration of nervous structures; the various modifications which have been proposed have been designated to bring one type of structure more into prominence than another. Much of the classic work in tracing nerve tracts, and in demonstrating fine nerve endings in tissue, was carried out by these methods. This, as are all the other classes, is subdivided according to the purpose for which the technique is intended.

The second class of stains employs a relatively new method, in which silver is adsorbed on the tissues from a silver proteinate solution, sometimes in the presence of metallic copper. These techniques have the advantage that no special preparation of the tissues is required and they may therefore be used on ordinary paraffin sections.

The next great class, designated MS 33 below, is of the most varied application. Workers in this group, with which the names of Bielschowsky, Cajal, and del Río-Hortega are associated, were able to adapt silver-staining techniques to the demonstration of the connective tissues of the central nervous system, through the discovery that prior treatment of the tissues with a variety of solutions (varying from uranium nitrate to alcoholic extract of cork crumbs) prevented the staining of nervous elements and brought into contrast their supporting structures. If the silver is deposited from a colloidal environment, which may be produced either from solutions of gelatin or in other ways, there is a complete inhibition of the absorption of silver, either by nerves or brain connective tissue, with the result that these techniques are commonly employed for the demonstration of spirochetes in tissues and in smears. In general the techniques of class MS 33 are more certain and more accurate than those of the last class, in those cases in which it is desired to show a specified structure, but are less useful when it is desired to secure a good general stain of nervous tissues.

The final class, here designated as MS 34, is known sometimes as the "dichromate-silver method," though other substances than dichromate have been employed. The techniques are experimental, yielding the most brilliant results when a successful impregnation is obtained, but for which it is almost impossible to specify conditions leading to success. Tissues are fixed for varying lengths of time in either potassium dichromate, dichromate-osmic acid, or dichromate-formaldehyde mixtures. The length of time is entirely critical, but results cannot be predicted or even reproduced with certainty. For this reason, it is usual to start with a large number of pieces in the preliminary fixative, remove groups of these to silver at frequent intervals, and extract from each group a number of pieces after varying times in the silver. Among the numerous pieces thus treated, one may be found which will show the required condition. This condition is curious and depends entirely upon the fact that there is not, as one might anticipate, a uniform precipitate of silver chromate or dichromate throughout the tissues. In certain cases, under conditions which it must again be emphasized cannot be anticipated, isolated nerve cells, with all their dendrites, will become impregnated with a dark-colored precipitate, while neighboring cells and neighboring dendrites will remain entirely unaffected. This is undoubtedly the best method by which the structure of such cells may be demonstrated. Unsuccessful impregnations show either a uniform granular precipitate throughout the whole tissue or else no staining of any kind whatever. The nature of the material precipitated onto the cell is unknown, though it has the peculiar property of being unstable unless exposed to oxygen. For this reason such preparations cannot be mounted in the conventional manner under a coverslip, but must be placed upon a slide and varnished either with balsam, dammar, or one of the special media recommended.

The fugitive nature of the stain produced by this last class, and the moderately fugitive nature of those obtained from the previous two classes, may be improved in either of two ways. The silver complex may be changed into a gold complex, or quite possibly to a colloidal dispersion of metallic gold, by a process analogous to photographic toning, in which treatment by gold chloride, either alone or in some combination, results in the replacement of silver with gold. This technique may be applied to any material, but in the formulas which follow it has only been specified if it is indicated by the original author. The second, and more satisfactory, method of securing permanency is to change the silver complexes, whatever they may be, to metallic silver itself. There are many methods by which this can be achieved, the simplest being to expose the sections to a weak (10%) solution of hydrobromic acid until the silver complex has been changed to silver bromide. The sections are then exposed to bright light to render the bromide unstable, and this compound is then reduced to metallic silver with ordinary photographic developers. Though Globus proposed the use of hydrobromic acid for quite another purpose, this technique is often associated with his name.

The most important consideration in securing successful results by any silver technique is the absolute purity of all the ingredients used and the absolute cleanliness of the glassware employed. Ordinary distilled water is insufficiently pure; triple-distilled water should be used. In many instances the slightest trace of an impurity at any stage of the proceedings will completely wreck what may be several weeks of subsequent work. The use of commercial formaldehyde, for example, in prior fixation should be avoided, and the grade sold as "analytical reagent" should be used. Another important step is to remove all traces of one solution before placing the object in the next. Thus, in those techniques in which the term *wash* is employed, it is understood that all traces of the previous reagent must be removed, preferably by running triple-distilled water, before going on to the next step. If running triple-distilled water is not available, it is necessary to make at least ten changes between large volumes of water. Another common cause of failure is the employment of too small volumes of reagents, many of which are weak solutions, but which are dependent for their success upon the maintenance of an excess of the solute. Even when working with pieces as small as a few-millimeter cube, it is rarely worth while to employ less than 50 milliliters of a solution, in which the object should, moreover, be gently agitated from time to time.

MS 31 METHODS USING SILVER NITRATE

31.0 Typical Examples

Demonstration of the nervous elements of the retina by the method of Balbuena 1922

This technique is included for two reasons. First, it is the most complex silver nitrate technique which has yet been developed; second, the excellence of the results obtained in a satisfactory preparation justify this complexity. As the technique involves the utilization of a large number of somewhat unusual reagents, it is best to gather these first. They will be given in the numbered sequence in which they are employed: 1. AMS 11.2 Cajal 1910a. This is the pyridine alcohol of the well-known Cajal techniques, and is made by adding 50 milliliters of pyridine to 200 milliliters of absolute alcohol. The solution is stable indefinitely. 2. AMS 11.2 Balbuena 1922. This is Balbuena's "alcoholic extract of cork crumbs." It is prepared by placing one inch of cork crumbs on the bottom of a 250-milliliter bottle. The crumbs are best prepared by cutting small pieces (of less than one-millimeter side) from a fresh bottle cork. The bottle is then filled with 70% alcohol and shaken at daily intervals until the solution is a dark yellow-brown color. The reagent is then filtered from the cork crumbs and may be stored indefinitely. 3. MS 31.1 Balbuena 1922 (Balbuena's silver stain). This is prepared by dissolving 0.13 grams of silver nitrate in 250 milliliters of triple-distilled water. After solution is complete 2.5 milliliters of pyridine are added. This solution will remain stable for a considerable time, if it is preserved in the dark. 4. AMS 21.1

Balbuena 1922. This is Balbuena's developer, which requires the use of two solutions. The first of these is an alcoholic extract of amber. This is best prepared by taking 70 milliliters of commercially available oil of amber and adding this to 180 milliliters of 80% alcohol. These are shaken together at daily intervals for seven days, at the end of which time the alcoholic extract is separated in a separatory funnel. This remains stable indefinitely. The second solution required for Balbuena's developer is a solution of 2.5 grams of hydroquinone in 250 milliliters of triple-distilled water. This should be prepared as it is required, for it is very unstable. 5. AMS 22.1 Balbuena 1922, which is Balbuena's toning solution. It is a buffered solution of gold chloride prepared by dissolving 2.5 grams of sodium borate in 250 milliliters of triple-distilled water and then adding to this solution of 0.25 grams of gold chloride. This solution also remains stable indefinitely if kept in the dark. 6. A 5% solution of sodium thiosulfate.

There will also be required for purposes of embedding; absolute alcohol, a mixture of absolute alcohol and ether in equal proportions, and the solutions of celloidin, given above as the standard requirements for celloidin embedding in Chapter 13. If the celloidin block is to be set, as is best in this instance, with the aid of anhydrous chloroform, this reagent will also be required. Having made sure that these reagents are available, one must next secure the material on which to operate.

The retina of a rabbit is an excellent material on which to start. The eyelids are removed from a freshly killed rabbit and the eyeball removed from the orbit. The eye is then carefully washed in triple-distilled water, and an area about one-millimeter square is cut about three millimeters to one side of the point of entry of the optic nerve. This usually demonstrates best the nervous elements of the retina. Many of these blocks may, of course, be taken from the same eye. These blocks are placed in the alcoholic pyridine fixing solution in a chemically clean vessel. About 25 milliliters of the fixative should be used for a piece of retina of the size indicated, and overnight fixation will be ample. The small pieces are removed directly from the fixative to absolute alcohol, in which they should remain at least 12 hours, being gently agitated at intervals to prevent the accumulation of diluted alcohol on the bottom of the chemically clean, stoppered vessel containing them. The absolute alcohol should then be replaced for a period of at least 24 hours by a mixture of equal parts of absolute alcohol and ether. It cannot be emphasized too frequently that the ether used for dehydration of specimens intended for celloidin embedding should be of the grade sold as "dried over sodium" and not the water-saturated material commonly sold for anesthesia. The material is next transferred to the thinnest of the three solutions of celloidin for a period of not less than 12 hours. It is then transferred to the intermediate solution of celloidin for a further period of 24 hours, and finally placed in the thickest solution for a further 24 hours. With fragments as small as this, the simplest hardening technique is to remove the piece from the syrupy solution in a clean, dry pipet, and to express the drop containing the piece from the end of the pipet directly into about ten milliliters of anhydrous chloroform. Again it must be emphasized that this chloroform must be specially dried, preferably over calcium chloride, if the material is to cut well. This small drop of celloidin should remain in the chloroform only long enough to harden, and should under no circumstances be permitted to remain until the chloroform has penetrated to the contained fragment of retina. A period of about 30 seconds will probably be sufficient before the drop of celloidin is removed to clean, 70% alcohol, where it may remain until it is convenient to continue the process.

After not less than one hour in the 70% alcohol, the drop of hardened celloidin is removed and trimmed until only about one millimeter of celloidin remains on top of the fragment of retina. The trimmed block is now placed in the alcoholic extract of cork where it may remain almost indefinitely. Balbuena, in his original method, suggests between 2 and 20 days. After the fragment has been (to quote Balbuena) "sensitized" in the alcoholic extract of cork, it is again removed to clean, 70% alcohol and washed until the greater part of the brown color has left the superficial layers of celloidin. The fragment is then oriented in thick syrupy celloidin, on the surface of a block of wood adapted to being held in the object holder of a sliding microtome, and the block, with the contained fragment, is then placed under a bell jar with chloroform, or allowed to evaporate in dry air until such time as it is hard enough to cut. Sections are cut with a knife which has been moistened in 70% alcohol and then accumulated in 70% alcohol until a sufficient number have been secured.

The sections are transferred directly from 70% alcohol to a chemically clean watch glass containing the silver-staining solution. This is best held on a small tripod and is warmed, after the sections have been placed in it, until it begins to steam. The flame is then removed, the reagent allowed to cool down until steam is no longer evident, and then reheated to steaming. This cycle of heating and permitting to cool is repeated until the sections have become yellowish. This may take anywhere from three to ten minutes according to the extent to which they have been previously sensitized in the alcoholic extract of cork. As soon as they are yellow-brown, they are allowed to cool in the silver solution. When this has reached room temperature, two or three drops of the alcoholic extract of amber are added to render the solution cloudy. Sufficient extract of amber should be added to render the silver solution definitely milky but not creamy.

As soon as this condition has been reached, add to the mixture as much of the hydroquinone solution as one has added extract of amber. The watch glass is then gently shaken backward and forward until the hydroquinone solution, the milky precipitate of oil of amber, and the original silver solution are thoroughly homogenized. The sections should be watched in this bath as they darken. If, after about five minutes, the sections have not become a definite dark brown, a fresh bath should be prepared by taking more of the original silver stain, rendering it milky with the extract of amber, and then adding to it the required quantity of the hydroquinone solution. The sections should then be removed from the exhausted solution and placed in the fresh one. It is rarely necessary to make more than two changes, or to wait more than 10 or 15 minutes, before the sections have become satisfactorily browned. When this has occurred they are removed to triple-distilled water where they are very thoroughly washed in at least five successive changes. The sections are removed from the distilled water directly to the gold toning solution, the dish containing which should be rocked gently backward and forward as though one were developing a photographic plate in a dish. Under this treatment the sections will be seen to change slowly from brown to a dark bluish purple. This change will normally take not more than a minute or two, and if it is not taking place sufficiently rapidly, it indicates either an insufficient washing of the section or that the gold has become decomposed through prolonged storage. Additional washing or the substitution of a freshly prepared gold solution will insure satisfactory toning within a few moments.

When toning is complete the sections are fixed in the 5% sodium thiosulfate bath, which removes from them the last traces of unwanted silver material. The sections are then washed in at least three changes of triple-distilled water. One of the sections may then be taken, rapidly dehydrated in alcohol, cleared, and examined under a coverslip with the highest power of the microscope. If the nervous elements are not stained at all, the whole batch of sections may be thrown away, and the operation carefully reviewed to decide the point at which the mistake occurred. If, alternatively, the entire section is found to be too greatly blackened, the situation may often be improved by prolonged soaking in thiosulfate solution. If, however, directions have been followed carefully, it is probable that the nervous structures of the retina will be displayed better than they can be by any other technique. If this is the case, the sections may be removed, dehydrated, cleared, and mounted in balsam in the ordinary manner.

Demonstrations of neuroblasts and axons of the developing spinal cord of a three-day chicken embryo by the method of Cajal 1910b

This technique may be divided into three stages: first, the removal of the chicken embryo from the yolk, and its fixation; second, staining in silver nitrate; third, developing the stain. For the first operation it is necessary to assemble three fingerbowls, two Syracuse watch glasses, a four-ounce, chemically clean, glass-stoppered bottle, scissors, and forceps. It is, of course, also necessary to have an egg which has been incubated for 72 hours. The reagents required are a liter of normal saline heated to around 37°C.; about 4 ounces of chemically pure alcohol, which may be either the ordinary commercial absolute alcohol or the latter diluted to 95% as specified in the original formula; and a solution of 1.5% silver nitrate in triple-distilled water. A chemically clean eye-dropper type pipet is also required.

One technique for removal of chicken embryo from the yolk has been described in Chapter 20, but a variation of this technique is required in the present case. First of all, fill three fingerbowls to within about one inch from the top with the normal saline. Break the egg into one of the fingerbowls. Breaking an egg, after 72 hours of incubation, into a fingerbowl in such a manner as to avoid also breaking the yolk, is an art to be learned only with practice. The inexperienced should submerge the egg in saline, break out the air space so as to cause the embryo to drop away from the shell, and then remove the shell, piece by piece, from one end of the egg, until a hole is left of sufficient size for the yolk and attached embryo to be slid from it into the normal saline. Before going further, the embryo is examined and a piece of filter paper taken of a size which will approximately fit one of the Syracuse watch glasses. A hole is then cut in this filter paper of a size that will leave about a ¼-inch gap around the embryo itself.

The next stage is to take a pair of large scissors and make as few cuts as possible around the outside of the extra-embryonic area, so as to isolate the entire blastoderm containing the embryo. The fewer the cuts which are made, and the larger the scissors used, the less will be the leakage of yolk into the surrounding normal saline. It would be ideal if it were possible to remove the embryo with only four cuts, but this requires a larger pair of scissors than is possessed by most technicians. Whatever method is adopted, the utmost care should be taken to get as little yolk as possible distributed through the normal saline. A common cause of failure in this metal-staining technique is the carrying over of a considerable quantity of yolk to the final dish of saline. As soon, therefore, as the embryo has been separated from the yolk, it is taken with a pair of forceps and pulled gently backward and forward through the saline in the first fingerbowl until it appears to be yolk-free. It is then picked up, preferably in a spoon, transferred to the second fingerbowl of clean saline, and again washed. Transference to the third fingerbowl, where a continual rinsing of the embryo backward and forward should fail to disclose the slightest milky trace of yolk coming from it, completes the washing. If, however, milky trails of yolk are still observed coming from the embryo, it must be washed in a fourth batch of saline. Next take a chemically clean Syracuse watch glass, and transfer the embryo so that it lies in the watch glass with its ventral surface uppermost. This can most readily be established by observing the entry of the vitelline veins and arteries into the embryo. The saline carried over with the embryo is now removed with an eye dropper.

The piece of filter paper with the hole in it is now dipped into clean saline and dropped on top of the embryo in such a manner that the embryo is centered in the hole. Next take the tip of a pair of fine forceps and make, as it were, a series of dots with these forceps on top of the filter paper in the region where the extra-embryonic membranes lie under it. Each time the tip of the forceps is pressed down on the filter paper, it causes the adhesion of the membrane to the paper. Fifty or 60 such dots, evenly spaced around the extra-embryonic membrane, will be none too many to insure proper adhesion. Now place a few drops of alcohol on the filter paper without getting any on the embryo itself. The purpose of this is to insure the adhesion of the embryo to the filter paper for ease in after-handling. Next place a few drops on top of the embryo itself, wait a moment or two, and then very carefully and slowly fill the watch glass with alcohol. Leave it for three or four minutes and then, pressing downward on the filter paper with the end of the pipet, move the whole filter paper backward and forward to make sure that the embryo is adhering to the filter paper and not to the watch glass. If the filter paper moves without the embryo, thus indicating that the adhesion of the embryo is to the watch glass, it is almost certain that the embryo has been placed upside down in the watch glass (that is, with its ventral surface against the glass) and there is nothing which can be done about it save to start with a new embryo. If, however, the embryo is attached to the filter paper, it may be picked up with a pair of forceps and removed to a stoppered, four-ounce jar of alcohol. This jar must be chemically clean. Tip the jar upside down from time to time to make sure that the water coming out of the embryo does not dilute the alcohol on the bottom. The embryo should remain in alcohol for at least 24 hours.

Make up the solutions which will be required. These are: 1.5% silver nitrate, of which 100 milliliters should be placed in a wide-mouthed, chemically clean, stoppered bottle; and the developer (AMS21.1 Cajal 1910, Chapter 24) which is prepared by dissolving 2.5 Gm of pyrogallic acid in 250 milliliters of water and 15 milliliters of 40% formaldehyde.

The hardened embryo is removed from the bottle of alcohol, and drained by touching the corner to a filter paper to remove as much of the alcohol as possible. It is then dropped into the silver nitrate solution which has been heated to 35°C. It will immediately turn slightly brown, and will float at the top for some time. While it is still floating, place it in an oven at 35°C., in the dark, and leave it for four or five days. It should, however, be examined at daily intervals, in case some material has been carried in which is causing the precipitation of the silver. This will immediately become apparent if the inside of the bottle or the floor of the bottle becomes covered with a brownish or black stain. Should this be observed, immediately remove the embryo to a fresh 1.5% silver nitrate.

When the embryo has been sufficiently impregnated, it is washed in triple-distilled water. Damage from shrinkage will be minimized if the wash water be heated to about 25°C., on the assumption that the developing solution which will be used next will be at about 20°C. It is not necessary, nor indeed desirable, to remove much of the silver nitrate, the main purpose of the rinse being to avoid carrying over the silver nitrate solution to the developing solution. This latter should be in a chemically clean, wide-mouthed, stoppered bottle, and at least 100 milliliters will be required for the development, which is carried out at room temperature, preferably in the dark, for about 24 hours. The embryo will become black in the developer, and there is no means of finding out whether the impregnation has been successful until it has been sectioned.

Paraffin sections about eight microns thick are now prepared, mounted on slides, dewaxed, and graded down through alcohol into water in which they can be examined under a low-power objective. They should at this point show neuroblasts and neurofibrils completely blackened, with little or no blackening of other portions of the embryo, save the periphery

on which some deposition of black material is inevitable.

If the sections on examination should prove to be uniformly blackened throughout, indicating either overimpregnation or overdevelopment, or far more probably the utilization of impure reagent, nothing can be done about it save to throw the sections away and start with a fresh embryo. If, however, the impregnation is not sufficiently heavy—that is, if the neuroblasts and neurofibrils are perfectly apparent but are only stained a light brown rather than the dense black which should be observed—they may be toned, and at the same time increased in contrast, with Cajal's gold toning solution, which will be found in Chapter 24 as AMS 22.1 Cajal 1910. Slides are taken directly from distilled water and placed in this solution, and examined at intervals. They will turn from a brown to a purplish shade, and will become darker in so doing. The reaction may be stopped at any point by removing the sections from the toning solution and washing them in distilled water.

When the desired degree of intensity has been reached, the sections are thoroughly washed in distilled water, upgraded through alcohols, and mounted under a coverslip in balsam after the usual reagents.

Demonstration of spirochetes in sections by the method of Dieterle 1927

This is a simple method for the demonstration of spirochetes in post-mortem material. It can be used after many kinds of fixation, though it is usually preferable to take the formaldehyde-fixed material. This is sectioned either by the paraffin or the freezing technique, the latter being so customary in pathological work, that it has given rise to the supposition that this method alone can be used. Better demonstrations for teaching, as distinct from diagnostic, purposes are, however, obtained from paraffin sections of about eight to ten microns in thickness. These sections are mounted on slides in the normal way and the slides are accumulated in distilled water. Four solutions are required, two of which must be maintained at 55°C. The stain depends for its effectiveness, first, on the inhibition of the staining of nervous elements by exposure to uranium nitrate, and second, on the selective deposition of the silver from a colloidal environment which is, in this case, produced with gum mastic.

All four solutions should be prepared before the sections are started. The first solution is 1% uranium (uranyl) nitrate in 70% alcohol. Both the metallic salt and the alcohol itself should be chemically pure, should be kept in chemically clean bottles, and used in chemically clean dishes. The next solution is a 10% solution of gum mastic in absolute alcohol. This is best prepared by selecting clear, transparent, light-colored pieces of gum mastic from a large quantity of the gum, grinding the selected pieces of gum mastic of the required weight with dry sand in a mortar, then flooding this mixture with absolute alcohol, and shaking until solution is complete. The sand is then removed by filtration through glass wool or some other relatively coarse material. The third requirement is a 1% solution of silver nitrate in triple-distilled water and must again, of course, be maintained in chemically clean bottles. The fourth solution, which is the developer, is very complicated, but is necessary in the peculiar circumstances under which this technique is employed. The formula will be found under AMS 21.1 Dieterle 1927; but it is so difficult to make up that the brief description there given must be augmented. In the first place, mix 150 milliliters of triple-distilled water with 30 of reagent grade acetone. The technique will be seriously impaired if a low quality of acetone is employed. In this mixture, dissolve first 4½ grams of hydroquinone, and after the solution is complete, a ¾-gram of anhydrous sodium sulfite. When the solution of sodium sulfite is complete, add first 30 milliliters of pyridine, and second 30 milliliters of 40% neutralized formaldehyde. This forms, when it has been brought by triple-distilled water to a total of 270 milliliters, a relatively stable solution. To this then add, drop by drop, ten milliliters of a 10% solution of gum mastic. This emulsion is stable for some days, and

can usually be re-emulsified by shaking, should it tend to separate.

When these solutions have been prepared, and an adequate supply of chemically clean coplin jars provided, the sections are immersed for 30 minutes at 55°C. in the uranium nitrate solution. They are then washed in at least three changes of triple-distilled water before being placed in 90% alcohol for two minutes. When they are sufficiently dehydrated they are flooded with 10% gum mastic, or placed in a jar of 10% gum mastic for about 30 seconds. It is less essential to impregnate each individual section than to insure that there is a solid film of the solution over the surface of the slide. Each slide is then removed individually, drained by one corner to remove surplus gum mastic, and the back of the slide lightly wiped. They are then rinsed very, very briefly in 90% alcohol to remove the remains of the gum mastic from the back of the slide, and to make sure that drops of gum mastic do not remain between the sections. Immediately after this brief rinse, they are dropped into triple-distilled water where the gum mastic is, of course, precipitated in a colloidal form over the surface and through the material of each section. Each slide is best handled individually in its successive changes through alcohol, mastic, and water, all the slides then being accumulated together in triple-distilled water.

The utmost care must be taken to provide a chemically clean coplin jar in which to place the silver nitrate solution which is next used. This is preheated to 55°C., preferably by leaving it for some hours in the embedding oven. It is then removed briefly from the oven, the slides are dropped into it, and it is returned to the oven for from one to six hours. It is essential that it be kept in the dark during this period. After removal from silver nitrate the sections should be a very pale yellow color. If they appear blackened, it is usually from some impurity in the gum mastic, and there is nothing to do save to take a fresh sample of gum and to experiment with it.

After removal from silver nitrate, the sections are washed in at least three changes of triple-distilled water. It is essential at this stage to remove the whole of the silver nitrate from the gum mastic complex which covers the sections.

After the sections have been adequately washed, they are placed in the milky developing solution for from 5 to 15 minutes, or until they become dark brown. They should not turn completely black, and it is much better to develop them too little than too much. After removal from the developing solution, they are thoroughly washed in several changes of triple-distilled water. This is essential, because the developing solution itself will tend to darken by oxidation, and, if left in the tissue, will itself become so dark that it will mask the spirochetes. The sections are then placed in 95% alcohol, in which they are left until it is apparent, on examination under a low power on the

microscope, that the gum mastic has been removed. If many slides are being treated in one coplin jar, it is usually better to treat them for about five minutes in a first bath of alcohol and then to pass them to a second, clean alcohol bath for at least ten minutes. A very simple test is to lift the slide from the alcohol and to permit it to drip into some convenient vessel of distilled water. If the least cloudiness is observed, the slide must be placed in clean alcohol and re-treated. This must be repeated until such time as the drops of alcohol falling from the surface fail to go cloudy in distilled water. The sections are then treated in acetone (to remove any alcohol-insoluble fraction of the gum mastic which may remain), cleared in xylene, and mounted in balsam. Successful preparations show spirochetes in black against a gray background.

31.1 Staining Solutions

In all these solutions the silver nitrate is first dissolved in water. The other ingredients are then mixed and added to the silver solution.

31.1 Balbuena 1922   21344, **20**:31
FORMULA: water 100, silver nitrate 0.05, pyridine 1

31.1 Bauer 1944   608b, **20**:297
FORMULA: water 50, 95% alc. 50, acetic acid 0.2, silver nitrate 1.5

31.1 Cajal 1910   21344, **8**:5
FORMULA: water 72, silver nitrate 1.4, 95% alc. 28

31.1 Cajal 1921   21344, **19**:71
FORMULA: water 100, silver nitrate 2, pyridine 2

31.1 Cajal 1925   21344, **23**:23
FORMULA: water 60, silver nitrate 1.2, pyridine 2, 90% alc. 30

31.1 Cajal 1925 *test.* **1933** *ips.*   Cajal and de Castro 1933, 262
FORMULA: water 100, silver nitrate 2, pyridine 3, 40% formaldehyde 5

31.1 Cajal 1929   21344, **26**:1
FORMULA: water 100, silver nitrate 2, pyridine 0.3

31.1 Davenport 1930   1879, **24**:690
FORMULA: water 10, silver nitrate 10, 90% alc. 90, nitric acid 0.4

31.1 Lauda and Rezek 1928   22575, **269**:218
FORMULA: dissolve with heat 0.1 gelatin in 100 water. Cool. Add 3 silver nitrate.

31.1 Levaditi *test.* **1916 Warthin**   4349, **6**:56
FORMULA: water 90, pyridine 10, silver nitrate 0.9

31.1 McManns 1943   11431, **55**:503
FORMULA: water 100, silver nitrate 20, chloral hydrate 1

31.1 Podhradszky 1934   23632, **50**:285
FORMULA: water 10, 95% alc. 90, silver nitrate 10, nitric acid 0.3

31.1 del Río-Hortega 1921   3232, **21**:1
FORMULA: water 100, silver nitrate 2, pyridine 1, 95% alc. 5

31.1 del Río-Hortega 1932 *test.* **1933 Cajal and de Castro**
                                        Cajal and de Castro 1933, 262
FORMULA: water 100, 95% alc. 1.5, silver nitrate 2, pyridine 1.5

31.1 Shanklin 1951   Cowdry 1952, 270
FORMULA: water 100, silver nitrate 10, pyridine 1

31.2 NEUROLOGICAL METHODS

31.21 NERVE CELLS AND PROCESSES

31.21 Ascoli 1911   3381, **25**:177
REAGENTS REQUIRED: *A.* 5% silver nitrate in 95% alc.; *B.* 10% silver nitrate; *C.* AMS
21.1 Ascoli 1911; *D.* glycerol; *E.* AMS 22.1 Cajal 1910
METHOD: [leeches, slit open and tied, not pinned, round a cork] → *A*, till hard, few mins.
→ *A*, fresh solution after removal from cork, 24–48 hrs. at 40°C. → *B*, 24–48 hrs.
→ rinse → *C*, 5–8 hrs. → wash → *D* → teased preparations → *E*, 5 mins. → M 11.1
Apáthy 1892
RECOMMENDED FOR: leeches.

31.21 Balbuena 1922   21344, **20**:31
REAGENTS REQUIRED: *A.* AMS 12.1 Cajal 1910a; *B.* AMS 12.1 Balbuena 1922; *C.* MS
31.1 Balbuena 1922; *D.* AMS 21.1 Balbuena 1922; *E.* AMS 22.1 Balbuena 1922; *F.* 5%
sodium thiosulfate
METHOD: [small pieces] → *A*, 12–48 hrs. → [sections by celloidin technique] → *B*, 2 to
20 days → rinse, 70% alc. → drain → 20 ml. *C.* heated to steaming, 3–10 mins. →
cool → add to sections in 20 ml. *C*, 2 or 3 drops *D* (*A* sol.) → shake gently → add 2 or
3 drops *D* (*B* sol.) → shake gently, leave 10–15 mins. → wash → *E*, 5 mins. → *F*, 2
mins. → balsam, via usual reagents
RECOMMENDED FOR: retina.
NOTE: A detailed description of this technique is given under MS 31.0 above.

31.21 Bartelmez 1915   11135, **25**:87
REAGENTS REQUIRED: *A.* F 0000.0010 Bartelmez 1915; *or* F 0000.0010 Bartelmez 1915;
B. 1.0% silver nitrate; *C.* 1.5% silver nitrate; *D.* 2% silver nitrate; *E.* AMS 21.1
Cajal 1910
METHOD: [fish larvae] → *A*, 60–90 mins. → 80% alc., wash → wash → *B*, 24 hrs. 35°C.
→ *C*, 24 hrs. 35°C. → [repeat *B* → *C* → *D* cycle, till material becomes brown] →
rinse → *E*, 24 hrs. → wash → [sections by paraffin technique]
RECOMMENDED FOR: fish larvae.

31.21 Blair and Davies 1935   590, **69**:303
REAGENTS REQUIRED: *A.* water 81, 40% formaldehyde 9, ammonia 5; *B.* pyridine; *C.* 2%
silver nitrate; *D.* DS 21.1 Noguchi 1913
METHOD: [pieces fixed in neutralized formaldehyde] → *A*, 2 days → wash, 2 days →
B, 2 days → thorough wash, distilled water → *C*, 4 days, 35°C. → thorough wash →
D, 24 hrs. → wash → [sections]
RECOMMENDED FOR: nerves in heart.

31.21 Boule 1908   15063, **10**:15
REAGENTS REQUIRED: *A.* F 0000.1010 Boule 1908 or AMS 12.1 Boule 1908; *B.* 3% silver
nitrate in 15% alcohol; *C.* Boule 1908 AMS 21.1
METHOD: [small pieces] → *A*, 24–48 hrs. → drawn or blot → *B*, 7 days, 35°C. → rinse,
15% alcohol → *C*, 24 hrs. → [section by paraffin technique]

31.21 Buxton *test.* **1930 Eltringham**   Eltringham 1930, 91
REAGENTS REQUIRED: *A.* 1% silver nitrate; *B.* 1.5% silver nitrate; *C.* 1% gold chloride;
D. 2% pyrogallol
METHOD: [fresh material] → *A*, 10 days, in dark → [paraffin sections] → water → *B*, 10
mins., bright sunlight → wash → *C*, 2 mins. → *D*, 5 mins. → wash → balsam, via
usual reagents
RECOMMENDED FOR: insect brains.

31.21 Cajal 1910a   *methods 1, 1A, 1B, 1C—auct.*   21344, **8**:3

REAGENTS REQUIRED: *A*. 1.5% silver nitrate (*or* see below); *B*. AMS 21.1 Cajal 1910; *C*. AMS 22.1 Cajal 1910

METHOD 1: [fresh tissue] → *A*, 3–4 days, 35°C. → rinse → *B*, 24 hrs. → [section by paraffin technique, bring sections to water] → *C* (optional), till faint stains sufficiently darkened → balsam via usual reagents

RECOMMENDED FOR: nerve cells and processes in embryos in lower mammals.

Method 1A: Substitute 5% silver nitrate for *A* above.

RECOMMENDED FOR: sensory nerve endings, invertebrates.

Method 1B: Substitute 0.75% silver nitrate for *A* above.

RECOMMENDED FOR: very young embryos.

Method 1C: Substitute MS 31.1 Cajal 1910 for *A* above.

RECOMMENDED FOR: human tissues and embryos.

31.21 Cajal 1910b   *methods 2, 2A, 2B, 2C, 2D—auct.*   21344, **8**:7

REAGENTS REQUIRED: *A*. 95% alcohol (*or* see below); *B*. 1.5% silver nitrate; *C*. AMS 21.1 Cajal 1910; *D*. AMS 22.1 Cajal 1910

METHOD 2: [fresh tissue] → *A*, 24 hrs. → drain or blot → *B*, 4–5 days, 35°C. → rinse → *C*, 24 hrs. → [section by paraffin technique, bring sections to water] → *D* (optional), till faint stains darkened → balsam, via usual reagents

RECOMMENDED FOR: general use.

Method 2A: Substitute AMS 12.1 Cajal 1910d, for *A* above.

RECOMMENDED FOR: general use when method #2 is unsatisfactory.

Method 2B: Substitute AMS 12.1 Cajal 1910a, for *A* above.

RECOMMENDED FOR: peripheral nerve endings.

Method 2C: Substitute AMS 12.1 Cajal 1910e, for *A* above.

RECOMMENDED FOR: spinal cord.

Method 2D: Substitute AMS 12.1 Cajal 1910, for *A* above, and precede *A* by 24 hrs. in allyl alcohol.

RECOMMENDED FOR: human cerebrum and cerebellum.

31.21 Cajal 1910c   *methods 3, 3A, 3B—auct.*   21344, **8**:9

REAGENTS REQUIRED: *A*. AMS 12.1 Cajal 1910 (*or* see below); *B*. 1.5% silver nitrate; *C*. AMS 31.1 Cajal 1910; *D*. MS 22.1 Cajal 1910

METHOD 3: [fresh tissue] → *A*, 20 to 48 hrs. → drain or blot → *B*, 4 days at 40°C. or until light gray → rinse → *C*, 24 hrs. → [sections by paraffin technique, bring sections to water] → *D* (optional) till faint stains darkened → balsam, via usual reagents

RECOMMENDED FOR: neurofibrils of large cells.

Method 3A: Substitute AMS 12.1 Cajal 1910f for *A* above.

RECOMMENDED FOR: buds of Auerbach.

Method 3B: Substitute AMS 12.1 Cajal 1910g for *A* above.

RECOMMENDED FOR: buds of Held.

31.21 Cajal 1910d   *methods 4, 4A—auct.*   21344, **8**:11

REAGENTS REQUIRED: *A*. 4% neutral formaldehyde; *B*. AMS 12.1 Cajal 1910; *C*. 1.5% silver nitrate; *D*. AMS 21.1 Cajal 1910; *E*. AMS 22.1 Cajal 1910

METHOD 4: [fresh tissue] → *A*, 6–8 hrs. → running water, 6 hrs. → *B*, 24 hrs. → drain or blot → *C*, 4 days at 40°C. → rinse → *D*, 24 hrs. → [section by paraffin technique, bring sections to water] → *E* (optional), till faint stains darkened → balsam, via usual reagents

RECOMMENDED FOR: arborizations in adult cerebellum.

Method 4A: Substitute fixative of class F 0000.1000 for *A* above.

RECOMMENDED FOR: neurofibrils of large cells.

31.21 Cajal 1910e   *method 5—auct.*   21344, **8**:12

REAGENTS REQUIRED: *A*. 50% pyridine; *B*. pyridine; *C*. 90% alcohol; *D*. 1.5% silver nitrate; *E*. AMS 21.1 Cajal 1910; *F*. AMS 22.1 Cajal 1910

METHOD 5: [fresh tissue] → *A*, 6 to 8 hrs. → *B*, 18–24 hrs. → running water 6 hrs. → *C*, 24 hrs. → drain or blot → *D*, 4–5 days, 35°C. → rinse → *D*, 24 hrs. → [section by paraffin technique, bring sections to water] → *F* (optional), till faint stains darkened → balsam, via usual reagents

RECOMMENDED FOR: neurogenesis and regenerative processes.

31.21 Cajal 1910f   *methods 6, 6A—auct.*   21344, **8**:14

REAGENTS REQUIRED: *A*. 10% chloral hydrate; *B*. AMS 12.1 Cajal 1910 (or see below); *C*. 1.5% silver nitrate; *D*. AMS 21.1 Cajal 1910; *E*. AMS 22.1 Cajal 1910

METHOD 6: [fresh tissue] → *A*, 24 hrs. → rinse → *B*, 24 hrs. → drain or blot → *C*, 4–5 days, 40°C. → rinse → *D*, 24 hrs. → [section by paraffin technique, bring sections to water] → *E* (optional), till faint stains darkened

RECOMMENDED FOR: Purkinje cells, motor end plates.

Method 6A: Omit *B* from above.

31.21 Cajal 1921   21344, **19**:71

REAGENTS REQUIRED: *A*. AMS 31.1 Cajal 1921; *B*. 95% alcohol; *C*. AMS 21.1 Cajal 1921; *D*. AMS 22.1 Cajal 1921

METHOD: [sections of formaldehyde material by freezing technique] → wash → *A*, 12–48 hrs. or till light brown → *B* (optional), 30 secs. → blot or drain → *C*, 24 hrs. → *D*, till axons of medullated fibers → balsam, via usual reagents

RECOMMENDED FOR: axons of medullated fibers.

31.21 Cajal 1925a   21344, **23**:237

REAGENTS REQUIRED: *A*. MS 31.1 Cajal 1925; *B*. AMS 21.1 Cajal 1925; *C*. 0.2% gold chloride; *D*. 5% sodium thiosulfate.

METHOD: [30–40 μ sections, by freezing technique, of formaldehyde material] → *A*, few mins. or till light brown → rinse, 95% alcohol → *B*, 5–15 mins. → wash → *C* (optional), till required shade → *D*, 5 mins. → wash → balsam, via usual reagents

RECOMMENDED FOR: axons.

NOTE: This method is frequently confused in the literature with MS 33.21 Cajal 1925.

31.21 Cajal 1925b *test.* **1933** *ips.*   Cajal and de Castro 1933, 362

REAGENTS REQUIRED: *A*. AMS 12.1 Cajal 1925; *B*. 2% silver nitrate; *C*. AMS 21.1 Cajal 1925; *D*. 0.2% gold chloride; *E*. 5% sodium thiosulfate

METHOD: [frozen sections of formaldehyde-fixed material] → *A*, 1–2 hrs. → quick wash → *B*, 1–5 mins., 45°–50°C. → 95% alc., quick rinse → *C*, 1–3 mins. → wash → *D*, till gray → *E*, 5 mins. → balsam, via usual reagents

RECOMMENDED FOR: nerve endings in tongue muscle.

31.21 Cajal 1929   21344, **26**:1

REAGENTS REQUIRED: *A*. AMS 11.1 Cajal 1929; *B*. AMS 12.1 Cajal 1929; *C*. MS 31.1 Cajal 1929; *D*. AMS 21.1 Cajal 1929; *E*. any AMS 22.1 sol.

METHOD: [fragments of fresh tissue] → *A*, 1–2 days → frozen sections → *B*, till required → *C*, 10 hrs. → 95% alc., 24 hrs. → *D*, 12 hrs. → wash → *E*, 10 mins. → balsam, via usual reagents

RECOMMENDED FOR: sections of cerebellum.

31.21 Cajal 1927 *test.* **1933** *ips.*   Cajal and de Castro 1933, 188

REAGENTS REQUIRED: *A*. AMS 12.1 Cajal 1927; *B*. 1.5% silver nitrate; *C*. AMS 21.1 Cajal 1910

METHOD: [fragments of fresh tissue] → *A*, 24–48 hrs. → wash, overnight → *B*, 3 days, 40°C. → rinse → *C*, 24 hrs. → [sections]

RECOMMENDED FOR: nerve fibers.

31.21 Cajal 1930 *test.* **1933** *ips.*   Cajal and de Castro 1933, 190

REAGENTS REQUIRED: *A*. 5% neutralized formaldehyde; *B*. 70% pyridine; *C*. 1.5% silver nitrate; *D*. AMS 21.1 Cajal 1910

METHOD: [fragments of fresh tissue] → *A*, 2–3 days → wash → *B*, 1–2 days → running water, 24 hrs. → *C*, 3 days, 37°C. → wash → *D*, 24 hrs. → celloidin sections

RECOMMENDED FOR: brains of small mammals.

31.21 de Castro 1926   21344, **23**:427

REAGENTS REQUIRED: *A.* AF 21.1 de Castro 1926; *B.* 0.3% ammonia in 95% alcohol; *C.* 15% silver nitrate; *D.* AMS 21.1 Cajal 1910; *E.* 0.2% gold chloride; *F.* 5% sodium thiosulfate

METHOD: [fresh material] → *A*, till decalcified → wash, 24 hrs. → slice, 1 mm. thick → *B*, thorough wash → wash → *C*, 5–7 days, 37°–40°C. → wash → *D*, 3–4 hrs. → wash → [sections] → *E*, 1–5 mins. → *F*, 5 mins. → wash → balsam, via usual reagents

RECOMMENDED FOR: nerves in teeth.

31.21 Chor 1933   1879, **29**:344

REAGENTS REQUIRED: *A.* 1% ammonia in 95% alc.; *B.* pyridine; *C.* 2% silver nitrate; *D.* AMS 21.1 Chor 1933

METHOD: [fresh muscle] → *A*, 24 hrs. → wash → *B*, 48 hrs. → thorough wash → *C*, in dark, 72 hrs. → rinse → *D*, 6–8 hrs. → rinse → 95% alc., → [paraffin sections by usual techniques]

RECOMMENDED FOR: motor end plates in primate biceps.

31.21 Cowdry 1912   10157, **29**:1

REAGENTS REQUIRED: *A.* 1.5% silver nitrate; *B.* AMS 21.1 Cowdry 1912; *C.* 0.1% gold chloride; *D.* 5% sodium thiosulfate

METHOD: [pieces fixed in F 0000.0010 Carnoy 1887] → water → *A*, 3 days at 40°C. → rinse → *B*, 24 hrs., in dark → [paraffin sections] → water → *C*, 2 hrs. → rinse → *D*, 5 mins. → balsam, via usual reagents

RECOMMENDED FOR: nerve fibrils.

31.21 Davenport 1930   1879, **24**:690

REAGENTS REQUIRED: *A.* MS 31.1 Davenport 1930; *B.* AMS 21.1 Davenport 1930; *C.* 0.01% gold chloride; *D.* 5% sodium thiosulfate

METHOD: [celloidin sections mounted on slides and varnished with 2% celloidin] → 80% alc., 5 mins. → *A*, overnight or till yellow → alc., rinse → *B*, 2 mins. → alc., wash → *C* (optional), till desired color → *D* (optional), 2 mins. → ether-alcohol to remove celloidin → balsam, via usual reagents

RECOMMENDED FOR: neurofibrils.

31.21 Davenport, Windle, and Beech 1924   20540b, **9**:5

REAGENTS REQUIRED: *A.* 2% ammonia in 95% alcohol; *B.* 5% pyridin; *C.* 1.5% silver nitrate; *D.* 4% pyrogallic acid

METHOD: [fresh embryos] → *A*, 2 days → *B*, 24 hrs. → wash, 1–3 hrs. → *C*, 2–3 days, 37°C. → wash 20 mins. (12 mm. embryos) to 1 hr. (20 mm. embryos) → *D*, 4 hrs. → wash → section

RECOMMENDED FOR: embryos.

31.21 Dogiel *test.* 1933 Cajal and de Castro   Cajal and de Castro 1933, 357

REAGENTS REQUIRED: *A.* 1.5% formic acid in 90% alc.; *B.* 2.5% silver nitrate; *C.* AMS 21.1 Cajal 1910

METHOD: [pieces of fresh tissue] → *A*, 1–2 days → *B*, rinse → *B*, fresh sol., 5–6 days, 36°C. → wash → *C*, 24 hrs. → [sections]

RECOMMENDED FOR: corpuscles of Grandry and Herbst.

31.21 da Fano 1920   11360, **40**:157

REAGENTS REQUIRED: *A.* AMS 11.1 da Fano 1920; *B.* 1.5% silver nitrate; *C.* AMS 21.1 Cajal 1914; *D.* 0.2% gold chloride; *E.* 5% sodium thiosulfate

METHOD: [small fragments fresh tissue] → *A*, 6–8 hrs. → rinse → *B*, 24–48 hrs. → rinse → *C*, 24–48 hrs. → wash → [section by paraffin technique, bring section to water] → *D*, 2 hrs. → *E*, 5 mins. → balsam, via usual reagents

31.21 Favorsky 1930   766, **70**:376

REAGENTS REQUIRED: *A.* 10% ammonia in 95% alcohol; *B.* pyridine; *C.* 2% silver nitrate; *D.* AMS 21.1 Cajal 1910a

METHOD: [pieces from F 0000.0010 Favorsky 1930] → 50% alc., wash → *A*, 2 days → wash → *B*, 1–2 days → wash → *C*, 4–10 days, 37°C. → rinse → *D*, 24 hrs. → wash → [paraffin sections]

31.21 Foley 1938 20540b, **13**:5

REAGENTS REQUIRED: *A*. pyridine; *B*. 1% ammonia in 80% alcohol; *C*. 40% silver nitrate; *D*. MS 33.1 Davenport 1930; *E*. AMS 21.1 Davenport 1930; *F*. 0.2% gold chloride; *G*. 5% sodium thiosulfate

METHOD: [sections of material from F 5000.1010 Bouin 1897 or F 5000.1080 Foley 1938] → *A*, 1 hr. → abs. alc., rinse → [varnish on slide with celloidin] → *B*, 12–24 hrs. → 80% alc., rinse → *C*, 6–8 hrs. 37°C. → *D*, 16–24 hrs. → 95% alc., rinse → *E*, till fine axons chocolate brown → 95% alc., rinse → tap water, wash → *F*, 10 mins. → wash → *G*, 3–5 mins. → wash → dammar, via alcohol and acetone

RECOMMENDED FOR: axons in picric fixed material.

31.21 Foley 1939 763, **73**:465

REAGENTS REQUIRED: *A*. AMS 12.1 Foley 1939; *B*. a graded series of 50%, 40%, 30%, 20%, and 10% alcohol each containing 15% pyridine; *C*. a graded series of 10%, 20%, 30%, 40%, 50%, 60%, 70%, 80%, and 90% aqueous pyridine; *D*. pyridine; *E*. 10% silver nitrate; *F*. AMS 21.1 Ranson 1914

METHOD: [stretched nerves] → *A*, 4°C., 24 hrs. → *B*, 30 mins. in each → *C*, 30 mins. in each (in 50% pyridine remove nerve from stretcher and thread through block of cerebral cortex preserved in 50% pyridine) → *D*, 24 hrs. → *C*, in reverse order, 30 mins. in each → water, thorough wash → *E*, 3–5 days, 37.5°C. → rinse → *F*, 2 days → [paraffin sections]

31.21 Gooding and Stewart 1937 11977, **7**:596

REAGENTS REQUIRED: *A*. 0.3% ammonia in 90% alcohol; *B*. 5% nitric acid; *C*. 2% silver nitrate; *D*. AMS 21.1 Gooding and Stewart 1937

METHOD: [pieces of teeth] → *A*, 48 hrs. → rinse → *B*, 48 hrs. → running water, 24 hrs. → *C*, 4–6 days, 37°C. → rinse → *D*, 1–2 days, 37°C. → wash → [paraffin or frozen sections]

RECOMMENDED FOR: nerves in pulp of teeth.

31.21 Gurdjian 1927 1135, **43**:1

REAGENTS REQUIRED: *A*. 1% ammonia in 95% alc.; *B*. AMS 11.2 Cajal 1910d; *C*. 0.75% silver nitrate; *D*. AMS 21.1 Ranson 1914

METHOD: [whole brain stems] → *A*, 10–20 days, changing daily → drain and blot → *B*, 3–5 days, changing daily → rinse → *C*, 2–4 wks., changing twice weekly → rinse → *D*, 7–10 days → [sections by paraffin technique]

31.21 Huber and Guild 1913 763, **7**:253

REAGENTS REQUIRED: *A*. 1% ammonia in 95% alc.; *B*. 7% nitric acid; *C*. pyridine; *D*. 2% silver nitrate; *E*. AMS 21.1 Ranson 1914

METHOD: [entire head, taken from animals injected via the heart with *A*] → *A*, 2–4 days → wash → *B*, till decalcified → wash → *A*, 3 to 8 days → rinse → *C*, 24 hrs. → *D*, 3 to 5 days, 35°C. in dark → rinse → *E*, 24 to 48 hrs. → [paraffin sections]

31.21 Jahnel 1917 14370, **42**:17

REAGENTS REQUIRED: *A*. 10% formaldehyde; *B*. 1% uranium nitrate; *C*. 95% alcohol; *D*. 0.5% silver nitrate; *E*. AMS 21.1 Ranson 1914

METHOD: [fresh tissue] → *A*, 15 days *or* [old formaldehyde-fixed material] → *B*, 1 hr., 37°C. → wash → *C*, 1 wk. → rinse → *D*, 1 wk., 37°C., in dark → wash, in dark → *E*, 1–2 days, in dark → wash → [sections by paraffin technique]

31.21 Liesegang 1911 11848, **3**:1

REAGENTS REQUIRED: *A*. 1% silver nitrate; *B*. AMS 21.1 Liesegang 1911

METHOD: [sections of formaldehyde-fixed material by freezing technique] → *A*, heated if necessary, till yellow → pour off *A*, leaving thin layer, add *B* in excess → wash → balsam, via usual reagents

31.21 McManus 1943 11431, **55**:503

REAGENTS REQUIRED: *A*. MS 31.1 McManus 1943; *B*. AMS 21.1 Bodian 1936; *C*. 1% gold chloride; *D*. 2% oxalic acid; *E*. 5% sodium thiosulfate

METHOD: [4–6 μ paraffin sections] → water → *A*, 30 mins., 60°C. → wash → *B*, 10 mins. → wash → *C*, 10 mins. → rinse → *D*, till fibers distinct → wash → *E*, 5–10 mins. → wash → balsam, via usual reagents

RECOMMENDED FOR: nerve fibers in spinal cord.

31.21 Miller 1944 *test.* **1944 Randall**　　　　　　　　20540b, **19**:122

REAGENTS REQUIRED: *A.* 20% silver nitrate; *B.* MS 33.1 Gros-Schultze (1938); *C.* 4% formaldehyde; *D.* 2% gold chloride; *E.* water 100, 40% formaldehyde 1, oxalic acid 2; *F.* 5% sodium thiosulfate

METHOD: [sections of formaldehyde-fixed material] → *A*, 1–1½ hrs. → rinse → *B*, 3 mins.→ rinse → *C*, 1 min. → wash → *D*, 10 mins. → wash → *E*, 20 secs. → wash → *F*, 2 mins. → wash → balsam, via usual reagents

RECOMMENDED FOR: nerve trunk of oligochaetae.

31.21 de No 1926 *test.* **1933 Cajal and de Castro**　　　Cajal and de Castro 1933, 368

REAGENTS REQUIRED: *A.* 50% pyridine; *B.* 3% nitric acid; *C.* 0.1% ammonia; *D.* 15% pyridine in 50% alc.; *E.* 2% silver nitrate; *F.* AMS 21.1 Cajal 1910

METHOD: [fresh tissue] → *A*, 24 hrs. → wash, 24 hrs. → *B*, till decalcified → wash → *C*, 24 hrs. → *D*, overnight → *E*, 6–7 days, 37°C. → wash → *F*, 24 hrs. → wash → [celloidin sections]

RECOMMENDED FOR: nerve endings in structures requiring decalcification.

31.21 Okada 1929　　　　　　　　　　　　　　　8542a, **7**:403

REAGENTS REQUIRED: *A.* 0.02% sodium hydroxide in abs. alc.; *B.* 1.5% silver nitrate; *C.* AMS 21.1 Okada 1929; *D.* 5% sodium thiosulfate

METHOD: [1 mm. slices of fresh tissue] → *A*, 6–12 hrs. → thorough wash → *B*, 3–5 days, 37°C. → *C*, 1–2 mins. → [paraffin sections] → *D*, 15 mins. → wash → balsam, via usual reagents

RECOMMENDED FOR: neurofibrils and pericellular net.

31.21 Perez 1931　　　　　　　　　　　　　　　21344, **27**:187

REAGENTS REQUIRED: *A.* 15% chloral hydrate; *B.* 0.2% ammonia in abs. alc.; *C.* 1.5% silver nitrate; *D.* ADS 21.1 Cajal 1910a

METHOD: [2 mm. slices of fresh skin] → *A*, 24 hrs. → rinse → *B*, 24 hrs. → wash, till rehydrated → *C*, 7 days, 37°C. → wash → *D*, 24 hrs. → wash → [paraffin sections]

RECOMMENDED FOR: Meissner's bodies in human skin.

31.21 Podhradszky 1934　　　　　　　　　　　23632, **50**:285

REAGENTS REQUIRED: *A.* MS 31.1 Podhradszky 1934; *B.* AMS 21.1 Podhradszky 1934; *C.* 1% gold chloride in 95% alcohol; *D.* 5% pyrogallic acid in 95% alcohol

METHOD: [5 μ sections of F 0000.1010 Podhradszky 1934 fixed material, varnished to slide with collodion] → 80% alc. → *A*, in dark, 12 hrs., 15°C. → 1 hr., 37°C. → 95% alc., rinse → *B*, till reduced → 95% alc., wash → *C*, till gray → 95% alc., wash → *D*, 3 mins. → abs. alc., rinse → balsam, via xylene

31.21 Rachmanov *test.* **1946 Roskin**　　　　　　　Roskin 1946, 257

REAGENTS REQUIRED: *A.* 10% silver nitrate; *B.* AMS 21.1 Rachmanov (1946); *C.* 5% sodium thiosulfate

METHOD: [sections of alcohol-fixed material] → water → *A*, 24 hrs., 37°C. in dark → wash → *B*, 1–3 mins. → wash → *C*, 3–5 mins. → balsam, via usual reagents

31.21 Ranson 1914　　　　　　　　　　　　　　766, **46**:522

REAGENTS REQUIRED: *A.* 1% ammonia in 95% alc.; *B.* pyridine; *C.* 2% silver nitrate; *D.* AMS 21.1 Ranson 1914

METHOD: *A*, 48 hrs. → rinse → *B*, 24 hrs. → *C*, 3 days, 35°C., in dark → rinse → *D*, 24 hrs. → [sections by paraffin technique]

31.21 Rasmussen 1938　　　　　　　　　　　　7802, **23**:263

REAGENTS REQUIRED: *A.* 0.2% ammonia in abs. alc.; *B.* 3% nitric acid; *C.* 0.15% ammonia in 80% alc.; *D.* pyridine; *E.* 2% silver nitrate; *F.* 0.75% silver nitrate; *G.* 4% pyrogallol

METHOD: [small pieces fresh hypophysis] → *A*, 2–3 days → running water, 12 hrs. → *B*, 2 hrs. → rinse → 80% alc., several changes, few hrs. → *C*, overnight → *D*, 12 hrs → thorough wash → *E*, in dark, 24 hrs. → *F*, in dark, 24 hrs. → *E*, in dark, 24 hrs. → rinse → *G*, 24 hrs. → wash → [paraffin sections]

RECOMMENDED FOR: nerve fibers in hypophysis.

31.21 Sand 1910 6593, **12**:128

REAGENTS REQUIRED: *A.* 10% nitric acid in acetone; *B.* 20% silver nitrate; *C.* AMS 21.1 Sand 1910; *D.* AMS 23.1 Dand 1910; *E.* 5% sodium thiosulfate

METHOD: [small pieces fresh tissue] → *A,* 1 hr. → *A,* fresh solution, 24 hrs. → *A,* fresh solution, 24 hrs. → [sections by paraffin technique, using acetone for dehydration; bring sections to water, via acetone] → *B,* 3 hrs., 37°C. → *C,* 10 mins. → rinse → *D,* 5 mins. → wash → *E,* 15 secs. → wash → balsam, via usual reagents

NOTE: This method was republished later (Sand 1915: 4349, **5**:71).

31.21 Schultze *test.* **1948 Romeis** Romeis 1948, 418

REAGENTS REQUIRED: *A.* 0.5% sodium hydroxide; *B.* 2% silver nitrate; *C.* water 95, AMS 21.1 Schultze (1948) 5

METHOD: [30–40 μ frozen sections of formaldehyde-fixed material] → wash → *A,* 1 day → wash, till wash water alkali-free (test with phenolphthalein) → *B,* 16–24 hrs. → *C,* till completely reduced → wash → balsam, via usual reagents

RECOMMENDED FOR: nerve bundles in cerebrum.

METHOD FOR CELLS IN CEREBRUM: Substitute 0.04% sodium hydroxide for *A* and 0.5% silver nitrate for *B.*

METHOD FOR MEDULLA, AND CEREBRAL, SPINAL, AND SYMPATHETIC GANGLIA: Substitute 0.8% sodium hydroxide for *A* and 10% silver nitrate for *B.*

METHOD FOR CEREBELLUM: Substitute 0.16% sodium hydroxide for *A* and 0.25% silver nitrate for *B.*

METHOD FOR PERIPHERAL NERVES: As for medulla and ganglia, but with a 1% dilution of AMS 21.1 Schultze (1948) substituted for *C.*

NOTE: The methods of **Lobo 1937** (*test.* Romeis 1948, 420) are essentially the same save that MS 33.1 Lobo 1937 is substituted for *B,* above, and that *A* is used at 60°C. for 15 minutes.

31.21 Schultze and Stohr *test.* **1933 Cajal and de Castro**

Cajal and de Castro 1933, 198

REAGENTS REQUIRED: *A.* 0.8% sodium hydroxide; *B.* 2% silver nitrate; *C.* ADS 21.1 Schultze and Stohr 1933; *D.* Any AMS 22.1 formula

METHOD: [frozen sections of formaldehyde-fixed material] → *A,* 1 day → wash, 1 hr. → *B,* overnight → *C,* till reduced → *D* → balsam, via usual reagents

RECOMMENDED FOR: nerve fibers in sections of nerve tissue.

31.21 Tello 1932 *test.* **1933 Cajal and de Castro** Cajal and de Castro 1933, 369

REAGENTS REQUIRED: *A.* 50% pyridine; *B.* AF 21.1 Tello 1932; *C.* 1% ammonia in 95% alc.; *D.* 1.5% silver nitrate; *E.* AMS 21.1 Cajal 1910

METHOD: [fresh tissue] → *A,* 24 hrs. → wash, 24 hrs. → *B,* till decalcified → wash, 24 hrs. → *C,* 24 hrs. → *D,* 5–7 days, 37°C. → wash → *E,* 24 hrs. → wash → [celloidin sections]

RECOMMENDED FOR: nerve endings in structures requiring decalcification.

31.21 Uyama 1926 8542a, **4**:389

REAGENTS REQUIRED: *A.* 3% silver nitrate; *B.* AMS 21.1 Uyama 1926

METHOD: [washed, enucleated, eye] → *A,* 3–5 days, 37°C. → rinse → *B,* 12–36 hrs. → wash → [paraffin sections]

RECOMMENDED FOR: nerve net in retina.

31.21 Walgren 1930 *test.* **1946 Roskin** Roskin 1946, 232

REAGENTS REQUIRED: *A.* AMS 11.1 Cajal 1933a; *B.* 1% silver nitrate; *C.* AMS 21.1 Cajal 1910; *D.* 0.05% potassium permanganate in 0.1% sulfuric acid; *E.* 1% oxalic acid

METHOD: [fresh fragments] → *A,* 5–9 days → rinse → *B,* 1–2 days → wash → *C,* 1–2 days → paraffin sections → water → *D,* few moments → rinse → *E,* few moments → [repeat *D* → *E* cycle till differentiation complete] → wash → balsam, via usual reagents

31.21 Willard 1935 17510, **78**:475

REAGENTS REQUIRED: *A.* AMS 13.1 Willard 1935; *B.* 2.5% silver nitrate; *C.* AMS 21.1 Willard 1935

METHOD: [fresh tissue] → *A*, 24 hrs. → wash → 96% alc., 24 hrs. → wash → *B*, 9–12 days, 37.5°C. → rinse → *C*, 12–24 hrs. → [15 μ to 30 μ sections by paraffin techniques]
RECOMMENDED FOR: innervation of adrenal.

31.22 NEUROGLIA

31.22 Bolsi 1927 *test.* 1933 Cajal and de Castro　　　　Cajal and de Castro 1933, 274
REAGENTS REQUIRED: *A*. AMS 11.1 Cajal 1914; *B*. AMS 11.1 Noguchi 1913; *C*. AMS 13.1 Bolsi 1927; *D*. 2% silver nitrate; *E*. AMS 24.1 Bolsi 1927; *F*. 5% sodium thiosulfate in 50% alc.
METHOD: [pieces of fresh tissue] → *A*, 24–48 hrs. → *B*, 1 or more months → wash → [frozen sections] → water → *B*, 10 mins. 45°–50°C. → cool → *C*, 5 mins. → *D*, 5 mins. → *E*, 5 mins. → *F*, 5 mins. → balsam, via carbol-xylene
RECOMMENDED FOR: microglia.

31.22 Cajal 1925 *test.* 1933 *ips.*　　　　　　Cajal and de Castro 1933, 262
REAGENTS REQUIRED: *A*. AMS 11.1 Cajal 1913; *B*. 5% formaldehyde; *C*. MS 31.1 Cajal 1925; *D*. 0.2% gold chloride; *E*. 5% sodium thiosulfate
METHOD: [pieces of fresh tissue] → *A*, 24 hrs. → *B*, till required → [frozen sections] → *C*, till dark chestnut, 5–10 mins. → wash → *D*, till violet → *E*, 5 mins. → wash → balsam, via usual reagents
RECOMMENDED FOR: macroglia and microglia.

31.22 Lobo 1937 *test.* 1948 Romeis　　　　　Romeis 1948, 420
REAGENTS REQUIRED: *A*. AMS 12.1 Lobo 1937; *B*. 4% formaldehyde; *C*. 0.04% sodium hydroxide; *D*. MS 31.1 Lobo 1937; *E*. AMS 21.1 Lobo 1937; *F*. 0.2% gold chloride; *G*. 5% sodium thiosulfate
METHOD: [fresh tissue] → *A*, (see note below for time) → *B*, till required → [30–40 μ frozen sections] → wash → *C*, 5–8 mins., 60°C. → wash, till wash water alkali-free when phenolphthalein tested → *D*, overnight, 60°C. → rinse → *E*, 3–5 mins. → wash → *F*, 10–15 mins. → *G*, 5 mins. → balsam via usual reagents
RECOMMENDED FOR: microglia (3–5 days in *A*), protoplasmic glia (15–30 days in *A*).

31.22 Merland 1935　　　　　　　　　4285a, **12**:290
REAGENTS REQUIRED: *A*. AMS 11.1 Merland 1935; *B*. 10% silver nitrate; *C*. AMS 21.1 Merland 1935; *D*. 10% sodium thiosulfate
METHOD: [frozen section of F 8000.1000 Merland 1935 material] → *A*, changed frequently, till silver nitrate test shows all bromide eliminated → *A*, fresh solution, 40 mins., 56°C. → rinse → *B*, 30–60 mins. 56°C. (till ochre) → wash → *C*, till reduced → *D*, 5 mins. → balsam, via usual reagents
RECOMMENDED FOR: astrocytes.

31.3 CYTOLOGICAL METHODS

31.31 GOLGI APPARATUS

31.31 Cajal 1912　*see* MS 31.31 Cajal 1914 (note)

31.31 Cajal 1914　　　　　　　　　21344, **12**:127
REAGENTS REQUIRED: *A*. AMS 11.1 Cajal 1914; *B*. 1.5% silver nitrate; *C*. AMS 21.1 Cajal 1914
METHOD: [Small pieces of fresh tissue] → *A*, 10–14 hrs. → rinse → *B*, 36–48 hrs. → rinse → *C*, 8–24 hrs. → wash → [paraffin sections by usual techniques]
RECOMMENDED FOR: Golgi network.
NOTE: This method is assigned, without reference, to **Cajal 1912** by Cajal and de Castro 1933, 203.

31.31 Golgi 1908a *test.* 1933 Cajal and de Castro　　　Cajal and de Castro 1933, 201
REAGENTS REQUIRED: *A*. F 8000.1000 Golgi 1908; *B*. 1% silver nitrate; *C*. AMS 21.1 Cajal 1914; *D*. AMS 22.1 Golgi 1908; *E*. AMS 23.1 Golgi 1908; *F*. 1% oxalic acid
METHOD: [fresh tissue] → *A*, 6–8 hrs. → wash → *B*, 3 hrs. to some days → quick rinse → *C*, 12 hrs. → wash → 3 to 5 μ sections → *D*, 10–30 mins. → *E*, till differentiated → *F*, to stop differentiation → [counterstain, if desired] → balsam, via usual reagents
RECOMMENDED FOR: Golgi network.

31.31 Golgi 1908b *test.* **1933 Cajal and de Castro**   Cajal and de Castro 1933, 201
 REAGENTS REQUIRED: *A.* AMS 11.1 Cajal 1908; *B.* AMS 12.1 Cajal 1910; *C.* 2% silver
 nitrate; *D.* AMS 21.1 Cajal 1910
 METHOD: [pieces of tissue] → *A*, 24 hrs. → wash, 4–6 hrs. → *B*, 24 hrs. → quick rinse →
 C, 5 days, 37.5°C. → quick wash → *D*, till reduced → [sections]
 RECOMMENDED FOR: Golgi network.

31.31 Rojas 1917   21344, **15**:30
 REAGENTS REQUIRED: *A.* AMS 11.1 Rojas 1917; *B.* 1.5% silver nitrate; *C.* AMS 21.1
 Rojas 1917
 METHOD: [fresh nerves] → *A*, 24 hrs. → running water, 24 hrs. → *B*, 48 hrs. → wash →
 C, 24 hrs. → wash → tease → glycerol
 RECOMMENDED FOR: demonstration of Golgi apparatus in wholemounts.

31.31 Weatherford *test.* **1938 Mallory**   Mallory 1938, 113
 REAGENTS REQUIRED: *A.* F 8000.1000 da Fano 1920; *B.* 5% trichloracetic acid; *C.* 1.5%
 silver nitrate; *D.* AMS 21.1 Cajal 1910; *E.* 0.2% gold chloride; *F.* 25% sodium
 thiosulfate
 METHOD: [fresh tissue] → *A*, 6–8 hrs. → wash → *B*, changed daily till ammonium ox-
 alate calcium test is negative → 80% alc. thorough wash → *A*, 1 hr. → quick wash →
 C, 36–48 hrs. → rinse → *D*, 8–24 hrs. in dark → wash → [4–8 μ sections] → water →
 E, 5–10 mins. → *F*, 10–15 mins. → [DS 11.21 counterstain, if required] → balsam, via
 usual reagents
 RECOMMENDED FOR: Golgi bodies in tissues requiring decalcification.

31.32 OTHER CYTOLOGICAL METHODS

31.32 Chatton and Lwoff 1930   6630, **104**:834
 REAGENTS REQUIRED: *A.* F 80000.1000 da Fano 1920 100, sodium chloride 1; *B.* V 22.1
 Chatton and Lwoff 1930; *C.* 3% silver nitrate
 METHOD: [live protozoa, concentrated on slide] → *A*, on slide, 5 mins. → drain → *B*,
 1 drop at 25°C. → cool to solidify → *C*, on slide, 5 mins. in dark → rinse → bright
 light till sufficiently reduced → wash → balsam, via usual reagents
 RECOMMENDED FOR: impregnation of basal bodies and nerve net in Ciliata.
 NOTE: **Chatton and Lwoff 1940** (6630, **134**:229) recommend development in 0.1% hydro-
 quinone.

31.32 Kingsbury and Johannsen 1927   Kingsbury and Johannsen 1927, 83
 REAGENTS REQUIRED: *A.* AMS 11.1 Kingsbury and Johannsen 1927; *B.* 1% silver nitrate;
 C. AMS 21.1 Kingsbury and Johannsen 1927
 METHOD: [small pieces of fresh tissue] → *A*, 8–12 hrs. → rinse → *B*, 24 hrs. → wash → *C*,
 24 hrs. → [wholemount or section]
 RECOMMENDED FOR: demonstration of invertebrate striped muscle.

31.4 HISTOLOGICAL METHODS

31.41 RETICULAR FIBERS

31.41 Cajal 1907 *test.* **1933** *ips.*   Cajal and de Castro 1933, 290
 REAGENTS REQUIRED: *A.* AMS 13.1 Cajal 1907; *B.* water 50, 95% alc. 50, ammonia 0.3;
 C. 1.5% silver nitrate; *D.* AMS 21.1 Cajal 1910
 METHOD: [pieces of fresh tissue] → *A*, 24 hrs. → running water, 24 hrs. → *B*, 1 day →
 rinse → *C*, 5 days, 37°C. → wash → *D*, 24 hrs. → wash → [sections]

31.41 Cajal *test.* **1933** *ips.*   Cajal and de Castro 1933, 290
 REAGENTS REQUIRED: *A.* AMS 11.1 Cajal 1933; *B.* 0.3% ammonia in 95% alc.; *C.* 2%
 silver nitrate; *D.* AMS 21.1 Cajal 1910
 METHOD: [pieces of fresh tissue] → *A*, 24 hrs. → thorough wash → *B*, 24 hrs. → wash
 → *C*, 3–4 days, 37°C. → wash, 1 min. → *D*, 24 hrs. → wash → [celloidin sections]

31.42 OTHER HISTOLOGICAL METHODS

31.42 Lauda and Rezek 1928   22575, **269**:218
REAGENTS REQUIRED: *A*. 0.25% ammonia in 95% alcohol; *B*. MS 31.1 Lauda and Rezek 1928; *C*. AMS 21.1 Lauda and Rezek 1928
METHOD: [fresh tissue] → *A*, 24 hrs. → wash → *B*, 3–4 days → wash → *C*, 24 hrs. → wash → 95% alcohol → [paraffin sections]
RECOMMENDED FOR: general histology of kidney.

31.42 Lillie 1928   23632, **45**:380
REAGENTS REQUIRED: *A*. 2.5% silver nitrate; *B*. AF 21.1 von Ebner (1891b); *C*. 18% sodium chloride
METHOD: [formaldehyde-fixed bones with fixative thoroughly washed out] → *A*, 37°C., 4–5 days → thorough wash → *B*, till decalcified → *C*, till acid-free → [paraffin sections]
RECOMMENDED FOR: structure of bone.

31.42 Kossa 1901   2526, **29**:163
REAGENTS REQUIRED: *A*. 5% silver nitrate; *B*. 1% pyrogallol; *C*. 5% sodium thiosulfate
METHOD: [frozen sections of undecalcified material] → water → *A*, 10–60 mins., in strong light → wash → *B*, 1–3 mins. → rinse → *C*, 3–5 mins. → thorough wash → balsam, via usual reagents

31.42 Kossa *test.* **1933 Cajal and de Castro**   Cajal and de Castro 1933, 315
REAGENTS REQUIRED: *A*. 0.2% silver nitrate; *B*. any DS 11.42 solution
METHOD: [paraffin sections] → water → *A*, ½ hr. → wash → *B*, till counterstained → balsam, via usual reagents

31.5 BACTERIOLOGICAL METHODS

31.51 METHODS FOR SPIROCHETES

31.51 Armuzzi and Stempel 1924 *test.* **1928 Schmorl**   Schmorl 1928, 40b
REAGENTS REQUIRED: *A*. pyridine; *B*. 5% uranium sulfate; *C*. 2% silver nitrate; *D*. AMS 21.1 Armuzzi and Stempel 1924
METHOD: [frozen sections of formaldehyde-fixed material] → *A*, 1½ hrs. → wash → 95% alc., 1 hr. → water, 1 min. → *B*, 2 hrs. → rinse → *C*, 2½–3 hrs., 37°C. → rinse → *D*, 10 mins. → thorough wash → balsam, via usual reagents

31.51 Bauer 1944   608b, **20**:297
REAGENTS REQUIRED: *A*. MS 31.1 Bauer 1944; *B*. AMS 21.1 Bauer 1944
METHOD: [blocks of formaldehyde-fixed and nitric acid-decalcified jaws] → running water wash, 2 days → *A*, changed when cloudy, 18 days, in dark, 37°C. → wash, 1 day → *B*, changed when cloudy, 48 hrs. in dark → wash → [paraffin sections]
RECOMMENDED FOR: spirochetes in tooth buds and jaws.

31.51 Cajal *test.* **1933** *ips.*   Cajal and de Castro 1933, 192
REAGENTS REQUIRED: *A*. 5% formaldehyde; *B*. MS 31.1 Cajal 1929; *C*. AMS 21.1 Cajal 1910
METHOD: [fresh tissues] → *A*, 2 days → 95% alc., 24 hrs. → *B*, 2 days, 37°C. → wash → *C*, 24 hrs. → [section]
RECOMMENDED FOR: spirochetes in sections.

31.51 Cajal and de Castro 1933   *see* MS 31.51 Noguchi (1913) (note)

31.51 Dieterle 1927   1879, **18**:73
REAGENTS REQUIRED: *A*. 1% uranium nitrate in 70% alc.; *B*. 10% gum mastic in abs. alc.; *C*. 1% silver nitrate; *D*. AMS 21.1 Dieterle 1927
METHOD: [sections, preferably of formaldehyde-fixed material] → *A*, 30 mins., 55°C. → wash → 90% alcohol, 2 mins. → *B*, 30 secs. → drain → rinse, 90% alcohol → rinse, water → *C*, 1 to 6 hrs., 55°C. in dark → wash → *D*, 5–15 mins. → wash → 96% alcohol till all traces of *B* removed → balsam, via acetone
RECOMMENDED FOR: spirochetes in sections.

31.51 Eyene and Sternberg *test.* **1916 Warthin**   4349, **6**:71

REAGENTS REQUIRED: *A.* 1% silver nitrate; *B.* AMS 21.1 Eyene and Sternberg (1916); *C.* 10% sodium thiosulfate

METHOD: [thin sections of formaldehyde-fixed material] → wash → *A*, 30 mins., in dark, 37.5°C. → *B*, 1–2 mins. → *C*, 1–2 mins. → wash → balsam, via usual reagents

31.51 Farrior and Warthin   1930 623, **14**:394

REAGENTS REQUIRED: *A.* 1% silver nitrate at pH 4.4; *B.* AMS 21.1 Farrier and Warthin 1930; *C.* 5% sodium thiosulfate

METHOD: [sections of formaldehyde-fixed material] → *A*, 30 mins., 37°C., in dark → *B*, till brownish black → *C*, 5 mins. → wash → balsam, via usual reagents

31.51 Hertzman *test.* **1938 Mallory**   Mallory 1938, 293

REAGENTS REQUIRED: *A.* pyridine; *B.* 1% uranium nitrate; *C.* 0.25% silver nitrate; *D.* AMS 21.1 Hertzman 1938

METHOD: [frozen sections of formaldehyde-fixed material] → *A*, 10 mins. → wash → *B*, 15 mins., 37°C. → rinse → *C*, 15–30 mins., 50°–60°C. → *D*, till dark brown, 50°–60°C. → warm water, wash → balsam, via usual reagents

31.51 Jahnel *test.* **1933 Cajal and de Castro**   Cajal and de Castro 1933, 384

REAGENTS REQUIRED: *A.* pyridine; *B.* 4% formaldehyde; *C.* 1% uranium nitrate; *D.* 1.5% silver nitrate; *E.* AMS 21.1 Noguchi 1913

METHOD: [2–4 mm. slices of alcohol- or formaldehyde-fixed material] → *A*, 1–3 days → thorough wash → *B*, 24 hrs. → *C*, 1 hr., 37°C. → wash → *D*, 5–8 days in dark, 37.5°C. → wash → *E*, 1–2 days in dark → [paraffin sections]

NOTE: *see also* MS 31.51 Levaditi 1905 (note).

31.51 Krajian 1935   1829, **32**:764

REAGENTS REQUIRED: *A.* 1% sodium cobaltinitrite; *B.* AMS 12.1 Krajian 1933; *C.* 0.75% silver nitrate; *D.* AMS 21.1 Krajian 1933

METHOD: [frozen sections of formaldehyde material] → *A*, 5 mins. → wash → *B*, 15 mins., 67°C. → wash → *C*, 1 hr., 67°C. → rinse → *C*, 15–25 secs. → wash → balsam, via usual reagents

NOTE: *see also* MS 33.51 Krajian 1933.

31.51 Krajian 1938   1829, **38**:427

REAGENTS REQUIRED: *A.* AMS 21.1 Krajian 1933; *B.* 0.5% mastic in 95% alcohol; *C.* 1% silver nitrate; *D.* AMS 21.1 Krajian 1933

METHOD: [air-dried smears of exudate] → *A*, 5 mins., 37°C. → wash → *B*, poured on slide → drain and breath on surface till cloudy → rinse → *C*, on slide warmed to bubbling, 3 mins. → *C* (repeat) → drain → *D*, 2 mins. → wash → dry

31.51 Krantz 1924   14674, 608

REAGENTS REQUIRED: *A.* 0.1% silver nitrate; *B.* AMS 21.1 Krantz 1924

METHOD: [sections of formaldehyde-fixed material] → water → *A*, 24 hrs., 60°C. → wash → *B*, 30–60 mins. → wash → balsam, via usual reagents

31.51 Knowles, Gupta, and Basu 1932 *test.* **1938 Hunter**

                                  20540b, **13**:46

REAGENTS REQUIRED: *A.* 0.3% silver nitrate; *B.* 1% hydroquinone

METHOD: [1 mm. slices of formaldehyde-fixed material, washed free of fixative] → *A*, 37°C., 24 hrs. → wash, till free from silver → *B*, 24 hrs. → [paraffin sections]

RECOMMENDED FOR: spirochetes in avian tissues.

31.51 Levaditi 1905   6630, **58**:845

REAGENTS REQUIRED: *A.* 4% formaldehyde; *B.* 2% silver nitrate; *C.* AMS 21.1 Levaditi 1905

METHOD: [fresh tissue] → *A*, 24 hrs. or till required → 90% alc., 24 hrs. → water, till rehydrated → *B*, 3–6 days, 37°C. → rinse → *C*, 1–3 days in dark → wash → [5 μ paraffin sections]

NOTE: Schmorl 1928, 403 recommends the substitution of AMS 21.1 Levaditi and Manuelian 1906 for *C* above; Jahnel *test.* 1933 Cajal and de Castro 384 recommend the substitution of AMS 21.1 Jahnel 1933 for *C* above.

31.51 Levaditi *test.* **1916 Warthin**   4349, **6**:56
REAGENTS REQUIRED: *A.* MS 31.1 Levaditi (1916); *B.* AMS 21.1 Levaditi (1916)
METHOD: [pieces of formaldehyde-fixed, and alcohol-hardened, tissue] → water → *A*,
2–3 hrs. → *B*, 6–9 hrs. → thorough wash → [paraffin sections]

31.51 Manouelian 1918   6630, **131**:759
REAGENTS REQUIRED: *A.* 4% formaldehyde; *B.* 1% silver nitrate; *C.* AMS 21.1 van
Ermenger 1894
METHOD: [small fragments of tissue] → *A*, 1–2 hrs. → 95% alc. till *A* removed → water,
till alc. removed → *B*, 1–12 hrs. 50°C. → rinse → *C*, 1–24 hrs. → 5 μ sections → bal-
sam, via usual reagents
RECOMMENDED FOR: spirochetes in sections.

31.51 Murray and Fielding *test.* **1937 Findlay**   11360, **57**:138
REAGENTS REQUIRED: *A.* 1% silver nitrate; *B.* 1% pyrogallol
METHOD: [pieces fixed overnight in F 0000.1010 Murray and Fielding 1937] → 70% alc.,
30 mins., 50°C. → *A*, 30 mins., 50°C. → wash → *B*, 1 hr., 50°C. → [paraffin sections]
RECOMMENDED FOR: *Leptospira icterohaemorrhagica* in sections.

31.51 Nakano 1912 *test.* **1928 Schmorl**   Schmorl 1928, 404
REAGENTS REQUIRED: *A.* 4% formaldehyde; *B.* 1.5% silver nitrate; *C.* AMS 21.1 Levaditi 1905
METHOD: [thin slices] → *A*, 10–20 mins., 37°C. → 95% alc., 3–5 hrs. → wash → *B*, 4–5
hrs. in dark, 50°C. → rinse → *C*, 4–10 hrs., 50°C. → wash → [paraffin sections]

31.51 Noguchi 1913 *test.* **Schmorl 1928**   Schmorl 1928, 407
REAGENTS REQUIRED: *A.* AMS 11.1 Noguchi 1913; *B.* 1.5% silver nitrate; *C.* AMS 21.1
Noguchi 1913
METHOD: [5–7 mm. slices of formaldehyde-fixed brain tissue] → *A*, 5 days → thorough
wash → 95% alc., 3 days → water, till rehydrated → *B*, 3 days, 37°C. → wash → *C*,
1–2 days → wash → [paraffin sections]
NOTE: **Cajal and de Castro 1933**, 383 recommend AMS 21.1 Cajal 1910 in place of *C*
above.

31.51 Para 1946   1789a, **42**:649
REAGENTS REQUIRED: *A.* 1% uranium nitrate; *B.* 1.5% silver nitrate; *C.* MS 33.1 Steiner
1937 80, 10% rosin in 95% alc. 20; *D.* AMS 21.1 Levaditi 1905
METHOD: [paraffin sections] → water → *A*, 30 mins. → rinse → *B*, 2 hrs., 56°C. → rinse
→ *C*, 1 hr. → rinse → *D*, 10–15 mins. → balsam, via usual reagents
NOTE: This is the preferred technique. The original offers 3 alternatives to *A*, 3 alterna-
tives to *C*, and 3 possible substitutes for rosin in *C*.

31.51 Schmorl 1928   *see* MS 31.51 Levaditi 1905 (note)

31.51 Steiner 1922   14674, 121
REAGENTS REQUIRED: *A.* % gum mastic in 95% alc.; *B.* 0.1% silver nitrate; *C.* A 2.5,
95% alc. 25, water 75; *D.* 5% hydroquinone
METHOD: [frozen sections of formaldehyde-fixed material] → *A*, 1–2 mins. → short wash
→ *B*, 24 hrs., 37°C. → wash, 37°C. → *C*, 10 mins. → rinse → *D*, 4–6 hrs. → thorough
wash → balsam, via usual reagents

31.51 Steiner 1937   11284, **23**:315
REAGENTS REQUIRED: *A.* AMS 12.1 Steiner 1937; *B.* 0.1% silver nitrate; *C.* 3% gum
mastic in abs. alc.; *D.* AMS 21.1 Steiner 1937
METHOD: [frozen sections of formaldehyde-fixed material] → water → abs. alc. → *A*,
6–8 mins. → wash, till gum-free → *B*, heated till bubbles appear and cooled 20–30
mins. → 95% alc., wash → *C*, 2 mins. → wash till gum-free → *D*, heat to boiling,
cool → balsam, via usual reagents

31.51 Steiner 1939   11284, **25**:204
REAGENTS REQUIRED: *A.* AMS 12.1 Steiner 1939; *B.* 0.1% silver nitrate; *C.* 12.5% gum
mastic in abs. alc.; *D.* AMS 21.1 Steiner 1939

METHOD: [10 μ paraffin sections] → abs. alc. → A, 1–1½ mins. → thorough wash → B, 1–1½ hrs., 100°C. → abs. alc. via graded alcohols → C, 5 mins. → wash → D, 5 mins. → [counterstain, if desired] → balsam, via usual reagents

31.51 Steiner and Steiner 1944   11284, **29**:868
REAGENTS REQUIRED: A. 1% uranium nitrate; B. 1% silver nitrate; C. 2.5% gum mastic in abs. alc.; D. AMS 21.1 Steiner and Steiner 1924
METHOD: [paraffin sections] → water → A, 3 mins. → wash → B, 2 hrs., 56°–58°C. → wash → dehydrate → C, 5 mins. → drain → D, 12–15 mins. → wash → balsam, via usual reagents

31.51 Warthin 1916   4349, **6**:71
REAGENTS REQUIRED: A. 2% silver nitrate; B. AMS 21.1 Levaditi 1905
METHOD: [pieces of F 8000.1000 Warthin 1916 fixed, and alcohol-hardened, material] → wash → A, 2 days in dark, 37.5°C. → wash, in dark → B, 48 hrs., in dark → wash → [paraffin sections]

31.51 Warthin-Starry 1929 *test.* Langeron 1942   Langeron 1942, 629
REAGENTS REQUIRED: A. 1% nitric acid; B. 2% silver nitrate; C. AMS 21.1 Warthin-Starry 1929; D. 5% sodium thiosulfate
METHOD: [sections of formaldehyde-fixed material on slides] → A, 1–30 mins. → rinse → B, 30 mins. to 2 hrs., 55°C., in dark, by dipping section bearing slide into stain, placing another slide on top and laying this sandwich in half its depth of stain → remove cover slide, lay section bearing slide, sections up, in 3 mm. layer C till brown → wash, warm water → D, 2 mins. → wash → balsam, via usual reagents
RECOMMENDED FOR: spirochetes in section.

31.51 Yamamoto 1909   23681, **20**:153
REAGENTS REQUIRED: A. 4% formaldehyde; B. 5% silver nitrate; C. AMS 21.1 Yamamoto 1909
METHOD: [thin slices] → A, 24 hrs. → 95% alc., 1 hr. → running water, 24 hrs. → dist. water, 1 hr. → B, 47 hrs., 37°C. → rinse → C, changed after 1 hr., and whenever turbid, 24 hrs., 37°C. → wash → [celloidin sections]

31.52 OTHER BACTERIOLOGICAL METHODS

31.52 van Ermengen 1894   23684, **15**:969
REAGENTS REQUIRED: A. 1% silver nitrate; B. AMS 21.1 van Ermengen 1894
METHOD: [bacterial smears, fixed 30 mins. in F 1000.0019 van Ermengen 1894] → water, wash → 95% alc., wash → A, on slide, 15–30 sec. → B, added to A on slide, 30 secs. → A, dropped on mixture on slide till ppt. occurs → water, wash → dry
RECOMMENDED FOR: demonstration of bacterial flagella.

31.52 Steiner 1950   591b, **20**:489
REAGENTS REQUIRED: A. AMS 12.1 Steiner 1950; B. 0.1% silver nitrate; C. 2% mastic in abs. alc.; D. 5% pyrocatchol
METHOD: [8 μ paraffin sections of formaldehyde-fixed tissues] → abs. alc. → A, 5 mins. → water, changed till no longer milky → B, 14–16 hrs., 60°C. → thorough wash → abs. alc. via graded alcs. → C, 5 mins. → D, 1 hr., 60°C. → wash → balsam, via usual reagents
RECOMMENDED FOR: microorganisms in tissues.

31.6 OTHER SILVER NITRATE METHODS

31.6 Gomori 1940   16913, **44**:250
REAGENTS REQUIRED: A. 0.5% silver nitrate; B. 5% sodium acid phosphite; C. 2% sodium thiosulfate
METHOD: [alcohol-fixed teeth] → A, 1 day → wash, 1 day → B, 1 day → wash → C, 12 hrs. → [sections]
RECOMMENDED FOR: carious lesions in teeth.

31.6 Hanazawa 1917   *Dent. Cosmos*, **59**:125
REAGENTS REQUIRED: A. 2% silver nitrate; B. any AMS 21.1 formula; C. 5% sodium thiosulfate

METHOD: [ground sections of teeth] → *A*, 2–5 days → wash → *B*, till sufficiently reduced → water → *C*, 2–3 mins. → wash → balsam, via usual reagents

RECOMMENDED FOR: dentine.

31.6 Holmes 1900   11373, **16**:371

REAGENTS REQUIRED: *A*. 0.75% silver nitrate; *B*. 0.2% sodium thiosulfate; *C*. sat. aq. sol. picric acid

METHOD: [eggs of Planorbis] → *A*, in direct sunlight, till cells clearly demarcated → rinse → *B*, wash → wash → *C*, 10 mins. → 70% alc., wash → balsam, via usual reagents

RECOMMENDED FOR: demarcation of cell outlines in invertebrate embryos.

31.6 Roskin 1946   Roskin 1946, 292

REAGENTS REQUIRED: *A*. 2% silver nitrate; *B*. 2% hydroquinone

METHOD: [specimens fixed in F 0000.1010 Roskin 1946] → wash → *A*, 10–18 days, 37°C., in dark → wash, in dark → *B*, 18–38 hrs., in dark → wash → balsam, via usual reagents

RECOMMENDED FOR: general structure in wholemounts of small fresh-water oligochaetae.

MS 32 METHODS USING PROTEIN SILVER

These methods, usually referred to as *Bodian Techniques* (see MS 32.1 Bodian 1936 below) are the only silver methods which give satisfactory staining of nervous structures in paraffin sections mounted on the slide. The original method, and most of the modifications, call for Protargol, a proprietary compound conforming to the specifications for "Protein silver, strong, U. S. P. XI." The restricted availability of Protargol has lead the author to specify "silver protein" in the methods which follow; all samples of "silver protein, strong," however, do not give satisfactory results, and some selection may be necessary. Confusion is sometimes caused by the designations "strong" and "mild" as applied to pharmacopeial preparations since the mild contains about three times as much (19% to 25%) silver as does the strong (7.5% to 8.5%). The strength, or mildness, from the pharmacopeial point of view, depends on the quantity of ionic silver which is found in solutions of the compound. A method of preparation from gelatin is given by Moskowitz 1950 (20540b, **25**:17).

32.0 TYPICAL EXAMPLE

Preparation of a transverse section of the sciatic nerve of a cat to demonstrate axis-cylinders by the method of Davenport, Windle, and Rhines 1947

This method departs from the classic Bodian technique in that metallic copper is not used in combination with silver protein to impregnate the nerves. The method is, however, simple and certain, and is recommended in those cases in which absolute certainty of impregnation of axis-cylinders is required.

Since the method of fixation is an integral part of this technique, the removal and the fixation of the sciatic nerve will first be described. The fixative recommended is a mixture of formamide and paranitrophenol, and is given under the heading F 9000.4000 Davenport, Windle, and Rhines 1947 in Chapter 18. Care must be taken to secure pure formamide, as the commercial grade is worthless for the purpose. About 100 milliliters of fixative will be required, and it is prepared by dissolving 5 grams paranitrophenol in 45 milliliters of 95% alcohol, and then adding to the mixture 10 grams of formamide. After all these ingredients are mixed, 45 milliliters of distilled water is added.

The cat has been selected, rather than the rabbit recommended in other examples, because of the relatively large size of the sciatic nerve. A freshly killed cat should be secured and the skin removed from the lateral side of the upper part of the leg. This exposes the biceps femoris muscle which may be lifted by slipping the handle of the scalpel under it and running the scalpel down from the origin towards the insertion. The aponeurosis at the knee can then be cut, either with a scalpel or scissors, and the muscle laid back to expose the sciatic nerve. If this operation is skilfully done there will be no bleeding.

Before removing the nerve it is desirable to have some form of stretcher which may be used to keep it straight during the process of fixation. The simplest method is to use the nerve as the string of a bow, the bow itself being made either from a fine sliver of bamboo, or from some thin plastic which will apply the required tension. The author prefers the small stiffening devices which are sold for insertion into the collars of men's shirts. These are usually about 2 inches long by ⅛ of an inch wide, and may be cut down the middle with a sharp knife to make two bows from each. The selected piece is laid down flat alongside the nerve, which has been freed from the fascia with some blunt-pointed instrument, and one end of the bow tied firmly to the nerve with a piece of surgical silk. The bow is then bent very slightly—from ⅛ to ¹⁄₁₆ of an inch, given sufficient tension—and the other end similarly lashed to the nerve with surgical silk. The required piece of nerve is then severed and lifted out, using the bow as a handle, and transferred to about 100 milliliters of fixative, preferably being suspended in the fixative by a thread tied around the bow. In the fixative recommended with this technique, from 24 to 48 hours are sufficient.

The usual precautions with regard to the purity of the reagents employed and chemical cleanliness of the glassware must be observed in staining the sections. Staining and washing is most conveniently done in rectangular jars, and it is best to use a single jar for all the staining, fixing, and toning operations, though the usual jars of xylene and alcohols will be required for deparaffinizing and dehydrating. The solutions required in order of their use are:

A. 5% silver nitrate. This presents no difficulty in preparation provided that reagent grades of silver nitrate and triple-distilled water are employed in chemically cleaned glassware.

B. 0.2% silver protein. The simplest way to dissolve the silver protein is to sprinkle the dry powder on the surface of the water. The mixture should not be stirred, but the powder should be allowed to drop through the water of its own weight. When no further silver protein is left on the surface, the material may be stirred rapidly and then placed on one side for use.

C. Davenport's developer, the formula for which is given under AMS 21.1 Davenport, Windle, and Rhines 1947 in Chapter 24. To prepare the solution 5 grams of sodium sulfite are dissolved in 100 milliliters of water. When solution is complete, 1 gram of hydroquinone is added and allowed to dissolve completely before adding a ½-gram of potassium metaborate, which is commercially available under the trade name of Kodalk.

D. 0.2% gold chloride.

E. 0.4% oxalic acid.

F. 5% sodium thiosulfate.

The technician should now have in front of him two jars of xylene, one jar of absolute alcohol, one jar of 95% alcohol, one jar of 70% alcohol, one jar of 50% alcohol, one jar of distilled water, and one jar of 5% silver nitrate. He should also have available in beakers a sufficient quantity of the silver protein solution, the developer, the gold chloride, the oxalic acid, and the sodium thiosulfate to fill one of the jars. It is to be presumed that the nerve has been sectioned by the ordinary paraffin technique and the sections, of a thickness of from eight to ten microns, mounted on glass slides. Each slide is then warmed until the wax melts and is dropped into the jar of xylene. When the slides have been in the first jar of xylene long enough for the wax to have been removed, they are transferred to the second jar of xylene for a minute and then run down the series to the jar of distilled water. If the slide, on removal from distilled water, appears to be greasy, it must be run up the series through the alcohols again into xylene, and then down. If the least trace either of wax or xylene remains in the section, staining cannot be carried out. The slides are transferred one at a time to the jar of 5% silver nitrate, which is then placed in the paraffin embedding oven (presumably at a temperature of about 60°C.) where they remain for approximately one hour. While they are in the oven a beaker full of distilled water should be heated to a temperature of 30°C. to 40°C. At the end of the hour, the jar of silver nitrate containing the slides is removed from the oven, and the silver nitrate is either thrown away or poured back into a bottle for further use. The jar is then filled with the warm distilled water and rocked slowly backward and forward for about 30 seconds. This first wash water is thrown away and replaced by a second, which is again used for 30 seconds and, in its turn, thrown away and replaced by a third change for a further period of 30 seconds. Immediately after this third wash, the jar is filled with silver protein solution and left at room temperature for about one hour. The silver protein solution is then thrown away—it is impossible to use this solution more than once—and the jar is rapidly filled with distilled water, which is instantly poured off again. The purpose of this wash is to remove the silver protein from the glass slide and jar without removing any appreciable quantity from the sections. The jar is then filled with the developing solution and rocked gently backward and forward for one or two minutes. The developing solution is then poured away and the jar containing the slides left under a running tap for several minutes; running distilled water is better if it is available.

If tap water is used, the jar and slides should be rinsed with a couple of changes of distilled water before pouring in the gold chloride toning solution. This is left until the yellow color of the silver stain has been replaced by the gray color of the gold, when the slides may again be rinsed in tap water, and the jar filled with the oxalic acid solution. This stage is rather critical and must be watched carefully. The oxalic acid causes great darkening and, if allowed to act too long, will destroy the sharp differentiation of the stain. The slides should be watched carefully, and the oxalic acid should be poured off and replaced by running tap water as soon as the first signs of darkening are apparent. This may be anywhere from $\frac{1}{4}$ to $\frac{3}{4}$ of a minute. Darkening will continue for some time after the slides have been in tap water; if one waits until they have become dark before starting the washing, the preparation will be spoiled. After the oxalic acid has been thoroughly washed off, the jar should be filled with sodium thiosulfate for one to two minutes, and then placed in running tap water until all traces of the fixative have been removed.

Each slide is then individually removed from the jar and run up through the series of the alcohols and xylene. After each is cleared in xylene it may be removed and mounted in balsam, which gives a permanent preparation.

32.1 Neurological Methods

32.1 Bacsich 1938 test. 1948 Romeis   Romeis 1948, 422

REAGENTS REQUIRED: *A.* 1% protein silver in a jar, on the bottom of which has been placed 2–3 Gms. of *clean* metallic copper for each 100 ml.; *B.* AMS 21.1 Bodian 1936; *C.* AMS 22.1 Bodian 1936; *D.* AMS 22.1 Bacsich 1938; *E.* 5% sodium thiosulfate; *F.* abs. alc. 50, ether 50

METHOD: [celloidin sections of formaldehyde-fixed material, attached to slide with V 21.1 Mayer 1884 and varnished with celloidin] → *A*, 1 hr., 36°C. → wash → *B*, till sections are as dark as possible → wash, 1 min. each in 3 changes of water → *C*, 5 mins. → wash → *D*, 5 mins. → wash → *E*, 5 mins. → wash → 95% alc. till dehydrated → *F*, to remove celloidin → balsam, via usual reagents

32.1 Bodian 1936   763, **65**:89

REAGENTS REQUIRED: *A.* 1% protein silver in a jar, on the bottom of which has been placed 2 or 3 Gms. of *clean* metallic copper per 100 ml.; *B.* AMS 21.1 Bodian 1936; *C.* AMS 22.1 Bodian 1936; *D.* 5% sodium thiosulfate

METHOD: [paraffin sections of formaldehyde-fixed material] → water → *A*, 12–48 hrs. at 37°C. → wash → *B*, 10 mins. → wash → *C*, 5–10 mins. → wash → *D*, 5–10 mins. → balsam, via usual reagents

32.1 Davenport, McArthur, and Bruesch 1939   20540b, **14**:22

REAGENTS REQUIRED: *A*. 10% silver nitrate; *B*. 0.2% protein silver; *C*. AMS 21.1 Davenport, McArthur, and Bruesch 1939; *D*. 0.1% gold chloride; *E*. 1% diaminophenol hydrochloride

METHOD: [paraffin sections of material fixed 2 to 12 hrs. in F 0000.0023 Davenport, McArthur, and Bruesch 1939] → wash → *A*, 1 hr., 58–62°C. → wash → *B*, 1 hr. → quick rinse → *C*, 1 min. → wash → *D*, till color gray → wash → *E*, dropped on slide, few secs. → wash → balsam, via usual reagents

RECOMMENDED FOR: general nervous histology.

32.1 Davenport, Windle, and Rhines 1947   Conn and Darrow 1947 1C2, 24

REAGENTS REQUIRED: *A*. 5% silver nitrate; *B*. 0.2% protein silver; *C*. AMS 21.1 Davenport, Windle, and Rhines 1947; *D*. 0.2% gold chloride; *E*. 0.4% oxalic acid; *F*. 5% sodium thiosulfate

METHOD: [paraffin sections of material fixed in F 9000.4000 Davenport, Windle, and Rhines 1947] → water → *A*, 1 hr., 58–62°C. → wash, 3 changes, 30 secs. each → *B*, 1 hr. → quick rinse → *C*, 1 min. → wash, running water → *D*, till gray → rinse → *E*, 15–45 secs. till darkening starts → rinse → *F*, 1–2 mins. → wash → balsam, via usual reagents

RECOMMENDED FOR: axis-cylinders.

NOTE: A detailed description of the application of this technique is given under MS 32.0 above. The method of **Dawson and Barnett 1944** for argentophil granules differs from the above in that the "*B* → rinse → *C*" cycle is repeated.

32.1 Dublin 1944   1829, **50**:361

REAGENTS REQUIRED: *A*. 1% protein silver; *B*. 1% hydroquinone; *C*. 0.5% gold chloride; *D*. 2% oxalic acid; *E*. 5% sodium thiosulfate; *F*. water 100, acetic acid 0.1, ponceau 2R 0.75; azophloxine 0.125; *G*. 0.1% acetic acid; *H*. water 100, acetic acid 0.1, phosphotungstic acid 1.5, orange G 1; *I*. water 100, acetic acid 0.1, light green 0.02

METHOD: [6–8 μ sections of formaldehyde-fixed material] → water → *A*, 2–4 hrs. → rinse → *B*, 5 mins. → rinse → *C*, till gray → rinse → *D*, 5 mins. → rinse → *E*, 5 mins. → wash → *F*, 5 mins. → *G*, rinse → *H*, 5 mins. time → balsam, via usual reagents

RECOMMENDED FOR: skin.

32.1 Foley 1943   20540b, **18**:27

REAGENTS REQUIRED: *A*. water 50, 95% alc. 50, ammonia 1; *B*. 1% protein silver in dish containing copper foil varnished with 0.5% celloidin; *C*. water 50, 95% alc. 50, protein silver 0.5, pyridine 1 in dish containing copper foil varnished with 0.5% celloidin; *D*. AMS 21.1 Foley 1943; *E*. 0.2% gold chloride in 0.1% acetic acid; *F*. 2% oxalic acid; *G*. 5% sodium bisulfite; *H*. DS 11.41 Einarson 1932; *I*. 5% phosphotungstic acid; *J*. water 97, acetic acid 3.2, anilin blue 0.004, fast green FCF 0.2, orange G 0.8

METHOD: [25 μ frozen sections of formaldehyde-fixed material] → *A*, 24 hrs. → *B*, 6–8 hrs., 37°C. → *C*, 1–2 days, 37°C. → 50% alc., rinse → *D*, 10 mins. → wash → *E*, 10 mins. → *F*, 1–3 mins. → rinse → *G*, 3–5 mins. → wash → *H*, overnight → wash → *I*, 30 mins. → *J*, 1 hr. → 95% alc., till differentiated → balsam, via butyl alcohol and cedar oil

32.1 Humphreys 1939   608b, **15**:151

REAGENTS REQUIRED: *A*. AMS 12.1 Humphreys 1939; *B*. 2% protein silver (in jar containing 10 Gm. metallic copper per 100 ml.); *C*. AMS 21.1 Humphreys 1939; *D*. 1% gold chloride; *E*. water 99, 40% formaldehyde 1, oxalic acid 2

METHOD: [blood vessels dissected from formaldehyde-fixed material] → thorough wash → *A*, 4 hrs. → wash, 2 hrs. → *B*, 6–24 hrs. → wash → *C*, till completely reduced → *D*, till gray → wash → *E*, till blue → balsam, via usual reagents

RECOMMENDED FOR: perivascular nerves in wholemounts of intracerebral vessels.

32.1 MacFarland and Davenport 1941   20540b, **16**:53

REAGENTS REQUIRED: *A*. 1% thallium nitrate; *B*. 1% protein silver; *C*. 0.1% oxalic acid; *D*. AMS 21.1 Bodian 1936; *E*. 0.2% gold chloride; *F*. AMS 21.1 MacFarland and Davenport 1941; *G*. 5% sodium thiosulfate

METHOD: [15 μ paraffin sections of F 0000.4000 MacFarland and Davenport 1941 material] → water → A, 1–2 days, 60°C. → wash → B, 1–2 days, 37°C. → quick rinse → C, till differentiated, 7–15 secs. → wash, 1 min. → D, 3–5 mins. → wash → E, 5–10 mins. → wash, $\frac{1}{2}$ min. → F, till sufficiently darkened, 15–30 secs. → balsam, via usual reagents

RECOMMENDED FOR: nerve fibers in adrenal glands of mammals.

32.1 Rogoff 1946   20540b, **21**:59

REAGENTS REQUIRED: A. 1% protein silver in a jar on the bottom of which has been placed 4–6 Gm. clean metallic copper per 100 ml.; B. AMS 21.1 Bodian 1936; C. AMS 22.1 Bodian 1936; D. 2% oxalic acid; E. 5% sodium thiosulfate

METHOD: [paraffin sections of mosquito larvae fixed in F 4000.0040 Petrunkewitsch 1933] → water → A, 36 hrs., 37°C. → wash → B, 5–10 mins. → wash → C, 2–5 mins. → quick rinse → D, 2–5 mins. → wash → E, 5–10 mins. → wash → balsam, via usual reagents

RECOMMENDED FOR: cephalic ganglia of mosquitos.

32.1 Silver 1942   20540b, **17**:123

REAGENTS REQUIRED: A. 0.2% protein silver; B. AMS 22.1 Silver 1942

METHOD: [frozen, celloidin or paraffin sections of formaldehyde-fixed material, loose or on slide, but with embedding material removed] → water → equal parts A and B, 45°C., till stained, 2–3 hrs. → wash → balsam, via usual reagents

RECOMMENDED FOR: nuclei, fine fibers, nerve terminations.

NOTE: this method may be adapted to myelin sheaths by mordanting tissues for 1 week in 3% potassium dichromate

32.1 Stage 1936   20540b, **11**:155

REAGENTS REQUIRED: A. 10% protein silver; B. 0.5% gold chloride; C. AMS 21.1 Stage 1936; D. 5% sodium thiosulfate

METHOD: [2 mm. slices fresh brain tissue] → A, 2–20 days → 70% alc., rinse → [celloidin, via graded alcs. and alc.-ether] → [section 10–20 μ] → 80% alc. → B, till gray white, about 1 min. → wash, 15 secs., or till differentiated → dissolve celloidin → balsam

NOTE: sections should not be exposed to alcohol lower than 85% between A and B.

32.1 Ungewitter 1943   20540b, **18**:183

REAGENTS REQUIRED: A. 25% chloral hydrate in 50% alc.; B. 1% protein silver in jar containing 2–3 Gm. metallic copper per 100 ml.; C. AMS 21.1 Ungewitter 1943; D. 1% silver nitrate

METHOD: [fresh tissue] → A, 24 hrs. → [paraffin sections] → water → B, 24 hrs. → rinse → C, 5–10 mins. → wash → D, 10–20 mins. → wash → [repeat $C → D$ cycle till sufficiently stained] → balsam, via usual reagents

32.2 OTHER PROTEIN SILVER METHODS

32.2 Dawson and Barnett 1944   *see* MS 32.1 Davenport, Windle, and Rhines 1947

32.2 Dublin 1943   *Tech. Bull.*, **4**:127

REAGENTS REQUIRED: A. 1% protein silver; B. 1% hydroquinone; C. 0.5% gold chloride; D. 5% oxalic acid; E. 10% sodium thiosulfate

METHOD: [paraffin sections of formaldehyde-fixed material] → water → A, overnight, 37.5°C. → rinse → B, 10 mins. → rinse → C, 5 mins. → rinse → D, 5 mins. → rinse → E, 5 mins. → wash → balsam, via usual reagents

RECOMMENDED FOR: demonstration of melanin.

32.2 Moskowitz 1950   20540b, **25**:17

REAGENTS REQUIRED: A. 0.5% potassium permanganate; B. 5% oxalic acid; C. 1% protein silver; D. water 100, sodium sulfite 5, hydroquinone 1; E. 0.2% gold chloride; F. 2% oxalic acid; G. 5% sodium thiosulfate

METHOD: [smears fixed in F 3000.0000 Schaudin 1893 and well washed] → A, 2 mins. → wash → B, 2 mins. → thorough wash → C, 36 hrs. at 35°C. → rinse → F, 3 mins. → wash → G, 8 mins. → thorough wash → balsam, via usual reagents

RECOMMENDED FOR: extra-nuclear structures in protozoa.

MS 33 METHODS USING SILVER DIAMMINE

33.0 Typical Examples

Demonstration of the nerve endings in the taste buds by the method of Bielschowsky 1904

This method is one of the best of the silver diammine techniques for the purpose of showing nervous structures, the demonstration of which is the subject of the next two examples, rather than connective tissues.

In every type of metal staining so far described, emphasis has been laid on the necessity of securing pure reagents. This warning is the more necessary in the present instance because such common reagents as sodium hydroxide and formaldehyde are included among the materials required. The sodium hydroxide employed must be of the analytical grade (purified by alcohol) and if possible free from all traces of chlorides. The formaldehyde employed must be of analytical reagent grade and must be neutralized by the addition of analytical reagent grade borax. The term *neutrality* in this instance may be extended to include any pH between 7 and 7.5, but under no circumstances may an acid formaldehyde be employed.

The first stage in the preparation is the preservation of small blocks of tissue likely to contain taste buds, in 8% neutralized formaldehyde. These may easily be obtained from a rabbit, in which form the taste buds are concentrated on the lateral surface of the ridges which comprise the foliate papillae. Secure a freshly killed rabbit and disarticulate the lower jaw completely, cutting with scissors through the disarticulated joint. A large sharp scalpel or cartilage knife is then passed under the tongue to sever its attachments. The lower jaw is removed, and the tongue left in place. The latter can now be removed entire, washed free of extravasated blood, and placed with the dorsal surface uppermost on any convenient surface. Examination of the posterior region of the tongue will show two oval bulges at the lateral portions of the posterior region. Each of these oval bulges (the foliate papillae) consists of many parallel transversely arranged ridges with deep grooves between them. Taste buds are closely concentrated on the lateral surfaces of these ridges. Each ridge should be severed from its base by running a cartilage knife or razor roughly parallel to the surface of the tongue. A sufficient number of ridges thus removed may be placed until required in the neutralized 8% formaldehyde, which is to be changed after six hours. The length of time allowed for hardening in the formaldehyde is immaterial, but should not be less than one month.

Three or four days before proceeding with the staining technique, the pieces should be removed from formaldehyde and placed directly into pure pyridine for about three days. It is probable that the main function of the pyridine is to cause a differential shrinkage of the nervous elements, which will thus become more apparent on subsequent staining. The success of subsequent operations depends on the removal of every trace of both formaldehyde and pyridine from the pieces before they are placed in the silver staining solution. Though one could in theory achieve this by washing in running triple-distilled water, the quantities of water required would be so great that the process is not practical. It is therefore recommended that the pieces be washed in running tap water for at least 24 hours (double the time will not hurt them) and then rewashed in triple-distilled water to remove impurities which may have come from the tap water. The second wash should either be in running triple-distilled water, or alternatively in not fewer than five changes of large volumes of triple-distilled water changed daily.

Before proceeding further it is necessary to make up the Bielschowsky stock silver solution (MS 33.1 Bielschowsky 1902) used in this technique. First secure a chemically clean 500-milliliter beaker, a chemically clean 250-milliliter graduated flask, a chemically clean glass stirring rod, and a chemically clean buret. Place 120 milliliters of triple-distilled water in the beaker and add to it 2.4 grams of reagent-grade silver nitrate. When the solution is complete add one milliliter of a 40% solution of sodium hydroxide prepared from analytical reagent-grade NaOH dissolved in triple-distilled water. Mix thoroughly until the curdlike precipitate is uniformly distributed through the mass. From the buret add reagent-grade ammonia to this curdy material, stirring vigorously after the addition of each drop. As soon as the curdy precipitate is seen to be clearing up, add one drop about every ten seconds, stirring vigorously between additions. It is as well to put the solution in a good light against a black background so as to detect the exact moment at which the last of the precipitate has vanished. It is fatal to the technique to add too much ammonia, but it does not particularly interfere with the stain if a slight excess of the precipitated silver hydroxide is present. Some authors have accordingly recommended that after the end point of the reaction has been reached (that is, when the precipitate has been exactly redissolved) one or two drops of a very weak solution of silver nitrate should be added so that the faintest opalescence is produced. The solution is then transferred to a graduated flask and made up to a total volume of 250 milliliters with triple-distilled water. This is the stock solution which in the present technique is diluted 40 stock to 60 triple-distilled water before use.

This staining solution is used after pretreatment with 3% silver nitrate, immersion in which is the next step. This 3% silver nitrate should be in a chemically clean stoppered bottle. To it the well-washed pieces of tongue are removed from triple-distilled water, and there incubated at 36°C. for three days. This reaction is best conducted in the dark, and like reactions in all other silver techniques must be watched closely to make sure that no impurities present in the solution or in the bottle cause a precipitate of metallic silver or of silver salts. If the least cloudiness is seen in the solution, or if a black precipitate appears to be accumulating on the bottom, the pieces should immediately be removed to a fresh solution.

After three days, each piece of tongue is removed from the silver nitrate solution and rinsed briefly in a large volume of triple-distilled water. The object of this rinse is not so much to remove silver nitrate from the interior of the material as to prevent carrying over excess silver nitrate solution into the silver stain. When the pieces have been freed from the surface-adherent silver nitrate solution, they are transferred to the diluted staining solution, where they remain at room temperature for 24 hours. They are then washed in running distilled water for at least 24 hours, or in three changes of large volumes of triple-distilled water changed at intervals of about 12 hours, before being placed in a fresh batch of 8% neutralized formaldehyde.

The washing which precedes immersion in formaldehyde is one of the most critical steps of the entire technique, for if silver stain or silver nitrate is carried over into the reducing solution, the preparation will be spoiled through a general deposition of silver proteinates.

After remaining in the neutral formaldehyde overnight, the pieces are washed thoroughly in tap water. Sections are then prepared by the ordinary paraffin technique. When dealing with materials as strongly muscularized as is tongue, however, it is desirable to use benzene as a clearing agent in order to prevent the muscle from becoming brittle and thus interfering with subsequent sectioning. After the sections have been mounted on a slide, they are passed down to water, thoroughly washed, and then examined under a high power of the microscope.

If the sections clearly display the nerve endings in the taste buds, they may be again upgraded through the successive strengths of alcohol, dehydrated, and mounted in balsam. If, as is frequently the case, the nerve endings are only lightly stained, the sections placed in a very weak solution of gold chloride (0.004%) until the pale brown color of the nervous material has been replaced by the dark purple of gold. After this treatment the sections are rinsed for a few minutes in 5% sodium thiosulfate to remove any residual silver which has not been replaced by the gold, washed thoroughly in either tap water or distilled water, dehydrated, and mounted in balsam.

Demonstration of oligodendria and microglia by the method of Penfield 1938

This is one of the most complex of the silver staining techniques, but the complexities are justified by the relative certainty with which results may be obtained. A relatively large number of reagents are required and it is best to make sure that all of these are available before starting the technique. These reagents are described below in the order in which they are required.

First is Cajal 1913 formol-bromide solution (AMS 11.1 Cajal 1913—Chapter 24). This is made by adding 38 c. milliliters of neutralized 40% formaldehyde to 212 milliliters of triple-distilled water. The formaldehyde must be of reagent grade and should have been neutralized with reagent-grade borax. The term *neutral* refers in this instance to any pH between about 7 and 7.6. Five grams of reagent-grade ammonium bromide are then added. This solution is stable indefinitely.

The next three reagents required are a 1% dilution of ammonia, 2% hydrobromic acid, and 5% sodium carbonate. Both the acid and the carbonate must be of the finest grade available; the latter in particular must be chloride-free.

The silver stain used is a dilution of del Río-Hortega 1921 silver carbonate (MS 33.1 del Río-Hortega 1921). This is prepared from a 10% solution of pure silver nitrate in triple-distilled water, a 5% solution of reagent-grade sodium carbonate (also in triple-distilled water), and ammonia. Place 30 milliliters of 10% silver nitrate in a 250-milliliter beaker and add to this, with constant agitation, 120 milliliters of sodium carbonate solution. The solution is now allowed to stand until the silver carbonate has fallen to the bottom. Then as much as possible of the supernatant liquid is poured from the top. The beaker is then filled with a fresh batch of triple-distilled water, thoroughly agitated, and again allowed to settle. The supernatant liquid is poured off and the process repeated about three times. The precipitate may alternatively be accumulated on a chemically clean filter paper on chemically clean glassware and washed by passing considerable volumes of triple-distilled water through it. Whatever method may be adopted, the silver carbonate is collected in approximately 100 milliliters of triple-distilled water; and reagent-grade ammonia is added drop by drop, with agitation between drops, until the carbonate is just dissolved. It is essential that the ammonia should not be in excess. At the moment when the precipitate is seen to be clearing up, the rate of addition of ammonia should be reduced to one drop every 10 seconds. The beaker should be observed in a good light against a black background. When the carbonate is dissolved, make up the solution with triple-distilled water to a volume of 240 milliliters. For purposes of the present technique, this stain is diluted 56 of the solution just described to 44 of triple-distilled water.

One requires also a 0.4% neutralized formaldehyde solution (that is, one milliliter of neutralized formaldehyde diluted with 99 milliliters of water), a 0.2% solution of gold chloride, and the usual 5% solution of sodium thiosulfate. All these reagents except the diluted stain are stable. The latter may usually be kept some weeks in a well-stoppered bottle, preferably in the dark.

Since the method of Penfield is designed to show both oligodendria and microglia, considerable care must be taken to make sure that the former are present in a normal condition in the brain at the time it is fixed. Oligodendria (McClung 1929, 362) will be distorted almost beyond recognition if the death of the animal from which they are taken is preceded by coma or deep stupor. Under these circumstances it is best to kill the rabbit used for the preparation by a sharp blow on the occipital region rather than by the more conventional method of chloroform or ether.

Having killed the rabbit, fasten it face down on a convenient dissecting board, skin the head, remove the parietal and frontal bones with bone forceps, flood the brain with the formaldehyde-bromide as a hemostatic measure, and then remove small pieces from the white matter of the cerebrum or from such other portions of the brain as it is desired to study. The white matter of the cerebrum is recommended as a material because of the relative certainty with which the supporting elements within it may be demonstrated. The tissue is best removed in blocks of about ½ cm. cube, and as the author has elsewhere indicated, it is preferable to use for this purpose the broken edge of a coverslip rather than steel instruments. Three or four of these blocks are removed to the formaldehyde-bromide solution in a chemically cleaned stoppered bottle and permitted to remain there until such time as one is ready to proceed with the preparation. It is stated by McClung 1929, 379 that one week in this solution gives excellent results; but the original recommendation of Penfield does not place any time limit on the preliminary hardening.

When one is ready to prepare and stain sections it is simplest to erect a sort of production line of glass dishes containing the successive solutions and water for the intermediate washings. The size and shape of these dishes is not of the slightest importance provided that they are chemically cleaned. Dishes in which it is intended to leave the reagents exposed for any length of time should be made of pyrex glass and furnished with some kind of lid. In the writer's experience the most readily available and useful dish is a deep pyrex petri dish at least 15 millimeters in depth, even though these dishes require rather large volumes of solution. Twelve such dishes should be chemically cleaned (that is, soaked in dichromate-sulfuric cleaning mixture), washed in tap water, soaked in distilled water, and dried under dust-free conditions.

The first dish should contain triple-distilled water. The blocks of tissue are placed on a freezing microtome and sectioned to a thickness of from 15 to 25 microns, and the sections are taken off on a wet knife and accumulated in this dish. When a sufficient number have been accumulated, one may proceed with the staining.

In another dish place the 1% ammonia, and transfer to it the sections from the dish of triple-distilled water. Here they may remain overnight to insure the complete washing out of formaldehyde and the neutralization of any residual acid which may be present.

The next morning fill another dish with 2% hydrobromic acid and transfer the sections to it one at a time, being careful to pick them up with a glass utensil. It will be found that a 22 × 15 mm. coverslip is excellent for this purpose. As soon as enough sections have been accumulated in the hydrobromic acid, the dish is placed for one hour on the surface of a water bath which is maintained at from 37° to 40°C. While these sections are being treated, fill three more dishes with water and a fourth with the 5% sodium carbonate. The dish containing the sections is now removed from the bath and, again with a glass utensil, the sections are removed to the first dish of wash water. Here they remain for about five minutes while the dish is gently rocked at intervals. All the sections are next removed to the second dish of water for at least 30 minutes of rocking at intervals; and then to the third dish for not less than 15 minutes of similar washing. While the washing in the third dish is being concluded the next dish is filled with 5% sodium carbonate. All the sections are transferred to this and permitted to remain for about one hour, though they may be left two or three times as long without interfering with subsequent stages of the technique.

Next take four clean dishes. Fill the first of these with triple-distilled water, the second with the diluted silver stain, the third with triple-distilled water, and the fourth with 0.4% neutralized formaldehyde. Take the first of the sections from the sodium carbonate, rinse it in the first dish of distilled water, and pass it to the dish of diluted silver stain. There it should remain for a period of three minutes. It is then removed, rinsed in the next dish of distilled water, and passed into the dish of formaldehyde. It should turn a dull steel-grey color almost immediately. If the first section does not turn this color, take a second section from the sodium carbonate, rinse it, place it in the reduced silver solution for four minutes, rinse it again, and transfer it in its turn to the formaldehyde. If this section does not then turn grey, repeat the process with another section, leaving it in the reduced silver solution for five minutes. By this method one may establish the period of time necessary to secure adequate impregnation of sections in the particular batch with which one is dealing. As soon as this has been established four or five sections may be taken at a time, placed in the silver, and gently rocked to make sure that some sections do not rest on top of others. Next, the sections are removed all at the same time to the distilled water, in which they are rinsed; and then to the formaldehyde, in which they may be accumulated. The whole batch of sections may thus be passed through stain and accumulated in formaldehyde.

Now take four more clean dishes. In the first of these place distilled water; in the second, the gold chloride toning solution; in the third, the 5% solution of sodium thiosulfate; and in the fourth, another bath of distilled water. The entire batch of sections is now taken at one time from the formaldehyde, placed in the distilled water, and there rocked gently to and fro. If there are many sections, change the water so as to insure thorough washing. When they have been sufficiently washed, the entire batch is transferred to the next dish containing the gold chloride. In this solution the dull steel-grey of the sections changes to the purplish-blue-grey of gold-stained material. They should be left until the change is complete—usually within a few minutes. It does not in the least matter if they are left for several hours.

The sections are next taken all at one time from the gold chloride solution and passed without preliminary washing to the sodium thiosulfate solution. This removes from them the silver salts which may not have been completely replaced by the gold. Four or five minutes is sufficient for this change. The sections should certainly not be left here longer than about ten minutes for there is some risk of removing the stain. After the thiosulfate treatment they are passed to the next dish of dis-

tilled water, in which they must be rocked back and forth. If any considerable number of sections is included in the batch, this distilled water should be changed once or twice, since it is necessary to remove all thiosulfate from the sections before mounting them. Now take an entirely new batch of dishes containing the customary dehydrating and clearing agents, run the sections through, and mount them in balsam.

This technique may be modified to show astrocytes, and thus present a very complete picture of the supporting structures of the cortex of the cerebrum. Simply leave the sections too long in the silver stain. This will result in a less clear picture of the oligodendria and microglia, but may be desirable for class demonstration purposes. To achieve this result leave them in the silver staining solution until they have changed to a definite dark straw color. This will usually require from five to ten minutes, and may be judged by eye without difficulty. The rest of the process is in every way similar. If the reader is trying this technique for the first time, it might be of interest for him to leave two or three sections in the silver stain while he is taking the remainder through the test of the technique.

Demonstration of microglia by the technique of del Río-Hortega 1921b

The last example demonstrated the use of del Río-Hortega's silver-carbonate technique for the demonstration of both oligodendroglia and microdendroglia. The present method demonstrates the use of del Río-Hortega's silver-hydroxide technique for a differential demonstration of microglia. The technique is much quicker and shorter than that of Penfield and is to be recommended where the demonstration of oligodendroglia is not required.

The procedure of securing the blocks of tissue and fixing them in Cajal's formaldehyde ammonium-bromide mixture is identical with that of the last example, to which reference should be made. Pieces of tissue, however, are fixed in a slightly different manner. They are allowed to remain in a large volume of the formaldehyde bromide for from two to three days at room temperature before being removed to a fresh batch of bromide in a chemically clean beaker which is then raised to a temperature of 55°C. for about ten minutes. The bromide is then cooled to room temperature and sections taken from it by the freezing technique described in Chapter 15. Sections should be about 25 microns in thickness, and cut with a knife moistened in distilled water. Sections are removed from this knife to a weak solution of ammonia, where they may remain until required; certainly at least overnight.

Before proceeding further it is necessary to make up the customary solutions. The only one presenting any difficulty is the silver complex of del Río-Hortega. This is given below as MS 33.1 del Río-Hortega 1916. All that has already been said about the necessity of the absolute chemical cleanliness of the glassware and the purity of reagents can be repeated at this point. Triple-distilled water, reagent-grade sodium hydroxide, and reagent-grade ammonia are essential.

Place 50 milliliters of 10% silver nitrate in a chemically clean 500-milliliter beaker and add to it, with constant stirring, 3.5 milliliters of 40% sodium hydroxide. Stir until the white curd of silver hydroxide is uniformly distributed. Then while still stirring add about 250 milliliters of triple-distilled water. Allow the precipitate to settle, pour off the supernant liquid, and add a further 250 milliliters of triple-distilled water. This washing by decantation should be repeated at least three times, and the precipitate allowed to settle after the last washing until all but 50 milliliters of the wash water can be discarded. The wet precipitate is then removed to a chemically cleaned graduated cylinder and the volume brought up to 75 milliliters before being transferred back to the beaker. Ammonia is added drop by drop until the precipitate is just redissolved. As has been recommended in previous examples, the ammonia should be added slowly. When there are signs that the precipitate is clearing up, the drops should be added at intervals of from 10 to 15 seconds, with constant stirring between additions. A strong

light and a dark background assist in determining the end point of the reaction. The mixture is now placed in a graduated flask and brought up to a volume of 250 milliliters with triple-distilled water. In the present method this staining solution is used at full strength.

Other solutions also required are: a 4% solution of neutralized formaldehyde (remember that reagent-grade formaldehyde neutralized to a pH between 7 and 7.5 with reagent-grade borax must of necessity be employed), a 2% solution of gold chloride, and the regular fixing solution of sodium thiosulfate. As in the last example, it is recommended that staining be carried out in chemically cleaned petri dishes. In the present instance not more than half a dozen such dishes will be required. In the first of these place triple-distilled water; in the second, the stain; in the third, triple-distilled water; in the fourth, the neutralized formaldehyde; in the fifth, triple-distilled water; and in the sixth and seventh, the gold chloride and the fixative. Now take sections from the weak ammonia, place them in the first dish of triple-distilled water, and rock them back and forth until they are alkali-free. A trial section is placed in the silver staining solution for approximately three minutes, then removed from the stain, rinsed rapidly in the next dish of distilled water, and placed in the neutralized formaldehyde. There, in from three to five minutes, it should have assumed a clear grey color, which will not become appreciably darker for another five minutes. This reaction time indicates that three minutes in the stain is satisfactory. If the darkening is too great or appears too quickly, the time that the section is left in the stain must be reduced. On the other hand, if the section fails to darken, the time must be increased. When the correct time has been established, all the sections may be passed successively through the stain, the distilled water, and the neutralized formaldehyde. After a maximum time of approximately ten minutes in the formaldehyde, the sections are removed to the next dish of triple-distilled water and thoroughly washed before being toned for ten to twenty minutes and fixed for five minutes.

They may then be mounted in balsam in the ordinary manner.

It will be immediately apparent that this method is both quicker and simpler than the method of Penfield; but it does not give such certain results, nor does it stain oligodendria except by an occasional accident which cannot be forecast. In the author's opinion it is less generally satisfactory than Penfield's technique even for the demonstration of microglia.

33.1 STAINING SOLUTIONS

The solutions of diammino silver used in these techniques are usually prepared by precipitating silver nitrate with sodium hydroxide and then adding ammonia drop by drop until the precipitate is just redissolved. It is much better to have a faint opalescence remain than to use too much ammonia. Some authors (Fontana 1912, Masson 1928, Gomori 1937)[1] recommend a second addition of a few drops of silver nitrate solution to insure an excess of this reagent; but see Gros-Schultze 1938 below, in which an excess of ammonia is used. Sodium hydroxide as the initial precipitant is sometimes replaced by potassium hydroxide (Foot 1927a, Gomori 1937), sodium carbonate (Cajal 1925, del Río-Hortega 1917, 1921, 1923, and 1927), lithium carbonate (Foot 1927b, Laidlaw 1929, del Río-Hortega 1919), or potassium

oxalate (Herrera 1932). Ammonia is used to produce as well as to dissolve the original precipitate by Fontana 1912, Gros-Schultze 1938, Lillie 1948, Masson 1928, and Weil and Davenport 1933. Triethanolamine is used both as precipitant and solvent by Zettnow 1891. Gomori 1936 used methenamine, and Herrera 1912 used ethylamine, for the same purpose.

Most of the solutions contain radicals derived from the original silver nitrate as well as from the precipitant and solvent. On the contrary, the precipitate is washed after either filtration or decantation in the formulas of Foot 1927b, Jalowy 1937, Landlaw 1929, and del Río-Hortega 1916 and 1921.

The result of all this is of course to provide solutions of diammino silver of various strengths and with various impurities. The table below summarizes the solutions recommended, listing (1) grams of silver per liter, (2) reagent used to produce the original precipitate, and (3) reagent used to dissolve this precipitate. Many of these solutions may appear to be identical, but most authors are insistent that the staining solution must be prepared by the method and in the concentration which they recommend. The original specifications are therefore given immediately following this table. For the sake of uniformity each formula has been adjusted to a final volume of 100.

SUMMARY OF DIAMMINO SILVER STAINING SOLUTIONS

Author	Gms Ag/L	Precipitant	Solvent
Agduhr 1917	3.2	NaOH	NH_4OH
Arcadi 1948	6.3	Na_2CO_3	NH_4OH
Belezky 1931	57	Na_2CO_3	C_5H_5N
Bensley and Bensley 1938a	0.6	NaOH	NH_4OH
Bensley and Bensley 1938b	12.7	NaOH	NH_4OH
Bertrand and Guillain 1934	4.4	Na_2CO_3	NH_4OH
Bielschowsky 1902	6.1	NaOH	NH_4OH
Cajal 1920a	7.6	NaOH	NH_4OH
Cajal 1920b	1.9	NaOH	$NH_4OH + C_5H_5N$
Cajal 1925	3.8	Na_2CO_3	$NH_4OH + C_5H_5N$
Cajal (1933)	6.3	NH_4OH	NH_4OH
del Carpio 1930	0.6	NaOH	NH_4OH
Cone and Penfield 1929	3.2	Na_2CO_3	NH_4OH
Fajersztajn 1901	12.7	NH_4OH	NH_4OH
da Fano 1914	12.7	NaOH	NH_4OH
da Fano 1919	15.9	NaOH	NH_4OH
Fontana 1912	1.6	NH_4OH	NH_4OH

[1] Literature references to the authors cited in this and the next two paragraphs and in the table which follows are given in the descriptions of the preparation of the solutions.

SUMMARY OF DIAMMINO SILVER STAINING SOLUTIONS—*(Continued)*

Author	Gms Ag/L	Precipitant	Solvent
Foot 1924	15.9	NaOH	NH_4OH
Foot 1927a	0.6	KOH	NH_4OH
Foot 1927b	6.3	$LiCO_3$	NH_4OH
Gatenby and Stern 1937	25.4	NaOH	NH_4OH
Glees, Meyer, and Meyer 1946	63	NH_4OH	NH_4OH
Gluck 1938	6.3	NH_4OH	$NH_4OH + C_5H_5N$
Gluckman 1943	95	NH_4OH	NH_4OH
Gomori 1937	25.4	KOH	NH_4OH
Gomori 1946	1.9	$C_6H_{12}N_4$	$C_6H_{12}N_4$
Gordon 1936	3.2	$NH_4OH + NaOH$	NH_4OH
Gordon and Sweets 1936	6.3	$NH_4OH + NaOH$	NH_4OH
Gros-Schultze (1938)	127	NH_4OH	NH_4OH
Herrera 1932	3.2	$K_2C_2O_4$	$C_2H_5NH_2$
Holmes 1942	0.06	NH_4OH	NH_4OH
Jalowy 1937	12.7	NaOH	NH_4OH
Kalwaryjski 1938	31.7	NH_4OH	NH_4OH
King 1937	12.7	NaOH	NH_4OH
Krajian 1933	18.4	NaOH	NH_4OH
Laidlaw 1929	30.5	$LiCO_3$	NH_4OH
Lawrentjew (1933)	127	NH_4OH	NH_4OH
Levi 1907	21.5	NaOH	NH_4OH
Lillie 1948	31.8	NH_4OH	NH_4OH
Lobo 1937	31.7	C_5H_5N	C_5H_5N
Long 1948	79	L_1CO_3	NH_4OH
Maresch 1905	63.5	NaOH	NH_4OH
Masson 1928	15.9	NH_4OH	NH_4OH
Patton 1907	6.3	NaOH	NH_4OH
Penfield 1935	127	NH_4OH	NH_4OH
del Río-Hortega 1916	12.7	NaOH	NH_4OH
del Río-Hortega 1917a	15.9	Na_2CO_3	NH_4OH
del Río-Hortega 1917b	15.9	Na_2CO_3	$NH_4OH + C_5H_5N$
del Río-Hortega 1919	7.9	$LiCO_3$	NH_4OH
del Río-Hortega 1921	7.9	Na_2CO_3	NH_4OH
del Río-Hortega 1923	7.9	Na_2CO_3	NH_4OH
del Río-Hortega 1927	12.7	Na_2CO_3	NH_4OH
del Río-Hortega 1932	7.9	$LiCO_3$	$NH_4OH + C_5H_5N$
Robb-Smith 1937	18	NaOH	NH_4OH
Rogers 1931	61	NaOH	NH_4OH
Romanes 1946	0.45	NH_4OH	NH_4OH
Wallart 1935	58	NH_4OH	NH_4OH
Weber 1944	15.9	NH_4OH	NH_4OH
Weil and Davenport 1933	15.9	NH_4OH	NH_4OH
Wolff 1905	63.5	NaOH	NH_4OH
Zettnov 1891	2.5	$N(CH_2CH_2OH)_3$	$N(CH_2CH_2OH)_3$

33.1 Agduhr 1917   23632, **34**:1

PREPARATION: Mix 5 10% silver nitrate with 1 25% sodium hydroxide. Dilute to 100 and add just enough ammonia to redissolve ppt.

33.1 Amprino 1936   *see* MS 34.1 Amprino 1936

33.1 Arcadi 1948   20540b, **23**:77

PREPARATION: To 10 10% silver nitrate add 30 5% sodium carbonate. Add just enough ammonia to dissolve ppt. and dilute to 100.

33.1 Belezky 1931   22575, **282**:214

PREPARATION: To 50 each of 17% silver nitrate and 10% sodium carbonate add just enough pyridine to dissolve ppt.

33.1 Bensley and Bensley 1938a Bensley and Bensley 1938, 109
PREPARATION: Add 0.1 40% sodium hydroxide to 10 1% silver nitrate. Add just enough ammonia to redissolve ppt. Dilute to 100 ml.

33.1 Bensley and Bensley 1938b Bensley and Bensley 1938, 109
PREPARATION: Add 0.75 40% sodium hydroxide to 100 2% silver nitrate. Add just enough ammonia to redissolve ppt.

33.1 Bertrand and Guillain 1934 6630, **115**:706
PREPARATION: To 7 10% silver nitrate add 27 5% sodium carbonate and then just enough ammonia to dissolve ppt. Dilute to 100.

33.1 Bielschowsky 1902 15058, **21**:579
PREPARATION: Add 0.4 40% sodium hydroxide to 48 2% silver nitrate. Add just enough ammonia to dissolve the ppt. Dilute to 100 ml.

33.1 Cajal 1920a *test.* **1933** *ips.* Cajal and de Castro 1933, 253
PREPARATION: To 12 10% silver nitrate add 0.5 40% sodium hydroxide. Wash ppt. by decantation. Suspend ppt. in 100 water. Add just enough ammonia to dissolve ppt.

33.1 Cajal 1920b *test.* **1933** *ips.* Cajal and de Castro 1933, 253
PREPARATION: Dilute 25 MS 33.1 Cajal 1920a to 100. Add 1 pyridine.

33.1 Cajal 1925 21344, **2**:157
PREPARATION: Prepare 50 MS 33.1 del Río-Hortega 1921 (below). Add 1.5 pyridine. Dilute to 100.

33.1 Cajal *test.* **1933** *ips.* Cajal and de Castro 1933, 319
PREPARATION: To 100 1% silver nitrate add just enough ammonia to redissolve the ppt. first formed.

33.1 del Carpio 1930 *test.* **1932 Findlay** 11360, **52**:155
PREPARATION: To 1 10% silver nitrate add 0.3 40% sodium hydroxide. Add just enough 20% ammonia to dissolve ppt. and dilute to 100.

33.1 Cone and Penfield *test.* **1929 Anderson** Anderson 1929, 90
PREPARATION: Add 5 10% silver nitrate to 20 5% sodium carbonate. Add just enough ammonia to dissolve ppt. Dilute to 100.

33.1 Craigie 1928 *see* MS 33.1 Zettnov 1891 (note)

33.1 Davenport, Windle, and Beech 1934 20540b, **9**:5
PREPARATION: Add 5 ammonia to 40 2% sodium hydroxide. Add just enough (about 40) 8.5% silver nitrate to give a slight permanent opalescence.

33.1 Debauche 1939 *see* MS 33.1 Rogers 1931 (note)

33.1 Fajersztajn 1901 *test.* **1933 Cajal and de Castro** Cajal and de Castro 1933, 223
PREPARATION: To 100 2% silver nitrate add just enough ammonia to redissolve the ppt. first formed.

33.1 da Fano 1914 2190, **3**:14
PREPARATION: Add 0.2 40% sodium hydroxide to 10 20% silver nitrate. Add just enough ammonia to dissolve ppt. Dilute to 100.

33.1 da Fano 1919 11454, **52**:1919
PREPARATION: As da Fano 1914 above but diluted to 80 instead of 100.

33.1 Fontana 1912 7176, **55**:1003
PREPARATION: To 100 0.25% silver nitrate add ammonia until ppt. first formed is just redissolved. Then add 0.25% silver nitrate drop by drop until a faint permanent opalescence is produced.

33.1 Foot 1924 11284, **9**:778
PREPARATION: Add 1 40% sodium hydroxide to 25 10% silver nitrate. Add just enough ammonia to dissolve ppt. Dilute to 100.

33.1 Foot 1927a 1887a, **4**:42
PREPARATION: Add 0.1 40% potassium hydroxide to 10 1% silver nitrate. Add just enough ammonia to redissolve ppt. Dilute to 100 ml.

33.1 Foot 1927b 1887a, **4**:212
PREPARATION: To 10 10% silver nitrate add 10 sat. aq. sol. (*circ.* 1.5%) lithium carbonate. Allow ppt. to settle. Decant. Wash ppt. by decantation several times. Suspend washed ppt. in 25 water. Add enough ammonia to not quite dissolve ppt. Dilute to 100. Filter.

33.1 Gatenby and Stern 1937 Gatenby and Painter 1937, 487
PREPARATION: Add 0.6 ml. 40% sodium hydroxide to 20 20% silver nitrate. Add just enough ammonia to dissolve ppt. Dilute to 100. Filter.

33.1 Glees, Meyer, and Meyer 1946 11025, **80**:101
PREPARATION: To 100 10% silver nitrate in 50% alc., add just enough ammonia to redissolve the ppt. first formed.

33.1 Gluck 1938 *test.* **1939 Foot** 4349, **19**:169
PREPARATION: To 10 10% silver nitrate add 0.5 40% sodium hydroxide. Wash ppt. by decantation and add just enough ammonia to dissolve ppt. Dilute to 100, and add 2 pyridine.

33.1 Gluckman 1943 4285a, **20**:132
PREPARATION: To 100 15% silver nitrate add just enough ammonia to redissolve the ppt. first formed.

33.1 Gomori 1937 608b, **13**:993
PREPARATION: Mix 10 10% potassium hydroxide with 40 10% silver nitrate. Add ammonia till ppt. dissolved. Add 10% silver nitrate drop by drop until ppt. just redissolves on shaking. Dilute to 100 ml.

33.1 Gomori 1946 591b, **10**:177
PREPARATION: Add 5 5% silver nitrate to 100 3% methenamine. Shake until ppt. is dissolved.

33.1 Gordon 1936 11284, **22**:294
PREPARATION: To 5 10% silver nitrate add just enough ammonia to redissolve ppt. first formed. Add 5 3% sodium hydroxide. Again add just enough ammonia to dissolve ppt. Dilute to 100.

33.1 Gordon and Sweets 1936 608b, **12**:545
PREPARATION: To 10 10% silver nitrate add just enough ammonia to redissolve ppt. first formed. Add 10 3% sodium hydroxide. Again add just enough ammonia to dissolve ppt. Dilute to 100 ml.

33.1 Gros-Schultze *test.* **1938 Mallory** Mallory 1938, 227
PREPARATION: Prepare a stock solution by adding just enough ammonia to 100 20% silver nitrate to redissolve the ppt. first formed. Prepare working solution by adding about 2 (more or less according to experience) ammonia to 100 stock.
NOTE: This solution is given as "Gros" (without reference) by Cajal and de Castro 1933, 178.

33.1 Gros 1933 *see* MS 33.1 Gros-Schultze 1938 (note)

33.1 Herrera 1932 *test.* **1933 Cajal and de Castro** Cajal and de Castro 1933, 275
PREPARATION: To 20 5% potassium oxalate add 5 10% silver nitrate and 0.3 abs. alc. Add just enough 33% ethylamine to dissolve ppt. Dilute to 100.

33.1 Holmes 1942 11431, **54**:132
PREPARATION: To 100 0.01% silver nitrate add 1 drop ammonia.

33.1 Jalowy 1937 23639b, **27**:667
PREPARATION: Add 1 40% sodium hydroxide to 20 10% silver nitrate. Mix thoroughly and filter. Wash ppt. thoroughly and suspend in 20 water. Add just enough ammonia to dissolve ppt. Dilute to 100 ml.

33.1 Kalwaryjski 1938 *test.* **1939 Findlay**　　　　　　11360, **59**:36
　　PREPARATION: To 50 10% silver nitrate add 50 ammonia.

33.1 King 1937　　　　　　　　　　　　　　　1879, **38**:362
　　PREPARATION: Add 20 10% silver nitrate to 80 5% sodium carbonate. Add just enough ammonia to dissolve ppt.

33.1 Krajian 1933　　　　　　　　　　　· 1789a, **16**:376
　　PREPARATION: Add 1 10% sodium hydroxide to 29 10% silver nitrate. Add just enough ammonia to dissolve ppt. Dilute to 100.

33.1 Laidlaw 1929　　　　　　　　　　608b, **5**:239
　　PREPARATION: To 16 60% silver nitrate add 185 sat. aq. sol. (*circ.* 1.5%) lithium carbonate. Wash ppt. by decantation three or four times and suspend washed ppt. in 60 water. Add just enough ammonia to dissolve ppt. and dilute to 100.

33.1 Lawrentjew *test.* **1933 Cajal and de Castro**　　　Cajal and de Castro 1933, 361
　　PREPARATION: To 100 20% silver nitrate add not quite enough ammonia to redissolve ppt. first formed. Immediately before use add from 3% to 8% (according to experience) ammonia.

33.1 Levi 1907　　　　　　　　　　14225, **18**:292
　　PREPARATION: Mix 17 20% silver nitrate with 17 40% sodium hydroxide. Add just enough ammonia to dissolve ppt. Dilute to 100 ml.

33.1 Lillie 1948　*see* MS 33.1 Weil and Davenport 1933 (note)
　　PREPARATION: To 20 ammonia add 10% silver nitrate, drop by drop, until a faint permanent-opalescence is produced. Dilute to twice the volume.

33.1 Lobo 1937 *test.* **1948 Romeis**　　　　　Romeis 1948, 418
　　FORMULA: water 62.5, 95% alc. 37.5, silver nitrate 1.25, pyridine 2.5

33.1 Long 1948　　　　　　　　　　20540b, **23**:69
　　PREPARATION: To 10 50% silver nitrate add, drop by drop with constant agitation, 100 sat. sol. lithium carbonate. Wash ppt. 5 times by decantation. Add not quite enough ammonia to dissolve ppt. Dilute to 100, filter, heat to 50°C. for 30 minutes in open vessel, cool, filter.

33.1 Maresch 1905　　　　　　　　　23681, **17**:641
　　PREPARATION: To 100 10% silver nitrate add 0.5 40% sodium hydroxide. Add just enough ammonia to dissolve ppt.

33.1 Martinez 1931　*see* MS 34.1 Martinez 1931

33.1 Masson 1928　　　　　　　　　608b, **4**:181
　　PREPARATION: Add to 12.5 20% silver nitrate enough ammonia to redissolve ppt. first formed. Then add 20% silver nitrate drop by drop until a slight permanent turbidity is produced. Dilute to 100.

33.1 Paton 1907　　　　　　　　　1424b, **18**:567
　　PREPARATION: Add 1 4% sodium hydroxide to 100 1% silver nitrate. Add just enough ammonia to dissolve ppt.

33.1 Penfield 1935　　　　　　　　608b, **11**:1007
　　PREPARATION: To 100 20% silver nitrate add just enough ammonia to redissolve ppt. first formed, then add 3 drops excess ammonia.

33.1 del Río-Hortega 1916　　　　　　21344, **14**:181
　　PREPARATION: To 20 10% silver nitrate add 1.4 40% sodium hydroxide. Add just enough ammonia to dissolve ppt. Dilute to 100 ml.
　　NOTE: Cajal and de Castro 1933, 211 wash the ppt. by decantation before re-solution.

33.1 del Río-Hortega 1917a　　　　　　21344, **15**:367
　　PREPARATION: To 25 10% silver nitrate add 75 5% sodium carbonate. Add just enough ammonia to dissolve ppt.

33.1 del Río-Hortega 1917b   21344, **15**:367
PREPARATION: To 100 MS 33.1 del Río-Hortega 1917a add 1 pyridine.

33.1 del Río-Hortega 1919   3231, **9**:68
PREPARATION: To 50 ml. sat. aq. sol. (*circ.* 1.5%) lithium carbonate add 12 10% silver nitrate. Allow ppt. to settle and wash by decantation. Add just enough ammonia to dissolve ppt. Dilute to 100.

33.1 del Río-Hortega 1921   3232, **21**:14
PREPARATION: To 50 5% sodium carbonate add 12 10% silver nitrate. Leave ppt. settle and wash by decantation. Add just enough ammonia to dissolve ppt. Dilute to 100.

33.1 del Río-Hortega 1923   21344, **21**:95
PREPARATION: To 50 5% sodium carbonate add 12.5 10% silver nitrate. Add just enough ammonia to dissolve ppt. Dilute to 100 ml.

33.1 del Río-Hortega 1927   3232, **27**:199
PREPARATION: To 80 5% sodium carbonate add 20 10% silver nitrate. Add just enough ammonia to dissolve ppt.

33.1 del Río-Hortega 1932 *test.* **1933 Cajal and de Castro**
                              Cajal and de Castro 1933, 263
PREPARATION: To 100 MS 33.1 del Río-Hortega 1917 add 1 pyridine.

33.1 Robb-Smith 1937   11431, **45**:312
PREPARATION: To 28.5 10% silver nitrate add 0.6 10% sodium hydroxide. Add just enough ammonia to redissolve precipitate and dilute to 100.

33.1 Rogers 1931   763, **49**:81
PREPARATION: To 48 20% silver nitrate add just enough ammonia to redissolve the ppt. first formed. Then add 0.5 ammonia and 48 water.
NOTE: **Debauche 1939** (20540b, **14**:121) differs only in using twice as much 10% silver nitrate.

33.1 Romanes 1946   11025, **80**:205
PREPARATION: To 2 5% silver nitrate add just enough ammonia to redissolve the ppt. first formed. Dilute to 100. To this add 33 1% gelatin, 2.5 0.5% tannic acid, and 1 pyridine.

33.1 Steiner 1937   11284, **23**:293
PREPARATION OF STOCK SOLUTIONS: I. Dissolve 1 silver nitrate in 20 water. Add ammonia until ppt. first formed is not quite dissolved. Dilute to 100. II. Dissolve 0.2 silver nitrate in 100 boiling water. Add 0.165 sodium potassium tartrate and boil till ppt. turns grey. Filter hot. III. 25% gum arabic.
WORKING SOLUTION: stock I 40, stock II 60, stock III 4

33.1 Wallert 1935   4285a, **12**:254
PREPARATION: To 100 10% silver nitrate add 1.5 40% sodium hydroxide. Add just enough ammonia to dissolve ppt.

33.1 Weber 1944   4285a, **21**:45
FORMULA: To 25 10% silver nitrate add not quite enough ammonia to redissolve ppt. first formed. Dilute to 100.

33.1 Weil and Davenport 1933   21458, **14**:95
PREPARATION: To 40 ammonia add just enough 10% silver nitrate (about 60) to produce a permanent opalescence.

33.1 Wolff 1905   766, **26**:135
PREPARATION: To 100 10% silver nitrate add 40% sodium hydroxide until no further ppt. is produced. Then add just enough ammonia to dissolve ppt.

33.1 Zettnov 1891   23684, **11**:689
PREPARATION: To 100 0.4% silver nitrate add triethanolamine until ppt. first formed is just redissolved.
NOTE: **Craigie 1928** (3566, **9**:55) is identical.

33.2 Neurological Methods

33.21 Nerve Cells and Processes

33.21 Agduhr 1917 23632, **34**:1

REAGENTS REQUIRED: *A.* 20% neutralized formaldehyde; *B.* 3% silver nitrate; *C.* MS 33.1 Agduhr 1917; *D.* 0.5% acetic acid; *E.* 0.004% gold chloride; *F.* 5% sodium thiosulfate

METHOD: Fix *A*, 5 days → wash → *B*, 6 days in dark → wash → *C*, 20 hrs. → *D*, 1 hr. → wash, 1 hr. → *A*, 1 to 4 days → [section by paraffin technique, bring sections to water] → *E*, 1 hr. → *F*, 2 mins. → balsam, via usual reagents

NOTE: Agduhr emphasized the need for thorough washing, particularly between *A* and *B* and for the use of large volumes (100 ml. for 5 mm. cubes) of *A*.

RECOMMENDED FOR: neurofibrils.

33.21 Bielschowsky 1904 *method for pieces—auct.* 11478, **3**:169

REAGENTS REQUIRED: *A.* 8% neutralized formaldehyde; *B.* pyridine; *C.* 3% silver nitrate; *D.* MS 33.1 Bielschowsky 1902 40 ml., water 60 ml.; *E.* 0.004% gold chloride; *F.* 5% sodium thiosulfate

METHOD: [Fix *A*, 1 month or till required] → *B*, 3 days → running water, 24 hrs. → distilled water, wash → *C*, 3 days, 36°C. → rinse → *D*, 24 hrs. → wash → *A*, 10 hrs. → [sections by paraffin technique, bring sections to water] → *E*, 1 hr. → *F*, 2 mins. → balsam, via usual reagents

33.21 Bielschowsky 1905 *see* MS 33.21 Bielschowsky 1910

33.21 Bielschowsky 1908 *test.* 1933 Cajal and de Castro

Cajal and de Castro 1933, 365

REAGENTS REQUIRED: *A.* 8% formaldehyde; *B.* 5% nitric acid; *C.* 4% silver nitrate; *D.* MS 33.1 Bielschowsky 1902; *E.* 0.2% gold chloride; *F.* 5% sodium thiosulfate

METHOD: [fresh tissue] → *A*, till hardened → *B*, till decalcified → wash, till acid-free → *A*, 24 hrs. → wash → [frozen sections] → water → *C*, 24 hrs. in dark → rinse → *D*, till brown, 20 mins. → wash → *A*, 10–15 mins. → rinse → *E*, till grey → *F*, 5 mins. → balsam, via usual reagents

RECOMMENDED FOR: nerve endings in structures requiring decalcification.

33.21 Bielschowsky 1910 *method for sections—auct.* 11478, **3**:169

REAGENTS REQUIRED: *A.* 2% silver nitrate; *B.* MS 33.1 Bielschowsky 1904; *C.* 8% neutral formaldehyde; *D.* 0.004% gold chloride; *E.* 5% sodium thiosulfate

METHOD: [sections by freezing technique, of formaldehyde-fixed material, from which the formaldehyde must be completely washed out before sectioning] → *A*, 24 hrs. in dark → rinse → *B*, 15 to 20 mins. → wash → *C*, 15 to 30 mins. → wash → *D*, 1 hr. → *E*, 2 mins. → balsam, via neutral reagents

NOTES: **Bielschowsky 1905** (11478, **4**:227) varies from above in substituting a few seconds in 2% acetic acid for the wash between *B* and *C* above. **Favorsky 1906** (11478, **6**:260) substitutes 10% silver nitrate for *A* above. **Boeke 1910** (766, **35**:193) substitutes his F 0000.1000 for plain formaldehyde in fixation; otherwise his method is essentially that above

RECOMMENDED FOR: peripheral nerve endings.

33.21 Boecke 1910 *see* MS 33.21 Bielschowsky 1910 (note)

33.21 Cajal 1925 21344, **23**:157

REAGENTS REQUIRED: *A.* AMS 11.1 Cajal 1913; *B.* MS 33.1 Cajal 1925 33.1; *C.* 4% neutralized formaldehyde; *D.* 0.2% gold chloride; *E.* 5% sodium thiosulfate

METHOD: [sections by freezing technique of materials hardened 5–30 days in *A*] → *A*, 4 hrs. → wash → *B*, warming if necessary, till dark amber → wash → *C*, 1 min. → *D*, till required color → *E*, 2 mins. → balsam, via usual reagents

NOTE: This technique is frequently confused with MS 31.21 Cajal 1925.

RECOMMENDED FOR: cerebellum.

33.21 Davenport, Windle, and Beech 1934   20540b, **9**:5

REAGENTS REQUIRED: *A.* 50% pyridine; *B.* 1.5% silver nitrate; *C.* MS 33.1 Davenport, Windle, and Beech 1934; *D.* 0.4% formaldehyde

METHOD: [embryos fixed 2 days in F 0000.1020 Davenport, Windle, and Beech 1934] → wash, 1 hr. → *A*, 1–2 days → wash, 2–4 hrs. → *B*, 3 days, 37°C. → wash, 20 mins. (12 mm. embryos) to 1 hr. (20 mm. embryos) → *C*, 6–24 hrs. → wash, 15 mins. → *D*, same time as *C* → wash → [section]

RECOMMENDED FOR: embryos.

33.21 Debauche 1939a   20540b, **14**:121

REAGENTS REQUIRED: *A.* 1% ammonia; *B.* 2% ammonia; *C.* 20% silver nitrate; *D.* ammonia; *E.* 1.2% formaldehyde; *F.* 1% gold chloride; *G.* 5% sodium thiosulfate

METHOD: [tissue fragments fixed in F 5000.1010 Debaissieux 1935] → *A*, 2–6 hrs. → [frozen 25 μ sections] → *B*, 15 mins. → *C*, 45°C. till light brown → *D*, added drop by drop to *C* containing sections until ppt. first formed is not quite redissolved → rinse → *E*, till rich brown → *F*, till deep blue → *G*, 10 mins. → wash → balsam, via usual reagents

RECOMMENDED FOR: invertebrate neurology in free sections.

NOTE: This method was republished by the same author (1939: 966, **59**:23). It may be applied to sections cut by the paraffin technique, if the wax is removed and the impregnation conducted before the section is attached to a slide.

33.21 Debauche 1939b   20540b, **14**:21

REAGENTS REQUIRED: *A.* 2% ammonia; *B.* 10% silver nitrate; *C.* MS 33.1 Debauche 1939; *D.* 1.2% formaldehyde; *E.* 1% gold chloride; *F.* 5% sodium thiosulfate

METHOD: [serial sections from E 21.1 Debauche 1939 blocks of F 5000.1010 Debaissieux 1935 fixed material] → water → *A*, 10 mins. → quick rinse → *B*, 10 mins. 45°C. → *C*, 1–5 mins. → quick rinse → *D*, till rich brown → *E*, till blue → *F*, 5 mins. → wash → balsam, via usual reagents

RECOMMENDED FOR: invertebrate neurology in serial sections.

33.21 Doinikow *test.* **1933 Cajal and de Castro**   Cajal and de Castro 1933, 341

REAGENTS REQUIRED: *A.* 8% formaldehyde; *B.* pyridine; *C.* 2% silver nitrate; *D.* MS 33.1 Bielschowsky 1902

METHOD: [blocks of fresh tissue] → *A*, some months → wash → *B*, 24–48 hrs. → running water, 24 hrs. → distilled water, some hrs. → *C*, 4–5 days, 35°C. → rinse → *D*, 48 hrs. → thorough wash → *A*, 48 hrs. → wash → [celloidin sections]

RECOMMENDED FOR: regenerating nerve fibers.

33.21 da Fano 1914   2190, **3**:14

REAGENTS REQUIRED: *A.* 2% silver nitrate; *B.* MS 33.1 da Fano 1914; *C.* 8% neutralized formaldehyde; *D.* 0.004% gold chloride; *E.* 5% sodium thiosulfate

METHOD: [small pieces, fixed in formalin or F 7000.1000 Orth 1896] → wash → [sections by freezing technique] → wash → *A*, in dark, 6 hrs. to 3 days → *B*, 20 to 30 mins. → wash → *C*, 15–20 mins. → wash → *D*, 1 hr. → *E*, 2 mins. → balsam, via usual reagents

33.21 da Fano 1919   11454, **52**:1919

REAGENTS REQUIRED: *A.* pyridine; *B.* 2% silver nitrate; *C.* MS 33.1 da Fano 1919 33.1; *D.* 8% neutralized formaldehyde; *E.* 0.004% gold chloride; *F.* 5% sodium thiosulfate

METHOD: [pieces, fixed 8% formaldehyde, 1–2 months] → wash → [sections by freezing technique] → wash → *A*, 6–12 hrs. → wash → *B*, 24–48 hrs. → rinse → *C*, 15 to 20 mins. → rinse → *D*, 2–3 hrs. → wash → *E*, 1 hr. → *F*, 2 mins. → balsam, via usual reagents

33.21 da Fano 1920   11454, **53**:1919

REAGENTS REQUIRED: *A.* pyridine; *B.* 8% formaldehyde; *C.* 2% silver nitrate; *D.* MS 33.1 da Fano 1919; *E.* 8% neutral formaldehyde; *F.* 0.004% gold chloride; *G.* 5% sodium thiosulfate

METHOD: [pieces, fixed 8% formaldehyde, 1–2 months] → wash → [sections by freezing technique] → wash → *A*, 4 to 12 hrs. → wash → *B*, 24 hrs. 37°C. → *C*, 1–2 days → rinse → *D*, 30 mins. → rinse → *E*, 2–3 hrs. → wash → *F*, 1 hr. → *G*, 2 mins. → balsam, via usual reagents

NOTE: The method above is the most complex of eight published in the same paper; the others: (a) reverse steps A and B above; (b) substitute 60% methyl alcohol for A above; (c) as b but with order of A and B reversed as in (a); (d) reverse steps A and B, substituting AMS 11.1 da Fano 1920 for A; (e) substitute AMS 11.1 da Fano 1920b for A; omit B; (f) substitute 50; pyridine for A; omit B; (g) omit A and B.

RECOMMENDED FOR: neurofibrils (original and a) in adult (f) and embryonic (g) material, general neurological staining (e), and pericellular baskets (b, c, d).

33.21 Fajersztajn 1901 *test.* 1933 Cajal and de Castro   Cajal and de Castro 1933, 223
REAGENTS REQUIRED: A. MS 33.1 Fajersztajn 1901; B. 2% formaldehyde; C. 0.2% gold chloride; D. 5% sodium thiosulfate
METHOD: [frozen sections of formaldehyde material] → water → A, 5–10 mins. → B, few moments → C, till violet → D, 5 mins. → wash → balsam, via usual reagents
RECOMMENDED FOR: axis cylinders in ganglia, cerebellum, spinal cord.

33.21 Favorsky 1906   *see* MS 33.21 Bielschowsky 1910 (note)

33.21 Finel 1947   6630, 141:198
REAGENTS REQUIRED: A. 20% silver nitrate; B. 40% formaldehyde; C. MS 33.1 Gros (1938); D. 1% ammonia; E. 0.1% acetic acid
METHOD: [paraffin sections of F 5000.1010 Bouin 1897] → water → blot → A, 24 hrs., 37°C. → blot → B, on slide, 1–2 secs. → blot → C, till sufficiently differentiated about 30 secs. → D, wash → E, rinse → balsam, via usual reagents

33.21 Glees, Meyer, and Meyer 1946   11025, 80:101
REAGENTS REQUIRED: A. 0.1% ammonia in 50% alcohol; B. 10% silver nitrate; C. 4% formaldehyde; D. MS 33.1 Glees, Meyer, and Meyer 1946; E. 5% sodium thiosulfate
METHOD: [15 μ frozen sections of formaldehyde material] → A, 24 hrs. → wash → B, till brown, 1–5 days → C, 1 hr. → wash → D, 30–60 secs. → C, 5 mins. → wash → E, 10 mins. → wash → balsam, via usual reagents

33.21 Gros-Schultze *test.* 1938 Mallory   Mallory 1938, 227
REAGENTS REQUIRED: A. 20% silver nitrate; B. 20% formaldehyde; C. MS 33.1 Gros-Schultze 1938; D. 20% ammonia; E. 0.5% acetic acid; F. 1% gold chloride; G. 5% sodium thiosulfate
METHOD: [frozen sections of formaldehyde-fixed material] → A, in dark, 5–20 mins. → B, 4 washes in 4 successive portions → C, till axis cylinders differentiated → D, rinse → E, rinse → F, 1 hr. → G, 1 min. → wash → balsam, via usual reagents
RECOMMENDED FOR: nerve endings.
NOTE: Cajal and de Castro 1933, 178 give this technique as "Gros." Szatmari 1936 (23639b, 24:239) precedes A, above, with 24 hours soaking in pyridine which is then thoroughly washed out.

33.21 Holmes 1942   11431, 54:132
REAGENTS REQUIRED: A. xylene 30, acetic acid 70; B. MS 33.1 Holmes 1942; C. AMS 21.1 Holmes 1942; D. 0.2% gold chloride; E. 2% oxalic acid; F. 5% sodium thiosulfate
METHOD: [15 μ paraffin sections of formaldehyde material] → A, 1 hr. → water, via graded alcs. → B, 5–24 hrs. 37°C. → rinse → C, 30 secs. → thorough wash → D, 3–5 mins. → rinse → E, 5–10 mins. → F, 5 mins. → wash → balsam, via usual reagents

33.21 Kernohan 1930   21400a, 49:58
REAGENTS REQUIRED: A. 20% silver nitrate; B. MS 33.1 Bielschowsky 1902 20, water 80; C. 4% formaldehyde; D. 0.2% gold chloride; E. 2% sodium thiosulfate
METHOD: [sections either by paraffin or collodion techniques] → wash → A, 1 hr. → wash → B, 1 to 4 mins. → wash → C, 1 min. → D, 2 mins. → E, 2 mins. → balsam via usual reagents

33.21 Landau 1940   4285a, 17:65
REAGENTS REQUIRED: A. 10% neutralized formaldehyde; B. 20% silver nitrate; C. MS 33.1 Gros-Schultze (1938); D. 0.04% neutralized formaldehyde; E. 0.2% gold chloride; F. 5% sodium thiosulfate; G. 10% potassium iodide

METHOD: [paraffin sections of formaldehyde material] → *A*, 24 hrs. in dark → *B*, 1–2 hrs. 35°–40°C., in dark → rinse → *C*, 5 mins. → add few drops *D* to *C* → repeat additions of *C* till sections sufficiently stained → thorough wash → *E*, till blue grey → *F*, 5 mins. → *G*, till differentiated → wash → balsam, via usual reagents, *or* M 11.1 Landau 1940

33.21 Lobo 1937   *see* MS 33.21 Schultze (1948) (note)

33.21 Miskolczy *test.* **1933 Cajal and de Castro**   Cajal and de Castro 1933, 341
REAGENTS REQUIRED: *A*. 10% silver nitrate; *B*. MS 33.1 Cajal 1925; *C*. 0.5% acetic acid; *D*. 8% formaldehyde; *E*. 0.2% gold chloride
METHOD: [blocks of formaldehyde fixed material] → [graded alcs. till dehydrated] → xylene, 2–3 hrs. → [graded alcs., till rehydrated] → water → *A*, 2–7 days → wash → *B*, 2–5 hrs. → wash → *C*, 10–30 mins. → wash → *D*, 24 hrs. → wash → [paraffin sections on slide] → water → *E*, 5–10 mins. → wash → balsam, via usual reagents
RECOMMENDED FOR: axis cylinders.

33.21 Paton 1907   14246, **18**:576
REAGENTS REQUIRED: *A*. 4% neutralized formaldehyde; *B*. 1% silver nitrate; *C*. MS 33.1 Bielschowsky 1902; *D*. 2% acetic acid; *E*. AMS 21.1 Paton 1907; *F*. 0.004% gold chloride; *G*. 5% sodium thiosulfate
METHOD: [whole fish embryos] → *A*, 1 to 5 days → wash → *B*, 4 to 7 days → rinse → *C*, 24 hrs. → wash → *D*, 5 to 15 mins. → wash → *E*, 12 hrs. → [sections by paraffin technique, bring sections to water] → *F*, 1 hr. → *G*, few minutes → balsam, via usual reagents

33.21 Penfield 1935   608b, **11**:1007
REAGENTS REQUIRED: *A*. water 50, citric acid 10.5, 40% formaldehyde 50; *B*. 20% silver nitrate; *C*. 20% formaldehyde; *D*. MS 33.1 Penfield 1935; *E*. 20% ammonia; *F*. 5% acetic acid; *G*. any AMS 22.1 formula; *H*. 5% sodium thiosulfate
METHOD: [small blood vessels dissected from material perfused for 3 days with *A*] → wash → *B*, 2 hrs. → *C*, 4 changes, each 100 ml. → *D*, till stained → *E*, 1–2 mins. → *F*, till neutral → *G*, till toned → *H*, 10 mins. → wash → balsam, via usual reagents
RECOMMENDED FOR: perivascular nerves of pia mater.

33.21 Pullinger 1943   11431, **55**:97
REAGENTS REQUIRED: *A*. 0.1% ammonia; *B*. MS 33.1 del Río-Hortega 1917a; *C*. 4% formaldehyde
METHOD: [cornea fixed *in situ* by injection of formaldehyde, 1 day, then cut from eye and fixed 3 more days] → wash → *A*, overnight → wash → *B*, 37°C., 4 hrs. → wash → *C*, 15 mins. → [sections]

33.21 Rogers 1931   763, **49**:81
REAGENTS REQUIRED: *A*. 10% formaldehyde; *B*. 3% ammonia in 90% alc.; *C*. 40% silver nitrate; *D*. MS 33.1 Rogers 1931; *E*. 4% acetic acid; *F*. 0.3% gold chloride in 1% acetic acid; *G*. 4% oxalic acid; *H*. 5% sodium thiosulfate
METHOD: [fresh tissue] → *A*, 1 wk. → wash → *B*, 1 day → [paraffin sections] → *C*, 13 hrs. → 80% alc., wash → *D*, 20 mins. → *E*, wash → *A*, 2–5 mins. → *F*, 10–15 mins. → wash → *G*, if stain not sufficiently intense → *H*, 5 mins. → wash → balsam, via usual reagents
RECOMMENDED FOR: axis cylinders and nerve endings.

33.21 Romanes 1946   11025, **80**:205
REAGENTS REQUIRED: *A*. MS 33.1 Romanes 1946; *B*. AMS 21.1 Romanes 1946; *C*. 0.3% gold chloride in 2% acetic acid; *D*. 2% oxalic acid in 0.04% formaldehyde; *E*. 5% sodium thiosulfate
METHOD: [paraffin sections] → water → *A*, 4–24 hrs. 58°C. → rinse → *B*, 5 mins. → [repeat *A* → *B* cycle if insufficiently stained] → wash → *C*, 5 mins. → rinse → *D*, 10–15 mins. → wash → *E*, 5 mins. → wash → balsam, via usual reagents

33.21 Schutz 1908   15058, **27**:909

REAGENTS REQUIRED: *A.* 2% silver nitrate; *B.* MS 33.1 Bielschowsky 1904; *C.* 8% neutralized formaldehyde; *D.* 1% acetic acid; *E.* 0.02% gold chloride; *F.* 5% sodium
thiosulfate

METHOD: [sections by freezing technique of formaldehyde fixed material] → wash → *A,*
24 hrs. in dark → wash → *D,* 10 mins. → *E,* 30–49 mins. (till dark grey) → rinse →
F, 2 mins. → balsam, via usual reagents

33.21 Szatmari 1936   *see* MS 33.21 Gros-Schultze 1938 (note)

33.21 Szepsenwol 1938   6630, **120**:689

REAGENTS REQUIRED: *A.* F 0000.1030 Szepsenwol 1935; *B.* 1% silver nitrate; *C.* 3%
silver nitrate; *D.* MS 33.1 Bielschowsky 1902 10, water 90

METHOD: *A.* 10 to 20 days, 55°C. → running water, 24 to 48 hrs. → *B,* 1 to 3 days, 35°C.,
in dark → *C,* 7 to 10 days, 35°C., in dark → wash → *D,* several hrs. → wash → *E,*
12 to 15 hrs. → paraffin sections via cedar oil

NOTE: This method is a slight modification of **Szepsenwol 1937** (4285a, **14**:168).

33.21 Wallart 1935   4285a, **12**:254

REAGENTS REQUIRED: *A.* AMS 12.1 Wallart 1935; *B.* 2% silver nitrate; *C.* MS 33.1
Wallart 1935; *D.* 4% neutralized formaldehyde

METHOD: [3–5 mm. slices of formaldehyde material] → *A,* 6 hrs. → thorough wash →
B, 5 days, 37°C. → rinse → *C,* 1–2 days → wash → *D,* 12–18 hrs. → wash → [par-
affin sections] → AMS 22.1 treatment → balsam, via usual reagents

RECOMMENDED FOR: nerves in organs rich in lipids.

33.21 Weber 1944   4285a, **21**:45

REAGENTS REQUIRED: *A.* AMS 12.1 Weber 1944; *B.* water 50, isopropanol 25, dioxane 25;
C. 1% pyridine; *D.* 3% silver nitrate; *E.* MS 33.1 Weber 1944; *F.* AMS 21.1 Weber
1944

METHOD: [small fragments] → *A,* 0°C., allow to rise to room temperature → 55°C., 1
month → *B,* wash, 30 mins. → *C,* wash 12 hrs. → wash, till wash-water no longer
gives chloride test for silver → *E,* 24 hrs. → *F,* 24 hrs. → paraffin, via usual reagents
→ [5 μ sections] → balsam

33.22 NEUROGLIA

33.22 Achucarro 1911   3231, **1**:139

REAGENTS REQUIRED: *A.* sat. aq. sol. tannic acid; *B.* MS 33.1 Bielschowsky 1902 4,
water 96; *C.* 4% formaldehyde

METHOD: [sections, by freezing technique, of formaldehyde-fixed material] → *A* →
warm till steaming → rinse → *B,* 10 mins. → *C,* 10 mins. → wash → balsam, via
usual reagents

RECOMMENDED FOR: macroglia.

33.22 Arcadi 1948   20540b, **23**:77

REAGENTS REQUIRED: *A.* ammonia; *B.* 2% hydrobromic acid; *C.* MS 33.1 Arcadi 1948;
D. 0.4% formaldehyde; *E.* 5% sodium thiosulfate

METHOD: [15 μ frozen sections] → *A,* 100 ml. jar → displace *A* with slow stream of water
over 24 hr. period → *A,* fresh solution → wash as before → *A,* fresh solution, 7 mins.
→ *B,* 1 hr., 38°C. → wash → *C,* 30–45 mins. → wash → *D,* 30 secs. → wash → *E,* 2
mins. → wash → balsam, via usual reagents

RECOMMENDED FOR: oligodendria in material stored for many years in formaldehyde.

33.22 Barker 1934   11977, **7**:293

REAGENTS REQUIRED: *A.* AMS 11.1 Cajal 1913; *B.* 0.5% ammonia; *C.* MS 33.1 del
Río-Hortega 1917a; *D.* 1% formaldehyde; *E.* 0.2% gold chloride; *F.* 5% sodium
thiosulfate

METHOD: [3 mm. slices of fresh tissue] → *A,* 3 days → [25 μ frozen sections] → water →
A, 10 mins., 55°C. → wash → *B,* 2 mins. → wash → *C,* 3 mins. → rinse → *D,* 1 min.
→ wash → *E,* 5 mins. → *F,* 1 min. → wash → balsam, via usual reagents

RECOMMENDED FOR: microglia.

33.22 Belezky 1931   22575, **282**:214

REAGENTS REQUIRED: *A*. MS 33.1 Belezky 1931; *B*. 4% neutralized formaldehyde
METHOD: [sections by E 11.1 Belezky 1931] → water, wash → *A*, few secs. → wash →
B, till blackened → balsam, via usual reagents
NOTE: *A* may be diluted and used for a longer period.

33.22 Bertrand and Guillain 1934   6630, **115**:706

REAGENTS REQUIRED: *A*. AMS 11.1 Bertrand and Guillain 1934; *B*. pyridine; *C*. 0.2%
hydrofluoric acid; *D*. 5% sodium carbonate; *E*. MS 33.1 Bertrand and Guillain 1934;
F. 2% formaldehyde; *G*. 0.2% gold chloride; *H*. 5% sodium thiosulfate
METHOD: [fresh ganglia] → *A*, 4–7 days, renewed daily, 4°–5°C. → wash → 12 μ frozen
sections → *B*, 12–24 hrs. → *C*, 1 hr., 37°C. → wash → *D*, 4 hrs. → *E*, till yellow →
rinse → *F*, till brown → wash → *G*, till grey → *H*, 10 mins. → wash → balsam, via
usual reagents
RECOMMENDED FOR: oligoglia in spinal and sympathetic ganglia.

33.22 Bolsi *test*. **1933 Cajal and de Castro**   Cajal and de Castro 1933, 261

REAGENTS REQUIRED: *A*. AMS 13.1 Bolsi 1933; *B*. MS 33.1 Cajal 1920; *C*. 2% formal-
dehyde; *D*. 0.2% gold chloride; *E*. 5% sodium thiosulfate
METHOD: [frozen sections of formaldehyde fixed material] → *A*, 30 mins., 50°C. → wash
→ *B*. 5–10 mins. → wash → *C*, till reduced → *D*, till violet → *E*, 5 mins. → balsam,
via usual reagents
RECOMMENDED FOR: macroglia.
NOTE: **Cajal and de Castro** (*loc. cit*.) suggest substitution of their AMS 13.1 for *A* above.

33.22 Cajal 1920 *test*. **1933** *ips*.   Cajal and de Castro 1933, 253

REAGENTS REQUIRED: *A*. AMS 11.1 Cajal 1913; *B*. AMS 11.1 Cajal 1920; *C*. MS 33.1
Cajal 1920b; *D*. 6% neutralized formaldehyde; *E*. 0.2% gold chloride; *F*. 6% sodium
thiosulfate
METHOD: [small pieces] → *A*, 4 days → frozen sections → *B*, 4 hrs., 37°C. → wash → *C*,
40°–45°C., till deep brown → rinse → *D*, few moments → thorough wash → *E*, 10–20
mins. → rinse → *F*, 5 mins. → wash → balsam, via clove oil and xylene
RECOMMENDED FOR: macroglia.

33.22 Cajal and de Castro 1933   *see* MS 33.22 Bolsi (1933) (note)

33.22 Cone and Penfield *test*. **1929 Anderson**   Anderson 1929, 90

REAGENTS REQUIRED: *A*. 0.1% ammonia; *B*. 5% hydrobromic acid; *C*. 5% sodium
carbonate; *D*. MS 33.1 Cone and Penfield (1929); *E*. 0.5% formaldehyde; *F*. 0.2%
gold chloride; *G*. 5% sodium thiosulfate
METHOD: [20 μ sections by freezing technique] → *A*, overnight → wash → *B*, 1 hr., 37°C.
→ wash → *C*, 1 hr. → *D*, 3–5 mins., or till brown → *E*, 1 min. with agitation → wash
→ *F*, till grey → *G*, 5 mins. → balsam, via usual reagents
RECOMMENDED FOR: microglia.

33.22 Gans *test*. **1933 Cajal and de Castro**   Cajal and de Castro 1933, 277

REAGENTS REQUIRED: *A*. 2.5% ammonium bromide; *B*. 0.1% ammonia; *C*. MS 33.1 del
Río-Hortega 1921; *D*. 0.4% formaldehyde; *E*. 0.2% gold chloride; *F*. 5% thiosulfate
METHOD: [25 μ frozen sections of formaldehyde fixed material] → *A*, 2 hrs., 37°C. → *B*,
quick rinse → *C*, 2 hrs. → rinse → *D*, 5 mins. → *E*, 15 mins. → *F*, 5 mins. → balsam,
via usual reagents
RECOMMENDED FOR: microglia.

33.22 Herrera 1932 *test*. **1933 Cajal and de Castro**   Cajal and de Castro 1933, 275

REAGENTS REQUIRED: *A*. AMS 11.1 Herrera 1932; *B*. MS 33.1 Herrera 1932; *C*. 4%
formaldehyde
METHOD: [pieces of fresh tissue] → *A*, 2 to 20 days → 25 μ frozen sections → water → *B*,
1 min. → rinse → *C*, 5 mins. → wash → balsam, via usual reagents
RECOMMENDED FOR: microglia.

33.22 Ingleby 1929   4349, **12**:91

REAGENTS REQUIRED: *A*. AMS 11.1 Cajal 1913; *B*. 10% tannic acid; *C*. 1% ammonia;
D. MS 33.1 da Fano 1919; *E*. 8% formaldehyde; *F*. 0.2% gold chloride; *G*. 5% sodium
thiosulfate

METHOD: [slices of brain tissue] → A, 2–4 days → wash → [15 μ frozen sections] → B, 5–7 mins., 50°C., then cool 10 mins. → C, till pliable → D, till yellow-brown → rinse → E, 1 min. → wash → F, till grey → G, 5 mins. → wash → balsam, via usual reagents

NOTE: F 5000.1010 Ingleby 1925 may be substituted for A if the time be reduced to 1 day.

33.22 King 1937 1879, **38**:362

REAGENTS REQUIRED: A. 1% ammonia; B. 5% ammonium bromide; C. AMS 11.3 King 1937; D. 3% sodium sulfite; E. MS 33.1 King 1937; F. 4% formaldehyde

METHOD: [frozen sections of formaldehyde-fixed material] → A, till required → B, 10 mins., 50°C. → C, 2 mins. → rinse → D, 2–3 mins. → E, 3 changes, 1 min. each → rinse → F, till brown → wash → balsam, via usual reagents

RECOMMENDED FOR: microglia and oligodendroglia.

33.22 McCarter 1940 608b, **16**:233

REAGENTS REQUIRED: A. 1% ammonia; B. 4% hydrobromic acid; C. 5% sodium carbonate; D. 5% ammonium alum; E. MS 33.1 del Río-Hortega 1917a; F. 0.4% formaldehyde; G. 0.2% gold chloride; H. 5% sodium thiosulfate

METHOD: [20 μ frozen sections of formaldehyde material] → A, few mins. to overnight, according to age → B, 37°C., 1 hr. → wash → C → equal volume D, added to C (ignore precipitate), leave 1 hr.–3 days → wash → E, 2–5 mins. → F, 10 mins. → wash → G, till blue-grey → H, 5 mins. → balsam, via usual reagents

RECOMMENDED FOR: oligodendria and microglia.

33.22 Penfield 1928 608b, **4**:153

REAGENTS REQUIRED: A. AMS 11.1 Cajal 1913; B. 1% ammonia; C. 2% hydrobromic acid; D. 5% sodium carbonate; E. MS 33.1 del Río-Hortega 1921 56, water 44; F. 1% formaldehyde; G. 0.2% gold chloride; H. 5% sodium thiosulfate

METHOD: [fresh tissue] → A, until wanted → [sections, by freezing technique] → A, 5 mins. → B, overnight → C, 1 hr., 38°C. → wash → D, 1 hr. → rinse → E, 3–5 mins. or till light brown → rinse → F, 1 min. with agitation → wash G, till blue grey → H, 5 mins. → balsam, via usual reagents

RECOMMENDED FOR: microglia.

33.22 Penfield 1924 3464, **47**:430

REAGENTS REQUIRED: A. AMS 11.1 Cajal 1913; B. MS 33.1 del Río-Hortega 1921; C. 1% formaldehyde; D. 0.2% gold chloride; E. 5% sodium thiosulfate

METHOD: [blocks of fresh tissue] → A, 48 hrs. → 95% alcohol, 36–48 hrs. → wash → sections, by freezing technique → wash → B, 30 mins. to 2 hrs. or until light brown → C, with agitation, 1 min. → D, till preferred color → E, 1 min. → balsam, via usual reagents

RECOMMENDED FOR: oligodendroglia.

33.22 Polak 1947 18794, **61**:508

REAGENTS REQUIRED: A.1% uranium acetate; B. MS 33.1 del Río-Hortega 1917a; C. 1% formaldehyde; D. 0.2% gold chloride; E. 5% sodium thiosulfate

METHOD: [5–10 μ sections of formaldehyde material] → water → A, 24 hrs. → B, till transparent, 15–60 secs. → rinse → C, till brown → rinse → D, till grey → rinse → E, 5 mins. → balsam, via usual reagents

33.22 del Río-Hortega 1916 21344, **14**:181

REAGENTS REQUIRED: A. 8% formaldehyde adjusted with ammonia to pH 8; B. 10% tannic acid; C. 0.1% ammonia; D. MS 33.1 Bielschowsky 1902 2, water 98

METHOD: Fix A, 2 to 3 days → [sections by freezing technique] → B, heated till steaming, 10 mins. → cool → C, till again flexible → D, till dark yellow → rinse → A, 10 mins. → balsam, via usual reagents

NOTE: del Río-Hortega for A specifies the pH as that which gives a blue reaction with litmus.

RECOMMENDED FOR: protoplasmic astrocytes.

33.22 del Río-Hortega 1917   21344, **15**:367
REAGENTS REQUIRED: *A.* MS 33.1 del Río-Hortega 1917b; *B.* 8% neutralized formaldehyde; *C.* 0.2% gold chloride; *D.* 5% sodium thiosulfate
METHOD: [sections by freezing technique of AMS 11.1 Cajal 1913 fixed material] → wash → *A*, 45°C., till black → rinse → *B*, 30 secs. → wash → *C*, till bluish → *D*, 5 mins. → wash → balsam, via usual techniques
RECOMMENDED FOR: astrocytes.
NOTE: Cajal and de Castro 1925 p. 255 cite this (without journal reference) as "**Río-Hortega 1918**" and recommend it for macroglia.

33.22 del Río-Hortega 1918   21344, **15**:165
REAGENTS REQUIRED: *A.* AMS 13.1 del Río-Hortega 1916; *B.* 0.1% ammonia; *C.* MS 33.1 del Río-Hortega 1916 10, water 90; *D.* 8% neutralized formaldehyde
METHOD: [sections, by freezing technique, of formol material] → *A*, 5 mins. 45°C. → *B*, till transparent → *C*, 1st dish, 1 min. → *C*, 2nd dish, 1 min. → *C*, 3rd dish, till brown → quick rinse → *D*, 30 secs. → wash → balsam, via usual techniques
RECOMMENDED FOR: protoplasmic neuroglia.

33.22 del Río-Hortega 1919   3231, **9**:68
REAGENTS REQUIRED: *A.* 4% formaldehyde; *B.* MS 33.1 del Río-Hortega 1917 26, water 74; *C.* 0.4% neutralized formaldehyde; *D.* 0.2% gold chloride; *E.* 5% sodium thiosulfate
METHOD: [smears, or small pieces] → *A*, 24 hrs. → [section pieces by freezing technique] → wash → *B*, 5 to 10 mins. → *C*, till reduced → *D*, 30 secs. to 1 min. → *E*, 1 min. → wash → balsam, via usual reagents

33.22 del Río-Hortega 1921a   3232, **22**:1
REAGENTS REQUIRED: *A.* 4% formaldehyde adjusted to pH 8 with ammonia; *B.* MS 31.1 del Río-Hortega 1921; *C.* MS 33.1 del Río-Hortega 1917a 29, water 71, pyridine 1; *D.* 0.4% formaldehyde
METHOD: [sections by freezing technique of formaldehyde material] → *A*, 1 min. 50°C. → *B*, 50°C. till brown → wash → *C*, 50°C. till dark brown → wash → *D*, 5 mins. → balsam, via usual reagents
RECOMMENDED FOR: oligodendria.

33.22 del Río-Hortega 1921b   3232, **22**:1
REAGENTS REQUIRED: *A.* AMS 11.1 Cajal 1913; *B.* 0.1% ammonia; *C.* MS 33.1 del Río-Hortega 1921; *D.* 4% neutralized formaldehyde; *E.* 0.2% gold chloride; *F.* 5% sodium thiosulfate
METHOD: Fix small pieces *A*, 2–3 days room temperature, then raise to 55°C. 10 mins. → [25 μ sections by freezing technique] → *B*, wash → *C*, 3 mins. → *D*, 10 mins. → wash → *E*, 10 to 20 mins. → *F*, 5 mins. → balsam, via S 41.1 del Río-Hortega (1938)
RECOMMENDED FOR: microglia.

33.22 del Río-Hortega 1923   21344, **21**:95
REAGENTS REQUIRED: *A.* 2% silver nitrate 100, pyridine 1.5; *B.* 1% pyridine; *C.* MS 33.1 del Río-Hortega 1923 100, pyridine 1.5; *D.* 4% formaldehyde; *E.* 0.2% gold chloride; *F.* 5% sodium thiosulfate
METHOD: [frozen sections of formaldehyde-fixed material] → wash → *A*, 50°C. till brown some hrs. → *B*, wash → *C*, 50°C. till sepia → wash → *D*, 10 mins. → *E*, till violet → *F*, 30 secs. → blot on slide → 95% alc., dropped on slide → balsam, via S 41.1 del Río-Hortega (1938)
RECOMMENDED FOR: neuroglia in pineal.

33.22 del Río-Hortega 1927   3232, **27**:199
REAGENTS REQUIRED: *A.* AMS 11.1 Cajal 1913; *B.* 5% sodium sulfite *or B.* AMS 13.1 del Río-Hortega 1927; *C.* MS 33.1 del Río-Hortega 1927; *D.* 0.4% neutralized formaldehyde; *E.* 0.2% gold chloride; *F.* 0.5% sodium thiosulfate
METHOD: [fix small pieces *A*, 2–3 days room temperature then raise to 55°C. 10 mins.] → [25 μ sections by freezing technique] → *B*, either solution, several hours → *C*, 1st dish, 1 min. → *C*, 2nd dish, 2 mins. → *D*, 10 mins. → *E*, 10–20 mins. → *F*, 5 mins. → balsam, via S 41.1 del Río-Hortega (1938)
RECOMMENDED FOR: microglia.

33.22 del Río-Hortega 1928 *test.* **1933 Cajal and de Castro**

Cajal and de Castro 1933, 280

REAGENTS REQUIRED: *A.* AMS 11.1 Cajal 1913; *B.* 0.1% ammonia; *C.* MS 33.1 del Río-Hortega 1927; *D.* 0.4% formaldehyde; *E.* 0.2% gold chloride; *F.* 5% sodium thiosulfate

METHOD: [pieces of fresh tissue] → *A*, 48 hrs. → *A*, 10 mins. 45°–50°C. → [15 μ to 20 μ frozen sections] → *B*, 10 mins. → wash → *C*, 5–15 mins. → *D*, 5 mins. → *E*, 15 mins. → *F*, 5 mins. → balsam, via usual reagents

RECOMMENDED FOR: oligodendria.

33.22 del Río-Hortega 1932 *test.* **1933 Cajal and de Castro**

Cajal and de Castro 1933, 263

REAGENTS REQUIRED: *A.* AMS 11.1 Cajal 1913; *B.* 0.1% ammonia; *C.* AMS 13.1 del Río-Hortega 1932; *D.* MS 31.1 del Río-Hortega 1932; *E.* MS 33.1 del Río-Hortega 1932; *F.* 0.1% formaldehyde; *G.* 0.2% gold chloride; *H.* 5% sodium thiosulfate

METHOD: [pieces of fresh tissue] → *A*, till required → [frozen sections] → *B*, wash → *C*, 10 mins. → *D*, 10–15 mins., 45°–50°C. → *E*, till deep brown → 80% alc., wash → 95% alc., wash → *F*, 2–3 mins. → *G*, till slate gray → *H*, 5 mins. → balsam, via usual reagents

RECOMMENDED FOR: glioblasts.

33.22 del Río-Hortega *test.* **1933 Cajal and de Castro**   Cajal and de Castro 1933, 268

REAGENTS REQUIRED: *A.* AMS 11.1 Cajal 1914; *B.* AMS 11.1 del Río-Hortega 1923a; *C.* 0.1% ammonia; *D.* MS 33.1 del Río-Hortega 1933; *E.* 4% formaldehyde; *F.* 0.16% gold chloride; *G.* 5% sodium thiosulfate

METHOD: [2–3 mm. slices fresh material] → *A*, 2–3 days → *B*, 2–3 days, 25°–35°C. → [frozen sections] → *C*, thorough wash → wash → *D*, 45°–50°C., till deep straw colored → wash → *E*, few mins. → *F*, 15 mins. → *G*, 5 mins. → balsam, via usual reagents

RECOMMENDED FOR: gliosomes.

33.22 del Río-Hortega 1933   *see* MS 33.23 del Río-Hortega 1933

33.22 del Río-Hortega 1929   3232, **30**:1

REAGENTS REQUIRED: *A.* 0.1% ammonia; *B.* MS 33.1 del Río-Hortega 1917 90, pyridine 10; *C.* 0.2% neutralized formaldehyde; *D.* 1% gold chloride; *E.* 5% sodium thiosulfate

METHOD: [sections by freezing technique of material fixed in F 7000.1000 del Río-Hortega 1929] → *A*, quick rinse → wash → *B*, at 55°C. till light brown → wash, 50% alc. → *C*, 5 mins. → *D*, 30 secs. to 1 min. → *E*, 1 min. → wash → balsam via usual, reagents

33.22 Rodriguez *test.* **1933 Cajal and de Castro**   Cajal and de Castro 1933, 285

REAGENTS REQUIRED: *A.* AMS 11.1 Rodriguez 1933; *B.* equal parts *A* and 3% ammonium oxalate; *C.* MS 33.1 Herrera 1932; *D.* 0.4% formaldehyde

METHOD: [pieces of fresh tissue] → *A*, 1–3 days → [25 μ–30 μ frozen sections] → *B*, 24 hrs. → quick wash → *C*, 1 min. → *D*, 5 mins. → balsam, via usual reagents

RECOMMENDED FOR: oligodendria.

33.22 Weil and Davenport 1933   21458, **14**:95

REAGENTS REQUIRED: *A.* MS 33.1 Weil and Davenport 1933; *B.* 6% formaldehyde

METHOD: [celloidin sections] → water → *A*, 15–20 secs. → rinse → *B*, until brown → wash → balsam, via usual reagents

RECOMMENDED FOR: microglia.

33.22 Winkler 1935   23430, **153**:160

REAGENTS REQUIRED: *A.* 2% hydrobromic acid; *B.* 2.5% sodium carbonate; *C.* MS 33.1 del Rio-Hortega 1916 20, water 80; *D.* 8% formaldehyde

METHOD: [frozen sections of formaldehyde material] → wash → 0.3% alcohol, 2–8 hrs. → wash → *A*, 14–24 hrs. → wash → *B*, 6–24 hrs. → *C*, ½–2 mins. → rinse → *D*, till reduced → DS 13.11 May and Grünwald 1902, 24 hrs., if plasma cell staining required → balsam, via usual reagents

RECOMMENDED FOR: microglia and plasma cells.

33.23 OTHER NEUROLOGICAL METHODS

33.23 Cajal *test.* **1933** *ips.*   Cajal and de Castro 1933, 319
REAGENTS REQUIRED: *A.* AMS 11.1 Cajal 1933a; *B.* MS 33.1 Cajal 1933b; *C.* AMS 21.1 Cajal 1933
METHOD: [pieces of fresh nerve] → *A*, 24 hrs. → thorough wash → *B*, 48 hrs. → wash → *C*, 6–12 hrs. → teased preparations or celloidin sections
RECOMMENDED FOR: Schwann cells.

33.23 Cajal *test.* **1933** *ips.*   Cajal and de Castro 1933, 343
REAGENTS REQUIRED: *A.* AMS 11.1 Cajal 1933b; *B.* water 100, MS 33.1 Bielschowsky 1902 1; *C.* AMS 21.1 Cajal (1933)
METHOD: [pieces of fresh nerve] → *A*, 24 hrs. → wash → *B*, several hrs. → rinse → *C*, several hrs. → teased preparations
RECOMMENDED FOR: peritubular connective sheath.

33.3 CYTOLOGICAL METHODS

33.3 Fieandt and Sazen 1936   23632, **53**:125
REAGENTS REQUIRED: *A.* 4% neutralized formaldehyde; *B.* 3% silver nitrate; *C.* MS 33.1 del Río-Hortega 1916; *D.* 0.5% acetic acid; *E.* 0.02% gold chloride; *F.* 5% sodium thiosulfate
METHOD: [20–30 μ celloidin sections of material fixed in F 7000.1010 Wittmaak (1910) and decalcified by AF 21.1 Fieandt and Sazen 1936] → [4–6 μ paraffin sections *neither deparaffined nor attached to slide*] → wash, 2 days → *A*, 3 days 37°C. → wash, 24 hrs. → *B*, 3½ days, 37°C. → rinse → *C*, 6 hrs. → *D*, 15 mins. → *A*, 10 mins. → wash, 15 mins. → *E*, 2 hrs., 37°C. → *F*, 2 mins. → wash, 12 hrs. → [attach to slide] → balsam, via usual reagents
RECOMMENDED FOR: Golgi apparatus in cells of inner ear.

33.3 Pritchard 1951 *test.* **1952 Cowdry**   Cowdry 1952, 212
REAGENTS REQUIRED: *A.* MS 33.1 Foot 1927a 50, water 50, ammonia 0.1; *B.* 0.04% formaldehyde; *C.* 2% potassium ferricyanide
METHOD: [sections of tissue fixed in F 7000.1000 Régaud 1910 or F 3700.1000 Helly 1903 and post-chromed 3 days in 3% potassium dichromate] → water → *A*, 20 secs., with constant agitation → *B*, large volume, 20 secs. → wash → *C*, till differentiated → wash → [counterstain, if desired] → balsam, via usual reagents
NOTE: Régaud fixation for mitochondria: Helly for Golgi.

33.3 del Río-Hortega 1916   21344, **14**:181
REAGENTS REQUIRED: *A.* 4% formaldehyde; *B.* 3% tannic acid; *C.* 1% ammonia; *D.* MS 33.1 del Río-Hortega 1916 10, water 90 (3 dishes required); *E.* 1% gold chloride (2 dishes required); *F.* 5% sodium thiosulfate
METHOD: *A*, 10 days → [sections by freezing technique] → *B*, heated till steaming, 5 mins. → *C*, till flexibility restored → *D*, 1st dish, 1 min. → *D*, 2nd dish, 1 min. → *D*, 3rd dish, 2 mins. → wash → *E*, 1st dish, 5 mins. → *E*, 2nd dish, 55°C., 20 mins. → *F*, 2 mins. → wash → balsam, via usual techniques
RECOMMENDED FOR: mitochondria.

33.3 del Río-Hortega 1916 *test.* **1933 Cajal and de Castro**
      Cajal and de Castro 1933, 211
REAGENTS REQUIRED: *A.* 3% tannin; *B.* 0.75% ammonia; *C.* MS 33.1 del Río-Hortega 1916 10, water 100; *D.* 0.2% gold chloride; *E.* 5% sodium thiosulfate
METHOD: [5 μ sections by freezing technique of formaldehyde-fixed material] → *A*, 5 mins., 50°–55°C. → *B*, till flexibility and transparency regained → *C*, 1 min. in 3 successive baths → thorough wash → *D*, 10 mins. 40°–45°C. → *E*, 5 mins. → thorough wash → balsam, via usual reagents
RECOMMENDED FOR: centrosomes in nerve cells.

33.3 del Río-Hortega *test.* **1933 Cajal and de Castro**   Cajal and de Castro 1933, 267

REAGENTS REQUIRED: *A.* AMS 11.1 Cajal 1914; *B.* AMS 11.1 del Río-Hortega 1933; *C.* 0.1% ammonia; *D.* MS 33.1 del Río-Hortega 1917; *E.* 0.2% formaldehyde; *F.* 0.16% gold chloride; *G.* 5% sodium thiosulfate

METHOD: [2–3 mm. slices of fresh material] → *A*, 2–3 days → *B*, 2–3 days, 25°–35°C. → [frozen sections] → *C*, till flexible → wash → *D*, 1–5 mins. → wash → *E*, 5 mins. → *F*, 15 mins. → *G*, 5 mins. → balsam, via usual reagents

RECOMMENDED FOR: mitochondria.

33.3 del Río-Hortega 1925   3231, **25**:34

REAGENTS REQUIRED: *A.* AMS 11.1 Strong 1903; *B.* 1% ammonia; *C.* AMS 33.1 del Río-Hortega 1921 56, water 44; *D.* 1% formaldehyde; *E.* 0.2% gold chloride; *F.* 5% sodium thiosulfate

METHOD: [small blocks] → *A*, 2–8 days → [10 μ sections by freezing technique] → *B*, very brief wash → wash → *C*, 5 mins. → rinse, 15–20 secs. with *very* gentle agitation → *D*, till grey → wash → *E*, 15 mins. → *F*, 5 mins. → balsam, via usual techniques

NOTE: This formula can be modified to stain gliosomes differentially by (1) adding 1% pyridine to *C* and staining at 50% *C* till sections turn brown and (2) increasing to 10% the concentration of *D*. All other steps are the same.

33.3 del Río-Hortega *test.* **1933 Cajal and de Castro**   Cajal and de Castro 1933, 269

REAGENTS REQUIRED: *A.* AMS 11.1 del Río-Hortega 1933b; *B.* 0.1% ammonia; *C.* 2% silver nitrate; *D.* MS 33.1 del Río-Hortega 1917; *E.* 0.4% formaldehyde; *F.* 0.16% gold chloride; *G.* 5% sodium thiosulfate

METHOD: [2–3 mm. slices of fresh tissue] → *A*, 3 or 4 days, on ice → [frozen sections] → *B*, thorough wash → wash → *C*, 15 mins. → rinse → *D*, 1 min. → rinse → *E*, 1 min. → *F*, 15 mins. → *G*, 5 mins. → balsam, via usual reagents

RECOMMENDED FOR: mitochondria in nerve cells.

33.4 HISTOLOGICAL METHODS

33.41 RETICULUM FIBERS

33.41 Amprino 1936   *see* MS 34.31 Amprino 1936

33.41 Bensley and Bensley 1938a   Bensley and Bensley 1938, 109

REAGENTS REQUIRED: *A.* 1% potassium permanganate; *B.* 5% oxalic acid; *C.* ADS 12.2 Lugol (1905) *D.* 5% sodium thiosulfate; *E.* sat. sol. tannic acid in 95% alc.; *F.* 0.1% ammonia; *G.* MS 33.1 Bensley and Bensley 1938a; *H.* 8% formaldehyde; *I.* 0.2% gold chloride

METHOD: [sections] → water → *A*, 1–5 mins. → *B*, till bleached → wash → *C*, 3–5 mins. → wash → *D*, till bleached → wash → *E*, 5 mins., 56°C. → *F*, rinse → *G*, 5–10 mins., 56°C. → wash → *H*, 5 mins. → wash → *I*, till violet → *D*, 5 mins. → wash → balsam, via usual reagents

33.41 Bensley and Bensley 1938b   Bensley and Bensley 1938, 109

REAGENTS REQUIRED: *A.* 2% silver nitrate; *B.* MS 33.1 Bensley and Bensley 1938b; *C.* 8% neutralized formaldehyde

METHOD: [sections] → water → *A*, overnight → *B*, 15–30 mins. → rinse → *C*, 3 mins. → balsam, via usual reagents

33.41 del Carpio 1930 *test.* **1932 Findlay**   11360, **52**:155

REAGENTS REQUIRED: *A.* 0.25% potassium permanganate; *B.* 5% oxalic acid; *C.* 2% silver nitrate; *D.* MS 33.1 del Carpio 1930; *E.* 4% neutralized formaldehyde; *F.* 0.2% gold chloride; *G.* 5% sodium thiosulfate

METHOD: [sections, already dye-stained] → water → *A*, 15–20 mins. → rinse → *B*, till bleached → wash → *C*, 24 hrs. → rinse → *D*, 30 mins. → double rinse → *E*, 15 secs. → wash → *F*, till gray → wash → *G*, 5–10 mins. → wash → balsam, via usual reagents

RECOMMENDED FOR: reticular fibers in sections previously dye-stained.

33.41 Foot 1924   11284, **9**:778

REAGENTS REQUIRED: *A.* ADS 12.2 Lugol (1905); *B.* 1% sodium thiosulfate; *C.* 0.25% potassium permanganate; *D.* 5% oxalic acid; *E.* 2% silver nitrate; *F.* MS 33.1 Foot 1924; *G.* 2% formaldehyde; *H.* 1% gold chloride; *I.* DS 11.121 Weigert 1903; *J.* DS 12.221 Weigert 1904

METHOD: [6 μ sections of F 3700.0010 Zenker 1894 material] → water → *A*, 5 mins. → *B*. ½ min. → *C*, 5 mins. → *D*, 15–30 mins. → wash → *E*, 48 hrs. → rinse → *F*, 30 mins, → rinse → *G*, 30 mins. → *H*. 1 hr. → wash → *I*, 1 min. → tap water, till blue → *J*, 30 secs. → balsam, via usual reagents

33.41 Foot 1927a   1887a, **4**:136

REAGENTS REQUIRED: *A, B, C, D*, as MS 33.41 Foot 1924; *E.* AMS 11.1 Foot 1927; *F.* 0.1% ammonia; *G.* MS 33.1 Foot 1927a; *H.* 8% neutral formaldehyde; *I.* AMS 22.1 Foot 1927; *J.* 5% sodium thiosulfate

METHOD: [material as for MS 33.41 Foot 1924] → *A* → *B* → *C* → *D*, as MS 33.41 Foot 1924 → water → *E*, 15 mins. at 37°C. → *F*, 30 secs. → rinse → *G*, 5 mins. in each of 2 changes → wash → *H*, 3 mins. → *I*, 3 mins. → rinse → *J*, 3 mins. → wash → balsam, via usual reagents

33.41 Foot 1927b   1887a, **4**:212

REAGENTS REQUIRED: *A, B, C, D* as MS 33.41 Foot 1924; *E.* Foot MS 33.1 1927b; *F.* 8% neutral formaldehyde; *G.* 0.2% gold chloride; *H.* 5% sodium thiosulfate; *I.* DS 11.123 Harris 1900; *J.* DS 12.221 van Gieson 1890

METHOD: [material as for AMS 33.41 Foot 1924] → *A* → *B* → *C* → *D*, as AMS 33.41 Foot 1924 → water → *E*, 15 mins. at 45°C. → wash → *F*, 2 mins. → rinse → *G*, 2 mins. → *H*, 2 mins. → wash → *I*, 3–5 mins. → tap water, till blue → *J*, 45 secs. → balsam, via usual reagents

33.41 Gluck 1938 *test*. **1939** Foot   4349, **19**:169

REAGENTS REQUIRED: *A.* ADS 12.2 Gram 1880; *B.* 5% sodium thiosulfate; *C.* AMS 11.1 Cajal 1913; *D.* MS 33.1 Gluck 1938; *E.* 2% formaldehyde; *F.* 0.2% gold chloride

METHOD: [sections of F 3700.0000 Zenker 1894] → water → *A*, 4–8 hrs. → 70% alc., wash → water → *B*, 5 mins. → thorough wash → *C*, 24 hrs., 37°C. → wash → *D*, 5 mins. → rinse → *E*, 5 mins. → wash → *F*, till gray → *B*, 5 mins. → wash → balsam, via usual reagents

33.41 Gridley 1951   *Tech. Bull.*, **21**:71

REAGENTS REQUIRED: *A.* 0.5% periodic acid; *B.* 2% silver nitrate; *C.* MS 33.1 da Fano 1919; *D.* 1.2% formaldehyde; *E.* 0.5% gold chloride; *F.* 5% sodium thiosulfate

METHOD: [6 μ sections] → water → *A*, 15 mins. → rinse → *B*, 30 mins. → wash → *C*, 15 mins. → rinse → *D*, 3 mins. → wash → *E*, 5 mins. → wash → *F*, 5 mins.

33.41 Gomori 1937   608b, **13**:993

REAGENTS REQUIRED: *A.* 1% potassium permanganate; *B.* 2% potassium metabisulfite *C.* 2% ferric alum; *D.* MS 33.1 Gomori 1937; *E.* 4% formaldehyde; *F.* 0.2% gold chloride; *G.* 2% sodium thiosulfate

METHOD: [paraffin sections, brought to water, of formaldehyde-fixed material] → *A* 1–2 mins. → rinse → *B*, 1 min. → wash → *C*, 2 mins. → wash → *D*, 1 min. → quick rinse → *E*, till reduced → wash → *F*, 10 mins. → rinse → *B*, 1 min. → wash → *G*, 1 min. → wash → balsam, via usual reagents

33.41 Gordon and Sweets 1936a   608b, **12**:545

REAGENTS REQUIRED: *A.* 0.5% potassium permanganate 95, 3% sulfuric acid 5; *B.* 1% oxalic acid; *C.* 2.5% ferric alum; *D.* MS 33.1 Gordon and Sweets 1936; *E.* 4% formaldehyde; *F.* 0.2% gold chloride; *G.* 5% sodium thiosulfate

METHOD: [sections, on slide, from formaldehyde or F 3000.1010 material] → water → *A* 5 mins. → wash → *B*, till white → wash → *C*, 15–20 mins. → wash → *D*, few secs. — rinse → *E*, till reduction complete → wash → *F*, 1–3 mins. → wash → *G*, 5 mins. — balsam, via usual reagents

RECOMMENDED FOR: reticulum of spleen.

33.41 Gordon and Sweets 1936b   608b, **12**:545

REAGENTS REQUIRED: *A.* 0.5% potassium permanganate 95, 3% sulfuric acid 5; *B.* 1% oxalic acid; *C.* 2.5% ferric alum; *D.* MS 33.1 Foot 1927a; *E.* 4% formaldehyde; *F.* 0.2% gold chloride; *G.* 5% sodium thiosulfate

METHOD: [sections from formaldehyde or F 5000.1010 Bouin 1897 material] → water → *A*, 1–5 mins. → wash → *B*, till white → wash → *C*, 15 to 30 mins. → wash → *D*, few secs. → *E*, till brown → wash → *F*, 1–3 mins. → wash → *G*, 5 mins. → wash → balsam, via usual reagents

RECOMMENDED FOR: reticulum of spleen.

33.41 Jalowy 1937   23639b, **27**:667

REAGENTS REQUIRED: *A.* MS 33.1 Jalowy 1937; *B.* 1% ammonia; *C.* 10% neutralized formaldehyde

METHOD: [sections of formaldehyde fixed materials] → water → *A*, 5–30 mins. 30°C. → rinse → *B*, rinse → *C*, 2–10 mins. → balsam, via usual reagents

RECOMMENDED FOR: collagen and reticular fibers in skin

33.41 Krajian 1933   1789a, **16**:376

REAGENTS REQUIRED: *A.* 10% ammonia; *B.* 0.3% potassium permanganate; *C.* 1.5% oxalic acid; *D.* 5% silver nitrate; *E.* 33.1 Krajian 1933; *F.* 12% formaldehyde

METHOD: [5–10 μ sections by freezing technique of formaldehyde-fixed material] → water → *A*, 15 mins. 60°C. → wash → *B*, 5 mins. → rinse → *C*, till decolorized → wash → *D*, 1 hr. 60°C. → *E*, 15 mins. 60°C. → wash → *F*, 1–3 mins. 60°C. → wash → balsam, via aniline and xylene

RECOMMENDED FOR: reticular and collagen fibers in frozen sections.

33.41 Laidlaw 1929   608b, **5**:239

REAGENTS REQUIRED: *A.* 1% iodine in 95% alc.; *B.* 5% sodium thiosulfate; *C.* 0.5% potassium permanganate; *D.* 5% oxalic acid; *E.* MS 33.1 Laidlaw 1929; *F.* 0.4% formaldehyde; *G.* 0.2% gold chloride

METHOD: [sections of F 5000.1010 Bouin 1897 fixed material] → water → *A*, 3 mins. → rinse → *B*, 3 mins. → rinse → *C*, 3 mins. → wash → *D*, 5 mins. → wash → *E*, 10 mins. → wash → *F*, 10 mins. → rinse → *G*, 10 mins. wash → balsam, via usual reagents

RECOMMENDED FOR: reticulum fibers in skin.

33.41 Levi 1907   14425, **18**:292

REAGENTS REQUIRED: *A.* 2% silver nitrate; *B.* MS 33.1 Levi 1907; *C.* 5% formaldehyde; *D.* 0.5% gold chloride; *E.* 5% sodium thiosulfate

METHOD: [paraffin sections of F 3700.0010 Zenker 1897 fixed material] → water → *A*, 24 hrs. → *B*, 20–40 mins., till brown → rinse → *C*, 5–10 mins. → wash → *D*, 2 hrs. → wash → *E*, 10–15 mins. → wash → balsam, via usual reagents

RECOMMENDED FOR: reticulum fibers in lymphatic glands.

33.41 Lillie 1948   Lillie 1948, 187

REAGENTS REQUIRED: *A.* 0.5% potassium permanganate; *B.* 5% oxalic acid; *C.* 1% uranium nitrate; *D.* MS 33.1 Lillie 1948; *E.* 4% formaldehyde; *F.* 0.2% gold chloride; *G.* 5% sodium thiosulfate

METHOD: [paraffin in sections varnished on slide with colloidin] → *A*, 2 mins. → wash → *B*, 2 mins. → wash → *C*, 5–10 secs. → *D*, on slide 3 mins. → rinse, *E*, 2 mins. → wash → *F*, 2 mins. → wash → *G*, 2 mins. → wash → balsam, via usual reagents

33.41 Long 1948   *see* MS 33.44 Long 1948

33.41 Maresch 1905   23681, **17**:641

REAGENTS REQUIRED: *A.* 2% silver nitrate; *B.* MS 33.1 Maresch 1905; *C.* 8% formaldehyde; *D.* 0.2% gold chloride in 0.2% acetic acid; *E.* 5% sodium thiosulfate

METHOD: [sections of formaldehyde fixed material] → *A*, 12–24 hrs. → rinse → *B*, 2–30 mins. → wash → *C*, 1 hr. → *D*, 1 hr. → *E*, 30 mins. → balsam, *via* carbol-xylene

RECOMMENDED FOR: reticulum fibers in liver.

33.41 Negrin 1941   1887a, **31**:108

REAGENTS REQUIRED: *A*. 10% sodium cyanide; *B*. MS 33.1 del Río-Hortega 1921; *C*. 1% pyridine; *D*. 0.4% neutralized formaldehyde; *E*. 10% potassium thiocyanate; *F*. 1% gold chloride; *G*. 5% sodium thiosulfate

METHOD: [sections] → water → *A*, 10–20 mins., 50°C. → thorough wash → *B*, 10–20 mins., 50°C. → *C*, wash → *D*, 1–3 mins. → *E*, till differentiated → thorough wash → *F*, 5 mins. → wash → *G*, 2 mins. → wash → balsam, via usual reagents

33.41 Perdrau 1921   11431, **24**:117

REAGENTS REQUIRED: *A*. 0.25% potassium permanganate; *B*. DS 21.212 Weigert 1885; *C*. ADS 21.1 Pal 1887 sols. *A* and *B*; *D*. 2% silver nitrate; *E*. MS 33.1 da Fano 1919; *F*. 8% neutralized formaldehyde; *G*. 5% sodium thiosulfate

METHOD: [sections of formaldehyde fixed material] → *A*, 10 mins. → wash → *B*, 2 hrs. → wash → *C*, (*A*) 15–20 secs. → *C*, (*B*) few secs. → wash → *D*, in dark, 12 hrs. → *E*, 20–30 mins. → wash → *F*, 15 mins. → wash → *G*, 5 mins. → wash → balsam, via usual reagents

33.41 del Río-Hortega 1916a   21344, **14**:181

REAGENTS REQUIRED: *A*. 1% tannic acid in 95% alcohol; *B*. MS 33.1 del Río-Hortega 1916 10, water 90 (3 dishes required); *C*. 8% neutralized formaldehyde

METHOD: [sections (see note below)] → *A*, 5 mins. at 55°C. → quick rinse → *B*, 1st dish, 1 min. → *B*, 2nd dish, 1 min. → *B*, 3rd dish, 2 mins. → wash → *C*, 30 secs. → wash → balsam, via usual reagents

NOTE: del Río-Hortega (*loc. cit.*) specifies formaldehyde material. **Gatenby and Stern** (Gatenby and Painter 1937, 549) state that alcohol or "Bouin" (presumably F 5000.1010 Bouin 1897) material may be used provided that it be "re-formalized" for a few days; Cajal and de Castro 1933, 291, suggest that material from this fixative be stored in 4% formaldehyde.

33.41 del Río-Hortega 1916b   21344, **14**:181

REAGENTS REQUIRED: *A*. 1% tannic acid in 95% alc.; *B*. MS 33.1 del Río-Hortega 1916 10, water 90 (3 dishes required); *C*. 1% gold chloride; *D*. 5% sodium thiosulfate

METHOD: [sections by freezing technique of formaldehyde material] → *A*, 5 mins., 55°C. → rinse rapidly → *B*, 1st dish, 1 min. → *B*, 2nd dish, 1 min. → *B*, 3rd dish, till dark brown → thorough wash → *C*, 30 to 40 mins., 40°C. → *D*, 5 mins. → wash → balsam, via usual reagents

33.41 Robb-Smith 1937   11431, **45**:312

REAGENTS REQUIRED: *A*. 10% ammonia; *B*. 0.25% potassium permanganate; *C*. 1.5% oxalic acid; *D*. 5% silver nitrate; *E*. AMS 33.1 Robb-Smith 1937; *F*. 15% formaldehyde; *G*. 0.2% gold chloride; *H*. 5% sodium thiosulfate

METHODS: [paraffin ribbons dried on slide, wax *not* removed] → *A*, 15 mins. → wash → *B*, 5 mins. → wash → *C*, till bleached → wash → *D*, 1 hr. → rinse → *E*, 15 mins. → wash → *F*, 3 mins. → wash *G*, 3 mins. → *H*, 1 min. → wash → dehydrate → xylene, till wax removed → balsam

33.41 Snessarew 1910   766, **36**:40

REAGENTS REQUIRED: *A*. 5% ferric alum; *B*. 10% silver nitrate; *C*. MS 33.1 Bielschowsky 1902; *D*. 8% formaldehyde

METHOD: [sections by freezing technique of formaldehyde fixed material] → *A*, 4 days changed daily → wash → *B*, 48 hrs. → rinse → *C*, 24 hrs. → wash → *D*, till blackened → balsam, via usual reagents

33.41 Studricka 1906   23632, **23**:416

REAGENTS REQUIRED: *A*. 3% silver nitrate; *B*. MS 33.1 Wolff 1905; *C*. 4% formaldehyde *D*. 0.5% gold chloride; *E*. 5% sodium thiosulfate

METHOD: [sections of fixed and decalcified material] → *A*, 4 days → wash → *B*, till yellow-brown → rinse → *C*, till dark brown → *D*, till gray-black → wash → *E*, 1 hr → wash → balsam, via usual reagents

RECOMMENDED FOR: reticulum fibers in cartilage, bone, and dentine.

NOTE: **Zimmermann 1908** (23632, **25**:8) differs only in reducing *A* to 2 days and in diluting *B* fourfold.

33.41 Urechia and Nagu 1931   6630, **106**:498

REAGENTS REQUIRED: *A*. AMS 11.1 Cajal 1913; *B*. sat. sol. ammonium sulfide; *C*. MS 33.1 del Río-Hortega 1917a; *D*. 50% alc.; *E*. 0.4% formaldehyde; *F*. 0.2% gold chloride; *G*. 5% sodium thiosulfate

METHOD: [fresh tissue] → *A*, 3–4 days → sections by freezing technique → *B*, 15–30 mins. → wash → *C*, 2–4 hrs. → *D*, quick wash, 2 changes → *E*, 5–10 mins. → *F*, 15 mins. → wash → *G*, 5 mins. → wash → balsam, via usual reagents

RECOMMENDED FOR: reticulum fibers in nervous tissues.

33.41 Wilder 1935a   608b, **11**:817

REAGENTS REQUIRED: *A*. 10% phosphomolybdic acid; *B*. 1% uranium nitrate; *C*. MS 33.1 Foot 1927a; *D*. AMS 21.1 Wilder 1935; *E*. 0.2% gold chloride; *F*. 5% sodium thiosulfate

METHOD: [sections of F 3700.1000 or .1010 material] → water → *A*, 1 min. → wash → *B*, 5 secs. → rinse → *C*, 1 min. → 95% alc. quick rinse → *D*, 1 min. → wash → *E*, 1 min. → rinse → *F*, 1–2 mins. → [dye stains as in MS 33.41 Foot 1924 to 1927b, if required] → balsam, via usual reagents

RECOMMENDED FOR: reticulum of spleen.

33.41 Wilder 1935b   608b, **11**:817

REAGENTS REQUIRED: *A*. 1% potassium permanganate; *B*. 5% oxalic acid; *C*. 1% uranium nitrate; *D*. Bielschowsky 1902 MS 33.1; *E*. AMS 21.1 Wilder 1935; *F*. 0.2% gold chloride; *G*. 5% sodium thiosulfate

METHOD: [sections] → water → *A*, 1 min. → rinse → *B*, 1 min. → wash → *C*, 5–10 secs. → rinse *D*, 1 min. → 90% alc., rinse → *E*, 1 min. → rinse → *F*, 1 min. → rinse → *G*, 1 min. → wash → balsam, via usual reagents

RECOMMENDED FOR: reticulum fibers.

33.41 Zhookin 1937   11284, **22**:1284

REAGENTS REQUIRED: *A*. 0.001% potassium permanganate; *B*. MS 33.1 Lawrentjew (1933); *C*. 0.04% formaldehyde, pH 7; *D*. 0.2% gold chloride; *E*. 5% sodium thiosulfate

METHOD: [frozen sections of formaldehyde material] → water → *A*, 20 secs. → rinse → *B*, 2–3 mins. → rinse → *C*, till reduced → wash → *D*, 1 min. → *E*, 5 mins. → wash → balsam, via usual reagents

33.41 Zimmermann 1908 *see* MS 33.41 Studnicka 1906 (note)

<h2 style="text-align:center">33.42 SELECTIVE STAINING OF SPECIAL CELLS</h2>

33.42 Gluckman 1943   4285a, **20**:63

REAGENTS REQUIRED: *A*. MS 33.1 Gluckman 1943; *B*. 5% sodium thiosulfate

METHOD: [paraffin sections of F 5000.1010 Bouin 1897 material] → water → *A*, 10 mins., 60°C. → *B*, 30 secs. → wash → balsam, via usual reagents

RECOMMENDED FOR: argentiphil cells of intestine.

33.42 Gomori 1946   519b, **10**:177

REAGENTS REQUIRED: *A*. 5% chromic acid; *B*. 1% sodium bisulfite; *C*. MS 33.1 Gomori 1946 50, water 50, sodium borate 0.2; *D*. 0.1% gold chloride; *E*. 2% sodium thiosulfate

METHOD: [sections] → water → *A*, 1–1½ hrs. → wash → *B*, 1 min. → wash → *C*, 1–3 hrs. till glycogen granules dark brown → wash → *D*, 5 mins. → *E*, 5 mins. → wash → [counterstain if desired] → balsam, via usual reagents

RECOMMENDED FOR: glycogen.

33.42 Jacobson *see* MS 33.42 Masson 1923b (note)

33.42 Masson 1923a *test.* **1937 Duthie**   Gatenby and Painter 1937, 414

REAGENTS REQUIRED: *A*. 0.003% ammonia; *B*. MS 33.1 Fontanna 1912; *C*. AMS 22.1 Cajal 1910; *D*. 2% sodium thiosulfate

METHOD: [frozen sections formaldehyde fixed materials] → *A*, 2–3 hrs. → *B*, in dark, 36 hrs. → wash → *C*, 10 mins. → wash → *D*, 1 min. → wash → balsam, via usual reagents

RECOMMENDED FOR: argentophil cells.

33.42 Masson 1923b *test.* **1948 Lillie** *cit.* **Lee**   Lillie 1948, 102

REAGENTS REQUIRED: *A.* MS 33.1 Fontana 1912; *B.* 0.1% gold chloride; *C.* 5% sodium thiosulfate

METHOD: [sections of formaldehyde material] → water → *A*, 12–48 hrs. in dark → wash → *B*, 4–6 mins. → wash → *C*, 1 min. → wash → [counterstain if required] → balsam, via usual reagents

RECOMMENDED FOR: argentaffin cells.

NOTE: Lillie (*loc. cit.*) states that **Lison** (no ref.) "used the sequence given above" and that **Jacobson** (no ref.) omitted the gold chloride.

33.42 Masson 1928   608b, **4**:181

REAGENTS REQUIRED: *A.* 0.1% ammonia; *B.* MS 33.1 Masson 1928; *C.* AMS 22.1 Cajal 1948

METHOD: [2–3 mm. slices of F 5000.1010 Bouin 1897 fixed material] → wash → *A*, 24 hrs. → rinse → *B*, 24 hrs. → rinse → *C*, 24 hrs. → [sections]

RECOMMENDED FOR: argentaffin cells.

33.42 Ogata-Ogata 1923   2526, **71**:376

REAGENTS REQUIRED: *A.* 1% ammonia; *B.* MS 33.1 Maresch 1905 50, water 50; *C.* 3% sodium thiosulfate; *D.* 4% formaldehyde

METHOD: [small blocks of fresh tissue] → *A*, 1–2 hrs. in dark → *B*, 3–5 hrs. in dark → *A*, 30 mins. changed several times, in dark → *C*, 1 hr. in dark → wash → *D*, 1–2 days → [frozen sections]

RECOMMENDED FOR: chromaffin cells.

33.42 Shanklin 1951   Cowdry 1952, 270

REAGENTS REQUIRED: *A.* MS 31.1 Shanklin 1951; *B.* 5% sodium sulfite; *C.* 0.6% pyridine; *D.* MS 33.1 del Río-Hortega 1927; *E.* AMS 21.1 Shanklin 1951; *F.* 0.2% gold chloride; *G.* 5% sodium thiosulfate

METHOD: [7–10 μ sections of formaldehyde material] → water → *A*, 24°C. 24 hrs. → wash → *B*, 1 hr. → *C*, 1–2 mins. → wash → *D*, 2–5 mins. → rinse → *E*, 1 min. → rinse → *F*, 1 min. → *G*, 1–2 mins. → wash → [counterstain if desired] → balsam, via usual reagents

RECOMMENDED FOR: parenchyma of pineal.

33.43 DEMONSTRATION OF CALCIFIED AND OSSIFIED MATERIAL

33.43 Gomori 1933   608b, **9**:253

REAGENTS REQUIRED: *A.* 1.5% silver nitrate; *B.* water 100, sodium hypophosphite 5, 0.5% sodium hydroxide 0.2; *C.* 5% sodium thiosulfate; *D.* 7% sulfosalicylic acid

METHOD: [blocks of tissue or embryos not more than 2 mm. thick] → 95% alc. 2–4 days → wash → *A*, 6–10 days, changed once or twice → thorough wash → *B*, 4–8 days → wash → *C*, 2 days → wash → *D*, till decalcified, 1–3 days → sections → [counterstain if desired]

RECOMMENDED FOR: demonstration of calcium in tissues.

33.43 Orban *test. circ.* **1938 Wellings**   Wellings *circ.* 1938, 190

REAGENTS REQUIRED: *A.* 0.25% potassium permanganate; *B.* 5% oxalic acid; *C.* 2% silver nitrate; *D.* MS 33.1 Bielschowsky 1902; *E.* 2% formaldehyde; *F.* 1% gold chloride; *G.* 5% sodium thiosulfate

METHOD: [celloidin sections of decalcified, F 3700.1010 Heidenhain 1916 fixed, teeth] → water → *A*, 5 mins. → wash → *B*, 15 mins. → wash → *C*, 24 hrs., in dark → wash → *D*, 30 mins. → wash → *E*, 30 mins. → wash → *F*, 1 hr., wash → *G*, 2 mins. → wash → balsam, via usual reagents

RECOMMENDED FOR: general structure of tooth pulp, and particularly development of dentine from it.

33.44 OTHER HISTOLOGICAL METHODS

33.44 Jacobson 1939   11431, **49**:1

REAGENTS REQUIRED: *A.* MS 33.1 Fontana 1912; *B.* 5% sodium thiosulfate

METHOD: [sections of formaldehyde material] → water → *A*, 12–24 hrs. → wash, 1 min. → *B*, 1 min. → wash → balsam, via usual reagents

RECOMMENDED FOR: differentiation of argentophil cells in gastrointestinal tract.

33.44   Long 1948   20540b, **23**:69

REAGENTS REQUIRED: *A*. 0.25% potassium permanganate; *B*. 5% oxalic acid; *C*. 10% silver nitrate; *D*. MS 33.1 Long 1948; *E*. 0.05% ammonia; *F*. 0.4% neutralized formaldehyde; *G*. 0.2% gold chloride; *H*. 5% sodium thiosulfate; *I*. 0.1% azocarmine in 1% acetic acid; *J*. 5% phosphotungstic acid; *K*. water 99, acetic acid 1, *either* light green SFY (adult tissues) *or* fast green FCF (embryonic tissues); *L*. 1% acetic acid

METHOD: [sections of F 3700.1010 Heidenhain 1916 after removal of mercury with iodine] → water → *A*, 2 mins. → wash, 5 mins. → *B*, 2 mins. → thorough wash → *C*, 12 hrs., in dark → wash → *D*, 25–30 mins., 40–45°C. → *E*, one dip → *F*, 10–20 mins. → wash → *G*, 15–30 mins. → rinse → *H*, 2 mins. → wash → *I*, 15–30 mins. → rinse → *J*, 3–6 hrs. → rinse → *K*, 3 mins. → rinse → *L*, rinse (or longer if differentiation necessary) → dammar, via isopropyl alcohol and xylene

RECOMMENDED FOR: differentiation of reticular fibers (dense purple), collagen (green), and myofibrils (red).

33.44   McIndoo 1928   1789a, **6**:598

REAGENTS REQUIRED: *A*. 10% formaldehyde; *B*. MS 33.1 del Río-Hortega 1919 50, water 50, pyridine 1; *C*. 20% formaldehyde buffered to pH 7; *D*. 2% sodium thiosulfate

METHOD: [small pieces] → *A*, 20 days → [frozen sections] → *B*, in watch glass heated to steaming, till brown → rinse → *C*, 1 min. → rinse → *D*, 1 min. → wash, 2–3 days → balsam, via usual reagents

RECOMMENDED FOR: demonstration of bile capillaries.

33.44   del Río-Hortega 1926   3231, **26**:107

REAGENTS REQUIRED: *A*. MS 33.1 del Río-Hortega (1933); *B*. 0.4% formaldehyde; *C*. 5% sodium thiosulfate

METHOD: [frozen sections of formaldehyde material] → water → *A*, till brown, 50°–55°C. → wash → *B*, 5–10 mins. → *C*, 5 mins. → wash → balsam, via usual reagents

RECOMMENDED FOR: epithelial fibrils.

33.5   BACTERIOLOGICAL METHODS

33.51   METHODS FOR SPIROCHETES

33.51   Ferguson *test*. 1916 Warthin   4349, **6**:56

REAGENTS REQUIRED: *A*. 2% silver nitrate; *B*. MS 33.1 Bielschowsky 1902; *C*. 8% formaldehyde; *D*. 0.01% gold chloride in 0.01% acetic acid; *E*. 5% sodium thiosulfate

METHOD: [sections] → water → *A*, 12–24 hrs. → *B*, 15–30 mins. → rinse → *C*, 3 mins. → wash → *D*, 2 mins. → wash → *E*, 1 min. → balsam, via usual reagents

33.51   Fontana 1912   7176, **55**:1003

REAGENTS REQUIRED: *A*. F 0000.1010 Fontana 1912; *B*. AMS 13.1 Fontana 1912; *C*. MS 33.1 Fontana 1912

METHOD: [fresh smears] → *A*, 2 mins. → wash → *B*, 5 secs., 40°C. → wash → *C*, dropped on slide and warmed, 2–30 secs. → repeat, until sufficiently darkened → wash → dry → balsam, if permanent preparation is required

NOTE: **Langeron 1942**, 636 recommends F 0000.1010 Ruge 1942 in place of *A* above.

33.51   Gordon 1936   *see* 33.6 Gordon 1936

33.51   Lancelin, Séguy, and Debreuil 1926   6630, **94**:557

REAGENTS REQUIRED: *A*. F 0000.1010 Fontana 1912; *B*. AMS 13.1 Fontana 1912; *C*. MS 33.1 Fontana 1912; *D*. AMS 22.1 Lancelin, Séguy, Debreuil 1926

METHOD: [fresh smears] → *A*, 2 mins. → wash → *B*, 5 secs., 40°C. → wash → *C*, dropped on slide and warmed, 20–30 secs. → rinse → *D*, till sufficiently darkened → dry → balsam, if permanent preparation required

33.51   Krajian 1933 *test*. 1935 abstract   20540b, **10**:1935

REAGENTS REQUIRED: *A*. 2% sodium cobaltinitrite; *B*. AMS 12.1 Krajian 1933; *C*. MS 33.1 Krajian 1933; *D*. AMS 21.1 Krajian 1933

METHOD: [5 μ frozen sections of formaldehyde material] → *A*, 5 mins. → wash → *B*, 15 mins. → rinse → *C*, 15–25 secs. → wash → *D*, 5 mins. → wash → balsam, via usual reagents

NOTE: See also Krajian MS 31.51 Krajian 1935.

33.51 Langeron 1942   *see* MS 33.51 Fontana 1912 (note)

33.51 Séguin 1939   829, **10**:838
REAGENTS REQUIRED: *A*. AMS 21.1 van Ermengen 1940; *B*. 33.1 Fontana 1912; *C*. 0.5% gold chloride; *D*. 0.25% platinic chloride
METHOD: [osmic fixed smears] → dry → abs. alc. 10 mins. → dry → *A*, on slide, 10 mins. → thorough wash → *B*, 10 mins. → wash → *C*, few mins. → rinse → *D*, few mins. → dry

33.51 Steiner 1937   11284, **23**:293
REAGENTS REQUIRED: *A*. 1.5% ammonia; *B*. MS 33.1 Steiner 1937
METHOD: [air-dried films] → *A*, till dehemoglobinized → wash → *B*, on slide, 40–90 mins. → drain → wash → dry

33.52 OTHER BACTERIOLOGICAL METHODS

33.52 Craigie 1928   3566, **9**:55
REAGENTS REQUIRED: *A*. AMS 13.1 Zettnow 1891; *B*. MS 33.1 Craigie 1928; *C*. 0.03% gold chloride
METHOD: [smears from formolized suspensions] → dry, 37°C. → heat, 100°C., 5 mins. → water, 5 mins. → rinse → dry, 100°C., 5 mins. → *A*, 5–10 mins., 100°C. → wash → *B*, on slide, warmed to steaming and held warm till smear brown → wash → *C*, 30 mins. → wash → dry
RECOMMENDED FOR: bacterial smears.

33.52 Novel 1939   857, **63**:302
REAGENTS REQUIRED: *A*. water 100, tannic acid 10, ferrous sulfate 16, magenta 0.4; *B*. MS 33.1 Fontana 1912
METHOD: [air dry smears] → *A*, 1–1½ min. → rinse → *B*, till chocolate, ½ to 1½ min. → rinse → dry
RECOMMENDED FOR: bacterial flagella.

33.52 Zettnow 1891   23684, **11**:689
REAGENTS REQUIRED: *A*. AMS 13.1 Zettnow 1891; *B*. MS 33.1 Zettnow 1891
METHOD: [Smear preparations on coverslip] → *A*, in dish heated on water bath, 5–7 mins. → water, wash → *B*, poured on slip, heated to steaming till margin blackens → wash → dry
RECOMMENDED FOR: bacterial flagella.

33.6 OTHER SILVER DIAMMINE METHODS

33.6 Gordon 1936   11284, **22**:294
REAGENTS REQUIRED: *A*. 2.5% ferric alum; *B*. water 100, gelatin 1, 2% sodium carbonate 0.1; *C*. MS 33.1 Gordon 1936; *D*. AMS 21.1 Gordon 1936
METHOD: [formaldehyde fixed smears] → *A*, 10 mins. → wash → *B*, dip, drain → quick rinse → *C*, 5–15 mins. → wash at 60°C. → *D*, till reduced → wash → balsam, via usual reagents
RECOMMENDED FOR: blood smears containing parasites.

33.6 Haymaker and Sanchez-Perez 1935   19938, **82**:355
REAGENTS REQUIRED: *A*. water 90, 40% neutralized formaldehyde 10, sodium chloride 0.45; *B*. 0.5% ammonia; *C*. MS 33.1 Haymaker and Sanchez-Perez 1935; *D*. MS 33.1 del Río-Hortega 1923 50, water 50; *E*. 0.4% formaldehyde; *F*. 0.2% gold chloride; *G*. 1% sodium thiosulfate
METHOD: [clots on coverslip] → *A*, 24 hrs. → *B*, 5 mins. → wash → *C*, 40°C. till clot yellows (about 10 mins.) → wash → *D*, 40°C. till clot brown (about 9 mins.) → wash → *E*, 5 mins. → *F*, 40°C. till violet (about 10 mins.) → *G*, 5 mins. → wash → balsam, via usual reagents
RECOMMENDED FOR: cells in tissue culture.

33.6 Kalwaryjski 1938 *test*. **1939 Findlay**   11360, **59**:36
REAGENTS REQUIRED: *A*. ADS 12.2 Lugol; *B*. 2.5% sodium thiosulfate; *C*. MS 33.1 Kalwaryjski 1938; *D*. 5% sodium thiosulfate

METHOD: [pieces of fresh muscle infested with Trichinella] → A, 10 mins. → wash → B, till muscle (*not* worms) decolorized → wash → C, till worms are iodine free → wash → D, till muscle colorless → wash → balsam, via usual reagents

RECOMMENDED FOR: Trichinella in muscles.

MS 34 METHODS USING SILVER IN COMBINATION WITH OTHER METALS

34.0 TYPICAL EXAMPLES

Demonstration of the Purkinje cells in the cerebellar cortex by the method of Golgi 1875

This method is not one which can be recommended to anybody who desires hurriedly to produce a slide. It is an experimental method given here for those who have a genuine interest in the production of beautiful slides. The two other Golgi processes given under MS 34.21 below are considerably quicker but they are less certain and give less opportunity for experiment. By the method about to be described it is possible, with patience, to secure a better slide than can be obtained by any other method.

The first step is to make up at least 100 milliliters of Müller's 1859 dichromate-sulfate (Chapter 18 F 7000.0000 Müller 1859) and weigh out, into each of three small tubes or capsules, one gram of finely powdered potassium dichromate. Next prepare about 250 milliliters of a 0.75% solution of silver nitrate and secure two chemically cleaned 100-milliliter stoppered bottles and a chemically clean crystallizing dish of about 30 milliliter capacity.

Kill a rabbit, tie it face down on a board, skin the head, and remove the parietal and frontal bones with bone forceps. The cerebellum should then be washed free of extravasated blood with normal saline or triple-distilled water, and blocks of the cerebellar cortex removed with the broken edge of a coverslip or with a stainless steel knife. (Many failures in using this technique are due to cutting blocks of material with an ordinary steel scalpel.) The blocks should measure about ½ mm. to ¾ mm. cube. At least 30 are required for experimental purposes. These blocks are now placed in the stoppered bottle of Müller's fluid (F 7000.0000 Müller 1859). It is desirable to place a half-inch layer of fat-free cotton or fine glass fiber on the bottom of the bottle to prevent the pieces of material from pressing against the glass. The pieces should be left in Müller's fluid for five days, and the bottle gently shaken daily to avoid exhausting the fixative in the vicinity of the pieces. On the fifth day add one of the one-gram bottles or capsules of dried potassium dichromate, tip the bottle up and down until the chemical is thoroughly dissolved, and then let it stand five days longer. On the tenth day add another gram of potassium dichromate and let it stand five days longer. On the fifteenth day remove two or three of the blocks and place them without washing in about 25 milliliters of 0.75 silver nitrate in the crystalizing dish. Add one gram of potassium dichromate to the fluid which holds the remaining blocks, dissolve as before, and leave for two days more.

Returning now to the two blocks which, for experimental purposes, have been put in the silver solution: these should be agitated rapidly to keep the precipitate from adhering to the surface as it forms. The silver nitrate after a few minutes should be poured off and replaced with fresh solution. This process of pouring off the contaminated solution and adding fresh is continued until the pieces rest at the bottom and no longer exude streams of a silver chromate precipitate. After they have remained in this satisfactory condition for about ten minutes they are removed to a stoppered bottle containing 100 milliliters of fresh 0.75% silver nitrate. There they may remain indefinitely. They should be marked in some manner, preferably by notching the edge, so that they can be identified.

Two more blocks should be removed from the dichromate solution at intervals of a day, washed, as has been described above, in successive portions of silver nitrate solution, notched by a different system, and transferred to the large bottle of silver nitrate at intervals of a day until all the blocks have been transferred. There will finally be 30 blocks covering 15 periods of immersion in the dichromate solution. It must be emphasized that the success of the process depends on the length of time the blocks stay in the dichromate. As for the length of time in silver nitrate, it should not be less than 48 hours, but it may be extended for several weeks with the assurance that the impregnation will not be affected. Forty-eight hours after the last of the blocks has been placed in silver nitrate, pour off the solution, add about 50 milliliters of triple-distilled water, tip the bottle up and down once, pour off the distilled water, and fill the bottle with 90% alcohol. After 24 hours the alcohol is replaced, and the process repeated as often as the reagent becomes discolored.

Though it is perfectly possible to obtain adequate sections by freezing techniques, it is usually better to use the celloidin method. An objection has always been that prolonged exposure to strong alcohol tends to remove the stains; but this has not been the author's experience.

To avoid wasting time preparing sections from unsatisfactory blocks, reject the hopeless cases by an examination of a freshly cut surface under a binocular microscope. For this purpose arrange the blocks in order of their removal from the dichromate. Examine first the block which has been hardened for the longest time. Slice one of the faces of this block with a razor-sharp scalpel and examine it under the surface of 95% alcohol with a binocular microscope. It will almost invariably appear as a uniform sheet of chrome yellow, at best only slightly granular. This indicates, as anticipated, that the block has been in the dichromate too long. Next take the block which has remained for the least time in the dichromate and slice its edge. It is almost certain to have a pale, transparent, cheesy appearance without any opaque yellow speckling. This indicates, as anticipated, that the block has been for too short a time in the dichro-

mate. Work through the series, taking blocks alternately from groups impregnated for a long and for a short time. It soon becomes apparent that the plain opacity of the long-impregnated blocks begins to break up into speckles, whereas golden yellow opaque spots begin to appear in the cheesy, transparent, under-impregnated blocks. Somewhere between these two lies the perfect specimen, preferably one lying intermediate between the two which have been reached as the end points of unsatisfactory material.

As has been stated, it is customary to section blocks of Golgi-impregnated material by the freezing technique, on the ground that the prolonged immersion in alcohol necessary for celloidin sectioning tends to degrade the finer details of the preparation. This has not been true in the writer's experience, unless dehydration has been unnecessarily prolonged. It is usually sufficient to put the selected block in about 25 milliliters of absolute alcohol for about two hours. Next, replace the absolute alcohol with a mixture of equal parts of absolute alcohol and ether and let stand two hours longer. Then place the block for about three hours in the thin, or first, solution of celloidin customarily employed for embedding. Since it will probably now be toward the end of the day, it is the author's custom to transfer the block directly from the thin syrupy solution of celloidin to the thickest solution of celloidin and to leave the material in this overnight. It may be removed from this thick syrup next morning and hardened by whatever technique is customary. In this instance immersion in 70% alcohol is probably simplest. When the celloidin is hardened, sections about 25 microns thick are cut with a knife moistened with 70% alcohol and accumulated in 70% alcohol. Each section is then separately removed to a slide and examined under medium power of an ordinary microscope. One or two sections will soon be found which will demonstrate to perfection the aborizations of Purkinje cells. These sections should be transferred to a separate watch glass of 70% alcohol. When sufficient sections showing the required structure have been accumulated, they may be mounted in cedar oil. This type of mounting is necessary, since it is a peculiarity of this technique that sections prepared by it may not be mounted under the surface of a coverslip or they will bleach within an interval varying from a few months to a year; whereas if they are merely varnished to a slide they may be preserved indefinitely. In the present instance they may be dehydrated in absolute alcohol, as it does not matter whether or not the celloidin is dissolved from the section. If one is dealing with brittle material or with material for which the celloidin forms the chief support, it is essential to complete the dehydration in some alcohol in which celloidin is not soluble. Golgi himself recommended guaiacol. Whatever medium is used for dehydration, clearing should always be carried out in cedar oil.

When it is required to make a more permanent preparation of an individual mount, it is simplest to take it from the thin cedar oil, lay it on a slide, blot the cedar oil from it with the finest filter paper available, and place over the surface a layer of the kind of thickened cedar oil once sold for use with oil immersion objectives and still obtainable from some suppliers as "cedar oil (special for microscopy)." This oil hardens in about 48 hours. Two layers will give enough protection, and the only objection to this method of mounting is the tendency of dust to accumulate on the surface. When this has happened to the extent that examination of the specimens is becoming difficult, it is only necessary to wash off the cedar oil with absolute alcohol and replace it with fresh cedar oil. Such drastic treatment may not even be necessary, and it is often possible to remove the dust with a cloth moistened in cedar oil.

Those who are not prepared to indulge in the many experimental processes mentioned in this technique are recommended to the technique of Golgi 1880 which is universally known as "Golgi's quick process." This involves osmic-dichromate fixation and the entire operation may be concluded in as little as three or four days. It does not, however, yield results so beautiful, nor is it always possible to secure results at all. The advantage of the present slow method is that, since numerous blocks are removed at intervals, one is certain to find at least one which has the correct degree of impregnation.

Demonstration of the structure of the superior cervical ganglion by the method of Kolossow 1896

This is an interesting mixed silver-osmic method which is ideally suited for the demonstration of nerve fibers in cells within sympathetic ganglia, a subject most difficult to impregnate by other silver techniques. Only two solutions are required. The first is Kolossow's 1897 osmic-dichromate fixative (see in Chapter 18, F 1700.0000 Kolossow 1897) and the second, the silver-osmic stain of Kolossow (see MS 34.1 Kolossow 1897), which is prepared by adding to 250 milliliters of triple-distilled water, first five grams of silver nitrate and then, when this has been completely dissolved, one gram of osmic acid.

The easiest material on which to become acquainted with this technique is the anterior (or superior) sympathetic cervical ganglion of a rabbit. Before commencing the dissection of the rabbit it is as well to prepare an adequate supply of the fixative solution and to store this in a chemically clean glass-stoppered bottle. A rabbit is then killed and tied, ventral side uppermost, on a dissecting board. A loop of cord is passed around the anterior region of the head, which is drawn over the edge of the board so as to stretch the neck as far as possible. The neck is then skinned and the superficial fascia removed, the muscles being pulled laterally away from the trachea. If this is done in about the central region of the neck, two nerves will immediately become apparent. The smaller of these is the descending ramus of the hypoglossal and the larger is the fused tenth nerve and sympathetic nerve from the ganglion sought. This larger nerve is then followed forward by parting the fascia of the muscle to a region just behind the tympanic bulla. Here it will be found to split into two, each of the two smaller tributaries swelling, after a distance of about one half inch, into a ganglion. The larger of these two ganglia, which is also the one closer to the surface of the neck, is the ganglion nodosum of the vagus nerve; while the smaller is the anterior (or superior) cervical sympathetic ganglion which is the one sought. This ganglion is then cut out from the surrounding tissue and dropped directly into the fixative, where it should remain for approximately three days. It is difficult to gauge the exact time and it might be well to remove the ganglion from the other side and place it in the same solution. One ganglion may then be removed from solution at the end of two days and the other at the end of four days, with reasonable certainty that one or the other will be in a condition suitable for staining. When the ganglion is removed from the fixing solution it should be rinsed very briefly in distilled water, drained of distilled water on the surface of filter paper, and then transferred directly to the staining solution which is of course kept in a chemically clean stoppered bottle. It remains in the staining solution for from two to three days and is then placed in 90% alcohol. Sections are prepared either in celloidin or by the freezing technique and are mounted in exactly the manner described for the method of Golgi given in the last example.

Demonstration of the neurons and dendrites of the brain of a rabbit embryo by the method of Windle 1926

This is a mixed dichromate-osmic-silver method, of the same general type as Golgi's mixed process (MS 34.21 Golgi 1900) but better and more certain for embryonic material. Only three solutions are required. The first of these is a 3.5% solution of reagent-grade potassium dichromate in triple-distilled water. The second is Windle's 1926 osmic-dichromate fixative (see, in Chapter 18, F 1700.0000 Windle 1926). The third is 0.75% silver nitrate. The brain of a 14-day rabbit embryo is used in the following example. At least a liter of the first solution and half a liter of the second will be required.

Secure a rabbit on the fourteenth day of gestation and kill it, preferably by a blow on the head. Lay the rabbit, ventral side uppermost, on a dissecting board, tying its four legs outward so as to leave the abdomen stretched. Remove the skin with extreme care, washing away the milk with a stream of water, and remove as many as possible of the milk glands from the abdominal surface so as to leave the muscular layer exposed. Remove the greater part of the abdominal wall, disclosing the two uteri, one on each side. These will contain a series of globular expansions, each about the size of the egg of a bantam hen. Two ligatures should be tied between each pair of these globular expansions and the uterus cut between the ligatures, the resultant pieces being removed separately to a clean dish. It will be found on examination that the uterus is not uniformly swollen but is extended to one side more than the other. Each piece is pinned down with the largest expansion uppermost. With a sharp knife, cut horizontally across the top of the globular expansion. With a little practice it is by this means possible to remove a large area without liberating much blood. Each embryo will then be seen clearly and should be removed with a spoon to a dish of normal saline, where it is rinsed to remove as much as possible of the extravasated blood before being transferred to a clean dish of saline for the removal of the membranes. The embryo is now placed in a bottle which contains a large volume of 3.5% potassium dichromate. On the bottom of the bottle there should be a layer of fat-free cotton or fine glass fiber. The bottle should be gently agitated at intervals to prevent the accumulation of exhausted fixative on the bottom. After about two days in potassium dichromate, the embryo will be hard enough to handle with safety. It should be removed to a clean dish of potassium dichromate, in which the skin is carefully dissected away from the upper portion of the head, the rudiments of the skull removed, and the entire brain passed, with extreme care and without any washing at all, into the osmic-dichromate solution. Here it should remain three days more. It is then removed from the osmic-dichromate solution and passed to another large volume of 3.5% potassium dichromate. The purpose of this is to wash out the osmic acid without removing any of the dichromate. It is safer to leave the embryo at least a week in this solution and desirable to change the dichromate at least once during this period. The brain may now be removed, placed on a pad of chemically pure filter paper, and left there until as much as possible of the surface-adherent dichromate has been removed from it. It is then placed in a clean crystallizing dish containing from 25 to 50 milliliters of the silver nitrate solution, and rocked back and forth to prevent the precipitate of silver chromate from settling on the surface of the brain. After about ten minutes of agitation, the now cloudy silver nitrate should be removed and replaced with a fresh batch of silver nitrate; and the process repeated until no further precipitate washes off into the silver nitrate solution. The brain is then removed to a fresh batch of at least 100 milliliters of silver nitrate and stored in a dark cupboard for from seven to ten days. The bottle should be examined at daily intervals and the solution changed at any time, whenever either a yellow precipitate is accumulating at the bottom of the bottle or a brownish stain is appearing on the sides. At the end of ten days the brains are removed to a large bottle of 95% alcohol after having been cut in half by a sagittal section. They may remain in alcohol until required or, as soon as dehydration is complete, may be sectioned by the celloidin technique. These sections are then cleared and mounted under cedar oil just as though they were Golgi preparations.

34.1 Staining Solutions

In most cases, the two metals are supplied from separate simple solutions recorded under the individual techniques.

34.1 Amprino 1936   4285a, **13**:223
   PREPARATION: To 20 20% chromic acid add slightly more 10% potassium hydroxide than is necessary to change color from red to yellow. Add 25 this solution to 75 10% silver nitrate. Wash ppt., suspend in 100 water, and add just enough ammonia to secure complete solution.

34.1 Berkely 1897   10920, **6**:1
   PREPARATION: To 100 1% silver nitrate add 10 0.25% phosphomolybdic acid.

34.1 Hill 1896   3464, **9**:1
   FORMULA: water 100, silver nitrate 0.8 gm., formic acid 0.1

34.1 Juschtschenko test. **1933 Cajal and de Castro**   Cajal and de Castro 1933, 124
   FORMULA: water 100, silver nitrate 2.5, osmic acid 0.5

34.1 Kolossow 1897 test. **da Fano 1928**   Gatenby and Cowdry 1928, 608
   FORMULA: water 100, silver nitrate 2, osmic acid 0.4

34.1 Martinez 1931 test. **1932 Findlay**   11360, **52**:152
   PREPARATION: To 50 10% silver nitrate add 50 2% sodium tungstate and then just enough ammonia to redissolve the ppt.

34.1 Oliveira 1936   22575, **298**:523
   PREPARATION: To 5 10% silver nitrate add 10 5% potassium dichromate. Collect ppt. and wash till washings are color-free. Suspend ppt. in 40 water and add just enough ammonia to dissolve ppt. Dilute to 85.

34.1 Rénaut test. **1907 Böhm and Oppel** cit. **Régaud**   Böhm and Oppel 1907, 387
   FORMULA: water 100, osmic acid 0.15, picric acid 0.6, silver nitrate 0.25

34.2 Neurological Methods

34.21 Nerve cells and processes

34.21 Andriesen 1894   see MS 34.21 Golgi 1880 (note)

34.21 Berkely 1897   10920, **6**:1
   REAGENTS REQUIRED: A. F 7000.0000 Müller 1859; B. F 1700.0000 Berkely 1897; C. 0.25% silver nitrate; D. MS 34.1 Berkely 1897

METHOD: [large pieces] → *A*, 2 wks. or until firm → [3 mm. slices from *A*] → *B*, 3 days → drain or blot → 25 ml. *C*, agitate gently → repeat successive washings in 25 ml. *C*, till no further ppt. appears in solution → *D*, 2–3 days at 26°C. → 90% alcohol, rinse → [frozen, celloidin, or freehand sections] → dammar *or* cedar oil *without cover*

34.21 Bolton 1898   *see* MS 34.21 Gerota 1896 (note)

34.21 Brookover 1910   *see* MS 34.21 Golgi 1880 (note)

34.21 Bubenaite 1929   23632, **46**:359
REAGENTS REQUIRED: *A*. 2.5% potassium dichromate; *B*. 2% silver nitrate
METHOD: [pieces of formaldehyde-fixed material] → *A*, 2 days, 34°C. → *B*, rinse → *B*, fresh solution, 1–2 days, 34°C. → wash → [paraffin sections]
RECOMMENDED FOR: ganglion cells.

34.21 Cajal 1890   *see* MS 34.21 Golgi 1880 (note)

34.21 Cajal 1891   *Cajal's double impregnation—auct.*   6011, **8**:130
REAGENTS REQUIRED: *A*. F 1700.000 Golgi 1880; *B*. 0.75% silver nitrate; *C*. F 1700.0000 Cajal 1891
METHOD: [small blocks, fresh tissue] → 100 ml. *A*, 2–3 days → drain → 25 ml. *B*, agitate gently → repeat successive washings in 25 ml. *B*, until no further ppt. appears in solution → 100 ml. *B*, 24 to 48 hrs. → rinse → *A* or *C*, 1–2 days → drain → wash in *B* as above → 100 ml. *B*, 36–48 hrs. → 90% alc. quick wash → sections, either frozen, freehand or collodion → dammar *or* cedar oil *without cover*
NOTE: **Durig 1895** (766, **10**:659) substitutes Durig 1895 F 7000.1000 for *A* and *C* above.

34.21 Durig 1895   *see* MS 34.21 Cajal 1891 (note)

34.21 Fish 1895   *see* MS 34.21 Golgi 1880 (note)

34.21 Gerota 1896   10157, **13**:108
REAGENTS REQUIRED: *A*. 4% neutralized formaldehyde; *B*. 4% potassium dichromate; *C*. 0.5% silver nitrate
METHOD: [whole brains] → *A*, very large volumes, 1–2 wks. → [small pieces from *A*] → *B*, 3–5 days → drain, or blot → 25 ml. *C*, agitate gently → repeat successive washings to 25 ml. *C*, until no further ppt. appears in solution → 100 ml. *C*, 10–20 days → 95% alcohol quick wash → [sections, either freehand, frozen or collodion] → dammar, or cedar oil, *without cover*
NOTE: **Bolton 1898** (11360, **20**:244) differs from above in substituting 1% ammonium dichromate for *B*, and 1% silver nitrate for *C*.

34.21 Golgi 1875 *test.* **1903** *ips.*   *Golgi's slow process—auct.*
                                                Golgi 1903, **1**:128
REAGENTS REQUIRED: *A*. F 7000.0000 Muller 1859; *B*. potassium dichromate; *C*. 0.75% silver nitrate
METHOD: [small blocks, fresh tissue] → 100 ml. *A*, 5 days → add 1 gm. *B*, leave 5 days → add 1 Gm. *B*, leave 5 days → add 1 Gm. *B*, leave until sufficiently hardened → drain or blot → 25 ml. *C*, agitate gently → repeat successive washings until no further ppt. appears in solution → 100 ml. *C*, 24 to 48 hrs. → 90% alc., changed when discolored, till required → [sections, either frozen, freehand, or collodion] → dammar, or cedar oil *without cover*
NOTE: A detailed description of this technique is given under MS 34.0 above.

34.21 Golgi 1880 *test.* **1903** *ips.*   *Golgi's quick process—auct.*
                                                Golgi 1903, **1**:162
REAGENTS REQUIRED: *A*. F 1700.0000 Golgi 1880; *B*. 0.75% silver nitrate
METHOD: [small blocks, fresh tissue] → 100 ml. *A*, 2 to 3 days → drain → 25 ml. *B*, agitate gently → repeat successive washings in 25 ml. *B* until no further ppt. appears in solution → 100 ml. *B*, 24 to 48 hrs. or until required → 90% alc. quick wash → [sections, either frozen, freehand, or collodion] → dammar or cedar oil *without cover*
NOTE: **Cajal 1890** substitutes F 1700.0000 Cajal 1890 for *A* above. **Lachi 1895** (14425, **5**:15) substitutes F 7000.1000 Lachi 1895 for 48 hours for *A* above. **dell' Isola 1895**

(3248, 2) substitutes F 1700.1000 dell' Isola 1895 for *A* above. **Strong 1895** (266, 10:494) substitutes F 7000.1000 Strong 1895 for *A* above. **Fish 1895** (21400a, 17:319) substitutes either F 1700.1000 Fish 1895 or F 7000.1000 Fish 1895 for *A* above using 3 days in both *A* and *B*. **Brookover 1910** (11135, 20:49) precedes *A* by fixation in 4% neutralized formaldehyde. **Vassale and Donaggio 1895** (14425, 6:82) substitute their F 7000.2000 for *A* above. **Andreizen 1894** (3579, 1:909) substitutes his method (F 1700.0000) of fixation for *A* above. **Hill 1896** (3464, 9:1) substitutes MS 34.1 Hill 1896 for *B* above. **Sehrwald 1889** (23632, 6:456) and **Mann 1902** (*test.* da Fano 1936 in Gatenby and Painter 1937, 509) coat the object with 10% gelatin before transferring to silver.

34.21 Golgi 1900 *test.* **1903** *ips. Golgi's mixed process—auct.*

Golgi 1903, **2**:685

REAGENTS REQUIRED: *A.* 2% potassium dichromate; *B.* F 1700.0000 Golgi 1900; *C.* 0.75% silver nitrate

METHOD: [small blocks of fresh tissue] → *A*, 2 to 30 days → *B*, 3 to 19 days → drain or blot → 25 ml. *C*, agitate gently → repeat successive washings in 25 ml. *C* until no further ppt. appears in solution → 100 ml. *C*, 24 to 48 hrs. or until required → 90% alc., quick wash → [sections, either frozen, freehand, or collodion] → dammar, or cedar oil, *without cover*

34.21 Golgi *test.* **1933 Cajal and de Castro**   Cajal and de Castro 1933, 357

REAGENTS REQUIRED: *A.* F 8000.1000 Lawrentjew (1933); *B.* 2% silver nitrate; *C.* AMS 21.1 Cajal 1914

METHOD: [pieces of tissue] → *A*, 8–10 days → *B*, rinse → *B*, fresh sol., 5–7 days → wash → *C*, 24 hrs. → sections

RECOMMENDED FOR: nerve endings.

34.21 Hill 1896   *see* MS 34.21 Golgi 1880 (note)

34.21 dell' Isola 1895   *see* MS 34.21 Golgi 1880 (note)

34.21 Juschtschenko *test.* **1933 Cajal and de Castro**   Cajal and de Castro 1933, 124

REAGENTS REQUIRED: *A.* F 1700.0000 Cajal 1890; *B.* MS 34.1 Juschtschenko (1933)

METHOD: [sympathetic ganglia] → *A*, 1–5 days → quick wash → blot dry → *B*, 2–3 days → [section] → dammar, or cedar oil, *without cover*

RECOMMENDED FOR: sympathetic ganglia.

34.21 Kolossow 1897 *test.* **da Fano**   Gatenby and Cowdry 1928, 608

REAGENTS REQUIRED: *A.* F 1700.0000 Kolossow 1897; *B.* MS 34.1 Kolossow 1897

METHOD: [whole ganglia] → *A*, 1–7 days → rinse and blot → *B*, 2–3 days → 90% alc., quick wash → [sections either frozen, freehand, or collodion] → dammar or cedar oil *without cover*

RECOMMENDED FOR: sympathetic ganglia.

NOTE: A detailed description of this technique is given under MS 34.0 above.

34.21 Kopsch 1896   766, **11**:727

REAGENTS REQUIRED: *A.* F 7000.1000 Kopsch 1896; *B.* 3.5% potassium dichromate; *C.* 0.75% silver nitrate

METHOD: [small pieces, fresh tissue] → 100 ml. *A*, 24 hrs. in dark → 100 ml. *B*, 48 hrs. → drain → 25 ml. *C*, agitate gently → repeat successive washings in 25 ml. *C* until no further ppt. appears in solution → 100 ml. *C*, 2 to 6 days → 95% alc., quick wash → [sections, either freehand, frozen, or collodion] → dammar, or cedar oil, *without cover*

NOTE: **Schreiber 1898** substitutes his F 7000.1000 for *A* above and his F 7000.1000 for *B* above.

34.21 Lachi 1895   *see* MS 34.21 Golgi 1880 (note)

34.21 Lawrentjew *test.* **1933 Cajal and de Castro**   Cajal and de Castro 1933, 359

REAGENTS REQUIRED: *A.* F 8000.1000 Lawrentjew 1933; *B.* 8% neutralized formaldehyde; *C.* 20% silver nitrate; *D.* MS 33.1 Lawrentjew 1933; *E.* 30% ammonia; *F.* 0.3% gold chloride; *G.* 5% sodium thiosulfate

METHOD: [fresh pieces] → *A*, 1 hr. → *B*, 4–6 days → wash → [frozen sections] → *C*, 1–5 mins. → *B*, 1–2 mins. → *D*, till nerve endings clearly shown → *E*, 1 min. → wash → *F*, till gray → *G*, 5 mins. → balsam, via usual reagents
RECOMMENDED FOR: peripheral nerve endings.

34.21 Mann 1902   *see* MS 34.21 Golgi 1880 (note)

34.21 Sala 1891   23632, **9**:389
REAGENTS REQUIRED: *A*. F 1700.0000 Golgi 1880; *B*. 0.75% silver nitrate
METHOD: [entire ganglion] → *A*, 3 days → rinse → *B*, 2–3 days → rinse → *A*, 4 days → wash → sections by freezing technique → dammar or cedar oil *without cover*

34.21 Sánchez *test.* **1933 Cajal and Castro**   Cajal and Castro 1933, 128
REAGENTS REQUIRED: *A*. F 7000.1000 Sánchez 1933; *B*. 0.5% silver nitrate; *C*. 0.75% silver nitrate
METHOD: [invertebrates] → *A*, changed daily, 3–5 days → *B*, with agitation, 1–2 mins. → *C*, 2–3 days → *A*, with agitation, 1–2 mins. → *A*, changed daily, 1–3 days → *B*, with agitation, 1–2 mins. → *C*, 1–3 days → [celloidin sections]
RECOMMENDED FOR: nerve fibers in invertebrates.

34.21 Schreiber 1898   *see* MS 34.21 Kopsch 1896 (note)

34.21 Sehrwald 1889   *see* MS 34.21 Golgi 1880 (note)

34.21 Smith 1930   *Turtox News*, **8**:91
REAGENTS REQUIRED: *A*. 4% potassium dichromate; *B*. 0.75% silver nitrate
METHOD: [2 mm. slices of formaldehyde material] → rinse → *A*, 3–5 days → wash → blot → *B*, 15 mins. with constant agitation → *B*, fresh solution, 24 hrs. → section
RECOMMENDED FOR: general neurology.

34.21 Smirnow 1895   1780, **52**:201
REAGENTS REQUIRED: *A*. F 7000.1000 Smirnow 1895; *B*. 3.5% potassium dichromate; *C*. F 1700.1000 Smirnow 1895; *D*. 0.5% silver nitrate; *E*. 1.0% silver nitrate
METHOD: [fresh whole cerebellum] → *A*, 1–8 wks. → [split halves from *A*] → *B*, 2–5 wks. → [1 cm. slices from *B*] → *C*, 7 to 10 days → drain or blot → 100 ml. *D*, 24 hrs. → *E*, 36–48 hrs. → [frozen, celloidin, or freehand sections] → dammar, or cedar oil, *without cover*

34.21 Strong 1895   *see* MS 34.21 Golgi 1880 (note)

34.21 Timofecheff *test.* **1933 Cajal and de Castro**   Cajal and de Castro 1933, 125
REAGENTS REQUIRED: *A*. F 1700.0000 Timofecheff 1933; *B*. water 100, silver nitrate 1, formic acid 0.01, sodium sulfate 0.001
METHOD: [pieces of fresh tissue of 1 cm. side] → *A*, 6–7 days → quick wash blot → *B*, 2–3 days → [section]
RECOMMENDED FOR: nerve endings in male sex organs.

34.21 Vassale and Donaggio 1895   *see* MS 34.21 Golgi 1880 (note)

34.21 Windle 1926   11135, **40**:229
REAGENTS REQUIRED: *A*. 3.5% potassium dichromate; *B*. F 1700.0000 Windle 1926; *C*. 0.75% silver nitrate
METHOD: [fetal brains] → *A*, 48 hrs. → *B*, 72 hrs. → *A*, 5–6 days → drain or blot → 25 ml. *C*, agitate gently → repeat successive washings in 25 ml. *C*, till no more ppt. produced in solution → 100 ml. *C*, 7–10 days in dark → [half brains from *C*] → 95% alcohol, till dehydrated → [sections by celloidin technique] → dammar, or cedar oil *without cover*
NOTE: A detailed description of this technique is given under MS 34.0 above.

34.22 NEUROGLIA

34.22 Cajal *test.* **1933** *ips.*   Cajal and de Castro 1933, 282
REAGENTS REQUIRED: *A*. 6% formaldehyde; *B*. F 7000.1000 Cajal 1933; *C*. 1% silver nitrate; *D*. 1% silver nitrate in 1% chloral hydrate

METHOD: [small pieces of fresh tissue] → *A*, 2–5 days → *B*, 3–5 days → *C*, with rapid agitation → *C*, fresh sol. → repeat till clouds of ppt. cease → *D*, 2 days → 90% alc. wash → [paraffin sections] → dammar or cedar oil *without cover*
RECOMMENDED FOR: oligodendria.

34.22 Martinez 1931

3232, **31**:653

REAGENTS REQUIRED: *A*. AMS 11.1 Cajal 1913; *B*. 0.5% ammonia; *C*. MS 34.1 Martinez 1931; *D*. 4% formaldehyde; *E*. 0.2% gold chloride; *F*. 5% sodium thiosulfate
METHOD: [fresh pieces] → *A*, 1 hr., 55°C. → wash → [frozen sections] → *B*, 5 mins. → rinse → *C*, 15 mins. → wash → *D*, till pale yellow → wash → *E*, 5 mins. → *E* (fresh solution), 15 mins., 50°C. → *F*, till purple → wash → balsam, via usual reagents

34.22 del Río-Hortega 1928 *test.* 1933 Cajal and de Castro

Cajal and de Castro 1933, 281

REAGENTS REQUIRED: *A*. F 7000.1000 del Río-Hortega 1928; *B*. 1.5% silver nitrate
METHOD: [fresh blocks of tissue] → *A*, renewed daily, 2–3 days → rinse → *B*, 2 or 3 days → 90% alc., wash → [paraffin sections] → dammar or cedar oil *without cover*
RECOMMENDED FOR: oligodendria.

34.3 HISTOLOGICAL METHODS

34.31 RETICULUM FIBERS

34.31 Amprino 1936

4285a, **13**:223

REAGENTS REQUIRED: *A*. 2% tannin in 95% alc.; *B*. MS 34.1 Amprino 1936 30, water 100; *C*. 15% formaldehyde
METHOD: [sections of formaldehyde-fixed material] → water → *A*, 30–40 mins., 55–58°C. → water → *B*, few mins. → *B* (fresh solution), few mins. → *B* (fresh solution), till light yellow → rinse → *C*, till reduced → balsam, via usual reagents

34.31 Oliveira 1936

22575, **298**:523

REAGENTS REQUIRED: *A*. 10% phosphomolybdic acid; *B*. 1% uranium nitrate; *C*. MS 33.1 Foot 1924; *D*. AMS 21.1 Oliveira 1936a; *E*. MS 34.1 Oliveira 1936; *F*. AMS 21.1 Oliveira 1936b; *G*. 0.2% gold chloride; *H*. 5% sodium thiosulfate
METHOD: [paraffin sections] → *A*, 1 min. → rinse → *B*, 5 secs. → quick rinse → *C*, 1 min. → 95% alc., rinse → *D*, 1 min. → wash → *E*, 15–20 mins. 56°C. → wash → *F*, 1 min. → wash → *G*, 5–10 mins. 56°C. → *H*, 6–10 mins. → thorough wash → balsam, via usual reagents

34.31 Oppel 1890

766, **4**:144

REAGENTS REQUIRED: *A*. 5% potassium chromate; *B*. 0.75% silver nitrate
METHOD: [small pieces alc. fixed material] → water → *A*, 24 hrs. → wash → *B*, 24 hrs. → wash → [frozen tangential sections]
RECOMMENDED FOR: lattice fibrils in liver.

34.32 OTHER HISTOLOGICAL METHODS

34.32 Kupffer 1889

20188, **5**:219

REAGENTS REQUIRED: *A*. F 1700.0000 Cajal 1890; *B*. 0.75% silver nitrate
METHOD: [small pieces of liver] → *A*, 24 hrs. → wash → *B*, 48 hrs. → [sections]

34.32 Martinotti 1888 *test.* 1889 Behrens, Kossel, and Schiefferdecker

Behrens, Kossel, and Schieffer-decker 1889, 211

REAGENTS REQUIRED: *A*. 2% arsenic trioxide; *B*. F 7000.0000 Müller 1859; *C*. water 12, silver nitrate 8, glycerol 80; *D*. 0.75 sodium chloride
METHOD: [small pieces] → *A*, till decalcified → wash → *B*, 15 mins. → rinse → *C*, 24–48 hrs. → rinse → sections → 95% alc. → *D*, few minutes → balsam, via usual reagents
RECOMMENDED FOR: elastic fibers.

34.32 Régaud and Dubreuil 1903 *test.* 1907 Böhm and Oppel

Böhm and Oppel 1907, 175

REAGENTS REQUIRED: *A*. 1% protein silver 50, 1% osmic acid 50; *B*. any DS 11.2 stain
METHOD: [fix flat sheet of epithelium in *A*] → wash → *B*, till nuclei are stained
RECOMMENDED FOR: delineation of cell outlines in epithelium.

34.32 Rénaut *test.* **1907 Böhm and Oppel** *cit.* **Régaud** Böhm and Oppel 1907, 387
REAGENTS REQUIRED: *A.* MS 34.1 Rénaut (1907)
METHOD: "*A*" is copiously injected into the testes, which are then hardened in alcohol.
Frozen sections are then mounted in balsam and exposed to light.
RECOMMENDED FOR: demonstration of lymph vessels in testes.

34.32 Schultze 1907 1780, **69**:544
REAGENTS REQUIRED: *A.* water 100, silver nitrate 2, osmic acid 0.1; *B.* 1% hydroquinone
METHOD: [pieces of tissue] → *A*, 30 mins. → rinse → *B*, 24 hrs. → wash → balsam, via
usual reagents
RECOMMENDED FOR: demonstrating outlines of epithelial cells.

34.4 CYTOLOGICAL METHODS

34.4 Aoyama 1930 23632, **46**:490
REAGENTS REQUIRED: *A.* F 8000.1000 Aoyama 1930; *B.* 1.5% silver nitrate; *C.* AMS 21.1
Aoyama 1930
METHOD: [small pieces] → *A*, 3–4 hrs. → rinse → *B*, 10–15 hrs., 25°C. → rinse → *C*, 5–10
hrs. → [paraffin sections]
RECOMMENDED FOR: Golgi network.

34.4 Bubenaite 1937 *test.* **1937 Gatenby and Painter** Gatenby and Painter 1937, 313
REAGENTS REQUIRED: *A.* 4% formaldehyde; *B.* 25% potassium dichromate; *C.* 2%
silver nitrate
METHOD: *A*, 1–2 days → rinse → *B*, 2 days 35°C. → rinse → *C*, wash, renewing solution
when necessary, till no further ppt. occurs in solution → *C*, fresh solution, 1 to 2 days
35°C. → [sections]
RECOMMENDED FOR: Golgi apparatus.

34.4 Golgi-Verratti *test.* **Cajal and de Castro** Cajal and de Castro 1933, 200
REAGENTS REQUIRED: *A.* F 1270.0000 Veratti 1890; *B.* water 100, potassium dichromate
2, copper sulfate 1; *C.* 1% silver nitrate
METHOD: [fragments of fresh tissue] → *A*, 3–4 wks. → wash → *B*, overnight → *C*, 4–8
hrs. → [sections]
RECOMMENDED FOR: Golgi apparatus.

34.4 Veratti *see* MS 34.4 Golgi-Veratti 1933

34.5 BACTERIOLOGICAL METHODS

34.5 Fontana 1923 9170, **64**:234
REAGENTS REQUIRED: *A.* F 0000.1010 Ruge 1942; *B.* 0.75% neoarsphenamine *or* AMS
13.1 Iron 1924; *C.* Fontana 1912 MS 33.1
METHOD: [fresh smears] → *A*, 2 mins. → wash → *B*, dropped on slide and warmed, 20–30
secs. → wash → *C*, dropped on slide and warmed, 20–30 secs. → repeat until sufficiently darkened → wash → dry → balsam
RECOMMENDED FOR: spirochetes in smears.

34.5 Safford and Fleisher 1931 20540b, **6**:43
REAGENTS REQUIRED: *A.* AMS 13.1 Safford and Fleisher 1931; *B.* MS 33.1 Fontana 1912
METHOD: [moist smears] → *A*, heated to steaming, 2 mins. → wash → dry → *B*, heated
to steaming, 1–2 mins. → wash → dry
RECOMMENDED FOR: bacterial flagella.

34.5 Williams *test.* **1924 Mallory and Wright** Mallory and Wright 1924, **279**
NOTE: This method involves a proprietary developer of undisclosed formula and **cannot**
be further noticed.

35 OTHER SILVER METHODS

35.1 STAINING SOLUTIONS

35.1 David 1934 23684, **132**:240
PREPARATION: Dissolve 1 silver nitrate in 4 water. Add to 1.2 sodium sulfate in 2 hot
water. Wash ppt. by decantation and suspend in 100 water.

35.1 Lugaro 1932 *test.* **1933 Cajal and de Castro**   Cajal and de Castro 1933, 260
Stock I. 9% sodium thiosulfate; Stock II. 2% silver bromide in 9% sodium thiosulfate;
Stock III. 0.3% silver iodide in 9% sodium thiosulfate

		I	II	III
Working solutions	A	4	16	1
	B	5	15	2
	C	6	14	4
	D	7	13	5
	E	8	12	6
	F	9	11	7
	G	10	10	8
	H	11	9	12

35.2 NEUROLOGICAL METHODS

35.2 Lugaro 1932 *test.* **1933 Cajal and de Castro**   Cajal and de Castro 1933, 260
REAGENTS REQUIRED: *A*. MS 35.1 Lugaro 1932; *B*. 8% formaldehyde
METHOD: [pieces fixed 3–8 days in 7% formaldehyde on ice] → 10 ml. *A* in flask in dark,
3 hrs. → 7 ml. *B* added to flask, 5–8 days → wash → frozen sections → balsam, via
usual reagents
RECOMMENDED FOR: neuroglia.
NOTE: Any one of the eight working solutions given under 33.1 Lugaro 1932, or an as-
sortment of them, may be selected.

35.3 OTHER METHODS

35.3 David 1934   23684, **132**:240
REAGENTS REQUIRED: *A*. ADS 12.2 David 1934; *B*. MS 35.1 David 1934
METHOD: [heat-fixed smear] → *A*, 10 mins. → wash → heat dry → *B*, heated to steam-
ing, till brown → wash → dry
RECOMMENDED FOR: bacterial flagella.

MS 40 Other Metals

41.1 STAINING SOLUTIONS

41.1 del Río-Hortega 1927 *test.* **1933 Cajal and de Castro**
                                        Cajal and de Castro 1933, 279
FORMULA: water 94.5, hydrochloric acid 5.5, potassium ferrocyanide 2.25

41.2 NEUROLOGICAL METHODS

41.2 Azoulay 1894   4956, **49**:924
REAGENTS REQUIRED: *A*. 0.5% ammonium vanadate; *B*. 2.5% tannin
METHOD: [thin celloidin sections of dichromate fixed material] → *A*, poured over section
on slide, 2–30 secs. → rinse → *B*, poured over section on slide, 20–30 secs. → [repeat
A → rinse → *B*, till staining sufficient] → balsam, via usual reagents
RECOMMENDED FOR: cerebellum.

41.2 Cox *test.* **1933 Cajal and de Castro**   Cajal and de Castro 1933, 130
REAGENTS REQUIRED: *A*. F 3700.0000 Cox 1895; *B*. 5% sodium bisulfite
METHOD: [large pieces] → *A*, 2–3 months → 90% alc., till mercuric chloride extracted →
[celloidin sections] → *B*, till dark brown → M 23.1 Cox 1891
RECOMMENDED FOR: general neurology.

41.2 Flater 1895   1780, **45**:158
REAGENTS REQUIRED: *A*. 4% potassium dichromate; *B*. 0.1% mercuric chloride
METHOD: [whole brains] → *A*, 2–3 months → 0.5 mm. slices → *B*, changed when dis-
colored, 9–12 months → wash → [celloidin sections] → balsam, via carbol-xylene
RECOMMENDED FOR: brains of small vertebrates.

41.2 Golgi 1878   Golgi 1903, **1**:143
REAGENTS REQUIRED: *A*. 1% potassium dichromate; *B*. 1.5% potassium dichromate; *C*.
2% potassium dichromate; *D*. 1% mercuric chloride
METHOD: [large pieces] → *A*, 1 month → *B*, 1 month → *C*, 1 month or till required →
1–2 cm. cube blocks → *D*, changed daily, till block is decolorized → wash → [cel-
loidin sections] → wash → AMS 24.1 Golgi (1937) → M 23.1 mountant
RECOMMENDED FOR: axis cylinder and dendrites in brain.

41.2 Krohntal 1899   23632, **16**:235
REAGENTS REQUIRED: *A*. F 8000.1000 Krohntal 1899; *B*. water 90, 40% formaldehyde 10,
hydrogen disulfide to sat.
METHOD: [fresh tissue] → *A*, 4–5 days → *B*, with agitation, few mins. → *B*, changed
daily, 5 days → [celloidin sections]
RECOMMENDED FOR: general neurology.

41.2 Pollaillon *test. circ.* **1938 Wellings**   Wellings *circ.* 1938, 132
REAGENTS REQUIRED: *A*. 10% ferric chloride; *B*. 30% tannic acid
METHOD: [sections to water] → *A*, 24 hrs. → wash → *B*, till dark enough → wash →
M 11.1 mountant
RECOMMENDED FOR: nerve fibers in teeth.

41.2 vom Rath 1895   *see* F 1250.0010 vom Rath 1895

41.2 del Río-Hortega 1927 *test.* **1933 Cajal and de Castro**
                                         Cajal and de Castro 1933, 278
REAGENTS REQUIRED: *A*. AMS 11.1 Cajal 1913; *B*. 0.1% ammonia; *C*. 10% hydrochloric
acid; *D*. MS 41.1 del Río-Hortega 1927; *E*. 1% sodium carbonate; *F*. 0.1% hydrochloric acid
METHOD: [blocks of fresh tissue] → *A*, some days → [20–25 μ frozen sections] → *B*,
thorough wash → thorough wash → *C*, 1 min. → *D*, 50°–60°C., with gentle rocking,
until solution begins to cloud → *E*, until sections transparent → *F*, few secs. → [re-
peat *D* → *E* → *F* cycle until stain satisfactory] → [counterstain in any DS 11.21
formula if desired] → balsam via usual reagents
RECOMMENDED FOR: pathological microglia.

41.2 van der Stricht 1895   *see* F 1200.0000 van der Stricht 1895

41.2 Wolters 1891   *see* DS 21.212 Wolters 1891

41.3 HISTOLOGICAL METHODS

41.3 Foster 1934   20540b, **9**:91
REAGENTS REQUIRED: *A*. water 1, tannic acid 1, sodium salicylate 1; *B*. 3% ferric
chloride
METHOD: [sections] → water → *A*, 10 mins. → wash → *B*, several mins. → wash →
counterstain, if required → balsam, via usual reagents
RECOMMENDED FOR: cell walls of apical meristem.

41.3 Hogan *test.* **1883 Cole**   Cole 1883, 5
REAGENTS REQUIRED: *A*. 10% ferric chloride in 90% alc.; *B*. 2% pyrogallol in 90% alc.
METHOD: [sections] → 90% alc. → *A*, 2 mins. → 90% alc., rinse → *B*, till sufficiently
stained → 90% alc., wash → water → glycerol → M 10 mountant
RECOMMENDED FOR: general histology.

41.3 Hogan *test.* **1878 Marsh**   Marsh 1878, 71
REAGENTS REQUIRED: *A*. 2% ferric chloride in 90% alc.; *B*. 2% pyrogallol in 95% alc.
METHOD: [sections] → 90% alc. → *A*, 2 mins. → alc., rinse → *B*, 2 mins. → alc. wash →
balsam, via usual reagents
RECOMMENDED FOR: cartilage.

41.3 Kenney 1928   1887a, **5**:283
REAGENTS REQUIRED: *A*. water 90, 40% formaldehyde 10, sodium sulfantimonate 1
METHOD: [pieces] → *A*, 24 hrs. → wash → [sections]
RECOMMENDED FOR: reticulum fibers.

41.3 Leber 1860   1789a, **14**:3

REAGENTS REQUIRED: *A.* 1% ferric chloride; *B.* 5% potassium ferrocyanide
METHOD: [small fragments] → *A,* 5 mins. → rinse → *B,* 2–3 mins.
RECOMMENDED FOR: delineation of cell outlines.

41.4 OTHER METHODS

41.4 Fol 1883   23635, **38**:491

REAGENTS REQUIRED: *A.* 1% ferric chloride; *B.* 1% gallic acid in 95% alc.; *C.* 0.1%
hydrochloric acid in 70% alc.
METHOD: [living Tintinnopsidae] → *A,* till dead → wash, 70% alc. → *B,* 1 day → *C,* till
differentiated → balsam, via usual reagents
RECOMMENDED FOR: marine Tintinnopsidae.

41.4 Sander 1935   23454, **116**:335

REAGENTS REQUIRED: *A.* water 99, sulfuric acid 1, potassium permanganate to sat.
METHOD: [heat-fixed smear] → *A,* 2 mins. → wash → dry
RECOMMENDED FOR: spores in bacteria.

24

Accessory Metal Staining Solutions

Decimal Divisions Used in Chapter

AMS 10 Solutions Used Before Staining

AMS 10.0 GENERAL OBSERVATIONS

As Chapter 18 has been devoted to fixative formulas, it appears necessary to justify the retention in this place of formulas used to fix materials before metal staining techniques. Formulas are retained in this section only when they are not considered by the author to be adapted to any other purpose. Fixatives developed for use prior to silver staining which would appear to have applications outside this specific field are given in Chapter 18. It is impossible, moreover, to distinguish in many of the formulas given in this chapter among those intended to fix the tissues, those designed to serve as mordants, and those supposed to exercise some physical effect so as to render more apparent some structure in the material after it has been metal-stained. Solutions of uranium, cobalt, and the like, might be considered chemical mordants which would render materials subsequently stained more clearly apparent: the reverse is the case. These materials are used mostly as inhibitors which, by preventing the absorption of various metal-stains upon the nervous elements of nervous structures, permit the demonstration of their supporting or connective tissues. The exact role played by pyridine, so frequently an ingredient of this group of solutions, is again doubtful; it has been suggested that it may cause no more than the differential shrinking of certain structures, particularly neurofibrillae, with the result that they become mechanically differentiated. It is recognized that the division into aqueous and alcoholic solutions is untenable on scientific grounds, but it is retained on grounds of convenience.

AMS 11 FORMALDEHYDE MIXTURES

AMS 11.1 FORMULAS

11.1 Bertrand and Guillain 1934   6630, **115**:706
FORMULA: water 86, 40% formaldehyde 14, ammonium bromide 2, pyridine 0.3

11.1 Cajal 1904 *test.* **1933 Cajal and de Castro**   Cajal and de Castro 1933, 189
FORMULA: water 100, 40% formaldehyde 25, ammonia 1

11.1 Cajal 1908 *test.* **1933** *ips.*   Cajal and de Castro 1933, 201
FORMULA: 40% formaldehyde 50, acetone 50, ammonia 0.2

11.1 Cajal 1913   21344, **11**:255
FORMULA: water 85, neutralized 40% formaldehyde 15, ammonium bromide 2

11.1 Cajal 1914   21344, **12**:127
FORMULA: water 64, 40% neutral formaldehyde 12, 95% alc., uranium nitrate 0.8

11.1 Cajal 1920 *test.* **1933** *ips.*   Cajal and de Castro 1933, 254
FORMULA: water 100, 40% formaldehyde 12, ammonium bromide 6

11.1 Cajal 1929   21344, **26**:1
FORMULA: water 100, 40% formaldehyde 15, chloral hydrate 5

11.1 Cajal *test.* **1933** *ips.*   Cajal and de Castro 1933, 290
FORMULA: water 37.5, 40% formaldehyde 37.5, pyridine 25

11.1 Cajal *test.* **1933a** *ips.*   Cajal and de Castro 1933, 319
FORMULA: water 100, 40% formaldehyde 15, uranium nitrate 1

11.1 Cajal *test.* **1933b** *ips.*   Cajal and de Castro 1933, 343
FORMULA: water 65, pyridine 25, 40% formaldehyde 12

11.1 da Fano 1920a   11360, **40**:157
FORMULA: water 100, neutralized 40% formaldehyde 15, cobalt nitrate 1

11.1 da Fano 1920b   11454, **53**:1919
FORMULA: water 40, 40% formaldehyde 10, pyridine 50

11.1 Foot 1927   1887a, **4**:42
FORMULA: water 100, tannic acid, 0.15, ammonium bromide 3.5, 40% formaldehyde 5

11.1 Herrara 1932 *test.* **1933 Cajal and de Castro**   Cajal and de Castro 1933, 276
FORMULA: water 75, 40% formaldehyde 15, pyridine 2.5, acetone 2.5, ammonium oxalate 3

11.1 Kingsbury and Johannsen 1927   Kingsbury and Johannsen 1927, 83
FORMULA: water 15, 40% formaldehyde 100, uranium nitrate 0.15

11.1 Klatzo 1952   *Lab. Invest.*, **1**:346
FORMULA: water 90, 40% formaldehyde 10, potassium dichromate 5, chloral hydrate 3

11.1 Lobo 1937 *test.* **1948 Romeis**   Romeis 1948, 420
FORMULA: water 83, 40% formaldehyde 20, ammonium bromide 2.7

11.1 Merland 1935   4285a, **12**:290
FORMULA: water 100, 40% neutralized formaldehyde 10, cobalt nitrate 2

11.1 Noguchi 1913 *test.* **Schmorl 1928**   Schmorl 1928, 407
FORMULA: water 75, 40% formaldehyde 15, acetone 5, pyridine 5, ammonium bromide 3

11.1 Raileanu 1939   6630, **104**:285
FORMULA: water 90, 40% neutralized formaldehyde 10, ammonium bromide 6

11.1 del Río-Hortega 1925   *see* AMS 11.1 Strong 1903

11.1 del Río-Hortega *test*. **1933a Cajal and de Castro**   Cajal and de Castro 1933, 267
FORMULA: water 90, 40% formaldehyde 10, ferric alum 7

11.1 del Río-Hortega *test*. **1933b Cajal and de Castro**   Cajal and de Castro 1933, 269
FORMULA: water 90, 40% formaldehyde 10, ammonium bromide 2, ferric alum 7

11.1 Rodriguez *test*. **1933 Cajal and de Castro**   Cajal and de Castro 1933, 285
FORMULA: water 75, 40% formaldehyde 15, acetone 2.5, pyridine 2.5, potassium oxalate 3

11.1 Rojas 1917   21344, **15**:30
FORMULA: water 80, 40% formaldehyde 12, pyridine 20, manganese nitrate 1

11.1 Strong 1903   11135, **13**:296
FORMULA: water 90, 40% formaldehyde 10, ferric alum 6
NOTE: The formula of del Río-Hortega 1925 (3231, **25**:34) does not differ significantly.

AMS 12 ALCOHOL MIXTURES

12.1 FORMULAS

12.1 Balbuena 1922   21344, **20**:31
PREPARATION: Macerate cork crumbs in 70% alc. till a dark yellow-brown solution is obtained

12.1 Boule 1908   15063, **10**:15
FORMULA: 95% alc. 80, 40% formaldehyde 20, acetic acid 0.4, ammonia 0.04

12.1 Cajal 1910a   21344, **8**:1
FORMULA: abs. alc. 90, pyridine 10

12.1 Cajal 1910d   21344, **8**:1
FORMULA: 95% alc., 100, chloral hydrate 2

12.1 Cajal 1910e   21344, **8**:1
FORMULA: 95% alc. 100, nicotine 1

12.1 Cajal 1910f   21344, **8**:10
FORMULA: 95% alc. 80, glycerol 16, ammonia 0.8

12.1 Cajal 1910g   21344, **8**:11
FORMULA: 95% alc. 100, ethylamine 1

12.1 Cajal 1925 *test*. **1933** *ips*.   Cajal and de Castro 1933, 363
FORMULA: water 50, 95% alc. 50, ammonia 1

12.1 Cajal 1927 *test*. **1933 Cajal and de Castro**   Cajal and de Castro 1933, 188
FORMULA: 95% alc. 100, pyridine 40, chloral hydrate 4

12.1 Cajal 1929   21344, **26**:1
FORMULA: 70% alc. 100, ammonia 0.2

12.1 Foley 1939   763, **73**:465
FORMULA: 95% alc. 50, water 50, pyridine 15, ammonia 1, potassium dichromate 1.5

12.1 Humphreys 1939   608b, **15**:151
FORMULA: 95% alc. 90, 40% formaldehyde 5, acetic acid 5

12.1 Krajian 1933   623, **17**:127
FORMULA: 95% alc. 40, acetone 40, glycerol 20, formic acid 12, uranium nitrate 4

12.1 Steiner 1937   11284, **23**:315
FORMULA: abs. alc. 100, uranium nitrate 0.8, gum mastic 3

12.1 Steiner 1939   11284, **25**:204
FORMULA: abs. alc. 100, gum mastic 12, uranium nitrate 0.8

12.1 Steiner 1950   591b *Tech. Bull.*, **20**:489
FORMULA: abs. alc. 100, uranium nitrate 1, mastic 1

12.1 Wallart 1935   4285a, **12**:254
FORMULA: abs. alc. 30, pyridine 30, ether 30, ammonia 0.03

12.1 Weber 1944 *SW16—auct.*   4285a, **21**:45
FORMULA: isopropanol 45, dioxane 45, water 10, 40% formaldehyde 20, acetic acid 2, formic acid 2, chloral hydrate 5, cobalt nitrate 0.3
NOTE: The acids are added immediately before use.

13 OTHER MIXTURES

13.1 FORMULAS

13.1 Bolsi 1927 *test.* **1933 Cajal and de Castro**   Cajal and de Castro 1933, 274
FORMULA: water 80, glycerol 20, ammonia 0.3

13.1 Bolsi *test.* **1933 Cajal and de Castro**   Cajal and de Castro 1933, 261
FORMULA: water 60, acetone 20, pyridine 20, ammonia 4

13.1 Cajal 1907 *test.* **1933** *ips.*   Cajal and de Castro 1933, 290
FORMULA: 33% acrolein 10, water 90

13.1 Cajal and de Castro 1933   Cajal and de Castro 1933, 261
FORMULA: hydrogen peroxide (3%) 100, oxalic acid to sat.

13.1 David 1934   *see* ADS 12.1 David 1934

13.1 Fontana 1912   7176, **55**:1003
FORMULA: water 100, tannic acid 5, phenol 1

13.1 King 1937   1879, **38**:362
FORMULA: water 30, ammonia 30, pyridine 30

13.1 Löffler 1890   *see* DS 23.215 Löffler 1890 (sol. *A*)

13.1 del Río-Hortega 1918   21344, **15**:165
FORMULA: water 100, ammonium bromide 1, tannic acid 3

13.1 del Río-Hortega 1932 *test.* **1933 Cajal and de Castro**
                                                               Cajal and de Castro 1933, 263
FORMULA: water 30, ammonia 30, pyridine 30

13.1 Safford and Fleisher 1931   20540b, **6**:43
FORMULA: water 100, picric acid 0.25, tannic acid 5, ferrous sulfate 7.5

13.1 Tron 1924   2190, **13**
FORMULA: water 100, neoarsphenamine 0.7, acetic acid 0.4

13.1 Willard 1935   17510, **78**:475
FORMULA: water 40, 95% alc. 40, pyridine 20, chloral hydrate 2.5

13.1 Zettnow 1891   23684, **11**:689
FORMULA: water 115, tannic acid 5, antimony potassium tartrate 0.75
PREPARATION: Dissolve the acid in 100 water at 60°C.; add the tartrate dissolved in 15 water.

AMS 20 Solutions Used after Staining

20.0 GENERAL OBSERVATIONS

It is extraordinary how far the science of microtomy as it is seen in these formulas has lagged behind the photographic methods which it is supposed to resemble. (Whether this resemblance is justified has already been questioned.) Photographic developers are designed to reduce to metallic silver, particles of silver bromide which have been rendered unstable through the absorption of photon energy. Neither silver bromide nor light enters into the majority of metal staining reactions. The best that can be said of these organic reducing agents, therefore, is that they will under certain empirically established conditions reduce either to the metallic form, or in most cases to metallic oxides or proteinates, some unstable metallic complex which has formed on the surface of the cell which it is desired to demonstrate. None of the more recent photographic developing techniques appears to have been tried, and the majority of the formulas given below appear entirely barbaric to a practical photographer. No formula has been included in this section unless it is specifically recommended by the original author of one of the metal stains given above. Most of the more successful metal stains are reduced with the aid of formaldehyde, and it remains yet to be demonstrated clearly that any of these pseudophotographic developers are indeed an improvement over this simple reagent.

21 DEVELOPING SOLUTIONS

21.1 FORMULAS

21.1 Armuzzi and Stempel *test.* **1928 Schmorl**   Schmorl 1928, 406
FORMULA: water 100, gum arabic 12, hydroquinone 0.25

21.1 Ascoli 1911   3381, **25**:177
FORMULA: water 90, sodium sulfite, cryst. 10, amidol 0.5

21.1 Balbuena 1922   21344, **20**:31
FORMULA: *A.* digest 30 oil of amber with 70 of 70% alcohol 1 week, separate; *B.* 1% hydroquinone
NOTE: The original calls for *Tinctura succini* for solution *A.* This tincture is not in the Spanish Pharmacopaeia, the formula given above being from the Portuguese (*test.* Squire 1899 *Companion to the Pharmacopaeia,* p. 612). Langeron 1942, 627 uses *teinture alcoolique du succin (du Codex)* which is prepared (*test.* Squire, *loc. cit.*) by macerating 1 part powdered amber in 10 parts 80% alcohol. This would have a very much lower oil content.

21.1 Bauer 1944   608b, **29**:297
FORMULA: water 100, gallic acid 1.43, tannic acid 0.86, sodium acetate 2.86

21.1 Boccardi 1886 *test.* **Lee 1905**   Lee 1905, 252
FORMULA: water 80, formic acid 20, oxalic acid 0.3

21.1 Bodian 1936   763, **65**:89
FORMULA: water 100, sodium sulfite 5, hydroquinone 1

21.1 Boule 1908   15063, **10**:15
FORMULA: water 100, 40% formaldehyde 6, 95% alc. 15, hydroquinone 1

21.1 Cajal 1910a   21344, **8**:3
FORMULA: water 250, 40% formaldehyde 15, pyrogallol 2.5

21.1 Cajal 1910b   21344, **8**:3
FORMULA: water 250, 40% formaldehyde 15, hydroquinone 2.5
NOTE: Cajal (*loc. cit.*) sometimes substituted 5 ml. pyridine, and sometimes 1.25 Gms. sodium sulfite for the formaldehyde.

21.1 Cajal 1914   21344, **12**:127
FORMULA: water 100, hydroquinone 2, sodium sulfite, anhyd. 0.75, 40% formaldehyde 4
NOTE: Cajal and de Castro 1933, 202, refer this formula, without reference, to **Golgi 1908.**

21.1 Cajal 1921   21344, **19**:71
FORMULA: water 70, 40% formaldehyde 30, hydroquinone 0.3

21.1 Cajal 1925   21344, **23**:237
FORMULA: water 70, 40% formaldehyde 20, hydroquinone 0.3, acetone 15

21.1 Cajal 1929   21344, **26**:1
FORMULA: water 65, acetone 15, 40% formaldehyde 20, hydroquinone 0.3

21.1 Cajal *test.* **1933** *ips.*   Cajal and de Castro 1933, 320
FORMULA: water 100, 40% formaldehyde 7.5, sodium sulfite, anhydrous 0.25, hydro-
    quinone 1.5

21.1 Chor 1933   1879, **29**:344
FORMULA: water 95, 40% formaldehyde 5, pyrogallol 4

21.1 Cowdry 1912   10157, **29**:1
FORMULA: water 100, pyrogallol 1, 40% formaldehyde 5

21.1 Davenport 1930   1879, **24**:690
FORMULA: 95% alc. 100, 40% neutralized formaldehyde 2, pyrogallol 2, 50% dextrin 0.4

21.1 Davenport, McArthur, and Bruesch 1939   21540b, **14**:23
FORMULA: stock I. water 90, sodium sulfite 10; stock II. water 95, sodium bisulfite 5,
    diamminophenol hydrochloride 1
WORKING SOLUTION: stock I 100, stock II 20

21.1 Davenport, Windle, and Rhines 1947   Conn and Darrow 1947, I-C2:24
FORMULA: water 100, sodium sulfite dessic. 5, hydroquinone 1, potassium metaborate 0.5

21.1 Dieterle 1927   1879, **18**:73
FORMULA: water 60, acetone 12, hydroquinone 1.8, sodium sulfite 0.3, pyridine 12, 40%
    neutral formaldehyde 12, water, *q.s.* to bring volume to 25; 10% sol. gum mastic in
    abs. alc. add 10 just before use

21.1 van Ermengen *test.* **1942 Langeron**   Langeron 1942, 831
FORMULA: water 100, gallic acid 2, tannic acid 1, sodium acetate 4

21.1 van Ermengen 1894   23684, **15**:969
FORMULA: water 100, gallic acid 1.5, tannic acid 0.8, sodium acetate 2.9

21.1 Eyene and Sternberg *test.* **1916 Warthin**   4349, **6**:71
FORMULA: water 100, gelatin 3, gum arabic 15, silver nitrate 0.8, hydroquinone 0.75
PREPARATION: Dissolve each ingredient in part of the water. Mix in order given.

21.1 Farrier and Warthin 1930   623, **14**:394
STOCK SOLUTIONS: I. 5% gelatin, II. 2% silver nitrate, III. 5% hydroquinone
WORKING SOLUTION: melt 75 stock I at 45°C., add 15 stock II and then 5 stock III

21.1 Faulkner and Lillie 1945   20540b, **20**:81
FORMULA: water 96, acetate buffer (pH 3.6) 4, silver nitrate 0.3, hydroquinone 0.15,
    gelatin 4
PREPARATION: Dissolve ingredients separately in buffered water. Mix immediately
    before use.

21.1 Foley 1943   20540b, **18**:27
FORMULA: water 85, acetone 15, sodium sulfite, anhydrous 2, boric acid 1.4, hydro-
    quinone 0.3

21.1 Golgi 1908   *see* AMS 21.1 Cajal 1914 (note)

21.1 Gomori 1933   *see* MS 33.1 Gomori 1933, sol. *B*

21.1 Gooding and Stewart 1937   11977, **7**:596
FORMULA: water 95, 40% formaldehyde 5, pyrogallol 2

21.1 Gurdjian 1927   *see* AMS 21.1 Ranson 1914 (note)

21.1 Holmes 1942   11431, **54**:132
FORMULA: water 100, sodium sulfite, anhydr. 5, sodium bisulfite 2.5, p-diammino benzene
    hydrochloride 0.5

21.1 Heitzman *test.* **1938 Mallory**   Mallory 1938, 293
FORMULA: 5% gelatin 75, 2% silver nitrate 15, 1% hydroquinone 2.5

21.1 Hewer 1933   *see* AMS 21.1 Ranson 1914 (note)

21.1 Huber and Guild 1913   *see* AMS 21.1 Ranson 1914 (note)

21.1 Humphreys 1939   608b, **15**:151
FORMULA: water 100, hydroquinone 5, sodium sulfite 10

21.1 Jahnel 1917   *see* AMS 21.1 Hanson 1914 (note)

21.1 Jahnel *test.* **1933 Cajal and de Castro**   Cajal and de Castro 1933, 384
FORMULA: water 100, acetone 10, pyridine 10, pyrogallol 4

21.1 Kallius 1893   764, **2**:271
FORMULA: water 66, 95% alc. 34, hydroquinone 0.08, sodium sulfite 0.8, potassium
carbonate 1.6
NOTE: **Curreri 1908** (766, **32**:432) recommends gold toning after this.

21.1 Kingsbury and Johannsen 1927   Kingsbury and Johannsen 1927, 83
FORMULA: water 100, 40% formaldehyde 6, hydroquinone 2, magnesium sulfate "a
minute quantity"

21.1 Kolossow 1892   23632, **9**:38
PREPARATION: Mix 20 25% tannin with 20 25% pyrogallol. Filter. Add to filtrate 35
water, 15 95% alc. and 10 glycerol.

21.1 Krajian 1933   623, **17**:127
FORMULA: water 60, acetone 10, pyridine 10, 40% formaldehyde 10, hydroquinone 1.2,
sodium sulfite 0.25, sat. sol. gum mastic in 95% alcohol 10, V 21.1 Mayer 1884 0.05
NOTE: **Krajian 1935** (1829, **32**:764) is identical. **Krajian 1938** (1829, **38**:427) omits the
Mayer's albumen.

21.1 Kranz 1924   14674, 608
FORMULA: water 100, gum arabic 12.5, pyrogallol, 1

21.1 Krautz 1924 *test.* **1928 Schmorl**   Schmorl 1928, 405
FORMULA: water 100, gum arabic 8, pyrogallol 0.2

21.1 Lauda and Rezek 1928   22575, **269**:218
FORMULA: dissolve with heat 0.1 gelatin in 100 water. Cool. Add 3 hydroquinone

21.1 Levaditi 1905   6630, **8**:845
FORMULA: water 100, 40% formaldehyde 5, pyrogallol 3

21.1 Levaditi and Manouélian 1906   6630, **60**:134
FORMULA: water 90, acetone 10, pyrogallol 3.6

21.1 Levaditi *test.* **1916 Warthin**   4349, **6**:56
FORMULA: water 77, acetone 8, pyridine 15, pyrogallol 3

21.1 Liesegang 1911   11848, **3**:1
PREPARATION: To 50 of a 50% solution of gum arabic add 50 20% potassium hydrosulfide.
NOTE: The *potassium hydrosulfide* referred to is most easily prepared by passing H_2S into
20% KOH to saturation. The solution is very unstable.

21.1 Lobo 1937 *test.* **1948 Romeis**   Romeis 1948, 420
FORMULA: water 70, 40% formaldehyde 19, acetone 11, hydroquinone 0.3

21.1 MacFarland and Davenport 1941   20540b, **16**:53
FORMULA: water 100, oxalic acid 2, 40% formaldehyde 1

21.1 Noguchi 1913 *test.* **Schmorl 1928**   Schmorl 1928, 407
FORMULA: water 95, 40% formaldehyde 5, pyrogallol 4

21.1 Okada 1929   8542a, **7**:403
FORMULA: water 100, 40% formaldehyde 5, pyrogallol 2

21.1 Oliveira 1936a   22575, **298**:523
FORMULA: water 100, 40% neutralized formaldehyde 3, 0.01 uranium nitrate

21.1 Oliveira 1936b   22575, **298**:523
FORMULA: water 70, 40% formaldehyde 30, hydroquinone 0.3

21.1 Paton 1907   14246, **18**:576
FORMULA: water 80, hydroquinone 0.8, 40% formaldehyde 8

21.1 Podhradszky 1934   23632, **50**:285
FORMULA: water 95, 40% formaldehyde 5, pyrogallol 5

21.1 Pritchard *test.* **Böhm and Oppel 1907**   Böhm and Oppel 1907, 438
FORMULA: water 98, formic acid 1, amyl alc. 1

21.1 Ranson 1914   766, **46**:522
FORMULA: water 95, 40% formaldehyde 5, pyrogallol 4
NOTE: The formulas of **Gurdjian 1927** (11135, **43**:1), **Hewer 1933** (11025, **67**:350) **Huber and Guild 1913** (763, **7**:253) and **Jahnel 1917** (14370, 42) are essentially the same.

21.1 Rachmanov *test.* **1946 Roskin**   Roskin 1946, 257
STOCK SOLUTIONS: I. water 100, borax 0.8, sodium sulfite 4, II. water 100, p-aminophenol sulfate 0.4, hydroquinone 1, sodium sulfate (crystal) 0.8
WORKING SOLUTION: stock I 50, stock II 50.
NOTE: It might be presumed that the "sulfate" in II was a misprint for "sulfite," but the Russian words are quite distinct. Roskin does not cite the original source.

21.1 Rojas 1917   21344, **15**:30
FORMULA: water 80, 40% formaldehyde 5, sodium sulfite, anhydrous 0.25, hydroquinone 1
NOTE: Romeis 1948, 456 gives the third ingredient as *"sulphat."*

21.1 Romanes 1916   11025, **80**:205
FORMULA: water 100, sodium sulfite, crystal 10, pyrogallol 1, hydroquinone 1

21.1 Schultze *test.* **1948 Romeis**   Romeis 1948, 418
FORMULA: water 100, hydroquinone 2.5, 40% formaldehyde 5

21.1 Schültze and Stöhr *test.* **1933 Cajal**   Cajal 1933, 363
STOCK SOLUTION: water 100, hydroquinone 2.5, 40% formaldehyde 5
WORKING SOLUTION: stock 1, water 19

21.1 Shanklin 1951   Cowdry 1952, 270
FORMULA: water 90, 40% formaldehyde 10, pyridine 1.3

21.1 Stage 1936   20540b, **11**:155
FORMULA: water 70, neutralized formaldehyde 30, hydroquinone 0.3

21.1 Steiner 1937   11284, **23**:315
FORMULA: water 100, hydroquinone 5, 6% gum mastic in abs. alc. 0.2

21.1 Steiner 1939   11284, **25**:204
FORMULA: water 100, hydroquinone 5, 12.5% gum mastic in abs. alc. 0.5

21.1 Steiner and Steiner 1944   11284, **29**:868
STOCK SOLUTIONS: I. 0.6% hydroquinone, II. 2.5% gum mastic in abs. alc. III. Dissolve, with boiling, 0.2 silver nitrate and 0.165 sodium potassium tartrate in 100 water. Cool, filter.
WORKING SOLUTION: stock I 60, stock II 20, stock III 20

21.1 Ungewitter 1943   20540b, **18**:183
FORMULA: water 100, p-methylaminophenol sulfate 0.2, sodium sulfite (dessic.) 10, hydroquinone 0.5, sodium borate 0.1

21.1 Uyama 1926   8542a, **4**:389
FORMULA: water 100, 40% formaldehyde 12.5, pyrogallol 1.75

21.1 Warthin-Starry 1929 *test.* **1942 Langeron**   Langeron 1942, 630
STOCK SOLUTIONS: I. 10% gelatin; II. 10% starch; III. 2.5% hydroquinone in 40% acetone; IV. 2% silver nitrate
PREPARATION: Prepare 50 ml. each I and II, dissolving the first with warm and the second with boiling. Mix. Take 6 ml. III and add to mixture.
WORKING SOLUTION: immediately before use mix 5 parts of the above mixture with 1 part stock IV

21.1 Weber 1944   4285a, **21**:45
FORMULA: water 100, 40% formaldehyde 5, hydroquinone 2, sodium citrate 1

21.1 Wilder 1935   608b, **11**:817
FORMULA: water 100, 40% neutralized formaldehyde 0.5, uranium nitrate 0.015

21.1 Willard 1935   17510, **87**:475
FORMULA: water 90, 40% neutralized formaldehyde 10, hydroquinone 1

21.1 Yamanoto 1909   23681, **20**:153
FORMULA: water 100, pyrogallol 2, tannic acid 1

22 TONING OR METAL EXCHANGE SOLUTIONS

Toning depends for its value on the fact that a solution of gold will replace metallic silver, or many silver compounds, in the solid state. The principle use is either to render more apparent weakly stained materials, or to improve the keeping qualities of the preparations on the ground that gold is less subject to natural deterioration than is silver. The simple solutions of gold chloride usually employed are listed with the staining techniques in Chapter 22.

22.1 FORMULAS

22.1 Balbuena 1922   21344, **20**:31
FORMULA: water 100, sodium borate 1, gold chloride 0.1

22.1 Bodian 1936   763, **65**:89
FORMULA: water 100, gold chloride 1, acetic acid 0.1

22.1 Cajal 1910   21344, **8**:1
FORMULA: water 100, ammonium thiocyanate 3, sodium thiosulfate 3, 1% gold chloride 0.2

22.1 Cajal 1921   21344, **19**:71
FORMULA: water 100, ferric alum 4, oxalic acid 1

22.1 Cajal *test.* **1948 Lillie**   Lillie 1948, 101
FORMULA: water 100, ammonium thiocyanate 3, sodium thiosulfate 3, gold chloride 0.01

22.1 Cajal and de Castro 1933   *see* AMS 24.1 Cajal and de Castro 1933

22.1 Foot 1927   1887a, **4**:43
FORMULA: water 100, gold chloride 0.2, mercuric chloride 0.5

22.1 Golgi 1908 *test.* **1933 Cajal and de Castro**   Cajal and de Castro 1933, 202
STOCK SOLUTIONS: I. water 100, sodium thiosulfate 3, ammonium thiocyanate 3; II. 1% gold chloride
WORKING SOLUTION: stock I. 100; stock II. 1.5

22.1 Lancelin, Séguy, and Dubreuil 1926   6630, **94**:557
FORMULA: 1% sodium thiosulfate 30, 1% ammonium thiocyanate 30, 1% gold chloride 30

22.1 Sand 1910   6593, **12**:128
FORMULA: water 85, 2% solution ammonium thiocyanate 15, 2% gold chloride 3

22.1 Simard and Campenhout 763, **53**:143

STOCK SOLUTIONS: I. 6% ammonium thiocyanate; II. 6% sodium thiosulfate; III. 2% gold chloride

WORKING SOLUTION: stock I. 50; stock II. 50; stock III. just enough to produce ppt.

23 DIFFERENTIATING SOLUTIONS

23.1 FORMULAS

23.1 Golgi 1908 *test.* **1933 Cajal and de Castro**   Cajal and de Castro 1933, 203

FORMULA: water 100, sulfuric acid 0.1, potassium permanganate 0.05

24 FIXING SOLUTIONS

Solutions of sodium thiosulfate are employed to "fix" photographic images because both silver chloride and silver bromide are readily dissolved by them, whereas metallic silver is soluble only with difficulty. While it is doubtful how far silver bromide enters into any metal staining reaction, it is inevitable that when tissues are exposed to solutions of silver salts a certain amount of silver chloride is formed. As this substance is unstable in the presence of light, it seems reasonable that it should be removed either by simple thiosulfate or by one of the solutions given below. Care must be exercised, however, not to remove the silver from fine structures by prolonged exposure to sodium thiosulfate. Most of the formulas given are combined toning and fixing solutions.

24.1 FORMULAS

24.1 Bolsi 1927 *test.* **1933 Cajal and de Castro**   Cajal and de Castro 1933, 274

FORMULA: water 95, 40% formaldehyde 5, gum arabic 0.05

24.1 Cajal 1913   21344, **11**:255

FORMULA: water 70, sodium thiosulfate 5, 95% alc. 30, sodium metabisulfite 10

NOTE: The original formula calls for "liquid sodium bisulfite." The quantity of dry salt above presumes that Cajal was employing the common technical solution of 38° Be which contains approximately 50% by weight of the dry salt. To restore the original formula 20 Gms. of solution should be substituted.

24.1 Cajal 1925   *see* MS 31.1 Cajal 1925b

24.1 Cajal and de Castro 1933   Cajal and de Castro 1933, 130

FORMULA: water 100, sodium thiosulfate 25, ammonium thiocyanate 2, potassium alum 1, lead acetate 1, gold chloride 0.2

24.1 Golgi *test.* **1937 Gatenby and Painter**   Gatenby and Painter 1937, 513

STOCK SOLUTION: water 100, sodium thiosulfate 15.5, potassium alum 2, ammonium thiocyanate 1, sodium chloride 4. Let stand 1 week. Filter.

WORKING SOLUTION: "used working solution" 40, stock 50, 1% gold chloride 7

24.1 Raileanu 1930   6630, **104**:285

FORMULA: water 62, 95% alc. 38, sodium thiosulfate 1.2

25

Solvents and Oils

S 00 General Observations

Solvents and oils are used in microscopical technique principally for the purpose of preparing objects for mounting whole in resinous media (Chapter 6) or for section cutting after embedding in one of the ways discussed in Chapters 12 through 15. At one time these reagents and mixtures of them could be clearly divided into two groups: those intended for the removal of water (*dehydrating agents*) and those intended for the removal of alcohol (*clearing agents*). These two groups are recorded under S 10 and S 20 below. For the past decade, however, a number of reagents have been recommended which may be used either for dehydration or clearing. These, which are given under S 30 below, are referred to as *universal solvents* for the reason that they are miscible with water and with resinous mounting media and with wax embedding media.

S 10 Dehydrating Agents

The function of a dehydrating agent as the name indicates is to extract water from the tissues in order that some other solvent not miscible with water may be substituted. Ethanol is the solvent most commonly used in making microscope slides and is referred to throughout the present work either as *abs. alc.* or 95% *alc.*, as the case may be. Where *alc.* or *alcohol* is referred to without qualification the ordinary 95% alcohol (190 proof alcohol) of commerce is intended.

Most good dehydrating agents are naturally hygroscopic and should therefore always be stored over some dehydrating agent which will remove from them the water that they absorb from the air. Weight for weight there is no dehydrating agent as efficient as anhydrous sodium sulfate, but the solubility of this in some dehydrating reagents renders it dangerous to use. The only all-round dehydrating agent which can be recommended is calcium sulfate, commercially available in suitable form as *Drierite*.

It is not usual to include glycerol as a dehydrating agent even though it will, in point of fact, readily extract water from tissues. The advantage of glycerol is that it permits the transfer of material from water to absolute alcohol without the danger of collapse. Objects may be placed in dilute glycerol, the glycerol concentrated by evaporation, and the most delicate material then transferred to absolute alcohol. This reverses the direction of osmotic pressure so that the pressure tends to keep the object expanded.

S 11 PHYSICAL PROPERTIES OF DEHYDRATING AGENTS

Name	Other names	Boiling point °C	Evaporation rate (ethanol = 100)	Suitability for use with stained material	Solvent action on Canada balsam	Solvent action on nitro-cellulose
Acetone	..	56	340	+++	+++	++
Allyl alc.	..	97.1	?	++	?	0
Diethylene glycol	..	245	<1	?	+++	++
Dipropylene glycol	..	231.8	<1	+	++	+++
Ethanol	95% alc., abs. alc.	78.3	100	+++	+++	*
Ethylene glycol monomethyl ether	methyl cellosolve	124.5	14	+	+++	++
Glycerol	..	..	..	+	0	0
Isopropanol	Isopropyl alc., propanol 2	82.3	88	+++	?	0
Methanol	methyl alc., wood alc.	64.5	207	+++	+++	++
Propylene glycol	..	188.2	<1	++	+	0
Triethylene glycol	..	287	<1	+	+	+++

* Alcohol is not a solvent for nitro-cellulose but is an excellent cosolvent with ether. A 50-50 mixture is usually employed.

S 20 Clearing Agents

The phrase *clearing agent*, as an alternative to the more correct *de-alcoholization agent*, is used because the high refractive index usually renders the object more or less transparent. Clearing agents are required either before resinous mounting media or before wax embedding media. It is recommended in general that essential oils be used for preparing wholemounts and that the synthetic clearing agents be used before embedding.

S 21 ESSENTIAL OILS

Essential oils are the natural oils collected from the leaves, stems, flowers, and fruits of plants. The table below presents the important characteristics of those commonly employed in microscopical technique. The column showing the strength of alcohol from which specimens may be transferred to the oil in question supposes the oil to be anhydrous. Most essential oils, as they occur in commerce, are water-saturated and this water must be removed with some dehydrating agent before they are used. It must be remembered that "miscibility with Canada balsam," shown in the seventh column, does not of necessity mean that these oils are miscible with any other resin used for mounting; and, particularly, when synthetic mounting media are employed, preliminary tests should always be made. The column showing the "solubility of nitrocellulose in" each oil should be consulted before clearing nitrocellulose-sections, to make sure that the support will not be dissolved while the specimen is cleared.

21 PHYSICAL PROPERTIES ESSENTIAL OILS

Name	Other names	Refractive index	Lowest-strength alcohol from which objects may be transferred	Suitability for use with stained materials	Miscibility with molten paraffin	Miscibility with Canada balsam	Solubility of nitrocellulose in
Oil of bay	Oil of myrcia	1.51	80%	?	?	∞	0
Oil of bergamot	..	1.46	90%	++	∞	∞	+
Oil of cajeput	..	1.47	80%	+++	∞	∞	0
Oil of caraway	..	1.50	90%	+	∞	∞	..
Oil of cedar wood	..	1.50	95%	+++	∞	∞	0
Oil of chenopodium	Oil of American wormseed	1.47	80%	+	∞	∞	0
Oil of cinnamon	Oil of cassia	1.6	95%	+	∞	∞	0
Oil of citronella	..	1.47	90%	++	∞	∞	0
Oil of clove	..	1.53	75%	+++	∞	∞	++
Oil of Cretan origanum	Oil of Cretan thyme	?	90%	++	∞	∞	
Oil of eucalyptus	..	1.46	80%	++	∞	∞	0
Oil of juniper	..	1.48	100%	++	+	∞	0
Oil of lavender	..	1.46	80%	++	∞	∞	0
Oil of lemon	..	1.47	95%	+	∞	∞	0
Oil of lilac	..	1.48	90%	+++	?	+++	0
Oil of marjoram	Oil of origanum (*in error*)	?	90%	++	∞	∞	0
Oil of origanum	Oil of wild marjorum	?	90%	++	∞	∞	0
Oil of thyme	Oil of origanum (*in error*)	1.50	90%	+++	∞	∞	0
Oil of turpentine	Turpentine, Gum turpentine	1.47	95%	0	∞	∞	0
Oil of white cedar	Oil of thuja	?	75%	++	∞	∞	0
Oil of wintergreen	Methyl salicylate	1.54	100%	+++	∞	∞	0

S 22 SYNTHETIC CLEARING AGENTS

These materials are more usually employed before embedding either in wax or in nitrocellulose, and data is, therefore, not available as to the lowest strength of alcohol from which the transfer can be made, since it is customary to dehydrate completely before either of these processes. A column has been included, however, which shows the solubility of water in these reagents (*not* the solubility of these reagents in water) which may serve as an indication of their sensitivity to imperfect dehydration. If they are to be used to clear objects before making whole-mounts in resinous media, it must be remembered that the miscibility of these solvents with Canada balsam is not of necessity the same as their miscibility with any other resin used for the mounting.

22 PHYSICAL PROPERTIES OF SYNTHETIC CLEARING AGENTS

Name	Other names	Refractive index	Boiling point	Evaporation rate (ethanol = 100)	Solubility of water in	Suitability for use with stained materials	Miscibility with molten paraffin	Miscibility with Canada balsam	Solubility of nitrocellulose in
Amyl acetate	..		141	?	2%	0	++	∞	∞
Aniline	aniline oil	1.59	184	?	12%	0	∞	++	0
Benzene	benzol	1.50	80	185	0.06%	+++	∞	+++	0
Butyl chloride	..	1.40	78.6	..	0.08%	?	+++	∞	0
Carbon disulfide	..	1.63	46.3	?	?	++	∞	∞	0
Carbon tetrachloride	..	1.46	76.7	?	>0.01%	+++	∞	∞	0
Chloroform	..	1.45	61.5	?	?	+++	∞	∞	0
Creosote, wood	Beechwood creosote	?	200+	?	..	+	∞	∞	0
Dichlorethyl ether	..	?	178.5	?	0.28%	++	+++	+++	*
Ethyl acetate	..	1.44	77.1	180	3.3%	..	0	+++	+++
Ethyl benzoate	..	1.51	212	?	>0.01%	+++	∞	∞	0
Ethylene dichloride	..	?	85.6	?	0.15%	++	∞	∞	*
Ethylene glycol monoethyl ether acetate	cellosolve acetate	?	156.4	6	6.5	?	?	+++	+++
Ethyl ether	ether, sulfuric ether	1.30	34.6	970	1.3	+++	0	∞	*
2-Heptanol	methyl amyl carbinol	1.42	162	?	5.2%	+	∞	∞	0
Hexanol	amyl carbinol	1.47	157.2	?	7.2%	+	∞	∞	0
Isopropyl acetate	..	?	88.4	150	1.8%	0	∞	∞	0
Methyl benzoate	oil of niobe	1.52	199	?	>0.01%	+++	∞	∞	0

22 PHYSICAL PROPERTIES OF SYNTHETIC CLEARING AGENTS—
(Continued)

Name	Other names	Refractive index	Boiling point	Evaporation rate (ethanol = 100)	Solubility of water in	Suitability for use with stained materials	Miscibility with molten paraffin	Miscibility with Canada balsam	Solubility of nitrocellulose in
Methyl salicylate	oil of wintergreen	1.54	222	..	>0.01%	+++	∞	∞	0
Pheynl salicylate	Salol	..	173	..	>0.1%	++	∞	∞	0
Pinene	..	1.47	155	..	>1%	+	∞	∞	0
Terpineol	..	1.48	219.8	>0.1	5%	+++	?	+++	0
Toluene	toluol	1.50	110.6	70	0.05%	+++	∞	∞	0
Xylene	xylol	1.50	138	19	>0.01%	++	∞	∞	0

* These materials are not in themselves solvents of nitrocellulose but are excellent cosolvents when mixed with ethanol. A 50-50 mixture of the solvent with ethanol is usually employed.

S 30 Universal Solvents

These materials are coming more and more into favor as a means of avoiding the use of two solutions, either before mounting in resinous media or embedding in wax. Though they are undoubtedly suitable for routine procedures, the writer prefers not to employ them for delicate objects, particularly those containing cavities which may become distorted through heavy diffusion currents and osmotic differences. The danger in the use of these materials lies both in the original transfer from water into them and in the transfer from them to paraffin. Unless time is the essence of the technique employed, it is recommended that dehydration be conducted with mixtures of these solvents with water and that the transfer to wax be through graded mixtures of solvent with wax.

31 PHYSICAL PROPERTIES OF UNIVERSAL SOLVENTS

Name	Other names	Refractive index	Boiling point °C.	Evaporation rate (ethanol = 100)	Solubility of water in	Suitability for use with stained materials	Miscibility with molten paraffin	Miscibility with Canada balsam	Solubility of nitrocellulose in
Acetic acid	..	1.37	118	?	∞	0	0	+++	..
Butanol	n-butyl alc., propyl carbinol	1.34	117.7	?	20%	++	∞	∞	*
Cresol	..	..	180–200	..	50%	0	∞	∞	0
Diacetone alcohol	diacetone	1.30	169	4	∞	?	0	∞	++
Diethylene dioxide	dioxane	1.42	101.5	?	∞	+++	∞	∞	*
Diethylene glycol monobutyl ether	butyl carbitol	?	230.4	<0.1	∞	+	∞	∞	+++

31 PHYSICAL PROPERTIES OF UNIVERSAL SOLVENTS—(*Continued*)

Name	Other names	Refractive index	Boiling point °C.	Evaporation rate (ethanol = 100)	Solubility of water in	Suitability for use with stained materials	Miscibility with molten paraffin	Miscibility with Canada balsam	Solubility of nitrocellulose in
Diethylene glycol monoethyl ether	carbitol	?	201.9	<0.1	∞	++	∞	∞	+++
Diethylene glycol monoethyl ether acetate	carbitol acetate	?	217.7	<0.1	∞	+	∞]	+++	+++
Dimethoxytetra ethylene glycol	..		276	?	∞	+	∞	∞	0
Diethylene glycol monomethyl ether	methyl carbitol	?	194.2	<0.1	∞	++	∞	∞	+++
Ethylene glycol monobutyl ether	butyl cellosolve	?	171.2	0.2	∞	++	∞	∞	+++
Ethylene glycol monoethyl ether	cellosolve	..	135.1	9	∞	+++	∞	∞	+++]
Ethylene glycol monomethyl ether acetate	methyl cellosolve acetate	?	144.5	11	∞	?	?	+++	++
Phenol	carbolic acid	1.54	182	..	∞	0	∞	∞	0
Triethylene glycol methyl ether acetate	methoxytriglycol acetate	?	244	>0.1	∞	?	∞	+++	++
Triethyl phosphate	..	..	21.5	>0.1	∞	?	∞	∞	0

* These materials are not in themselves solvents of nitrocellulose but are excellent cosolvents when mixed with ethanol. A 50-50 mixture of the solvent with ethanol is usually employed.

S 40 Recommended Mixtures

The majority of the mixtures given below were designed to produce materials having properties not available in solvents which could have been secured in the days when the mixtures were developed. Thus many of them consist of mixtures of phenol with some clearing agent notoriously sensitive to water. Phenol is an excellent coupler and permits xylene to be used with, say, 70% alcohol. These mixtures are included in the present place only because they are widely recommended in the literature. The modern worker would be well advised to seek in the tables given above some pure solvent having characteristics of the mixtures given below, and to substitute this pure solvent for the mixture which he had intended to use.

41.1 FORMULAS

41.1 Amann 1899a   23632, **16**:38
FORMULA: chloral hydrate 50, p-chlorphenol 50

41.1 Amann 1899b   23632, **16**:38
FORMULA: chloral hydrate 60, phenol 30

41.1 Apáthy *test.* **Guyer 1930** *cit.* **Kornhauser**   Guyer 1930, 65
FORMULA: chloroform 30, origanum oil 30, cedar oil 30, abs. alc. 7.5, phenol 7.5
RECOMMENDED FOR: clearing celloidin blocks prior to double embedding.

41.1 Apáthy *test.* **1942 Langeron**   Langeron 1942, 438
FORMULA: chloroform 32, oil of thyme 16, oil of cedar 32, alcohol 8, phenol 8

41.1 Cole 1903   Cross and Cole 1903, 193
FORMULA: phenol 100, glycerol 3
RECOMMENDED FOR: clearing arthropod material before mounting in glycerol.

41.1 Cole 1947   20540b, **22**:103
FORMULA: xylene 60, toluene 12, beechwood 12, aniline 12

41.1 Dunham *test.* **1937 Gatenby and Cowdry**   Gatenby and Cowdry 1937, 108
FORMULA: white oil of thyme 75, clove oil 25
RECOMMENDED FOR: clearing celloidin sections.

41.1 Eycleshymer *test.* **1915 Chamberlain**   Chamberlain 1915, 36
FORMULA: cedar oil 30, bergamot 30, phenol 30

41.1 Gage 1890   21400a, **12**:120
FORMULA: turpentine 60, phenol 40, 95% alc. *q. s.* to complete solution

41.1 Gage 1896a   Gage 1896, 176
FORMULA: xylene 75, castor oil 25
RECOMMENDED FOR: clearing and hardening nitrocellulose blocks.

41.1 Gage 1896b   Gage 1896, 176
FORMULA: turpentine 70, phenol 30

41.1 Gatenby and Painter 1937   Gatenby and Cowdry 1937, 108
FORMULA: creosote 40, bergamot oil 30, origanum oil 10, xylene 20
RECOMMENDED FOR: clearing celloidin sections.

41.1 Gothard *test.* **1929 Anderson**   Anderson 1929, 128
FORMULA: creosote 50, cajuput 40, xylene 50, abs. alc. 160

41.1 Maxwell 1938   20540b, **13**:93
FORMULA: oil of cedar 30, oil of thyme 40, xylene 15, abs. alc. 15

41.1 Minot *test.* **1928 Schmorl**   Schmorl 1928, 162
FORMULA: oil of thyme 80, oil of cloves 16

41.1 del Río-Hortega *test.* **1938 Mallory**   Mallory 1938, 249
FORMULA: xylene 80, phenol 10, creosote 10

41.1 Weigert 1891   7276, **17**:1184
FORMULA: xylene 35, aniline 65

41.1 Weigert *test.* **1938 Mallory**   *carbol-xylol—compl. script*

Mallory 1938, 98

FORMULA: xylene 75, phenol 25

41.1 Zirkle 1930   19938, **71**:103

REAGENTS REQUIRED: *A.* 5% alc.; *B.* 11% alc.; *C.* 18% alc.; *D.* 30% alc.; *E.* 45% alc. 90, n-butanol 10; *F.* 62% alc. 80, n-butanol 20; *G.* 77% alc. 65, n-butanol 35; *H.* 90% alc. 45, n-butanol 55; *I.* abs. alc. 25, n-butanol 75; *J.* n-butanol

METHOD: [water] → *A*, 1–5 hrs. → *B*, 1–5 hrs. → *C*, 1–5 hrs. → *D*, 1–5 hrs. → *E*, 1–5 hrs. → *F*, 12 hrs. → *G*, 1 hr. → *H*, 1 hr. → *I*, 1 hr. → *J*, several changes if necessary, till dehydration complete → [paraffin]

NOTE: This is the well-known "Zirkle's butyl alcohol schedule for plant tissues." It is equally applicable to animal tissues.

26

Mounting Media

M 00 Generalities

A mountant is a material in which an object may be permanently preserved for microscopical examination and which has inherent in it the property of holding the coverslip in place. There is a tendency to confuse mountants with preservative media, which are dealt with in Chapter 17. A preservative is a material in which an object may be permanently preserved but which does not have in it the inherent property of holding the coverslip in place, and which must, therefore, be sealed with cement or by some other method.

Mountants may be divided into three groups according to the treatment which the object must receive before mounting. The first group (M 10 below) contains those mountants which are miscible with water, and to which, therefore, the object may be directly transferred either from water or from glycerol. The second class (M 20 below) comprises those mountants which are miscible with alcohol and to which objects may therefore be transferred after dehydration but without having passed through a clearing agent. The third class of mountants (M 30 below) are the conventional resins and

balsams to which objects can be transferred only after they have been dehydrated and cleared in the usual
manner.

M 10 Mountants Miscible with Water

This section may be divided into three
groups. M 11 contains conventional gum
arabic media (of which Farrants' is the
type) to which objects may be transferred either directly or from water. These
media should be far more widely used
than is commonly the case, for a great
deal of time is wasted in dehydrating and
in transferring to balsam objects which were
better mounted in gum arabic. The second
group (M 12) contains glycerol jellies
which are widely used by botanists and to
a lesser extent by zoologists for the preparation of Crustacea. These media have the
disadvantage that they must be melted
before use and are, therefore, not nearly
as simple to use as the gum arabic media.
The third group, M 13, which will probably become more numerous as time goes
on, employs water-thickening agents other
than gum arabic or gelatin. Any one of
these three groups may be mixed with
stains for special purposes and the best
known media of this type are those of
Zirkle, some of which will be found in each
of the three sections.

11 GUM ARABIC MEDIA

11.1 FORMULAS

11.1 Allen *test.* **1937 Gatenby and Cowdry**   Gatenby and Cowdry 1937, 221
FORMULA: water 45, glycerol 11, 40% formaldehyde 4.5, gum arabic 45
PREPARATION: Dissolve gum arabic in water. Mix formaldehyde in the glycerin and add
slowly, with constant stirring, to gum.

11.1 André *test.* **1942 Langeron**   Langeron 1942, 930
FORMULA: water 50, glycerol 20, gum arabic 30, chloral hydrate 200
PREPARATION: Dissolve gum arabic in water. Mix glycerol in gum and add chloral
hydrate.

11.1 Apáthy 1892   23632, **89**:1065
FORMULA: water 30, gum arabic 30, levulose 30
PREPARATION: Dissolve gum arabic in water. Add levulose to solution.
NOTE: Much grief in the prevention of bubbles may be avoided by reducing the water to
20 and using commercial levulose syrup in place of the dry sugar.

11.1 Berlese *test.* **1929 Imms**   4184, **20**:165
FORMULA: water 10, acetic acid 3, dextrose syrup 5, gum arabic 8, chloral hydrate 75
PREPARATION: Dissolve the acid in the water with the syrup and gum arabic. Add
chloral hydrate to the solution.
NOTE: **Swan 1936** (4184, **27**:389) states that Berlese first disclosed the formula to
Davidson in 1919, who communicated it to Lee by whom it was published in 1921.
Doetschman 1944 (21400a, **63**:175) uses three times as much water in his formula for
"Berlese."

11.1 Brun 1889   *see* P 12.3 Brun 1889

11.1 Chevalier 1882   Chevalier 1882, 319
FORMULA: water 60, gum arabic 20, glycerol 20

11.1 Davies *circ.* **1865**   Davies, 82
FORMULA: water 30, gum arabic 30, glycerol 30, arsenic trioxide 0.1

11.1 Doetschman 1944   21400a, **63**:175
FORMULA: water 35, glycerol 20, dextrose syrup 20, gum arabic 20, chloral hydrate 20,
sat. aq. sol. magenta 0.3

11.1 Doetschman 1944   *see also* M 11.1 Berlese (note)

11.1 Ewig *test.* **1944 Doetschman**   21400a, **63**:175
FORMULA: water 35, glycerol 12, dextrose syrup 3, gum arabic 20, chloral hydrate 30

11.1 Fabre-Domergue 1889   *see* P 12.3 Fabre-Domergue 1889

11.1 Farrants *test.* **1880 Beale**   Beale 1880, 68
FORMULA: water 40, glycerol 20, gum arabic 40
NOTE: This mixture requires a preservative. Arsenic, camphor, and phenol have all been recommended. If only dirty gum arabic is available the mixture may be filtered through glass wool. The author's name is almost always misspelled "Farrant."

11.1 Faure 1910   979, **8**:25
FORMULA: water 50, chloral hydrate 50, gum arabic 30, glycerol 20

11.1 Gater 1929   4184, **19**:367
FORMULA: water 10, acetic acid 2.7, gum arabic 8, chloral hydrate 74, glucose syrup 5, cocaine hydrochloride 0.3

11.1 Gerlach 1885   *see* P 12.3 Gerlach 1885

11.1 Highman 1946   1789a, **41**:559
FORMULA: water 50, gum arabic 25, sucrose 25, potassium acetate 25

11.1 Hogg 1883   Hogg 1883, 237
FORMULA: water 75, gum arabic 25, phenol 5
PREPARATION: Dissolve gum arabic in 25 water. Dissolve phenol in 50 water and mix with gum.

11.1 Hoyer 1882   2981, **2**:23
FORMULA: water 50, gum arabic 50, chloral hydrate 2
PREPARATION: Use water and chloral hydrate to dissolve gum.

11.1 Landau 1940   4285a, **17**:65
FORMULA: water 30, gum arabic 30, dextrose 30, glucose 5

11.1 Langerhaus 1879   23833, **2**:575
FORMULA: water 20, glycerol 25, gum arabic 60, phenol 1
PREPARATION: Dissolve gum in 20 water and filter. Add glycerol and phenol to filtrate.

11.1 Lieb 1947   *Abopon mountant—auct.*   591b, **17**:413
This involves a proprietary product of secret composition and cannot, therefore, be further noticed.

11.1 Lillie and Ashburn 1943   1789a, **36**:432
FORMULA: water 100, gum arabic 50, sucrose 50, thymol 0.1

11.1 Marshall 1937   11977, **7**:565
FORMULA: water 50, gum arabic 0.5, gum tragacanth 1.5, P 12.2 Archibald and Marshall 1931 50
PREPARATION: Dissolve gum arabic in water with gum tragacanth with boiling. Cool. Mix P 12.2 Archibald and Marshall 1931 with gums. Filter.

11.1 Martin 1872   Martin 1872, 169
FORMULA: water 50, gum arabic 50, glycerol 25, camphor 0.2

11.1 Morrison 1942   *Turtox News*, **20**:157
FORMULA: water 50, glycerol 20, acetic acid 3, gum arabic 40, chloral hydrate 50

11.1 Robin 1871a   Robin 1871, 372
FORMULA: water 45, gum arabic 15, glycerol 30

11.1 Robin 1871b   Robin 1871, 372
FORMULA: water 100, gum arabic 50, glycerol 50

11.1 Robin 1871c   Robin 1871, 372
FORMULA: water 60, gum arabic 20, glycerol 20

11.1 Schweitzer 1942 *test.* **1946 Roskin**   Roskin 1946, 200
FORMULA: water 65, gum arabic 20, chloral hydrate 8, glycerol 7

11.1 Semmens 1938a   *CS12—auct.*   *Microscope,* **2**:120
FORMULA: water 40, gum arabic 20, DS 11.23 Belling 1921

11.1 Semmens 1938b   *CS13—auct.*   *Microscope,* **2**:120
FORMULA: water 45, gum arabic 10, chloral hydrate 25, acetic acid 37.5, carmine 0.5
PREPARATION: Dissolve the chloral hydrate in 25 acetic acid with 25 water, raise to
   boiling, stir in carmine, cool, and filter. Dissolve the gum in 20 water and 12.5 acetic
   acid. Mix the solutions.

11.1 Swan 1936   4184, **27**:389
FORMULA: water 20, gum arabic 15, chloral hydrate 60, glucose syrup 10, acetic acid 5

11.1 Womersley 1943   21654, **67**:181
FORMULA: water 100, 95% alc. 50, gum arabic (powder) 40, phenol 50, chloral hydrate
   50, glucose syrup 10, lactic acid 20
PREPARATION: Mix alc. and powdered gum to a smooth paste. Flood 100 water onto
   paste. Stir rapidly. Leave 2 hours, then filter. Evaporate till volume 100. Grind phenol
   and chloral hydrate in a mortar till solution complete. Add to solution. Add syrup
   and lactic acid to mixture.

11.1 Zirkle 1940   20540b, **15**:144
FORMULA: water 65, formic acid 41, gum arabic 10, sorbitol 10, ferric nitrate 0.5, carmine
   0.5
PREPARATION: Dissolve the gum in the solvents. Incorporate the iron and then the dye.
NOTE: See also M 12.1, M 13.1 Zirkle 1940.

12 GELATIN MEDIA

It is presumed, in all the formulas that follow, that a gelatin is employed which will
give a crystal-clear solution in water. Such purified gelatins are today available on the
market for bacteriological use. If commercial gelatin is being used, it is necessary that
it should first be clarified, and directions for doing this are given in all the older formulas. Soak the gelatin overnight, drain it carefully, and then melt it on a water bath
at about 40°C. Then add, for each 100 milliliters of the fluid so produced, the whites of
two fresh eggs. These are mixed thoroughly with the molten gelatin and the temperature
of the water bath is then raised to boiling and left until the whole of the egg white is
coagulated. The medium must not be stirred during this time. The egg white coagulates
in large lumps, which may readily be strained out through cheesecloth, and which retain,
attached to them, all the fine particles which cause cloudiness of the gelatin.

12.1 FORMULAS

12.1 Baker 1944   Baker 1944, 173
FORMULA: water 65, gelatin 5, glycerol 35, cresol 0.25
PREPARATION: Soak gelatin in 25 water for 1 hour, then melt at 60°C. Mix glycerol in 40
   water with cresol, then heat to 60°C. and mix with gelatin.

12.1 Beale 1880   Beale 1880, 67
FORMULA: clarified gelatin 50, glycerol 50

12.1 Brandt 1880   23632, **2**:69
FORMULA: gelatin 40, glycerol 60, phenol 0.5
PREPARATION: Soak gelatin in water for 24 hours. Drain and melt. Mix glycerol and phenol
   with molten gelatin. Clarify *s.a.*

12.1 Bruere and Kaufmann 1907   4349, **2**:11
FORMULA: gelatin about 25, glycerol about 50, water *q.s.*, 40% formaldehyde 0.1
PREPARATION: Soak the gelatin overnight. Drain, melt, and add an equal volume of
   glycerol. Clarify *s.a.*, filter, and add formaldehyde.

12.1 Carleton and Leach 1938   Carleton and Leach 1938, 115
FORMULA: water 60, gelatin 10, glycerol 70, phenol 0.25
PREPARATION: Melt gelatin in water at 80°C. Raise glycerol and phenol to 80°C. and add.

12.1 Chevalier 1882   Chevalier 1882, 297
FORMULA: water *q.s.*, gelatin 25, pyroligneous acid 10
PREPARATION: Soak the gelatin in water, drain, and melt. Add pyroligneous acid to molten gelatin.

12.1 Deane *test.* **1877 Frey**   Frey 1877, 135
FORMULA: water 30, gelatin 15, glycerol 55
PREPARATION: Dissolve gelatin in water with heat and add glycerol.

12.1 Dean *test.* **1880 Beale**   Beale 1880, 67
FORMULA: gelatin 30, honey 120, 95% alc. 15, creosote 0.2
PREPARATION: Soak gelatin overnight. Drain. Melt on water bath. Heat honey on water bath. Mix with gelatin. Mix creosote in alc. and add to mixture when cooled to about 35°C. Filter.

12.1 Delépine 1915   4349, **5**:71
FORMULA: gelatin 5.2, sat. sol. arsenic trioxide 19, glycerol 71
PREPARATION: Dissolve gelatin in hot arsenic solution, add glycerol.

12.1 Fischer 1912   23632, **29**:65
FORMULA: water 100, sodium borate 2, gelatin 10, glycerol 17
PREPARATION: Dissolve ingredients with heat and maintain at 40°C. until the medium remains liquid on cooling to room temperature.

12.1 Forbes 1943   21400a, **62**:325
FORMULA: water 40, gelatin 9, glycerol 50, phenol 0.6

12.1 Geoffroy 1893   11074, **7**:55
FORMULA: water 100, chloral hydrate 10, gelatin 4

12.1 Gerlach 1885   *see* P 12.3 Gerlach 1885

12.1 Gilson *test.* **1905 Lee**   Lee 1905, 273
PREPARATION: Soak gelatin in water overnight, drain, and melt. To 50 of this add 50 glycerol and enough chloral hydrate to bring the total volume to 50.

12.1 Guyer 1930   Guyer 1930, 96
FORMULA: water 50, gelatin 8, glycerol 50, egg white (fresh) about 10, phenol 0.25
PREPARATION: Soak gelatin in water overnight. Dissolve with gentle heat. Add egg white to warm gelatin. Autoclave 15 minutes at 15 lbs. and filter. Add glycerol and phenol to filtrate.

12.1 Heidenhain 1905   23632, **20**:328
FORMULA: water 60, gelatin 13, glycerol 10, 95% alc. 20
PREPARATION: Dissolve gelatin in water with glycerol. Add alc. drop by drop to solution.

12.1 Kaiser 1880   3445, **1**:25
FORMULA: water 40, gelatin 7, glycerol 50, phenol 1

12.1 Kisser 1935   23632, **51**:372
FORMULA: water 60, glycerol 50, gelatin 16, phenol 1

12.1 Klebs *test.* **1877 Frey**   Frey 1877, 135
PREPARATION: Soak isinglass in water, drain, and melt. Add enough glycerol to increase volume by one half.

12.1 Legros *test.* **1871a Robin**   Robin 1871, 371
FORMULA: water 20, gelatin 10, glycerol 30, sat. aq. sol. arsenic trioxide 30
PREPARATION: Melt gelatin in water. Mix glycerol and arsenic with molten gelatin.

12.1 Legros *test.* **1871b Robin**   Robin 1871, 372
FORMULA: water 50, gelatin 10, arsenic trioxide 0.3, glycerol 30, phenol 0.1
PREPARATION: Soak gelatin in 20 water some hours and melt. Dissolve arsenic in 30 water and add to molten gelatin. Add glycerol and phenol to mixture.

12.1 Martindale *test.* **1884 Cole** Cole 1884b, 49
FORMULA: water 50, gelatin 5, 95% alc. 3, egg white 3, glycerol 50, salicylic acid 0.25
PREPARATION: Soak gelatin in water and melt. Add alc. to molten gelatin. Add remaining ingredients to mixture at 30°C. Mix well and heat to 100°C. for 5 minutes and filter.

12.1 Moreau 1918 5293, **34**:164
FORMULA: water 42, gelatin 7, glycerol 50, phenol 1
PREPARATION: Soak gelatin in water and melt. Add glycerol and phenol to molten gelatin.

12.1 Muir *test. circ.* **1938 Wellings** Wellings *circ.* 1938, 146
FORMULA: sat. aq. sol. thymol 100, glycerol 5, gelatin 10, potassium acetate 0.5

12.1 Nieuwenhuyse 1912 *test.* **1915 Kappers** 4349, **5**:116
REAGENTS REQUIRED: *A.* 30% gelatin; *B.* 4% formaldehyde
METHOD: Sections on slide are covered with a fairly thick layer of *A* and, after chilling, placed in *B* for 30 mins. Air dry at 30°C. until transparent.

12.1 Nordstedt 1876 *test.* **1883 Behrens** Behrens 1883, 180
FORMULA: water 42, gelatin 14, glycerol 56

12.1 Roskin 1946 Roskin 1946, 123
FORMULA: water 42, gelatin 7, glycerol 50, phenol 0.5
PREPARATION: Soak gelatin in water 2 hours. Melt. Incorporate glycerol. Filter.

12.1 Roudanowski 1865 11024, **2**:227
FORMULA: water *q.s.*, gelatin 20, glycerol 50
PREPARATION: Soak gelatin in water overnight. Drain and melt. Mix glycerol with molten gelatin.

12.1 Schact *test.* **1883 Behrens** Behrens 1883, 181
FORMULA: water 36, gelatin 12, glycerol 48

12.1 Squire 1892 Squire 1892, 84
FORMULA: water 25, gelatin 6.5, glycerol 50, chloroform 0.6, egg white 5
PREPARATION: Soak gelatin in water 24 hours, drain. Mix glycerol in 25 water with 0.1 chloroform, heat, and add to soaked gelatin. Heat to solution. Add egg white and clarify *s.a.* Filter. Add enough water to make filtrate 100. Add 0.5 chloroform and stir well.

12.1 Wood 1897 3430, **24**:208
FORMULA: water 100, clarified gelatin 20, glycerol 10, 40% formaldehyde 1
PREPARATION: Dissolve gelatin in water with glycerol on water bath. Add formaldehyde immediately before use.

12.1 Wotton and Zwemer 1935 *see* M 12.1 Zwemer 1933 (note)

12.1 Yetwin 1944 11428, **30**:201
FORMULA: water 83, gelatin 5, glycerol 17, chrome alum 0.3, phenol 0.3

12.1 Zirkle 1937a 19938, **85**:528
FORMULA: water 50, acetic acid 50, glycerol 1, gelatin 10, dextrose 4, ferric chloride 0.05, carmine to sat.

12.1 Zirkle 1937b *see* DS 11.23 Zirkle 1937

12.1 Zirkle 1940a 20540b, **15**:143
FORMULA: water 60, acetic acid 50, gelatin 10, sorbitol 10, ferric nitrate 0.5, carmine 0.5
PREPARATION: Mix all ingredients except dye. Bring to boil and add dye. Boil 5 minutes. Do not filter.
NOTE: See also M 11.1 and M 13.1 Zirkle 1940.

12.1 Zirkle 1940b 20540b, **15**:143
FORMULA: water 55, acetic acid 45, gelatin 10, gluconic acid 15, ferric nitrate 0.5, carmine 0.5
PREPARATION: As Zirkle 1940a.

12.1 Zirkle 1947   20540b, **22**:87
FORMULA: water 45, acetic acid 30, lactic acid 15, gelatin 10, orcein to sat.
PREPARATION: Dissolve the gelatin in water. Add other ingredients, boil 2–3 minutes.

12.1 Zwemer 1933   *Glychrogel—auct.*   763, **57**:41
FORMULA: water 80, gelatin 3, glycerol 20, chrome alum 0.2, camphor 0.1
PREPARATION: Dissolve gelatin in 50 water with heat. Add glycerol to hot solution. Dissolve chrome alum in 30 water and add to hot mixture. Filter, then add camphor.
NOTE: This formula was republished by **Wotton and Zwemer 1935** (20540b, **10**:21).

13 OTHER WATER-MISCIBLE MOUNTANTS

13.1 FORMULAS

13.1 Archibald and Marshall 1931   16035, **23**:272
FORMULA: water 60, gum tragacanth 0.5, alc. *q.s.*, gum acacia 1.5, lactic acid 12, glycerol 12, phenol 12
PREPARATION: Add enough alcohol to gum tragacanth to make thin paste. Flood 10 water on paste with constant stirring. Dissolve gum acacia in 50 water. Mix with tragacanth mucilage. Add acid, glycerol, and phenol to mixed gums. Filter.
RECOMMENDED FOR: wholemounts of invertebrate larvae.

13.1 Bernhardt 1943   1752, **48**:533
FORMULA: water 1, glycerol 2, phenol 1, lactic acid 1

13.1 Downs 1943   19938, **97**:639
STOCK SOLUTION: dissolve 15 polyvinyl alc. in 100 water at 80°C.
WORKING FORMULA: stock 56, lactic acid 22, phenol 22
NOTE: The same formula was republished, with proper acknowledgment, by **Huber and Caplin 1947** (1829, **56**:763) to whom the medium is often attributed.

13.1 Huber and Caplin 1947   *see* M 13.1 Downs 1943 (note)

13.1 Jones 1946   16730a, **21**:85
FORMULA: water 35, polyvinyl alc. 6.3, sat. sol. picric in abs. alc. 18, lactophenol 45
FORMULA: mix polyvinyl alc. to a paste with the picric solution. Add water to paste and stir to jelly. Add lactophenol to jelly and heat to transparency on water bath.

13.1 Gray and Wess 1950   11360, **70**:290
FORMULA: water 30, lactic acid 15, glycerol 15, 70% acetone 20, polyvinyl alc. 6
PREPARATION: Add the acetone slowly and with constant stirring to the dry resin. Mix half the water with the lactic acid and glycerol and add to resin mixture. Add remaining water slowly and with constant stirring. Heat on a water bath until clear.

13.1 Monk 1938   19938, **88**:174
FORMULA: levulose syrup 35, pectin gel 35, water 20, thymol 0.1

13.1 Monk 1941   21400a, **60**:75
FORMULA: dextrose syrup 30, pectin gel 30, water 30
NOTE: *Karo* brand dextrose and *Certo* brand pectin are specified in the original of both of Monk's formulas.

13.1 Roudanowski 1865   11024, **2**:227
FORMULA: water *q.s.*, isinglass 5, glycerol 8
PREPARATION: Leave isinglass in water and soak overnight. Drain and melt. Add glycerol to molten material.

13.1 Watkin 1925   *see* DS 21.41 Watkin 1925

13.1 Zirkle 1937   19938, **85**:528
FORMULA: DS 11.23 Belling 1921 80, levulose syrup 10, pectin jelly 10
NOTE: The original specifies *Karo* brand levulose syrup and *Certo* brand pectin jelly.

13.1 Zirkle 1940a   20540b, **15**:142
FORMULA: water 60, acetic acid 50, dextrin 10, sorbitol 10, ferric nitrate 0.5, carmine 0.5
PREPARATION: Dissolve dextrin in water. Add other ingredients in order given. Boil, cool, and filter.
NOTE: See also M 11.1 and 12.1 Zirkle 1940.

13.1 Zirkle 1940b   20540b, **15**:144
FORMULA: water 55, acetic acid 55, sorbitol 5, pectin gel 10, levulose syrup 10, ferric nitrate 0.5, carmine 0.5
PREPARATION: Mix all ingredients except pectin. Leave some days. Filter. Incorporate pectin.
NOTE: The original calls for *Certo* brand pectin and *Karo* brand levulose syrup.

M 20 Mountants Miscible with Alcohol

Media of this type, into which objects may be mounted directly from alcohol without the necessity of clearing, fall into three classes. In the first class (M 21) are the media based on gum mastic; in the second (M 22) are the media based on Venice turpentine. Both these media are regularly used for objects which are considered too delicate to withstand the action of a clearing agent. The third class (M 23), containing the gum sandarac media, comprise those formulas which are usually referred to as *neutral mountants*. These are widely used both for substances which are considered too delicate to preserve in Canada balsam, which involves prior clearing, or for sections which have been stained in material which fades rapidly under the influence of acid balsam. Many are derived from the original *euparal* of Gilson, the formula for which has never been disclosed and which is a preparatory substance of secret composition. These media have a refractive index much lower than the gum mastic or gum turpentine media so that they cannot satisfactorily be used for thick objects. It may be pointed out that "dry" Canada balsam is soluble in absolute alcohol and has from time to time been recommended. It is the writer's experience that this solution is not satisfactory, for mounts made with it darken more rapidly than those made from balsam which has been dissolved in hydrocarbons.

21 GUM MASTIC MEDIA

21.1 FORMULAS

21.1 Artigas 1935   13461, **10**:71
FORMULA: 95% alc. 100, gum mastic 30, beechwood creosote 100
PREPARATION: Dissolve gum in alc. Centrifuge or filter. Add creosote and evaporate till no alc. remains.
RECOMMENDED FOR: nematode worms after clearing in creosote.

21.1 Hoyer 1921   6630, **84**:814
PREPARATION: Suspend mastic in a cloth bag in a considerable volume of 95% alc. Withdraw bag in which remain gross impurities. Shake solution thoroughly, allow to settle, and decant clear solution. Evaporate to required consistency.

22 VENICE TURPENTINE MEDIA

22.1 FORMULAS

22.1 Langeron 1942   *Venice turpentine-alcohol*   Langeron 1942, 654
PREPARATION: Dilute crude Venice turpentine with an equal volume of 95% alc. Mix well and allow impurities to settle. Decant and re-evaporate to convenient consistency.

22.1 Vosseler 1889   23632, **6**:292
FORMULA: 95% alc. 50, Venice turpentine 50
PREPARATION: Mix ingredients. Allow to settle. Decant.

22.1 Wilson 1945   20540b, **20**:133
FORMULA: Venice turpentine 25, phenol 50, proprionic acid 35, acetic acid 10, water 20
PREPARATION: As M 22.1 Zirkle 1940.

22.1 Zirkle 1940   20540b, **15**:147
FORMULA: water 25, acetic acid 15, proprionic acid 35, phenol 55, Venice turpentine 20,
ferric nitrate 0.5, carmine 0.5
PREPARATION: Mix the Venice turpentine with the proprionic acid. Add the phenol and
acetic acid. Then add the water, in which the ferric nitrate has been dissolved, slowly
and with constant stirring. Incorporate the dye in this mixture.
NOTE: See also M 31.1 Zirkle 1940.

M 23 GUM SANDARAC MEDIA

23.1 FORMULAS

23.1 Armitage 1939   *Microscope*, **3**:215
PREPARATION: To 100 of a syrupy filtered solution of gum sandarac in dioxane add the
fluid produced by the mutual solution of 3 salol and 2 camphor.

23.1 Buchholz 1938   20540b, **13**:53
FORMULA: oil of eucalyptus 60, paraldehyde 30, gum sandarac to give required consistency

23.1 Cox 1891   1780, **37**:16
FORMULA: alcohol 150, sandarac 150, turpentine 60, camphor 30, lavender oil 45, castor
oil 0.5
PREPARATION: Dissolve sandarac in alc. Dissolve camphor in turpentine and then mix in
alc. solution. Add oils to mixed solutions.

23.1 Denham 1923   *Camphoral—auct.*   11360, **43**:190
STOCK I: chloral hydrate 50, camphor 50
PREPARATION OF STOCK I: Grind ingredients in a mortar till solution complete.
STOCK II: gum sandarac *q.s.*, isobutyl alc. *q.s.*
PREPARATION OF STOCK II: Make a thin solution of the ingredients. Shake with activated
charcoal. Filter. Evaporate to a thick syrup.
WORKING MEDIUM: stock I 60, stock II 30

23.1 Gilson 1906   *Euparal—compl. script.*   6011, **23**:427
NOTE: This is a proprietary mixture of secret composition and cannot be further noticed.
The reference cited does not disclose the composition.

23.1 Mohr and Wehrle 1942   20540b, **17**:157
FORMULA: camsal 10, gum sandarac 40, eucalyptol 20, dioxane 20, paraldehyde 10
NOTE: Camsal is produced by the mutual solution of equal quantities of camphor and
phenyl salicylate (salol). This medium may be diluted with dioxane. It may be
colored green (in imitation of green euparal) by adding a solution of copper oleate in
eucalyptol.

23.1 Shepherd 1918   21400a, **37**:131
FORMULA: sandarac 30, eucalyptol 20, paraldehyde 10, camsal 10
NOTE: Camsal is a mixture of equal parts camphor and phenyl salicylate. Shepherd
(*loc. cit.*) recommends dissolving the sandarac in 150 abs. alc., filtering under anhydrous condition and re-evaporating to dryness.

24 OTHER ALCOHOL-MISCIBLE MEDIA

24.1 FORMULAS

24.1 Hanna 1949   11360, **69**:25
FORMULA: sulfur 40, phenol 100, sodium sulfide 2

24.1 Seiler 1881   21400a, **3**:60
FORMULA: Canada balsam 40, abs. alc. 60

M 30 Mountants Not Miscible with either Alcohol or Water

The great majority of all mounts are prepared in these media of which Canada balsam (mixtures containing which form the first class, M 31), is the best known. Gum damar (M 32) is a substance which is so variable in composition that it is difficult to recommend it. It has less tendency to become either yellow or acid with age than has balsam, provided that one secures a good specimen. But there are numerous accounts in the literature of mounts which have become granular within a few years of having been made. It would appear probable that these mounts were made from an impure sample of the gum, and the worker who wishes to use damar media is recommended to be very particular as to his source of supply. The next class (M 33) covers the few other natural resins which have from time to time been proposed for mounting media as well as mixtures of these resins with Canada balsam and with gum damar. The last class (M 34 below) is likely to increase very rapidly with time. It includes numerous synthetic resins which have been proposed as a substitute for the natural resins usually employed. No methcrylate mixtures are included since there is abundant evidence in the literature (Richards and Smith 1938: 19938, **87**:374) that they are worthless. Unfortunately, many authors have proposed media based on resins of which only a trade name is quoted. These have not been included since they are almost impossible to duplicate. Formulas using trade names have, however, been included if a reasonable chemical identification of the resin is given in the original description.

31 CANADA BALSAM MEDIA

Canada balsam is the natural exudate of *Abies balsamea*. It consists of a resin (*Canada resin* in the formulas given below) dissolved in a variety of hydrocarbons. The material sold on the market as *dried balsam* has had the lower boiling-point natural hydrocarbons driven off with heat but the higher boiling-point fractions, which act as natural plasticizers, remain. This dried balsam is commonly used as a 40 % solution in xylene or benzene. If true Canada resin is used, a plasticizer must be added. A method of purifying Canada balsam is given by Bensley and Bensley 1938, 38. *Neutral balsams* are a delusion and some M 34 formula should be used in their place.

31.1 FORMULAS

31.1 Apáthy 1909   8338, **22**:18
FORMULA: Canada balsam 50, cedarwood oil 25, chloroform 25

31.1 Becher and Demoll 1913   Becher and Demoll 1913, 107
FORMULA: Canada resin 40, abs. alc. 40, terpineol 20

31.1 Curtis 1905 *salicylic balsam—compl. script.*   1863, **17**:603
FORMULA: dried Canada balsam 30, sat. sol. salicylic acid in xylene, 70

31.1 Hays 1865   21400a, **1**:16
FORMULA: Canada balsam 50, chloroform 50
PREPARATION: Mix ingredients and allow to stand 1 month. Decant. Evaporate to required consistency.

31.1 Sahli 1885   23632, **2**:5
NOTE: This paper is often quoted as recommending a solution of balsam in cedar oil. Sahli recommends only that sufficient of the oil used for clearing be left to soften the balsam.

31.1 Semmens 1938 *CS15a—auct.*   *Microscope*, **2**:166
FORMULA: Dried Canada balsam 40, xylene 20, DS 12.16 McLean 1934b 20
NOTE: The substitution of DS 12.16 McLean 1934a (eosin) gives *CS15b* and McLean 1934a (erythrosin) gives *CS15c*.

31.1 Zirkle 1940   20540b,**15**:149
FORMULA: water 20, acetic acid 15, proprionic acid 40, phenol 65, oleic acid 10, dried
Canada balsam 10, ferric nitrate 0.5, carmine 0.5
PREPARATION: Mix the balsam with the acetic and proprionic acids. Add the oleic acid
and then the phenol. Incorporate the water in which the ferric nitrate has been dissolved. Then mix in the dye.

32 GUM DAMAR MEDIA

Gum damar is the natural exudate of *Shorea wiesneri*, but it is almost always adulterated and usually contains solid impurities. The raw gum should be dissolved in
chloroform, filtered, and evaporated until the chloroform is driven off. The purified gum
is then dissolved in benzene or toluene to a suitable consistency.

M 32.1 FORMULAS

32.1 Cooke *circ.* **1920**   Cooke *circ.* 1920, 49
PREPARATION: Warm together till dissolved equal parts of gum damar, benzene, and
turpentine. Filter. Evaporate to desired consistency.

32.1 Vögt and Jung *test. circ.* **1890 Francotte**   Francotte, 248
FORMULA: Canada balsam 30, benzene 100, gum damar 30
PREPARATION: Dissolve ingredients separately, then mix solutions.

33 OTHER RESINS AND MIXED RESINS

33.1 FORMULAS

33.1 Artigas 1935   *see* M 21.1 Artigas 1935

33.1 Chevalier 1882   Chevalier 1882, 327
FORMULA: chloroform 90, rubber 3, gum mastic *q.s.* to give required consistency

33.1 Frémineau *test.* **1883 Chevalier**   Chevalier 1882, 297
FORMULA: Canada balsam 60, gum mastic 20, chloroform *q.s.* to give required fluidity

33.1 Lacoste and de Lachand 1943   4285a, **20**:159
FORMULA: toluene 100, rosin 120

33.1 Noyer 1921   6630, **84**:814
PREPARATION: Take decanted solution of mastic from M 21.1 Noyer 1921 and evaporate
to dryness. Redissolve in xylene. This solution was once known in commerce as
erenol.

33.1 Rehm 1893   23632, **9**:387
FORMULA: benzene 100, rosin 10

33.1 Seiler 1881   Seiler 1881, 90
FORMULA: naphtha 17, turpentine 15, Canada balsam 45, damar 23
NOTE: Seiler (*loc. cit.*) recommended this either as a mountant or as a ringing cement.

33.1 Southgate 1923   3566, **4**:44
PREPARATION: Digest 200 crude Yucatan elemi in the cold with 200 95% alc. Filter and
evaporate filtrate to dryness and redissolve in benzene to a suitable consistency.
NOTE: The solution of amyrin-free gum elemi thus obtained is stated to preserve Giemsa
or other DS 13.1 stains indefinitely.

34 SYNTHETIC RESINS

34.1 FORMULAS

34.1 Déflandre 1933   *Bul. soc. franc. microsc.,* **2**:67
FORMULA: coumarone resin 20, xylene 80, monobromonaphthalene 1

34.1 Déflandre 1947   *Kumadex—auct.*   Déflandre 1947, 96
     PREPARATION: Mix 3 parts of a syrupy solution of a coumarone resin in xylene with 1
     part of Canada balsam.

34.1 Fleming 1943   11360, **63**:34
     FORMULA: Naphrax 40, xylene 59, dibutyl phthallate 1
     NOTE: The resin mentioned is a high refractive index (1.7–1.8) naphthalene derivative,
     the synthesis of which is fully described in the reference cited.

34.1 Gray and Wess 1951a   11360, **71**:197
     FORMULA: ethyl cellosolve 68, isoamyl phthalate 12, polyvinyl acetate 20
     RECOMMENDED FOR: sections.

34.1 Gray and Wess 1951b   11360, **71**:197
     FORMULA: ethyl cellosolve 50, isoamyl phthalate 10, polyvinyl acetate 40
     RECOMMENDED FOR: wholemounts.

34.1 Groat 1939   763, **74**:1
     FORMULA: toluene 40, "nevillite 1" or "V" 60
     NOTE: The nevillites are mostly hydrogenated coumarones of which clarite (nevillite 1)
     is the best known. Nevillite V is a naphthaline polymer.

34.1 Kirkpatrick and Lendrum 1939   *DPX—auct.*   11431, **49**:592 4
     FORMULA: xylene 80, tricresyl phosphate 15, "Distrene-80" 10
     NOTE: Distrene-80 is a polystyrene with a molecular weight of about 80,000.

34.1 Skiles and Georgi 1937   19938, **85**:367
     FORMULA: vinylite 20, xylene 80
     METHOD: used to varnish bacterial films

34.1 Wicks, Carruthers, and Ritchey 1946   20540b, **21**:121
     FORMULA: "Piccolyte" 60, xylene 40
     NOTE: There are a whole series of beta-pinene polymers marketed under the general
     name "piccolyte." The authors cited found "WW-85," "WW-100," "S-85," and
     "S-100" the most suitable.

27

Embedding Media

E 00 General Observations

The term *embedding media* covers all those materials which are used to surround, impregnate, and support specimens which are being sectioned. The technique of section cutting is discussed in Chapters 10 through 15. Embedding media may be divided into those which are miscible with water (E 10) and to which, therefore, objects may be transferred without special preparation, and those which are not miscible with water (E 20) and thus require preliminary treatment of the specimen.

E 10 Media Miscible with Water

Water-miscible embedding media are in some cases intended for surrounding an object which is to be frozen before it is cut, and in other cases intended to be hardened by other means and cut without freezing. No general division between these two groups is possible because many media are suitable for both purposes. When, however, no specific method is given, it is to be presumed that the media are intended for objects to be cut on a freezing microtome in the manner described in Chapter 15.

E 11.1 FORMULAS

11.1 Anderson 1929   Anderson 1929, 129
  FORMULA: syrupus simplex (B.P.) 45, dextrin 14, 80% alc. 45
  PREPARATION: Boil the dextrin in the syrupus simplex till solution complete. Add alc.
  little by little with constant shaking.

11.1 Apáthy *test.* **1948 Romeis**   Romeis 1948, 108
  FORMULA: water 87.5, glycerol 12.5, gelatin 25
  METHOD: [object from water] → 50% glycerol → 30% embedding medium, 40°C., 24
  hrs. → embedding medium, 40°C. 24 hrs. → dessicator, 50°C. till volume reduced to
  half → cast as block → cool → 95% alc. 24 hrs. → terpineol, 24 hrs. → [section]

11.1 Belezky 1931 22575, **282**:214

REAGENTS REQUIRED: *A*. water 75, phenol 7.5, gelatin 25; *B*. 4% neutralized formaldehyde

METHOD: [small pieces] → *A*, 2–3 hrs., 37°C. → cool → cut small blocks containing pieces from mass → *B*, 2–5 days → [frozen sections]

11.1 Blank and McCarthy 1950 11284, **36**:776

FORMULA: Carbowax 4000 90, Carbowax 1500 10

METHOD: [fixed and washed tissues] → water → "wax," 56°C. till impregnated → [block]

NOTE: The Carbowaxes (products of the Carbide and Chemical Corporation) are solid polyethylene glycols. "1500" has about the consistency of petroleum jelly, "4000" about that of 58° paraffin; other grades are available. All grades are water soluble, which makes embedding easy, but it is very difficult to flatten ribbons before they disintegrate.

11.1 Brunotti 1892 11074, **6**:194

REAGENTS REQUIRED: *A*. water 100, gelatin 10, acetic acid 15, mercuric chloride 0.5; *B*. 5% potassium dichromate

METHOD: [water] → 1 part *A*, 3 parts water, till impregnated → *A*, till impregnated → *B*, dropped in with as much *A* as possible adhering

11.1 Bunge *test.* **1877 Frey** Frey 1877, 71

FORMULA: egg white 72, 10% sodium carbonate 7.5, tallow 27

PREPARATION: Whip egg white and sodium carbonate together. Melt tallow and incorporate with egg white.

METHOD: embed from water. Harden in alcohol

11.1 Chatton 1923 6630, **88**:199

FORMULA: water 100, agar 1.3, 40% formaldehyde 2.5

PREPARATION: Dissolve agar in boiling water. Add formaldehyde to hot solution.

METHOD: [object from water] → surface of thin slab cast from medium → pour just liquid medium on top, allow to set → 95% alc.

NOTE: This is primarily intended for setting and orienting small objects, the block being re-embedded in paraffin.

11.1 Clark 1947 11431, **59**:337

REAGENTS REQUIRED: *A*. 12.5% gelatin; *B*. 25% gelatin; *C*. 2% formaldehyde; *D*. 0.5% gelatin; *E*. 40% formaldehyde

METHOD: [pieces of formaldehyde fixed material] → thorough wash → *A*, 24 hrs. 37.5°C. → *B*, 24 hrs. → [make block and refrigerate—trim block] → *C*, 24 hrs. → [frozen sections] → 50% alc. → *D*, few moments → place on *clean* slide → drain → vapor from *E*, 1 hr., 27°C. → *C*, till required

RECOMMENDED FOR: fatty tissues.

NOTE: A detailed description of this technique is given in Chapter 15.

11.1 Cole 1884 Cole 1884, 39

FORMULA: water 24, gum arabic 36, sugar 18, water 16

RECOMMENDED FOR: use on freezing microtomes.

11.1 Cutler 1935 1887a, **20**:445

REAGENTS REQUIRED: *A*. 95% alc. 50, glycol stearate 50; *B*. glycol stearate

METHOD: [fixed tissues] → 95% alc., via graded series → *A*, 56°C., 12–24 hrs. → *B*, 24–48 hrs. → [make block]

NOTE: Ribbons may be attached to slide and processed exactly as paraffin ribbons.

11.1 Flemming *test.* **1877 Frey** Frey 1877, 71

FORMULA: hard soap 75, 95% alc. 25

11.1 Frey 1877 Frey 1877, 71

FORMULA: isinglass 30, water *q.s.*, glycerol 30

PREPARATION: Soak isinglass in water. Drain. Melt. Mix glycerol with molten isinglass.

METHOD: embed from 50% glycerol. Harden in alcohol

11.1 Gaskell 1912   *see* E 11.1 Romeis 1948

11.1 Gerlach 1885   *see* M 12.1 Gerlach 1885

11.1 Godfrin *test.* **1942 Langeron** *cit.* **Brunotte 1889**   Langeron 1942, 440
FORMULA: water 25, glycerol 20, gelatin 2.5, 90% alc. 150, castor oil soap 50
PREPARATION: Dissolve gelatin in water with glycerol on water bath. Mix oil in alc. and add to hot solution.
METHOD: [woody tissues] → 95% alc. in vacuo to remove air → water, some hrs. → medium, freshly prepared → continue heating till skin forms on surface → withdraw object

11.1 Gräff 1916   *see* E 11.1 Romeis 1948

11.1 Hartley 1938   *Microscope,* **2**:46
FORMULA: water 20, glycerol 40, gum arabic 20, thymol 0.1
METHOD: [bundles of textile fibers] → medium, till saturated → dry → section
RECOMMENDED FOR: transverse sections of textile fibers.

11.1 Heringa and ten Berge 1923   23632, **40**:166
METHOD: [object washed free of fixative] → 10% gelatin, 2–5 hrs., 37°C. → 20% gelatin, 37°C., 10 mins. → [make block, cool] → [frozen sections] → sat. sol. thymol → attach to slides with V 21.2 Heringa and ten Berge 1923 → stain

11.1 Kaiser 1880   *see* M 12.1 Kaiser 1880

11.1 Langeron 1942   Langeron 1942, 439
FORMULA: water 60, gum arabic 20, glycerol 20
RECOMMENDED FOR: use on freezing microtome.

11.1 Lebowich 1936   1887a, **22**:782
FORMULA: 56°C. paraffin 80, stearic acid 20, diethylene glycol 1.5, ethanolamine 1.5
PREPARATION: Mix completely the molten waxes, preferably with high-speed electric mixer. Add other reagents and continue mixing 30 minutes at 85°C.
REAGENTS REQUIRED: *A.* acetone; *B.* soap from above
METHOD: [fixed material] → *A*, till dehydrated → *B*, 56°–62°C. (in vacuo for large objects), till impregnated → [cast in block and section] → [mount sections by V 21.3 Lebowich 1936]

11.1 Lubkin and Carsten 1942   19938, **97**:168
FORMULA: water 80, polyvinyl alc. 16, glycerol 20
PREPARATION: Dissolve the alc. with continuous stirring at 75°–85°C. Incorporate glycerol while cooling.
METHOD: Place well-washed tissue blocks in medium in covered dishes. Heat to 56°C. for 2 hrs. daily. When solidified (8–9 days), trim and cut as though the block were nitrocellulose.

11.1 Nicolas 1896   2844, **3**:274
REAGENTS REQUIRED: *A*. 3% gelatin; *B*. 10% gelatin; *C*. water 90, gelatin 20, glycerol 10; *D*. 5% formaldehyde
METHOD: [water] → *A*, 1–2 days, 25°C. → *B*, 1–2 days, 25°C. → *C*, 2–3 days 35°C. → [transfer to paper box, cool] → *D*, till hard enough to cut

11.1 Pickworth 1934   11025, **69**:62
FORMULA: water 100, phenol 1, gum arabic 25

11.1 Pölzam *test. circ.* **1890 Francotte**   Francotte, *circ.* 1890, 287
FORMULA: dried hard soap 15, glycerol 35, 95% alc. 50
PREPARATION: Boil ingredients with reflux to a syrupy mass.
METHOD: [objects too delicate for paraffin embedding] → 95% alc. → medium at 30–40°C. → [cool as block] → [section]

11.1 Romeis 1948   Romeis 1948, 109
FORMULA: water 75, phenol 0.75, gelatin 25
METHOD: [object washed free of fixative] → 50% embedding medium, 24 hrs., 37°C. →
embedding medium, 30 mins. → [set as block; evaporate till surface tacky] → 10%
formaldehyde, 1–2 days → [frozen sections]
NOTE: This is a synthesis by Romeis (*loc. cit.*) of the methods of **Gaskell 1912** (11431,
20:17), and **Graff 1916** (14674, **63**:1482).

11.1 Salkind 1916   6630, **79**:16
REAGENTS REQUIRED: *A*. cherry gum 25, water 50, lead subacetate solution (N.F. VI) 25,
acetic acid 1.5; *B*. ammonia
PREPARATION: Dissolve gum in water. Mix lead subacetate solution and acetic acid and
add to filtrate.
METHOD: [water] → *A*, till impregnated → [paper boat] → vapor of *B*, till hard enough
to cut
NOTE: The original method, and also the citation in Gatenby and Cowdry 1937, 108
call for "Extract of Saturne" (*sic*). Gray 1816 (*Treatise on Pharmacology*, 318) refers to
a solution obtained by boiling litharge with distilled vinegar as "Goulard's Extract
of Saturn." The *Merck Index*, 1940, 315 refers to the NF solution given above as
"Goulard's Extract." Whether or not the strength of Salkind's solution was that of
the NF does not appear to be ascertainable.

11.1 Samuel 1944   11025, **78**:173
REAGENTS REQUIRED: *A*. 0.65% agar in 2% formaldehyde; *B*. 1.3% agar in 2% formaldehyde
METHOD: [small objects] → film of *B* cast on slide → *A*, around but not over object →
film of *B* over object → paraffin

11.1 Tobias 1936   Tobias 1936, 74
FORMULA: water 60, gum arabic 40, phenol 0.5

11.1 Webb 1890   11360, 113
FORMULA: water 100, phenol 2.5, dextrin *q.s.* to give a thick syrup

11.1 Zwemer 1933   763, **57**:41
REAGENTS REQUIRED: *A*. 5% gelatin; *B*. 10% gelatin; *C*. 4% formaldehyde
METHOD: [formaldehyde fixed tissues] → *A*, 24 hrs., 37.5°C. → *B*, 12 hrs. 37.5°C. →
[cast block] → *C*, till required → [sections by freezing technique]

E 20 Embedding Media Not Miscible with Water

Before material can be embedded in these media for cutting, it must be subjected to
whatever treatment is specified in Chapters 12 through 14. In general, however, this
treatment consists of the removal of water from the specimen with a dehydrating agent
and the substitution for the dehydrating agent of a solvent which is itself miscible with
the embedding material. Three main types of media are distinguished in the present
chapter. First (E 21.1) come the numerous wax media which have been suggested to replace straight paraffin in the production of sections; second, nitrocellulose media, more
commonly referred to as "*celloidin*," in which there are few media but a considerable
number of methods, particularly for double embedding; third (E 23) resinous materials
which are intended for the inclusion of matter from which sections are to be ground, as
indicated in Chapter 10, rather than cut.

21 WAX MEDIA

The original method of cutting sections embedded in wax, which is described in detail
in Chapter 12, was to dehydrate the specimen with alcohol, to remove the alcohol either
with an essential oil or a hydrocarbon, and then to embed the material in straight paraffin. This technique has been modified both through the introduction of substitutes for,
or adjuvants to, paraffin, and by the introduction of other solvents. In the section which

follows, therefore, the formulas which may be used to replace paraffin are given and also some techniques by which any material may be embedded in any selected formula.

21.1 FORMULAS

21.1 Altmann *test.* **1942 Langeron**   Langeron 1942, 422
FORMULA: 60°C. paraffin 85, tristearin 10, beeswax 5

21.1 Beyer 1938   591b, **2**:173
FORMULA: paraffin 100, rubber 2, beeswax 0.5

21.1 Bragg 1938   23639b, **28**:154
REAGENTS REQUIRED: *A*. water 20, 95% alc. 40, aniline 30; *B*. 95% alc. 30, aniline 60;
C. aniline; *D*. aniline 50, toluene 50; *E*. toluene; *F*. sat. sol. 53° paraffin in toluene;
G. 53° paraffin
METHOD: [embryos in 70% alc.] → *A*, 2–6 hrs. → *B*, 2–6 hrs. → *C*, 1 hr. or till clear →
D, 1–6 hrs. → *E*, 1–3 hrs. → *F*, 1–4 hrs. → *G*, 3–4 hrs., 56°C. → [cast in block]
NOTE: This is recommended for heavily yolked embryos.

21.1 Débauche 1939   20540b, **14**:121
FORMULA: paraffin 80, beeswax 20

21.1 Dufrénoy 1935   6630, **119**:375
METHOD: [water] → 50% methylal, 30 mins. → methylal, 30 mins. → methylal 2, liquid
petrolatum 3, 30 mins. → methylal 1, liquid petrolatum 3, 30 mins. → liquid petrolatum, 30°C., 30 mins. → [paraffin]

21.1 Gray 1941   U.S. Patent 2,267,151
FORMULA: paraffin (MP 58°C.) ⸌70, rubber 5, beeswax 5, spermaceti 5, nevillite "5"
("clarite") 15
NOTE: This composition melts at about 50°C. but will cut 5 μ ribbons at a room temperature of 85°F. By increasing the resin to 30 it is possible to cut 1 μ ribbons.

21.1 Gudden *test.* **1895 Rawitz**   Rawitz 1895, 31
FORMULA: stearic acid 48, lard 48, beeswax 2

21.1 Hance 1933   19938, **77**:353
STOCK: Dissolve about 20 crude rubber, in small pieces, in 100 paraffin heated to smoking.
WORKING FORMULA: paraffin 100, stock 4–5, beeswax 1

21.1 Hetherington 1922   11428, **9**:102
METHOD: [nematodes] → F 0000.0010 Hetherington 1922 → methyl salicylate → wax

21.1 Johnston 1903   11032, **6**:2662
FORMULA: paraffin 99, asphalt 0.1, para rubber 1
PREPARATION: Heat ingredients to 100°C. with occasional stirring for 48 hours. Decant.

21.1 Hsii and Tang 1939a   20540b, **14**:151
FORMULA: Japan wax 90, beeswax 10

21.1 Hsii and Tang 1939b   20540b, **14**:151
FORMULA: Japan wax 30, paraffin 70

21.1 Larbaud 1921   *see* E 21.1 Peeters 1921

21.1 Langeron 1942   Langeron 1942, 415
METHOD: [water] → 95% alc. → amyl alc. 24 hrs. → liquid petrolatum, 2–3 changes in
24 hrs. → [paraffin]

21.1 Maxwell 1938   20540b, **13**:93
FORMULA: paraffin 56–58° 100, rubber paraffin (see E 21.1 Hance 1933) 4–5, bayberry
wax 5–10, beeswax 1

21.1 Peeters 1921   6630, **85**:15
METHOD: [95% alc.] → amyl alc. → amyl alc., fresh portion, 52°C. → equal parts
   paraffin and amyl alc. 52°C. → paraffin
NOTE: Larbaud 1921 (6628, **172**:1317) uses butyl alc. by the same technique.

21.1 Pohlman *test.* **1930 Guyer**   Guyer 1930, 43
FORMULA: 52° paraffin 10, bayberry wax 1

21.1 Ruffini 1927   Ruffini 1927, 28
FORMULA: paraffin (MP 52°–54°C.) 100, beeswax 10, lard 15

21.1 Seiler 1881   Seiler 1881, 48
FORMULA: paraffin 65, tallow 35

21.1 Sherman and Smith 1938   591b (tech suppl.), **2**:171
PREPARATION OF STOCK: To 100 paraffin (MP 55°C.) at 78°C. add 12.5 crepe rubber at
   the rate of about 3 every 12 hours; continue heating till homogeneous.
WORKING MEDIUM: paraffin (MP 55°C.) 100, stock 2.5, beeswax 5

21.1 Spee 1885   23632, **2**:7
METHOD: Heat paraffin of 50°C. melting point until it turns yellow.

21.1 Steedman 1947   17510, **88**:123
FORMULA: ethylene glycol monostearate 10, ethylene glycol distearate 73, stearic acid 5,
   ethyl cellulose 4, castor oil 8

21.1 Steedman 1949   14900, **164**:1084
FORMULA: diethylene glycol distearate 80, ethyl cellulose (low viscosity) 4, stearic acid 5,
   castor oil 4, diethylene glycol monostearate 5
NOTE: This composition melts at 53°C. but cuts well at 80°–90°F.

21.1 van Walsem 1892   22238, **1**:32
FORMULA: paraffin MP 55°C. 95, beeswax 5
RECOMMENDED FOR: very large sections.

21.1 Waterman 1939   20540b, **14**:55
FORMULA: paraffin 80, stearic acid 16, spermaceti 3, bayberry wax 1
NOTE: This mixture melts about 3°C. below the melting point of the paraffin base, but it
   is sufficiently hard to cut good sections at room temperatures.

22 NITROCELLULOSE MEDIA

Nitrocellulose is a very loose term covering a large number of mixtures of chemical
compounds. These mixtures are usually differentiated according to the viscosity of a
standard solution which is tested by timing the rate of fall of a steel ball. A half-second
nitrocellulose would, therefore, be of low viscosity and a thirty-second nitrocellulose of
very high viscosity. Only the very low viscosity nitrocelluloses are suitable for embedding, and the term *celloidin* (a registered trademark), is now used for any nitrocellulose
suitable for the purpose. In the section which follows, are given mostly methods rather
than formulas.

22.1 FORMULAS

22.1 Bauer 1941   23632, **58**:44
METHOD: [object, washed free of fixative] → equal parts pyridine and 4% celloidin,
   24 hrs. → 9% celloidin, 24 hrs. → [make block]

22.1 Brown 1948   20540b, **23**:83
REAGENTS REQUIRED: *A*. 2% celloidin; *B*. 4% celloidin; *C*. 6% celloidin; *D*. chloroform;
   E. benzene; *F*. sat. sol. paraffin in benzene; *G*. paraffin
METHOD: [perfectly dehydrated specimens] → *A*, 12–24 hrs. → *B*, 12–24 hrs. → *C*, 2–4
   days → *D*, vapor, till firm → *E*, 6–12 hrs. in each of three changes → *F*, 37°C., 1 day
   → *G*, 12–24 hrs. in each of three changes

22.1 Espinasse *test.* **1937 Gatenby and Painter** Gatenby and Painter 1937, 96
REAGENTS REQUIRED: *A.* methyl benzoate 100, celloidin 1
METHOD: abs. alc. → *A*, till permeated → benzene → paraffin

22.1 Field and Martin 1894 23632, **11**:6
METHOD: Dissolve celloidin moistened with toluene in a mixture of equal parts toluene and abs. alc. to give a thick solution. Warm to 25°C. and add, little by little, as much paraffin as the solution will take up. Pass object to mass from equal parts toluene and abs. alc. When impregnated transfer to a sat. sol. paraffin in chloroform. Evaporate solvents at 56°C. and treat block as paraffin block.

22.1 Heinz 1923 14674, **70**:913
REAGENTS REQUIRED: *A.* abs. alc. 50, ether 50; *B.* methyl salicylate 50, ether 25, abs. alc. 25, celloidin 1; *C.* chloroform; *D.* sat. sol. paraffin in chloroform
METHOD: [pieces from abs. alc.] → *A*, 12 hrs. → *B*, 24 hrs. → *C*, 12 hrs. → *D*, 12 hrs. → [paraffin]

22.1 Jordan and Heather 1929 20540b, **4**:121
FORMULA: abs. alc. 25, ether 25, methyl salicylate 25, celloidin 1
METHOD: [fixed and dehydrated pieces] → 50:50 ether abs. alc., 8 hrs. → celloidin mixture 24 hrs. → sat. sol. paraffin in chloroform 2–3 hrs. → paraffin, 2 changes, till permeated → [make block]

22.1 Peterfi 1921 23632, **38**:342
FORMULA: methyl benzoate 100, collodion 1
METHOD: [abs. alc.] → methyl benzoate → medium, till perfectly clear → cedar oil → paraffin

22.1 Reichardt and Wetzel 1928 23632, **45**:476
REAGENTS REQUIRED: *A.* methyl benzoate; *B.* 1% celloidin in methyl benzoate; *C.* 10% paraffin in methyl benzoate; *D.* paraffin (50°C.)
METHOD: [objects to be embedded] → abs. alc. till perfectly dehydrated → *A*, till clear → *B*, 3–5 days → *C*, 1–2 days, 40°C. → *D*, 1 day → [make block]

22.1 Richardson 1934 11571b, **13**:81
FORMULA: celloidin 110, abs. alc. 25, ether 110
PREPARATION: Leave celloidin in alc. overnight. Mix ether in alc. solution and leave several days.
METHOD: [formol fixed material] → acetone 2 hrs. → clove oil, till clear → celloidin, 6 hrs. → [prepare block in usual manner]

22.1 Seki 1937a 23639b, **27**:278
METHOD: [dehydrated object] → methanol, 24 hrs. → equal parts methanol and ether, 12 hrs. → 1% celloidin in methanol 12 hrs. → [evaporate to ⅔rds volume] → chloroform, 24 hrs. → anhydrous butyl alc., 12–24 hrs. → benzene, 3–5 hrs. → sat. sol. paraffin in benzene, 35°C., ½–1 hr. → paraffin

22.1 Seki 1937b 23639b, **27**:282
METHOD: [dehydrated object] → 2% celloidin in methanol, 1 day → 4% celloidin in methanol, 2 days → 8% celloidin in methanol, 4 days → [set in block] → 3% chloroform in 70% alc., 1 day → section

22.1 Stepanow 1900 23632, **17**:185
REAGENTS REQUIRED: *A.* clove oil; *B.* ether 80, abs. alc. 4, clove oil 20, celloidin 6
METHOD: [dehydrated tissues] → *A*, 3–6 hrs. → *B*, 3–24 hrs. → [cast block, allow to evaporate until transparent] → chloroform

22.1 Tschernyachinsky 1930 23632, **47**:200
METHOD: [objects impregnated with 8% celloidin in abs. alc.-ether] → equal parts 8% celloidin and clove oil, 2–24 hrs. → chloroform, 30 mins. → sat. sol. paraffin in chloroform 56°C. 1 hr. → paraffin

22.1 Wolf 1939   23632, **56**:57

METHOD: [object, washed free of fixative] → laboratory glycerol, 6 hrs. → anhydrous glycerol, 6 hrs. → wipe free from glycerol → suspend in 8% celloidin, 2 days → [make block]

23 RESINOUS MEDIA

Resinous media, as has been explained in Chapter 10, are used for supporting materials from which sections are to be ground rather than cut. No specific mixtures have been recommended for this purpose, though Canada balsam, damar, and ordinary resin have all been employed. The only formula at present occupying this section is designed to permit cutting thin sections in a polymerized resin, instead of a material hardened by evaporation, as are the nitrocelluloses of the last section.

23.1 FORMULAS

23.1 Bourdon 1943   4285a, **20**:46

PREPARATION: Catalyze vinyl acetate with 3% benzoyl peroxide and warm till syrupy. Embed in this material impregnated, after dioxane dehydration, with vinyl acetate. Polymerize at 37°C. for 48 hours followed by 48 hours at 56°C. Cut as though the block were made of nitrocellulose. Sections of 2 μ–3 μ may be obtained.

24 OTHER MEDIA

Three media, which cannot justifiably be included in either of the previous divisions, are given under this heading.

24.1 FORMULAS

24.1 Barlow 1938 *test.* **1938 "A.B."**   *Microscope*, **2**:150

FORMULA: paraffin (43°C.) 45, ethyl cellulose (low viscosity) 10, stearic acid 15

24.1 Brain 1950   11360, **70**:313

STOCK SOLUTIONS: I. 1% celloidin in 98% alc.; II. 1% celloidin in abs. alc.; III. 2.5% celloidin in methyl salicylate

NOTE: Stock solutions I and II are prepared by dilution from a 30% solution of celloidin in the usual 50:50 alc.-ether mixture.

REAGENTS REQUIRED: *A*. 2% gelatin; *B*. 10% gelatin; *C*. AF 21.1 Brain 1950; *D*. stock I; *E*. stock II; *F*. 60 stock II, 30 stock III; *G*. 50 stock II, 50 stock III; *H*. 30 stock II, 60 stock III; *I*. stock III; *J*. benzene; *K*. 60 benzene, 30 paraffin; *L*. 50 benzene, 50 paraffin; *M*. 30 benzene, 60 paraffin; *N*. paraffin 56°MP

METHOD: [well-washed, formaldehyde-fixed material] → *A*, 4 days, 37°C. → *B*, few hrs. 37°C. → [cast in block of *B*] → *C*, changed daily, until decalcification complete (45 days for mouse jaws) → running water, 24 hrs. → 50% alc., 30 mins., 37°C. → 70% alc., 30 mins., 37°C. → 90% alc., 30 mins., 37°C. → *D*, 1½ hrs., 37°C. → *E*, 3 changes, each 30 mins., 37°C. → *F*, 1 hr., 37°C. → *G*, 1 hr., 37°C. → *H*, 1 hr., 37°C. → *I*, 4 days, 37°C. → *J*, 2 changes each 2½ hrs., 37°C. → *K*, 1 hr., 45°C. → *L*, 1 hr., 45°C. → *M*, 1 hr., 45°C. → *N*, 3 changes each 8 hrs., 58°C. → [cast block in *N*]

RECOMMENDED FOR: teeth, particularly for showing relation of enamel to dentine.

24.1 Cutler 1935   1887a, **20**:445

METHOD: glycol stearate used as paraffin but embedding from 95% alc.

28

Various Formulas

V 00 General Observations

This chapter includes those formulas which cannot reasonably be placed in any other section. It is divided into three main and two subsidiary divisions. The formulas in the first division (the cements, lutes, and varnishes—V 10) were at one time of more interest to microtomists than is now generally the case. This indicates less a reduction in the value of the formulas than it does the changing fashion in the preparation of microscope slides. It is now the custom, greatly to the detriment of the art, to use for mounting only those materials which themselves support and cement the coverslip in position. The writer has elsewhere in the present work expressed his opinion of the undesirability of this custom, and it is to be hoped that the inclusion of many of these older formulas for cements and varnishes, designed to attach the coverslip to the slide and to preserve within it a fluid medium,

650

may encourage mounters to revert to fluid mounts. The next section (on adhesives—V 20) is self-explanatory, though few people today seem to think it necessary to cause to adhere to a slide any object except a paraffin ribbon, or, even in that case, to realize that materials other than egg albumen may be used with advantage. The next section (on media for injection—V 30) contains many formulas which cannot be ignored by any preparer of microscope slides whether for teaching or research purposes. The two last sections (on cleaning methods and formulas—V 40, and miscellaneous formulas—V 50) are of little importance but provide a final resting-place for formulas which the writer considers worth publishing but which cannot be placed elsewhere.

V 10 Cements, Lutes, and Varnishes

These materials are used for two purposes. The first is the attachment of objects, either supporting structures such as cells (see Chapters 1–3) or objects for examination, to slides; or second, they are used to seal edges of coverslips in order to retain under the cover some mounting medium. The formulas are here divided into those which are in fluid form and those which must be melted before application. It must be remembered, however, that the majority of the solid cements may be dissolved in a suitable solvent and used as though they were fluid. If this is done, it is well to heat the dried cement to get rid of the last trace of solvent.

Care must be taken, in following old directions as to the sealing of microscopical preparations, that one uses actually the material intended by the writer and not that which at the present time passes under the same name. Thus the modern marine glue bears no relation at all to the solution of shellac in gutta percha which was the marine glue used by the early microtomists. The formula given below (V 12.2 Harting 1880) is very close to the original marine glue, but there is no means of finding out whether or not it is identical with the material ("G 4") specified by the early writers and blindly copied by many later ones. Another source of constant confusion is gold size. This was originally partially polymerized and oxidized linseed oil diluted with turpentine, and was specified for the use of gilders because it remained tacky for a long time, thus enabling the leaf gold to be applied to a complex ornament over a long period. Modern varnishes having the same property of remaining tacky are available on the market under the name of *gold size*, but are entirely unsuitable for the preparation of microscope slides. Another misunderstood term is *sealing wax*. In the earlier days sealing wax contained considerable quantities of Venice turpentine and of beeswax, as well as the shellac of which it is now almost completely composed. In the following pages will be found formulas giving so far as is possible the original ingredients.

Shellac itself is a term capable of misinterpretation. Orange shellac is a natural exudate, caused by insect damage, from the bark of many resinous trees. It is a mixture of alcohol-soluble resins and naphtha-soluble waxes. White shellac is produced by the action of chlorine on alkaline-aqueous solutions (in part "soaps") of orange shellac. The alcohol-soluble fraction of this chlorinated shellac polymerizes very rapidly, at temperatures just below its melting point, into a material which is insoluble in alcohol or any other common solvent. Hence a "cell" turned from V 11.2 Gage 1901 (below) can be used for an alcohol mount if the dewaxed shellac called for in the formula is prepared from white shellac and the ring-baked. Bellido 1927 (11360, **47**:27) specifies heat treatment for shellac cells used in the mounting of diatoms in bromonaphthalene.

The only confusion which is likely to arise among solvents is in the use of the term *benzine*, a petroleum fraction nowadays sold as ligroin. It has none of the properties of *benzene* nor should it be confused with the low-boiling-point petroleum ether which is sometimes specified in its place.

11 FLUID AT ROOM TEMPERATURES

11.1 AQUEOUS BASE

11.1 Bellido 1897 *test.* **1927** *ips.*   11360, **47**:9
FORMULA: water 48, acetic acid 50, abs. alc. 2, gelatin 6
PREPARATION: Soak gelatin in water overnight. Melt at 90°C. and add other ingredients.
NOTE: Don Ernesto Caballero Bellido's Spanish writings fall naturally under the name "Caballero." The present writer uses "Bellido" because that is the last name under the title of the English paper cited. The Royal Microscopical Society avoids the dilemma neatly by omitting any reference to this paper in the author index of the volume in question.

11.1 Caballero 1897   *see* V 11.1 Bellido 1897 (note)

11.1 Semmens 1938   *CS11—auct.*   *Microscope*, **2**:120
FORMULA: water 65, acetic acid 25, gum arabic 20

11.1 Spence 1938   *see* V 11.1 Gage 1901 (note)

11.2 NONAQUEOUS BASE

11.2 Beale 1880a   *Gold size*   Beale 1880, 54
FORMULA: linseed oil 100, red lead 4, umber 1.5, white lead 5, yellow ochre 5
PREPARATION: Mix oil, red lead, and umber thoroughly. Boil 3 hours. Allow to settle. Decant clear fluid. Grind white lead and yellow ochre together. Mix with boiled oil. Reboil 3 hours. Allow to stand. Decant.

11.2 Beale 1880b   *Brunswick black*   Beale 1880, 55
FORMULA: Trinidad asphalt 50, boiled linseed oil 50, turpentine 100
PREPARATION: Boil asphalt in linseed oil for some time. Cool. Mix turpentine with cooled mass.
NOTE: Beale directs that $4\frac{1}{2}$ oz. of linseed oil be boiled with half an ounce of litharge "until quite stringy."

11.2 Beale 1880c   *Sealing wax varnish*   Beale 1880, 55
FORMULA: 95% alc. 100, sealing wax 40
NOTE: This cement should be made with a sealing wax of the period, not with the modern variety which is mostly rosin. A typical contemporary recipe is: 5 parts shellac, 9 parts Venice turpentine, 7 parts rosin, 6 parts pigment. (Spon, *Workshop Receipts*, 2nd series. London 1883).

11.2 Beale 1880d   *Damar cement*   Beale 1880, 55
FORMULA: benzene 60, gum damar 40

11.2 Beale 1880e   *Cement for glass*   Beale 1880, 60
FORMULA: chloroform 65, rubber 1, gum mastic 35
PREPARATION: Dissolve chloroform in rubber. Add gum mastic to solution. Digest at 50°C. 1 week. Allow to settle. Decant.

11.2 Behrens 1883   Behrens 1883, 192
FORMULA: abs. alc. 50, ether 10, turpentine 50, copal in fine powder 50
PREPARATION: Dissolve ingredients with prolonged but very gentle heat.

11.2 Bell's cement
This was a proprietary product of secret composition; the formula appears to have been lost.

11.2 Bellido   *see* V 11.2 Hitchcock 1884 (note)

11.2 Bénoit-Bazille *test.* **1942 Langeron**   Langeron 1942, 666
FORMULA: turpentine 30, asphalt 20, gold size 50
PREPARATION: Dissolve asphalt in turpentine. Add gold size to solution.

11.2 Brooke *test.* **1880 Beale**   *flexible Brunswick black*   Beale 1880, 55
FORMULA: Brunswick black 90, rubber solution 10
NOTE: Beale does not specify proportions. Those given have served the author.

11.2 Carnoy *test.* **1937 Gatenby and Cowdry**   Gatenby and Cowdry 1937, 232
FORMULA: tolu balsam 40, Canada balsam 20, chloroform 30, shellac 20
PREPARATION: Mix tolu balsam and Canada balsam with heat. Cool. Dissolve chloroform in shellac. Add to cooled mixture.
NOTE: The cement is to be diluted with chloroform until it flows freely from the brush.

11.2 Chevalier 1882   Chevalier 1882, 305
FORMULA: asphalt 15, turpentine 15, gold size 60
PREPARATION: Dissolve asphalt in turpentine. Add gold size to solution.

11.2 Davies *circ.* **1865**   Davies, 24
FORMULA: rubber 0.5, ligroin 70, asphalt 30
PREPARATION: Dissolve rubber in ligroin. Dissolve asphalt in solution.

11.2 Eulenstein *test.* **1880 Beale**   *Brunswick black*   Beale 1880, 55
FORMULA: Brunswick black 50, gold size 50, Canada balsam 5

11.2 Frey 1877   Frey 1877, 133
FORMULA: chloroform 80, rubber 1.25, gum mastic 20
PREPARATION: Dissolve chloroform in rubber 1.25. Add gum mastic in fine powder to solution.

11.2 Gage 1901   Gage 1901, 204
FORMULA: V 11.2 Hitchcock 1884 100, Venice turpentine 2, castor oil 2
NOTE: Spence **1938** (*Microscope*, **2**:127) omits the Venice turpentine.

11.2 Gram-Rützon *test.* **1883 Behrens** *cit.* **Poulsen**   Behrens 1883, 191
FORMULA: abs. alc. 25, ether 50, Canada balsam 25, shellac 25

11.2 Groves *test.* **1883 Hogg**   Hogg 1883, 246
FORMULA: chloroform 50, gum mastic 50, bismuth nitrate *q.s.*
PREPARATION: Dissolve chloroform in gum mastic. Add enough bismuth nitrate to form a thick cream with gum solution.

11.2 Hitchcock 1884 *test.* **Gage 1901**   Gage 1901, 204
PREPARATION: Half fill a bottle with shellac. Fill with 90% alc. and leave to complete solution. Place in a separatory funnel with one-half its volume of naphtha. Shake well, allow to separate, retain the alc. fraction, and evaporate to suitable consistency.
NOTE: This method of dewaxing shellac is said by Spence **1938** (*Microscope*, 2:127) to be due to **Pelz,** about 1876. It is certainly German in origin, since *benzol* (an obvious mistranslation of *benzin*) is frequently specified. **Bellido 1897** (11360, **47**:9) merely decants the clear supernant fluid from an alcoholic solution of shellac which has stood for some weeks.

11.2 Hogg 1883a   Hogg 1883, 221
FORMULA: gum damar 20, turpentine 20, gum mastic 20, chloroform 40
PREPARATION: Dissolve gum damar 20 and turpentine with heat. Cool. Filter. Dissolve gum mastic and chloroform in cold. Filter. Mix with filtered damar.

11.2 Hogg 1883b   Hogg 1883, 222
FORMULA: acetic acid 90, gum ammoniac 2, gelatin 20
PREPARATION: Dissolve gum ammoniac in acetic acid. Dissolve gelatin in gum solution.
NOTE: This formula wets glass readily and was originally designed for sealing glycerol mounts.

11.2 James 1885   11360, 1101
FORMULA: gum damar 40, ligroin 100, zinc oxide *q.s.*
PREPARATION: Dissolve gum damar in ligroin. Heat zinc oxide to dryness. Cool. Moisten with benzine. Add damar solution with constant stirring. Leave 12 hours. Decant from any gross particles.

11.2 Kitton *test.* **1883 Hogg**   Hogg 1883, 247
   FORMULA: *A.* white lead 30, red lead 30, litharge 30, turpentine *q.s.* to make a paste;
      B. gold size
   NOTE: For use mix about 3 parts *B* with 1 of *A.* This mixture sets very rapidly and forms
      a very hard cement which may be used for the preparation of cells.

11.2 Mohr and Wehrle 1940   *Cellobalm—auct.*   20540b, **15**:173
   FORMULA: toluene 77, ethyl cellulose 7.7, Canada balsam 15

11.2 Pelz   *see* V 11.2 Hitchcock 1884 (note)

11.2 Perruche 1939   *Bull. soc. franc. microsc.*, **8**:147
   FORMULA: benzene 100, aluminum stearate 1.5
   USE: For making water-repellent barriers for the temporary restraint of aqueous fluids on
      slides.

11.2 Robin 1871   *flexible asphalt cement*   Robin 1871, 379
   FORMULA: carbon disulfide 60, asphalt 30, Venice turpentine 10

11.2 Rousselet 1898   11479, **7**:93
   FORMULA: benzene 40, gum damar 25, gold size 30
   PREPARATION: Dissolve benzene in gum damar. Mix gold size with solution.

11.2 Seiler 1881   *see* M 33.1 Seiler 1881

11.2 Semmens 1937   *Microscope*, **1**:5
   PREPARATION: Dissolve 25 gum damar in 250 each of chloroform and xylene. Filter and
      evaporate to 100.
   RECOMMENDED FOR: ringing lactophenol mounts.

11.2 Spence 1938   *see* V 11.2 Gage 1901 (note)

11.2 Thiersch *test.* **1871 Robin**   *blue varnish*   Robin 1871, 381
   FORMULA: 95% alc. 100, shellac 60, spirit blue 1, castor oil 0.4

11.2 Woohead *test.* **1884 Cole**   Cole 1884b, 50
   FORMULA: benzene 50, gum damar 50, zinc oxide 6
   PREPARATION: Dissolve gum damar in benzene. Grind zinc oxide with solution.

11.2 Zimmermann *test.* **1883 Behrens**   Behrens 1883, 191
   FORMULA: shellac 50, 95% alc. 100, anilin green 2
   PREPARATION: Dissolve ingredients. Filter. Evaporate to required consistency.

12 SOLID AT ROOM TEMPERATURES (APPLIED MOLTEN)

12.1 AQUEOUS BASE

12.1 de Groot 1904   23833, **28**:406
   FORMULA: zinc oxide 25, water 90, gelatin 20
   PREPARATION: Mix zinc oxide with a little water to make a paste. Add rest of water
      gradually to secure smooth suspension. Heat to 80°C. on water bath. Dissolve gelatin
      in hot suspension.
   NOTE: This cement is excellent for making alcohol-resistant glass-to-glass seals.

12.1 Marsh 1878   Marsh 1878, 45
   FORMULA: gelatin 100, water *q.s.*, creosote 0.6
   PREPARATION: Mix gelatin and water and soak for 12 hours. Drain. Melt. Add creosote to
      molten gelatin.

12.1 Reuter *test.* **1938 Carleton and Leach**   Carleton and Leach 1938, 116
   FORMULA: water 100, gelatin 20, potassium dichromate 0.5
   PREPARATION: Dissolve gelatin in 90 water at 80°C. Add potassium dichromate dis-
      solved in 10 water.

12.1 Rüyter 1934   4285a, **11**:410
   PREPARATION: Saturate 100 water with oil of thyme. Soak 20 gelatin overnight. Melt. Add thyme water to make 100. Add 10 5% potassium dichromate. Keep in dark.
   NOTE: This formula is identical with **Rüyter 1935** (23632, **51**:374).

12.1 Seiler 1881   Seiler 1881, 93
   FORMULA: acetic acid 100, gelatin 27, gum ammoniac 2.2
   PREPARATION: Dissolve the gum in the acid. Filter. Warm and dissolve gelatin.
   NOTE: Seiler (*loc. cit.*) recommends that the cooled ring should be painted with 2% potassium dichromate and exposed to light.

12.2 NONAQUEOUS BASE

12.2 Apáthy 1889   23632, **6**:164
   FORMULA: paraffin 60°C. 50, Canada balsam 50
   PREPARATION: Heat ingredients till golden brown.
   NOTE: The identical composition can be achieved by dissolving 45 parts Canada resin in 55 parts molten wax.

12.2 Beale 1880a   *marine glue*   Beale 1880, 55
   FORMULA: ligroin 100, Para rubber 50, shellac 50
   PREPARATION: Dissolve Para rubber in half ligroin with gentle heat. Dissolve shellac in half ligroin with gentle heat. Cool. Mix thoroughly.
   NOTE: The mixture may either be evaporated until solvent free, in which case it is used as a thermoplastic cement, or diluted with more ligroin for use as a varnish.

12.2 Beale 1880b   *French cement*   Beale 1880, 59
   FORMULA: rubber 100, lime *q.s.*
   PREPARATION: Melt the rubber over an oil bath. Add the lime, little by little, until the mixture thickens. Scrape into a mortar and heat with a pestle until cool enough to knead with the hands.
   NOTE: The cement, when cool, should be of the consistency of stiff modelling clay. It is remarkably waterproof and adheres perfectly to glass.

12.2 Belling 1926   2975, **50**:160
   FORMULA: paraffin 50, gum mastic 50

12.2 Cigalas *test.* **1942 Langeron**   Langeron 1942, 677
   FORMULA: beeswax 70, rosin 30, lard 10
   PREPARATION: Dissolve ingredients together.
   NOTE: This is an excellent waterproof cement for temporary aquaria or for mending leaks.

12.2 Coburn 1915   4349, **5**:71
   FORMULA: white lead ground in oil 50, raw linseed oil 7, rosin 29, 95% alc. 7, shellac 7
   PREPARATION: Mix the oil with the white lead and raise to the melting point of the rosin which is then incorporated. While cool but still liquid, stir in the shellac dissolved in the alc.

12.2 Fant 1932   *in verb.*
   FORMULA: anhydrous lanolin 30, rosin 55, "dried" Canada balsam 10
   PREPARATION: Melt ingredients together.
   NOTE: This formula was verbally communicated to the author by Fant in 1932 and by the author communicated to others. This lead to an unsigned note in Watson's *Microscope Record* 1934, attributing the composition to Gray; the error has been perpetuated by Gatenby and Cowdry 1937, 230, and others.

12.2 Gage 1896   Gage 1896, 179
   FORMULA: V 11.2 Hitchcock 1884 100, castor oil 10, Venice turpentine 10

12.2 Gray 1934   *see* V 12.2 Fant 1932 (note)

12.2 Griffiths *test circ.* **1865 Davies**   Davies, 22
   FORMULA: rosin 50, beeswax 10, red ochre 10, Canada balsam 20

12.2 Harting *test.* **1880 Beale**   *gutta percha cement*   Beale 1880, 56
FORMULA: turpentine 90, gutta percha 6, shellac 6
PREPARATION: Dissolve turpentine in gutta percha with stirring at 50°C. Strain. Dissolve shellac in strained fluid at 60°C. Continue heating until a test drop placed on a cool surface becomes reasonably hard.
NOTE: This is to be used as a thermoplastic cement, particularly for attaching hard rubber cells.

12.2 Hood and Neill 1948   20540b, **23**:217
FORMULA: asphalt 42, Canada balsam 15, paraffin (48°C.) 28, pitch 15

12.2 Kroenig 1886   1780, **27**:657
FORMULA: beeswax 20, rosin 80

12.2 Lataste *test.* **1942 Langeron**   Langeron 1942, 677
FORMULA: paraffin 60, rubber scrap 30
PREPARATION: Heat paraffin and rubber scrap till solution takes place, taking equal precautions against fire and suffocation of the technician.

12.2 Martin 1872   Martin 1872, 169
FORMULA: rosin 80, beeswax 20, tallow 10, oil color as desired

12.2 Mendeleef *test.* **1942 Langeron**   Langeron 1942, 677
FORMULA: beeswax 12.5, rosin 50, ochre 20, linseed oil 0.5
PREPARATION: Melt wax. Add rosin when hot. Stir to perfect mixture. Grind ochre and oil to a paste. Add to hot mixture.
NOTE: Any other appropriate pigment may be used in place of the ochre.

12.2 Muir and Judah 1915   4349, **5**:71
FORMULA: Trinidad asphalt 85, boiled linseed oil 12, oil of amber 3
PREPARATION: Raise the oils to boiling and add 25 asphalt, boil 30 minutes and cool. Remelt and add remaining asphalt in 4 portions, cooling and remelting between each addition. Boil 45 minutes after last addition.

12.2 Noyer 1918   6630, **81**:741
FORMULA: rosin 80, lanolin 20
PREPARATION: Melt together.

12.2 Oschatz 1842 *test.* **1847 Cooper**   Cooper 1847, 207
FORMULA: sealing wax 50, white lead ground in oil 50
PREPARATION: Melt ingredients together.

13 OTHER CEMENTS, LUTES, AND VARNISHES

13.1 FORMULAS

13.1 Langeron 1942   Langeron 1942, 327
FORMULA: white beeswax 65, Venice turpentine 35
RECOMMENDED FOR: rolling into pellets to support coverslip.

13.1 Martin 1872   *dead black varnish*   Martin 1872, 172
PREPARATION: Mix lamp black and gold size in a mortar to a thick cream.

V 20 Adhesives

The adhesives given in the present section may be distinguished from the cements, lutes, and varnishes of the last section by the use to which they are put. A cement or varnish is required to have properties other than that of causing one object to adhere to another. The adhesives most commonly employed in microtomy are those used to attach sections in paraffin ribbons to a slide. It is not absolutely necessary to use an adhesive for this purpose, because a section of animal material, flattened with distilled water on a chemically clean slide, will remain attached through most subsequent manipulations. When an adhesive for paraffin ribbons is used, it may be applied in either of two ways without regard to the specifications given by the inventor: the material may be first smeared on the slide, or it may be diluted considerably with water and this diluted adhesive used to flatten the section. It may be thought curious that formulas for label adhesives should be included, but there is certainly no commoner reason for the loss of a valuable preparation than the detachment of the label. It is warmly recommended that one of those formulas be employed which contain a small quantity of glycerol for the purpose of preventing the absolute hardening of the adhesive. The entire label and not only the adhesive upon it should be moistened to avoid a differential contraction in drying, which invariably strips the adhesive from the glass.

21 FOR ATTACHING SECTIONS TO SLIDES

21.1 For Attaching Paraffin Ribbons

21.1 Artschwäger 1919   *see* V 21.1 Szombathy 1918 (note)

21.1 Böhm and Davidoff 1905   *Japanese method—compl. script.*

Böhm and Davidoff 1905, **30**

REAGENTS REQUIRED: *A.* V 21.1 Mayer 1884; *B.* 0.5% gum arabic
METHOD: slides are *very* thinly coated with *A* and then dried at 70°–80°C. to coagulate albumen. Sections are flattened on the slide with warm *B*.
NOTE: In European literature, other than English, this method is fairly universally known as the "Japanese method" (cf. Cajal and de Castro 1933, 65; Spielmeyer 1924, 48)

21.1 Claoué 1920 *test.* **1942 Langeron**   Langeron 1942, 481

FORMULA: alcohol 50, ether 50, pyroxylin 0.4, castor oil 3, camphor 2
PREPARATION: Dissolve alcohol, ether, and pyroxylin. Add castor oil and camphor to solution.
METHOD: applied at any time from a drop bottle. The slide should be blotted free of excess reagent before the adhesive is applied.
RECOMMENDED FOR: cementing in place sections which have loosened

21.1 Cobe and Schoenfle 1946   *Tech. Bull.*, **7**:31

PREPARATION: In 100 boiling 0.2% potassium dichromate dissolve 0.02 gelatin. Boil 5 minutes, cool, filter.
METHOD: flatten ribbons on bath of warm solution, strand on slide, and dry.

21.1 Crabb 1935   19938, **80**:530

REAGENTS REQUIRED: *A.* colloidin USP 40, abs. alc. 20, ether 20, amyl acetate 20; *B.* collodion USP 50, abs. alc. 25, ether 25
METHOD: [ribbons, spread and flattened on slide and thoroughly dried] → *A*, flooded on slide, 30 secs. → blot → *B*, flooded on slide → drain → dry → 70% alc., 5 mins. → 95% alc., quick wash → xylene

21.1 David 1935   19938, **82**:179

FORMULA: water 100, "waterglass" 1, ammonia 1

21.1 Gravis 1889   4992, **15**:72

FORMULA: water 100, agar 0.1, camphor 0.1
PREPARATION: Dissolve agar in water with boiling. Filter. Add camphor to filtrate.

21.1 Haupt 1930   *see* V 21.1 Szombathy 1918 (note)

21.1 Heidenhain 1905   23632, **22**:331

FORMULA: water 75, albumen 2, 95% alc. 25
PREPARATION: Dissolve albumen in 50 water. Filter. Mix 95% alc. with 25 water. Add to filtered solution.

21.1 Hollande 1911   1823, **13**:171

FORMULA: garlic 50, water 80, chloroform 1
PREPARATION: Crush ingredients. Triturate. Leave 24 hours. Filter.
NOTE: For some reason this appears to work better than a pectin solution of comparable strength.

21.1 Land *test.* **1915 Chamberlain**   Chamberlain 1915, 114
REAGENTS REQUIRED: *A*. 1% gum arabic; *B*. 0.5% potassium dichromate
METHOD: Smear *A* on slide. Flood with *B*. Warm to flatten sections. Drain, dry.

21.1 Lillie 1945   20540b, **20**:99
FORMULA: water 100 dried egg albumen 5, sodium chloride 0.5, glycerol *q.s.*, 0.01%
merthiolate 0.5
PREPARATION: Shake the water, albumen, and sodium chloride gently together till dissolved. Filter. Add glycerol to make double volume of filtrate. Add merthiolate to mixture.

21.1 Masson 1928   608b, **4**:181
REAGENTS REQUIRED: *A*. 0.25% gelatin; *B*. 40% formaldehyde
METHOD: flatten sections on *A*. Drain. Expose to vapor of *B* at 50°C., 20 mins. to overnight.

21.1 Masson *test.* **1942 Langeron**   Langeron 1942, 476
REAGENTS REQUIRED: *A*. 1% gelatin; *B*. 95% alc. 80, 40% formaldehyde 20
METHOD: [paraffin ribbons] → float on *A* and warm to flatten → drain → dry heat to melt paraffin → xylene, till wax removed → abs. alc. → *B*,, 5 mins. → 50% alc.

21.1 Mayer 1884   11360, **4**:317
FORMULA: fresh egg white 50, glycerol 50, sodium salicylate 1
PREPARATION: Agitate ingredients at intervals for some days. Filter.
RECOMMENDED FOR: spreading in thin layer on slide; or, diluted 20:1 with water, flattening sections.

21.1 McDowell and Vassos 1940   1789a, **29**:432
FORMULA: water 90, starch 3, 10% hydrochloric acid 0.5, thymol 0.1
PREPARATION: Mix starch in 30 water to make a smooth paste. Raise 60 water to boiling. Add to starch paste. Add hydrochloric acid to starch. Boil 5 minutes. Cool. Add thymol to cooled starch.

21.1 Moreau 1918   5293, **34**:164
REAGENTS REQUIRED: *A*. 0.01% gelatin, freshly prepared; *B*. 90% alc. 80, 40% formaldehyde 20
METHOD: sections are flattened on warm *A* and dried. After passage through benzene and abs. alc., *B* is applied from a drop bottle.

21.1 Régaud *test.* **1942 Langeron**   Langeron 1942, 481
REAGENTS REQUIRED: *A*. collodion USP 20, ether 40, abs. alc. 40; *B*. 70% alc.
METHOD: [sections attached to slide but apparently loose] → abs. alc. → *A*, 2 mins. → drain → *B*, → stain, etc.
RECOMMENDED FOR: cementing in place paraffin sections which appear loose after dewaxing.

21.1 Reinke *test.* **1928 Schmorl**   Schmorl 1928, 77
FORMULA: egg albumen 50, glycerol 50
PREPARATION: Beat egg white until stiff. Leave till the mass has reverted to a clear fluid. Filter and add an equal volume of glycerol.

21.1 Rüyter 1931a   23632, **47**:226
FORMULA: water 80, V 21.1 Mayer 1884 1, acetone 20, methyl benzoate 0.3
PREPARATION: Mix 21.1 Mayer 1884 with water. Mix acetone and methyl benzoate and add to first mixture.
METHOD: use to float and flatten ribbon
RECOMMENDED FOR: attaching ribbons from double-embedded (nitrocellulose-paraffin) blocks.

21.1 Rüyter 1931b   23632, **48**:226
FORMULA: water 80, acetone 20, methyl benzoate 0.6
METHOD: flood under ribbons on slide. Warm. Dry.
USE: as Rüyter 1931a

21.1 Schneidau 1937   21559, **56**:258
FORMULA: water 100, egg albumen 0.06, glycerol 1.6, sodium salicylate 0.06
RECOMMENDED FOR: flattening and fixing paraffin ribbons.

21.1 Spoerri 1939   19938, **90**:260
FORMULA: water 100, starch 3, hydrochloric acid 0.2
PREPARATION: Suspend the starch in 30 water; add 70 boiling water and stir. Add acid
  and boil 5 minutes.

21.1 Szombathy 1918   23632, **34**:334
REAGENTS REQUIRED: *A*. water 100, gelatin 1, glycerol 15, sodium salicylate 0.2; *B*. water
  98, 40% formaldehyde 2
METHOD: coat slide thinly with *A*. Flood with *B* on which sections are flattened in the
  usual manner. Dry.
NOTE: This method is usually known to botanists from a paper by **Artschwäger** 1919
  (3430, **67**:373). **Haupt 1930** (20540b, **5**:97) substitutes 2 phenol for the salicylate in
  A above.

21.2 FOR ATTACHING SECTIONS IN NITROCELLULOSE

21.2 Heringa and ten Berge 1923   23632, **40**:166
REAGENTS REQUIRED: *A*. 3% gelatin; *B*. 5% sodium sulfate
METHOD: [coat slides with *A*] → dry → soak in *B*, 2 hrs. → wash → dry

21.2 Langeron 1942a   Langeron 1942, 482
REAGENTS REQUIRED: *A*. V 21.1 Mayer 1884; *B*. oil of cloves; *C*. abs. alc.; *D*. abs. alc. 50,
  ether 50
METHOD: [section from 70% alc.] → press to slide coated with *A* → blot with considerable pressure → *B*, from drop bottle, few mins. → *C*, in jar, 15 mins. → *D*, till nitrocellulose dissolved → abs. alc. → stain, etc.

21.2 Langeron 1942b   Langeron 1942, 483
REAGENTS REQUIRED: *A*. water 100, gelatin 10, phenol 0.5; *B*. 4% formaldehyde; *C*. abs.
  alc.; *D*. abs. alc. 50, ether 50
METHOD: [section from 70% alc.] → press to slide coated with *A* → blot thoroughly →
  B, 5 mins. → *C*, 2–3 mins. → *D*, till nitrocellulose dissolved → abs. alc. → [stain, etc.]

21.2 Linstaedt 1912   763, **6**:445
REAGENTS REQUIRED: *A*. water 100, dextrin 3, sucrose 3; *B*. 4% celluloid in acetone;
  C. 1% celloidin in ether-alc.
METHOD: coat glass plates with *A* and dry; spray or dip coat with *B*; store till required.
  Arrange sections on water film on coated plate; blot; spray with *C*. When partially
  dry dip in 70% alc., then in water till celluloid sheet bearing sections can be detached.
RECOMMENDED FOR: preparation of sheets of sections which may be cut up with scissors,
  after staining, for issue to classes.

21.2 Rüyter 1931   *see* V 21.1 Rüyter 1931

21.3 FOR ATTACHING INDIVIDUAL SECTIONS REQUIRING STAINING

21.3 Altmann 1894 *test.* **1905 Böhm and Davidoff**   Böhm and Davidoff 1905, 78
REAGENTS REQUIRED: *A*. 3% gutta percha in chloroform; *B*. collodion USP
METHOD: Slide is coated with *A*, dried and stored. When warmed, coated slides become
  tacky. Sections are pressed to tacky surface, cooled, and varnished with *B*.

21.3 Chiovenda 1936 *test.* **1937 Foot**   4349, **17**:173
FORMULA: water 84, V 21.1 Reinke (1928) 12, glycerol 4, merthiolate 9.5
METHOD: soak sections in adhesive; strand on clean slide; drain; dry at 30–40°C.; place
  in abs. alc.

21.3 Fol *test.* **1937 Gatenby and Cowdry**   Gatenby and Cowdry 1937, 116
FORMULA: water 72, 95% alc. 30, acetic acid 7, gelatin 1.5, chrome alum 0.1
PREPARATION: Dissolve acetic acid in gelatin with heat. Mix 95% alc. in 70 water and
  add to solution. Dissolve chrome alum in 2 water and add to mixture.
METHOD: clean slides are dipped and dried. When again moistened, the surface becomes
  sticky without dissolving.

21.3 Heringa 1924   6630, **91**:931
REAGENTS REQUIRED: *A*. 3% gelatin; *B*. 2.5% sodium sulfate
METHOD: [clean slides] → *A*, dip → dry → *B*, 1 hr. → water, thorough wash → dry
NOTE: Slides so treated are soaked for a few moments in water before having sections pressed to them.

21.3 Langeron 1942   Langeron 1942, 678
FORMULA: water 81, gum arabic 30, aluminum sulfate 0.6
PREPARATION: Dissolve gum arabic in 75 water. Dissolve aluminum sulfate in 6 water and add to gum solution.

21.3 Lebowich 1936   1887a, **22**:782
REAGENTS REQUIRED: *A*. 0.5% gelatin in 1% (of "3%") hydrogen peroxide; *B*. 2% neutralized formaldehyde; *C*. 2.5% gum arabic
METHOD: Dip chemically clean slide in *A*. Drain and dry. Dip in *B*. Drain and store. Use *C* to float and flatten sections. Drain, dry section in place.
NOTE: This technique was originally intended for use with E 11.1 Lebowich 1936. **Moritz 1939** (20540b, **14**:17) recommends 0.25% gelatin in *A*.

21.3 Masson *test.* **1942 Langeron**   Langeron 1942, 457
REAGENTS REQUIRED: *A*. 70% alc.; *B*. 70% alc. 50, ether 50; *C*. abs. alc. 50, ether 50, pyroxylin 0.25; *D*. 80% alc.
METHOD: [sections floating in *A*] → strand on slide → *B*, from drop bottle → *C*, in jar, cautious dip → drain → *D*

21.3 Moritz 1939   *see* V 21.3 Lebowich 1936 (note)

21.3 Obregia 1890   15058, **9**:295
REAGENTS REQUIRED: *A*. dextrose syrup 60, dextrin syrup 20, 95% alc. 40; *B*. 2% celloidin
METHOD: Coat slides with *A*, very thinly. Dry *slowly*. Flatten section on sticky surface. Heat to 60°C. Remove paraffin with solvent. Remove solvent with abs. alc. Pour on *B*. Dry. Strip film with sections attached.
NOTE: The strength of syrup is not important. The consistency should be about that of the simple syrup of the pharmacopeia.

21.3 Schällibaum 1883   1780, **22**:689
FORMULA: 2% pyroxylin 20, oil of cloves 80
METHOD: [make thin layer on slide] → press on section → dry 10 mins. → heat to 50°C.

21.3 Windeholz 1923   7276, **70**:877
FORMULA: "waterglass" 30, water 70
METHOD: spread a thin film on slide; leave till just dry; strand section on film. Blot and leave 15 mins.
NOTE: "Waterglass" is a commercial solution of sodium silicate of very variable composition.

21.3 Zimmermann 1896   Zimmermann 1896, 40
REAGENTS REQUIRED: *A*. V 21.1 Gravis 1889; *B*. collodion USP 5, abs. alc. 25, ether 75
METHOD: sections → flattened on slide using *A* → drain → dry → varnish in place with *B*

22 FOR ATTACHING WHOLE OBJECTS TO SLIDES

22.1 FOR OBJECTS REQUIRING FURTHER MANIPULATION

22.1 Chatton and Lwoff 1930   6630, **104**:834
FORMULA: water 100, gelatin 10, sodium chloride 0.05
RECOMMENDED FOR: attaching fixed protozoans on slide before silver staining. Use at 25°C.

22.1 Giesbrecht 1881   23833, **4**:255
REAGENTS REQUIRED: *A*. 1% shellac to 95% alc.; *B*. clove oil
METHOD: Coat slides thinly with *A*. Dry. Moisten with *B*. Arrange objects on oil film and then evaporate oil at 60°C.

22.2 For Objects Not Requiring Further Manipulation

22.2 Gage 1896   Gage 1896, 180
FORMULA: V 22.3 Gage 1896 50, acetic acid 25, water 25
RECOMMENDED FOR: a thin layer is dried on a slide or coverslip. Objects are arranged on this and then caused to adhere by breathing on them.

22.2 Martin 1872a   Martin 1872, 169
FORMULA: chloroform 80, gutta percha 20, tallow 5

22.2 Martin 1872b   Martin 1872, 169
FORMULA: rosin 75, beeswax 15, Canada balsam 5

22.2 Meakin 1939   *Microscope,* **3**:17
FORMULA: water 12.5, dextrin 25, glycerol 75, phenol 3
PREPARATION: Dissolve dextrin in water with heat. Add other ingredients.
USE: attaching minute objects, particularly butterfly scales.

22.3 Label Adhesives

22.3 Gage 1896   Gage 1896, 179
FORMULA: water 30, 95% alc. 30 acetic acid 30, gelatin 25, glycerol 10
PREPARATION: Dissolve acetic acid in gelatin with occasional shaking at about 30°C. Add water, 95% alc., and glycerol in order given after solution of gelatin is complete.

22.3 Marpmann 1886   23328, **2**:151
FORMULA: water 70, 95% alc. 5, gum arabic 18, gum tragacanth 5, glycerol 23, oil of thyme 0.4
PREPARATION: Dissolve gum arabic in 35 water. Mix gum tragacanth and 95% alc. to make a smooth cream. Flood 35 water on tragacanth cream. Leave 3 hours. Combine with gum arabic solution. Mix glycerol with the oil of thyme and combine with mixed gums.

22.3 Martin 1872   Martin 1872, 171
FORMULA: water 30, gum arabic 30, gelatin 15, glycerol 1.5, camphor 0.1
PREPARATION: Dissolve gum arabic in warm water. Let gelatin soak overnight. Drain. Melt. Mix with warm gum. Add glycerol and camphor to mixture.

23 OTHER PURPOSES

23.1 Formulas

23.1 Apáthy 1912   23632, **29**:449
FORMULA: abs. alc. 50, ether, 50, celloidin 16, clove oil 33
PREPARATION: Dissolve ether and celloidin in abs. alc. Add clove oil to solution.
RECOMMENDED FOR: attaching celloidin blocks to wood blocks.

23.1 Rossi-Régaud *test.* **1927 Ruffini**   Ruffini 1927, 39
FORMULA: collodion USP 25, ether 35, abs. alc. 40
NOTE: The formula here given has been adjusted from that cited by Ruffini to compensate for the difference between US and Italian pharmacopeial collodion.

30 Injection Media

There is a widespread delusion that the only materials which may be used for injection are those suspended in a colloid. Actually any material of a particle size too great to pass through the walls of the vessel may be used and will be held in place either in a wholemount or in the course of sectioning, just as are the blood corpuscles. Injection media should always be strained before use, since the entire injection may be destroyed through one large particle choking off the major vessel through which the injection is being inserted. The writer's preference is always for those injection methods, whereby one inserts first one material in solution, and then, after it, another which will cause the injection mass to precipitate in place. A solution of lead acetate, followed by one of potassium dichromate, may be used to fill the very finest capillaries with an opaque yellow pigment. This is one of the oldest known methods of injection and cannot be equaled by any of the more modern substitutes.

31 FOR INJECTION AT ROOM TEMPERATURE

31.1 FORMULAS

31.1 Altmann 1878 *test.* **1893 Schaffer**   23632, **10**:191
FORMULA: olive oil 50, 95% alc. 25, ether 25
METHOD: small pieces of decalcified bone are impregnated *in vacuo*, washed in water, stained in 1% osmic acid for 24 hrs., and then sectioned.

31.1 Beale 1880a   Beale 1880, 111
FORMULA: water 30, 95% alc. 15, acetic acid 0.5, glycerol 60, ammonium hydroxide 0.3, carmine 0.6
PREPARATION: Dissolve the carmine in 5 water with the ammonia. Mix the acetic acid with 30 glycerol. Add this, with constant stirring, to the carmine solution. Mix 30 glycerol, 15 alc., and 25 water. Add this to carmine-acid mixture.

31.1 Beale 1880b   Beale 1880, 109
FORMULA: water 123, 95% alc. 30, glycerol 12, potassium ferrocyanide 0.8, ferric chloride 0.6
PREPARATION: Dissolve the potassium ferrocyanide in 24 water with 6 glycerol. Dissolve ferric chloride in 24 water with 6 glycerol. Add slowly, with constant agitation, to the ferrocyanide solution. Mix alc. in 75 water. Add to blue solution slowly and with constant agitation.

31.1 Beale 1880c   Beale 1880, 111
FORMULA: water 32, 95% alc. 10, glycerol 45, carmine 0.4, ammonium hydroxide 0.2, acetic acid 0.3
PREPARATION: Mix carmine with water to make paste. Add ammonia to dissolve paste. Add 15 glycerol to carmine solution. Mix 15 glycerol with acetic acid. Add slowly, with constant stirring, to carmine. Add 15 glycerol, alc., and 32 water to mixture in order given.

31.1 Beale 1880d   Beale 1880, 363
FORMULA: water 30, glycerol 60, potassium ferrocyanide 0.2, ferric chloride 0.13, hydrochloric acid 0.1
PREPARATION: Dissolve potassium ferrocyanide in 30 glycerol. Dissolve ferric chloride in 30 glycerol and add slowly, with constant agitation, to the ferrocyanide. Mix hydrochloric acid with water. Add slowly, with constant agitation, to the blue mixture.

31.1 Bensley 1929   590, **40**:146
PREPARATION OF STOCK SOLUTION: Dissolve 0.4 silver nitrate in 10 water. Add 5% sodium phosphate drop by drop until no further ppt. forms. Wash by decantation. Accumulate ppt. in 3 parts water. Add 2.8 citric acid to wet ppt. Dilute with water to 100.
PREPARATION OF WORKING SOLUTION: stock 25, 1% sodium citrate 75
METHOD: inject after washing out blood with sodium citrate. Fix injected pieces in 4% formaldehyde. Cut frozen sections and develop with any AMS 21.1 formula.

31.1 Brucke 1865   1780, **1**:87
FORMULA: 2.17% potassium ferrocyanide 20, 12% sodium sulfate 80, 10% ferric chloride 20
PREPARATION: Mix 40 sodium sulfate with potassium ferrocyanide. Mix 40 sodium sulfate with ferric chloride. Add to above solution slowly and with constant stirring.

31.1 Doyère 1841 *test.* **Cooper 1847**   Cooper 1847, 156
REAGENTS REQUIRED: *A.* solution of potassium chromate; *B.* solution of lead acetate
METHOD: inject *A* through an artery until it runs from a vein. Then inject *B*.

31.1 Frey 1877a   Frey 1877, 111
FORMULA: water 100, lead acetate 30, potassium chromate 14
PREPARATION: Dissolve lead acetate in 50 water. Dissolve potassium chromate in 50 water. Add to acetate solution slowly and with constant stirring.

31.1 Frey 1877b   Frey 1877, 118
FORMULA: water 100, barium chloride 40, sulfuric acid *q.s.*, glycerol 10, alc. 10
PREPARATION: Dissolve barium chloride in water. Add sulfuric acid by drop till no further ppt. forms. Leave 24 hours, then pour off one-half of supernatant fluid. Add glycerol and alc. to residue.

31.1 Mayer 1888   14246, **8**:307
FORMULA: water 105, potassium ferrocyanide 2, ferric chloride 1
PREPARATION: Dissolve potassium ferrocyanide in 5 water. Add ferric chloride and 100 water to ferrocyanide solution slowly and with constant agitation.

31.1 Mayer 1910   Lee and Mayer 1910, 250
FORMULA: water 100, gelatin 10, chloral hydrate 10
PREPARATION: Melt gelatin in water. Add chloral hydrate to hot solution.

31.1 Mozejko 1910   23632, **27**:374
FORMULA: water 100, gelatin 7.5, sodium salicylate 12.5
PREPARATION: Melt gelatin in water. Add sodium salicylate to hot mixture.

31.1 Pearl 1902   *see* V 31.1 Tandler 1901 (note)

31.1 Ranvier 1875   Ranvier 1875, 120
FORMULA: V 31.1 Beale 1880b 80, glycerol 20

31.1 Richardson *test.* **1880 Beale**   Beale 1880, 110
FORMULA: water 30, 95% alc. 4, glycerol 60, potassium ferrocyanide 0.65, ferrous sulfate 0.33
PREPARATION: Dissolve the potassium ferrocyanide in 15 water with 30 glycerol. Dissolve the ferrous sulfate in 15 water with 30 glycerol. Add slowly and with constant stirring to ferrocyanide solution. Add 95% alc. to mixture.

31.1 Richardson *test.* **1877 Frey**   Frey 1877, 117
FORMULA: water 100, potassium ferrocyanide 3.3, ferrous sulfate 1
PREPARATION: Dissolve potassium ferrocyanide in 50 water. Dissolve ferrous sulfate in 50 water. Add slowly, with constant stirring, to ferrocyanide.
NOTE: Frey (*loc. cit.* p. 118) states that if the quantities of salts be doubled, glycerol may be substituted for half the water.

31.1 Robin 1871a   Robin 1871, 33
FORMULA: glycerol 100, acetic acid 5, carmine 3
PREPARATION: Grind carmine in 50 glycerol to a smooth mass. Mix acetic acid in 50 glycerine and add drop by drop, with constant stirring, to carmine until pH about 4.

31.1 Robin 1871b   Robin 1871, 34
FORMULA: sat. sol. (*circ.* 30%) potassium ferrocyanide 13, glycerol 64, sat. sol. (*circ.* 32%) copper sulfate 23
PREPARATION: Mix ferrocyanide in 32 glycerol. Mix the copper sulfate in 32 glycerol. Add to ferrocyanide drop by drop with constant agitation.

31.1 Robin 1871c   Robin 1871, 35
FORMULA: sat. sol. (*circ.* 30%) potassium ferrocyanide 45, glycerol 50, 27% ferric chloride 1.5
PREPARATION: Mix the ferrocyanide in 25 glycerol. Mix ferric chloride in 25 glycerol. Add drop by drop, with constant stirring, to ferrocyanide solution.

31.1 Robin 1871d   Robin 1871, 36
FORMULA: water 70, glycerol 100, cadmium sulfate 30, sodium sulfide 20
PREPARATION: Dissolve cadium sulfate in 40 water with 50 glycerol. Dissolve sodium sulfide in 30 water with 50 glycerol. Mix slowly and with constant stirring into cadmium solution.

31.1 Seiler 1881   Seiler 1881, 78
FORMULA: water 100, gelatin 4.5, silver nitrate 0.2
PREPARATION: Add the silver dissolved in 35 water to the gelatin dissolved in 65.
METHOD: drain blood vessels and fill with medium. Develop in any AMS 21.1 formula.
RECOMMENDED FOR: demonstration of endothelium of blood vessels.

31.1 Tandler 1901   23632, **18**:22
FORMULA: water 100, gelatin 5, potassium iodide 6
PREPARATION: Melt gelatin in water. Add potassium iodide to hot mass. Cool.
NOTE: **Pearl 1902** (11032, **5**:1736) is essentially the same.

31.1 Thoma 1899   1739, **74**:270
FORMULA: water 60, glycerol 40, indigo-carmine 0.15, sodium chloride 1
PREPARATION: Dissolve indigo-carmine in 50 water. Add glycerol to solution. Dissolve
sodium chloride in 10 water. Add slowly to mixture with constant agitation.

31.1 Hagmann 1940   20540b, **15**:115
REAGENTS REQUIRED: *A.* water 90, acetic acid 10, Santomerse no. 3 1, trypan blue 2;
    B. water 75, 40% formaldehyde 10, acetic acid 15, barium chloride 40
METHOD: chloroformed insects are placed under vacuum in a device which permits their
being dropped into *A* in vacuo. After 15 mins. the pressure is released and the insects
transferred to *B* for not less than 3 hrs. Specimens may be stored in 70% alc., mounted
in balsam, and sectioned by celloidin or paraffin techniques. *Santomerse* is a wetting
agent.
RECOMMENDED FOR: injection of insect trachea.

32 FOR INJECTION WARM

32.1 FORMULAS

32.1 Bensley *test.* **1929 Moore** *cit.* **Knouff**   4349, **12**:55
PREPARATION OF COLLOIDAL CARMINE: Dissolve 40 carmine in 100 water with 40 am-
monia. Leave mixture 12–24 hours. Filter. Boil filtrate until ammonia-free. Add 95%
alc. in excess to filtrate to precipitate carmine. Filter. Dry ppt.
WORKING MASS: Dissolve carmine from above in 50 water. Soak 25 gelatin in 25 water.
Melt and mix with carmine.

32.1 Carter 1862   *Arch. Med.,* **3**:287
FORMULA: water 90, acetic acid 5, gelatin 12, ammonia 5, carmine 6
PREPARATION: Dissolve carmine in ammonia. Melt 9 gelatin in 60 water. Mix with
carmine. Dissolve 3 gelatin in 30 water with acetic acid. Add slowly with constant
agitation to hot carmine-gelatin mixture.

32.1 Fol 1883   23635, **38**:492
STOCK I: Soak 100 gelatin in water. Drain. Melt.
STOCK II: Warm carmine in 75 water with 25 ammonia. Leave overnight. Filter. Add
acetic acid drop by drop until color changes to bright red.
PREPARATION OF STOCK MASS: Stock I 100; stock II 100. Add the carmine solution to the
molten gelatin. Stir well. Chill and shred the chilled mass. Wash the shreds in running
water overnight. Drain, remelt, and cast in sheets. Dry sheets.
PREPARATION OF WORKING MASS: Soak stock mass in enough water to cover. Soak 10
minutes. Drain. Melt.

32.1 Fol 1884   Fol 1884, 13
PREPARATION OF STOCK MASS: Soak 50 gelatin in sheets in V 32.1 Fol 1883, stock II for
48 hours. Drain. Rinse. Transfer rinsed sheets to 100 0.1% acetic acid solution. Leave
overnight. Wash 3 hours in running water. Dry.
PREPARATION OF WORKING MASS: As Fol 1883

32.1 Frey 1877   Frey 1877, 112
FORMULA: water *q.s.*, gelatin 25, sat. aq. sol. (*circ.* 40%) barium chloride 50, sulfuric acid
q.s.
PREPARATION: Add acid to barium chloride until no further ppt. produced. Soak gelatin
in water. Drain. Melt and incorporate with barium sulfate.

32.1 Harting *test.* **1877a Frey**   Frey 1877, 111
FORMULA: water 60, gelatin 20, lead acetate 5, potassium dichromate 2.7
PREPARATION: Dissolve lead acetate in 20 water. Dissolve dichromate in 40 water. Mix
slowly and with constant agitation with acetate solution. Heat to 35°C. Soak gelatin
in water. Drain. Melt and incorporate with warm lead chromate mass.

32.1 Harting *test.* **1877b Frey**   Frey 1877, 112
FORMULA: water 11.5, gelatin 25, lead acetate 25, sodium carbonate 25
PREPARATION: Dissolve lead acetate in 6.5 water. Dissolve sodium carbonate in 5 water.
Mix slowly and with constant agitation with acetate solution. Heat to 35°C. Soak
gelatin in water. Drain. Melt and mix with lead carbonate.

32.1 Hoyer 1882   2981, **2**:19
FORMULA: water 80, gelatin 20, glycerol 10, silver nitrate 2, 1% pyrogallic acid 2, chloral
hydrate 2
PREPARATION: Soak gelatin in 30 water a few hours. Melt. Dissolve silver nitrate in 50
water. Mix with gelatin. Add 1% pyrogallic acid to mixture. Agitate few minutes. Add
glycerol and chloral hydrate to mixture.

32.1 Krause 1909   23632, **26**:1
FORMULA: water 2000, sodium borate 100, carmine 1.5, gelatin 100, 2% HCl *q.s.*,
camphor 0.3
PREPARATION: Dissolve carmine in water with sodium borate with boiling. Cool. Chill.
Soak gelatin in chilled carmine solution 2–3 days. Drain. Rinse. Transfer rinsed sheets,
with added hydrochloric acid, to solution, 6 hours. Drain. Wash. Drain. Melt. Add
camphor to molten mass. Cool.

32.1 MacCallum 1926   590, **38**:153
FORMULA: water 30, gelatin 7, carmine 4, ammonia 4
PREPARATION: Dissolve carmine in ammonia. Add 20 water. Leave 24 hours. Filter. Boil
filtrate to volume 10. Add 10 water to reduced filtrate. Again boil to volume 10. Soak
gelatin in water. Melt. Mix with carmine solution.

32.1 Moore 1929   4349, **12**:55
FORMULA: water 90, gelatin 25, carmine 6, ammonia *q.s.*, potassium iodide 5, acetic acid
q.s.
PREPARATION: Melt gelatin in 60 water. Soak. Mix carmine in 30 water. Add enough
ammonia to dissolve carmine. Add potassium iodide to carmine solution. Mix with
gelatin at 25°C. Add enough acetic acid to give pH 7.2.

32.1 Robin 1871a   Robin 1871, 23
FORMULA: lard 40, spermaceti 40, beeswax 10, turpentine 15

32.1 Robin 1871b   Robin 1871, 32
FORMULA: water 60, glycerol 30, gelatin 10, arsenic trioxide 0.5, phenol 0.1
PREPARATION: Melt the gelatin in water with arsenic trioxide. Add glycerol and phenol
to the solution.
NOTE: This mass may be mixed with any pigment.

32.1 Robin 1871c   Robin 1871, 40
FORMULA: water 130, gelatin 15, silver nitrate 30
PREPARATION: Dissolve gelatin in 100 water with heat. Cool to 30°C. Dissolve silver
nitrate in 30 water. Warm to 30°C. Mix with gelatin.

32.1 Stirling *test.* **Cole 1884**   Cole 1884b, 29
FORMULA: water 50, gelatin 25, acetic acid *q.s.*, carmine 4, ammonia 4
PREPARATION: Soak gelatin in water. Drain. Melt. Make to 50. Mix ammonia in 50
water and carmine. Leave overnight. Filter. Add acetic acid to filtrate drop by drop
until color changes. Add to molten gelatin.

32.1 Thiersch 1865   1780, **1**:148
FORMULA: water 65, gelatin 15, carmine 10, ammonia 10
PREPARATION: Mix carmine in 30 water with ammonia. Leave overnight. Agitate. Filter.
Dissolve gelatin in 35 water with heat. Add to filtrate.

32.1 Thiersch *test.* **1871 Robin**   Robin 1871, 36

FORMULA: water 140, gelatin 60, potassium dichromate 7.5, lead nitrate 10

PREPARATION: Dissolve 30 gelatin in 70 water with potassium dichromate. Cool to 30°C. Dissolve 30 gelatin in 70 water with lead nitrate. Cool to 30°C. Mix slowly and with constant agitation into dichromate solution. Raise, while constantly stirring, to 100°C. Strain.

32.1 Thiersch *test.* **1877 Frey**   Frey, 1877, 113

FORMULA: stock I sat. aq. sol. (*circ.* 16%) ferrous sulfate; stock II sat. aq. sol. (*circ.* 33%) potassium ferrocyanide; stock III sat. aq. sol. (*circ.* 10%) oxalic acid; stock IV gelatin, soaked, strained, and melted

WORKING INJECTION MASS: Mix stock I 6 and stock IV 15 at about 60°C. Cool to 30°C. Mix stock II 12, stock IV 30, stock III 12 at about 60°C. in order given. Cool to 30°C. Add previous mixture to this slowly and continuously with constant stirring. Without ceasing to stir, raise temperature slowly to 100°C. Strain for use.

NOTE: This really excellent blue injection mass fell into disrepute through Robin's unfortunate mistranslation (Robin 1871, p. 35) of Thiersch's original directions. Thiersch took "*eine kalt gesättigte Lösung von schwefelsaurem Eisenoxydul,*" which was rendered by Robin as "*une solution froide saturée de protoxyde de fer.*" The wide circulation by Robin of these very obviously impossible directions led to the dropping of the method from the literature.

32.1 Thiersch *test.* **1877 Frey**   Frey 1877, 115

FORMULA: water 22, gelatin 40, potassium chromate 1, lead nitrate 5

PREPARATION: Dissolve potassium chromate in 12 water. Soak 20 gelatin in water. Drain. Melt and incorporate with chromate solution. Keep at 35°C. Dissolve lead nitrate in 10 water. Soak 20 gelatin in water. Drain. Melt and incorporate at 35°C. with lead solution. Then add to lead gelatin mixture at 35°C. slowly and with constant stirring. Raise to 100°C., stirring at intervals for 1–2 hours. Strain.

32.1 Woodhead *test.* **Cole 1884**   Cole 1884b, 29

FORMULA: water 100, gelatin 10, carmine 4, ammonia 8, acetic acid *q.s.*

PREPARATION: Dissolve carmine in ammonia. Soak gelatin in water. Melt at 40°C. Add to carmine. Add acetic acid to mixture, drop by drop, until color changes.

V 40 Cleaning Methods and Formulas

In addition to the five standard methods given below, many people clean slides by flaming them with a bunsen burner. It is difficult to find a satisfactory cloth with which to dry slides after they have been washed, and unless a piece of old linen is available it is usually better to rinse in alcohol and air dry. It was at one time customary to store all clean slides and covers in 95% alcohol, which was alleged to prevent deterioration of the surface.

There is no known method of removing surface cloudiness from an old slide made of bad quality glass.

41.1 METHODS AND FORMULAS

41.1 acid alcohol—*compl. script.*

METHOD: dip slides in acid alcohol and dry without rinsing. **Masson 1929** (4349, **12**:81) recommends 10% nitric acid in 95% alc.; **Gray** (1952, 113) prefers 1% acetic acid in 70% alc.

41.1 Lysol

METHOD: heat Lysol to about 150°C. Dip slide and rinse off in water.

NOTE: This method will even remove resin, lacquers, varnishes, and paraffin.

41.1 scouring powder

METHOD: make a thin cream of any kitchen scouring powder and water. Dip slides, air dry, and repack in boxes. Polish with cloth before use.

41.1 sulfuric-dichromate—*compl. script.*

FORMULA: to 40 sat. aq. sol. potassium dichromate add, with due precautions, 60 sulfuric acid

METHOD: soak slides and covers for about a day; wash thoroughly in running water
NOTE: The cleaning solution may be used as long as any crystals remain at the bottom.

41.1 trisodium phosphate
METHOD: soak slides overnight in a 15% solution of trisodium phosphate. Rinse and dry.

V 50 Miscellaneous Formulas

51.1 FORMULAS

51.1 André *test.* **1942 Langeron**   Langeron 1942, 930
FORMULA: water 30, acetic acid 30, chloral hydrate 40
RECOMMENDED FOR: reswelling dried arthropods.

51.1 Baker 1941   11360, **61**:75
FORMULA: water 36, 95% alc. 54, glycerol 10
RECOMMENDED FOR: softening materials already embedded in paraffin which have
   proved too tough to cut. The block should be soaked until experiment shows that the
   material will cut.

51.1 Foster and Gifford 1947   20540b, **22**:129
FORMULA: 95% alc. 80, glycerol 10, hydrofluoric acid 10
RECOMMENDED FOR: softening refractory plant materials before sectioning.

51.1 Gifford 1950a   20540b, **25**:161
FORMULA: water 36, 95% alc. 54, acetic acid 10
RECOMMENDED FOR: softening paraffin-embedded plant tissues after the block has been
   trimmed to expose a surface of the material.

51.1 Gifford 1950b   20540b, **25**:161
FORMULA: water 32, 95% alc. 48, acetic acid 20
RECOMMENDED FOR: as above, but with very refractory material.

51.1 Guyer 1930   Guyer 1930, 30
FORMULA: abs. alc. 55, ether 45, pyroxylin 7, camphor 0.3
PREPARATION: Dissolve ether in abs. alc. with pyroxylin. Add camphor to solution.
RECOMMENDED FOR: sealing, by dipping, stoppers, or corks of vials.

51.1 Hetherington 1922   11428, **9**:102
FORMULA: water 25, lactic acid 50, 95% alc. 25
RECOMMENDED FOR: reswelling of dried plant specimens.

51.1 Langeron 1942   Langeron 1942, 852
FORMULA: paraffin 65, rubber 35
RECOMMENDED FOR: bottom of small dishes for dissection.

51.1 Lendrum 1944   20540b, **19**:143
FORMULA: glycerol 90, aniline 10
RECOMMENDED FOR: as V 51.1 Baker 1941.

51.1 Schmorl 1928   Schmorl 1928, 90
FORMULA: anhydrous chloroform 32, oil of thyme 16, oil of cedarwood 32, abs. alc. 8,
   phenol 8
RECOMMENDED FOR: storage of celloidin blocks

51.1 Vesseler 1891   23632, **7**:461
FORMULA: beeswax 60, Venice turpentine 30
RECOMMENDED FOR: wax for supporting specimens.

51.1 Wilson 1946   *Tech. Bull.*, **7**:57
FORMULA: abs. alc. 100, celloidin 4, gum mastic 0.625
PREPARATION: Dissolve celloidin in 75 alc., 25 ether. Evaporate ether and add gum dis-
   solved in 25 alc.
RECOMMENDED FOR: varnishing edge of microtome knife to prevent striations in sections
   caused by minute nicks in edge of knife.

Abbreviations Used

The abbreviations used in this work have been drawn from three sources. The first group, invented by the author for bibliographic purposes, is explained fully, with examples, in the introduction. The second group consists of standard pharmaceutical abbreviations, such as *a.a.* and *s.a.* used to abbreviate the directions given for the preparation of solutions. The third group contains the common abbreviations such as *q.v.* and *loc. cit.* employed in written English. The list which follows contains the meaning of all abbreviations used in the book.

a.a.	of each the amount indicated
abs. alc.	absolute alcohol
auct.	author
BP	British Pharmacopoeia
cf.	compare
circ.	approximately
cit.	quoting
compl. script.	numerous writings
Gm.	gram
in litt.	received as an unpublished written communication
in verb.	received verbally
loc. cit.	the place [already] quoted
ml.	milliliter
n.d.	no date
N.F.	National Formulary
op. cit.	the work [already] quoted
ppt.	precipitate
q.s.	enough
q.v.	which see
s.a.	in the customary manner
sat.	saturated
sat. alc. sol.	saturated alcoholic solution
sat. aq. sol.	saturated aqueous solution
sic	exactly as shown
sol.	solution
test.	according to
test. ips.	according to himself
USP	United States Pharmacopeia

Books and Periodicals Cited

A. Books

The following list of books is not intended to be a complete bibliography but only a list of books cited in the preceding pages. A complete bibliography of books on microtechnique has been prepared under the joint authorship of the present writer and his wife (Gray and Gray. *Bibliography of Books on Microtechnique*. Dubuque, Iowa, Wm. C. Brown Co., 1954).

Cited as	Title
Alzheimer 1910	*see* Nissl and Alzheimer 1910
Anderson 1929	Anderson, J. How to stain the nervous system. Edinburgh, E. Livingstone, 1929.
Apáthy 1896–1901	Apáthy, Stefan. Die Mikrotechnik der thierischen Morphologie, Zwei Abtheilung. Braunschweig, Harald Bruhn, 1896–1901.
Baker 1945	Baker, John R. Cytological technique, 2nd ed. London, Methuen, 1945.
Beale 1880	Beale, Lionel S. How to work with the microscope, 5th ed. London, Harrison, 1880.
Beccari 1946	Beccari, Nello. Elementi di technica microscopica, 4th ed. riveduta di U. Ignesti. Milan, Societa Editrice Libraria, 1946.
Becher 1921	Becher, Siegfried. Untersuchungen über Echtfärbung der Zellkerne mit künstlichen Beizenfarbstoffen. Berlin, Borntraeger, 1921.
Becher and Demoll 1913	Becher, S., and R. Demoll. Einführung in die mikroskopische Technik. Leipzig, Quelle und Meyer, 1913.
Behrens 1883	Behrens, Wilhelm. Hilfsbuch zur Ausführung mikroskopischer Untersuchungen im botanischen Laboratorium. Braunschweig, Harald Bruhn, 1883.
Behrens, Kossel, and Schiefferdecker 1899	Behrens, W., A. Kossel, and P. Schiefferdecker. Die Gewebe des menschlichen Körpers und ihre mikroskopische Untersuchung, erste Band: Das Mikroscop und die Methoden der mikroskopischen Untersuchung. Braunschweig, Harald Bruhn, 1889.
Belling 1930	Belling, John. The use of the microscope, 1st ed. New York, McGraw-Hill, 1930.
Bensley and Bensley 1938	Bensley, R. R., and S. H. Bensley. Handbook of histological and cytological technique. Chicago, University of Chicago Press, 1938.
Besson 1904	Besson, Albert. Technique microbiologique et sérothérapique. Paris, Baillière, 1904.
Böhm and Oppel 1907	Böhm, Alexander, and Albert Oppel. Manuel de technique microscopique, traduit de l'allemand par Étienne de Rouville, 4th ed. Paris, Vigot, 1907.
Boitard 1921	Boitard. Nouveau manuel complet du naturaliste préparateur, Nouvelle ed. par Maigne. Paris, Mulo, 1921.

Cited as	Title
Boneval 1890	Boneval, René. Nouveau guide pratique de technique microscopique appliquée à l'histologie et à l'embryogénie. Paris, Maloine, 1890.
Cajal and de Castro 1933	Ramón y Cajal, S., and F. de Castro. Elementos de técnica micrográfica del sistema nerviosa. Madrid, Tipografía Artística, 1933.
Carleton and Leach 1938	Carleton, H. M., and E. H. Leach. Histological Technique. 2nd ed. London and New York, Oxford University Press, 1938.
Carnoy 1884	Carnoy, Jean Baptiste. La biologie cellulaire. Paris, Doin, 1884.
Carpenter 1891	Carpenter, William B. The microscope and its revelations, 7th ed. edited by W. H. Dallenger. Philadelphia, Blakiston, 1891.
Chamberlain 1915	Chamberlain, Charles J. Methods in plant histology, 3rd ed. Chicago, University of Chicago Press, 1915.
Chamberlain 1932	*Idem.* 5th ed. 1932.
Chevalier 1882	Chevalier, Arthur. L'étudiant micrographe, 3rd ed. Paris, Chevalier, 1882.
Clayden 1948	Clayden, E. C. Practical section cutting and staining. Brooklyn, N. Y., Chemical Publishing Co., 1948.
Cole 1883	Cole, Arthur C. Studies in microscopical science, 2 vol. London, Baillière, Tindall and Cox, 1883–1884.
Cole 1884	———— The methods of microscopical research. n. d., bound with Cole 1883, vol. 2.
Conn 1946	Conn, H. J. Biological stains. Geneva, N. Y., Biotech Publications, 1946.
Cooper 1847	Cooper, Daniel. The microscopic miscellany; being selections from the Microscopic Journal. London, privately printed, 1847.
Cowdry 1943	Cowdry, E. V. Microscopic technique in biology and medicine. Baltimore, Williams and Wilkins, 1943.
Cowdry 1952	———— Laboratory technique in biology and medicine, 3rd ed. Baltimore, Williams and Wilkins, 1952.
Cross and Cole 1903	Cross, M. I., and Martin J. Cole. Modern microscopy, 3rd ed. London, Baillière, Tindall and Cox, 1903.
Davies *circ.* 1865	Davies, Thomas. The preparation and mounting of microscopic objects. New York, William Wood, *circ.* 1865.
Davies 1880	———— The preparation and mounting of microscopic objects, edited by John Mathews. London, David Bogue, 1880.
Deflandre 1947	Deflandre, G. Microscopie pratique, 2nd ed. Paris, Lechevalier, 1947.
Dobell 1919	Dobell, Clifford. The amoebae living in man. London, John Bale, Sons and Danielsson, 1919.
Ehrlich, Krause, *et al.* 1910	Ehrlich, Paul, Rudolf Krause, Max Mosse, Heinrich Rosin, and Karl Weigert. Enzyklopädie der mikroskopischen Technik, 2nd ed., 2 vol. Berlin, Urban und Schwarzenberg, 1910.
Eltringham 1930	Eltringham, H. Histological and illustrative methods for entomologists. Oxford, Clarendon, Press, 1930.
Fischer 1899	Fischer, Alfred. Fixirung, Färbung und Bau des Protoplasmas. Jena, Fischer, 1899.

Cited as	Title
Flemming 1882	Flemming, Walther. Zellsubstanz, Kern und Zelltheilung. Leipzig, Vogel, 1882.
Francotte *circ.* 1890	Francotte, P. Manuel de technique microscopique. Paris, Lebègue, *circ.* 1890.
Frei-Sulzer 1946a	Frei-Sulzer, M. Mikroskopische Untersuchungsmethoden. Zürich, André Schlegel, 1946.
Frei-Sulzer 1946b	——— Lohnende Objekte für mikroskopische Untersuchungen und ihre Präparation. Zürich, André Schlegel, 1946.
Frey 1877	Frey, Heinrich. Das Mikroskop und die mikroskopische Technik, 6th ed. Leipzig, Wilhelm Engelmann, 1877.
Friedlaender 1885	Friedlaender, Carl. The use of the microscope in clinical and pathological examinations, 2nd ed., translated by Henry C. Coe. New York, Appleton, 1885.
Friedlaender 1889	Mikroskopische Technik zum Gebrauch bei medicinischen und pathologisch-anatomischen Untersuchungen, 4th ed. by C. J. Eberth. Berlin, Fischer, 1889.
Gage 1896	Gage, Simon Henry. The microscope and microscopical methods, 6th ed. Ithaca, N. Y., Comstock, 1896.
Gage 1901	——— The microscope and an introduction to microscopic methods and to histology, 8th ed. Ithaca, N. Y., Comstock, 1901.
Gatenby and Cowdry 1928	Gatenby, J. Brontë, and E. V. Cowdry. Bolles Lee's microtomist's vade-mecum. Philadelphia, Blakiston, 1928.
Gatenby and Painter 1937	Gatenby, J. Brontë, and Theophilus S. Painter. The microtomist's vade-mecum (Bolles Lee), 10th ed. Philadelphia, Blakiston, 1937.
Gérard 1887	Gérard, R. Traité pratique de micrographie. Paris, Doin, 1887.
Golgi 1903	Golgi, Camillo. Opera omnia, 3 vol. Milan, Hoepli, 1903.
Graupner 1934	Graupner, Heinz. Mikroskopische Technik. Leipzig, Akademische Verlagsgesellschaft, 1934.
Gray 1952	Gray, Peter. Handbook of basic microtechnique. Philadelphia, Blakiston, 1952.
Griffith and Henfrey 1875	Griffith, J. W., and Arthur Henfrey. The Micrographic Dictionary, 3rd ed., 2 vol. London, John van Voorst, 1875.
Günther 1898	Günther, Carl. Einführung in das Studium der Bakteriologie mit besonderer Berücksichtigung der mikroskopischen Technik, 5th ed. Leipzig, Georg Thieme, 1898.
Gurr 1951	Gurr, Edward. Microscopic staining techniques No. 3. London, Gurr, 1951.
Guyer 1917	Guyer, Michael F. Animal micrology, 2nd ed. Chicago, University of Chicago Press, 1917.
Guyer 1930	*Idem.* 3rd ed. 1930.
Hager 1886	Hager, Hermann. Das Mikroskop und seine Aniwendung. Berlin, Julius Springer, 1886.
Hall and Herscheimer 1905	Hall, Walker, and G. Herscheimer. Methods of morbid histology and clinical pathology. Philadelphia, Lippincott, 1905.
Heidenhain 1892	Heidenhain, Martin. Festschrift Herrn A. von Kolliker zur Feier seines fünfzigjährigen medicinischen Doktorjubiläums. Leipzig, Wilhelm Engellmans, 1892.
Hogg 1883	Hogg, Jabez. The microscope. London, Routledge, 1883.

Cited as	Title
Johansen 1940	Johansen, Donald Alexander. Plant microtechnique. New York, McGraw-Hill, 1940.
Jones 1950	Jones, Ruth McClung. McClung's handbook of microscopical technique, 3rd ed. New York, Hoeber, 1950.
Kahlden 1894	Kahlden, C. von. Methods of pathological histology, translated and edited by H. Morley Fletcher. London, Macmillan, 1894.
Kahlden and Laurent 1896	Kahlden, C. von, and O. Laurent. Technique microscopique. Paris, Carré, 1896.
Kingsbury and Johannsen 1927	Kingsbury, B. F., and O. A. Johannsen. Histological technique. New York, Wiley, 1927.
Kisser 1926	Kisser, Josef. Leitfaden der botanischen Mikrotechnik. Jena, Fischer, 1926.
Langeron 1916	Langeron, M. Précis de microscopie, 2nd ed. Paris, Masson, 1916.
Langeron 1934	*Idem.* 5th ed. 1934.
Langeron 1942	*Idem.* 6th ed. 1942.
Langeron 1949	*Idem.* 7th ed. 1949.
Laporte 1946	Laporte, L. J. Ce qu'il faut savoir sur le monde microscopique. Paris, Lechevalier, 1946.
Ledermann 1903	Ledermann, R. Die mikroskopische Technik. Vienna, Alfred Hölder, 1903.
Lee 1885	Lee, Arthur Bolles. The microtomist's vade-mecum. London, Churchill, 1885.
Lee 1890	*Idem.* 2nd ed. 1890.
Lee 1901	*Idem.* 5th ed. 1901.
Lee 1905	*Idem.* 8th ed. 1905.
Lee and Mayer 1910	Lee, A. Bolles, and P. Mayer. Grundzüge der mikroskopischen Technik für Zoologen und Anatomen, 4th ed. Berlin, Friedländer, 1910.
Lillie 1948	Lillie, R. D. Histopathologic technic. Philadelphia, Blakiston, 1948.
Maggi 1895	Maggi, L. Tecnica protistologica. Milan, Hoepli, 1895.
Mallory 1938	Mallory, Frank Burr. Pathological technique. Philadelphia, Saunders, 1938.
Mallory and Wright 1897	Mallory, Frank Burr, and James Homer Wright. Pathological technique. Philadelphia, Saunders, 1897.
Mallory and Wright 1911	*Idem.* 5th ed. 1911.
Mallory and Wright 1924	*Idem.* 8th ed. 1924.
Marsh 1878	Marsh, Sylvester. Section cutting. London, Churchill, 1878.
Martin 1872	Martin, John H. A manual of microscopic mounting. London, Churchill, 1872.
Mayer 1920	Mayer, Paul. Zoomikrotechnik. Berlin, Bornträger, 1920.
McClung 1929	McClung, C. E. Handbook of microscopical technique. New York, Hoeber, 1929.
Meakin and Swatman 1949	Meakin, S. H., and C. C. Swatman. Mounting diatoms. London, Arthur Barron, 1949.
Meyer 1915	Meyer, Arthur. Erstes mikroskopisches Praktikum, 3rd ed. Jena, Fischer, 1915.

Cited as	Title
Nissl and Alzheimer 1910	Nissl, Franz von, and Alois Alzheimer. Histologische und histopathologische Arbeiten über die Grosshirnrinde. Jena, Fischer, 1910.
Patzelt 1948	Patzelt, Viktor. Anleitung zu mikroskopischen Untersuchungen. Vienna, Urban und Schwarzenberg, 1948.
Pollack 1900	Pollack, Bernard. Les méthodes de préparation et de coloration du système nerveux, traduit de l'allemand par Jean Nicolaide. Paris, Carré et Naud, 1900.
Pritchard 1851	Pritchard, Andrew. A general history of animalcules. London, Whittaker, 1851.
Prowazek 1922	Prowazek, S. von. Taschenbuch der mikroskopischen Technik der Protistenuntersuchung, 3rd ed., bearbeitet von V. Jollos. Leipzig, Barth, 1922.
Queckett 1855	Queckett, John. A practical treatise on the use of the microscope, 3rd ed. London, Baillière, 1855.
Ranvier 1875	Ranvier, L. Traité technique d'histologie. Paris, Savy, 1875.
Rawitz 1895	Rawitz, Bernhard. Leitfaden für histologische Untersuchungen. Jena, Fischer, 1895.
Richards 1949	Richards, Oscar W. The effective use and proper care of the microtome. Buffalo, American Optical Co., 1949.
Romeis 1948	Romeis, Benno. Mikroskopische Technik, 15th ed. Munich, Leibniz, 1948.
Roskin 1946	Roskin, G. E. Mikroskopecheskaya technika. Moscow, Sovetskaya Nauka, 1946.
Ruffini 1927	Ruffini, Angelo. Processi di tecnica embriologica ed istologica. Bologna, Licinio Cappelli, 1927.
Sass 1940	Sass, John E. Elements of botanical microtechnique. New York, McGraw-Hill, 1940.
Schmorl 1928	Schmorl, G. Die pathologisch-histologischen Untersuchungs-methoden, 15th ed. Leipzig, Vogel, 1928.
Schneider 1922	Schneider, Hans. Die botanische Mikrotechnik. Jena, Fischer, 1922.
Seiler 1881	Seiler, Carl. Compendium of microscopical technology. Philadelphia, Brinton, 1881.
Spielmeyer 1924	Spielmeyer, W. Technik der mikroskopischen Untersuchungen des Nervensystems. Berlin, Springer, 1924.
Squire 1892	Squire, Peter Wyatt. Methods and formulae used in the preparation of animal and vegetable tissues for microscopical examination. London, Churchill, 1892.
Stitt 1916	Stitt, E. R. Practical bacteriology, blood work and parasitology. 4th ed. Philadelphia, Blakiston, 1916.
Stitt 1920	Idem. 6th ed. 1920.
Stöhr 1901	Stöhr, Philipp. Textbook of histology including microscopical technique, 4th American ed. translated by Emma L. Bilstein and edited by Alfred Schafer. Philadelphia, Blakiston, 1901.
Tobias 1936	Tobias, J. Carroll. The student's manual of microscopic technique. London, Chapman and Hall, 1936.
Wellings circ. 1938	Wellings, A. W. Practical microscopy of the teeth and associated parts. New York, Staples, n.d. (circ. 1938).
Wethered 1898	Wethered, Frank J. Medical microscopy. Philadelphia, Blakiston, 1898.

Cited as	Title
Whitman 1885	Whitman, Charles Otis. Methods of research in microscopical anatomy and embryology. Boston, Cassino, 1885.
Wythes 1851	Wythes, Joseph H. The microscopist. Philadelphia, Lindsay and Blakiston, 1851.
Zimmerman 1893	Zimmerman, A. Botanical microtechnique, translated by James Ellis Humphrey. New York, Henry Holt, 1893.
Zimmerman 1896	——— Botanical microtechnique, translated by James Ellis Humphrey. Westminster, Archibald Constable, 1896.
Zinnser and Bayne-Jones 1939	Zinnser, Hans, and Stanhope Bayne-Jones. A textbook of bacteriology, 8th ed. New York, Appleton-Century, 1939.

B. Periodicals Not Cited in *World List*

Cited as	Title
Amer. J. Med. Tech.	The American Journal of Medical Technology. Houston, Texas.
Arb. bot. inst. Wurz.	Arbeiten der botanischer Institut der Universität Würzburg.
Arch. Biochem.	Archives of Biochemistry. New York.
Arch. Med.	Archives of Medicine. New York.
Bull. Amer. Soc. A. Microsc.	Bulletin of the American Society of Amateur Microscopists. Pittsburgh.
Bull. Soc. Franc. Microsc.	Bulletin de la société francaise de microscopie. Paris.
J. Pal.	Journal of Paleontology. Tulsa, Oklahoma.
Lab. Invest.	Laboratory Investigation. New York.
Micrologist	The Micrologist. Manchester, England.
Microscope	The Microscope and Entomological Monthly. London.
Microsc. Rec.	Watson's Microscope Record. London.
Mikroskopie	Mikroskopie. Zentralblatt für mikroskopische Forschung und Methodik. Vienna.
Rep. Mass. Gen. Hosp.	Annual Reports of the Massachusetts General Hospital. Boston.
Tech. Bull.	Technical Bulletin of the Registry of Medical Technologists. Muncie, Indiana.
Turtox News.	Turtox News. Chicago.
Ward's Bul.	Ward's Natural Science Establishment Bulletin. Rochester, New York.

C. Periodicals Listed in *World List of Scientific Periodicals* 2nd Edition 1934

Cited as	Title
65	Abhandlungen der Königlichen Sächsischen Gesellschaft (Akademie) der Wissenschaften, Mathematisch-Physische Klasse. Leipzig.
466	Allgemeine Zeitschrift für Psychiatrie und psychisch-gerichtliche Medizin. Berlin.
590	American Journal of Anatomy. Baltimore.
591	American Journal of Botany. Lancaster, Pennsylvania.
591b	American Journal of Clinical Pathology. Baltimore.
600a	American Journal of Hygiene. Baltimore.
608b	American Journal of Pathology. Boston.
617	American Journal of Public Health. New York.
618	American Journal of Public Hygiene and Journal of the Massachusetts Association of Boards of Health. Boston.
623	American Journal of Syphilis. St. Louis, Missouri.
626	American Journal of Tropical Medicine. Baltimore.

Cited as	Title
645	American Monthly Microscopical Journal. Washington, D. C.
651	American Naturalist. Boston.
665	American Review of Tuberculosis. New York.
763	Anatomical Record. Philadelphia.
764	Anatomische Hefte: Abteilung 1. Wiesbaden.
766	Anatomischer Anzeiger. Jena.
825	Annales de chimie (et de physique). Paris.
829	Annales de dermatologie et de syphiligraphie. Paris.
857	Annales de l'Institut Pasteur. Paris.
899a	Annales de parasitologie humaine et comparée. Paris.
915	Annales des sciences naturelles: (a) Botanique, (b) Zoologie. Paris.
966	Annales de la Société scientifique de Bruxelles. Louvain.
979	Annali di botanica. Rome.
988	Annali d'igiene (sperimentale). Turin.
1006	Annali di nevrologia. Naples.
1025	Annals of Applied Biology. Cambridge.
1032	Annals of Botany. London.
1048	Annals of Missouri Botanical Garden. St. Louis, Missouri.
1200	Annual Report of the Cancer Research Fund. London.
1683	Arbeiten aus den Zoologischen Instituten der Universität Wien und der Zoologischen Station in Triest. Vienna.
1739	Archiv für Anatomie und Physiologie. Leipzig.
1752	Archiv für Dermatologie und Syphilis. Vienna and Leipzig.
1756	Archiv für Entwicklungsmechanik der Organismen. Leipzig.
1780	Archiv für mikroskopische Anatomie (und Entwicklungsmechanik). Bonn.
1789a	Archiv für pathologische Anatomie. Bratislava.
1798	Archiv für Protistenkunde. Jena.
1799	Archiv für Psychiatrie und Nervenkrankheiten. Berlin.
1820	Archiv für Zellforschung. Leipzig.
1823	Archives d'anatomie microscopique. Paris.
1825	Archives de biologie. Paris.
1829	Archives of Dermatology and Syphilology. New York.
1843	Archives de l'Institut Pasteur de Tunis. Tunis.
1845	Archives of Internal Medicine. Chicago.
1852	Archives italiennes de biologie. Pisa.
1863	Archives de médécine expérimentale et d'anatomie pathologique. Paris.
1878a	Archives of Neurology and Psychiatry. Chicago.
1879	Archives of Neurology and Psychiatry. London.
1883	Archives of Ophthalmology. New York.
1886	Archives de parasitologie. Paris.
1887a	Archives of Pathology and Laboratory Medicine. Chicago.
1915	Archives de zoologie expérimentale et générale. Paris.
1946	Archivio per le scienze mediche. Turin.
1949	Archivio zoologico (italiano). Napoli.
2174	Atti dell'Istituto botanico della Università di Pavia. Milano.
2190	Atti della Società lombarda di scienze mediche e biologiche. Milano.
2526	Beiträge zur pathologischen Anatomie und zur allgemeinen Pathologie. Jena.
2626	Bericht der Deutschen Botanischen Gesellschaft. Berlin.
2627	Bericht der Deutschen Chemischen Gesellschaft. Berlin.
2701	Bericht der Naturforschenden Gesellschaft zu Freiburg im Breisegau.
2813	Berliner klinische Wochenschrift. Berlin.
2818	Berliner tierärztliche Wochenschrift. Berlin.
2842	Bibliographia zoologica. Leipzig.
2844	Bibliographie anatomique. Revue des travaux en langue française. Paris and Nancy.
2975	Biological Bulletin of the Marine Biological Laboratory. Wood's Hole, Massachusetts.
2981	Biologisches Zentralblatt. Leipzig.
3231	Boletín de la Sociedad española de biología. Madrid.

Cited as	Title
3232	Boletín de la Real Sociedad española de historia natural. Madrid.
3248	Bollettino della Reale Accademia medica. Genoa.
3381	Bollettino della Società medico-chirurgica. Pavia.
3389	Bollettino della Società zoologica italiana. Roma.
3430	Botanical Gazette. Chicago.
3432	Botanical Magazine. Tokyo.
3445	Botanisches Zentralblatt. Jena and Dresden.
3464	Brain: a Journal of Neurology. London.
3566	British Journal of Experimental Pathology. London.
3579	British Medical Journal. London.
3678	Bulletin de l'Académie Royale de Belgique, Classe des sciences. Brussels.
3919	Bulletin biologique de la France et de la Belgique. Paris.
4184	Bulletin of Entomological Research. London.
4285a	Bulletin d'histologie appliquée à la physiologie et à la pathologie et de technique microscopique. Paris.
4346	Bulletin international de l'Académie des sciences de Cracovie (de l'Academie polonaise des sciences). Cracow.
4349	Bulletin of the International Association of Medical Museums and Journal of Technical Methods. Montreal and Washington, D. C.
4604	Bulletin of the Museum of Comparative Zoology at Harvard College. Cambridge, Massachusetts.
4956	Bulletin et mémoires de la Société anatomique de Paris.
4992	Bulletin de la Société belge de microscopie. Brussels.
4999	Bulletin. Société botanique de France. Paris.
5133	Bulletin de la Société d'histoire naturelle d'Autun.
5293	Bulletin de la Société mycologique de France. Paris.
5310	Bulletin de la Société de pathologie exotique. Paris.
5392	Bulletin de la Société vaudoise des sciences naturelles. Lausanne.
5401	Bulletin de la Société zoologique de France. Paris
6011	Cellule. Lierre.
6593	Compte rendu de l'Association des anatomistes. Paris and Nancy.
6628	Compte rendu hebdomadaire des séances de l'Académie des sciences. Paris.
6630	Compte rendu hebdomadaire des séances et mémoires de la Société de biologie. Paris.
6816	Contributions to Embryology (Publications of the Carnegie Institution). Washington, D. C.
7033a	Cytologia. Tokyo.
7137	Denkschriften der Medizinisch-naturwissenschaftlichen Gesellschaft zu Jena.
7141	Dental Cosmos. Philadelphia.
7175	Dermatologische Studien. Hamburg.
7176	Dermatologische Wochenschrift. Leipzig.
7177	Dermatologische Zeitschrift. Berlin.
7276	Deutsche medizinische Wochenschrift. Leipzig.
7282	Deutsche Monatsschrift für Zahnheilkunde. Berlin.
7599	Edinburgh Medical Journal. Edinburgh.
7802	Endocrinology. Glendale, California.
7871	Entomological News. Academy of Natural Sciences, Philadelphia.
7936a	Ergebnisse der Anatomie und Entwicklungsgeschichte. Wiesbaden.
7962	Ergebnisse der Physiologie. Wiesbaden.
8338	Fauna und Flora des Golfes von Neapel und der Angrenzen Meeresabschnitte. Berlin.
8542a	Folia anatomica Japonica. Tokyo.
8545	Folia haematologica. Leipzig.
8645	Fortschritte der Medizin. Halle.
9170	Giornale italiano delle malattie veneree e della pelle. Milan.
9775	Hygiène de la viande et du lait. Paris.
9940	Indian Journal of Medical Research. Calcutta.
9943	Indian Medical Gazette. Calcutta.
10157	Internationale Monatsschrift für Anatomie und Physiologie. Leipzig.

Cited as	Title
10606	Jahrbuch für wissenschaftliche Botanik. Berlin.
10881q	Japanese Journal of Zoology. Tokyo.
10899	Jenaische Zeitschrift für Naturwissenschaft. Jena.
10919	Johns Hopkins Hospital Bulletin. Baltimore.
10920	Johns Hopkins Hospital Reports. Baltimore.
10996	Journal of the American Chemical Society. Easton, Pennsylvania.
11006	Journal of the American Medical Association. Chicago.
11022	Journal of the American Veterinary Medical Association. Ithaca, New York.
11024	Journal de l'anatomie et de la physiologie normales et pathologiques de l'homme et des animaux. Paris.
11025	Journal of Anatomy (and Physiology). London.
11032	Journal of Applied Microscopy (and Laboratory Methods). Rochester, New York.
11035	Journal of the Royal Army Medical Corps. London.
11056	Journal of Bacteriology. Baltimore.
11074	Journal de botanique. Paris.
11075	Journal of Botany, British and Foreign. London.
11130	Journal of the College of Science, Imperial University of Tokyo.
11135	Journal of Comparative Neurology (and Psychology). Philadelphia.
11139b	Journal du Conseil permanent international pour l'exploration de la mer. Copenhagen.
11147	Journal of Dental Research. Baltimore.
11189	Journal of Experimental Medicine. New York.
11211	Journal of Genetics. Cambridge.
11250	Journal of Infectious Diseases. Chicago.
11284	Journal of Laboratory and Clinical Medicine. St. Louis, Missouri.
11295	Journal of the Linnean Society (Botany). London.
11307	Journal des maladies cutanées et syphilitiques. Paris.
11343	Journal of Medical Research. Boston.
11360	Journal of the Royal Microscopical Society. London.
11373	Journal of Morphology (and Physiology). Boston.
11392	Journal of Neurology and Psychopathology. Bristol.
11428	Journal of Parasitology. Urbana, Illinois.
11431	Journal of Pathology and Bacteriology. London.
11454	Journal of Physiology. London and Cambridge.
11478	Journal für Psychologie und Neurologie. Leipzig.
11479	Journal of the Quekett Microscopical Club. London.
11560	Journal of State Medicine. London.
11571b	See 4349.
11587	Journal of Tropical Medicine (and Hygiene). London.
11597	Journal of Urology. Baltimore.
11689	Kansas University Science Bulletin. Lawrence, Kansas.
11796	Kitasato Archives of Experimental Medicine. Tokyo.
11848	Kolloidchemische Beihefte (Ergänzungschefte zur Kolloidzeitschrift). Dresden.
11976	Laboratory. Pittsburgh.
11977	Laboratory Journal. London.
11988	Lait. Lyons.
11995	Lancet. London.
13034	Medical Journal of Australia. Sydney.
13172	Medizinische Klinik. Vienna.
13367	Memoirs of the College of Science, Kyoto Imperial University. Kyoto.
13461	Memorias do Instituto de Butantan. São Paulo.
13465	Memorias do Instituto Oswaldo Cruz. Rio de Janeiro.
13495	Memorie della Reale Accademia delle scienze dell'Istituto di Bologna.
13497	Memorie della Reale Accademia delle scienze di Torino. Turin.
13685	Military Surgeon. Washington, D. C.
14246	Mitteilungen aus der Zoologischen Station zu Neapel. Berlin.
14352	Monatsschrifte für praktische Dermatologie. Leipzig and Hamburg.
14370	Monatsschrift für Psychiatrie und Neurologie. Berlin.

Cited as	Title
14425	Monitore zoologico italiano. Florence.
14555	Morphologisches Jahrbuch. Leipzig.
14674	Münchener medizinische Wochenschrift. Munich.
14706	Museums Journal. The Organ of the Museums Association. London.
14900	Nature. London.
14901	Nature. Paris.
14975	Naval Medical Bulletin. Washington, D. C.
15058	Neurologisches Zentralblatt. Leipzig.
15063	Névraxe. Recueil de neurologie normale et pathologique. Louvain.
16035	Parasitology. Cambridge.
16059	Pathologica. Genoa.
16155	Pflügers Archiv für die gesamte Physiologie der Menschen und der Tiere. Bonn.
16157b	Pharmaceutica Acta Helvetiae. Zürich.
16185a	Philadelphia Medical Journal. Philadelphia.
16273	Phytopathology. American Phytopathological Society. Ithaca.
16341	Polnisches Archiv für biologische und medizinische Wissenschaften. Lemberg.
16550	Presse médicale. Paris.
16592	Proceedings of the Royal Academy of Sciences. Amsterdam.
16599	Proceedings of the American Academy of Arts and Sciences. Boston.
16730a	Proceedings of the Royal Entomological Society of London. London.
16852	Proceedings of the New York Pathological Society. New York.
16913	Proceedings of the Society for Experimental Biology and Medicine. New York.
16916	Proceedings of the Royal Society of Medicine. London.
16953	Proceedings of the Washington Academy of Sciences. Washington, D. C.
16977	Processi verbali della Società toscana di scienze naturali in Pisa.
17035	Progrès médical. Paris.
17191a	Protoplasma. Leipzig.
17302	Public Health Reports. Washington, D. C.
17510	Quarterly Journal of Microscopical Science. London.
17770a	Recueil des travaux botaniques néerlandais. Société botanique néerlandaise, Nimègue.
18640	Report on (of Director of) Veterinary Research. Department of Agriculture, Union of South Africa, Pretoria.
18794	Revista de la Asociación Médica Argentina. Buenos Aires.
19076	Revue générale de botanique. Paris.
19219	Revue neurologique. Paris.
19227a	Revue de pathologie végétale et d'entomologie agricole. Paris.
19288	Revue suisse de zoologie et Annales de la Société zoologique suisse et du Muséum d'histoire naturelle de Genève. Geneva.
19353	Ricerche del Laboratorio di anatomia normale della Reale Università di Roma. Rome.
19443	Rivista di patologia nervosa e mentale. Florence.
19460	Rivista sperimentale di freniatria e medicina legale delle alienazioni mentali. Reggio-Emilia.
19704d	Sang: Biologie et pathologie. Paris.
19938	Science. New York.
20080	Semaine médicale. Paris.
20170	Sitzungsberichte der Kaiserlichen Akademie der Wissenschaften in Wien, Mathematisch-Naturwissenschaftliche Klasse, Abteilung I: Mineralogie, Krystallographie, Botanik, etc. Abteilung. IIa: Mathematik, Astronomie, Physik, etc. Abteilung IIb. Chemie. Abteilung III. Anatomie und Physiologie. Vienna.
20181	Sitzungsberichte des Deutschen Naturwissenschaftlich-medizinischen Vereins für Böhmen "Lotos" in Prag. Prague.
20188	Sitzungsberichte der Gesellschaft für Morphologie und Physiologie in München. Munich.
20189	Sitzungsberichte der Gesellschaft Naturforschender Freunde zu Berlin.
20214	Skandinavische Archiv für Physiologie. Leipzig.
20540b	Stain Technology. Geneva, New York.

Cited as	Title
20796	Svenska Akademiens Handlingar. Stockholm.
20936	Technical Bulletin. New York State Agricultural Experiment Station, Geneva, New York.
21344	Trabajos del Laboratorio de investigaciones biológicas de la Universidad de Madrid.
21400a	Transactions of the American Microscopical Society. Lancaster, Pennsylvania.
21458	Transactions of the Chicago Pathological Society. Chicago.
21559	Transactions and Annual Report. Manchester Microscopical Society, Manchester, England.
21652	Transactions of the Royal Society of Edinburgh. Edinburgh.
21654	Transactions of the Royal Society of South Australia. Adelaide.
21671	Transactions of the Royal Society of Tropical Medicine and Hygiene. London.
22073	University of California Publications in Botany. Berkeley.
22084	University of California Publications in Zoology. Berkeley.
22238	Verhandelingen der Koninklijke Akademie van wetenschappen: (a) Natuur-historische geologische en medische wetenschappen. (b) Wis- en natuurkundige wetenschappen. Amsterdam.
22246	Verhandlungen der Anatomischen Gesellschaft. Jena.
22264	Verhandlungen der Deutschen Pathologischen Gesselschaft. Jena.
22302	Verhandlungen der Physikalisch-medizinischen Gesellschaft zu Würzburg.
22575	Virchows Archiv für pathologische Anatomie und Physiologie und für klinische Medizin. Berlin.
23053a	Wissenschafthliche Ergebnisse der Deutschen Tiefsee-Expedition auf dem Damfer "Valdivia."
23253	Zapeske Kievskaho Obshchestva Estestvoesptateleye. Kiev.
23328	Zeitschrift für angewandte Mikroskopie und klinische Chemie. Leipzig.
23354	Zeitschrift für Biologie. Munich and Berlin.
23418	Zeitschrift für die gesamte Anatomie, Abteilung 1: Zeitschrift für Anatomie und Entwicklungsgeschichte. Abteilung 2: Zeitschrift für Konstitutionslehre. Abteilung 3: Ergebnisse der Anatomie und Entwicklungsgeschichte. Berlin.
23422	Zeitschrift für die gesamte experimentelle Medizin. Berlin.
23430	Zeitschrift für die gesamte Neurologie und Psychiatrie. Berlin.
23454	Zeitschrift für Hygiene und Infektionskrankheiten. Leipzig.
23507a	Zeitschrift für mikroskopisch-anatomische Forschung. Leipzig.
23543	Zeitschrift für physikalische Chemie, Stöchiometrie und Verwandtschaftslehre. Leipzig.
23632	Zeitschrift für wissenschaftliche Mikroskopie und für mikroskopische Technik. Leipzig.
23635	Zeitschrift für wissenschaftliche Zoologie. Leipzig.
23639b	Zeitschrift für Zellforschung und mikroskopische Anatomie. Berlin.
23681	Zentralblatt für allgemeine Pathologie und pathologische Anatomie. Jena.
23684	Zentralblatt für Bakteriologie, Parasitenkunde und Infektionskrankheiten. Jena.
23720	Zentralblatt für Innere Medizin. Leipzig.
23730	Zentralblatt für die medizinischen Wissenschaften. Berlin.
23732	Zentralblatt für Nervenheilkunde. Berlin.
23820	Zoologica. Orginalabhandlungen. Herausgegeben von C. Chun, Stuttgart.
23831	Zoologische Jahrbücher, Abteilung 1: Systematik (Ökologie), Geographie und Biologie. Abteilung 2: Anatomie und Ontogenie. Abteilung 3. Allgemeine Zoologie und Physiologie. Jena.
23833	Zoologischer Anzeiger. Leipzig.

Index

A

Abbott's method for bacterial spores, 484
Abbreviations, examples of use, 1–2
  list of, 669
Abies balsamea, 640
Abopon mountant, 632
Accelerators for metal stains, 613–615
Accessory dye staining solutions, 514–521
  decimal divisions of, 514
Accessory fixative solutions, 254–266
  decimal divisions of, 254
Accessory metal staining solutions, 613–621
  decimal divisions of, 612
  general remarks on, 612
Acetaldehyde, fixative combination with formaldehyde, 193
Acetic acid, as ingredient of,
  Alcorn and Yeager's preservatives, 177;
  Assier's preservatives, 76; Berlese's
  mountant, 631; Fol's adhesive for free
  sections, 659; Gage's adhesive, 661;
  Hogg's varnish, 653; macerating fluids,
  see under name of author, (262–263);
  Morrison's mountant, 632; Oudemann's
  preservative, 177; Pampel's preservative, 177; Railliet's preservatives, 177;
  Robin's preservatives, 177; Seiler's gelatin cement, 655; Semmen's gum arabic
  varnish, 652; Swan's mountant, 633;
  Wilson's Venice turpentine mountant,
  638; Zirkle's balsam, 640; Zirkle's dextrin mountant, 637; Zirkle's gelatin
  mountants, 635–636; Zirkle's pectin
  mountant, 637; Zirkle's Venice turpentine mountant, 638
  as solvent, 626
  effect on fixation, 189
  for,
    clearing slides, 131; clearing whole-
    mounts, 56; fixing pollen grains, 309;
    swelling arthropods, 667
  in fixative combinations with,
    alcohol, 189, 190; formaldehyde, 191;
    other ingredients, see under name of
    other ingredient; trichloroacetic acid,
    190
  physical properties of, 626
Acetic-iodine, as differentiator, 381

Aceto-carmines, 303
Acetone, as dehydrant in Lillie's stain, 381
  as ingredient of,
    Bolsi's accelerator, 616; Cajal's de-
    velopers, 616, 617; Cajal's formalde-
    hyde accelerator, 615; Claverdon's fixa-
    tive, 224; Foley's developer, 617; Her-
    rara's formaldehyde accelerator, 613;
    Jahnel's developer, 618; Levaditi and
    Manouelian's developer, 618; Lobo's
    developer, 618; Michaelis's double stain,
    345; Rodriguez's formaldehyde ac-
    celerator, 614; Rüyter's adhesive for
    nitrocellulose-paraffin ribbons, 658
  fixative combinations with,
    formaldehyde, 193; other ingredients
    see under name of other ingredient
  for,
    dehydrating, 333, 345, 348; dispersing
    polyvinyl alcohol, 636
  physical properties, 623
Achucarro's method for macroglia, 585
Acid alcohol, for,
    cleaning slides, 131, 666; differentiating
    stains, 519
Acid alizarine blue, in,
    Buzaglo's triple stain, 368; Korn-
    hauser's quadruple stain, 369, 370;
    Petersen's triple stain, 372
  staining combinations with,
    alizarine viridine and quinalizarine,
    368; anilin blue and orange G, 372; fast
    green FCF, orcein and orange G, 367,
    370
Acid-alum-hematoxylins, 289, 290
Acid-fast bacteria, in,
    sections, 495–498; smears, 476–478
  preparation of smear of, 469
  urea for differentiating, 520
Acid fuchsin, as,
    nuclear stain, 319, 357–362; plasma
    stain, 320, 321
  for staining,
    actinomyces, (Lignière), 504; adrenal
    cortex (Fujiware), 429; algae (Baum-
    gartel), 511; astrocytes (Beyer), 413;
    bacteria in sections (Fraenkel), 492;
    bacterial smears (Maneval), 473; bac-
    terial spores (Botelho), 485; blood

Bacteria—(*continued*)
differential staining of dead, 491
differentiation from mitochondria, 444
fat in, 491
Gram-positive, in sections, 493
in,
leukocytes, 490, 491; milk, 490, 491, 492; plant tissues, 444, 498
sections, mentioned in,
Holmes and French's triple stain, 352; Langeron's double stain, 353; Masson's double stain, 353; Masson's triple stain, 371; silver nitrate methods for, 563
Neisser's granules in, 489–490
polar bodies in, 491
Bacterial capsules, in sections, 498
in smears, 487–489
Bacterial flagella, dye staining methods for, 481–484
silver diammine methods for, 598
silver-iron method for, 608
silver nitrate methods for, 563
silver-sulfate method for, 609
Bacterial smears, 473–492
acid-fast, 476–478
Gram-positive, 474–476
mountant for, 641
silver diammine methods for, 598
Bacterial spores, general remarks, 467–468
permanganate stain for, 611
stains for, 484–487
Badertscher's method for sebaceous glands, 422
Bailey's method for, mitochondria, 441
neuroglea, 412
Bailey's mordant, 517
in Bailey's method for bacterial flagella, 481
Baillif and Kimbrough's method for blood, 416
Baird's method for connective tissue spreads, 394
Baker, on selection of grasshoppers, 310
on spermatogenesis in Triturus, 272
Baker's fixatives, calcium-formaldehyde, 236, 238
osmic-chromic-acetic, 200, 238
Baker's, glycerol jelly, 633
method for, Golgi bodies, 442
mitochondria, 441, 443
narcotic, 265
softening fluid for embedded objects, 667
Baker and Crawford on osmotic pressure of fixatives, 187
Baker and Thomas's fixative, 202, 238
in Baker and Thomas's method for mitochondria, 442
Balbiani's method for nuclei in ciliates, 434

Balbuena's alcoholic accelerator, 614
developer, 616
method for retina, 544–546, 551
silver staining solution, 550
toner, 620
Baley's fixative, 217, 238
in Baley's methods for pancreas, 428
Banard, machine for sealing glycerol mounts, 33
Bank and Davenport's fixative, 237
Barbadoes earth, separation of radiolarians from, 18
Barbrow's triple stain, 365
Bardelli and Cillé's method for Zymonema, 503
Barium chlorate, as ingredient of bleaching solutions, 262
Barium chloride, as ingredient of,
Frey's injection fluid, 663; Frey's injection mass, 664; Hagmann's injection fluid, 664
in Forsgren's triple stain, 423
Barium eosinate, 348
Barium peroxide, for ripening hematoxylin, 284
Bark, collecting animals from, 44
Barker's method for microglea, 585
Barlow's ethyl cellulose embedding medium, 649
Barnabo on pH of fixatives, 188
Barnett, *see* Dawson, 567
Barret's fixatives, 199, 238
Barreto's method for Negri bodies, 464
Barrett's method for pollen mother cells, 435
Bartelmez's fixatives, 189, 238, 239
in Bartelmez's method for brains in fish larvae, 551
Bartha, *see* Mitter, 437
Basal bodies in ciliates, 456, 559
Basement membrane, mentioned in Lillie's quadruple stain, 370
"Basic" dyes, 270, 271
Basic fuchsin, *see* Magenta
Basophil cells, of pituitary, 425–428
Bassal, *see* Morel, 286, 516
Bastian's preservative, 178
Basu, *see* Knowles, 567
Batillon's fixative, 228, 239
Bauer's, developer, 616
in Bauer's method for spirochetes in tooth buds, 560
fixative, 223
method for, neuroglea, 412
nitrocellulose embedding, 647
silver staining solution, 550
Bauer and Leriche's triple stain, 352
Baumgartel's method for, algae, 511
leprosy bacilli in sections, 495
Bay oil, physical properties of, 624

Nebel's, fixatives—*(continued)*
  osmic-platinic-chromium-thorinin, 196
  method for pollen tubes, 422
Needles, glass, for injection, 166
  hypodermic, conversion to injection needles, 165
Neelsen's method for acid-fast bacteria, 469, 477
Negri bodies, mentioned in Krajian's method for bacteria in sections, 494
  in section of guinea-pig brain, 460–461
  preparation of smears of, 75
  special methods for, 463, 464–467
Negrin's method for reticulum fibers, 594
Neill, *see* Hood, 656
Neisser's polychrome methylene blue, 490
  in, Cowdry's method for diphtheria, 489
    Neisser's method for diphtheria bacilli, 490
Neisser and Hueppe's method for bacterial spores, 486
Nelis's fixative, 213
Nelson's method for nerves in wholemounts, 406
Nematodes, collecting from, feces, 35
    moss, 45
  combined fixative and dehydrant for, 189
  fixation of, 36
  Hetherington's embedding method for, 646
  impregnating with glycerol, 32
  mastic mountant for, 637
  wholemount in glycerol, 35–37
Nemeč's fixatives, chromic-formaldehyde, 230, 249
  picric-acetic-sulfuric, 222
    in Nemeč's method for plastids, 450
Neoarsphenamine, as ingredient of Tron's accelerator, 615
  in Fontana's method for spirochetes, 608
Nereids, 53
Neri's method for Negri bodies, 466
Nerve cells, centrosomes in, 590
  mitochondria in, 591
Nerve endings, arsenic-silver method for, 605
  gold methods for, 534–536
  gold-dichromate method for, 541
  in,
    calcified structures, 556, 557; gland cells, 529; male sex organs, 606; tendons, 540; tongue, 553
  methylene blue method for, 403
  osmic method for, 529
  peripheral, 552, 606, 615
  protein silver method for, 568
  silver diammine method for, 581, 584
Nerve fibrils, 554
Nerve net, in ciliates, 559
Nerves, differentiation of anesthetized from normal, 404
  in, oligochaetes, 556

Nerves—*(continued)*
  in—*(continued)*
    teeth, 534–535, 610
    mentioned in,
      Hubin's triple contrast, 340; Mallory's triple stain, 360; Masson's double contrast, 337; Patay's triple stain, 339; Shumway's triple stain, 372
    regenerating, 582
Nervous tissues, dye-stains for, 395–416
  gold-arsenic method for, 540
  gold-dichromate methods, 540, 541
  gold-mercury methods for, 538–539
  gold-osmic methods for, 540, 541
  hematoxylin methods for, 403–409
  miscellaneous dye stains for, 409–411
  osmic methods for degenerative changes in, 528–529
  osmic-silver-dichromate methods for, 603–607
  protein silver methods, 566–568
  reticulum fibers in, 595
  silver nitrate methods for, 551–558
  silver-dichromate methods for, 603–607
  thiazin stains for, 401–403
Neubert's, double contrast, 326
  method for smooth muscle, 424
Neukirch's method for glycogen, 453
Neuman's, double contrast, 303
  method for nervous tissues, 407
Neurofibrils, Agduhr's method for, 581
  Bethe's method for, 402
  Cajal's method for, 552
  Cowdry's method for, 554
  Davenport's method for, 554
  Donaggio's method for, 402
  da Fano's method for, 583
  in spinal cord, 555
  Schultze and Stohr's method for, 557
Neurogenesis, 552, 553
Neuroglia, dye stains for, 411–415
  gold-mercury methods for, 536–538, 539
  in smears, 588
  silver bromide-chloride-thiosulfate method for, 609
  silver diammine methods for, 585–590
  silver-dichromate methods, 606, 607
  silver nitrate methods for, 558
  silver-tungstic method, 607
Neuroglia, *see also* Macroglia, Astrocytes, etc.
"Neutral" balsam, 639
"Neutral" dyes, 271
Neutral macerating fluids, 264
"Neutral mountants," 637, 638
Neutral red, as polychrome stain, 371
  for staining,
    bacterial flagella, (Gemelli), 482; blood, (Lightwood, Hawksley and Bailey), 418; blood, (Sabin), 419; blood, (Simpson),

28323